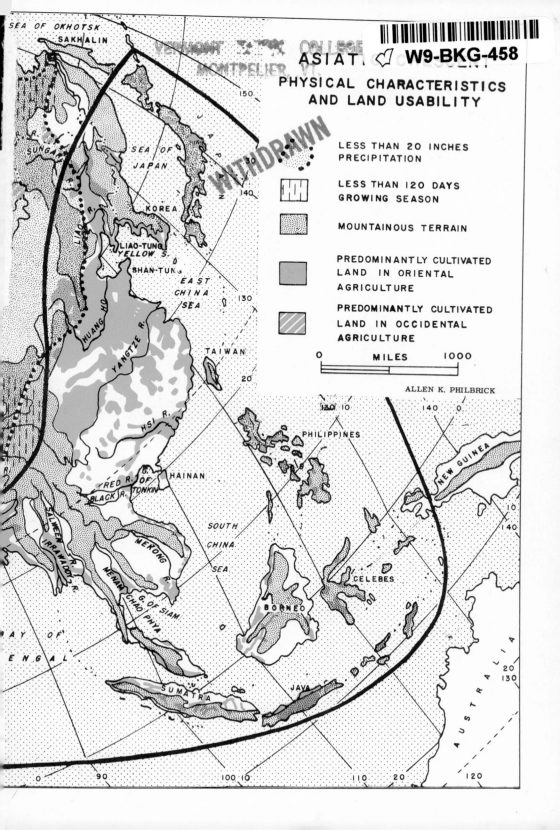

ASIATIC CRESCENT

PHYSICAL CHARACTERISTICS AND LAND USABILITY

LESS THAN 20 INCHES PRECIPITATION

LESS THAN 120 DAYS GROWING SEASON

MOUNTAINOUS TERRAIN

PREDOMINANTLY CULTIVATED LAND IN ORIENTAL AGRICULTURE

PREDOMINANTLY CULTIVATED LAND IN OCCIDENTAL AGRICULTURE

0   MILES   1000

ALLEN K. PHILBRICK

THE
PATTERN
OF
ASIA

Edited by

NORTON GINSBURG

Department of Geography
The University of Chicago

Co-authors

JOHN E. BRUSH

Department of Geography
Rutgers, the State University

SHANNON McCUNE,* Provost*

University of Massachusetts

ALLEN K. PHILBRICK

Department of Geography
Michigan State University

JOHN R. RANDALL

Department of Geography
Ohio State University

HEROLD J. WIENS

Department of Geography
Yale University

THE
PATTERN
OF
ASIA

Englewood Cliffs, N.J.   PRENTICE-HALL, INC.

Preface

This is a preface to be read. It is to be read because it explains a number of things that will make this book more comprehensible and valuable.

The book is organized into six large sections of differing lengths. The first is a general introduction to Asia; the second is concerned with East Asia; the third with Southeast Asia; the fourth with South Asia; the fifth with Southwest Asia; the sixth with the Soviet Union. The first and sixth divisions are the shortest. The introduction sets the scene for the chapters that follow and should be read first. Sections two and three are subdivided into an introductory chapter and then a chapter on each country or groups of countries within East Asia and Southeast Asia, respectively. Sections four and five, covering South Asia and Southwest Asia, respectively, include several chapters dealing with the realm as a whole, followed by more detailed treatments of individual countries or groups of them. This is a more-or-less traditional system of organization.

The book, however, has a theme which makes it distinctive. It emphasizes the changing political and economic geography of Asia and attempts to illustrate the various problems and potentials of the countries of Asia. The purpose is to provide not merely a random description, but to point toward a more basic understanding of the processes of change which are radically transforming the Asian landscape.

v

Although the existence of a theme makes possible a high degree of integrity, the several approaches of the co-authors have made for considerable diversity in the organization of, and emphases within, chapters. It can be argued that this is an advantage, since it brings several points of view to bear on a multifaceted Asia which cannot be regarded as a stamp from a single die. It also has certain disadvantages of which the authors are well aware, since comparability is sometimes made difficult and occasional contradictions may occur.

Such disadvantages have been coped with, in part, in several ways: (1) the general introduction provides an umbrella under which to bring the several points of view of the co-authors; (2) maps have been prepared which are in general parallel throughout the book, making comparisons easier; (3) photographic illustrations have been chosen and captioned with that same end in view. The results are as successful as, perhaps more successful than, could have been expected. In any event, the one great virtue remains: the individual characters of the various regions and countries in Asia are not obscured.

The maps, for the most part, are very complex. Some readers may at first find them difficult to interpret. This is not wholly chance, however. The maps were designed to act as references in themselves about which commentaries have been written. Thus, it is assumed that they will be referred to not merely once, but again and again, not simply as illustrations of what is written in words but as integral parts of the volume, worthy of continued study and interpretation. Because the maps tell so much, it has been impossible to include upon them all of the place names referred to in the book. This is another failing of which the authors are aware, although it is felt that the value of the maps as interpretive tools has thereby been increased. It is recommended, in any case, that the reader refer to some of the standard atlases, among which are *Prentice-Hall World Atlas, The Oxford Atlas, Goode's World Atlas,* and Bartholomew's *The Advanced Atlas of Modern Geography.* To the editor's knowledge, every place name cited appears within these atlases.

The problem of place names with regard to Asia is enormous. The romanization of the ideographic languages and the transliteration of the alphabetic languages present numerous difficulties. Wherever possible, the decisions of the United States Board on Geographic Names have been followed; however, diacritical markings in Arabic and Annamese, for example, have not been employed except in the case of Chinese place names.

For the most part, Chinese place names have been romanized according to the Wade-Giles standard system of romanization. This system is by no means wholly satisfactory, but it has the great virtue of providing a uniform system, as compared with the more common so-called "postal atlas" system which does not provide intrinsic uniformity and, indeed, is not a "system" at all. The authors feel that the Wade-Giles standard system is, in the long run, the more useful in spite of its drawbacks. Where the system is used for a fairly well-known place which may be better recognized under its traditional postal spelling, the postal spelling appears in parentheses at the time of first appearance; e.g., Ssu-ch'uan (Szechwan). In a few cases, the traditional spelling is so well-known that the standard spelling might mean confusion. In cases such as these, the postal spelling is used throughout the book, but the Wade-Giles spelling appears in parentheses when the name first appears. Examples are Peking (Pei-ching), Mukden (Shen-yang), Canton (Kuang-chou), and Amoy (Hsia-men). It is hoped that in later editions of the book the place names of other countries may be more completely standardized and that all diacritical markings will appear.

At the end of almost every chapter appears a selected bibliography of geographical concern. Not all publications related to that chapter have been included—only those which may be desirable for additional reading and which are assumed to be available in most reference libraries. Few references in foreign languages have been noted. Each bibliography is accompanied by a short commentary which should facilitate its use.

The Pattern of Asia has been in painful preparation for over five years. The term "painful" is appropriate because it almost exceeds the imagination to attempt to cram even into 907 pages the basic configurations of so huge a continent and so large a proportion of mankind. It represents the results of the intellectual energies not merely of its several co-authors and the editor, but also of innumerable colleagues who read, commented upon, and reread portions of the manuscript. To all these our very deepest thanks. Since noting them all at this point would add greatly to what is already a gigantic volume, it is hoped they will not take this over-all expression of thanks amiss; however, the editor cannot resist expressing his personal thanks especially to colleagues at the University of Chicago and the University of Washington, whose counsel he found indispensable.

NORTON S. GINSBURG

University of Chicago

Contents

CONTENTS

Plates

MAP CREDITS

All of the maps in this volume were prepared by Professor Allen K. Philbrick, with the exception of numbers 11, 12, 16, 18, 21, 22, 24, and 25. In many cases, data presented on the maps were gathered and ordered by him; in many other cases others of the co-authors contributed the basic data, and these were transferred into final map form. In one or two cases, with permission of the appropriate authority, maps from other publications were incorporated directly into the text as noted below.

Most of the maps represent the compilation of data from numerous sources and are, in effect, the result of formal research. In some cases, however, the maps were adapted from, and therefore are variants of, maps previously published. These also are noted below. The maps showing physiography are used with the kind permission of Professor A. K. Lobeck.

Map
9. Physiography from Lobeck.
14. Physiography from Lobeck.
15. After R. G. Hainsworth and R. T. Moyer, *Agricultural Geography of the Philippine Islands, A Graphic Summary,* 1945.
16. From *Area Handbook on the Philippines,* Chicago, 1956.
17. After the *Atlas von Tropisch Nederland,* 1938.
18. From N. S. Ginsburg and C. F. Roberts, Jr., *Malaya,* 1957.
20. From N. S. Ginsburg and C. F. Roberts, Jr., *Malaya,* 1957, after E. H. G. Dobby.
21. From B. P. Asanachinta, "Land Uses in Thailand" (unpublished master's thesis, University of Chicago, 1950).
22. From B. P. Asanachinta, "Land Uses in Thailand" (unpublished master's thesis, University of Chicago, 1950).
24. *Area Handbook on Cambodia,* Chicago, 1955.
25. From L. H. Gulick, Jr., "Rice Regions of French Indochina" (unpublished master's thesis, University of Chicago, 1948).
29. Physiography from Lobeck.
31. After International Bank for Reconstruction and Development, *The Economic Development of Ceylon,* 1953, and works by B. H. Farmer.
34. Physiography from Lobeck.
36. After *Great Soviet Atlas* and other sources.

Maps

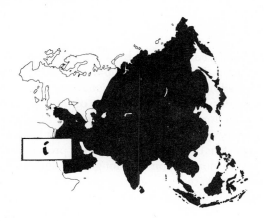

Asia

THE PHYSICAL BASIS

ASIA IS NOT ONE BUT MANY. ON THIS, THE LARGEST CONTINENT, LIVE 60 per cent of the people of the world, not evenly distributed throughout the vast extent of Asian territory, but localized in certain major concentrations, which form the core lands of the various Asian states. Size and diversity, both of physical elements and populations, are two of the distinctive qualities of Asia, shared with the other continents, but nowhere evidenced on so grand a scale.

Nevertheless, the history of the past few hundred years has been drawn in large part with Asia as an appendage of Europe, in effect a backwash area in the stream of international affairs. What Europe, and to a lesser extent the United States, willed was affirmed in Asia; what Asia willed had little consequence in the Occident. Indeed, it is safe to hold that Asia had no will, that it was subject to the control and manipulation of the West, and that it lacked in whole or in part the cohesiveness and integrated organization that are prerequisite to independent survival in a highly competitive and increasingly interdependent world.

Within the past half century, however, an Asian will has come into being, though amorphous and sometimes ephemeral in different places at different times. The culmination of this gradual growth of Asian self-consciousness followed the launching of the Pacific War by Japan in 1941.

1

The previous 70 years had been characterized by a series of wars that facilitated Japan's expansion onto the adjacent continent. With these wars went a concomitant channeling of vigorous nationalism, organized social effort, and natural resources into the development of an expanding economy and an ambitious plan for domination over much of eastern Asia. Thus when Japan's military program ended in failure (but only against the might of the strongest nation in the world) her professed intent of freeing Asia from Western domination had long since ignited the Asian imagination. The early successes of the Japanese, especially in Southeast Asia, fed fuel to the fires of Asian nationalism, diverse though they themselves might be. After the close of the second World War a number of newly independent countries made their appearance on the map of Asia, and in other places, where Europeans and Americans had been politically and economically dominant, there followed a further and sometimes complete loosening of the ties with the West.

Thus, since the war there has come to be not only a more diverse Asia, but a new Asia. It is with the new Asia that this volume is concerned, for the social, economic, and political geography of Asia is not what it was before, and even the physical bases underlying the various Asian states and regions must be assessed with new frames of reference and changing problems in mind.

The situation of Asia

What is known as the Asiatic continent is the northeasterly component of the Eurafrasian land mass. It is roughly quadrangular in form and covers approximately 18 million square miles, one-third the land surface of the earth (front end paper). The north-to-south extensions of this huge quadrangle range from latitudes 85°N. to beyond 10°S.; the west-to-east dimensions, from the western margins of Turkey eastward to the Bering Strait, range from longitudes 25°E. to 170°W., almost halfway around the world. To the north lies the Arctic Ocean; to the northwest, the plains of northern Europe and the mountainous shield of Scandinavia; to the southwest, the Mediterranean world with its serrated northern coasts and, beyond Suez, the deserts of North Africa; to the south, the Indian Ocean, into which projects the great peninsula of the Indian subcontinent; to the southeast, the attenuated peninsulas and archipelagoes of Malaysia, blending through a complex of island groups into Australasia and the southwest Pacific. In the east is the lengthy Pacific littoral, broken in the north by the peninsulas of Shan-tung, Liao-tung, and Korea; farther east lies an arced island chain centered upon the Empire of Japan.

In modern times access to Asia has been mostly over the seas and oceans that rim its more southerly coasts, and it is in the coastal regions that European influence has been most important. The opening of the Suez Canal in 1869 provided a convenient western gateway to much of coastal Asia; after 1860 the opening of Japan to foreign trade and the establishment of regular trans-Pacific steamship services provided an eastern entrance, but only over a sea of more than continental dimensions, the Pacific. Foreign access to much of Asia still is mainly maritime, but the improvement of land transportation in the Soviet Union has already increased the accessibility of central Asia, and air transportation, with its possibilities for trans-polar connections between North America and Asia, may alter the established patterns of accessibility (back end paper).

Economically and politically, Asia has begun to occupy relative to the rest of the world a position more in keeping with its area, resources, and population. The European tail no longer wags the Asiatic dog, although it remains remarkable that so seemingly minor an appendage of the great continent should continue to exert so important an influence upon Asian affairs. The unique place of the Soviet Union also has focussed attention on Asia, where Russian political imperialism and pressures seem to be most intense and potentially most effective. Thus, many of the Asian countries have gained the special attention of the United States, whose clear interest it is to maintain them as going concerns within which political decisions can be made without excessive interference from foreign powers, and especially from the Soviet Union. At the same time Asia— especially eastern Asia—has been acquiring a trans-Pacific world view, which has come to balance the traditional orientation westward toward Europe.

The increasing concern of the West with Asia and of Asia with the West must be seen together with the expansion of Occidental values and technologies throughout the world and the emergence of a closed world order in which the best of the "empty spaces" have long since been occupied. Each of the Western powers, with the possible exception of the Soviet Union, is finding necessary a global view of physical resources and the problems of their development, both of which Asia possesses in abundance.

The environmental pattern

Much of Asia appears singularly inhospitable to human occupance. Yet within Asia live one and a third billion people, some three-fifths of the population of the earth. What physical basis underlies this anomaly? (See end papers.)

Unique among the continents, Asia is mountain-hearted. Amidst the great mountain ranges appear extensive plateaus, some expressionless

Fig. 1 • This view from Landour hill, Mussoorie, Uttar Pradesh, India, encompasses the perennial snow and glaciers of the Great Himalaya, Jaonli to Kedarnath (22,000 to 23,000 feet); and forests and cultivated terraces on the slopes of the Lesser Himalaya. The Great Himalaya and associated ranges form one of the more formidable topographic barriers to communications in the world. Although crossed by numerous caravan routes, the highest passes are nearly three miles in height; no highways or railways pierce the mountain wall, and it was not until 1936 that the first airplane succeeded in crossing it safely. *(Stanley E. Brush.)*

and featureless, some severely broken into badlands of forbidding aspect. Nowhere in interior Asia is there a great fertile lowland comparable with that of the Mississippi basin, which comprises the agricultural heartland of North America and which admits to the interior both tempering winds from southerly latitudes and communications facilities. Nor are there great river basins, as yet undeveloped but well watered and forested, that reach into the very core of the continent, as do the Amazon in South America and the Congo and Zambezi in Africa. Rather, the physical character of Asia in some ways resembles that of Australia.

The core of the Asiatic mountain system lies in the vast complex of mountains and plateaus, focussing upon Tibet, that are bounded roughly on the south by the sweeping northwest-southeast arc of the Himalaya (Figure 1); on the west by the knotted Pamirs, the roof of the world; on the north by the T'ien Shan of China's Hsin-chiang (Sinkiang) Province; and to the east by the mountains of southwestern China. The geologic structure of this core is relatively little known and it cannot be clearly demarcated except in the south, where the Himalaya rise abruptly from the Indo-Gangetic plain. To the west, however, a chain of mountains and plateaus extends well into southwestern Asia and dominates the landscape in Iran (Persia), the Caucasus, and Turkey. To the north, the T'ien Shan are connected orographically with a parallel-trending chain, the Altai mountains of Mongolia, which are structurally related to and form part of the series of complex ranges in northeastern Siberia that continue into eastern Manchuria and Korea. In the far east appear the mountains of Japan, part of the zone of vulcanism rimming the Pacific through T'ai-wan, the Philippines, and the East Indian archipelago.

If all of the main ranges and plateaus on the mainland of the continent are considered together, they extend generally east-northeast and west-southwest for some 5,000 miles and constitute the largest body of highlands in the world. Within that upland mass are some of the world's highest mountains; these, when combined with the deserts that lie between certain of the ranges, form a continental barrier of unmatched impenetrability. Around the high uplands there are also great stretches of hill lands —as in southeastern China and in part of geologically ancient peninsular India—where elevations generally are lower but where high relief places limits on opportunities for both occupance and communications.

The mountain core acts as the hub of a colossal wheel, the spokes of which are formed by some of the greatest rivers of the world, spiralling outward from the rain-catching and snow-capped slopes of the Hindu Kush, Pamirs, Himalaya, Karakorum, Altyn Tagh, T'ien Shan, and the other ranges of the highland core. Not all of these rivers reach the sea, however. Within the continent are some five million square miles of interior drainage. Numerous rivers rising within or on the margins of the mountan core complex flow without tributaries for hundreds of miles across deserts and steppe until they disappear into great saline lakes, swamps, or wastes, or into the Aral or Caspian seas. Into the southern Caspian drain short swift rivers from the Elburz mountains of northern Persia, and from the north, European Russia, come the Ural River and the the giant Volga. Into the Aral Sea drain the northwest-flowing Syr and the Amu, the Oxus of ancient history. Into Lake Balkhash drains the Ili River from the slopes of the T'ien Shan, and through the Taklamakan (desert) of western Hsin-chiang Province the Tarim River flows into the ephemeral lake, Lop Nor. In general, these drainage systems offer limited opportunities for livelihood, and it is only in relatively small irrigated oases of intermontane basins that men in any numbers have settled permanently.

Yet the arid and mountainous heartland of Asia cannot be considered "dead." In the past it was from this heartland that nomadic peoples spilled over into Europe, the Middle East, India, and China, and brought under their sway vast empires, comparable in size and power to the largest the world has seen. Today, however, the direction of power flow has been reversed, and instead of invasions outward from Central Asia, the invasions, on a smaller scale and less violent, are inward. These take the form of the development of irrigated cotton agriculture in Soviet Turkestan and mineral explorations and exploitation and increased agricultural activity in Hsin-chiang and Mongolia. For the time being at least, the self-generation of political and military strength that characterized interior Asia in the past has ceased, as the tractor, truck, and airplane have made obsolete the mounted mobility of the nomad.

The rivers that flow northward, the Ob, the Yenisei, the Lena, and lesser streams, rise in the mountains of northern and northeastern Asia and cross extensive coastal lowlands before they enter the Arctic Ocean. For the most part these northern lowlands are too cold for permanent human occupance. Only in the northern latitudes of North America are there comparable areas of lowland in which cold forms so great a barrier to occupance; and only in relatively recent years in Siberia, as in Canada, have men attempted to settle in and exploit on a substantial scale the material resources of the taiga and tundra. In general the forest and mineral resources of this region, the magnets for attracting settlement, are matched elsewhere by more accessible resource associations that for the time being at least can be exploited more easily and cheaply.

The great rivers flowing eastward and southward define the Asia that is populous and developed (Figure 2). From a highly restricted area within the interior mountain core flow such rivers as the Indus, the Ganges, the Brahmaputra, the Irrawaddy, the Salween, the Mekong, the Yangtze (Yang-tzu), and the Huang To. To the west are few large streams other than those that contribute to the pattern of interior drainage, but the southeast-flowing Tigris and Euphrates provide a major exception in the valley setting in which the most ancient civilizations flourished and decayed. Between and beyond the major river basins flow such lesser yet large streams as the Narbada, Cauvery, Kistna, and Mahanadi of peninsular India, the Menam Chao Phya of Thailand, the Red and Black rivers of Indochina, the Hsi system of south China, the Huai of north China, and the Liao and Amur-Sungari systems of Manchuria and the Soviet Far East. Within the valleys of many of these rivers have developed the cultural cores of lasting civilizations and modern nations, and it is in them that most of the peoples of Asia live—and multiply.

Climatically, Asia is as varied as it is orographically and hydrologically.

Fig. 2 • Part of the lower Menam Chao Phya plain near Bangkok in Thailand as it appears during the dry season. The alluvial soils are occupied entirely by paddy fields demarcated by low bundings and by farmsteads, villages, or temples *(wat)*, rising like islands out of the plain. In the spring and summer the waters of the Chao Phya regularly flood much of the plain (see Map 21) and create an amphibious world foreign to Western agriculture but common to wet-rice-growing Asia. *(Helen Smith.)*

(See Plates A, B, C, D, E, and Maps 1 and 2.) The primary climatic quality of Asia is continentality. The seasonal heating and cooling of this, the world's largest land mass, makes for major seasonal variations in climate. In winter, when the interior regions are cold, a semipermanent high-pressure belt forms within the northern interior of the continent, and strong cold winds, outflowing as polar continental air masses from the anticyclones within the belt, bring winter to most of the continent. In summer, the rapid and continuous heating of the interior results in lower pressures and in the inflow of tropical maritime air from the continent's margins. Since the outflowing winds are land-originated and usually do not pass over large bodies of water, they are dry, and the winters also tend to be dry. Conversely, in the summer the generally weaker inflows of air from the eastern and southern seas are humid and carry with them the moisture that for much of Asia makes summer the rainier season.

Each continent exhibits this seasonal reversal of winds and rains, known as the *monsoon effect,* but nowhere are these reversals as notable as in Asia. In North America there is a smaller land mass in which cooling and heating takes place; in South America only a small part of the continent lies in the higher latitudes and the winter monsoon effect is minimized; as for Africa, no part of that continent lies within the higher latitudes, and the monsoon effects are restricted to relatively limited areas. Europe, as a westward-facing, ocean-fronting area, is most strongly influenced by the westerly winds of the upper middle latitudes, and the climate of Europe is predominantly maritime all the year round, except in the Mediterranean region. In Australasia, too, a relatively small area is involved, and maritime influences tend to predominate throughout the year, except in interior Australia, although during the northern winter the northeast trades, strengthened by outflows of air from the Asian continent, sweep across the equator into northern Australia.

In terms of temperatures, the alternation of seasons means little in the southeast Asian peninsulas and archipelagoes. These lie on or near the equator, and their mean temperature curves show little variation from month to month (Maps 1a, 1b, and 2 and Plates A and B). The same is true of southern India, and in the Arabian peninsula, where mean temperatures vary relatively little, the diurnal fluctuations of temperature are of considerably greater significance than any other. India, and to a degree southeastern Asia and parts of southwestern Asia, are protected from these cold dry winds of the interior by the mountain core and its major outliers. Parts of the southwest are touched by tongues of maritime air from the Mediterranean, making for milder winters than those in similar latitudes on the eastern side of the continent. North of India the mountain barrier prevents the flow of maritime air into the interior, and in summer a second major low-pressure area appears over the hot deserts of northwest India.

The interior regions, isolated as they are from the sea by great distances and mountain barriers, are dry, and they exhibit the extremes of seasonal and diurnal temperature variations that tend to characterize middle-latitude deserts. In eastern Asia temperature means vary primarily with latitude, and in this respect the east coast of China may be likened to that of eastern North America. Temperatures also vary notably with altitude. The Tibetan highlands lie well over 10,000 feet, and winters are cold while summers are at best cool. Even at much lower elevations mean temperatures are far below those in the coastal lowlands—especially in southern Asia where the "hill station," or mountain summer resort, is a distinctive occupance feature, developed usually by Europeans seeking relief from the high temperatures and humidities of the steaming lowlands of, for example, India and Java.

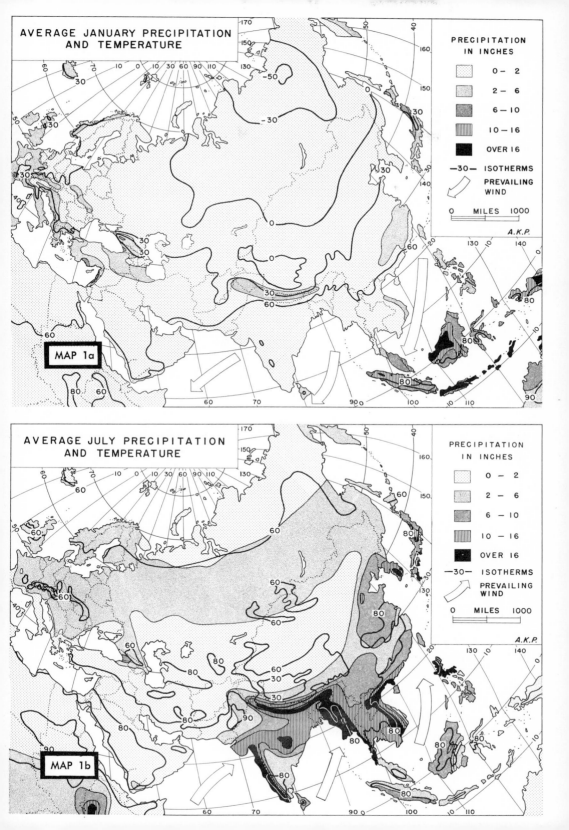

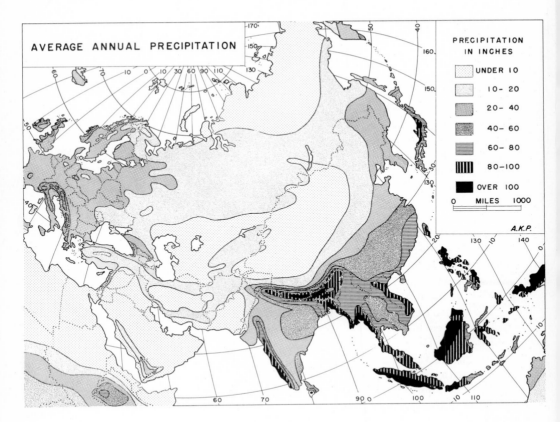

AVERAGE ANNUAL PRECIPITATION

PRECIPITATION
IN INCHES

UNDER 10
10- 20
20- 40
40- 60
60- 80
80-100
OVER 100

0   MILES   1000

A.K.P.

MAP 2

Although the greater part of Asia receives most of its rainfall in the summer (Map 1a) there are several major exceptions and many minor ones. The cyclonic storms that carry maritime air into the Mediterranean region in the winters are accompanied by rainfall, whereas in summer most of the region is overlain by a dry belt of higher pressures that moves northward from the Sahara. Thus much of the rainfall of southwestern Asia comes in the winter, and the summers are dry (Map 1b). Along eastward-facing coasts in southern Asia north of the equator, rainfall is heavy in the fall and winter when northeasterly winds of continental origin strike the coasts after passing over large bodies of water, as in southeastern India and along the east coasts of Malaya, Indochina, and the Philippines. Java and the Lesser Sunda Islands receive more rain in the summer, but the southern-hemisphere summer is the northern winter, and much of this precipitation has its source in reinforced winter trade winds from the northern hemisphere. In Japan, the west-facing coast of Honshu also receives its heaviest precipitation in winter, the source being the continental winds that cross the Sea of Japan and rise against the mountains of Honshu.

Everywhere, precipitation varies markedly owing to orographic factors. Much of interior Asia remains dry even in summer because rain-bearing winds of maritime origin cannot penetrate the mountain barriers (Map 2). High elevations in general depress mean summer temperatures, but at the same time some of the highest daytime temperatures in Asia are found in the protected depressions of the interior, such as the Tarim Basin. Exceptionally heavy precipitation in summer characterizes the west coast of India, where the Western Ghats rise precipitously from a narrow coastal plain, but on the plateau just to the east of the Ghats is a rain-shadow zone where summer rainfall is scanty and irregular. In North China, where summer rainfall is characteristic, precipitation decreases rapidly toward the interior because the moisture-bearing winds of summer tend to parallel the coast and those that do reach into the interior are too weak to rise over the plateau and low mountain rim of the north China plain. On a grand scale there is no better example of orographic influence on climate than high Tibet, which displays a tundra-like climate similar to that of northern Asia but at over 30 degrees of latitude farther south.

In the case of India, the barrier of the Himalaya has created what may be considered to be an autonomous climatic region, separated from the rest of Asia. Here is experienced the true summer monsoon, the sudden onslaught of rain-bearing winds from the southwest and south, which comes with trigger-like suddenness though not always with temporal regularity. The mechanism of the summer monsoon is not yet fully explained, but its impact appears to be derived from the attraction for the southeast trades of the southern hemisphere of the intense and concentrated low-pressure area in northwestern India. When the pressure in the Indian low falls below that of the climatic equator, the southeast trades are sucked violently across the equatorial doldrum belt of low pressure toward their new focus—bearing warm maritime air across the parched face of India. Conversely, in winter, winds from the continental interior are largely blocked by the mountain wall, while the winter cyclonic depressions that cross northern India from southwestern Asia are shallow and weak.

Vegetation cover in Asia displays diversities perhaps even greater than those of surface configuration and climate, since vegetation changes rapidly with the human occupance of regions, and in many areas the pre-occupance vegetation cover no longer can be described accurately. Much of northern Asia is covered by coniferous and mixed forests which stretch in an almost unbroken band from Scandinavia to the Bering Strait, with intermixtures of swamp and muskeg. To the south of the forests, but separated from them by a thousand-mile-long wedge of grasslands extend-

Fig. 3 • The shores of the Ch'ing Hai (Koko Nor) in China's Ch'ing-hai province are covered with sands, desert shrub, or short grass, in contrast with the tropical forests pictured in Figure 4. Here Golo tribesmen, a Mongol people, are wearing heavy sheep-skins as protection against the cold climate at an altitude of 10,000 feet. (Lt. Col. David R. Longacre.)

ing from the plains of European Russia, is a broad band of temperate desert shrub, broken by forests on the ridges of mountain ranges and by the occasional cultivated oases which are the chief sites of permanent habitation. In the mountain core region, mountain and high-plateau grass-land and shrub are most common, but in the protected dry valleys are found also vast areas of bare rock and shifting sand and of desert shrub and salt flats, as well as oases at the feet of mountains (Figure 3). These associations continue into southwestern Asia, merging on the one hand into the grassland of the Anatolian Plateau and the evergreen woodlands of the eastern Mediterranean coasts, and on the other into the low-latitude deserts of southern Persia, Iraq, Jordan, Israel, and Arabia.

In northern India the western deserts and savannah merge almost im-perceptibly eastward into deciduous and semideciduous monsoon forests and then into tropical rainforests and, along the Bengal coasts, swamp forests. In southern India much of the natural vegetation is or was that of a tropical savannah interspersed with salt flats in depressions or with mon-soon forests on uplands. Along the narrow rainy west coast, however, grow dense tropical rainforests.

In southeastern Asia most of the uplands on the mainland are in semi-deciduous monsoon forests in which such trees as teak and the Diptero-carps predominate, but toward the equator the tropical rainforest becomes increasingly common (Figure 4) and along the coasts may be great swamp forests. Along the eastern middle-latitude margins of Asia, the

Fig. 4 • Characteristic of the great tropical forests in southern and southeastern Asia are these in western New Guinea (Irian) near Sorong. Here a tree is being blasted out of the ground during road construction. *(Standard Oil Company, N.J.)*

subtropical forests of south China blend into the grasslands of north and northwest China and thence into the grasslands and surrounding mixed northern forests of Manchuria and the Soviet Far East. Offshore, the subtropical broadleaved evergreen forests of T'ai-wan and the Ryukyus merge into the deciduous and mixed forests of middle Japan and thence into the coniferous forests of northern Japan, Hokkaido, and Sakhalin. In much of southern and eastern Asia, also, except in areas of little rainfall or at higher latitudes, bamboos are an important vegetation element, widely disseminated and used in India, southeastern Asia, south and central China, and southern Japan.

Wherever men have settled and are engaged in permanent agriculture, vegetation no longer remains natural, and in many areas of denser settlement the original vegetation cover may have been entirely removed (Figure 2). Thus, the Indo-Gangetic and lower Chao Phya plains are almost totally covered with cropland, as are the lowlands of China and the valleys and basin bottoms of Japan. In these areas, and in many others throughout the more intensely occupied regions, imported plants may have replaced the indigenous ones; many of the important crops—maize, cassava, sweet potatoes, tobacco, and rubber—have been imported into Asia only in comparatively recent times. Further, in many forested areas the practice of shifting or fire-clearing cultivation, as well as ill-regulated forest exploitation, has resulted in the formation of vast areas of dense and often impenetrable thickets, the "jungle" of the tropics and subtropics.

Asian *soils* reflect the diversities of surface configuration, climate, and vegetation under which they were formed. By and large, northern Asia is covered by podzolic soils of varying but generally low fertility, often poorly drained in the lowlands and thin on the sloping uplands. Deep black prairie and chernozem soils underlie the grasslands of western Siberia, Manchuria, and Anatolia, while similarly deep but often saline soils are found beneath the semidesert and desert areas where sands and lithosols also are important. Red desert soils and sands cover much of Arabia and northwest India, while lighter desert soils are found in most of southwestern Asia. Huge areas in northwest China are covered with deep layers of wind-blown silt called *loess,* the soils of which are often of high fertility but are subject to extremes of gully and sheet erosion.

In lower latitudes most soils are characterized by the process of laterization under which fine clays, rich in aluminum and iron oxides and low in silica, accumulate, making for deep and nearly structureless soils of generally low fertility from which most plant nutrients have been leached by heavy rainfall. Although more resistant to erosion than soils formed under more temperate climatic conditions, the lateritic soils of the tropics also are subjected to higher and more intense rainfall. Erosion, therefore, is a grave problem in the tropical and subtropical regions. The reddish soils of southeastern China display both lateritic and podzolic qualities, as do those of southern Japan, but in much of northern China, Manchuria, and Japan, the predominant soils are gray-brown podzolics formed under forests and similar to those in the northeastern United States.

The most important soils in Asia, however, are those relatively immature soils of alluvial origin that are found in river valleys. Especially in the lower and middle latitudes, these are the soils that are richest in plant nutrients and in many cases maintain their fertility through periodic inundations by silt-bearing water from rivers in flood. The soils of

the Tigris-Euphrates valley, of the Indo-Gangetic plain, of the lower Irrawaddy, of the Chao Phya lowland in Thailand, of the deltas of the Mekong, Red, and Hsi rivers, of the Yangtze lowland and the north China
plain, of the lower valley floors of the innumerable lesser rivers of India,
Malaya, the East Indian archipelago, the Philippines, T'ai-wan, Korea,
and Japan, are soils that in large measure provide the peoples of Asia
with their sustenance. Yet not all of these soils are equally fertile. Those
in the subtropical and tropical zones are constantly subjected to high
precipitation and to leaching unless periodically renewed. Others are
subjected to such continual inundations and poor drainage that they cannot be utilized economically. Not least, many of the best soils have been
so long utilized for the production of crops that their fertility has been
drastically reduced.

Certain other immature soils also are locally important, especially in
southeastern Asia where soils have formed over recently deposited volcanic materials. Many of the soils formed over acidic ejecta are not very
fertile, prone as they are to rapid leaching. However, where the parent
volcanic materials are basic, the soils may be very rich and may retain
their fertility for long periods, especially if occasionally renewed by new
deposits of basic ejecta. Such soils help explain the enormous densities of
rural population in Java and in smaller areas in the Philippines. The infrequent renewals of such soils, however, may be associated also with
death and destruction for the communities occupying them.

In sum, Asia possesses a singularly limited agricultural resource base
and therefore offers more limited opportunities for productive agriculture
than its size might indicate (front end paper). It is doubtful whether with
present technologies more than 20 per cent of the total land area of Asia
is suitable for agriculture, and at least a quarter of this percentage consists of marginal land. Where middle-latitude soils are themselves suitable, lack of water is often a key factor. Most subtropical and tropical
soils are not very fertile, and even when relatively immature are subject
to rapid declines in fertility. Certainly, the assertion holds true that much
of predominantly agricultural Asia is unattractive for human occupance.
As will be seen later, not only is most of Asia unattractive to settlement,
but much of it is virtually unoccupied, although there are more people
more densely concentrated in Asia than in any other continent.

The pattern of non-agricultural resources

In effect, what has been out-
lined above is the basic resource base for Asian agriculture in terms of
the index variables—surface configuration, climate, vegetation, and soils.

It is true that such resources remain in very large part the basic resources for most of the world's population, but the possibilities for the economic development of national states and regional economies depend to an increasing degree on other resources—on forests, power resources, and minerals.

One of Asia's major resources is found in its *forests,* but many of these are remote and too inaccessible for immediate exploitation. In addition, those in the Soviet Union are for all practical purposes of little significance to the rest of Asia. In the mountains of west China and interior Asia are considerable reserves of timber, but these also are relatively inaccessible and of little general commercial importance. In southwestern Asia, forest resources are of minor importance and chiefly provide fuelwood. In Japan, Korea, and Manchuria, middle-latitude mixed and coniferous forests cover wide areas. In the case of Japan, however, cutting on a sustained-yield basis is insufficient to supply the domestic demand, and in both Korea and Manchuria the more easily accessible stands have long since been cut over. Neither Korea nor China is adequately supplied with wood for fuel, lumber, and pulp, although they conceivably could be made self-sufficient with afforestation and proper forest management and control.

In southern and southeastern Asia vast areas are covered by stands of tropical and subtropical forests within which are trees of high commercial value, such as teak and Philippine mahogany (*lauan*). However, not only are many of these forests difficult of access, but they consist primarily not of homogeneous stands of single species but of stands of many species intermixed (Figure 4). Cutting, therefore, must be selective, and selective cutting is costly. On the other hand, the growth rate in regions of warmer climates is much higher than in the middle and upper latitudes, and the potentials of these forests and of timber cropping in general also are much higher than in the north. Unfortunately the problem of the conversion of tropical hardwoods to pulp for paper and rayon has not yet been fully solved. Furthermore, since these forests are in general far removed from the major consuming centers in the southwest, in India, and in China, wood is at best a bulky, low-cost commodity, and transportation facilities are limited, it is questionable whether their timber can be transported economically to the consumer.

Of greater significance perhaps than wood in the nonagricultural resource complex are *power resources* which, in addition to fuelwood, the chief fuel in Asia, consist of coal, petroleum, natural gas, and water power.

Coal is found in many parts of Asia. One of the largest reserves is in northeastern Siberia, in the Lena River valley; but these deposits are among the least known in the world—and among the least accessible. Lesser deposits are mined west of Lake Baykal, north of Khabarovsk, and near Vladivostok. In western Soviet Asia, however, two major coal deposits are under vigorous exploitation: in the Kuznetsk basin and at Karaganda. Although some coal from the former measures have been shipped eastward to the Soviet Maritime Provinces, on the whole they are of little consequence to most of Asia. China has in Shan-hsi and Shen-hsi provinces some of the largest coal reserves in the world, but since these are neither wholly explored nor entirely accessible, most of China's production comes from substantial but lesser deposits in north China and Manchuria. Korea also possesses important coal deposits, chiefly anthracite, especially in the north, but the most fully exploited coal measures in eastern Asia are in Japan, the main fields being in northern Kyushu and in western Hokkaido. Low-grade coal is mined in northern T'ai-wan and to a lesser degree in the Philippines, Malaya, and western Sumatra. Indochina contains large deposits of anthracite in the northeast, exploited largely for export, but both Burma and Thailand are coal-short, and southeastern Asia is on the whole a coal-deficit region; coal has to be imported for use in the larger cities from Japan, China, and India. India's coal reserves are somewhat larger than those of Japan, are of high grade, and are localized primarily in the northeast, but Pakistan's reserves are very small and of poor quality. Southwestern Asia also is a major coal-deficit region, despite deposits in Iran, which are little exploited, and in Turkey, which are exploited more intensively.

Petroleum is far less well-distributed than coal. The most important known reserves are in southwestern Asia, at or near the head of the Persian Gulf. These account for about one-fifth of the world's production and contain over half its known reserves. In the southeastern corner of Asia is a second localization of deposits, smaller than the first but of special importance to eastern Asia. Production is concentrated largely in eastern Sumatra and coastal Borneo, with lesser production in Burma and Java. Minor deposits are known and exploited in Japan and Sakhalin island, and some production also appears in Assam and Kan-su and Hsin-chiang provinces of northwest China, but over most of the rest of Asia exploration has not reached the point where the extent of petroleum resources is known, although favorable formations are believed to exist in large parts of northern Siberia and Soviet Turkestan. Deposits of oil shales have been discovered and partially utilized, especially in Manchuria, and these may greatly extend Asia's petroleum-producing potential. Natural gas is of little importance in the energy-producing pattern of Asia, although it exists in association with petroleum deposits and has been used in a number of countries on a small scale.

Asia's water-power potential exceeds that of the other continents; it is more than twice that of the next largest continent, Africa. Yet in terms of developed water-power resources Asia ranks low on the list. Only in Japan, and to a lesser extent in Korea and Manchuria, have significant advances been made in the utilization of this inexhaustible resource (Figure 5). Many Asian rivers present grave problems of utilization. In the far north they flow mostly through nearly level featureless plains where dam sites are few and frozen ground is common, and in winter they are frozen for months at a time. In the high mountains the upper reaches of the rivers are so inaccessible and so far removed from potential markets that their harnessing would appear to be economically unsound. In some areas, as in Japan, streams seldom are dammed, because the lands to be flooded behind the dams are considered to be more useful as cultivated land. Much of the hydroelectric development now under way or contemplated in Asia, from the River Jordan, to the Damodar valley of India, to the Chao Phya in Thailand, to the Shinano River in Japan, is tied in with multipurpose projects in which flood control and irrigation are important elements.

In sum, the power potential of Asia is high, but the resource elements that contribute to that potential apparently are distributed in such a way as to leave certain areas power-short. Although mineral fuels can be transported for long distances, it is a costly business to carry north Chinese coal 3,000 miles to Singapore, unless transportation facilities are developed to the point where fuel carriage can be indirectly subsidized by more valuable cargoes moving in the opposite direction. Again, despite the fact that water-power resources are abundant, they also are highly localized and present engineering as well as fiscal problems that can be met only with difficulty. In terms of actual energy consumption, Asia, apart from the U.S.S.R., utilizes only 12 per cent of the world total and in terms of per-capita energy consumption lies at the bottom of the list.

The situation with regard to Asian *nonpower minerals* is similar. On an absolute basis Asia is mineral-wealthy; even on a per-capita basis it is far from poor; but in terms of production it ranks low on the world scale, although not so low as in its production of power. The locations of many of its minerals are disadvantageous, and even in the more densely populated countries there are vast areas that never have been mineralogically surveyed. An effective interpretation of the mineral potenial depends upon the continuous geological exploration of such areas as northeastern Siberia and the continental mountain core with its peripheral and associated uplands.

In general, all key metallic minerals are found in quantity in Asia. Iron-ore deposits among the largest and richest in the world are located in the Indian peninsula, occurring in the northeast in happy conjunction with coals of coking quality and with limestone. Iron ore also is mined in several places in Soviet Asia from Magnitogorsk to the Maritime Provinces. China possesses iron ore in moderate quantities in its central, northern, and northeastern regions, although its Manchurian ores are not of high grade; and northern Korea also possesses sizable deposits. Lateritic iron ores are mined in the Philippines, in Indochina, in Malaya, and in Indonesia, and although few of these deposits are of world importance, all are of great interest to Japan, which possesses only small deposits of its own.

Bauxite is mined in southeastern Asia in considerable quantities. Tin and tungsten are found in southwest China and in the southeastern countries, especially Thailand, Malaya, and Indonesia. India possesses the world's second largest deposits of manganese, and copper is found in marketable quantities in the arc of countries from India to Japan. The Philippines and Turkey are rich in chrome ores, and lead and zinc also

Fig. 5 • The Yang-tzu river gorge above I-ch'ang in central China is one of the great sources of hydroelectric power in Asia. As yet undeveloped, it is symbolic of the "white coal" resources of Asia. Many of the better Asian hydroelectric sites are inaccessible or are poorly located in relation to market areas and must await substantial economic development before becoming economically feasible. (Herold Wiens.)

are scattered widely, one of the major sources being pre-war Burma, although Soviet Asian production has since surpassed Burma's. Titanium ores are abundant in India, and nickel also is mined there as well as in the Soviet Union. Precious metals are no less widespread; gold has been one of the major metallic minerals produced in central India, eastern Siberia, Korea, T'ai-wan, and the Philippines.

Nonmetallic minerals are widely scattered. Salt comes primarily from the evaporation of sea water, although there are exceptions in the salt wells of Ssu-ch'uan (Szechwan). India is noted for its mica, Ceylon and Korea for their natural graphite. Potash is the distinctive product of the Dead Sea, but natural nitrates and phosphates, the bases for fertilizer industries, are not plentiful in Asia, unless the interior deserts prove more fruitful than is expected. Sulfur is produced in Japan; elsewhere it is available only in limited quantities, primarily in association with volcanic activity. In general, building stone is abundant, as is limestone for construction, smelting, and cement, except in the alluvial lowlands and in areas of recent volcanic eruptions and depositions.

As with fuels, the problem Asia faces with regard to minerals is in transporting them from their natural sites to the centers of demand. Because Asia itself, apart from the Soviet Union and Japan, is not a major consumer of minerals, either fuel or nonfuel, it ranks very high in terms of its mineral exports to the rest of the world, especially to western Europe and North America. Thus, Persian, Mesopotamian, and Arabian oil moves to the West; Indonesian and Bornean oil moves in part to Australia; Southeast Asian tin, bauxite, tungsten, chrome, and copper move to the United States and Europe; Dead Sea potash goes to Europe; Indian mica and Ceylonese and Korean graphite also move out of the continent. To a considerable extent this centrifugal flow of exports holds for Asian timber production: teak from India, Burma, and Thailand; and *lauan* (Philippine mahogany) from the Philippines. It is not strange, therefore, that one of the major non-Asian economic activities in Asia has been the exploitation of mineral and forest resources—the larger and more important producers or controllers of production being individuals or companies of Occidental origin.

At the same time, the flows of these raw materials within Asia itself are by no means inconsequential. Some Persian Gulf oil moves to India; Indian coal goes into southeastern Asia, as does Japanese coal; iron ore from India and southeastern Asia moves to Japan, as do lesser quantities of bauxite and the less important metallic minerals. It is important to note, however, that the chief Asian mineral importers are countries such as Japan and metropolises such as Singapore and Hongkong, which reflect or symbolize industrialization and the Western world, not traditional and indigenous Asia.

Asian Asia

PATTERNS AND PROBLEMS

THE PHYSICAL DIVERSITY OF ASIA THE CONTINENT IS MATCHED ONLY by its cultural heterogeneity. Just as there are several Asias definable in physical terms, so there are several Asias that can be distinguished on the basis of cultural differences. Most significant among these is the paradoxical division between the Asia that is Asian and the Asia that is not.

What is "Asian" Asia?

To a degree Asian Asia is a negative concept; it may be defined as that part of the Asiatic continent not fundamentally European in civilization. It does not include, therefore, most of Soviet Asia, which is culturally non-Asian, which is separated by vast distances from the parts of Asia that are, and which operates entirely as an appendage to the Russian heartland in Europe, spilling over into the western part of the Siberian plain and continuing eastward as a slender ribbon embracing the steel thread of the Trans-Siberian railway. Although the greater part of the Soviet Union lies in Asia, its traditional patterns of culture, whether Christian or Marxist, have long been oriented to and identified with Europe, despite the exotic overtones given to Russia long ago by Mongol conquerors. The fact that Russia borders upon most

21

of the rest of the Asian continent and that many minority groups are split by the 8,000-mile international boundary is exceptionally significant in Asian Asia's affairs. No discussion of the political and economic geography of the rest of the continent can help but return repeatedly to the political —and to a certain extent the cultural—influences that the Russian empire can and does bring to bear. Thus, although the Soviet Union lies outside the area of prime interest here, its areal relations with Asian Asia will be considered at length in Chapters XXXVIII and XXXIX.

Asian Asia also is a positive concept. It is the Asia that rims the southern and eastern margins of the great continent. This is the Asia that is populous; this is the Asia that is non-European, even if European-influenced. Here, in what is termed the *Asiatic Crescent,* in the valleys of the great rivers and in the oases of deserts and mountains, are the cores of lasting civilizations and modern nations. Very often these are separated from one another by expanses of largely unoccupied land—deserts, steppes, barren or forested mountains and plateaus—all of which singly or in association act as formidable barriers to communications (back end paper). Here also, all within a distance of some 750 miles from the sea, are some of the world's more densely populated regions, where the basis for livelihood is subsistence agriculture and where "vegetable" rather than "mechanical" civilizations predominate.

In terms of the problems and patterns of occupance and livelihood, Asian Asia displays in most of its parts similarities that provide a unity for geographic examination. This unity is further supported by the almost universal conflicts between nationalism and colonialism that characterize the area, providing the various countries within it with a uniformity of purpose and outlook in almost incongruous association with the cultural diversity that otherwise is apparent. In almost all of the Crescent, also, a revolution in social values is under way, termed by some a "revolution of rising expectations," by which the Asian peoples have set their eyes on goals of economic as well as political freedom and on the material attainments of the Western world.

Despite these unifying qualities, the Asiatic Crescent presents a range of cultural differences that is perhaps unmatched anywhere else in the world. From the western tip of the Crescent to its northeastern terminus in Hokkaido, its peoples present a near-infinite variety of languages, religions, ethnic complexes, personality structures, and forms of government and political control. Their patterns of occupance, though in some ways similar, range from the nomadic herding and transhumance of the Bedouin and Tibetan herdsman to the earth-bound solidity and permanency of the Chinese village. Furthermore, as already indicated in the previous chapter, the areal differentiation of natural conditions is fully as great from west to east as it is from north to south, and this is reflected in differences in numerous artifacts and cultural practices.

On the basis of these differences it is customary to divide the Crescent into four great realms or super-regions: Southwest Asia, South Asia, Southeast Asia, and East Asia. (These divisions provide the skeletal outline for the chapters that follow.) In addition, a fifth and essentially negative realm within the bow of the Crescent, Central or High Asia, sometimes is added: it consists of the associated high mountains, plateaus, and deserts that form the continental core lands. Since it possesses no political individuality, and since the bulk of this volume will be divided among major political units, High Asia will be treated together with the true Crescent countries, chiefly China, under the hegemony of which it falls.

It is considerably easier to establish a system of realms than it is to justify its validity. The great internal diversities that characterize each of the realms are reason enough for difficulty, and peripheral overlappings further complicate the task of classification. Thus, the concept of the realms must be regarded as a convenient, but by no means rigid, means for aiding understanding, which if carried to extremes may lead to oversimplification of complex reality.

Southwest Asia, which includes Turkey, Syria, Lebanon, Israel, Jordan, Iraq, Iran, and the Arabian peninsula, may be defined most briefly in terms of Islam and oil, nomadic herding and oasis agriculture, and its strategic crossroads position between Europe and the rest of the Crescent. Its unique natural quality lies in its aridity, although it shares this characteristic with interior Asia to the northeast, northern Africa to the west, and western Pakistan to the east, just as it also shares with these areas its predominantly Moslem faith.

South Asia includes India, Pakistan, Afghanistan, Ceylon, and the mountain states of Nepal, Bhutan, and Kashmir. The latter three possess a natural affinity with the mountain core, balanced by a traditional political orientation toward India. Afghanistan might well have been assigned to Southwest Asia, but its traditional political ties also have been with India. Moslem Pakistan itself in its western portion is little more than an extension of the Southwest Asian arid lands as they blend into humid Asia, but it is divided into two parts, the more populous eastern of which is imbedded in a regional matrix that is in both physical and cultural terms predominantly Indian. Ceylon differs culturally from the other countries primarily in that its religion is neither Islam nor Hinduism, but Theravada Buddhism. Yet, in spite of these great differences, South Asia may rightly be defined in terms of its Indian center of gravity, its former integration under British rule, the present membership of its countries in the British Commonwealth of Nations, its isolation from the rest of Asia by formidable mountain barriers, and its subjection to the far-from-uniform sway of the seasonal monsoon regime.

Southeast Asia—Burma, Thailand, the Associated States of Indochina, Malaya, Indonesia, British Borneo, and the Philippines—can best be defined initially in negative terms. It is neither Indian nor Chinese in culture, although it lies between the two and has been influenced substantially by both. It may also be identified by the strong maritime quality that its seas and its fragmented littoral impose, by its relatively less dense population and agricultural frontiers, and by its great diversity of ethnic groups, languages, religions, political systems, and states. Yet there are numerous connections with the other realms—ties, for example, with Pakistan and Southwest Asia through Islam in Indonesia and Malaya, and with South and East Asia by predominantly wet-rice agricultural lowlands, which are not far different from those in much of India and East Pakistan on the one hand and South China and Japan on the other.

East Asia, composed of China, Korea, and Japan, may best be identified in terms of two variables: a predominantly Sinitic culture and a largely middle-latitude position fronting the Pacific. However, Japan has long looked southward as well, and there are strong Malayan influences apparent in Japanese cultural forms. China's interests in Southeast Asia also are noteworthy. Japan's relatively advanced industrialization also helps differentiate East Asia from the other realms, as does the fact that non-Asian influences in the East Asian countries have never taken the form of full political control. Again, much of the diversity appearing in East Asian landscapes may be explained in terms of a degree of latitudinal and climatic diversity that is not duplicated in the other Asian realms.

Accessibility and communications

The Asiatic Crescent not only occupies the southern and eastern margins of Asia, but its commercial world view has been, at least since the middle of the nineteenth century, essentially maritime. This is true even though the indigenous Asian societies have by and large tried to maintain cultural isolation, as evidenced by the magnificent if ostrich-like refusal of eighteenth-century Imperial China to communicate with the West. With some exceptions the pressures upon the countries of the Crescent to look seaward have greatly increased since the close of the second World War, although the direct influences of the former imperial powers have declined substantially with the granting of political freedoms to their numerous former colonies and protectorates. At the same time, however, the rise of China as a major and aggressive power has created in its neighbors a new and singular awareness of its proximity.

Overland communications among the various Asian realms, and even among many of the individual countries within the realms, are remarkably few. Taking the Crescent as a whole, accessibility to interior Asia and the Soviet Union to the north is limited by the barrier of the mountain core and its associated ranges, plateaus, and desert wastes. The only railways connecting Crescent countries with the Soviet Union lie near the longitudinal extremes of the continent. In the west one railway runs eastward from Turkey into Soviet Armenia, though with a break in gauge near the border; a second line runs from Armenia only as far as Tabriz in northwestern Persia, but it does not connect with the main system that radiates outward from Tehran. In the east, a branch of the Trans-Siberian railway enters Manchuria at Man-chou-li, traverses that great region, and after crossing another international boundary terminates at Vladivostok. Several other Russian lines, parts of the Turk-Sib system, come close to the Persian and Afghan borders, but do not cross them. There is only one major rail connection across interior Asia at any point: a spur of the Trans-Siberian runs southward to Ulan Bator (Urga), the capital of Outer Mongolia, and thence to Kalgan in northern China. The Chinese also are constructing a railway northwestward across Ning-hsia and Hsin-chiang provinces to connect eventually with the Turk-Sib system. The only other railways leading to the outside world from the Crescent zone are one leading westward from European Turkey to Greece and Bulgaria, and a second along the eastern Mediterranean coast between Israel and Egypt, which was not, however, in commercial use in 1957.

Railway communications between the various realms are no less few. One line west from Pakistan just crosses the Persian border, but it is not connected with the sparse Iranian network. Similarly, no railways pierce the Himalayan barrier to the north of India-Pakistan, and there is no crossing of the difficult Burmese border ranges that separate India from Burma. Southeast Asia not only has no overland rail connections with South Asia, but its connections with China consist only of one meter-gauge line running from Hanoi in Tonkin to the Yün-nan boundary and a second line from Annam into Kuang-hsi province and thence into Hunan province and the main Chinese railway network.

Rail communications between individual countries within the realms are more numerous, but are still few in number. In Southwest Asia each country, except those of the Arabian peninsula, is connected with the others in the realm, although the lines are limited in number and they by no means provide the shortest distances between two points. In South Asia, however, India and Pakistan share a relatively dense railway net, one of the legacies of British rule. In Southeast Asia, Burma and Thailand have no operational rail connections; Thailand and Cambodia are linked by one operational line between Bangkok and Pnom Penh; and Thailand and Malaya share a line that connects Bangkok and Singapore. Indonesia and the Philippines, as island countries, have no rail links with the mainland. In the East Asian realm there are three major rail links, one of them double-tracked, between Manchuria and Korea. Between Japan and Korea differences in railway gauge prevent the operation of through-train ferries, although fast ferries make passenger and goods transfers quickly.

Highway communications between the Crescent and the rest of Eurasia are of even lesser dimensions than railway communications. Several passable roads connect eastern Turkey and northern Iran with the southernmost regions of the U.S.S.R. Several seasonal roads connect northern China with Outer Mongolia and Russia, the chief one trending northwestward through the so-called Kan-su (Ho-hsi) Corridor south of the Gobi. These and other routes through southern Hsin-chiang have for thousands of years been arteries of commerce between China and the West, but none of them can be regarded as a highway in the modern sense.

The realms similarly are isolated from each other by lack of highways across their forbidding boundaries. Southwest Asia has no paved roads leading into South Asia, although the famed Khyber and Bolan passes have many times provided ingress to India for invaders and traders—even before the time of Alexander. Northward from India are numerous trails into Tibet and China, but none of these is suitable for wheeled vehicles; eastward into Burma there exist only the seasonal and neglected Ledo (Union) Road of second-World-War fame from Assam and a lesser route through the state of Manipur midway along the Indo-Burmese boundary. Between Southeast Asia and China there are but a few connections, chief of which is the now little-used Burma Road between Lashio and K'unming.

Within the realms international highways link several of the countries of Southwest Asia, but even when paved they merely feed into little-developed national road systems. Only in South Asia does a well established highway system link the two main countries, and this is primarily the result of a division of what formerly had been an integrated system. In the Southeast Asian mainland countries, all-year roads connect northeastern Thailand with Indochina at three points, but there are no through routes between Thailand and Burma or between Thailand and Malaya. In East Asia the road links between Manchuria and Korea cannot compare with the railway connections, and neither country possesses well developed internal road systems.

In recent years the rapid development of air transportation has to a small degree countered the paucity of external and internal overland communications. Several major air lines link the countries of the Crescent westward with Europe and eastward across the Pacific with the United States. Some services have come to be operated also between Soviet territory and China and Korea. Most commercial services, however, tend to skirt the southern margins of the continent, following the curve of the Crescent itself. The main routes from London and western Europe to Tokyo do not follow the approximate Great Circle through Leningrad, Irkutsk, and Vladivostok, but instead follow a reverse arc through Rome, Cairo, Lydda, Basra, Karachi, Calcutta, Rangoon, Bangkok, and Hong-kong. That political factors encourage this routing is at once apparent, but it is even more significant that the major air services tend to serve the Asia that is both populous and Asian. In general, air services are locally important for the movement of passengers and especially valuable cargo and for the transport of mail and passengers from the outside world; they are of very minor—if increasing—importance in most movements of commercial freight and in the transport of Asians within the Crescent.

The main transport routes are marine. The coasts of the Crescent countries are rimmed with harbors of various capacities, among which are some of the world's major ports. Most of these latter are equipped with well developed port facilities, and to them come regularly scheduled ocean liners not much smaller than those that ply the North Atlantic. Many of them also act as entrepôts, among which coastal vessels, both Western and native, carry on extensive cabotage. Singapore and Hong-kong are famous entrepôts, but Bombay, Madras, Colombo, Calcutta, Rangoon, Penang, Manila, Jakarta, Shang-hai, Tientsin (T'ien-ching), Yokohama, and Kobe also have entrepôt functions. To a large degree the great port cities act as the centers of commercial and industrial activity; to a lesser degree they are centers of political activity and control.

The eastern maritime approaches to Asia follow two routes across the Pacific. One is nearest the Great Circle route across the North Pacific from the Pacific west coast of North America to Yokohama, Shang-hai, Hongkong, and Manila. The southern route via Honolulu is followed by most vessels that sail from North American Atlantic and Gulf ports and that enter the Pacific through the Panama Canal. These seaward approaches to Asia from the East cross what is in almost every respect, since the relative decline of Japan as a leading maritime power, an American sea.

The approaches from the west, however, are through the maritime gate at Suez (Figure 6), and the Indian Ocean is in shipping terms a European sea, as evidenced by the European flags that predominate within it. Singapore, overlooking the eastern entrance to the Indian Ocean, the Strait of Malakka, acts as a convenient point of division between the essentially European Indian Ocean and the predominantly American

Fig. 6 • Looking northward along the Suez Canal just north of the Great Bitter Lake. At the left is one of the control stations along the canal. Except at a few places and at one major by-pass, the canal is too narrow to permit the passage of two vessels without danger of their going aground. Thus, ships are piloted through the canal in convoys of half a dozen or more vessels. When sandstorms or fogs obscure visibility, ships tie up alongside the canal banks until they pass. This 100-mile ditch cut through the sandy isthmus connecting the Mediterranean with the Red Sea carries more than twice as much traffic as the Panama Canal. Through it passes most of the trade of Asia with western Europe. Through it also passes about two-thirds of the petroleum exported from the Near East. *(Wellington D. Jones.)*

North Pacific, although European, and particularly English, companies are engaged in trade along the Asian coasts east of Singapore to a degree symbolized by the commercial wealth and maritime importance of Hongkong. In addition, Japanese shipping, after a near-shattering decline at the end of the second World War, has begun to regain its previous importance in Far Eastern and, to a lesser degree, in trans-Pacific trade.

The ports of Southwest Asia, however—with the exception of Port Said, which is technically in Africa but acts as an entrepôt for part of the realm —tend to lie off the traditional ocean routes connecting Asia with western Europe and North America. Most of the Mediterranean ports are relatively small and are served by both large and small companies whose center of operations, with some exceptions, is the Mediterranean itself. Istanbul provides an exception, serving as the chief port for Turkey and as an entrepôt astride the narrow water gate separating the Black Sea, which is the most important maritime outlet for the Soviet Union, from the Mediterranean. Certain other Southwest Asian ports vie in shipping-tonnage terms with the major ports of the world, but these for the most part are special-function ports. For example, those located at the head of the Persian Gulf are devoted primarily to the export of petroleum products by tankers, many of which enter them in ballast.

The shipping routes that girt the Asiatic Crescent coasts extend for thousands of miles. The arterial trade route between Suez and Kobe covers 8,100 nautical miles by way of Aden, Colombo, and Singapore, nearly twice the distance from Seattle to Yokohama. The sea-route distance from Singapore to Kobe alone is some 3,100 nautical miles, approximately the same as that of the trans-Atlantic crossing from New York to Liverpool. The route from Suez to Bombay covers a similar distance, and the coastal route between Bombay and Calcutta measures 2,150 miles.

These great distances mean that the movement of freight even by sea, the cheapest medium of general cargo transportation, is costly. They mean also that freight rates within the area often are higher than those elsewhere, and this fact helps account for the pre-eminence in Asian pre-war shipping of the Japanese merchant marine, which had the great advantage of home ports on the very edge of the Crescent. In the postwar world, it means that the costs of commodities produced in the Western world frequently are higher to the Asian consumer, whose purchasing power is low to begin with, than to the consumer in western Europe or in the United States. Because of these great distances, also, vessels on the Europe—Suez—Indian-Ocean—Far-East route or the North-America—East-Asia—trans-Pacific route usually make numerous stops along the way, in contrast to vessels on the North Atlantic run, this latter run being an extreme example of a transoceanic ferry. Many vessels, both cargo and passenger carriers, find it profitable to participate in round-the-world services. In this connection it is important to note that the distance from American east-coast ports to Hongkong is about the same by way of the Atlantic and Suez as by way of Panama and the Pacific. Lastly, the strategic position of Colombo is reflected in the convergence of ocean routes upon it. As one of the major ports of call for shipping to and from Asia, Colombo acts as a focus of shipping services between Europe and South, Southeast, and East Asia, between Europe and Australia, and between East and South Africa and all but the westernmost parts of the Crescent.

The patterns of culture

The theme of diversity and complexity that applies to the Asian Crescent is well displayed in the distribution of ethnic, religious, and linguistic groups within it. (Maps 3, 18, 24, and 28b). In the Southwest, Arabs, Persians, and Turks are the

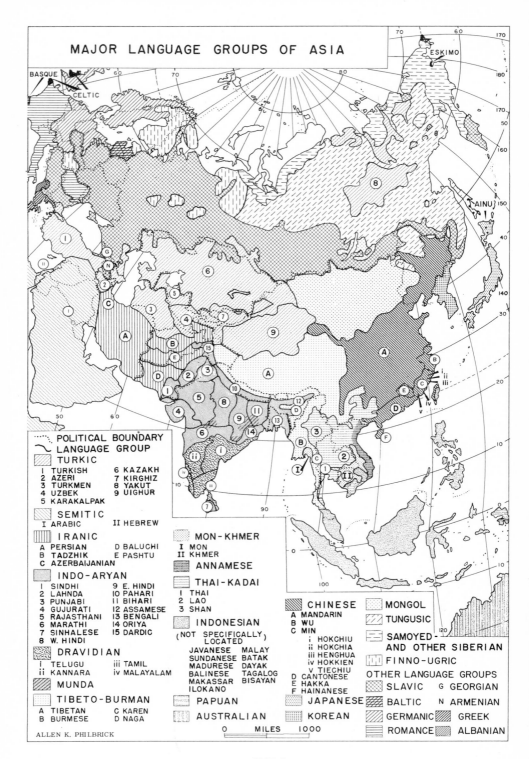

MAJOR LANGUAGE GROUPS OF ASIA

ESKIMO

BASQUE

CELTIC

AINU

POLITICAL BOUNDARY
LANGUAGE GROUP

TURKIC
1 TURKISH	6 KAZAKH
2 AZERI	7 KIRGHIZ
3 TURKMEN	8 YAKUT
4 UZBEK	9 UIGHUR
5 KARAKALPAK	

SEMITIC
I ARABIC   II HEBREW

IRANIC
A PERSIAN	D BALUCHI
B TADZHIK	E PASHTU
C AZERBAIJANIAN	

INDO-ARYAN
1 SINDHI	9 E. HINDI
2 LAHNDA	10 PAHARI
3 PUNJABI	11 BIHARI
4 GUJURATI	12 ASSAMESE
5 RAJASTHANI	13 BENGALI
6 MARATHI	14 ORIYA
7 SINHALESE	15 DARDIC
8 W. HINDI	

DRAVIDIAN
| i TELUGU | iii TAMIL |
| ii KANNARA | iv MALAYALAM |

MUNDA

TIBETO-BURMAN
| A TIBETAN | C KAREN |
| B BURMESE | D NAGA |

ALLEN K. PHILBRICK

MON-KHMER
I MON
II KHMER

ANNAMESE

THAI-KADAI
1 THAI
2 LAO
3 SHAN

INDONESIAN
(NOT SPECIFICALLY LOCATED)
JAVANESE	MALAY
SUNDANESE	BATAK
MADURESE	DAYAK
BALINESE	TAGALOG
MAKASSAR	BISAYAN
ILOKANO	

PAPUAN

AUSTRALIAN

CHINESE
| A MANDARIN |
| B WU |
| C MIN |
| i HOKCHIU |
| ii HOKCHIA |
| iii HENGHUA |
| iv HOKKIEN |
| v TIECHIU |
| D CANTONESE |
| E HAKKA |
| F HAINANESE |

JAPANESE

KOREAN

MONGOL

TUNGUSIC

SAMOYED- AND OTHER SIBERIAN

FINNO-UGRIC

OTHER LANGUAGE GROUPS
SLAVIC	G GEORGIAN
BALTIC	N ARMENIAN
GERMANIC	GREEK
ROMANCE	ALBANIAN

0   MILES   1000

MAP 3

predominant ethnic groups. Not only are these divided, however, among themselves into various national political units, but also there are important less numerous or minority peoples within the realm such as the Israelis, Kurds, Azerbaijanians, and Armenians. In South Asia the terms "Indian" and "Pakistani" refer to two nationalities rather than to ethnic entities, since each country contains numerous peoples having significant cultural distinctions—Afghans, Punjabi, Rajputs, Sikhs, Bengali, Tamils, and Nepalese, to name a few. In Southeast Asia the several separate political states each contain numerous minority peoples, such as the Shan and Karens in Burma and Thailand, the so-called Moi of Indochina, the Moros and Negritos of the Philippines, and the Menangkabau of Indonesian Sumatra or the Dyaks of Borneo (Kalimantan). It is possible to extend greatly the list of differing peoples in Indonesia if one recognizes the Javanese, Sudanese, Madurese, and Balinese, for example, as having distinctive ethnic character. In East Asia, China exhibits wondrous ethnic diversity, despite its vast and monolithic culture, especially in its marchlands, where Mongols, Tibetans, Uighurs, Uzbeks, Thai, and the aborigines of Taiwan form only a partial list of the minorities. In Korea and Japan ethnic homogeneity is perhaps greater than elsewhere; both represent Sinitic variants, though so differentiated with time that they have come to possess distinctive if related culture patterns of their own.

Religious differences within the Crescent are no less significant. Predominantly Islamic Southwest Asia includes important Christian enclaves, as in Lebanon, and a Judaic island in Israel. South Asia includes not merely Moslems and Hindus, but numerous Moslem and Hindu sects, as well as sizable minorities of Christians in the more urbanized areas, animists in the peninsular and Assamese hills, and Mahayana Buddhists in the northern mountain border regions. In Southeast Asia, Theravada Buddhism in Burma and Thailand contrasts with the Catholicism of the Philippines, the predominant Mohammedanism of Indonesia, and the Chinese eclecticism of the Annamese; animists hold firm in the sparsely populated uplands or peripheral islands of each country. In East Asia, the Confucian code of ethics dominates much of China, though in conflict with a rising tide of Communism and in association with impressive numbers of Moslems and Mahayana Buddhists among the minority peoples of the west and with Christians in the coastal areas of the east. In Japan Buddhism resides in peculiar amalgam with state Shintoism, both overlain with Chinese influences and underlain by a still-important animism, while in the larger cities Christianity has numerous converts.

Cultural complexity is further evidenced in terms of linguistic differences. The actual variety of languages and dialects in Asian Asia defies brief description, but in general there are differences of such dimensions that mutual incomprehensibility is the rule rather than the exception.

Arabic, Turkish, Hebrew, and Persian in the Southwest; Hindi and related dialects in northern India and Tamil, Malayalam, and Telegu in the
south; Burmese, Thai, Annamese, and the Malayan dialects in the southeast; and Chinese in its various forms, Korean, and Japanese in East Asia,
represent only a sample of the languages and dialects that are to a very
large degree mutually unintelligible, if not in written, then in spoken
form. The interchange of scripts, words, and ideas within languages that
further complicate the problem is indicated in the case of Chinese,
Korean, and Japanese. The latter two are much indebted to Chinese for
forms of writing and numerous words and sounds, but all three languages have different linguistic origins, and none of the three in colloquial
form is similar to the others.

The number of significantly differing languages and dialects within
certain countries has made it necessary to establish, or attempt to establish, so-called "national" or "official" languages. In China, where a common written language is shared by all ethnic Chinese, there are several
groups of 30 million persons or more who speak dialects not comprehensible to their ethnic brethren. Thus, there has been established a
national language, *kuo-yü* or the state language, based upon the Peking
dialect, sometimes referred to as Mandarin. In the Philippines, where
Malayan languages predominate, Tagalog has been established as the national language, although more people speak another Malayan language,
Bisayan, and English is commonly used as the *lingua franca* of commerce.
In Indonesia, where Malayan languages also predominate, dialectical differences have been so great that a national tongue, Bahasa Indonesia, has
been established, and the government has ordered the substitution of
Roman script for the traditional Arabic script which came with Islam
into Southeast Asia. In the Republic of India it is planned to establish
Hindi as the national language, over the objections of the Dravidian-
speaking peoples of the south and despite the use of English again as a
lingua franca. Similarly, Pakistan may establish Urdu, a Hindi variant,
as its national language, over the objections of the Bengalis in East
Pakistan. In Southwest Asia linguistic variations, though considerable,
have been limited by the widespread use of Arabic and Arabic scripts,
although shortly after the first World War Turkey officially replaced an
Arabic with a Roman script for its non-Semitic language, and in addition
linguistic enclaves are formed by minorities of varying ethnic derivations.

Patterns of population and settlement

Along with these cultural dif-
ferences among and within the realms and the countries that comprise

them, there are considerable differences in the distribution of populations (back end paper). In general, the population pattern of Asian Asia
is characterized by heavy densities in the better-watered and more fertile
coastal and fluvial lowlands, usually with relatively easy access to the sea.
Estimated average densities differ widely, however, from realm to realm:
in Southwest Asia, 30 per square mile; in Southeast Asia, 102 per square
mile; in South Asia, 233; and in East Asia as a whole, an estimated 150.

TABLE II-1

ESTIMATED POPULATION OF ASIA, 1954 °
(by realms)

Realm	Population in millions	Density per sq. mi.
East Asia	712	150
Southeast Asia	183	102
South Asia	489	233
Southwest Asia	67	30

° Source: UN, *Demographic Yearbook, 1955.*

In Southwest Asia population is concentrated largely in Mediterranean
coastlands, in small oases, in river basins such as that of the Tigris-
Euphrates, and in intermontane basins and plateaus, as in central Turkey
and northwestern Persia. Local variations in densities are very great, and
in some of the oases and irrigated basins rural densities of 1,000 per square
mile may be found.

In South Asia densities range from those of 2,000 per square mile in
portions of the Indo-Gangetic plain to almost uninhabited regions in
Kashmir. In general, the population map shows the heaviest population
densities in the plain and in the coastal lowlands of peninsular India. As
compared with Southwest Asia, however, there is a more even distribution of population in all but westernmost South Asia.

Southeast Asia is characterized by vast areas of sparsely populated
land, lying between relatively restricted population cores where local
densities run as high as in the north of India, but where gross population
densities are much less. Higher densities are associated with the fluvial
plains of the realm, with the notable exception of Java, where some of
the densest population groupings in Asia occur on uplands, as well as on
plains, that are nourished by basic ejecta from still active volcanoes.

In East Asia the same general pattern holds as in Southeast Asia but on
a much larger scale, with the bulk of the population residing in the
coastal and riverine lowlands of China, Japan, and Korea. However, most
of western China, Tibet, and Outer Mongolia have average densities of
only 7 per square mile, while portions of the lower Yangtze and Hsi river
plains and the coastal lowlands of Japan and Korea have densities approaching 2,000 per square mile. If the sparsely settled regions of interior

Asia are subtracted from the rest of East Asia, the remaining 55 per cent of the realm possesses an average density of over 200 per square mile, more nearly comparable with the 223 of South Asia than with the 150 of the whole. Even so, areas of sparse and scattered settlement, not only in China but also in Korea and Japan, account for by far the larger part of even the eastern portion of the realm.

Demographic patterns and trends throughout Asian Asia are characterized by very high birth rates in association with high death rates and very high infant mortality rates. In general, the rate of population increase as represented by the differences between crude birth and death rates is relatively low. The age distribution curves of the various national populations also resemble each other. The people of the Crescent in general are young, and they are young because they usually do not live long enough to become old. To cite an extreme example, in India, of every 100,000 male children born in a given year, only 34 per cent can expect to be alive at the age of 40; in the United States the equivalent percentage is over 85 per cent. In Thailand, a more nearly average case, 51 per cent can expect to be alive at 40. It should be noted, however, that the low life expectancy in most of Asia reflects very high infant mortality; even if this bias is accounted for, the life expectancy of the Indian child of 5 is only 39 years more.

Although the average *rate* of population increase in Asia is quite low, about the same as that of the United States, the actual annual increases are enormous owing to the huge populations involved. Thus, if the rate of increase for India is assumed to be a conservative 1.26 per cent, this means an annual increment of 4.5 millions and a decennial increase of about 50 millions. In China similar increases can be expected.

An even more serious problem arises from the trend toward declining death rates without concomitant declines in birth rates. In most regions, death rates have been declining steadily though slowly for decades. Thus, Java's population has multiplied fivefold since the first half of the nineteenth century, and Japan has increased her population two and one-half times since 1870. Death rates in certain other areas, as in Ceylon, T'ai-wan, Syria, Lebanon, and Malaya, have fallen very sharply since 1930 to European levels. In the cases of Ceylon and Taiwan at least, however, birth rates have not fallen similarly; and their rates of increase are between 3 and 4 per cent or more. Elsewhere, even in India and China, death rates have been declining, though they are still about three times the Western levels; however, birth rates have remained sufficiently high to create an ever-widening gap between births and death, with the overwhelming advantage to the former. Herein is one of the great problems of Asia: an uncoiling spiral of expanding population which cannot help but rapidly increase the pressure of Asians upon their physical resources.

The traditional Asian society is based upon the village community, and the bulk of Asians in all the countries of the Crescent live in hamlets or villages. Only in the more rugged and less densely populated regions are examples of dispersed settlement found. In almost all countries urbanism in the Western sense remains foreign to the traditional patterns of settlement, and the number of great multifunctional metropolises is notably few when considered in relation to the population numbers involved.

There were, of course, great cities in Southwest, South, East, and even in Southeast Asia before European influences made their appearance in force. Yet these cities for the most part performed a specialized function in that they were political centers, most often being the only political centers within their countries. They contained the seats of government, the sites of the royal palaces, the residences of the court nobles, and the homes and shops of countless artisans and other persons engaged in serving the needs of the court and its hangers-on. Essentially, this sort of city was parasitic in its functional relations with its hinterland, which in most cases included an entire country. The city performed few services for its hinterland other than administrative ones. In Edo, now called Tokyo, the seat of the Tokugawa Shogunate in pre-Meiji Japan, the produce of the nation pouring into the city was largely in the form of tax levies in grain and other tribute for which little was returned to the countryside. The same sort of functions characterized Ch'ang-an (now Hsi-an), capital of China during the Han dynasty; Hang-chou, capital of China during the later Sung; and Peking, capital during the Ming and Ch'ing reigns. Agra and Delhi, capitals of the Mogul empire in India, provide additional examples. If these great capitals were situated near tidewater or on navigable rivers it was in most cases sheer coincidence, since they were centers of societies that primarily were internally rather than externally oriented.

Within the past century there has been a rapid growth of cities on Western lines, especially along the seacoasts of the Asiatic Crescent and along the more modern communications routes within individual countries. Yet the relative rarity of such cities on a large scale is illustrated in the case of China, which in a population of nearly 600 millions has only seven cities of over one million population. In the United States, by comparison, there are 12 such cities in a population one-third the size. Even in relatively industrialized Japan, which contains six cities of about one million population or over, there is a peculiar lack of cities between 500,000 and one million.

Urbanization in Asia is of the greatest importance, nevertheless—if not in terms of the numbers of people directly involved in the process, then in terms of the increasingly important roles that the cities are playing in the processes of change that dominate the Asian scene.

Pluralism and the
problem of Asia

One of the major features of homogeneity in Asiatic Asia is a widespread cultural and economic pluralism, which to a high degree contains the kernel of the problem of Asia.

The world of the Asian village, agriculturally based, relatively small, restricted in outlook, inbred, and self-sufficient, contrasts with the world symbolized by the great and modern port cities of the Crescent, externally oriented and in contact with the one world of international commerce

Fig. 7 • The villages of Asia are based upon an agriculture that is substantially self-sufficient, as reflected in this wet-rice, terraced landscape in west-central Java near Bandung. *(Norton Ginsburg.)*

(Figures 7 and 8). This contrast is one aspect of the basic pluralism that appears almost everywhere in Asia. The two worlds, however, are not completely separated. Improved communications, the transition from a barter to a money economy, and some raising of educational levels, all have resulted in substantial increases in communication between the traditional village and the essentially foreign city. The consequence has been a gradual, if localized, decay in the stability and self-sufficiency of the traditional Asian systems of cultural and economic organization and the partial substitution of Western values. Another consequence has been the fostering in Asians of economic expectations that are not clearly ac-

Fig. 8 • In contrast to the Asian rural landscape is the urban landscape of the great cities such as Jakarta—Western-oriented, commercial, often politically dominant. *(Republic of Indonesia Information Office.)*

37

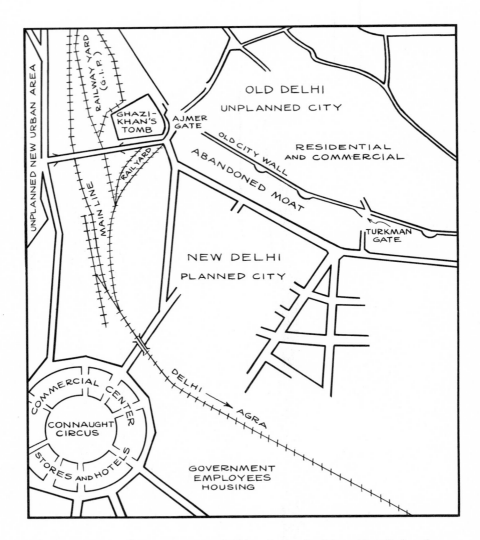

Fig. 9 • Rarely is the juxtaposition of old and new in Asian cities displayed more clearly than in the aerial photograph (opposite) of India's capital city, Delhi. The above diagram identifies the densely occupied, unplanned old city with its walls and moat, built after 1638 A.D., which appears in the upper right. The urban pattern is irregular; the crooked narrow streets and dwellings arranged about private courtyards suggest leaf veins and cells when viewed under the magnifying glass. Railways do not enter the city, but remain outside the wall. In contrast is the spacious governmental city with wide avenues laid out in geometric plan on the model of baroque cities such as Paris and Washington. At the lower left is Connaught Circus about which modern hotels and commercial buildings are grouped. Government buildings occupy the center of the photograph, and government employees' housing appears in the lower and lower right portions. (*Air Survey Company of India, Ltd.*)

companied by proportional increases in the opportunities for satisfying those expectations. Thus there has developed what some have termed a "revolt of the clerks," those Asians of some education but little opportunities, and on a broader basis the "revolution of rising expectations," the satisfaction of which is made all the more difficult by rapid population increases, by increasing pressures on the land, by inadequate transportation facilities, and by scarcities of capital and skilled labor forces.

Although the contacts between the indigenous and foreign cultures have been increasing rapidly, there are vast gaps still between them. In the plural economy, particularly, various sectors operate along parallel rather than interrelated lines. Three distinctive landscape phenomena may be used to illustrate the workings of this system: (1) the great city, (2) the plantation, and (3) the large-scale mining enterprise.

The first of these has already been discussed in related contexts. The impact of the *great city* upon the countryside cannot be minimized, but to a large extent its immediate influence is limited to a relatively restricted hinterland, and it remains basically non-Asian, an essentially foreign and anomalous element in the indigenous landscape. Although some of the modern coastal cities such as Hongkong and Singapore were founded within recent times by Europeans, most of the large metropolises were expanded from previously existing towns of much smaller size. In many cases a foreign "concession" or "cantonment" was tacked onto the older town, as in the case of several of the China treaty ports or certain of the Indian cities. In other cases the newly acquired commercial functions, and sometimes industrial and political functions, became localized in new areas adjacent to the old city; some of these areas in time became much larger than the old town (Figure 9). In some regions, where there have developed modern cities that have assumed the main commercial functions of the country and sometimes its chief political functions, there also remain older, traditional capitals which retain political significance or which remain cultural centers of importance. Thus, in Java there is modern Jakarta with its port of Tanjong Priok, and Jogjakarta, the traditional center; in Burma there are Rangoon and Mandalay; in Japan, Tokyo and the more ancient capital, Kyoto; in Turkey, Ankara and Istanbul, a variation on the pattern; and in China, Peking, Nanking, and Hsi-an versus Canton, Hongkong, Shang-hai, Ch'ing-tao, Tientsin, and Dairen. In some cases, of course, a traditional political and cultural capital also has become a modern commercial center, as have Delhi, Bangkok, Mukden, and Tokyo. However, especially in Delhi and Bangkok, the transformations have been accompanied by the addition of an essentially new and modern city along the peripheries of the old.

Since the second of the landscape features identifying the plural economy, the *plantation* or *estate,* is primarily a tropical and colonial phenomenon, it is not strange to find it chiefly in those tropical and sub-tropical areas of Asia where colonialism was practiced over long periods. The estate is a distinguishing feature of the rural occupance pattern in parts of India, Ceylon, Malaya, Indonesia, the Philippines, and Taiwan; it is less significant yet notable in Thailand, Indochina, and Burma; it is of little general significance in middle-latitude East Asia and in subhumid Southwest Asia. With some qualifications, the estate remains a foreign enclave in the country wherein it is sited; its relation to the indigenous economy is primarily through the value of its overseas exports to the con-trolling government; both the capital and management of the enterprise are in foreign hands. To some extent it may not be wholly isolated from the indigenous predominantly subsistence economies, since in Taiwan and Java, for example, individual farmers contract to sell their sugar cane to the sugar companies, which produce relatively little on their own lands. In many cases, also, the estates draw upon domestic labor forces, but it is also true that in Malaya, for example, the bulk of the rubber-estate labor is not Malay, but Chinese or Indian. In this instance, the dualistic quality of the plantation has developed into a truly plural one, with Europeans, Chinese, Indians, and Malays participating.

At an increasing rate, also, the products of the plantation are being produced by individual Asian "smallholders." About a third of the rubber of Malaya and Sumatra is produced by these entrepreneurs who own a few acres of trees and associated subsistence crop lands which carry them through adverse periods of low rubber prices. Similar conditions char-acterize the production of coconut products, which are produced largely by smallholders who keep one foot each in the commercial and local sub-sistence worlds. Where there is great domestic as well as foreign demand for a plantation product, however, as there is for tea in China and Japan, production generally takes place on small holdings rather than on true estates as in Assam and Ceylon. Similarly, rice is not produced on planta-tions even in the surplus trinity of Burma, Thailand, and Indochina, al-though production by tenants on subdivided large holdings is common; and the production of cotton in both India and China likewise takes place primarily on small holdings.

Mining illustrates even more clearly the role of foreign enterprise in the Crescent countries. With the exception again of Japan, and more recently of China and India, almost all large-scale mining activity has been as-sociated with foreign capital and management and an export trade. In Southwest Asia the petroleum resources, largest in the world, of Iraq, Iran, and the Arabian peninsula, have been exploited almost entirely by European companies, which pay royalties to the country involved (Fig-ure 10). The same is true of the petroleum resources of Indonesia, Burma, and British Borneo; of the tin of Malaya, Thailand, and Indonesia; of the

Fig. 10 • Characteristic of the role of foreign enterprise in developing the mineral resources of the Asiatic Crescent countries are the oil installations in Southwest Asia. Here at Abqaiq is one of the oil wells of the Arabian American Oil Company in Saudi Arabia, a tiny sample of the vast well system that has made Saudi Arabia the most important single oil-producing country in the Near East. In the foreground is a pipeline that supplies water to the settlements associated with the oil installations. These and other facilities act as focal attractions for the settlement of Arab nomads who pitch their tents or erect crude huts near them. Here, women and children are drawing water, the most significant natural resource other than petroleum in the dry Southwest, from the pipeline. Their encampment is in the middle ground. Note the complete absence of vegetation and the prevalence of a sandy surface. Elsewhere in the Near East, as in the vicinity of mines elsewhere in Asia, large permanent mining settlements have been constructed, largely by foreign enterprise. The larger part of the population in these "towns" is composed of semiskilled native or immigrant Asian workmen who have been trained with the foreign companies. The men thus acquire both new skills and a new awareness of the West which they might not obtain in any other way. (Standard Oil Co., N.J.)

iron ore of the Philippines, Malaya, and Indochina; of the lead, silver, and precious stones of Burma; and of the gold and chrome ores of the Philippines. In East Asia, Manchurian and Korean mineral production was developed by the Japanese, but in China proper the largest coal-mining enterprise was under British control. In Malaya, the foreign element inherent in the mining industry is further complicated by the ownership of many tin mines by Chinese and by the import of Chinese labor for most of the tin mines.

In general, mining activities have been isolated somewhat more than the estates from local societies, since the native Asian has not been able to compete with the mining company as he has with the estate. Yet the importance of foreign mineral exploitation to rulers and governments within the Crescent is almost incalculable. At the same time, the post-war trend has been toward nationalization in one form or another, and in Persia, Burma, Indonesia, and China, among others, private foreign ownership and exploitation of minerals has either been eliminated or severely curtailed.

The livelihood and developmental problems of Asia provide one major· unifying element in dealing with a part of the world of which the diversity may appear discouragingly great. In Asian Asia the basis for livelihood in every country, with the possible exception of Japan, is agriculture, often irrigated agriculture. Most of the population is rural and resides in small village occupance units. In almost all areas, in Japan to a lesser degree, agricultural productivity is low, technologies are primitive, if often effective, and major seasonal surpluses of labor are everywhere in evidence. The ratio of population to cultivated land is enormously high, absolutely as well as relative to Western standards, and this fact is all the more significant in the light of the relatively few livelihood opportunities other than agriculture. Industrialization has not taken place, or is taking place slowly, again with the Japanese exception, and where it is proceeding the problem of acquiring skilled labor in countries where practical literacy is shockingly low provides constant barriers to change and development.

In brief, the Crescent areas are characterized by poverty, by overpopulation relative to arable land and current agricultural practices, by potential or actual rapid increases in population, by folk societies ill-prepared for rapid social and economic change, by burgeoning nationalisms which in their often irrational orientations demand a paradoxical mating of painless industrialization with traditional noneconomic value systems. In addition, the basic problem is made even more difficult by the absence or limitation of well-rounded resource endowments for many individual countries, or even for groups of them, and by the processes of political and social change which are creating a fundamentally altered geography for Asia.

SELECTED GEOGRAPHICAL BIBLIOGRAPHY

1. Cressey, G. B. *Asia's Lands and Peoples.* New York: McGraw-Hill, 1951.
2. *Development of Upland Areas in the Far East.* New York: Institute of Pacific Relations, 1949 (2 volumes, mimeographed).
3. East, W. G., and O. H. K. Spate. *The Changing Map of Asia.* London: Methuen, 1950.

4. Gourou, P. *L'Asie*. Paris: Hachette, 1953.
5. Gregory, J. W., ed. *The Structure of Asia*. London: Methuen, 1929.
6. Kendrew, W. G. *Climate of the Continents,* chap. 18-26. Oxford: Clarendon Press, 1937.
7. Murphey, Rhoads. "New Capitals of Asia," *Economic Development and Cultural Change,* April, 1957, pp. 216-43.
8. Pelzer, K. J. *Population and Land Utilization,* Vol. I of *An Economic Survey of the Pacific Area*. New York: Institute of Pacific Relations, 1941.
9. Peterson, A. D. C. *The Far East*. London: Duckworth, 1949.
10. Rosinger, L. A., ed. *The State of Asia*. New York: Institute of Pacific Relations, 1951.
11. SCAP, Natural Resources Section. *Sources of Iron Ore in Asia,* Report No. 154. Tokyo: 1952.
12. Spencer, J. E., and W. L. Thomas. "Hill Stations and Summer Resorts of the Orient," *Geographical Review,* October, 1948.
13. Spencer, J. E. *Asia East by South*. New Work: Wiley, 1954.
14. Stamp, L. D. *Asia*. New York: E. P. Dutton, 1950.
15. Thompson, W. S. *Population and Peace in the Pacific*. Chicago: University of Chicago Press, 1946.
16. United Nations Economic Commission for Asia and the Far East. *Economic Survey of Asia and the Far East*. New York: (annual since 1947).
17. ————. *Flood Damage and Flood Control Activities in Asia and the Far East*. Bangkok: 1950.
18. Wickizer, V. D., and M. K. Bennett. *Rice Economy of Monsoon Asia*. Stanford: Food Research Institute, 1941.

Comments

The above listing includes only those references that deal with two or more of the four major Asian realms.

Cressey, East and Spate, Gourou, Peterson, Spencer, and Stamp are general texts. Cressey is the most complete descriptive reference source; East and Spate is most valuable for portraying the background and changes in Asia's political and social geography.

Pelzer is a convenient statistical reference for the prewar period in East and Southeast Asia. Postwar information and trends are found in the annual reports of the United Nations Economic Commission for Asia and the Far East. Wickizer and Bennett is the classic monograph on rice culture and trade in Asia other than in Southwest Asia. Rosinger is a useful summary of postwar political and economic developments in Asia outside of Southwest Asia by non-geographers.

In addition, valuable materials on Asian geography may be found in the journals, *Pacific Affairs, Far Eastern Survey,* and *Far Eastern Quarterly* (since 1957 the *Journal of Asian Studies*) although none are devoted primarily to geographical problems, and in the specialized publications of the United Nations and the American and British governments. Eight Asian countries have been covered in the series *Overseas Economic Surveys,* published by Her Majesty's Stationery Office, London, and several others are in preparation.

Asian map coverage is highly varied and at larger scales is both preliminary and incomplete. The National Geographic Society publishes good maps of

Asia and its major realms. Most of the continent is covered at 1:4,000,000 in a set published by the British Geographical Section, General Staff; the larger part of it covered at 1:1,000,000 in the *International Map of the World* series. Each country has been mapped in whole or part at larger scales, but only Japan, Korea, Taiwan, Java-Madura, Burma, India, Pakistan, and Israel, among the major countries or regions, have been covered fully by topographic quadrangles. At the time of writing, also, the *Oxford Economic Atlas of Asia* was in preparation.

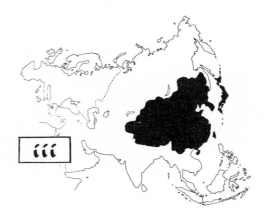

$\mathcal{E}$ast $\mathcal{A}$sia

AN INTRODUCTION

EAST ASIA IS UNIQUE AMONG THE OTHER REALMS OF ASIAN ASIA IN that none of the three countries that compose it—China, Japan, Korea—ever has been under the direct political control of a non-Asian country. That there have been considerable periods during which each of the three countries has been under the political, economic, or cultural domination of the others is well known. Yet, unlike Southwest Asia, South Asia, and most of Southeast Asia, the East Asian realm has remained free from foreign control, although foreign influences have played important roles in defining the positions of China, Korea, and Japan in the world political and economic order.

Whereas the rest of Asian Asia had been divided largely into colonial territories, mandates, and spheres of influence by the close of the first World War, the political independence from the West of the East Asian countries was at that time well defined. In general, their political independence has depended upon two factors that serve to set them off from the countries and regions of the rest of the Asiatic Crescent. These are the *geographical situation* of the realm and the remarkable *political and cultural stability* of the societies that reside within it.

East Asia and the "Far East"

East Asia, as its name implies, occupies most of eastern Eurasia. Farthest, therefore, from the centers of political power in western Europe, it long remained the least accessible of the Crescent realms to the imperial powers of Europe. It was as a consequence of this relative isolation that the term the "Far East" came to be applied to East Asia. However, the so-called "Far East" extends well into the interior of the Asiatic continent as western China, and in terms of overland, rather than maritime, communications, its westernmost regions lie nearer to Europe than all of Southeast Asia and much of South Asia. The total longitudinal spread of the realm amounts to some 70 degrees, and the east-west extension of China alone, the continental state, covers some 60 degrees, more than the breadth of the United States and about the same as the distance from the Urals to the English Channel. The dependence of the West on marine transportation to provide access to East Asia has tended to overestimate the maritime orientation and peripheral character of the East Asian countries and in turn—at least in the recent past—to blur the substantial continental interests of both China and Korea.

In another respect the phrase "Far East" has in recent times become even less meaningful, though it remains in common use. To the United States the eastern coasts of Asia are not so much the "Far East," though that they remain in some shipping and air-transport terms, but the "Farther West." The limits of the American *drang nach Westen* have not been the eastern or North American shores of the Pacific, but in a sense, especially since the Pacific War, the western or Asiatic shores. However, East Asia is *both* the farther east *and* the farther west, when accessibility in terms of the North American ecumene is considered. It is possible to travel from New York by sea or air to the East Asian coasts for about the same costs, either eastward across the Atlantic via Suez and Southeast Asia, or westward across the North American continent and thence across the Pacific. This duality of accessibility has led to round-the-world services of both shipping and air transport, although the most important routes still are the trans-Pacific shipping lanes that follow, as nearly as possible, a Great Circle route northwestward along the west coast of North America and then southwestward along the coasts of Asia.

In still another sense, however, the term "Far East" fails to take into account the changes in accessibility that are being brought about by technological developments in transportation. In terms of the most direct air route from the eastern United States to China, the "Far East" becomes also the "Farther North." The shortest air route from Washington, D.C., to Chungking (Ch'ung-ch'ing) runs neither west nor east but north, across Hudson Bay, the Arctic Circle, eastern Siberia, Lake Baykal, and Ulan Bator in Outer Mongolia. Although feasible neither commercially nor politically for the time being, this route possesses a strategic significance of breathtaking dimensions and a potential importance that may well alter the basic flow patterns studied by the economic geographer.

If the United States has the option of looking toward East Asia either to the east or to the west, East Asia has not merely an option but a need to look in both directions toward the "West," a term which itself repeats in reverse the conceptual errors associated with the "Far East." Indeed, in another sense East Asia must look not only in two directions, but in three: to the east across the Pacific toward the United States, to the southwest toward the Suez route and western Europe, and northwest toward the Soviet Union. If the western shores of the Pacific are in some respects to be considered an American frontier, they are even more directly a Russian frontier. Thus, East Asia lies between the two major opposing forces contending for world supremacy. The pressures resulting from this intermediate position were evidenced during the Chinese Civil War of 1946-9 and in the Korean War, which was fought over a Korea divided between the Russian "West" and a free "West," and were evidenced also in the anomalous position of Japan, which leans heavily toward the United States, if only out of animosity toward Russia, but which cannot ignore the proximity of the traditional enemy across the sea of Japan.

Cultural and political relations

The second factor that helped East Asia stave off direct control by the European countries was the remarkable cultural stability of the major East Asian societies. Although the cultural discrepancies and variations among the three nations were and are substantial, their similarities also have been great. Both Korea and Japan derive much of their cultural heritage from the monolithic culture of China, which in spite of great regional differences within China itself has been more important to more people for a longer continuous period than any other. When the Europeans first came to East Asia in numbers, the bulk of China, not merely in simple physical terms but also in terms of its ancient and highly developed social order, was so imposing that it was not until the middle of the nineteenth century, that certain internal weaknesses could be exploited to permit the acquisition of economic and then political rights and privileges. In like but lesser degree the isolation of Japan enforced by the Tokugawa Shogunate beginning in the mid-seventeenth century presented an impressive facade, which was at variance with the real stresses behind it.

In China, unlike India, the administrative and social structure of the state had been so highly developed and integrated over the centuries that China could not be swallowed piecemeal, but came to be regarded as one Leviathan-like *pièce de résistance* that no European country, nor America had it moved her, could contemplate without concomitant digestive rumblings of an economic and political nature. When some one country, as in the case of Germany shortly before the first World War, seemed disposed to attempt a carving of the whole, the other interested states collaborated in halting the operation. European preoccupation with China also gave Japan a breathing period in which to reorganize her society. It is exceptionally significant to note that the only successful severing of a major part of China between 1860 and 1931 was by Japan, which occupied peripheral T'ai-wan (1894), Korea (1910), and Manchuria (1932). The later alienation of Outer Mongolia under Russian influence also concerned a peripheral region, and Russian influences in Hsin-chiang province, least accessible from the Chinese ecumene, point toward another possible step in peripheral partition.

Until 1949 it was safe to say that among all the cultures in Asia the Chinese was the least affected by Western civilization. It was old, it was stable, and its adherents displayed a certain contempt for European cultural values, albeit tempered by a considerable respect for their associated technology. Since that date, rapid and radical changes in the Chinese social order have taken place, most recently along the lines of a particular Western ideology, Soviet Communism. This change, led as it was to a large degree by the Chinese intellectuals, could not have come so suddenly had it not been for the stresses occasioned by the long drawn-out struggle with Japan, which lasted for some 15 years, and by the presentation of a choice between Western ideologies, one of which, though the more unscrupulous by far, had the great advantage of relative freedom from the taint of imperialism that distorted the motives of the democratic powers.

The Chinese social order has definitely changed; but to what extent the new will be in amalgam with the old is one of the great questions of the century. Across the East China sea, however, Japan provides an example of a society in which new values have been added to and integrated within a traditional pattern of culture, the traditional pattern to a large degree retaining its identity and integrity, recoiling under the cultural impact and then rebounding.

Despite the cultural similarities among China, Japan, and Korea, their mutual political interrelations in modern times have been far from harmonious. The decline of China as a great power and her replacement in

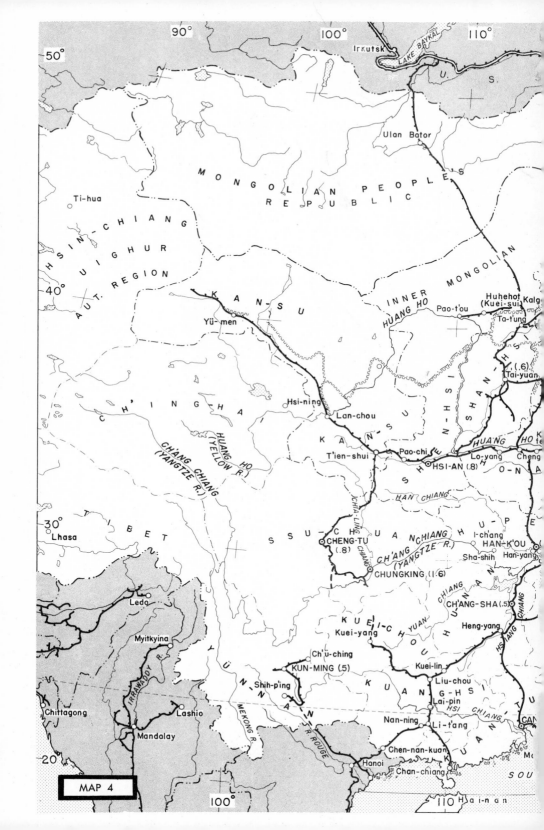

MAP 4

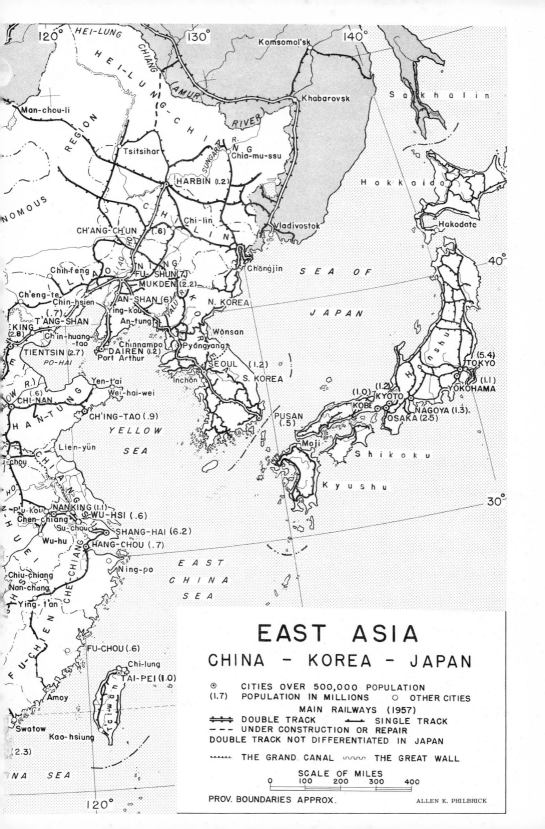

EAST ASIA
CHINA – KOREA – JAPAN

⊙ CITIES OVER 500,000 POPULATION
(1.7) POPULATION IN MILLIONS   ○ OTHER CITIES
MAIN RAILWAYS (1957)
⊩⊩⊩ DOUBLE TRACK   ⊢⊢⊢ SINGLE TRACK
– – – UNDER CONSTRUCTION OR REPAIR
DOUBLE TRACK NOT DIFFERENTIATED IN JAPAN

⌇⌇⌇ THE GRAND CANAL   ⌇⌇⌇ THE GREAT WALL

SCALE OF MILES
0   100   200   300   400

PROV. BOUNDARIES APPROX.   ALLEN K. PHILBRICK

East Asia by Japan was marked by the Sino-Japanese War of 1894, as a result of which Japan obtained control over T'ai-wan. The balance of power shifted from continental China to peripheral maritime Japan, who further established her position by defeating Imperial Russia in 1905, thereby gaining special rights in Manchuria, and by obtaining in 1910 complete domination over Korea, hitherto a vassal of China. Japan went on to dominate the East Asia political scene until her defeat in 1945, occupying Manchuria from 1932 onward.

The national antagonisms that accompanied Japan's rise to power served to accentuate among these three nations differences that still leave their mark upon political and social relationships. Japanese held Koreans and Chinese in some contempt as incompetents; Koreans regarded the Japanese as oppressors; and Chinese tended to regard them as barbarian dwarfs. The defeat of Japan, however, and China's rise as a great power have restored China as the mainspring in East Asia, while Japan's ambiguous political status has become a symbol of a world divided between the Soviet Union and its allies and the democratic West.

The resource base of East Asia

The term "East Asia" also may be misleading because not all of eastern Asia lies within that realm. Some of eastern Asia lies to the north; some to the south. East Asia as here defined should more properly be termed "Middle-latitude East Asia," since China, Japan, and Korea lie primarily in the middle latitudes (Map 4). The East Asian realm extends through 35 degrees of latitude, a distance of approximately 2,500 miles from the southernmost tip of Hai-nan island to the northernmost curve of the Amur River along the borders of Manchuria. This is the equivalent in North America of the latitudinal spread between Mexico City and Edmonton, Alberta.

The land area covered by the realm, therefore, is more than twice that of any of the other realms, although the term "subcontinent," often applied to India, is seldom used with regard to East Asia, probably because East Asia is not nearly so clearly demarcated by its land boundaries from the rest of the continent. It is not strange to find, therefore, that East Asia contains the most extensive resource base among the realms and in many respects, despite some major lacks, the richest. The distribution of resources is far from even, however, thereby providing one professed justification for the Japanese plan to unite eastern Asia, including Southeast Asia, into a so-called Greater East Asian Co-Prosperity Sphere.

To a very large degree the East Asia most significant in terms of livelihood is that part of the realm within 750 miles of the sea. Here is most of the agricultural land, densely occupied and for the most part localized on the plains of the great rivers and in the coastal and intermontane lowlands of south China, Korea, and Japan. Most of western China is not suited for sedentary agriculture, other than oasis agriculture, and annual rainfall averages less than 15 inches over two-thirds of China's territory; about 95 per cent of the cultivated land in China lies east of a *NNE-SSW* line connecting K'un-ming in Yün-nan (Yunnan) province with Tsitsihar (Ch'i-ch'i-ha-erh) in Hei-lung-chiang (Heilungkiang) province.

Climatically, East Asia is characterized by the seasonal shifts in winds and precipitation of the monsoon effect, by a great latitudinal spread, and by orographic factors, with maritime influences secondary but important, especially in Japan.

Strong outflows of polar continental air from the semipermanent winter anticyclone in northeastern Asia bring winter to most of the realm, the cold dry northerly winds reaching southward beyond T'ai-wan and Hong-kong. Winter is the dry season in the west and north of the realm and the drier season in the east and south where cyclonic lows, somewhat smaller and weaker but similar to those in the eastern United States, bring some rainfall to south China, southern Korea, and Japan. Between April and the end of September the polar front, which in January extends south of Hai-nan island, lies well to the north of the Amur, and in July the ephemeral intertropical front has bent northward from its January position just south of the equator so that it cuts meridionally across Southeast Asia.[1] It is this front that separates what might be termed "Monsoon Asia" from East Asia. The heating of the continent tends to draw tropical maritime air from the South China sea and the Philippine sea northwestward toward the continent. The result is a summer season of light, prevailingly southeasterly winds, which bring moisture to much of the realm. Of the two flows of air, however, the winter flow is by far the more powerful, unlike the Indian monsoon regime in which it is the summer flow that is most forceful.

Orographic factors are of considerable importance in the climatic patterns of East Asia. The mountains named Ch'in Ling, the eastern extension of the K'un-lun Shan, act as a major barrier to the cold northerly winds of winter and protect South China from their full strength. The Red Basin of Ssu-ch'uan (Szechwan) Province lies in the lee of of these mountains and their neighboring range, the Ta-pa Shan; the basin possesses a subtropical climate at a latitude of 30 degrees north. Similarly, southeastern Japan is protected from cold continental winds by the central mountains of Honshu. On the other hand, the great heights of the Tibetan plateau, over 10,000 feet, have led to a tundra-like climate, but at the latitude of Shang-hai. Local climatic variations due to orographic

[1] See Chapter XV.

PLATE A

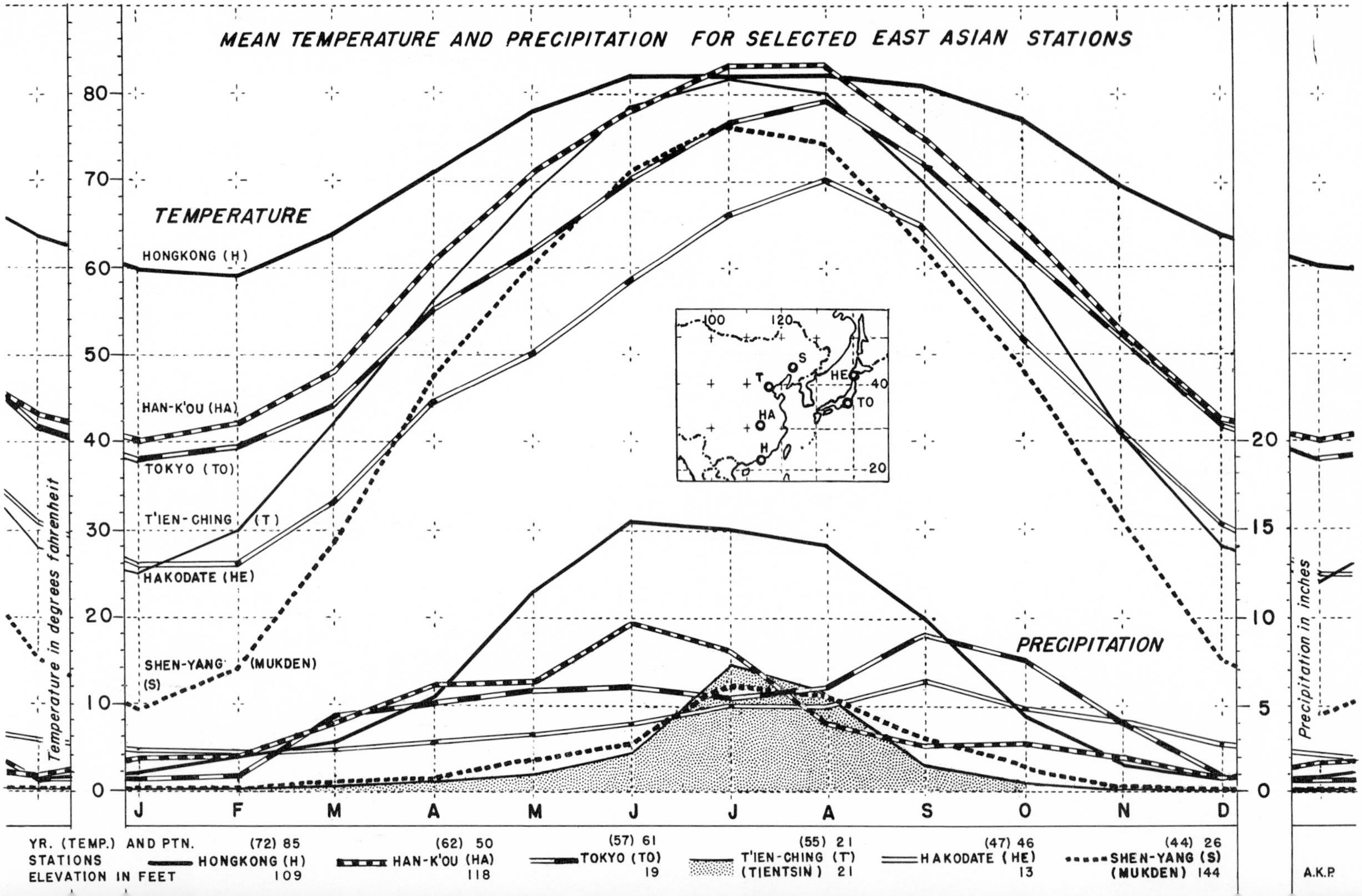

MEAN TEMPERATURE AND PRECIPITATION FOR SELECTED EAST ASIAN STATIONS
TEMPERATURE
HONGKONG (H)
HAN-K'OU (HA)
TOKYO (TO)
T'IEN-CHING (T)
HAKODATE (HE)
SHEN-YANG (S) (MUKDEN)
PRECIPITATION
Temperature in degrees fahrenheit
Precipitation in inches
80
70
60
50
40
30
20
10
0
20
15
10
5
0
J F M A M J J A S O N D
100
120
40
20
S
T
HA
H
HE
TO
YR. (TEMP.) AND PTN.
STATIONS
ELEVATION IN FEET
(72) 85 HONGKONG (H) 109
(62) 50 HAN-K'OU (HA) 118
(57) 61 TOKYO (TO) 19
(55) 21 T'IEN-CHING (T) (TIENTSIN) 21
(47) 46 HAKODATE (HE) 13
(44) 26 SHEN-YANG (S) (MUKDEN) 144
A.K.P.

factors, especially in terms of rainfall, are found everywhere in the hilly and mountainous portions of the realm.

Latitudinal influences on climate are more significant in East Asia than in any other part of the Asiatic Crescent. Plate A indicates that, in contrast to Southeast Asia particularly, differences in both rainfall and temperature curves in East Asia are correlated closely with latitudinal position. Although almost all of the realm displays a notably drier winter, total rainfall varies markedly from south to north. Even more noteworthy are the variations in winter temperatures, which range from a January mean at Hongkong of almost 60°F. to Mukden (Shen-yang) in Manchuria with a January mean of less than 10°.

Maritime influences also enter the climatic picture, especially in Japan and to a lesser degree along the China coast. In general, the ranges of temperatures between winter and summer are far less along the coasts than in the interior of China, and ranges even within interior Honshu contrast markedly with those along the Japan coasts. In general, also, the coastal areas tend to be somewhat more rainy, although where the prevailing winds during the summer tend to parallel a coast, as in the vicinity of Tientsin (T'ien-ching), this may not be the case. The Japan Sea coast of Honshu, however, receives its heaviest precipitation in the winter when dry northwesterly winds pick up moisture and become unstable as they cross the sea, then rise over the mountains of western Honshu. Similarly, northern T'ai-wan receives rain during the winter from northeasterly winds of continental origin that have crossed the seas south of Japan. Of great importance also is the warm tropical ocean current, the Kuro Shio, or Black Current, which runs northeastward from the South China Sea, warming the southern coasts of Japan and Korea; conversely, a more localized cold current flows down from the north along the northerly Japan coasts.

East Asian agriculture, associated for the most part with the areas of alluvial soils along the coasts and in the river valleys, is correlated closely with variations in rainfall and seasonal temperatures. From Hai-nan island, where the Peking government is planning rubber plantations, through Kuan-tung province, T'ai-wan, and adjacent areas, double-cropping of rice is common, and in some few areas in certain years three crops of rice are known to be raised. Northward in the Yangtze valley, double-cropping of rice alone is rare, but double-cropping of rice with other crops is the rule. As the length of the growing season diminishes northward, rice gives way to wheat, millet, and kao-liang (grain sorghum), and double-cropping diminishes, to become the exception in north China and Manchuria. In northwestern China, double-cropping is limited as much by lack of water as it is by a short growing season. In Korea there is no double-cropping of rice, although south of Seoul rice and a second crop are commonly raised on one piece of land, and dry crops often are double-cropped. In southern Japan double-cropping is the rule, although only in a few areas is double-cropping of rice practiced, but beyond about 37°N. double-cropping diminishes rapidly, especially in the uplands, until in Hokkaido it is not practiced at all.

The agricultural systems of East Asia closely resemble those of the rest of Asian Asia in that they are characterized by intense cultivation of a horticultural variety, small plots of land, and almost no mechanization. Irrigation, both controlled and natural, is widely practiced, and rice is the major crop for most of the realm. However, limits on rice cultivation are sufficiently well defined by precipitation and length of growing season so that about one-fourth of the population of the realm is not dependent upon rice as the main food staple, but on other grains, of which wheat is the most conspicuous, if not the most important.

In general, agriculture is even more intensively practiced in East Asia than in the rest of the Asian Crescent. Wherever climatic factors are favorable, multiple cropping is practiced, in striking contrast with large portions of South and Southeast Asia where the multiple-cropping index is low. Fertilization, primarily with farm-produced fertilizers, including nightsoils, is practiced on a scale unparalleled in the rest of Asia, and yields by and large are far higher than elsewhere. Japan leads the Asian world in per-acre yields of each crop of rice, although the climatically favored double-cropping rice region of South China produces more rice per acre with two crops. Japanese agriculture, though similar to that in China and Korea, depends more on commercial fertilizers.

In all the agricultural regions of the realm, the prime source of energy is human, with a secondary independence on animal power increasing southward. Animal husbandry is little practiced in these regions, despite the Chinese emphasis on scavenger swine and the increasing dependence on animal husbandry in the drier and colder regions of the continental north and west.

Nonagricultural resources exist in large quantities, but they are not well distributed throughout the realm, and there are major resource deficiencies. Coal is perhaps the most important and abundant resource. China contains some of the largest reserves in the world, and both Korea and Japan possess substantial coal supplies. In all three countries water power offers a major potential source of energy, exploited primarily in Japan and scarcely at all in China. Wood, either plain or in the form of charcoal, still is the major source of fuel within the realm as a whole. Petroleum in large quantities seems to be lacking, although considerable deposits are reported to have been discovered since 1950 in northwest China.

Metallic minerals are found widely scattered. Iron ore is present in fair quantities in central and north China, Manchuria, and north Korea, and tungsten and tin are major resources of southwest China. Japan is notoriously ill-supplied with metals other than copper. Many metals have been mined for centuries, but few in internationally significant quantities. Nevertheless, until mineralogical explorations, particularly in west China, have proceeded much further than they now have, it is unwise to conclude that commercially exploitable reserves of many metals do not exist. Nonmetallic minerals seem to be relatively abundant, again subject to the qualification that scientific exploration has yet to be accomplished over most of the realm. The salt of southwest and coastal north China, the graphite of Korea, and the sulfur of Japan are three nonmetallic minerals that are produced in especially important quantities.

Forest resources are widely scattered within the realm, but have long been severely depleted in agricultural China and southern Korea. The remaining great stands of timber lie for the most part in the least accessible regions of Manchuria, Korea, and Japan, and in the far distant mountains of west China. Local dependence on wood for fuel in China and Korea has resulted in so careful a search for combustible forest materials that natural regeneration of the forests has been impossible. About 60 per cent of Japan is still forested, but the annual cutting, considerably above the replacement rate, is resulting despite reforestation programs in a gradual depletion of reserves. Japan, however, is a special case, since in addition to demands for wood for fuel and construction, she also has a large demand for pulpwood to supply paper mills and rayon manufacturing plants. Thus, Japan remains a large wood importer.

Industrialization and trade

Although it is China that possesses the larger resource potential, it was Japan that first bridged the gap between a subsistence agrarian economy and an industrialized society. It was this transition, though based upon the shakiest of indigenous resource foundations, that enabled Japan to become the leader not only of East Asia but also for a time of Asians everywhere. Japan became the model, and to a degree still is for much of Asia, of an Asian country that had adapted the Western system of production to its own ends. The political impact of this accomplishment was further emphasized by Japan's early successes in the Pacific War and was little diminished by a later defeat that could be and is being explained in terms of Japan's facing the strongest countries of the Western World.

After 1920 Japan came to dominate the trade of East Asia. Both Korea and T'ai-wan were Japanese possessions, and their economies were in large part geared to that of Japan. Manchurian trade, both before and after its severance from China, was strongly oriented toward Japan, and China's trade, despite boycotts and competition with Europe and America, swung heavily toward Japan. The flow pattern was basically one of raw materials and foodstuffs moving toward Japan in Japanese bottoms, with manufactures moving outward from Japan chiefly for Asian markets.

Japan's Achilles' heel was her dependence on imported raw materials, which led to increasing costs of production and a gradual deterioration of Japan's comparative advantage in Asian markets. The war and the concept of the Greater East Asian Co-Prosperity Sphere both have been explained in terms of the necessity for controlling raw-material supplies. Japan's textile industry, most important in the export trade, was based in part on cotton from India and the United States, as well as from China, and on pulpwood from Canada; petroleum came primarily from the United States and secondarily from Southeast Asia; iron ore and pig iron came from Southeast Asia and India as well as East Asia, and scrap had its origin almost entirely in the United States. So long as Korea and T'aiwan remained within Japan's orbit, food imports were no problem, but since the war Japan, unable to supply more than 80 per cent of her domestic food needs, has found the food problem attaining paramount importance. No less difficult has been the problem of markets, especially since the close of the Chinese civil war, and the shutting off of China and Manchuria as markets for Japanese manufactures, for Japan—like Britain —must sell to survive.

In neither Korea nor China has industrialization proceeded as far as it has in Japan. Most of China's millions depend directly upon the land. Only in southcentral Manchuria and in the Europeanized coastal cities has manufacturing developed along modern lines. Thus, Mukden is the capital of an industrial region centered about Manchuria's coal and iron-ore resources, while Tientsin and Shang-hai are two examples of coastal great cities that possess industrial functions of note. In Korea, two regions in the north experienced industrial development on a substantial scale under Japanese initiative, based on local supplies of coal, iron ore, timber, hydroelectric power, and industrial crops. However, the main body of the Korean economy remains agricultural and little touched by these developments.

East Asia's population is the largest among the realms. If China's 1954 population is estimated to have been some 582 millions, then the total for the realm was 712 millions, or 48 per cent of all the people in Asian Asia. Densities differ markedly, from 156 per square mile in China to 346 in Korea and 619 in Japan, but in the densely occupied agricultural plains densities of 3,000 per square mile are not uncommon. Thus, even though agriculture in East Asia is more highly developed than elsewhere in the Asiatic Crescent, and though Asian industrial development has reached

Fig. 11 • East Asia contains more people than all the rest of Asian Asia combined. China alone contains the largest number of people of any country in the world. China's hundreds of millions, half of Japan's scores of millions, and most of Korea's tens of millions live in rural villages where the numbers of children appear overwhelming, as in this village in Shan-tung province. In this November picture many of the children wear very light clothing, since the days are warm even in late fall in north China's dry climate. But padded gowns, stuffed with cotton, as worn by the girl in the center background, are necessary for warmth during the cold nights and mornings. *(Norton Ginsburg.)*

its pinnacle in Japan, most East Asians are tied to the land. Fewer than 15 per cent of China's population live in cities; no more than 20 per cent in Korea, and less than 40 per cent in relatively urbanized Japan.

In East Asia, as in the other Asian realms, life remains basically agrarian. On agriculture depend the livelihoods of hundreds of millions of people. The futures of these people, stirred by new concepts about man and nature and by new technologies superior to their own, are here no more than elsewhere preordained by geographical conditions and relationships, but it is within these that China's destiny, the Korean dichotomy, and Japan's place in a shrinking world will be determined.

Japan

NATURAL RESOURCES

JAPAN'S SITUATION IN EAST ASIA IS A STRATEGIC ONE. THE STRAITS of Tsushima and Korea, which separate Japan from Korea, are together only some 116 miles in width. The Sea of Japan at its widest point measures approximately 550 miles from east to west. The distance from Hokkaido to the nearest point on the mainland U.S.S.R., however, is only 180 miles, and the width of the Soya Straits between Hokkaido and the Soviet island of Sakhalin is a mere 26 miles. Furthermore, Hokkaido is separated from the Russian-controlled Kuril islands by a distance of less than ten miles. This physical proximity of Russia to Japan is perhaps the single most strategic element in understanding Japan's postwar political geography.

The Japanese archipelago itself consists of four main islands—Hokkaido, Honshu, Shikoku, and Kyushu—and a number of lesser islands, of which Sado island, off the northwest coast of Honshu, is the largest (Map 5). Formerly, the Japanese Empire included the southern half of the island of Sakhalin, known to the Japanese as Karafuto, the Ryukyu Retto, T'ai-wan, Korea, the Kurils, known to the Japanese as the Chishima Retto, and Manchuria. As a result of the Pacific war, Japan lost Manchuria and T'ai-wan to China, Karafuto and the Kurils to Russia. Korea was freed from Japanese control, and the Ryukyus, including the stra-

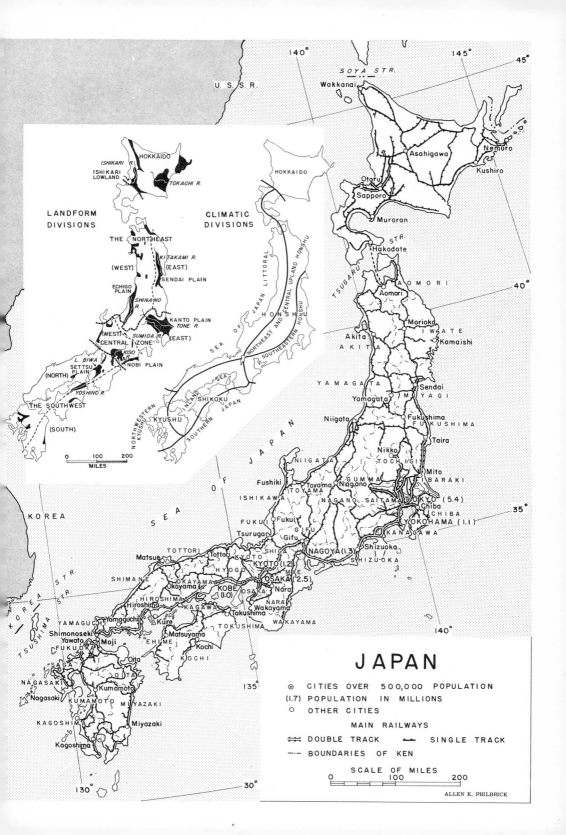

LANDFORM
DIVISIONS

CLIMATIC
DIVISIONS

ISHIKARI R.
HOKKAIDO
ISHIKARI
LOWLAND
TOKACHI R.

HOKKAIDO

THE NORTHEAST

(WEST)

KITAKAMI R.
(EAST)

SENDAI PLAIN

ECHIGO
PLAIN

SHINANO
R.

KANTO PLAIN
TONE R.

(WEST)
CENTRAL ZONE
(EAST)

SUMIDA R.

L. BIWA
SETTSU
PLAIN
(NORTH)

KISO
R.
NOBI PLAIN

YOSHINO R.

THE SOUTHWEST

(SOUTH)

SEA OF JAPAN LITTORAL

NORTHEAST AND CENTRAL UPLAND HONSHU

SOUTHEASTERN HONSHU

INLAND SEA

SHIKOKU

SOUTHERN JAPAN

NORTHWESTERN KYUSHU

KYUSHU

0   100   200
MILES

U.S.S.R.

SOYA STR.

Wakkanai

Asahigawa

Nemuro

Otaru

Kushiro

Sapporo

Muroran

STR.

Hakodate

TSUGARU STR.

AOMORI
Aomori

Morioka

Akita

IWATE

Kamaishi

AKITA

YAMAGATA

Sendai

Yamagata

MIYAGI

Niigata

Fukushima

FUKUSHIMA

Nikko

Taira

NIIGATA

TOCHIGI

Mito

Fushiki

Toyama

Nagano

GUMMA

IBARAKI

ISHIKAWA

TOYAMA

NAGANO

SAITAMA

TOKYO (5.4)

FUKUI

Fukui

GIFU

Chiba

CHIBA

Tsuruga

Gifu

SHIGA

NAGOYA(1.3)

Shizuoka

YOKOHAMA (1.1)

KANAGAWA

KOREA

SEA   OF   JAPAN

TOTTORI

KYOTO

MIE

SHIZUOKA

Matsue

Tottori

KYOTO(1.2)

Nara

SHIMANE

HYOGO

OKAYAMA

OSAKA (2.5)

Okayama

KOBE

NARA

Wakayama

HIROSHIMA

(1.0)

Hiroshima

KAGAWA

Takushima

WAKAYAMA

YAMAGUCHI

Kure

Matsuyama

TOKUSHIMA

Shimonoseki

Yamaguchi

EHIME

Kochi

Yawata

Moji

KOCHI

FUKUOKA

Oita

SAGA

OITA

MIYAZAKI

NAGASAKI

KUMAMOTO

Nagasaki

Kumamoto

KAGOSHIMA

Miyazaki

Kagoshima

JAPAN

⊙ CITIES OVER 500,000 POPULATION

(1.7) POPULATION IN MILLIONS

○ OTHER CITIES

MAIN RAILWAYS

⊨ DOUBLE TRACK   ⊢ SINGLE TRACK

-·- BOUNDARIES OF KEN

SCALE OF MILES

0   100   200

ALLEN K. PHILBRICK

tegic island of Okinawa, passed into a United Nations trusteeship administered by the United States. Japan's official land territory as of 1956 covered only 142,000 square miles, roughly the same area as the state of Montana, but inhabited by 90 million people. Japan's population density was 619 per square mile, as compared with Montana's 4, Korea's 346, the United Kingdom's 527, and the Netherland's 850.

Japan's strategic location along the shortest sea route between eastern Asia and western North America also is significant. Most of the major ocean routes between East Asia and North America are through Japan. Shipping en route to China, Hongkong, and often to Southeast Asia from the west coast of the United States customarily stops at Japanese ports. Japan also is the eastern terminus of the route connecting western Europe and the Mediterranean with the Orient through Suez, the Straits of Malakka, and the Straits of T'ai-wan. In political and military terms, the islands provide a major outpost of the non-communist world on the edge of East Asia and restrict Russian and Chinese access to the Pacific. Conversely, should Japan become allied with Chinese or Russian interests, the islands would act as a major barrier to Western ingress into Asia and the eastern Soviet Union.

Japan's geographical position has been compared often with that of the British Isles, which balance Eurasia on the west as Japan does on the east. The analogy holds to the extent that both the British and the Japanese islands are separated from the continental mainland by a narrow strait and a restricted sea and that both the islands themselves and the adjacent mainlands are densely populated. The physical geographies of the island groups, however, and the nature of their neighboring mainland areas differ substantially. England's early economic development and industrialization took place on what was for the times a natural resource base of considerable wealth, and occurred only after a long period of commercial expansion, which provided vast amounts of capital and experience for an industrial evolution. Furthermore, the mainland areas also were proceeding rapidly toward industrial development.

In the Far East, on the other hand, Japan fronts on a culture world that still remains primarily dependent upon agriculture of a subsistence sort and that is only now beginning to industrialize. Furthermore, Japan until 1867 had experienced two centuries of self-imposed isolation, with no remunerative trade or dependencies, and possesses a resource endowment of notably limited dimensions. That Japan became a world power was to a large extent in spite of rather than because of her restricted resource base, yet it is that resource base which provides the major setting and to a large degree the basic assets for Japanese livelihood.

Fig. 12 • The characteristic landscape of Japan is identified by sea and mountains in juxtaposition, by intensively cultivated lowlands in association with forested hilly outliers, by settlements clinging to shorelines and roads. Here is a spring view along the Inland Sea, Kagawa prefecture. *(U.S. Army.)*

Surface configuration and drainage

The Japanese archipelago is one of the chain of peninsulas and islands that borders the western Pacific. It also is part of a zone of vulcanism that rims most of the Pacific basin. In Japan, as well as in T'ai-wan, the Philippines, and part of the East Indian archipelago, geological structure and surface configuration record the prevalence of volcanic activity not only in the past but in the present. In Japan, concentrated in eastern Hokkaido, southwestern Hokkaido, central-north Honshu, southern Kyushu, and the Ryukyus, there are over 50 active volcanoes.

Most of Japan is in relatively steep slope, and two-thirds of the country is mountainous. Indeed, the islands may be described as the summits of a series of mountain ranges that rise from the floor of the Pacific and de-

63

fine the arced form of the archipelago. To the east of Japan is one of the world's great oceanic depressions with depths up to 34,000 feet; to the west is the Sea of Japan, a relatively deep arm of the ocean reaching depths of 11,000 feet, not merely a shallow, water-covered extension of the continental shelf, as is the Yellow Sea. "Forested mountains and the sea in juxtaposition" succinctly describes Japan's natural landscape; the Japanese word for landscape or scenery is *sansui*, from the two characters for "mountain" and "water" (Figure 12).

Human occupance in Japan is associated intimately with a limited number of lowlands, chiefly along the margins of the islands but including some intermontane basins. The total area of these lowlands is less than 25,000 square miles. Chief among these are the Kanto plain of eastern Honshu (3.2 million acres), the Ishikari-Yufutsu lowland of Hokkaido (0.5 million acres), the Echigo or Niigata plain of northwestern Honshu (0.45 million acres), the Nobi or Nagoya plain of eastcentral Honshu (0.45 million acres), the Sendai plain of northeastern Honshu (0.37 million acres), the Settsu or Kinai plain of central Honshu (0.31 million acres), and the Tsukushi lowland of northern Kyushu (0.3 million acres).

Each of these lowlands is of riverine origin, although each also has been subjected to marine influences. Evidences of fairly recent uplift are the natural terraces—sometimes called *di*luvial terraces as compared with the *al*luvium of the lowland floors—that appear on the inner margins of the coastal lowlands. In brief, each coastal lowland may be described as a great alluvial fan, or group of coalescing fans, constructed from the alluvium deposited by streams debouching from the interior highlands.

Drainage patterns reflect both the surface configuration and the relatively abundant rainfall that characterizes most of the country. Streams are short and swift, with steep gradients and extreme fluctuations of flow in accordance with variations in seasonal rainfall. Only two rivers are more than 200 miles in length, the Shinano River, which flows through the Niigata plain, and the Ishikari River in western Hokkaido. In each island the typical stream rises in the mountainous interior, flows through a relatively steep-walled young valley, bursts out of the uplands onto a plain, where it flows approximately at right angles to the sea within a diked channel higher than the immediately surrounding lowlands, and then enters the ocean (Figure 13). Channels are braided, and the streams are shallow and silt-laden. Floods are common and provide one of the major natural hazards to agricultural occupance in the lowlands. However, the fact that the main streams are higher than the plains offers one major advantage. The gravity flow of irrigation water onto paddy fields is made convenient. The streams' shallowness, on the other hand, prevents their use for navigational purposes, except by very small native boats and for floating logs down from the forested uplands.

The absence of navigable streams is countered to a degree by a shoreline that extends for 17,000 miles. Much of this coast contains embayments and coves, which provide Japan with her innumerable harbors. The Inland Sea itself may be considered one great harbor, with innumerable lesser harbors, some of considerable size lining its shores. The coasts of western Kyushu and southern Honshu also are spotted with natural harbors on which hundreds of fishing villages are sited.

Not all of the coastline is indented, however. Most of the Japan sea coast is smooth except at Wakasa Bay (on which the naval base of Maizuru is located) and at Toyama Bay (on which the port of Fushiki is situated) to the east of the Nodo peninsula. The coast of Honshu north from Tokyo Bay also is smooth to just beyond Sendai, where it becomes irregular once more. The coasts of Hokkaido also are quite regular, except in a few points, as at Muroran where a major port has developed. In general, where the lowland plains meet the sea, especially on the Japan seacoast, shorelines are smooth, and the streams that drain the lowlands often are partially blocked from the ocean by sand bars and ridges, which deflect their lower courses parallel to the shore. Even where there are natural sheltered harbors, as at Tokyo, Nagoya, and Osaka, stream deposition on the bay-head plains has led to shallow harbor waters. Thus, the deep-water ports for Tokyo and Osaka are Yokohama and Kobe respectively, at the foot of the upland margins of the plains, where inshore waters are deep and silting is not a major problem.

Fig. 13 • The rivers of Japan in their lower courses flow within channels raised above the level of the surrounding plains. The Tone River on the right is several feet above the village in Ibaraki prefecture to the left. The two are separated by a levee, partly natural, which has been artificially built up for flood protection. (U.S. Army.)

The land forms of Japan may be described in terms of a series of mountain arcs, generally north-south trending, which provide the ridge poles from which the rest of the country hangs. On the basis of these mountain arcs and the complex of landscape features associated with them, the country has been divided by Watanabe into four major landform regions: Hokkaido Proper, the Northeast, the Central Zone, and the Southwest (Map 5).[1]

(1) *Hokkaido Proper* includes all except the southwestern peninsula of the island. The V-shaped backbone of the region is composed of two mountain arcs, one from Karafuto to the north, the other from the Kurils to the northeast. In the eastern part of the region a series of volcanoes, still active, are conspicuous landscape features, but in general the mountainous topography is well rounded; there are extensive ash plateaus, wide river valleys, and extensive coastal terraces. The Ishikari plain is formed at the junction of the two major mountain arcs. Three smaller, but important, flat-bottomed basins are found in series to the northeast of the Ishikari.

(2) The *Northeast* region consists of the northern part of Honshu and the southwestern peninsula of Hokkaido. In general, the Honshu segment consists of narrow, segmented coastal plains and three major meridionally trending mountain ranges separated by a series of lowlands. The western part of the region consists of discontinuous coastal plains along the Sea of Japan, of which the Echigo or Niigata plain is the largest section, and of two parallel chains of young folded mountains rising to 8,000 feet and separated by a line of intermontane basins. The easternmost of the two mountain chains contains numerous volcanoes, a feature that appears also in southwestern Hokkaido.

The eastern part of the region consists of two segments of a mountainous upland running at a slight angle to the trend of the island and the western mountains. Separating them from each other and from the rest of the Northeast region is the Kitakami-Abukuma lowland, an elongated extension to the north and south of the Sendai plain. The mountains of the eastern subregion, though almost as high as those to the west, contain older crystalline rocks, but no volcanoes. The only coastal lowland is found where the Sendai plain meets the sea.

(3) The *Central Zone* consists of a great knotted complex of mountains running at right angles to the grain of the island arc and resulting from the meeting of the three great mountain systems that form the Japanese archipelago: the northeastern system, the southwestern system, and the Mariana system, which appears in the islands to the south of Tokyo. Here are the highest mountains of Japan, the Japanese Alps, which rise

---

[1] A. Watanabe, "Landform Divisions of Japan," *Bulletin of the Geographical Survey Institute* (Tokyo: Ministry of Construction, 1950), Vol. II, Part I, pp. 81-94.

to over 10,000 feet. Running north-south through the region is the trench
of the Fossa Magna, a great fault trough related to the Mariana system
and partially filled with volcanoes—among which Fuji at the southern
end of the depression is the largest. On the eastern margin of the region
is the Kanto plain, and to the south is the Nobi plain at the heads of
Sagami Bay and Ise Bay respectively, each of fault origin.

(4) The *Southwest* region includes the remainder of the archipelago—
southwestern Honshu, Shikoku, and Kyushu. The southern or Pacific side
of the region, sometimes termed the "Outer Zone of Southwest Japan,"
consists of the Kii peninsula, southern Shikoku, and southern Kyushu,
and is an area of young faulted mountains with few and small lowlands.
In southern Kyushu it includes an area of vulcanism, a reflection of the
Ryukyu mountain arc which enters Kyushu from the south. The northern
or "inner" half of the region consists of southwestern Honshu, or Chugoku,
an area of upfaulted granitic hills and mountains of mature, rounded relief; the great trough that forms the Inland Sea; northern Shikoku, which
bears a close physical resemblance to the Chugoku subregion; and northern Kyushu, which has developed from the same morphological processes, although sedimentaries are more common and volcanism, related
again to the Ryukyu arc, has marked much of the area. The Inland Sea
itself consists of a series of faulted depressions, associated with some
submergence, flooded by the sea, and dotted with innumerable islands
which are the irregular rims of the troughs.

Climate and soils

Japan is a middle-latitude
country. Its *climate* is characterized by marked winter and summer
seasons, which differ not merely in terms of rainfall variations as in southern Asia, but also in terms of extreme temperature changes as in other
middle-latitude regions. Four types of related influences contribute to
Japan's climatic pattern: (1) latitudinal, (2) monsoonal, (3) marine or
insular, and (4) altitudinal or topographic.

The climate of Japan may be likened to that of the east coast of North
America. Japan's north-south extension through 16 degrees of latitude,
from latitudes 30° to 46°N., is roughly equal to the range between Jack-
sonville, Florida, and Quebec, Canada. Southern Japan is a subtropical
land; Hokkaido displays high-latitude temperate qualities, with short
summers and long, hard winters. The frostless season varies from about
140 days in northern Hokkaido to 300 days in southern Japan.

Japan's situation on the margins of the world's greatest land mass
brings more marked seasonal contrasts of winds and rainfall than in
similar latitudes in eastern North America. In winter, Japan is under the

influence of the predominantly westerly and northwesterly winds that outflow from the northern interior of Asia and pour cold, dry, polar continental air over the archipelago. For the most part Japanese winters are considerably drier than the summers. Osaka, for example, receives between one and two inches of rainfall during each of the three winter months, as compared with five to seven inches in the three summer months. In summer the winds shift notably to the south and southeast and bathe Japan in humid tropical maritime air flows which bring the larger part of the year's precipitation. No part of Japan is dry, however, and there is no true dry season.[2] Cyclonic depressions move across Japan from the mainland throughout the year, especially in winter, and the rainfall associated with their fronts tends to smooth out the differences in precipitation between seasons.[3] In central and northern Japan most of the winter precipitation appears in the form of snow; in the far south snow is uncommon.

Japan's *insularity* also markedly affects the climatic pattern. The southern and southeastern coasts are washed by a warm current moving northeastward from the South China Sea along the coasts of East Asia. This current, similar to the Gulf Stream and known as the Japan Current or as the Kuro Shio, the Black Current, has an average minimum winter temperature of 68°F. and warms the coasts of southern Kyushu, Shikoku, and Honshu to about the latitude of Tokyo. A branch of the Kuro Shio, the Tsushima Current, creeps northward along the Japan Sea coast, but its influence is less than that of the parent stream. Conversely, a cold current, known as the Oya Shio, moves southward from the Bering Sea, cooling the northeastern coast of Honshu until it plunges below the waters of the Kuro Shio. Lesser cold currents, which tend to drift toward the continental shores of the Japan Sea, also affect the Japan Sea coast of Hokkaido.

The Sea of Japan itself acts as a powerful climatic influence, especially in winter. During that season the cold and stable air masses outmoving from the continent pass over the markedly warmer waters of this deep arm of the sea; their lower levels are warmed and become notably unstable as they absorb moisture. Thus, when the predominantly westerly winter winds strike the western side of Honshu, they tend to drop their newly acquired moisture. The Sea of Japan side of Japan, therefore, is an

[2] The driest parts of Japan are Hokkaido, which has 30-40 inches of rainfall and is near the northern limits of the influence of tropical maritime air, and the eastern Inland Sea area, protected in all directions by high barrier uplands and mountains, with 40-50 inches.

[3] In late spring extensive weak depressions tend to stagnate over the lower Yangtzu basin and then move very slowly northeastward over southern Japan. These are accompanied by light and continual rains which are known as the *baiu* or "plum rains."

area of abundant rainfall all year round, but with a marked winter, rather than a summer, maximum.

The *marine* component of Japan's climate also is reflected in the typhoons, which make their appearance in summer and early fall. An average of six or seven, originating for the most part in the Philippine Sea, pass over or near Japan each year, and others, which curve off short to the northeast or pass well to the south into China, also affect the archipelago. The torrential rains, floods, and high winds that accompany these storms do immense damage in terms of lives and property. In the summer of 1953 one such great storm left a million persons homeless and did some 280 million dollars' worth of property damage in northern Kyushu.

The fineness of Japan's *surface features* is reflected in similar variations in climate. Each valley or basin, each side of a mountain range or even of a single peak, each headland and each side of the headland, possesses a distinctive climate of its own. The western mountain slopes of Honshu, which force upward the moisture-laden winter winds from the Sea of Japan, provide one example of a major topographic influence on climate. Of equal significance is the altitudinal climatic zoning of the highlands with their alpine climates at highest altitudes. On a smaller scale, the interior intermontane basins generally are drier than the coastal plains, since they lie in the lee of surrounding mountains. More important is the example of the eastern part of the Inland Sea which, protected by mountains, is the driest part of Old Japan (Honshu, Kyushu, and Shikoku).

Japan has been divided into more than one system of climatic regions. According to Trewartha, there are three major regional divisions based upon the Koeppen climatic system: Hokkaido (*Dbf*), northern and mountainous central Honshu (*Daf*), and the remainder of Japan (*Caf*). A second descriptive system divides Japan into seven regions (Map 5 and Table 1):

(1) *Hokkaido* experiences long, cold winters and short, mild summers. Rainfall varies from 35 to 40 inches, and snow is common, lasting well into spring. The growing season varies between 130 and 150 days.

(2) *Northeast and Central Upland Honshu* also experiences long winters and mild summers. Though the winters are not quite as severe as in Hokkaido, precipitation is greater, from 40 to 60 inches, and in the mountain basins the growing season is longer, from 160 to 180 days. Extreme local variations are associated with altitude and surface configuration.

(3) *The Sea of Japan Littoral* extends from the southern tip of Hokkaido to near the southern tip of Honshu. This is the region of maximum winter precipitation (60 inches annually). Winters are more severe to the north, and summers are shorter; snow is known throughout the region, but the area of greatest snowfall is along the northern stretch of coast. The growing season varies from 220 days in the south to 175 days

in the north. Fogs are especially common in the fall and winter, and the southern part of the region is known as the *Sanin* or shaded part of Japan. The northern sector of the region experiences warmer summers than do its latitudinal equivalents on the Pacific side of Honshu, which is washed by the cool Oya Shio. Winters, however, tend to feel colder than on the east side of Honshu because of the high humidities and strong westerly winds, although temperatures are similar.

(4) *Southeastern Honshu,* with Tokyo at its midpoint, marks the transition from temperate to subtropical Japan. Summers are long, hot, and humid. Winters are drier and cool to cold. Autumn rains are associated with typhoons; early summer rains are associated with large, slow-moving lows which originate over the lower Yang-tze basin. The two combined create a bimodal rainfall curve, with early summer and early fall maxima. Annual precipitation ranges from 60 to 90 inches, and the growing season increases from 180 days in the north to 240 in the south.

(5) *The Inland Sea* region also exhibits a long growing season of some 220 days. Rainfall is markedly less than in southeastern Honshu, especially in the eastern part of the region where the rain-shadow effect of the surrounding mountains limits rainfall to some 40 inches. Summers are long and hot; winters are mild and relatively dry.

(6) *The Northwestern Kyushu* region also experiences long, hot summers and mild winters, but rainfall is much higher than in the Inland Sea region, averaging 60 to 80 inches, and temperatures are somewhat lower. The length of growing season is slightly less than to the east, but still between 200 and 220 days. Typhoons inflict serious damage from time to time, more than in the protected Inland Sea region.

(7) *Southern Japan*—southern Kyushu, southern Shikoku, and the Kii peninsula—experiences very mild winters and long, hot summers with a growing season of 240 to 300 days. Precipitation ranges up to 120 inches annually, and typhoons are more common here than elsewhere in Japan.

Of the five basic factors in soil formation (climate, slope, age, parent materials, and vegetation) climate is perhaps the most important. Thus, to a large degree Japan's *soils* reflect differences in climate, from the thin, greyish, podzolic soils of the north to the red and yellow lateritic soils of the south. In the two-thirds of Japan that is in steep slope, however, soils are shallow and are often so thin as to be virtually nonexistent. These soils are identified as lithosol associations and are predominantly under forest cover. In general, in central and northern Japan, where the surface layer is thick enough to be termed a soil, podzolization is the characteristic soil-forming process. In the south, the red and yellow color of the soil indicates the concentration of iron and aluminum oxides, which are identified with the process of laterization.

Unique to Japan are the considerable areas of so-called *ando,* or "dark

TABLE IV–1
SELECTED DATA FOR SEVEN MAJOR CLIMATIC REGIONS OF JAPAN *

	Fahrenheit temperatures		Frostless season (days)	Annual Precipitation (inches)	May-Sept. Precipitation (inches)	Mean cloudiness (days)		Mean relative humidity (%)
	Jan. mean	Aug. mean				July	Jan.	
Hokkaido (Asahigawa)	14.2	69.3	141	44.7	21.1	20.7	17.8	80.8
Northeast and central highland Honshu (Yamagata)	28.8	75.4	159	49.1	24.2	16.8	16.8	79.6
Sea of Japan Littoral (Niigata)	34.5	78.1	218	70.1	28.1	24.2	16.1	78.1
Southeast Honshu (Tokyo)	37.6	78.3	231	60.6	35.5	6.4	17.6	73.4
Inland Sea (Osaka)	39.6	81.1	223	52.5	31.5	5.8	11.9	73.7
Northwest Kyushu (Fukuoka)	40.6	79.5	206	62.6	38.3	12.7	13.2	77.5
Southern Japan (Kagoshima)	44.1	80.6	257	84.9	53.4	8.8	12.8	76.8

* After Ackerman.

soils," especially in southern Kyushu, Kanto, and southeastern Hokkaido, where acidic ash has been deposited from Japan's volcanoes.[4] These soils generally are dark but infertile. Other special soils are the sands and sandy loams found along the coasts, and the planosols, ill-drained dark soils with an impervious hardpan below, which are more the result of Japanese wet-rice agriculture on terraces and other uplands than the consequence of any natural soil-forming process.

Most important to the Japanese, however, are the alluvial soils, which account for 16 per cent of Japan's surface area and with which Japanese agriculture is intimately correlated. These alluvial soils are as immature as the lithosols of the mountains, but they derive fertility from the silt and clay brought down from the uplands and redeposited in the lowlands below. Nevertheless, many of these soils are ill-drained, which limits their utility, and centuries of hard usage have greatly diminished their fertility. Relatively high rainfall also has taken its toll of soil fertility, leaching plant nutrients down beyond the reach of plant roots. Since many of the streams that drain the lowlands flow through channels elevated above them, floods that might naturally fertilize the lowland soils often are destructive and in their fury strew sterile sands and gravels over what had been productive paddy fields (Figure 14).

In general, the soils utilized for agriculture in Japan will continue to be restricted to the limited areas of alluvial soils and adjoining terrace soils, some of which are *ando,* together with occasional well-drained sandy loams along stream margins and near the sea shore. Podzolic soils on terraces and more gentle slopes also can be and are made productive with fertilization and care. The fact that almost a third of Japan is covered by soils with some agricultural potential does not mean that cultivation over all of them is possible, since slope, indifferent fertility, and competing uses cut down severely on their usability.

Forest resources

More than 60 per cent of Japan's surface area is in productive forest, and these forests, which include some 1,100 species, form one of the major natural resources of the country. In addition to this 60 per cent, comprising 55 million acres out of Japan's total surface of 91 million acres, there are another 6.5 million acres (7.1 per cent) of so-called *genya,* or brushlands, or in Japanese, "wild fields."

Japan's forests may be divided into three major zones. First is the

---

[4] The word "ando" comes from the two Japanese characters meaning "dark" and "soil." Most *ando* are dark in color, and they are subdivided into two classes: brown and black.

Fig. 14 • Aftermath of a September flood in Nagasaki prefecture on Kyushu. The railroad bridge has been washed away, and houses and fields have been damaged. This is a common occurrence in all parts of Japan. Note the irregular pattern of the paddy fields, green and velvety before they yellow with maturity for the harvest. *(U.S. Army.)*

northern boreal zone of Hokkaido and its highland extension down into northern Honshu. The predominant trees in these forests are spruce, fir, larch, and birch. Second, a zone of mixed forests, largely deciduous, covers most of central Honshu down to the Inland Sea region. Oak, beech, and maple are the dominant species, but with large intermixtures of conifers of which *sugi* or Japanese cedar, *hinoki* or Japanese cypress, and certain large pines are most important, especially at higher altitudes. In southern Japan a broadleaved evergreen forest predominates, with live oak, laurel, and other hardwoods the most conspicuous species, but here also *sugi* and pine appear at higher altitudes or in planted stands. The camphor tree is an example of the numerous subtropical species that also are found. In all areas, large planted stands of pine and *sugi* are found in association with areas of natural forest.

In terms of acreages, about half of Japan's forests are broadleaved, 30 per cent are coniferous, and 20 per cent are mixed. A fraction of a per cent is in bamboo forest, located mostly in central and southern Japan, although almost every farmstead or village has its little grove of bamboo. Since some 60 per cent of the broadleaved forests, however, are in the form of so-called "coppice stands," used primarily for fuelwood and containing little timber of marketable size, most of Japan's timber supply must come from the coniferous forests.[5]

Not all of Japan's forests are accessible (Figure 15). Of the total forested area, including *genya*, of nearly 62 million acres, an estimated 6,260,000 acres, 10 per cent of the forested area and 24 per cent of the total volume of timber, are in inaccessible forests, as yet untapped, isolated by a lack of modern transportation facilities. In addition, about 9 per cent of the total forested area, five million acres, is in protective forests, which either are not open to lumbering or are used on a very limited

[5] The forests of Hokkaido and northern Honshu, largely coniferous, contain 45 per cent of the standing volume of Japan's forests.

Fig. 15 • Japan's forested areas frequently are reached only over poor unsurfaced roads, such as this one in Nagano prefecture on Honshu, heavy with mud. The size of the cut logs is typical of those from many of Japan's mixed coppice stands; they will be used primarily for fuel and pulping. Note the omnipresent power lines, found even in the less accessible areas. *(U.S. Army.)*

basis. Lastly, some seven million acres of forest have been cut over and are in need of reforestation, although they provide some fuelwood. In brief, the most accessible of Japan's forests are under vigorous exploitation; those less accessible, in northern Honshu or parts of eastern Hokkaido, have yet to be brought into productive use. The burden of forest exploitation, therefore, is not evenly distributed among all of Japan's forests.[6]

Wood and wood products provide one of the important bases both of the Japanese economy and of Japanese life. Except in the largest cities and for the buildings occupied by the wealthy or public buildings, house construction in Japan is almost entirely of wood. Cellulose from softwoods is the basis for one of the great rayon and paper industries of the world, and before the Pacific War, Japan ranked sixth among the nations of the world in the production of pulp. In addition, the primary fuel for cooking and heating in Japanese homes is wood or charcoal. Only in the larger cities and public buildings has wood been displaced as the main heating fuel, and that on a small scale and in very recent times. A further key use of the forests is to stabilize soils and water supply in the uplands. Clearance of the forest in many hilly and mountainous areas has resulted in severe soil erosion, in the silting of stream channels downstream, and in floods of serious consequences to agriculture.

The total need of Japan for wood and wood products of all kinds— timber, fuel, pulp, and general manufacturing—is estimated to be 2.6 billion cubic feet a year,[7] of which some 1.6 billion cubic feet is for fuel. Most of the remaining 1 billion cubic feet is for timber and general construction purposes; only 10 per cent is for pulping purposes. Even so, at present rates of exploitation, Japan is unable to satisfy her wood needs, and wood, especially for pulping purposes, is a major import. Since the estimated growth rate in the accessible Japanese forests is about 1.7 billion cubic feet a year, there is an anticipated deficit of some 900 million cubic feet a year if sustained yield practices are observed, more if the existing pattern of forest depletion is not changed. Formerly, Japan made up most of this deficit from the forests of Karafuto (southern Sakhalin) primarily,[8] Manchuria, and Korea. These sources of supply since the war have become only partially and not reliably available. In 1950, total timber and fuelwood production in Japan amounted to 1.7 billion cubic feet, of which fuelwood accounted for 65 per cent.

[6] The accessible coniferous forests, 15 per cent of the total forested area, supply some 85 per cent of all saw-timber cut.

[7] In 1943, under press of wartime conditions, peak Japanese production reached 3.4 billion cubic feet.

[8] In 1940 Karafuto alone contained nine major paper and pulp mills, with an annual output of 300,000 tons of pulp and 170,000 tons of paper, about 17 per cent of Japan's total consumption of pulp and paper.

Although Japan is famous for her prewar programs of reforestation and forest management, present forest exploitation is not carried on in keeping with modern forest management practices. Over half of the forests are privately owned, and customary practices are to clean-cut timber, even on steep slopes, and to follow with a clearing of underbrush for use as fuel and composting materials on the farms. This leaves whole hillsides exposed, and under the heavy rainfall that characterizes most of Japan soils erode rapidly with consequent flood damage to agricultural areas in the lowlands. Furthermore, exploitation of the forests is proceeding at a more rapid rate than growth under present conditions; during the war, cutting of coniferous saw-timber rose to five times the then growth rate. In addition, planted forests seldom are properly thinned, leading to smaller timbers, and clean-cutting prevents a natural reproduction of the forests.

On the 31 per cent of the total forest acreage that is state-owned, however, and on the 18 per cent of the forested areas owned by other public bodies, more rigid forest management is practiced. Most of the national forests are in Hokkaido, northern Honshu, and mountainous southern Kyushu, and many are inaccessible. The government is promoting reforestation with a vigorous program of indoctrination and subsidies. Between 1946 and 1950 some 7.1 million acres of land in slope were reforested. The inaccessible areas are slowly being opened to exploitation, but it is realized that much of the inaccessible forest area performs a major function of watershed protection and that this function must be continued.

Nonfuel mineral resources

Japan's position with regard to *metallic minerals* is especially weak. Although the variety of metallic minerals is extensive, Japan possesses reserves adequate to meet normal peacetime needs only in six—chromite, copper, gold, magnesium, silver, and zinc. It is known that Japan has not been thoroughly explored mineralogically, but the possibilities for large-scale new discoveries are slight. Only in the case of magnesium and lesser minerals derivable from sea water is there an anticipated unlimited natural supply, although, excepting salt, commercial production from sea water has yet to become significant.

Iron ore, the basic metallic mineral for any industrialized country, is available in very small quantities. Reserves of ore are estimated at about 20 million metric tons, half of which are associated with the largest iron mine in Japan at Kamaishi, Iwate Ken, in northeastern Honshu. Here are reserves of high-grade ores, which at present rates of consumption will have been depleted by 1970. Some bog iron is mined in Hokkaido. In all, only 1,140,000 metric tons of ore were mined in 1953. A larger reserve of ore, some 10 million recoverable tons, exists in the form of iron sands which are widely spread the length of Japan, but there are extreme technical difficulties of extraction owing to the low quality of the ore and the high percentage (about 17 per cent) of titanium. Some 220,000 tons are mined each year, and as costs come down with increased use of titanium by-products, more can be expected to be utilized. Japan also uses about 550,-000 metric tons a year of pyrite cinder, a by-product of sulfuric acid production from pyrites, as blast-furnace feed. Pyrites are abundant in Japan and, except for technological problems of use, offer a major additional source of iron. Nevertheless, Japan must continue to depend on foreign supplies of iron ore for most of her needs. These needs amount to over 6 million metric tons, including pyrite cinder, of which about 4.5 million tons are imported.

Most of the key lesser metals associated with the iron and steel industry are either lacking or available only in small quantities. Manganese, nickel, tungsten, molybdenum, vanadium, cobalt, and titanium resources supply only a small fraction of the domestic demand. Tin, mercury, and antimony reserves also are small, and the reserves of lead, though larger and able to supply about a fifth of the demand, are limited. Japan also is almost without bauxite; there are few aluminum shales; and the supplies of alunite are scattered. Prewar aluminum production was based almost entirely on bauxite imported from Southeast Asia, on aluminum shales from East Asia, and on alunite from Korea.

Among the metals available in substantial quantity, copper is perhaps the most significant. Although copper is not present in great abundance, the 1954 production of 69,000 metric tons of refined copper was sufficient to meet the demand, and production should be able to rise in the future as needs also expand. The chief exploited deposits are found in Akita, Tochigi, and Ibaraki Ken, north and northeast of Tokyo, and in Ehime Ken, in northern Shikoku (Figure 16). Chromite deposits also are believed sufficient for domestic needs. The chief mines are found in southern Hokkaido and in Toyama and Okayama Ken of southcentral Honshu, tapping reserves amounting to some 800,000 metric tons. In 1954, 11,600 metric tons of chromic oxide were produced. Zinc also is available in quantities sufficient to meet domestic demand, and deposits are estimated at some two million tons of metal. The chief mines, sometimes in association with lead mining, are located in Gifu Ken in central Honshu and in Iwate and Miyagi Ken, northern Honshu. Gold and silver are the last of the major minerals of which supplies are expected to meet Japan's needs, and veins of gold and silver are mined on both a large and small scale from Hokkaido to Kyushu. Most of the metals not in notable de-

Fig. 16 • The Ashio smelter in Tochigi prefecture, Honshu. Copper is one of the six metallic minerals available in relative abundance in Japan. Although this is mid-March, there is snow atop the mountains in the background. Note the complex masonry, typical of Japan, which reflects the use of local construction materials. *(U.S. Army.)*

ficiency in Japan, however, were imported in substantial quantity both before and during the Pacific war. If Japan's industrial capacity rises well above that of the immediate prewar period, as it already has done in certain sectors of the economy, domestic supplies even of these metals will have to be obtained from foreign sources.

The situation with regard to *nonmetallic minerals*, other than fuels, is much superior to that of the metals. Limestone, sulfur, building stones, clays, gypsum, arsenic, bismuth, cadmium, garnet, and other minerals are relatively abundant. Limestone is found in every island, and in places in convenient juxtaposition to coal, as in northern Kyushu. Sulfur, a characteristic product of areas of vulcanism, is one of Japan's few minerals of which there is an exportable surplus. Most of the production comes from pyrites, 1,124,000 metric tons in 1954; the balance from native sulphur deposits, 188,000 tons in 1954. The pyrite and sulphur deposits are widely scattered throughout the islands.

Japan lacks certain fine clays for her china industry and refractory uses, lacks graphite, phosphate rock and potash, diamonds, and micas, and is in short supply for numerous other minerals. The lack of fertilizer raw materials, other than nitrates which can be fixed from the air, is associated with a demand for these fertilizers larger than in any other country in Asia.

Conspicuous among Japan's mineral shortages is that of salt. Though surrounded by the sea, Japan produces only a fifth, 453,000 metric tons in 1954, of her needs. Most of Japan's salt-producing industry is located along the eastern shores of the Inland Sea, the area of lowest rainfall in Old Japan. Yet, the average rainfall in this region is over 40 inches, several more than Chicago, and though the winters are relatively dry, there is precipitation throughout the year. Therefore, complete solar extraction of the salt is impossible, although the brine can be concentrated. Thereafter, the brine must be heated and condensed over fires of charcoal or coal from Kyushu. In some cases, electrical means are used to evaporate the salt. Thus salt-making is expensive, much more so than along the Yellow Sea coast of China, or even the western shores of T'ai-wan. When charcoal is used, it places an added burden on regional fuel supplies, and the need for coal must be satisfied only in competition with other demands.

Fuel and energy resources

Japan's position with regard to energy resources is perhaps more favorable, despite key weaknesses, than for any other class of resources. However, of the five major sources of inanimate energy—coal, water power, petroleum, natural gas, and wood—Japan is highly deficient in two, petroleum and natural gas. For a nation the merchant marine of which is almost entirely dependent on oil for power, the lack of petroleum is a grave problem. This same deficiency is considered to have been one of the major factors contributing to Japan's defeat in the Pacific War.

Japan's known *petroleum* deposits are concentrated primarily in northwestern Honshu, in Niigata, Yamagata, and Akita Ken. A number of other districts may be proved productive, but an annual production of 349,000 metric tons (1955) accounts for less than 15 per cent of Japan's domestic needs. Some natural gas is produced in association with petroleum operations, but production represents only a minute fraction of Japan's consumption of inanimate energy.

On the other hand, *wood* is one of Japan's major energy sources. The importance of wood, or charcoal, in the Japanese way of life has already been indicated. About 21 per cent of the total energy, in thermal equivalents, produced in Japan is derived from wood. Almost every village in Japan has its local source of fuelwood. Thousands of charcoal kilns are found throughout the country, and even in the markets of the largest cities bundles of faggots or of charcoal are a conspicuous article of commerce. Most of the fuelwood is derived from coppice stands which are not suitable for timber production. Furthermore, the extent of these coppice areas, which account for some 36 per cent of the productive forests, is increasing at the expense of tall-timber stands. Existing demands for fuelwood are greater than the coppice woods' natural reproduction rate, and the toll of other forest capital being exacted to meet fuel needs is a threat to Japan's potential self-sufficiency in woods for other purposes.

The major source of energy in Japan, as in most countries, is *coal*. In terms of heat values, coal accounts for two-thirds of Japan's total production of fuel and energy. The total reserves of coal in Japan are estimated to be 17 billion tons, only a small fraction of China's reserves, but enough at present rates of consumption to last more than 200 years. Although never a major coal exporter, Japan helped fill the half-empty bottoms of her outgoing ships by loading coal for Hongkong and Southeast Asia. In terms of value, coal accounts for about half of all mineral production in Japan.

More than three-fourths of Japan's coal is a low-grade bituminous of Tertiary origin, with heating qualities well below that of West Virginia coals. Only 4 per cent is believed to be anthracite, and the remainder is subbituminous. Production costs have been high because of crooked and broken seams, thin measures, ground water in the mines, and the limited use of machinery. In certain areas of northern Kyushu the mines are under the sea, and the dangers of flooding are great. Before the second World War, per-ton costs were almost twice those in the United States, and the production per underground worker in Japan was about a third that in the United States. In addition, Japanese coal is high in ash and volatile matter, and its calorific value is relatively low.

The two major producing regions for coal are northern Kyushu and western Hokkaido. The northern Kyushu region produces about 55 per cent of the total national production, much of which is consumed in the area or is transported by coasting vessel to the consuming centers at the eastern end of the Inland Sea (Figure 17). Hokkaido contains more than half of the gross proved, probable, and possible reserves, but accounts for only a third of total production (43 million metric tons in 1955). The Hokkaido mines are centered in the Ishikari field of westcentral Hokkaido, where the possibilities for expansion of production are better than in Kyushu. There also are fields in eastern Hokkaido near the port of

Kushiro that contain substantial reserves, as yet little exploited. Hokkaido coal moves by barge and coasting vessel to the towns of northern Honshu and the industrial areas of Kanto, the Nobi plain, and even the eastern Inland Sea.

Of lesser importance is a third field, the Joban field, of Fukushima Ken in northeastern Honshu. It is the chief source of coal for the city of Tokyo, and most of it moves by rail rather than by sea. In addition, there are lesser fields in far northern Honshu and anthracite mines at the south-western tip of Honshu, geologically associated with the fields of northern Kyushu. Shikoku, however, is without known coal deposits. Lignite also is becoming a major fuel, and in 1953 1.49 million tons were produced. A major possible use for lignite is as a domestic fuel, thereby removing some of the fuel burden from the forests. Reserves are estimated at some 800 million recoverable tons, although actual reserves are perhaps twice as large. Workable lignite deposits are widely scattered throughout the archipelago.

Fig. 17 • The coal-mining town of Honami in Fukuoka prefecture, Kyushu. Piles of waste material from the mines tower over the town. In contrast to the industrialized Japan represented by the mines is the Shinto shrine, with its gate or *torii*, in the left middle-ground, a reflection of the dualism which characterizes Japan as well as the other countries of the Asiatic Crescent. *(U.S. Army.)*

Since little of Japan's coal is of coking quality, Japan has been dependent upon imports of coking coal for her iron-and-steel industry. Although the possibilities for coking poorer-grade coals economically are nearer to realization than ever before, Japan still looks abroad, chiefly to the Chinese mainland from which much of her coking coal came before the war. The loss of Karafuto also was a major blow to Japan, since almost 13 per cent of the production of coal in the Japanese Empire, exclusive of Manchuria and Korea, came from Karafuto during the war years.

Another major source of energy is *water power,* and in this resource Japan is perhaps most fortunate. The ample rainfall, swift streams, and high mountains of central Japan provide three of the five basic natural conditions for the development of hydroelectricity.[9] A conservative estimate of Japan's hydroelectric potential, on the basis of six-month minimum flow, is 12 million kilowatts. The Japanese already have developed 74 per cent of this potential, and in 1955 there was an installed capacity of 8.9 million kilowatts. Although there are hydroelectric plants on each major island of the archipelago, there is a major concentration of installations in central and northern Honshu. Plants in Tohoku (northeastern Honshu) and Chubu (central Honshu) account for about half of all hydroelectric energy generated (48.5 billion KWH in 1955), and these tend to be concentrated on the Japan Sea side of the island.

Most of the Japanese installations are small. Of some 1,450 hydroelectric stations in the country, 88 per cent have an installed capacity of less than 10,000 kilowatts and 47 per cent less than 1,000 kilowatts. Only a handful, a little over 1 per cent, have a capacity of more than 50,000 kilowatts. Most of the larger plants are in central Honshu (Figure 18). Smaller plants are widely scattered.

The efficiency of hydroelectric production suffers from the seasonal variations in rainfall, especially away from the areas of winter rainfall. Thus, in much of Japan there is a major decline in hydroelectric output during the winter months. This deficiency is accentuated by the lack of storage facilities.[10] The typical Japanese installation consists of a low dam that deflects water into twin penstocks. These penstocks carry the water down nearby slopes, sometimes through sizable tunnels, and thence into the plant itself. Such installations are known as "run-of-stream" plants and are relatively uncommon in the United States, for example, where storage facilities normally are planned for and constructed. The problem in Japan lies partially in the fact that the areas to be flooded behind high

[9] The fourth would be natural water-storage facilities, and the fifth, regularity of flow.

[10] The heavy loads carried by Japanese rivers restrict the life of the dam structures by rapid silting of reservoirs. The Japanese have customarily assumed a 25- to 30-year life for their dams before silting. However, most of the future hydro development will be associated with multipurpose storage dams, planned for longer life.

Fig. 18 • One of the larger hydroelectric installations in Japan at Ochiai in Gifu prefecture, central Honshu. In the photograph, the power station is just to the left of the dam. This type of low dam providing little water storage capacity is common in Japan, where high dams and large reservoirs have not been widely constructed. Note the partly forested, largely cleared steep slopes in the background and the intensively cultivated terraced slopes in the foreground. *(U.S. Army.)*

dams either contain valuable cropland or provide routes for communications facilities. In a rugged country like Japan where cropland is scarce and topographic features provide formidable barriers to communications, the submergence of these areas under reservoirs would be of considerable consequence. That the Japanese have no impractical bias against building storage dams, however, is indicated by their constructions of two of the world's largest dams in Korea and Manchuria. In any event, normal production from Japan's hydroelectric plants indicates that they operate at less than two-thirds of their installed capacity.

Thermoelectric plants supply most of the power necessary to meet the seasonal and regional deficits in hydroelectric power. In 1955 there were some 325 thermoelectric plants with an installed capacity of 5.6 million kilowatts. These, when combined with the hydroelectric plants, gave Japan in 1955 a total installed electrical generating capacity of 14.5 million kilowatts, roughly equivalent to the installed capacity in the states of Illinois and Michigan combined. It is planned to raise total capacity to 17 million kilowatts by 1959. The thermal plants also operate at less than capacity, and their average efficiency of output is calculated at about 40 per cent of capacity, but during the Pacific War output rose to about 75 per cent.

Most of the thermal plants are designed as standby or auxiliary plants for the hydroelectric system; this explains in part their low efficiency of operation. On the other hand many of the thermal plants, and in fact most of the larger ones, are located in areas where demand is greatest and where hydroelectric installations are unable to meet demands at any time of the year. Northern Kyushu and the Kinki region, which includes Osaka and Kobe, are two major loci of thermoelectric generation. Kanto (Tokyo) and Nobi (Nagoya) are another two, which are easily reached by hydroelectric installations in central Honshu but which need more energy than the hydroelectric plants can supply. Western Hokkaido is another center of thermal generation, in association with the coals of the Ishikari basin. Of the total amount of electrical power available, 65.2 billion KWH in 1955, more than three-quarters comes from hydroelectric plants. Only in the areas of thermal concentration noted above, and especially in the great cities, is thermal energy of prime importance.

Most of Honshu is covered by an integrated system of high-voltage lines that permit the transfer of power from surplus to deficit areas. However, the losses in transfer are great enough so that peripheral areas on the island are out of effective transfer range. Hokkaido and Shikoku are not connected with the main systems; Kyushu is, but it is so far removed from the centers of hydroelectric generation that it depends almost entirely on its thermal plants, which use locally produced coal.

In terms of *total energy* in electrical equivalents available to each Japanese, some 1,200 KWH per person, 44 per cent comes from coal and 37 per cent from hydroelectricity, most of the balance coming from fuelwood. Although this per-capita consumption of energy places Japan slightly above the world average, it is less than 10 per cent of the electrical equivalents available to each person in the United States.

SELECTED GEOGRAPHICAL BIBLIOGRAPHY

1. Ackerman, Edward A. *Japanese Natural Resources*. Chicago: University of Chicago Press, 1953.
2. *Climatographic Atlas of Japan*. Tokyo: Industrial Meteorological Association, 1948.
3. Ginsburg, N. S. "Japanese Natural Resources," in Hugh Borton, ed., *Japan*. Ithaca: Cornell University Press, 1951.

4. Okada, T. *Climate of Japan*. Tokyo: Central Meteorological Observatory, 1931.
5. SCAP, Natural Resource Section. *Reports*, especially Nos. 141, 149, 153, and 154. Tokyo: 1945–1952.
6. Swanson, C. L. W. "Reconnaissance Soil Survey of Japan," *Soil Science Society of America, Proceedings*, 1946, Vol. II, pp. 493-507.
7. Trewartha, G. T. *Japan: A Physical, Cultural, and Regional Geography*. Madison: University of Wisconsin Press, 1945.
8. U.S. Army Service Forces. *Civil Affairs Handbook: Japan*, sec. 6, "Natural Resources," No. M354.
9. U.S. Bureau of Mines. "Mineral Resources of Japan," *Foreign Minerals Survey*, Vol. 2, No. 5, October, 1945.
10. Watanabe, A. "Landform Divisions of Japan," *Bulletin of the Geographical Survey Institute*, Vol. II, Part I, pp. 81-94. Tokyo: Ministry of Construction, 1950.

Comments

The most valuable general study of Japanese resources is that of Ackerman, which covers in great detail almost every aspect of the resource problem, including trends and potentials. Trewartha is more general and is the basic text on Japanese geography. The *Reports* of the Natural Resources Section, Supreme Commander Allied Powers, are exceptionally valuable, if highly specific, studies of Japanese natural resources. Ackerman's study is based largely on the data in these reports. Okada is the basic source for climatic information. The *Climatographic Atlas* is in effect a supplement to Okada. Both contain extensive tables of climatic data.

Numerous journal articles and statistical publications also are available, but the selections here contain essentially all the basic materials necessary for an understanding of Japan's resource position.

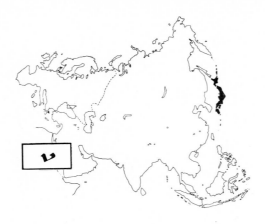

Japan

AGRICULTURE AND FOOD SUPPLY

ALTHOUGH JAPAN HAS PROCEEDED FURTHER ALONG THE ROAD TO industrialization than any other country in Asia, agriculture remains the chief occupation of its people, and it is largely upon their agricultural output that Japan's economic wellbeing depends. In 1956, 17,140,000 people, approximately 41 per cent of the total labor force, were dependent upon agriculture and forestry for their livelihood.

The pattern of agriculture

It is customary to think of Japan as being so densely occupied that there are only a few, small areas of sparse population. This conception of Japan and the Japanese landscape is misleading. The land-utilization map of Japan (Map 6) shows clearly that much of Japan, about three-fourths of its land surface, is sparsely occupied. Much of this area is in mountain forest or brushland; some is in wasteland. Although scattered settlements, some of them (at least in Old Japan) of great antiquity, are widely distributed in the area, it is possible to travel for miles without seeing permanent habitations. The lumber camp, the wood-gatherer's hut, the hovels of a shifting cultivator—these are the major features of occupance over extensive areas of densely populated Japan.

Fig. 19 • Agricultural land utilization in Japan is restricted to the intensively occupied coastal plains and riverine lowlands between forested interfluves. In this area just northwest of Kobe, paddy fields and some upland fields occupy the valleys of small streams rising in the hills which are covered by planted stands of Japanese cedar and by coppice stands of mixed trees. Note the terraces along the margins of the valleys, which reflect intensive land uses, the ponds and reservoirs that store irrigation water, and the irregularly shaped villages that hug the roads. The village at the right is a modified *strassendorf* type. (U.S. Army.)

The most significant fact about agricultural occupance in Japan is its extreme localization and concentration. A second is the remarkable areal correlation between population and cultivated land. A map of one is in effect a map of the other, and the low densities of the one reflect a scarcity of the other. Japan's density of population is slightly less than Belgium's, for example, but in terms of density per unit of cultivated land, Japan's is nearly twice as great as Belgium's, being 4,220 per square mile. The so-called physiological density of Japan's population is characteristically Asian and is probably the highest in the world. In the agricultural areas it is true that "there is no getting away from men anywhere."

The areas devoted to agriculture in Japan are extremely limited; only 15 million acres, 16.4 per cent of the total land surface area of Japan, is

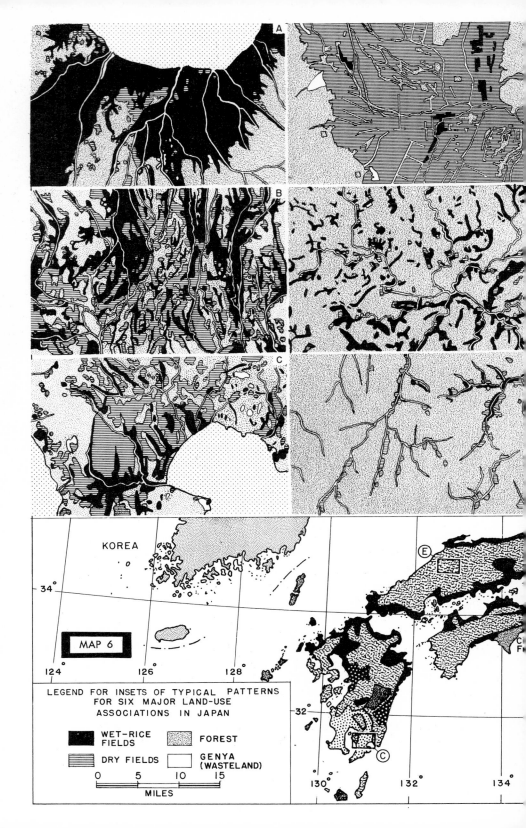

KOREA

34°

MAP 6

124°   126°   128°

LEGEND FOR INSETS OF TYPICAL PATTERNS
FOR SIX MAJOR LAND-USE
ASSOCIATIONS IN JAPAN

WET-RICE   FOREST
FIELDS

DRY FIELDS   GENYA
(WASTELAND)

0   5   10   15
MILES

E

32°

C

130°   132°   134°

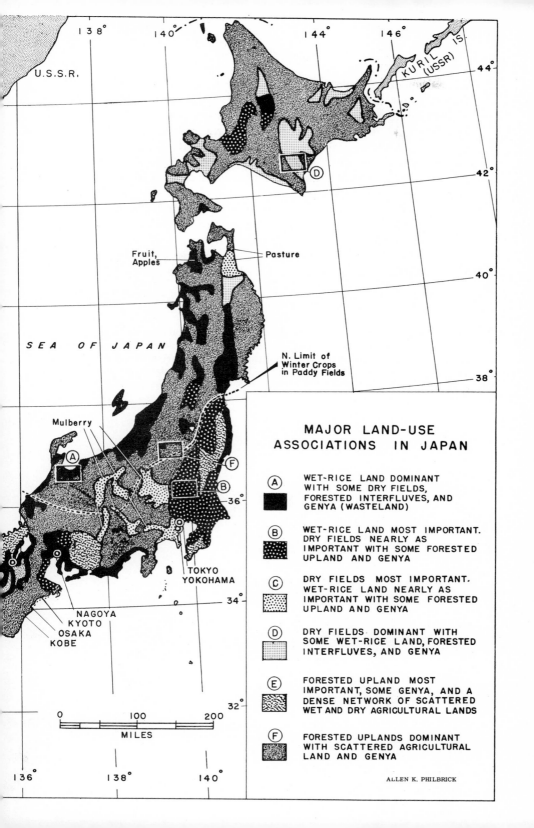

MAJOR LAND-USE
ASSOCIATIONS IN JAPAN

Ⓐ WET-RICE LAND DOMINANT
WITH SOME DRY FIELDS,
FORESTED INTERFLUVES, AND
GENYA (WASTELAND)

Ⓑ WET-RICE LAND MOST IMPORTANT.
DRY FIELDS NEARLY AS
IMPORTANT WITH SOME FORESTED
UPLAND AND GENYA

Ⓒ DRY FIELDS MOST IMPORTANT.
WET-RICE LAND NEARLY AS
IMPORTANT WITH SOME FORESTED
UPLAND AND GENYA

Ⓓ DRY FIELDS DOMINANT WITH
SOME WET-RICE LAND, FORESTED
INTERFLUVES, AND GENYA

Ⓔ FORESTED UPLAND MOST
IMPORTANT, SOME GENYA, AND A
DENSE NETWORK OF SCATTERED
WET AND DRY AGRICULTURAL LANDS

Ⓕ FORESTED UPLANDS DOMINANT
WITH SCATTERED AGRICULTURAL
LAND AND GENYA

ALLEN K. PHILBRICK

U.S.S.R.

KURIL IS.
(USSR)

Fruit,
Apples — Pasture

SEA OF JAPAN

N. Limit of
Winter Crops
in Paddy Fields

Mulberry

TOKYO
YOKOHAMA

NAGOYA
KYOTO
OSAKA
KOBE

0   100   200
MILES

in permanent cultivation. By far the greater part of this area is concentrated in the major lowlands and lesser coastal plans and intermontane basins in which Japan's population also is compressed (Figures 12 and 19). The land-utilization map shows the largest areas of cultivation to be the plains of Kanto, Nobi, Sendai, Ishikari, Niigata, Settsu, and Tsukushi, and the lesser lowlands. With the major exception of urban sites, almost all level or near-level areas are under cultivation, and cultivation has crept up onto the slopes that rim the lowlands.

One Japanese geographer has divided Japan into three major land-use regions: [1] (1) the Central Region, (2) the Frontier Region, and (3) Hokkaido. The Central Region contains central and southern Honshu, Shikoku, and all of Kyushu except the southernmost parts. It is divided in turn into a Core Zone—Northern Kyushu, the Inland Sea region, and the

[1] Y. Ogasawara, "Land Use of Japan," *Bulletin of the Geographical Survey Institute,* 1950, Vol. II, Part I, pp. 95-119.

Fig. 20 • There is an agricultural "frontier" zone in Japan, particularly in northern Honshu and parts of Hokkaido. In these areas are larger holdings, generally on poorer soils, with dispersed rather than concentrated settlement patterns. This is a farmstead in such a "frontier" area in Iwate prefecture, northeastern Honshu, which has been occupied for a relatively longer period than some farmlands in the forested hills beyond. Note the bunding between the fields. *(U.S. Army.)*

major lowlands of Honshu except for the Sendai Plain—and a Peripheral Zone. The Core Zone is the agricultural heartland of Old Japan, distinguished from the Peripheral Zone by a longer continuance of agricultural occupance, higher percentages of cultivated land, and lesser dependence on auxiliary economic activities such as silkworm raising or forest exploitation. The areas included within the so-called Frontier Region are characterized by lesser population densities, scattered occupance patterns, a high ratio of subsistence to cash crops, and relatively large areas in forest or pasture (Figure 20). Hokkaido is divided into two major regions, the west and the east. Both resemble the Frontier Region of Old Japan, but western Hokkaido is relatively densely occupied, whereas eastern Hokkaido is much less so.

The fact that the term "frontier" can be applied to large areas within Old Japan is especially significant since it accentuates the areal anomalies of agricultural localization within the archipelago. This is not to say that there is an extensive agricultural frontier region in Japan awaiting the pioneer settler. The frontier in Hokkaido is restricted to a few small areas. In Old Japan, the concept of the awaiting frontier is negated in large part by natural barriers of excessive slope and soil infertility, although there exist possibilities for upland development.

At the present time, Japanese agriculture is land-intensive; that is, emphasis is on high production per unit of land. To a degree, however, Japanese agriculture also may be described as labor-intensive, in that the present agricultural system is the one most productive, given existing technologies and crop combinations, of a man's time and energy.[2]

The intensity of pressures upon the cultivated areas in Japan is reflected in a number of agricultural practices which are identified closely with Japanese agriculture, and indeed with much of Asian agriculture, of which Japan has come to be a recognized prototype.

Over half of Japan's cultivated area is under *irrigation*. The irrigated areas are coincident with those areas under wet or irrigated rice, which occupies about 53 per cent of all cultivated land. Unlike several of the countries of Southeast Asia, Japan has little uncontrolled irrigation. Only where the steeper paddy terraces rise from the lowland rims may irrigation water be uncontrolled, but even in many such cases water is carried ingeniously from upland ponds and streams to the higher terraced fields and thence downward to the terraces below. Many of Japan's mountain streams are deflected by diversion dams through a network of canals and ditches which ultimately serve the individual paddy fields. In some cases, when a river flows upon an elevated bed, water may be deflected

[2] The acknowledged underemployment of farm labor for part of the year would appear to negate this argument, but the conspicuous labor shortages that exist in much of Japan during the planting and harvesting seasons indicate a need for more rather than less labor at those times.

to the fields without a major dam structure. Only in few instances, however, are gravity-flow systems sufficiently developed to permit the direct
irrigation of individual paddy fields. Generally, water is lifted from the
larger canals onto the fields or into the distributary ditches by hand- or
foot-operated pumps. Increasingly, small gasoline or electric pumps are
being used for this purpose.

Just as irrigation is one indication of land-intensive agriculture, so is
terracing another. Throughout Japan, except in the most level areas, some
terracing is practiced. In fact, many near-level areas under irrigated rice
also may be said to be terraced; the necessary levelling of each paddy
field for even distribution of water has the effect of creating low terraces,
even where the degree of slope is minute. In general, however, the term
refers to what are more properly called "bench terraces," which form
marked step-like patterns along the often steep lower slopes and drainage
courses of hills and mountains. Such terraces are carved laboriously out
of hillsides and are supported by retaining walls of earth, brush, masonry,
or boulders, some of which are several feet in height. The bench terraces
used for wet-rice cultivation are the relics of an age when the expenditure
of human energy on terrace construction and levelling was of little economic consequence. Today, the construction of such terraces has virtually
ceased as increased labor costs have made them uneconomic. On the
other hand, the number of terraces for dry or upland crops rapidly is increasing. Most terraces now being constructed are not fully levelled;
many are without retaining walls; and some are little more than enlarged
contoured plow ridges. In places, dry cultivation is proceeding without
terracing on slopes that are far too steep for normal agriculture. The resultant losses through soil erosion and decreases in stream and water
control are nationally significant.

Another characteristic of Japanese agriculture is *multiple-cropping*.
About one-third of the total cultivated area is double-cropped, and the
cropping index for the whole country is about 133 per cent. This is the
highest index of multiple-cropping for an entire country in Asia, although
in China, Southeast Asia, and India, multiple-cropping is regionally of
major importance—of least importance, perhaps, in Southeast Asia. The
nature of double-cropping in Japan varies significantly from region to
region. In general, more than one crop is raised in almost every *ken* in
Old Japan; in Hokkaido double-cropping is practically unknown for
obvious climatic reasons, and the cropping index there is less than one.
In northern Japan the cropping index is barely over 100 per cent, but it
increases rapidly to the south. The highest cropping indices are 191 per
cent in Kumamoto Ken and above 160 per cent in most of Kyushu and
much of Shikoku, although local variations are considerable.

South of the 37th parallel double-cropping of paddy fields is common.

North of that latitude it is rare, since the length of growing season to the north does not normally permit the growth of a crop of irrigated rice and then a second crop in the same field. The second crop in the double-cropped paddy fields, moreover, almost never is rice because of a growing season too short for two crops of rice, but generally is some other grain planted as a winter crop, or vegetables. Wheat, barley, millet, and soy beans are the most important of these second crops. Only in a few areas in southern Shikoku and the Kii peninsula are two crops of rice raised on one piece of land. Even where climatic conditions permit the raising of second crops on paddy land, double-cropping may not be possible for reasons of poor drainage. In the Kanto region alone, about 40 per cent of the paddy fields lie fallow in winter because of poor drainage conditions, and in all of Japan where climate permits the double-cropping of paddy fields, about 35 per cent of such fields lie fallow in winter. Farmers sometimes attempt to counter this problem by raising high mounded rows within their fields upon which dry winter crops are sown, but this is an exceedingly laborious undertaking, limited in economic practicability because less than half of the field is then cultivable. On upland fields winter grains normally are rotated with vegetables or with millets or corn.

Intercropping is another device, a variant of multiple-cropping, for making the most of a limited agricultural area: a late crop is planted between the rows of an earlier crop so that both can be harvested within a single growing season. This practice is more common on nonirrigated land, since second crops seldom can be planted in the paddy fields while they are still wet. In some cases, however, where drainage conditions permit, a winter crop of grain will be intersown with soybeans or vegetables, followed by a summer crop of rice or vegetables. In the truck-gardening areas about the great cities, three crops of vegetables commonly are obtained through intertillage. Intertillage also is significant in the raising of green manure crops on both upland and irrigated fields.

Transplantation is yet another time- and land-conserving practice, common to many other wet-rice areas in Asia. In short, the seed grain is planted in small, carefully prepared plots, known as seedbeds, which are perhaps one-tenth the area of the paddy fields (Figure 21). After a period of several weeks, when the rice plants are almost a foot high, the seedlings are gently uprooted from the flooded seedbed and transplanted to larger paddy fields. The advantages of the transplanting process are several. Most important is the fact that where the growing season is especially limited for multiple-cropping—and this is true of much of Japan—the time during which the seedlings are growing in the seedbeds permits the maturation of the winter or second crop of grains in the paddy fields. A second advantage is that pest and water control during the critical early period of rice growth is made easier. In this connection there also is

Fig. 21 • Seeding seedbeds in May in Shizuoka prefecture, central Honshu. The beds are small, permitting easier weed and water control during the early life of the rice plant and enabling winter crops to mature several weeks longer in the double-cropped paddy fields. The soil in the beds is soft, undifferentiated mud, fertilized with compost. Note the uplands in the background covered in part with tea, a famous product of Shizuoka Ken. (U.S. Army.)

a saving of irrigation water. Fourth, there is a saving of labor, since greater care can be lavished on the limited area of the seedbeds at a time when the second crop is about to be harvested and the paddy fields themselves have to be made ready for receiving the primary rice crop. Finally, there is some evidence that the slight damage to the seedling roots during transplantation stimulates later plant growth. In Hokkaido, however, where multiple-cropping is not practiced and the pressure on the land is less than in Old Japan, seed grain may be sown broadcast in the fields without transplanting. The relations between transplantation and yields, all other factors being equal, however, are uncertain.

Intensive fertilization is more characteristic of Japanese agriculture than of any other country in Asia, although the Chinese in restricted areas may match the intensity of Japanese fertilizer use. In Southeast Asia, and to a large degree in India, fertilization is much less intensive and over large areas scarcely is practiced at all. The importance of fertilizers in

Japan is indicated by the fact that they account for approximately one-third of the total production costs of rice.

Two kinds of fertilizers may be distinguished, organic and inorganic. Most of the organic fertilizers consist of so-called "farm manures," which are composed primarily of waste materials on the farm or available in the immediately adjacent areas—animal manures, straw, cut grass from road-sides and hillsides, leaves, and human excrement. In addition, human excrement, or nightsoil, is gathered in the urban areas and sold in the countryside. Since raw nightsoil is often harmful to growing plants and its bacterial content is dangerously high, the various fertilizer materials are stored with it in compost pits where decomposition takes place and the natural heat of fermentation destroys many of the harmful bacteria. Al-most every Japanese farm has a compost pit, and it is official government policy to encourage their construction and use. Before the war these local organic fertilizer materials were augmented by additions of commercial organic fertilizers such as bean and oil cake, imported largely from Man-churia, bone meal, seaweed, and fish cake. Although still important, the commercial organic fertilizers are much less significant in the fertilizer use pattern than before the war, since their price has risen drastically, and imports from other parts of East Asia have declined. In all, farm-originated fertilizers, all organic, accounted for 48 per cent of the nitrogen, 35 per cent of the phosphates, and 75 per cent of the potash consumed before the war.

What differentiates Japan from, for example, China, is the enormous use of commercial *inorganic* fertilizers. To maintain high yields, Japan's requirements for commercial fertilizers take the form of 2.25 million metric tons of ammonium sulfate equivalents (20 per cent N), 1.725 mil-lion metric tons of superphosphate (16 per cent P_2O_5), and 450,000 tons of potash equivalents (40 per cent K_2O). By 1950 the total commercial fertilizer consumption exceeded that of the prewar period, and basic re-quirements, except for potassic fertilizers, were close to being met. Japan is self-sufficient in the production of nitrogenous and phosphatic fer-tilizers, and in both cases has a surplus for export. However, Japan is without phosphate rock, and over a million tons of rock are imported annually. Most potassic fertilizers also are imported, since domestic sup-plies of raw materials are negligible.

In addition, green manures are valuable not only in adding nitrogen to the soil but in improving soil qualities, especially on upland fields. Lime-stone is available in large quantities, and close to a million tons a year are used to neutralize the acidity of Japanese soils. Other materials, such as rich mud from the beds of rivers, canals, and ponds, are applied as dressing to field surfaces.

Crops, crop associations,
and livestock

As in most Asian countries, the overwhelming emphasis in Japanese agriculture is on high calorie-producing crops. In Japan, of the total area *cropped* annually, approximately 17 million acres, almost 90 per cent, is in food crops. Between 75 and 80 per cent is in the so-called staple crops, lesser cereals, and pulses. Less than 5 per cent is in industrial and other nonfood crops, and a minute percentage is in forage crops. This is the characteristic cultivation pattern for most of Asia. Where pastoral industries are especially significant, as in central Asia or Southwest Asia, sedentary agriculture displays the same sort of pattern, although the areas in pasture, either natural or sown, become of primary rather than of negligible importance.

The single most important crop in Japan in terms of acreages, production, value, and general social significance is rice. Less than 5 per cent of the rice grown in Japan is upland or nonirrigated. Only a small fraction of the rice grown is glutinous as opposed to common, and most of it is used for confectionaries and the brewing of alcoholic beverages such as *sake*. The distribution of rice is closely associated with the lowland areas that also are the more densely populated parts of the country. Rice is least important in the northern and upland prefectures where irrigation water is not available or where the growing season is perilously short. In all, rice accounts for some 40 per cent of the total cropped acreage in Japan. Yields are among the highest in the world, being exceeded only in Italy and Spain where the average quality of the land under rice is higher than it is in Japan. Japan's production of approximately 79 bushels of rough rice per acre per crop can be compared with about 55 bushels in China, 50 in the United States, and 23 bushels in India, Burma, and Thailand, and even less in the Philippines. The actual annual yields per unit area, as differentiated from yields per harvest, are higher in south China, however, where there are considerable areas in which double-cropping of rice is practiced, giving higher per acre yields per year than in Japan.

Wheat and barley are the two most important grains other than rice in Japanese agriculture. Wheat, naked barley, and barley together account for about 23 per cent of the total cropped area, or more than half the area in rice. Wheat is grown widely in Japan, but the major concentrations are south of the 37th parallel where it is grown as a winter crop, often as a second crop in paddy fields. The barleys similarly are grown primarily as a winter crop, and their concentration also is south of the 37th parallel, although barley also is grown as a summer crop in Hokkaido. In the Inland Sea region and in Kyushu naked barley predominates; in Kanto, a second area of concentration, common varieties are dominant. Both are grown as winter crops on paddy fields or in rotation with other crops on dry fields. Yields of these grains are high by world standards. Japan's average wheat yield is nearly twice that of the United States, where yields in the Great Plains are relatively low, is comparable to that of France, but is below that of Great Britain and the Low Countries.

The other major staple crops are starchy tubers, among which sweet potatoes are the most important. Sweet potatoes and white potatoes together account for some 8 per cent of the total cropped area. Sweet potatoes are limited to the regions south of the 37th parallel and are most heavily concentrated in the Kanto region and in Kyushu, mostly on loose sandy or *ando* soils unsuited for rice cultivation. White potatoes are grown much more widely, but the bulk of their acreage is in Hokkaido where they compete with rice as the chief food staple. The expansion of the sweet-potato acreage in recent years is a reflection of the emphasis placed on high-calorie foods not only in Japan but also in China and Southeast Asia where similar increases have been displayed. Sweet potatoes are one of the few foods that provide more calories per acre on the average than rice and with considerably less labor input. The replacement of rice by sweet potatoes, however, is unlikely, since the difference in calories between the two foods is small; rice can provide additional nutrients in larger quantities than do sweet potatoes; and cultural preference is overwhelmingly oriented toward rice, since sweet potatoes are regarded as poor man's food.

In addition to these grains, oats, rye, buckwheat, corn, sorghums, and small millets are grown especially in the highland and "frontier" areas. Millet is a favorite crop in recently settled highland farms in northeastern Honshu and Hokkaido. Beans and peas of all kinds cover about 6 per cent of the total cropped area and are grown throughout the islands. Other vegetables, which account for some 5 per cent of the cropped area, are grown everywhere, usually as summer crops in rotation with winter grains on upland fields where climatic conditions permit, sometimes as intertilled crops giving several harvests per season on the better land near the urban markets. Although the giant radish, *daikon*, is characteristically Japanese, most of the vegetables are grown also in the United States, but in Japan their variety is less than it is either in the United States or China.

Fruit-tree crops occupy less than 2 per cent of the total cropped area, and tend to occupy marginal land unsuited for other kinds of production. Citrus fruits, chiefly *satsuma* oranges, are grown south of Kanto, chiefly in Shizuoka and Wakayama Ken, but also around the shores of the Inland Sea and in Kyushu. Other fruits are grown widely, seldom in orchards

except for notable concentrations in Akita and Aomori Ken in far northern Honshu. Oilseed crops, chiefly rape, occupy about the same acreage
as fruit crops, chiefly in southern Japan, in the vicinity of Nagoya, on the
southern shores of Lake Biwa, and in Kyushu. Crops such as rape and
sesame are important sources of the cooking oils and fats of which Japan
is notoriously short.

Industrial and fiber crops occupy less than 5 per cent of the cropped
area, although locally their importance to the village and the industrial
farmer may be considerable. Most important among these crops is the
mulberry, the leaves of which are used to feed silkworms. The raising of
silkworms is an important source of auxiliary income to the Japanese
farmer, although the market for and the price of silk have dropped remarkably since 1930 when the near-disastrous impact of the American
depression was followed by the introduction of synthetics and the substitution of nylon for silk stockings in the United States. As a result, the
total mulberry acreage declined from some 1,760,000 acres in 1930 to
440,000 in 1950. Chief concentrations of mulberry are in the intermontane basins of central Honshu, although it is an important feature of agricultural occupance in all except the northern prefectures of Honshu and
Hokkaido.

Tea also may be classified as an industrial crop, although it may be
considered a food crop. Much production comes from Shizuoka Ken and,
as tea is a subtropical plant, little is grown north of the 37th parallel.
Japanese tea is produced primarily for local consumption and not for
export. It is dried unfermented, or green, and does not find favor in the
European and American markets, which prefer the fermented dark teas
of Assam and Ceylon. Tea bushes characteristically are grown on upland
slopes unsuited for other crops. Production in 1956 (75,000 metric tons)
was about the same as that in 1910, despite considerable fluctuations
between, and it is unlikely that a notable expansion of production will
take place. Among other crops are tobacco, the most important, pyre-
thrum, mat rushes, hemp, flax, ramie, and jute.

The intensity of pressure upon agricultural land in Japan is reflected in
the minor importance of a livestock industry. Most of the cattle in Japan,
2,900,000 in 1954, are used as draft animals, yet there are only two to
every five farms. However, the number of cattle is increasing and by
1954 had nearly doubled the number in 1930. Cattle feed consists primarily of cuttings from roadsides and hill slopes. Horses are declining in
numbers, and there are about a million in Japan. Sheep and goats, however, have been increasing rapidly, especially in northern Honshu and
Hokkaido, although their contribution to the gross food supply is minute.
Most surprising is the small number of swine, only 745,000 being recorded
in 1954, or one to every seven farms. This is in remarkable contrast to

China, where almost every farm unit has a pig or two. Dairy cattle numbered 360,000 in 1954, or one to every 17 farms, but their numbers are increasing—especially near the larger cities, where the demand for dairy products is increasing, and in Hokkaido.

The areas of pasture in Japan have been estimated by the Ministry of Agriculture and Forestry at some 6,400,000 acres, of which over 5,000,000 acres consist of coppice and fuelwood stands. It is likely that this estimate is far too large, if considerations of slope, forage vegetation, and accessibility are taken into account. Most of the natural pastures are in the high uplands of northern Honshu, Hokkaido, and central Kyushu. Their carrying capacity is judged low, and the native pasture grasses are largely harsh and nonnutritious. Only in a few areas has improvement of the natural pasture taken place by the planting of other grasses. Moreover, so long as the chief function of cattle is to provide motive power on the farm or in the city, feed must be brought to the animals. In winter in much of Japan, they must be fed concentrated feeds; before the Pacific war a large proportion, over a million metric tons, was imported. Since the war, however, imported feed has been available only in small quantities, and this has been associated with a decline in the horse population.

Barnyard fowl also are surprisingly few in Japan. The total fowl population, chiefly chickens, in 1954 was about 30 millions, or five per farm unit. Again, a shortage of imported feed appears to be the major limiting factor in the support of the fowl population, since the prewar numbers of chickens were half again as great as in 1954.

Rural occupance and organization

The average Japanese farm unit is small, averaging less than 2.5 acres (or one hectare), but the variations in size from place to place are noteworthy. In Hokkaido, where settlement has been more recent, the average farm ranges from 10 to 12 acres. The size of farms decreases southward, and in Old Japan the average size is under 2 acres. In all Japan nearly two-thirds of the farm families cultivate under 2.5 acres. In general, those parts of the country that have been occupied the longest contain the smaller agricultural units.

Not only is the farm unit small, but it is highly fragmented. Each farm consists of six to 20 fields, some irrigated, some dry, scattered at considerable distances from the farmstead. This fragmentation is largely the result of ancient land-division practices whereby land was redistributed among villagers from time to time by the state or community. But for some centuries at least the Japanese have practiced primogeniture, whereby a farm unit is handed down intact to the oldest son. Postwar legislation under Occupation auspices directed that property be apportioned among the several children of the deceased, and this threatens to worsen the fragmentation problem. The scattered fields operated by one farmer present problems of accessibility and inconvenience that are unquestionably costly, and their excessive number takes its toll of arable land through boundary ridges, footpaths, and additional irrigation ditches. They offer a kind of insurance, however, in that the frequent disasters of storm or flood that strike the Japanese farmer seldom affect all of his scattered holdings.

In spite of the fragmentation and small holdings and dense population, the agricultural landscape of Japan is characteristically open and free from both fences and massive hedgerows. Property ownership is well known within the highly integrated rural communities, and low bundings and footpaths suffice to mark property lines between the fields.

The typical Japanese farmstead is not isolated, but as in most of Asian Asia tends to be associated with other farmsteads into a village.[3] Not all Japanese villages are compact, however. In Hokkaido isolated farmsteads are the rule rather than the exception, and in the uplands of Honshu and the ash plateau of central Kyushu dispersed or partially dispersed settlement is characteristic. The shapes of settlements also differ widely, and three types may be defined: First, the so-called *strassendorf,* or street settlement, which is an elongated ribbon of housing lining a single street. These are most common at the boundaries between hill and lowland or along beach ridges, as in the Echigo plain. A second form centers about a crossroads, but is loosely defined with a somewhat scattered appearance, as in southern Kyushu. A third is characteristic of the plains about Osaka, Lake Biwa, and Nara where early occupance was organized in the north Chinese fashion. These settlements are rectangular, extremely compact, and generally contain more than one street or crossroads.

Until 1947 a high rate of tenancy characterized Japanese agriculture; about two-thirds of the farmers rented all or part of their land, and as

[3] The organization of these villages along social geographical lines is quite complete, although not the same all over Japan. Commonly each village is termed a *buraku,* although where the settlements are very tiny, a *buraku* may include more than one such agglomeration of houses. The *buraku* in turn forms part of a larger areal unit known as an *ōaza,* which had official political status during the pre-Meiji period. The *ōaza* still has considerable cultural significance and economic importance in that irrigation facilities and property classifications are organized on *ōaza* lines. However, neither the *buraku* nor the *ōaza* are now legal entities, although in practice the *buraku* is the basic unit of political organization in Japan along unofficial lines. The next largest administrative unit, and the first nationally official one, is the *mura,* or township (often translated as "village"), which is composed of the *ōaza,* and the *buraku* within them. The *mura* thus may contain from five to 50 *actual* villages or *buraku.* Where there is a large settlement dominating the countryside, though not of city size, the term *machi,* or town, is used. Actually the *machi* resembles the *mura* in that a number of *buraku* are involved, and the distinction largely is one of population size and of the dominance of one settlement over others in the area.

much as 70 per cent of a harvest went to the landlord. During the Occupation legislation concerning land reform was passed, as a result of which by 1950 some 62 per cent of Japan's farmers wholly owned the land they cultivated, and only 5 per cent owned none of the land they cultivated. In terms of cultivated area, before reform 54 per cent was operated by owners, whereas after reform about 90 per cent was cultivated by owners. In addition, tenancy practices were revised and regularized. The reform has not been without problems, the influence of the landlords locally remaining strong, but the over-all result has been to lighten vastly the burden on the Japanese farmer.

That this burden remains heavy, however, is indicated by the marked dependency of the Japanese farmer on outside sources of income for his livelihood. In the past the chief sources of income were the raising of silkworms and the practice of rural handicrafts. In each of these cases technological change has resulted in a marked decrease in demand both for silk and handicraft products, with resulting rural depression, especially in the 1930's. In 1950, half of Japan's farm households had auxiliary occupations; in 1954, this number had risen to 60 per cent. In most cases the auxiliary occupations have come to mean part-time work in nearby towns and cities or full-time employment by members of the family who commute to and from the towns, although the time-honored practices of fishing, forestry, silkworm-raising, and mat-making still are of notable significance.

In general, Japanese agriculture is practiced to a large degree on the basis of cooperation among farmers in a village and even between villages. This cooperation had been formalized under the so-called Farmers' Organizations of prewar times. Since the war these organizations have been gradually replaced by cooperatives organized in more democratic fashion and along more modern lines. Compactness of settlement, fragmentation of land, and the need for group utilization of water resources, all have operated to reinforce the strong communal orientation of the farmer.

Fisheries

Japan is the leading fishing country in the world. Her production in 1955 of 4.7 million metric tons of marine products was nearly twice that of her nearest competitor, the United States. The waters about Japan are especially productive, as is to be expected from waters in which currents of different temperatures and salinities meet. In the colder waters of the north, where the Oya Shio moves down along the coasts of Hokkaido and northern Honshu, herring, cod, halibut, salmon, crab, and other cold-water fish are the basic marine products. In the south and east, where the warm Kuro Shio and its branches sweep northeastward along the south Honshu coast and through the straits of Korea and Tsushima, sardines, tuna, skipjack, seabreams, mackerel, and yellowtail are the dominant species. In the zones of mixing, which migrate seasonally, many of these species may be found.

Sardines and herring are the main species and account for a quarter of the total landings. Fluctuations in the catches of these two fish are primarily responsible for the variations in the total landings from year to year. Edible seaweeds are cultivated or gathered along most of the coasts, as are squid and shellfish of various sorts. A small but significant production of freshwater fish comes from pisciculture in ponds, reservoirs, lakes, and flooded paddy fields (Figure 22). Ninety per cent of the fish consumed are used as food; the remainder are made into fertilizer and oil. Except for the larger coastal cities, most of the marine products sold in local markets are preserved by salting or drying. Away from the coasts, very little salt-water fish, even preserved, is consumed.

The bulk of the catch comes from the waters within 20 miles of the Japanese coast, although Japanese fishing vessels have long scoured the

Fig. 22 • Most of Japan's animal protein comes from fish. In addition to the deep-sea fisheries, Japanese farmers raise carp and other fresh-water fish in ponds and in flooded paddy fields. Here a farm woman spreads moss and twigs laden with carp eggs in a paddy field in the Kanto region. *(U.S. Army.)*

Fig. 23 • Japan is the leading fisheries country in the world. Although the fishing industry is scattered in part among myriad small villages along the coasts, it tends to be concentrated in the larger ports. Here shark are being unloaded in Tokyo from a diesel-powered wooden fishing boat. The valuable livers are being removed; the rest of the fish will be used as food or fertilizer, and the skin will be made into leather. *(U.S. Army.)*

western and northern Pacific for their catch. As a result of the war, Japan lost her rights to fish in the waters off the coasts of the Kurils, Sakhalin, and Kamchatka, from which she obtained about 15 per cent of her total prewar catch. This loss, though significant in itself, is especially important since it was from these waters that Japan received not only large quantities of herring, cold-water seaweed, and other cold-water marine products, but also the valuable salmon and crab that provided one of the bases for Japan's fisheries exports. In addition, the coasts of Korea,[4] China, and the remainder of the U.S.S.R. have been closed to Japanese fishermen, with consequent restrictions on the size of catches from waters

[4] In 1952, South Korea established a line, the so-called "Rhee line," midway between Japan and Korea in the Sea of Japan, and forbade Japanese fishermen to move across it.

far removed from the Japanese coasts. In spite of these restrictions, fish products continue to account for 5 per cent of Japan's exports by value.

The fishing industry is centered in some 3,200 fishing villages distributed along the coasts of the islands. Nearly three million people are directly dependent for all or part of their livelihood upon fishing. Most of the fishing villages, however, also are dependent upon part-time farming, especially in the Inland Sea area, and this association is one of the typical features of the Japanese fishing complex. On the other hand, the large-scale fishing operations, which account for about a third of the total landings each year, are centered in the larger ports (Figure 23). Most of the larger motorized vessels also operate out of these ports. Of the 1.27 million gross tons of shipping engaged in fishing in 1955, over 78 per cent was motorized. The balance consisted of thousands of small vessels, constructed largely since the war, which operate mostly within sight of land.

Food supply and problems

Japan is not self-sufficient in foodstuffs. In 1956 Japan imported approximately 4.9 million tons of foodstuffs, the bulk of which consisted of grains, and imports are expected to rise by at least 200,000 tons per year. This represented about 15 per cent of Japan's food requirements on the basis of a daily per-capita food intake of 2,250 calories. In terms of total quantities of food produced in Japan itself, the imports amounted to about 12 per cent. Although yields per unit area have risen over those of the prewar period and the area of cultivation is increasing slightly, the total population has so increased that production increases have barely kept up with the rise in population. This relatively small percentage of Japan's food needs accounts for the second largest single group of imports into Japan by value.[5]

The Japanese diet is based primarily on calorie-rich grains and starchy tubers. Of all the calories consumed annually, about 67 per cent is accounted for by rice alone, 80 per cent by all grains, and about 92 per cent by grains and starchy tubers combined. The intake of animal protein is exceptionally low by Western standards, and the bulk of it (85 per cent) comes from marine products rather than meat. Some protein also comes from the soy beans which are consumed in the form of bean curd, or *tofu*, and soy sauce, but soy beans form a substantial import item in themselves.

[5] Imports of food also vary with the size of harvests in Japan, which may vary remarkably. For example, in 1953 the rice crop was 17 per cent less than that in 1952, thus necessitating larger imports of grains, among which wheat is becoming increasingly important.

One of the prime problems facing the Japanese is that of raising production so as to at least hold the line against the increasing food needs associated with population increases. It is anticipated that by 1970 Japan will have a population of more than 100 million. The Japanese government has succeeded in reclaiming some 1.25 million acres since the close of the war, some of which was land in military installations, and is planning to reclaim another 2.5 million acres. There are estimates of as much as 9 million acres of reclaimable land, but these generally are acknowledged to be high, and the total economically reclaimable area is believed to be closer to 4 million acres at a maximum. Most of this land is marginal land, the yields from which can be expected to be on the whole well below the national average.[6]

At the same time, improvements in the drainage of existing paddy fields will result in multiple-cropping where only single-cropping is now possible. Another possibility is the consolidation of fields into integrated farm units. It is expected that such consolidation, which was proceeding even before the war, will add as much as 10 per cent to the total cultivable area. Over 6 million acres gradually are being reorganized. New irrigation projects, generally in association with the expansion of hydroelectric installations, also will assist in raising production levels.

In addition, there are the possibilities of expanding yields by increased fertilization and mechanization. Japanese production of fertilizers can be expected to rise, but existing fertilizer production is based in part upon imported raw materials, and these also demand foreign exchange of which Japan is seriously short. At the same time there is serious doubt as to whether more fertilizers will pay for themselves in increased productivity. What is needed is a program of intensive research into fertilizer requirements and practices to determine much more accurately than can now be known the most efficacious use of fertilizer resources.

Mechanization is by no means a panacea for Japan's food deficit. The present system of agriculture—based as it is upon wet-rice agriculture; tiny fields, many of them terraced; and an intensive utilization of human energy—does not lend itself to easy or rapid mechanization. However, mechanization of water pumping for irrigation and of such auxiliary activities as threshing of grain has been proceeding for many years, and in this sense will continue as a major feature of the agricultural scene. The use of small portable "rototillers" suitable for use on small fields also has been increasing. Experiments in mechanization in India, Malaya, and Japan itself may in time indicate further possibilities for increased use of machines, but it will be many years before the tractor becomes part of Japanese agricultural technology.

[6] Nearly 2 million acres are in Hokkaido, but the Japanese government's first Five-Year Plan (1952–7) contemplated the reclamation of only 365,000 acres.

A more intensive use of the uplands offers better possibilities for increased production of foodstuffs. In the "frontier" upland areas especially, shifting agriculture, although illegal, is one common land-use practice. Although the acreage of these "fire fields," or *kaden*, is unknown, Trewartha estimates that 2.8 per cent of Japan's prewar farm families were engaged in the wasteful practice. However, the natural pastures and cutover areas in Japan conceivably can be converted to the development of a livestock industry on a vastly expanded scale. One chief barrier to such expansion is the belief, apparently sound, that the labor of one man in the rice fields results in greater food production than in pastoral activities. Other barriers are the lack of good natural pasturage, the low purchasing power of the Japanese people, the unattractiveness of the rigorous mountain pioneering life with its associated isolation from the rest of society, and the lack of winter feed. To a degree the increased cultivation of crops such as corn, which supply food both for human and animal consumption, would help alleviate some of these difficulties. At the same time, the demand in Japan for forest products indicates a necessity for the utilization of as much forested, or cut-over, area as possible for the production of wood.

Another possible source of additional food is through an enlarged fishing industry, which supplies the bulk of the animal protein in the Japanese diet. This will depend on the results of much-needed research into Japan's fisheries resources, the expansion of piscicultural activities, and the extension of fishing grounds into waters closed to Japan as a result of the war. More serious is the problem of the imminent depletion of the more accessible fisheries resources, a process which appears to have been proceeding since well before the war. As the technological aids to fishing raise the size of the catch, the drain upon the fisheries will increase, to the ultimate long-run disadvantage of the industry as a whole. Contrasting with the situation in the United States, there are few new species of marine life that remain to be tested by the Japanese as a possible source of food.

In connection with fishing, but also associated with the entire food industry, is the problem of storage and processing and of waste in general. It is estimated that up to 10 per cent of the total annual volume of foodstuffs in Japan is destroyed by spoilage, rodents, and other losses. Modern food preservation and transportation facilities are notoriously underdeveloped, and the practice of conservation so universally attributed to the Japanese is actually only along limited lines with notable sectors of wastage throughout the food-producing structure. At the same time, the Japanese level of food consumption is substantially higher on the whole than that in the rest of Asia, and food habits are as deeply ingrained as elsewhere. The major dietary shift in recent years has been toward an increasing use of wheat and wheat flour, especially in the urban areas, but this has served only to aggravate the food deficit, since Japan's wheat production is unable to meet the enlarged demands, these having been met by increased imports.

In summary, all the evidence indicates Japan's continued dependence upon imports for up to a fifth of her food needs, and only restricted possibilities for increasing food production to keep pace with a rapidly rising population.

SELECTED GEOGRAPHICAL BIBLIOGRAPHY

1. Ackerman, Edward A. *Japanese Natural Resources*. Chicago: University of Chicago Press, 1953.
2. Embree, John F. *Suye Mura*. Chicago: University of Chicago Press, 1939.
3. Espenshade, Ada. "A Program for Japanese Fisheries," *Geographical Review*, January, 1949, pp. 76-85.
4. Eyre, John D. "Elements of Instability in the Current Japanese Land Tenure System," *Land Economics*, August, 1952, pp. 193-202.
5. ———. "Water Controls in a Japanese Irrigation System," *Geographical Review*, April, 1955, pp. 197-216. See also Eyre, John D. "Japanese Land Development in Kojima Bay," *Economic Geography*, January, 1956, pp. 58-74.
6. Hall, R. B. "Some Rural Settlement Forms in Japan," *Geographical Review*, January, 1931, pp. 93-123.
7. SCAP, Natural Resources Section. *Reports*, especially Nos. 136, 143, 148, 152. Tokyo: 1945–52. See also Thompson, J. H. "Urban Agriculture in Southern Japan," *Economic Geography*, July, 1957, pp. 224-37.
8. Trewartha, Glenn T. *Japan: A Physical, Cultural, and Regional Geography*. Madison: University of Wisconsin Press, 1945.
9. ———. "Japan," in *The Development of Upland Areas in the Far East*. New York: Institute of Pacific Relations, 1949.

Comments

Japanese agriculture, fisheries, and food production are thoroughly discussed in Ackerman, upon which much of this chapter is based, and Trewartha. Trewartha also analyzes the Japanese rural occupance pattern in its prewar setting.

The SCAP *Reports* contain a diversity of information and are especially valuable for their postwar statistics to 1951. Number 143 lists Japanese crop and livestock statistics from 1878–1950; Number 148 discusses the postwar agricultural programs; Number 152 is concerned with fisheries development. Number 136 is entitled "The Japanese Village in Transition," and is a primarily sociological—but significantly geographical—appraisal of postwar changes in Japanese village structure and rural organization. It is particularly useful in comparison with Embree's pioneering study of a Japanese village.

Eyre's studies provide valuable descriptions of land reform and irrigation practices in Japanese villages, and Thompson deals with the specialized form of agriculture in and around Japan's larger cities.

Japan

INDUSTRY AND COMMERCE

THE RELATIVELY ADVANCED STAGE OF JAPAN'S INDUSTRIALIZATION and Westernization is reflected in the substantial percentage of her population engaged in nonagricultural occupations and in an even higher percentage of urbanization as measured by her urban population.

Population and urbanization

In 1955 about 41 per cent of the Japanese labor force of 41.8 million persons was in agricultural and forestry occupations and another 1.5 per cent was engaged in fishing. The next largest group of occupations is associated with commerce and services both in and out of government, and these account for about 32 per cent of the total. In comparison, about 17 per cent was employed in manufacturing. If all laborers and craftsmen other than those engaged in agriculture are considered, however, some 23 per cent of Japan's labor force was engaged in industrial occupations. This percentage is the highest in Asia, and compares not unfavorably with the 30 per cent thus engaged in the United States. The balance of the labor force includes the unemployed plus some unclassified residue.

Preliminary estimates for 1958 and projections into the future indicate trends toward greater concentrations in industrial occupations. This occupational structure is associated with an exceptionally high degree of education for an Asian country. Most Japanese are literate, although the effectiveness of that literacy is limited by the difficulties of the written Japanese language. In 1950 about 58 per cent of the adult population had received more than seven years of schooling. Higher education was much more limited, however, and only 19 per cent of the adult population had received ten or more years of education.

Over 40 per cent of the Japanese live in cities or urban areas of more than 30,000 population. This is the highest percentage of urban population in Asia, though it is far below the 60 to 80 per cent of urban population found in Western Europe and the United States. More than one-fourth of the Japanese live in cities of 100,000 or over, and about 15 per cent live in the largest cities, those over 980,000 population.

The cities of Japan are widely scattered throughout the archipelago. As of January 1, 1956, there were 97 cities of more than 100,000 population, and with only one exception every *ken* had at least one such city.[1] The greatest concentration of cities of size, however, is on the Pacific side of Japan, particularly in a belt extending from Kanto on the northeast to northern Kyushu on the southwest. The largest cities in Japan, as of the beginning of 1956 were: Tokyo, an estimated 7,000,000 (23 *ku*); Osaka, 2,547,000; Kyoto, 1,204,000; Nagoya, 1,337,000; Yokohama, 1,143,000; and Kobe, 979,000. These population data refer only to the central city and not to the metropolitan areas of which they are the nodes.

Tokyo and Yokohama generally are regarded as twin cities, but the area between them has been entirely built over. Osaka and Kobe similarly are twin cities, with Kobe acting as the port of Osaka, just as Yokohama acts as the main port for Tokyo. The Japanese are accustomed to associate these pairs of cities with a single name—*Kei-hin* for Tokyo and Yokohama, and *Han-shin* for Osaka and Kobe. In addition, each metropolis or pair is associated with a number of satellite cities, which serve to raise the total urban population in the metropolitan areas to almost twice that of the cities themselves.[2] For example, Kawasaki fills the gap between Tokyo and Yokohama, while Yokosuka, the naval base, is a southern extension

---

[1] The exception is Shimane Ken in southeastern Honshu. Its largest city, however, contained 97,000 persons at the beginning of 1956.

[2] The official Japanese designation for a city is *shi*. This areal administrative unit, however, need not be entirely built up, but may include some agricultural land. Several of the larger cities are set in political units that are not *ken* but on a par with them. Thus, Tokyo is in Tokyo *To*, Osaka is in Osaka *Fu*, and Kyoto is in Kyoto *Fu*. These units are similar to the *ken*, except that they are predominantly urban, while the *ken* are predominantly rural. The largest cities are in turn divided into *ku* or wards, and these in turn into *cho*. Tokyo officially is no longer, since 1943, incorporated as a *shi* or city, but is divided into a number of *ku*. However, unofficially,

of the Yokohama urbanized area. Similarly, Sakai is in effect a southern outlier of Osaka, although it is an independent *shi,* and there are a number of smaller *shi* between Osaka and Kobe, all of which together form one major urban complex.

Of the six great cities of Japan, two, Yokohama and Kobe, are modern Western-type cities, developed from small villages to serve as the ports of Tokyo and Osaka respectively. The sites of both are restricted, hugging the narrow coastal plain near the margins of the larger plains upon which each of their paired cities lies. The other four cities have developed from traditionally Japanese cores. Tokyo, formerly known as Edo, was the capital of Tokugawa Japan,[3] and developed first as a great political and administrative center. Dominated by a central palace fortress, it spread rapidly over the plain site it occupies, acquiring in the process the multifunctional characteristics of a great world metropolis. Kyoto is a more ancient capital than Tokyo and is one of the best examples of a great indigenously Asian city (Figure 24). To a degree, Kyoto, with its temples, shrines, palace, and universities, is the cultural center of Japan. It also is sited on an extensive plain, the Kyoto plain, and the street pattern of the city is notably rectangular, in the manner of the early Chinese capital upon which it was modeled.[4]

Osaka and Nagoya both are great multifunctional cities, and though sprung from native Japanese towns with castle centers, they have become less Japanese than Western. Both, however, retain the flat and monotonous skyline of the typical Japanese town; both are largely of wooden construction; both are sited on extensive lowland plains; both are cut through with canalized rivers upon which much of the intracity traffic is carried. Both also are major industrial and commercial centers, Osaka being known as the Chicago of Japan.

With the exception of Fukuoka (544,000) in northern Kyushu, there are no cities in Japan with populations greater than 500,000, other than the six largest cities. With the exception of one major area, the lesser cities of Japan are subordinated to the great cities, which in effect serve the entire archipelago, limited as it is in size and irregular as it is in shape.

---

its *ku* are regarded as forming one *de facto shi.* In 1956, there were 499 *shi* in Japan, counting Tokyo as one *shi.* All of these *shi* are over 30,000 population.

In general, a *shi* contains at least one major population cluster of 30,000 population. It is the size of this cluster that distinguishes it from a *machi,* which generally has a smaller urban center and a number of lesser agglomerated settlements separated by considerable areas of farmland or other nonurban land. The *mura* in general also contains a number of small population clusters, but is distinguished from the *machi* in that none is large enough to dominate the rest.

[3] The name Tokyo means "eastern capital," as distinguished from Kyoto, the ancient capital.

[4] Kyoto was founded in 793 A.D. At that time named Hei-an, it was laid out in the form of Ch'ang-an or Hsi-an, capital of the Chinese Sui dynasty.

Fig. 24 • Kyoto, the ancient capital and cultural center of Japan and Japan's third largest city. Kyoto is the most "Japanese" of the great cities of Japan and contains few of the industrial areas and squalid slums that characterize the industrial centers. However, it is a modern city as well, with broad avenues, tramways, and hotels. *(U.S. Army.)*

But each large plain or intermontane basin tends to have a good-sized city that acts as a regional capital (Figure 25). For example, in coastal Tohoku, the northeast, there is Sendai; in the inland basins of Tohoku, there are Morioka and Yamagata; in Hokuriku, northwestern Honshu, there is Niigata; in southern Kyushu, there is Kagoshima; in the Inland Sea region, there are Hiroshima, Takamatsu, and Okayama; and in southern Shikoku, there is Kochi. In Hokkaido the regional capital is Sapporo, with a lesser inland center at Asahigawa. Other cities of size, such as Hakodate, Otaru, and Muroran, all are ports. In northern Kyushu, however, there is an exceptional association of urban centers which in the aggregate have populations of metropolis size and which are strung out along the Kyushu shore—Moji, Kokura, Tobata, Yawata, Wakamatsu, and Shimonoseki across the straits in Honshu. To the west is Fukuoka, itself

111

a great city, and its associated cities inland, of which Kurume is the largest; then Nagasaki, Sasebo, Omuta, and Kumamoto. The entire group of cities is associated closely with the coal deposits of northern Kyushu, and together they form one of the larger industrial regions of Japan.

Most of the lesser cities and towns display predominantly Japanese characteristics. Skylines are low and level; few buildings are more than two stories in height, and most are of wooden construction except for government buildings and the central business districts. Most of them have level plain sites,[5] the majority being located on coastal plains and possessing port functions as well as others. Except for the newest industrial and commercial cities, such as Kobe, Yokohama, and Yawata, and the cities of more recently settled Hokkaido, most of the cities developed from what had been so-called castle towns, market towns, or station and

[5] One of the chief competitions for level land in Japan is between urban and agricultural land uses. As the cities expand, they tend to take out of production increasing amounts of the best arable land.

Fig. 25 • Kiryu city in Gumma prefecture, north of Tokyo, a textile-manufacturing city on the mountainous edge of the Kanto region and a regional capital. Note the Watarase River in the background upon the flood plain of which the city is sited. Note also the level skyline, except for smokestacks, which characterizes all except the largest Japanese cities. *(U.S. Army.)*

harbor towns, all dating back to feudal days. Most of the medieval towns, unlike those of China, for example, lacked city walls, although the castle towns contained a fortified place or castle sited on higher land and surrounded by walls of log pilings. It was not until the sixteenth century, and then under Portuguese influence, that the castles themselves were surrounded by the stone walls and moats that are identified with these structures today.

The structure of
Japanese industry

The rapid industrial development of Japan is one of the wonders of the world. With an extremely modest resource endowment and after a period of self-imposed isolation lasting some 200 years, Japan succeeded within a generation in becoming one of the industrial countries of importance and in 60 years had come to rank with the top ten in value of industrial output. By 1952 manufactural industries accounted for nearly a third of the estimated gross national income. Over one-fifth of the working population was employed in industry, and a number of cities were devoted primarily to manufacturing.

From the Restoration (1867) onward, the industrialization of Japan was characterized by a rapid development of export industries dependent for the most part on imported raw materials. The textile industry was the most important industry, as it has been in most countries entering upon industrialization. The participation of Japan in a number of wars with China and Russia, and in the first World War, led to an increasing diversification of industry both for home consumption and export. Heavy industries were established, largely with government subsidy or under government control. Labor was drawn initially from the skilled craftsmen who were employed at the shogunate or imperial courts or the courts of the lesser nobles, but a rapidly developed educational system, combined with the advice of foreign experts, resulted in the creation of a labor force especially highly skilled for Asia.

The maturation of Japan's industry is indicated by the decline in the importance of the textile industry. In 1923, the value of the textile output accounted for 44.6 per cent of all industrial production. By 1937, however, it had dropped to 28.5 per cent, while the metals and chemical industries had risen to 18 per cent each, and machinery output accounted for an additional 13 per cent of the total. By 1950, after the disastrous intercession of the Pacific war, textiles had dropped to less than 20 per cent of the total industrial production, and the value of metals manufactures, machinery, and chemicals had risen proportionately.

Japanese industry is still characterized by small-sized units and decentralization.[6] There are over 100,000 factories in Japan employing more than five persons. These had in 1950 some 3.8 million employees, averaging 38 employees to a single plant, including clerical help. One of the striking characteristics of Japanese industry is the apparent excess of employees at the white-collar level and in clerical positions. Another feature is the custom of farming out work to home workers on a piece-work basis. Some industries—the bicycle industry, for example—are based upon this system, which provides part-time employment for thousands in and around the industrial centers. The importance of cottage industry is indicated by the 110,000 so-called factories employing less than five persons each.

The close of the Pacific war left Japan's industrial plant in a shambles, but the recovery since 1946 has been rapid, and the general level of industrial and commercial activity in 1956 was about 200 as compared with 100 for the period 1932-6. This index is only of limited significance, however, since the 1932-6 averages were well below those of the later thirties. Population has increased by nearly 50 per cent, and the proportion of service activities also has risen greatly. Furthermore, although most industrial output has risen to about immediately prewar levels, the cotton textile industry remains depressed, and the output of cotton cloth in 1954, 2.7 billion square meters, was well below the 1937 output of 4 billions. The silk industry also is depressed, and has been since the early thirties, when the depression cut down exports to the United States, and the substitution of nylon for silk stockings cut the demand still further. The output of raw silk in 1953, some 14,700 metric tons, was only about a third of the output in the immediate prewar period.

The metals industries have recovered well. Iron and steel production is up to prewar levels; in 1955, pig-iron production amounted to 5.26 million metric tons and steel-ingot production to about 9 million tons, substantially higher than the prewar level.[7] Similarly, refined nonferrous metal production has reached postwar levels, with the notable exception of aluminum, production of which was 60,000 metric tons in 1955, about half the midwar peak. The greatest postwar achievements have been in machinery and metals manufacturing; textile machinery, transport machinery and rolling stock, engines, bicycles, sewing machines, clocks, watches, cameras, and electrical equipment are among the more important

[6] Physical decentralization is meant here. Actually Japanese industry, and trade as well, was dominated in prewar times by a relatively small number of giant holding companies, family-based, and known as *Zaibatsu*. Although the power of the *Zaibatsu* was greatly diminished by Occupation reforms, their strength has been increasing rapidly since the peace treaty was signed in 1952. Under this system of organization, factories, mines, banks, shipping companies, and insurance companies may all be affiliated into a virtually self-sufficient association.

[7] Most Japanese steel is produced by the open-hearth method, and the balance comes from electric furnaces. The steel industry uses a high ratio of scrap to pig iron.

rapidly expanding industries, the output of which is exceeding prewar figures. Similarly, the shipbuilding industry has staged a remarkable recovery from its immediately postwar decline, having suffered surprisingly little damage during the war. There are reported facilities for the production of 850,000 gross tons of shipping annually, which ranks Japan fourth after the United Kingdom, the United States, and Germany, and the demand for these facilities comes from both domestic and foreign sources, primarily the latter.[8]

Other industries also have come back to or exceeded prewar levels. The output of fertilizers—for example, nearly 3 million metric tons of ammonium sulfate annually—is far higher than previous output, and the production of cement similarly is at an all-time high. Paper and pulp both are being produced in record quantities, although at the expense of domestic forest resources, which are being sadly depleted. Pulp for rayon and rayon production itself, however, is about half of prewar levels; this carries over into the synthetic-fiber field the relatively depressed conditions characteristic of the textile industry as a whole. With regard to textiles it is important to note that the number of spindles operating in 1954 roughly equalled the 7.5 million spindles operating out of 12 million installed in 1936. Lower production, despite increases in plant efficiency as compared with the prewar period, has been a result of difficulties in obtaining raw materials and markets overseas. The expansibility of the cotton-textile industry is great, and the quality of Japanese machinery and output is high.

In addition, Japan has modified its policy of producing basic consumer goods for low-income markets in underdeveloped areas and is increasing its emphasis on higher-quality goods for more discriminating purchasers. The postwar camera industry is an example of this trend. Japanese optical goods for the first time are successfully competing with high-quality German manufactures. At the same time, Japan continues to produce large quantities of highly diverse, low-cost consumer goods—toys, mirrors, combs and other celluloid knickknacks, cheap pottery and glassware, trinkets, scarves, and the like, known collectively as "bazaar goods."

The pattern of Japanese industry

Most of Japan's industry is localized in an industrial belt which closely corresponds to the highly urbanized belt between Kanto and northern Kyushu. Very few major

[8] In 1956, ships ranked first among Japan's exports, and accounted for 12 per cent of her total exports.

manufacturing establishments, except for silk filatures, are found outside
this region. Steel installations at Kamaishi on the northeast coast of Honshu and Muroran in Hokkaido, based on local supplies of ore, provide two
major exceptions that prove the rule. Other exceptions are rice-milling,
fish-canning, and other food-processing plants, which are widely scattered throughout the country.

There are four major nodes within the industrial belt, each associated
with a great city or group of large cities, accounting for nearly 80 per cent
of all industrial output. The Kanto, or Kei-hin, region is the most important industrial area, centering about *Tokyo,* but including Yokohama,
Kawasaki, and Yokosuka. A large integrated iron-and-steel plant is under construction at Chiba, southeast of Tokyo, and lesser industrial establishments are found in the rings of cities that surround Tokyo in and
along the margins of the Kanto plain. The eastern quarter of Tokyo is the
main industrial area, with secondary concentrations in the northern part
of the city and along the west coast of Tokyo Bay down to Yokohama.
Before the war the region accounted for about 30 per cent of all industrial production in Japan, but the postwar percentage can be assumed to
be higher. Much of the coal for power, chemical industries, and space
heating comes by rail from the Joban fields, 100 miles to the northeast
in Fukushima Ken, and some comes by collier from Hokkaido. Electric
power is brought down from the system of hydroelectric installations in
the mountains to the west, and in Tokyo itself are the largest thermoelectric plants, coal-fueled, in Japan. Labor is concentrated in the city
proper, but workers from considerable distances in the Kanto area commute daily via a highly developed system of electric interurban lines.
The manufactures of the region are highly diversified, ranging from iron-
and-steel fabrications, to beer, to optical equipment of highest quality.
Tokyo also is the center of the printing and publishing industry.

Industrial dominance is supported by the associated concentration of
banking and other commercial facilities within Tokyo. The fact that Tokyo
was and is a political capital as well has helped supply and maintain a
large skilled-labor pool. That Tokyo and Yokohama are major ports also
is of major importance. Yokohama has long been the overseas port of
Tokyo, but shortly before the war the port of Tokyo itself was improved
enough to handle vessels drawing up to 23 feet, and overseas vessels of
small to medium size now use it directly. Tokyo is more important as a
center for the coastal trade, although Yokohama also is a major coastal
shipping focus. Of the major Japanese ports, Yokohama ranks first or second, depending upon its competitive relations with Kobe, but its trade
traditionally has been predominantly trans-Pacific, and it is at Yokohama
that vessels from the west coast of North America customarily stop first
on their way to the China seas and the straits region of Southeast Asia.

The second largest industrial node, of about equal importance to that of Kanto, is the so-called Kinki, or Han-shin, node, centering about the cities of *Osaka* and Kobe, and including Kyoto, Nara, Sakai, and by extension Wakayama on the south and Himeji on the west. Production in the area is as diverse as in the Kanto node, but there is even greater emphasis on heavier industries, although textile spinning in Osaka and weaving in the outlying centers are also basic industries. Shipyards, diesel-, steam- and electric-engine plants, steel-fabrication plants, textile mills, breweries, chemical plants, and cement plants provide the basis for the region's industrial establishment. There is greater dependence upon thermoelectric power than in Kanto, since Kinki is farther removed from the main centers of hydroelectric generation, but hydroelectricity nonetheless supplies the greater part of the electrical energy consumed. Coal comes almost entirely from northern Kyushu, with occasional shipments from Hokkaido.

Functionally, Osaka and Kobe are related in much the same manner as Tokyo and Yokohama. However, Osaka's naturally shallow harbor has been improved to take deep-draft vessels, although Kobe retains most of the overseas passenger traffic of the region. Osaka, Kobe, and Yokohama are the three major overseas ports of Japan; in 1953 Kobe handled about 35 per cent of Japan's foreign trade. Kobe has a greater industrial development than Yokohama, centering especially about the shipbuilding and steel-fabricating industries, although it is handicapped by an even greater lack of level land for industrial uses. The deep-water harbor, 16 miles west of Osaka, which provided the basic reason for Kobe's existence, also is a partial handicap to further expansion in that it makes land reclamation along the shore difficult. Kyoto, though within the Kinki region, is not a modern manufacturing city, but rather a center of arts and crafts, and it is from Kyoto that the better Japanese objects of art tend to come. Himeji, 40 miles to the west, is the site of a modern iron-and-steel plant which supplies demands within Kinki. A ring of satellite cities and suburbs is integrated into the complex, as in the Kanto region.

During the Tokugawa Shogunate, Osaka acted as the major commercial center for Japan, and it was here that there developed a class of entrepreneurs and merchants with accumulated capital and commercial experience. These bourgeois families to a large degree sparked Japanese economic development and certainly financed much of it from their profits in the domestic rice trade. The advantages of Osaka as an industrial city center about its central location, transportation facilities, and large level site which permitted expansion of urban occupance. The city is crisscrossed by canals which carry a large percentage of the local traffic. Industry is not as highly localized within the city as in Tokyo. Osaka's central business district is largely in Western-type buildings, but much of the city is typically Japanese in appearance; even many factories seem exotic and transitory. Unlike Tokyo, but like Kyoto, most of the city is laid out in a rectangular grid pattern. The key situation of Osaka-Kobe at the eastern head of the Inland Sea gives both of these ports a westward orientation in foreign trade and shipping, as reflected in the lesser importance of the North American trade as compared with Tokyo-Yokohama.

A third major industrial node centers about the city of *Nagoya*. Like Osaka and Tokyo, Nagoya is sited on a densely populated, low, alluvial plain, and nearby tidewater is shallow. The city also is dominated by a castle, one of the more striking in Japan, and owes much of its early importance to its function as a castle town and administrative center and to its location on the Tokaido, or Eastern Sea Road, the main highway connecting Kyoto and Tokyo (Edo) in feudal times. Nagoya's industrial complex is somewhat less diverse than that in Kanto or Kinki, and the value of production is about a third as large. Among the four major industrial nodes, Nagoya is the only one in which textiles are the most important product, but other light industries, especially pottery, also are significant. Before and during the war Nagoya became important as an aircraft manufacturing center, and since the war it has become a major automotive center.

Nagoya ranks high as a foreign-trade port, but well below the big three, although its port has been improved for deep-draft vessels. No separate deep-water port ever was developed for Nagoya, although Yokkaichi, some 18 miles to the southwest on Ise Bay, does serve as an important auxiliary port. The lack of a deep-water port, together with a poorly developed canal system within the city, retarded Nagoya's development until the Japanese railway system had been established. Another major factor acting to retard development has been Nagoya's location between the two largest commercial and industrial centers, Osaka and Tokyo, the hinterlands of which tend to close in on Nagoya from both the west and east. Nevertheless, the Ise Bay region is undergoing rapid industrial expansion, comparable to that in Kanto and Kinki. Nagoya's major source of electrical energy is from the hydroelectric installations in the nearby central mountain knot of Honshu. Coal comes both from northern Kyushu and Hokkaido, chiefly by water. The coastwise trade of the city is much greater than its overseas trade, much of the latter passing through Kobe on the one hand or Yokohama on the other.

The fourth major industrial node is that of *northern Kyushu*. Unlike the other three, this region is not dominated by any one city, but is characterized by several cities of middle size. The core of the region is composed of the group of cities near the shores of the Straits of Shimonoseki —Shimonoseki, Moji, Kokura, Tobata, Wakamatsu, Yawata. Extensions of this core are found at Fukuoka, some 25 miles to the southwest, the largest city in the region, and at Nagasaki, Saga, Omuta, and Kumamoto. In general, industrial occupance appears much more dispersed than in the other industrial nodes.

The northern Kyushu node differs from the others in that textiles are of slight importance in the industrial complex. Heavier industries predominate, and the largest iron-and-steel plant in Japan is located at Yawata. Other major industrial products are cement, chemicals, glass, steel fabrications, and machinery, although sugar refining, brewing, rice milling, distilling, and flour milling are other important industrial functions. Most of the industries depend upon the coal fields of northern Kyushu for fuel and for one of their basic raw materials. Hydroelectric power is of little importance. Several of the coastal cities are ports of some size, though generally of restricted depths, and are the major coal-exporting centers of Japan. Moji, Wakamatsu, and Nagasaki are particularly important in this regard. Since the core of the region lies at the western maritime entrance to Japan, it also is the center for a considerable import trade in foodstuffs and raw materials, many of which are processed locally. Taiwanese and Siamese rice, Australian wheat, Southeast Asian iron ore, Taiwanese sugar and molasses, Chinese coking coal, and Bornean and Persian Gulf crude petroleum are the sorts of imported raw materials that have become integrated into the industrial complex.

Trade

To an overwhelming degree the modern Japanese economy depends both upon imported raw materials and upon foreign markets for its manufactured goods. Its foreign trade accounted for 23 per cent of its national income in 1952. Before the Pacific war some 88 per cent of Japan's imports consisted of raw materials and foodstuffs; at the same time, 88 per cent of her exports consisted of manufactures. Since the natural resource base of Japan is inadequate to support her large and expanding population, Japan, like Britain, must look to the outside world for the means by which national livelihood can be supported.

Unlike Britain, which has long maintained worldwide trade connections, Japan's traditional trade orientations have been primarily in two directions, chiefly to Asian Asia on the one hand and to a lesser degree to North America. Although by the middle thirties Japan had succeeded in building up a substantial trade with Latin America and Africa, this trade accounted for only 6 to 8 per cent of her total trade by value. Trade with Europe was of minor importance, and the exchange with Australasia was of modest significance, both together accounting only for about

11 per cent of Japan's total trade. The trade with North America was primarily with the United States, and in 1936 this trade accounted for 22.6 per cent of Japan's imports and 16.4 per cent of her exports.

Japan's most important prewar trading areas lay within the Asiatic Triangle—the region extending eastward from Pakistan to Karafuto (southern Sakhalin). In 1936 the Triangle took 63 per cent of Japan's exports and supplied 54 per cent of her imports by value. Within the region, the Empire areas—Korea, Manchuria, T'ai-wan, and Karafuto—accounted for a third of the imports and 40 per cent of all exports by value. However, the United States was the single most important trading partner, with Korea a close second and Manchuria third. India and T'ai-wan were about of equal importance, each accounting for about 8 per cent of the total trade, and China proper and the Dutch East Indies followed, each with 3 to 4 per cent of the trade.[9] At the same time there was a trend toward the expansion of trade with Southeast Asia, which was in keeping with Japan's traditional orientation toward the *Nanyo,* or Southern Seas.

The close of the war found Japan stripped of her major prewar possessions in Asia. Korea, T'ai-wan, Karafuto, and Manchuria were no longer Japanese dependencies. This meant that the areas accounting for between 35 and 45 per cent of her total prewar trade were no longer under her control. For political reasons neither Karafuto nor Manchuria has been easily accessible for postwar trade. Furthermore, India, Pakistan, and Southeast Asia have been in the midst of political and consequent economic turmoil; markets have been limited and production down. In the absence of other alternatives, a large part of Japan's food requirements and raw materials has been supplied by the United States. Consequently, the postwar importance of the United States in Japan's import trade is much greater than before the war, and the United States import trade accounted for 31 per cent of the total in 1955. A large percentage of this trade was paid for by American aid programs, since the importance of the United States in Japan's export trade (22 per cent in 1955) is much smaller than in the import trade.

The most important markets for Japanese produce are in the Asiatic Triangle countries, which receive about 40 per cent of Japan's exports.

---

[9] After 1936 the intensification of Japanese developmental efforts in Manchuria, and to a lesser extent her occupation of north China, resulted in a great upswing in her export trade with these areas. This has led to the conclusion that the China trade was and should be the dominant trade in Japan's foreign commerce. It is a misleading conclusion, however, since the actual trade with China proper was of modest dimensions, though of strategic importance for certain imports, and the trade with Manchuria became increasingly one-sided as Japanese producers'-goods exports increased to that area. To the extent that over half of the goods sent to Manchuria after 1936 were bought and paid for directly or indirectly by Japanese government agencies, they constituted more of a drain upon the Japanese economy than a support for it.

Korea, T'ai-wan, and all of mainland China (including Manchuria), however, take only about 9 per cent of all exports, as compared with about 40 per cent before the war. Postwar exports to Indonesia and Pakistan are especially important, but India itself is far less important on the basis of prewar standards, since the Indian cotton textile industry completely satisfies the domestic market, and indeed textile exports have grown larger than those of Japan herself. Political considerations militate against the extension of the export trade with China, which accounts for less than 3 per cent of the total (as compared with over 20 per cent prewar), although Japanese commercial opinion is heavily in favor of reopening that trade on a large scale.

For many years Japan's trade has been characterized by an excess of merchandise imports over exports. In the past Japan was able to make up the trade deficit by so-called "invisible" exports in the form of shipping services, banking and insurance services, and tourism. Even before the Pacific war, however, rising costs of raw materials and restrictions on available markets made it increasingly difficult for Japan to balance her international accounts. In the postwar period this difficulty has vastly increased.

In 1955 Japan's imports consisted of about 29 per cent foodstuffs, 39 per cent nonfuel raw materials, and 12 per cent fuels. Rice from the United States and Thailand; wheat from the United States and Australia; sugar from T'ai-wan; soybeans from the United States; and vegetable oils from Southeast Asia, were the more important elements among the food imports.[10] Among the raw materials, cotton, chiefly from the United States and secondarily from Pakistan and Mexico, was by far the most important material. Iron ore and rubber from Southeast Asia, jute from Pakistan, wool from Australia, phosphate rock from the United States, bauxite from Indonesia, and salt from T'ai-wan were other major items.[11] Among the fuels, petroleum and petroleum products from the United States and Southwest Asia and coking coal from the United States and India were the major imports.[12]

Exports in 1955 consisted, as before the war, primarily of manufactures, of which about 18 per cent consisted of cotton textiles and 19 per cent of other textiles. Most of these textiles went to countries in

[10] Before the war the Japanese Empire was virtually self-sufficient in foodstuffs. Rice came to Japan proper from Korea and T'ai-wan, sugar from Taiwan, and soybeans and oilseeds for food, oil, animal feeds, and fertilizers from Manchuria.

[11] China proper was a major prewar supplier of raw cotton and other textile fibers, iron ore, salt, and cereals. However, it is unlikely that postwar China will be an important exporter of fibers, iron ore, or cereals. Manchuria supplied almost no iron ore but did export pig iron to Japan, another product unlikely to move in China's postwar export trade.

[12] China and Manchuria supplied the bulk of Japan's prewar imports of coking coal.

Southeast and South Asia, but not, as in the prewar period, to India. Some 31 per cent consisted of metal manufactures and machinery, which went chiefly to Asian countries. Among these metal products are semifinished steel, ships, and railway rolling stock, the latter going to such countries as Thailand, much of whose railway equipment is of Japanese origin. Much of the balance of exports consisted of a variety of goods, among which toys, pottery, glassware, optical goods, lumber products, coal, and cement were conspicuous. In addition, about 10 per cent of all exports normally consists of special foodstuffs, chiefly high-priced marine products such as canned tuna, which go primarily to the United States.

Although the recent value of Japan's trade is substantially higher than, for example, in 1936, the quantities are much smaller. The higher values are primarily reflections of inflationary forces associated in part with the Korean war and its aftermath. The adverse balance of merchandise trade in 1956 was the difference between exports valued at $2.5 billions and imports valued at $3.2 billions. In addition, there were outpayments for shipping and other services rendered by other countries. These deficits were countered by direct aid from the United States, and more important, by special procurement orders [13] placed in Japan by the United States for military supplies and by payments for services rendered U.N. troops and other personnel based in Japan in connection with the war. These procurement orders, combined with a considerable invisible income from services to other nations, contrived to give Japan a favorable international payments balance of $290 millions in 1956. The decline in the postwar trade, however, is indicated by the lower level of goods loaded and unloaded in 1954 (an estimated 39 million metric tons) as compared with 1937 (50 million tons).

In addition to the overseas trade, there is a vast internal trade within the archipelago itself, probably larger than that of any other Asian country. The bulk of this trade, which is much larger than the foreign trade, consists of grain moving from farm to city, coal moving from the fields of Hokkaido and Kyushu to the major consuming centers in central Honshu, and timber products moving from Hokkaido and northern Honshu to the south. In addition, there are heavy transshipments of bulky raw materials from the major foreign-trade ports to the larger cities.

Transportation

Japan is a maritime as well as a trading nation. In 1941 it had the third largest merchant marine in the

[13] All special procurement income, including direct U.S. aid, equalled $595 millions in 1956.

world, grossing 6.1 million tons. Most of the vessels in the fleet were modern; most were engaged in the carriage of cargoes both Japanese and foreign over the world ocean; many were engaged in the carriage of a so-called "third-country" trade, or trade between two countries other than Japan, thereby earning valuable foreign exchange. Between two-thirds and three-fourths of Japan's prewar commodity trade by volume was carried in Japanese bottoms.

Immediately after the close of the Pacific war that fleet lay at the bottom of the Pacific Ocean and its marginal seas. Japan then possessed only 750,000 gross tons of seaworthy merchant shipping, much of it old or hurriedly war-built and unfit for competition in the oceanic carrying trades. A vigorous series of shipbuilding programs, augmented by purchases from abroad, brought the Japanese merchant fleet to about 3.5 million gross tons by the end of 1955, of which 2.73 million tons were dry-cargo vessels. In line with the worldwide postwar emphasis on tankers, over one-fifth of the postwar fleet consists of tanker tonnage, as compared with only 7 per cent in the prewar year. Despite this expansion of the fleet, only 47 per cent of Japan's imports and about 44 per cent of Japan's exports were carried in Japanese bottoms in 1954. This meant the expenditure of valuable foreign exchange for shipping services provided by other nations. One of Japan's major objectives, and indeed necessities, is the further rebuilding of her merchant fleet at least to approximately the 1936 level, when it grossed 4 million tons.

In the prewar period the bulk of the Japanese fleet operated in Asian waters, although the Japanese flag was seen around the world. The western Pacific, and particularly its waters east of Hongkong, was a Japanese-dominated sea. Japan's strategic situation along the East Asian coast makes it likely that her fleet will once more dominate its waters, but this will depend upon the opening of Chinese and Korean ports to normal trade.

Not all of the shipping is engaged in overseas trade, however. In addition to the 3.5 million gross tons in the 1955 fleet, there were another 200,000 tons of railway ferries, whalers, tugs, dredgers, and other special vessels, plus the large fishing fleet, which does not normally engage in the carrying trade. Furthermore, 640,000 gross tons of shipping, chiefly vessels under 1,000 gross tons, normally are engaged in domestic cabotage,[14] although the tonnage thus engaged varies considerably from year to year and from season to season. In addition, there are another 770,000 gross tons of wooden vessels, most of them sail-powered, that ply the coasts of the archipelago and engage in the coastwise trade (Figure 26). In 1952 the total weight of coastwise cargoes amounted to 65 million

[14] Many of these are under 100 gross tons and therefore are not classified as part of the merchant fleet.

Fig. 26 • Vessels like these carry upwards of 5,000,000 metric tons of cargo per month along the coasts of Japan. Here, bundles of faggots are being carried aboard ship along the coasts of Mie prefecture in central Japan for shipment to the urban centers. The bulk of the coastwise trade consists of fuelwood, lumber, coal, sand, and gravel. *(U.S. Army.)*

metric tons, of which 40 per cent consisted of coal and the remainder of bulk cargoes such as oil, lumber, sands and gravels, metallic ores, and semifinished metals. Small wooden vessels carried about two-thirds of this volume.

The prewar shipping fleet was dominated by a handful of companies which in turn were linked with the giant holding companies of Japanese industry, the so-called *zaibatsu*. The postwar ownership pattern indicates a much greater spread of ownership and control. Certain of the major prewar companies such as N.Y.K. and O.S.K. still are leaders in the industry, but their share of tonnages is much smaller than it used to be, and several new companies have been founded since the war to challenge the old. Government subsidies are assisting in the expansion of the fleet by new construction in Japanese yards, and plans called for over 220,000 tons of new shipping each in 1955 and 1956.

Japan's railway network is the most extensive in East Asia and, except for India-Pakistan's, is the most highly developed in Asia as a whole. In 1955 there were 27,700 kilometers of mainline railways, of which 27.7 per cent were electrified and 72 per cent were government-owned. Only 9 per cent of the government railways are electrified, however, as compared with 78 per cent of the privately owned railways. Japan had 7.5 km. of line per 100 sq. km., as compared with Britain's 13.5 and Italy's 6.8. Chief motive power on the government mainlines is supplied by steam engines; oil-burning diesels have not yet come into use. All major lines are Cape gauge, 3 feet 6 inches. With few exceptions, the privately owned lines are feeders auxiliary to the government system, or short interurban lines. There are in addition more than 2,000 kilometers of tramways. Only 2,400 kilometers of mainline are double-tracked, and most of them are in the main line connecting Kanto with northern Kyushu via the tunnel under the Straits of Shimonoseki. In addition, there are shorter stretches of double trackage in the Kanto region and in the Ishikari lowland of Hokkaido.

The gross railway pattern is one of main lines paralleling the shore-line, with cross-island connections from Pacific coast to Sea of Japan coast on Honshu and similar cross connections on the other islands (Map 5). Most of the traffic, which amounts to nearly 190 million metric tons of freight per year, is carried along the main line connecting the six largest cities in Japan and northern Kyushu. Toward the end of the thirties a considerable increase in tonnage was carried to and from the Japan Sea coast and the Pacific coast as trade with Manchuria through north Korean ports increased, but this trade flow has ceased. Most of the freight consists of bulk commodities, coal alone accounting for one-fourth of all freight tonnage.

Japanese railways have greatly increased their operations since 1936. In that year 15.6 million ton-kilometers were recorded; in 1955, 42 million. Similarly, in 1936 over 36 million passenger-kilometers were run; in 1955, over 91 million passenger-kilometers. In part, the increases in passenger traffic are reflections of the greater mobility that is characterizing most of the peoples of Asia.

The development of railway and coastal shipping services, combined with the Shogunate policy of limited highway development, has resulted in a relatively underdeveloped highway system in Japan.[15] Although

[15] During Tokugawa times a skeletal system of post roads was expanded primarily for the use of official travellers and messengers. However, since the Shogunate's policy was one of divide and rule among the feudal nobles, other highways were little improved and were characterized by few bridges and many roadblocks about which settlement grew. The post roads nevertheless established the basic pattern of Japan's overland transportation system, and the famed Tokaido between Kyoto and Tokyo (Edo) is followed roughly by the present rail and road routes.

there are over 135,000 kilometers of roads in the archipelago, the only modern, surfaced roads are the less than 9,000 kilometers of national highways. Nevertheless, the highways are entering more prominently than ever before into the circulation of goods and people. The total amount of freight carried in trucks is estimated to be in the vicinity of 30 million metric tons a month, but most of it is carried on very short hauls, and the real importance of the road carriers is much less than these figures would indicate. The total number of both large and small automotive vehicles registered in Japan in 1955 was 1,300,000, chiefly trucks and busses. This represents a three-fold increase over 1940. It is clear that one of Japan's major needs is a more highly developed highway system. The fact that low purchasing power prevents the large-scale distribution of passenger automobiles is one major deterrent to implementing plans for the expansion of the road system.

Surface configuration also provides a major handicap to both road and railway building in Japan. The length of tunnels in the Japanese railway mainlines alone amounts to some 700 kilometers, or about 2.5 per cent of all railway mileage. In general, both railways and roads follow coastal plains or drainage courses, and this adds considerably to the mileage of both. Train ferries are operated between Aomori in northern Honshu and Hakodate in Hokkaido and across the Inland Sea from Honshu to Takamatsu on Shikoku.

Industrial and commercial problems

The justification for Japan's entering upon a war of aggression in the Pacific theatre in 1941, and indeed before that as early as 1931 with the so-called Manchurian Incident, was the need for two things: raw materials and markets. The problem of obtaining them is no less significant to postwar Japan than it was before, but Japan is no longer a first-class world power, and to a large degree her political and economic destiny lies beyond her control. In the prewar period Japan's access to raw materials was hampered by competition with other countries, particularly the imperialist countries with interests in Asia. By import restrictions these powers limited access to markets in their possessions and dependencies. Japan's movement into Manchuria and then China was rationalized as a countermove to these discriminations. At the same time, Japan was experiencing rising costs of both raw materials and production. This spiral of increasing costs, when associated with declining markets abroad, placed the Japanese economy on a precarious footing.

The same kind of uncertainty preoccupies postwar Japan. Where are the sources of raw materials? If they are primarily the United States, how will they be paid for? In the absence of a great demand for raw silk in the United States, the canned tuna, cameras, toys, chinaware and pottery, sewing machines, and bazaar goods can only begin to balance the merchandise trade between the two countries. As for western Europe, the trade between it and Japan has always been quite small. Both are raw-materials importing regions, and both have tended to be competitive in world markets for manufactures. Raw materials from Southeast Asia and South Asia, and to a lesser degree from other lesser developed regions of the world, seem to be the more likely possibilities, yet there is a great reluctance on the part of certain of the formerly occupied Southeast Asian countries, for example, to trade with Japan except on very favorable terms. Furthermore, production in many of the newly independent countries has declined, and surpluses are much smaller than they were.

Nevertheless, Japan is sending missions and consultants into Southeast and South Asia to advise on the development of resources and industries. To a degree, Japan offers one of the major possibilities for furthering economic development in other countries, and in so doing can pay her own way by supplying services and producers' goods. Japanese textile machinery, machine tools, and electrical equipment by and large have a high reputation in Asian markets, and in outfitting certain major industrial establishments with Japanese-made equipment, Japan will be guaranteeing herself markets for replacements and additional equipment as expansion of industry occurs in these nations.

At the same time, the ability of the newly industrializing countries to produce more of their consumer-goods needs, even with Japanese equipment, means declining markets for certain Japanese exports, textiles particularly. The concept of Japan as the workshop for Asia must be reconsidered in the light of this probable development. In addition, dependence upon Japanese know-how is anathema to certain countries, and each wishes for a kind of industrial self-sufficiency that in reality will be impossible to attain.

One hope of the Japanese is to reduce the prices of their exports abroad and continue to supply large quantities of both consumer and producers' goods, perhaps of increasingly high quality, even as the purchasing countries are themselves industrializing. This may take the form of the export of higher-count cotton goods, of artificial fibers that these countries will not be producing for some time, of machinery, and of transportation equipment. If this trend, already indicated, continues, it will bring Japan into even more direct competition with the western European industrial nations, especially Britain and Western Germany, which also depend largely on the export of higher quality and higher cost manufactures. To meet this challenge, Japan must reduce costs of manufacturing and costs of the finished product.[16] To do so, a reduction in transportation costs both for raw materials and for finished products is necessary, and this depends in large part on Japan's ability to transport her trade in her own ships. The enlargement of the merchant marine, therefore, is a basic element in Japan's struggle for economic stability and growth.

Geographically, Japan provides an ideal complement for the primarily agricultural and slowly industrializing countries of Asia. For example, in exchange for food from the three rice-exporting nations of Southeast Asia —Burma, Thailand, and Indochina—and in return for raw cotton, rubber, ores, vegetable oils, and tropical hardwoods from other tropical Asian nations, Japan can supply the necessary manufactured goods both for immediate consumption and for industrialization. Also, with the independence of these countries from Western domination, Japan may be able to provide many more of those invisible account items—shipping services, banking services, insurance—that were taken almost completely out of her hands at the end of the war. In short, Japan can be conceived of as a regional industrial and commercial center for the other Asian countries, political conditions permitting.

The role that Japan can play in assisting China to industrialize and expand its economic base also is significant, to both China and Japan. The possibilities of mutual trade agreements between Japan and China, however, seem slight and lie substantially out of Japan's control. Until such time as Japan, China, and Korea have reestablished normal political relations, Japan will be unable to perform the functions that her geographical position and stage of industrialization define for her in East Asia.

[16] One of the great advantages of Japanese industry has been its low labor costs. In the cotton textile industry, for example, large dormitories are maintained for female employees from the rural areas who are recruited for periods of several years, are kept wholly by the company, and are paid very modest wages. However, Japan's comparative advantage in labor costs has been decreasing steadily as the standard of living of the Japanese has risen and as other countries in Asia, such as India, have proceeded to industrialize. At the same time, the costs of raw materials have risen as Japan has had to compete in world raw material markets with such industrial giants as the United States and the western European countries. The result has meant higher costs of production and a declining comparative advantage for Japanese manufactures. Japanese steel, for example, manufactured from imported raw materials, is more expensive than that of the large steel-producing countries. It can sell on the world market only in times of great demand, as during the Korean conflict. Similarly, Japanese ships are excellently designed and built, but they cost more than ships built in British, Dutch, and German yards. However, because of a large shipbuilding capacity originally constructed with government subsidies before the war, the Japanese shipbuilders have been able to make deliveries earlier than the European yards, thus obtaining orders especially in times of shipping shortages.

SELECTED GEOGRAPHICAL BIBLIOGRAPHY

1. Cohen, J. B. *Japan's Economy in War and Reconstruction.* Minneapolis: University of Minnesota Press, 1949.
2. Erselcuk, M. "Iron and Steel Industry in Japan," *Economic Geography,* 1947.
3. Fisher, C. A. "The Expansion of Japan: A Study in Oriental Geopolitics," *Geographical Journal,* January-March, 1950, and April-June, 1950.
4. Ginsburg, N. S. *Japanese Prewar Trade and Shipping in the Oriental Triangle,* Research Paper Number 6. Chicago: University of Chicago, Department of Geography, 1949.
5. Great Britain, Board of Trade. "Japan," *Overseas Economic Surveys.* London: Her Majesty's Stationery Office, 1952.
6. Lockwood, W. *The Economic Development of Japan.* Princeton: Princeton University Press, 1955.
7. Orchard, J. E. *Japan's Economic Position.* New York: Whittlesey House, 1930.
8. Schumpeter, E. (ed.). *The Industrialization of Japan and Manchukuo.* New York: Macmillan, 1940.
9. Trewartha, G. T. *Japan: A Physical, Cultural, and Regional Geography.* Madison: University of Wisconsin Press, 1945.
10. U.S. Army Training Forces. *Civil Affairs Handbook: Japan.* Sections 1A, 8, 10, and 11; respectively, "Population Statistics," "Industry and Commerce," "Public Works and Utilities," "Transportation Systems." #M354.

Comments

Fisher's article provides an excellent historico-geographical canvas against which Japan's development stands forth. Lockwood carefully analyses Japan's industrialization. Prewar trade and shipping information also is found in Ginsburg and Trewartha; Schumpeter and Orchard provide adequate background for Japan's industrial development. Midwar and early postwar economic problems are described in Cohen, and the postwar economic situation is summarized in the British Board of Trade monograph.

Numerous statistical materials are issued by the relevant Japanese government offices, many of them in English or with English summaries. Most valuable are those, including the *Monthly Economic Reports,* of the Japanese Economic Stabilization Board. In addition, contemporary information may be found in the *Oriental Economist* and the *Far Eastern Economic Review,* and in the several yearbooks, official and unofficial published in Japan—*Jiji Nenkan, Asahi Nenkan,* and the *Japan Statistical Yearbook.*

Korea

THE STRATEGIC LOCATION OF KOREA IN THE HEART OF THE FAR EAST has been fundamental to its history. Around the peninsula lie the major powers of the western Pacific (See inset, Map 7). Each of them has striven for control of Korea. Despite these pressures the Korean people have been able to survive as a nation with their own culture and way of life.

Since the second World War Korea has been divided—first by the 38th parallel separating areas of different military and political control, and then by a battle line or a truce line. This division has brought into sharp focus the key significance of Korea's situation, for Korea has been in recent times, as in the past, a meeting place for differing and often hostile ideologies.

Korea's peninsular character also has been a critical factor in its history. It has acted as a bridge between the continent of Asia and the maritime powers. The narrow mountainous peninsula has been no easy highway, however. Often it has been a blind alley up which forces of aggression have spent themselves.

Korea is not large; its area is only 86,328 square miles, roughly the size of the state of Minnesota. As will be noted later, its mountainous character, its variations in climate, and its scattered resources make difficult

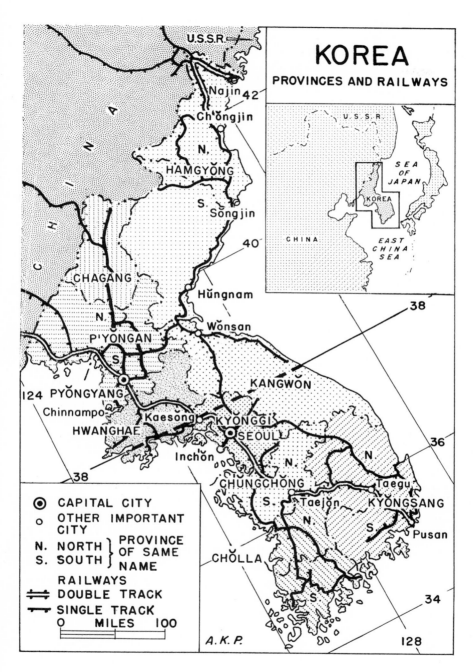

KOREA
PROVINCES AND RAILWAYS

CAPITAL CITY
OTHER IMPORTANT CITY
N. NORTH } PROVINCE OF SAME NAME
S. SOUTH }
RAILWAYS
DOUBLE TRACK
SINGLE TRACK
0   MILES   100

MAP 7

the utilization of its land. Yet, the population in 1957 was estimated to be 31 million people. Despite the tolls of war, people still crowd upon the land, and there is great need for rapid economic development. The future indeed looks grim, if the country continues to be divided, if struggles for power continue or threaten, and if population pressures mount as they have in the past. Future actions must take into account the geographic realities in Korea.

The physical basis for livelihood

Korea is a land of mountains; only one-fifth of the land is usable for agriculture. The rest has too steep slopes or too rocky or sandy soils. The mountain character of the peninsula thus limits severely the potentialities for economic development. However, in the mountain areas there are extensive forests, mineral deposits, hydroelectric power potentials, and small amounts of cultivable land. Thus the highlands are devoid neither of settlement nor of possibilities for economic development.

The northern interior of Korea, adjacent to Manchuria, is high and mountainous. These mountains are of a complex structure and have as their highest point, Paektu-san,[1] or White Top mountain. From this mountainous interior a major chain, the Taebaek-san, extends southward, parallel and near to the east coast. This range may be described simply as a block of diverse structure that has been uptilted to the east and downtilted to the west where it extends under the Yellow Sea. From the southern part of the Taebaek-san, an ancient elevated earth-fold forms a range, the Sobaek, extending to the southwest. Most of the mountains of Korea have been caused by block faulting or flexures of the earth's crust. In this way there have been exposed large areas of very ancient granites and metamorphic rocks, but in the northern interior and the two major offshore islands, Cheju and Ullung, volcanic activity has taken place in relatively recent times.

Despite the increasing utilization of the highlands in recent times, they have much less importance in the economic life of the peninsula than do the plains, which, though limited in size, provide the basic resource of the Korean people—land for agriculture. The plains fringe the coastal areas; they are narrow on the eastern side of the peninsula and relatively broad though irregular on the west. Most of the plains are caused by the downwarping or faulting of blocks of the earth's crust and by the erosional and depositional action of rivers. On the landward margins of the plains, the alluvial material laps around isolated hills or mountain spurs

[1] In Chinese, Pai-t'ou Shan.

like the sea around islands or headlands. Toward the headwaters of the streams the plains may consist only of narrow ribbons of flat land amidst a maze of hills and mountains (Figure 27). Just as there is a contrast between the mountain areas based upon granitic, metamorphic, sedimentary, or occasionally volcanic rock, so the plains have local differences based upon their geologic history and the nature and age of the depositional materials which form them. These variegated patterns of landforms, therefore, result in major differences in the amounts of land suitable for agriculture and the kinds of agriculture that can be practiced on them.

The second major physical factor in the economic development of Korea is its climate. Korea has a humid, continental climate. The range between the hot, moist summers and the cold, dry winters is great. However, there are some important differences between the north, where the

Fig. 27 • In eastcentral Korea, where the Taebaek and Sobaek ranges meet, most of the land surface is in steep slopes, many of them covered with second-growth forest suitable primarily for the production of fuelwood. The valley bottoms are narrow and are in cultivation only where the valley opens somewhat as the surrounding hills become lower, but local roads hug the valley bottom. Scenes similar to this one occur throughout highland Korea, but in areas adjacent to dense settlement the hillslopes are bare of vegetation, and eroded. Soil erosion is a curse with which Korea has been afflicted for centuries. (*Geographical Review.*)

severe winters limit the farmers to a single crop a year, and the south, where a winter second crop may be planted on the dry fields and the drained paddy fields. Thus, because of its milder winters, the south can support a denser agricultural population than the north. As has been noted in previous chapters, the climate of Korea is dominated by its position between continental Asia and the Pacific Ocean. The seasonal monsoonal air drifts, warm and moist maritime air in the summers and cold and dry continental air in winters, exert a major control over the climate of the peninsula. Nonperiodic cyclonic storms, typhoons, and convectional storms add variation to the seasonal climate and are major factors in the occurrence and distribution of precipitation. The hot weather and heavy rains of summer facilitate wet-rice cultivation. The daily changes in the weather occasioned by the effect of the movement of air masses as well as the seasonal changes play a large role in the lives of the Korean people.

The peninsular population

The peninsula, with its limited plains and its humid continental climate, has long been inhabited by a distinctive people, the Koreans. Though situated near powerful neighbors, they have been able to develop and maintain their own culture with its own language and way of life. Korean tradition and legend puts the founding of their civilization in B.C. 2333. This date does not stand historical examination, though it does appear from shell mounds and grave remains that there were people with a complex culture living in the peninsula centuries before the time of Christ. The influence of China was very strong, and Chinese colonies, later absorbed into Korean kingdoms, flourished at the start of the Christian era. Subsequently there were contests of power among different local kingdoms which controlled areas within the peninsula and adjacent Manchuria. Finally, in A.D. 668, the country was united under one political regime.

In later centuries when subjected to invasions from China and Japan, Korea attempted to be a "hermit nation," but with the impact of the Western World on the Far East, this isolationism was impossible to maintain. Weakened by internal dissension and an archaic form of government, the nation found the outside world a harsh one. Japan, after fighting China in 1894-1895 and Russia in 1904-1905, assumed a dominant position over Korea, which it annexed in 1910. For the next 35 years Korea (or Chosen as it was called by the Japanese)[2] was a colony of Japan. This long

---

[2] The Korean name for Korea is Choson or Tae Han. The name Korea stems from one of the ancient Korean kingdoms, Koryo, 918–1392 A.D.

period of foreign control had a profound effect on Korean life and economy, an effect that is still evident.

It appears from contemporary records (which must be used with caution) that Korea's population was stabilized at around six to seven million people during the decades before Korea was opened to the outside world in 1876. However, with the advent of a commercial economy, of better public health safeguards, and of relative peace, the population underwent an "explosive" increase. The first official census was taken in 1925 and revealed a population of 19,523,000; by 1944 this had grown to 25,900,142.[3] A very rough estimate of the Korean population for 1957 is 31,000,000. Not only is the number of persons less than would have been the case if the Korean war had not taken its great toll, but the distribution of people also has changed. The influx of refugees from the north and repatriates from Japan greatly increased the population in the south, so that this area, which had had the greater density before, acquired an even higher density.

During the last year of Japanese control some 71 per cent of the Korean people were engaged in agriculture and 10 per cent engaged in manual labor associated with mineral exploitation. The educational system (which may be characterized by the remark of a high Japanese government official: "The Koreans should be taught to follow, not to know") did not allow for the higher education of many Koreans. Only a handful of Koreans were permitted to occupy high positions in business, government service, and the professions.

The pattern of agriculture

Rice-dominated agriculture is the basic characteristic of the Korean economy, and has been for centuries. Korean farmers are diligent and skilled in meeting the demands for hand labor in rice cultivation. During the period of Japanese control rice cultivation expanded onto reclaimed land and was intensified on existing farm land through the introduction of better seeds and increased use of chemical fertilizers. The increased production that resulted was largely for the benefit of Japan, which normally took one-half of the Korean rice crop for its urban markets.

[3] Included in this figure were 708,448 civilian Japanese living mainly in the cities and 71,400 Chinese. At the same time, there were an estimated 1,550,000 Koreans living in Japan and 1,500,000 in China, mainly in Manchuria. An estimated 185,000 Koreans were resident in the Soviet Union. At the end of the second World War, the Japanese were repatriated and about two-thirds of the Koreans in Japan returned to Korea. Subsequently the movement of refugees from north to south Korea and the tremendous loss of life associated with the havoc of the Korean war have further confused the demographic picture.

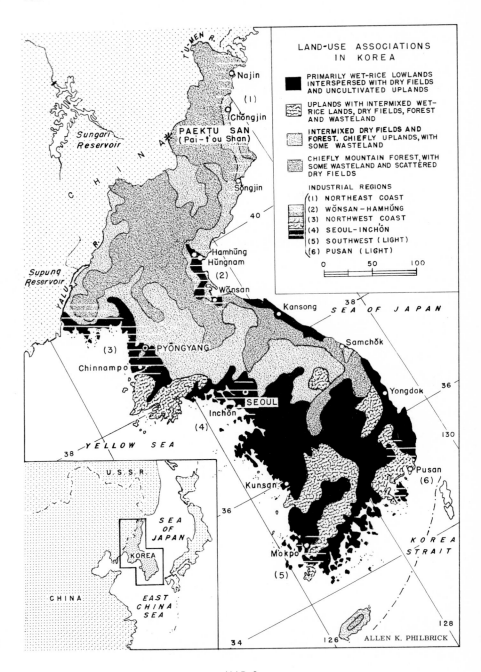

MAP 8

Though rice is the desired crop of all Korean farmers, obviously not all of the agricultural land is suited to its production (Map 8). In the south, on the hill slopes and on areas where paddy fields can not be developed because of sandy or gravel soils, are grown dry crops such as barley, wheat, mulberry, cotton, and vegetables. On the borders of the paddy fields soy beans often are planted. In the winter some of the dry fields are double-cropped with barley which provides food for many of the farm families who sell their rice. Some of the paddy fields are also double-cropped in those areas where the winters are not too severely cold and where the water can be quickly drained from the fields.[4] In northern Korea and in the mountain lands of the south, double-cropping is not possible because of the shortness of the growing season. In the uplands, where paddy fields cannot be developed, dry fields predominate. On these fields cereals—barley, corn, grain sorghum, and wheat—and native cotton and vegetables are grown. In the areas of most severe climates or poor soils, millet, rye, oats and potatoes are the major crops. In the more remote areas of the mountains, just as in some other parts of Asia, migratory, shifting fire-field agriculture is practised. In such pioneer regions the farmers plant crops after clearing the land by fire. This practice is wasteful of soils and forests which otherwise would be suitable for exploitation.

Under Japanese rule the increased commercialization of agriculture and emphasis upon rice production for export resulted in a rapid increase in tenancy. Japanese companies acquired large holdings and developed semimonopolistic marketing organizations. With the expulsion of the Japanese and the organization of new northern and southern regimes in Korea, one of the crying needs was for land reform. This took different forms. In North Korea the land was vested in communist-dominated committees which "gave" the land to the farmers. The farmers had to conform to the will of the committee and had to pay high taxes, equivalent to their former rents, for they did not receive clear title to their land. In South Korea the land was sold on a long-range credit basis to the farmers who thus had clear title to their land. Unfortunately, this program was put into operation very slowly in South Korea. With the outbreak of the Korean war, the whole commercial agricultural pattern was again violently disrupted. Many Korean farmers devoted themselves to virtual subsistence production, though government grain-collection programs to feed the urban centers and the armed forces were carried forward, sometimes by force.

---

[4] Almost as important as getting water *on* to paddy fields in Asia is getting it *off* so that the rice may mature quickly and be more easily harvested.

> **Mineral resources and
> industrial development**

The Japanese occupation and
postwar events greatly affected Korea's agricultural patterns, but the
really far-reaching changes took place in other facets of the economy.
Though for centuries there had been some limited mineral production,
mainly gold, copper, and iron workings, the Japanese introduced modern
mining and hydroelectric enterprises. As Japan became increasingly industrialized, and particularly after 1931 when Japan took over Manchuria
and began rapidly to develop her military strength, Korean resources became of greater significance and were exploited at an increasing rate. As
Table VII–1 shows, by 1944, the peak year for most mineral production,
there were produced in Korea 3,331,814 metric tons of iron ore, particularly from the Musan area in northeastern Korea, 4,530,263 tons of anthracite coal from scattered fields mainly in northwestern Korea, 2,518,513
tons of lignite and low-grade coal, mined in northeastern Korea for coal-
liquefaction plants, 103,306 tons of different types of graphite, 8,333 tons
of tungsten, and 5,193 tons of copper. In addition, there was a production
of other minerals—lead, zinc, manganese, and magnesite.

TABLE VII–1

PRODUCTION OF MAJOR MINERALS IN KOREA

(In metric tons)

	1938	1944
Anthracite coal	1,723,290	4,530,263
Lignite coal	1,696,061	2,518,513
Iron ore	768,000	3,331,814
Gold (in kilograms)	27,788	598
Copper	5,828	5,193
Amorphous graphite	44,815	74,879
Crystalline graphite	12,503	28,427
Tungsten ore	2,625	8,333
Lead	6,086	21,200
Zinc ore	9,167	
Zinc (metallic)		20,011
Manganese	780	33,584
Fluorspar	37,391	75,227
Magnesite	31,937	157,745

Source: The Bank of Korea, *Economic Review, 1949.* Table 51.

By 1944 the total installed capacity of hydroelectric plants was 1,426,-
790 kilowatts, and there were new plants under construction. In some of
the major cities and near the Yongwol coal mine were thermal power
plants, but their installed capacity was only one-tenth that of the hydro-

electric plants. Most of the hydroelectric plants were along the Yalu River and its tributaries, and 85 per cent of the water power was generated north of the 38th parallel.

The development of mineral and hydroelectric resources naturally was associated with a great increase in industrialization. Most of the industries were established by the Japanese for the primary or secondary processing of raw materials, these products then being sent to Japan for final consumption or further processing. Together with the industries there was a growth of many cities in Korea. Some were old centers that were expanded; others were virtually new urban centers. Seoul, the capital, had a population of almost a million in 1940; Pyongyang and Pusan had more than 250,000 each; and Taegu, Inchon, and Chongjin each had almost 200,000 people. The increased industrialization and urbanization were accompanied by a great development of railroads and highways. The network of railroads, roughly in the shape of an X with interconnecting lines (Map 7), gave the peninsula an adequate system over which to move export products to the ports, which also underwent substantial development.

These changes were correlated with the Japanese economic domination of Korea. When this control ended in 1945 and the 38th parallel divided the country, tremendous economic and industrial dislocations took place. There initially was some interchange between the two divisions, notably of electric power; this ceased in May, 1948, when the North Koreans cut off the electric current as a retaliatory measure after national elections were held in South Korea. During this period of postwar readjustment, divergent developments took place on either side of the 38th parallel. Some of the Japanese-sponsored enterprises had been uneconomic—based only upon wartime demands—and these ceased operation. Other industries deteriorated rapidly, in part because Japanese management and technicians could not be quickly replaced by Koreans, few of whom had been allowed to obtain higher educations or technical training. In both North and South Korea some new industries were developed to make up for shortages of materials normally obtained from the other zone.

With the outbreak of the Korean war in 1950, even greater catastrophes hit Korean industry. Air raids, ground warfare, scorched-earth tactics, all took a tremendous toll. It is difficult to assess exactly what remains of the industrial complex north of the truce line. U.S. Air Force commanders commented during the latter stages of the fighting that there was nothing left to bomb. Many of the industrial sections of the cities of South Korea were reduced to rubble during the fighting or were devastated by fires. Thus when Seoul was ultimately retaken by United Nations forces, the city's industrial plants were estimated to be 85 per cent destroyed.

As a consequence of these tragic developments, a tremendous amount of reconstruction has been necessary in Korea. The pattern of economic development under the Japanese shows the great potential that exists for industrialization. This pattern cannot, however, be duplicated. What actually may take place will depend in large part upon the nature of the political situation in Korea.

In view of probable long-standing political controls over Korean development and because of the considerable geographic differences between North and South Korea, it is worthwhile to consider these two regions in more detail.[5] Rather than utilize the truce-line, which was established along the fighting front in the summer of 1953, or the 38th parallel which was designed as a temporary boundary line for limited military purposes, traditional provincial boundaries may best be utilized to demarcate the boundary between these two regions.[6] It should be emphasized that the line is chosen for convenience in order better to depict the zone in which there is transition from north to south. This division is justified by factors of terrain and climate, as well as by historical tradition and present-day political realities. Though Korea may be unified, the differences between north and south, conditioned as they are by geographic diversities as well as historic developments, will remain.

North Korea

Mountainous North Korea is firmly tied to the continent of Asia. Though the Sea of Japan and the Yellow Sea influence its coastal areas, North Korea is continental rather than peninsular in character. Lofty Paektu-san, surrounding mountains, and lava-capped plateaus dominate the northern interior. The eastern escarpment of the mountain area is abrupt, and the hills and offshoots of the interior mountains make the eastern coastal area rugged with few valleys. In the west the descent from the mountainous interior is less abrupt; consequently, hills and plains are more extensive along the coast. In their lower courses the Yalu River and the Taedong River have created large flood plains, and in Hwanghae province are rather extensive areas of low hills and broad valleys, but even in these areas hills and mountains dominate the landscape. As a consequence, not only is the population sparse, but it is for the most part concentrated in the lowlands along the fringes of the northern division.

Extremely cold winters also are a factor in accounting for the low population density. Average winter temperatures in North Korea lie well be-

[5] The treatment of these two regions is adapted from Shannon McCune, *Korea's Heritage, A Regional and Social Geography* (Tokyo: Tuttle, 1956).

[6] These boundaries are the northern boundaries of Kyonggi and Kangwon provinces.

low freezing. For instance, Pyongyang, in the northwest, has an average January temperature of 17.6°F.; Wonsan, which is at the same latitude on the northeast coast, has an average January temperature of 25.2°, and Chunggangjin, which is located at the bend of the Yalu river, deep in the northern interior, has an average January temperature of −6°. One crucial consequence of this climatic fact is that North Korea has a short growing season, which means that with certain rare exceptions North Korean farmers are limited to one crop per year on a given piece of land.

In its original state North Korea was densely forested. Settlement slowly encroached upon these forested areas, and, more recently, commercial forestry made further inroads. At lower elevations much of the forest has been cut over, and growths of scrub oak, pine, and other less valuable trees have supplanted the natural vegetation. However, large areas of virgin forest, of spruce, fir, and larch still flourish in the drainage basin of the Yalu River.

In many respects North Korea has been, and still is, what might be called a "pioneer land" dominated by a "frontier spirit." Factors of terrain and climate called for ruggedness, persistence, and individual initiative on the part of its settlers and later inhabitants. In fact, the northerners often are inclined to think of themselves as brave, energetic, virile—as "tiger hunters"—in contrast with the South Koreans whom they call effeminate, indecisive, and unaggressive. On the other hand the South Koreans consider their northern neighbors to be uncouth, barbaric, volatile, and quixotic and themselves stable, cultured, and hard-working. Both pictures, of course, are overdrawn, reflecting regional prejudices. More important are the facts that the people of both areas speak the same language, follow the same cultural patterns, and possess an integrated historical background.

In modern times the industrialization of North Korea and the development of its mineral deposits and hydroelectric power resources caused a tremendous increase in the population, though the total is still much below that of South Korea. In 1940 the total population for the five northern provinces was 8,233,477, resulting in a density of 188.47 per square mile. By 1944 the population had grown to 8,859,710. In the postwar years, however, as the political dichotomy grew rigid and as many North Koreans moved south to escape communist domination, the population decreased. But immigrants from Manchuria, added to normal population growth, served to keep the total North Korean population at only slightly below the 1944 figure in the period after the second World War. The Korean war, the waves of refugees moving back and forth before the advancing armies, bombed-out cities, the presence of Chinese soldiers, and all the other effects of the military action have so confused the situation that it is no longer possible to give accurate population data. Reports have it that because of the war the North Korean population has been reduced by approximately half.

In the past the population of North Korea was centered largely in the valleys and plains along the northwestern coast. The area around Pyong-yang—where the Koguryo kingdom (B.C. 37-A.D. 688) had its capital—was the dominant political and economic center. The northeastern area was relatively isolated and undeveloped until recent decades when the Japanese developed hydroelectric and mineral resources for integration within their war economy. With the building of a railroad line between Pyongyang and the east coast in 1940 the northern realm became more closely knit.

Though North Korea was more industrialized by the Japanese than was its southern neighbor, its economy is still fundamentally agricultural and self-sufficient. In the coastal plains and the interior valleys rice is the principal crop. On fields that cannot be irrigated the farmer may plant dry crops, especially cereals such as wheat, grain sorghum, and corn. Native cotton and tobacco are specialty or cash crops. Fields with poor soils or fields in areas affected by severe climatic conditions are used for hardy cereals, such as millet, rye, and buckwheat. In general, the fields are larger than those in South Korea, but the amount of cultivated land in proportion to the total area is relatively low.

The farmer, for the most part, lives in villages located on the valley floors or on the lower slopes of the hills, though in distinction to this type of economy is another, that of the "fire-field" folk. These people are pioneer settlers who go into the forest lands, particularly on the hillslopes, clear their fields by burning, and plant crops for one, two, or three years. Then, as the fertility of their original field decreases or as the forest and brush vegetation encroaches upon them, they move on and clear a new patch. These "fire-field" folk generally live in dispersed settlements, and their homes are built of logs with shingled roofs.

In recent times, as population pressure increased and as better farming techniques became available, North Korean agriculture became more intensive. Under the Japanese particularly, new lands were reclaimed along the tidal flats of western Korea, and the stream valleys of northeastern Korea were used for well developed irrigation works. Some specialty crops were introduced, such as apples in Hwanghae and South Pyongan provinces. Considerable crop experimentation took place, and hardier types of early-maturing rice were planted in the interior valleys.

The forests are an important resource for the North Koreans, supplying them with much-needed fuel and charcoal. Under the Japanese, commercial forestry was developed along the headwaters of the Yalu and Tumen rivers, and wood-processing plants and lumber mills were established at cities along the rivers or near their mouths. Much of this lumber

Fig. 28 • The Supung dam on the Yalu River looking northeast and upstream. This dam is the largest in the Far East and one of the highest in the world. A lake extends beyond the dam for nearly 75 miles up the Yalu valley. Note the power station in the right foreground was bombed out by United Nations forces' air attacks. Hydroelectric power from the dam was divided evenly between Korea and Manchuria. Before the second World War, power from Supung accounted for about one-fourth of all the hydroelectric energy generated in Korea. The small amount of water below the dam is characteristic in February during the dry season. (U.S. Air Force.)

was exported from the producing areas, particularly to the urban markets in Korea and Japan.

In the early days, fishing had been a minor occupation or a supplemental activity for farmers living in the coastal areas or along the streams, but under the Japanese commercial fishing was introduced, particularly in northeastern Korea, where the cool waters of the south-flowing Liman current provided good fishing grounds. The introduction of power launches and better nets aided the rise of an important industry, and Korea became one of the leading fisheries countries of the world.

In modern times, it was in terms of mineral and hydroelectric development that the greatest transformation took place in the economy of North Korea. As the Japanese prepared for war, they thoroughly explored and exploited these resources. The headwaters of some of the north-flowing tributaries to the Yalu River were dammed and the water was then diverted south, over the divide and into valleys leading to the Sea of Japan. A number of such hydroelectric developments were built during the twenties and thirties. Equally important was the large dam built in the late thirties at Supung, some 50 miles from the mouth of the Yalu River in northwestern Korea. The hydroelectric plant at this dam provided power for both Manchuria and Korea (Figure 28). Concurrently, large-scale industrialization, emphasizing chemicals and associated products, took place in the areas adjoining these power projects (Map 8). The coal and iron-ore deposits near Pyongyang were exploited, as were the lignite resources in extreme northeastern Korea and the low-grade but very extensive iron-ore deposits at Musan in northeastern Korea. One of the region's most important industrial complexes was developed in Hungnam, based on hydroelectric power, and cities such as Pyongyang, Wonsan, Chongjin, and Sinuiju became populous urban centers.

Concurrently with this industrial activity the Japanese built a modern transportation network to integrate North Korea with the surrounding areas under their control. Ports along the coast—Chinnampo, on the Yellow Sea, and Wonsan, Songjin, Chongjin, along the Sea of Japan—rapidly were developed. A significant development was the creation of two modern ports in the extreme northeast of Korea, Najin and Unggi, to serve as outlets for the products of central and northern Manchuria. Also the Japanese continued the main-line, double-tracked railroad from Pusan in southeastern Korea, through Seoul, across northwestern Korea into Manchuria; and the east-coast line was extended through the Wonsan-Seoul corridor to connect with the main line. Branch lines were built inland, tapping the northern interior, particularly in regions possessing mineral or forest resources.

Little authentic information is readily available on the economic development of North Korea under the communist regime. Reports on industrial activity, on land reform, and on construction of new highways usually are put in general terms or percentage figures with no basic data. Two-year plans have been proclaimed, and grandiose programs have been advertised. From these and the reports of refugees who have continued to flee southward, certain trends seem evident. The economy of North Korea has been knit closely to the economy of the adjacent areas of Manchuria, North China, and the Soviet Far East. Hydroelectric power and mineral resources have been developed to supply those areas. It was in part because of these developments, as well as for strategic and political reasons, that the Chinese communist armies advanced into North Korea when the United Nations troops neared the Yalu River and its power plants.

Though initially there were close economic ties with the Soviet Union—

an economic and cultural pact was signed in Moscow in March, 1949—after the entry of Chinese troops and the long and devastating war (devastating especially to the North Korean economy) the Chinese communists replaced the Russians in North Korea. A pact calling for Chinese aid in North Korea's economic rehabilitation was signed in Peking in January, 1954. Some observers have stated that North Korea is becoming more a Chinese province than an independent country, and that its economic resources in the form of arable land, coal, iron-ore deposits, forests, and hydroelectric power are being used largely to benefit China.

South Korea

South Korea is much more peninsular and martime in character than is North Korea. Though it too is a land of mountains and valleys, the chief differences are that the mountains of the south are not so massive or high and that its plains are much more extensive. Consequently, the amount of cultivated land is greater, and the access from place to place is easier. In central Korea, the major range, the Taebaek, which runs north and south parallel to the eastern coast, slopes to the coast abruptly, but in the west the headwaters of the Han River have etched out more gentle slopes. Though there is a subdued extension of the Taebaek range to the southeast tip of Korea, more important is the Sobaek range in the southern part of the area. This range extends diagonally from the central Taebaek to the southwest, thus separating the Naktong river basin from the river basins of western Korea. Ancient earth folds truncated by erosion and different levels of alluvium give variation to the western hill lands and plains. The southwestern coast is a maze of islands and peninsulas, with structural lines going at cross angles. The two volcanic islands that lie offshore at some distance, small Ullung to the east and large Cheju to the southwest, also are grouped with South Korea.

South Korea is fortunate in having a comparatively mild winter climate, though with respect to some of the interior locations the term "mild" can hardly be used. The average January temperature at Seoul is 24°F., at Mokpo in the southwest it is 33.7°, and at Pusan in the southeast it is 35.6°. The relatively mild winters are important, particularly in the lowland areas along or near the coast, for in those areas winter cropping is possible. This means that two crops can be grown in a year, making possible higher population densities. This is perhaps the single most significant feature of the geography of South Korea as compared to that of North Korea.

The mountains and hills of South Korea were at one time covered by heavy forests, but farmers in search of wood and the ravages of uncontrolled insect pests have denuded many of the hills of their trees. Barren hill slopes are now a common characteristic in the densely populated areas. The remnants of fine forest stands are found only in the mountains and in protected sites around monasteries or graves. The Japanese attempt to foster a large-scale reforestation program was frustrated in part by their own need for wood during the second World War. In the chaotic postwar period, when the occupation authorities were unable to curtail the cutting of firewood and brüsh by the Korean farmers, more slopes were denuded, and again severe erosion set in.

The people of South Korea live within a predominantly agricultural

Fig. 29a • Most Koreans live in villages similar to this one near Seoul. Most of the houses are thatched-roofed, but some are tile-roofed. Almost all are either U-shaped or L-shaped and are surrounded by a wall. It is in the enclosed courtyards that much of Korean life centers about the drying and threshing of grains and beans, the manufacture of *kimchi* (the Korean national dish of pickled radish and spices), and the washing and drying of clothes. Each house has a vegetable garden and some fruit and mulberry trees. On the slopes about the village, upland crops are grown—wheat, barley, millet, rye, buckwheat, beans, and vegetables. On more level land off the picture to the right paddy is raised. The village is connected with its sister villages and the outside world by a poor, unsurfaced road. *(Geographical Review.)*

Fig. 29b • The market place at Kangnung on the Korean east coast. The farm women selling their produce have brought it in from their villages in wooden bowls carried on their heads. Each sale is characterized by much bargaining. The permanent stalls in the background sell processed and manufactured goods. Many of the women are wearing white, the traditional and favorite clothing color for Koreans. *(Shannon McCune.)*

folk society. They live in small villages, usually situated in the lee of a hillslope, and carry on intensive agriculture on the paddy fields located along the valley bottoms and on dry hillside fields (Figures 29a and 29b). Alluvial soils form their basic natural resource. Rice is the principal crop, and most of the agricultural activity is geared to its production. Much hand labor is required to prepare the fields, transplant the rice shoots, and harvest the grain. Arduously the paddy fields are drained and the earth heaped into ridges so that barley can be grown as a winter crop. Dry fields are planted with barley, wheat, and cotton. These supplemental crops provide the food staples for many of the farmers, rice being the commercial crop sold to the wealthy and the city dwellers.

During the period of Japanese control agriculture became increasingly commercialized, and the export of rice to Japan was expanded. South Korean farmers depended more and more upon rice as their cash crop while they ate imported Manchurian millet or cereals that they grew on dry fields or produced as winter crops in the paddy fields. As commercialization increased, tidal flats along the coast were reclaimed, and riverine plains were made to produce higher yields by large-scale irrigation projects. Finally, the introduction of more intensive methods of cultivation, including the application of commercial fertilizer, resulted in higher yields per acre, although these averaged only about half those of Japan. However, the benefit of all this agricultural development went mainly to Japanese companies and to wealthy landowners, both Japanese and Korean. The plight of the rural people was tragic in a land of plenty. Starvation was common.

Fishing along the coasts and the rivers of South Korea has long been a supplementary occupation for many Korean farmers (Figure 30). Under the Japanese some of the coastal fishing villages grew rapidly, particularly those along the eastern and southeastern coasts, where sardine catches were tremendous, but the disappearance of the schools of sardines in 1940 led to a severe decline in the fishing industry. In the postwar years rehabilitation of the industry was attempted; the Koreans took over the Japanese facilities and began using new fishing boats and nets, furnished as a part of American aid programs. One of the points of recent friction with Japan has been Korea's delimitation of its offshore fishing grounds, a measure designed to restrict the activities of Japanese fishermen in Korean waters.

The great increase in population in recent decades has become one of South Korea's most pressing problems. In 1940 the eight provinces that made up South Korea had a population of 16,101,558 and a population density of 38,655 per square mile. By 1944 the population had grown to 17,040,432. Although urbanization was rapid, there were too few industries to absorb the surplus of labor from the rural areas. As a consequence many Korean men migrated to Japan. Manchuria, too, attracted many migrants. Finally there was a shift to the northern province of Korea as industrialization increased there.

In the postwar period when many Koreans, mostly unskilled workers, returned from Japan where they had been working in mines and factories, the population pressure in South Korea became even more pronounced. Though the Japanese residents of Korea were sent home and thus gave slight relief, Japanese technical and administrative skills were sorely missed. The problem of population pressure was aggravated by the influx of refugees from North Korea who, now landless, crowded into the southern cities, as the natural growth of population continued. Meanwhile agricultural yields fell drastically from prewar levels because of a lack of fertilizer. The situation was relieved by stopping the export of large quantities of rice to Japan and by American economic assistance. On the whole, the splitting of the country by the 38th parallel probably caused more suffering in the South than in the North.

Most of the industries of South Korea, unlike those of North Korea where coal and iron deposits and hydroelectric power resources abound, were developed to meet consumer demands or to process agricultural products, particularly rice. A major consequence of industrialization under the Japanese was the undermining of the traditional village handicraft economy which for ages had produced the cloth, pottery, shoes, tools, household utensils, and nearly everything else needed by the rural population.

With industrialization came a revolution in transportation and communications. The Japanese developed the ports of Inch'on, Kunsan, Mokpo, and Pusan into major rice-exporting centers, with large warehouses and shipping facilities. These they connected with the agricultural

Fig. 30 • Nets drying on the gravel beach of a small east-coast village. In small sheltered bays are located many such fishing villages. Many of the fishermen also are engaged in part-time farming, and their terraced paddy fields may be seen in the background and at the left. The thatch-roofed house in the foreground is typical. More prosperous fisher-farmers are likely to have tile-roofed houses like the ones in the left background. In winter, the beach may be washed by breakers stirred by the predominantly northerly winds from the Sea of Japan, but the embayment is sheltered from the full force of the seas, and settlement has encroached upon the very margins of the strand. Note the sampan moored near the shore, typical of the non-motored smaller fishing vessels which predominate in the in-shore fishing along Korea's coasts. *(UNKRA.)*

hinterlands by modern highways and railway networks (Map 7). The main railway line, built for strategic purposes in the early days of the Japanese occupation, ran north from Pusan to Taegu in the rich Naktong river basin. Later, secondary rail lines branched from the main line to other parts of the Naktong basin. The main line was pushed across the Sobaek range and directly north to Seoul and from there into North Korea. In the west, a rail center was built at Taejon, with connections to Kunsan and later to Mokpo. Eventually the network was supplemented by branch lines as well as feeder bus and truck routes.

Realizing that the main line was vulnerable and overburdened, even though it was double-tracked in the 1930's, the Japanese developed alternate routes and facilities. One line was built north from Pusan, paralleling the main line, but tapping a different section of the Naktong basin. It crossed to the Sobaek range over a more difficult route which passed near the coal-mining areas at Yongwol, where Japanese exploitation was in progress. The line continued northward into the Han river basin and approached Seoul from the east. Another line, projected along the east coast, was not completed north of the port of Pohang. The port of Yosu, midway between Mokpo and Pusan, was connected with the railroad lines in southwest Korea and became an alternate port of some value. On the whole, South Korea was remarkably well supplied with transportation facilities.

In the postwar period South Korea's economic difficulties increased. Uncertainty about the political future, the influx of repatriates and refugees, and a vicious spiral of inflation—three factors among many—hampered the economy. One critical need was land reform, since this directly affected the lives of the bulk of the people. Very early in the occupation period, in an attempt to ease this problem, the American military government undertook a land reform program by promulgating a law reducing rents of tenants to one-third of the production of the primary crop of each farm from as much as two-thirds. Finally in the spring of 1947 provision was made for the sale and redistribution of the former Japanese-owned land to South Korean farmers. Some 687,000 acres were sold to 588,000 tenant families. As a result of this measure and pressures on Korean landlords to sell their land, tenancy dropped from 73 per cent of the farm families in 1945 to 40 per cent in 1948. In 1949 the Republic of Korea enacted a land-reform program which would have enabled 1,200,000 farmers to purchase 1,470,000 acres of land from Korean landlords. Unfortunately, this plan was not implemented before the communist aggression took place in June, 1950. The invaders immediately set up their own scheme, but it was rather crude, and soon they were driven out. Moreover most of the records of land ownership had been destroyed, and the influx of refugees confused matters even more. A land-reform plan was to have been carried out in 1951 and the year following, but by 1957 it had not yet been implemented fully.

To help the South Korean economy back on its feet after the expulsion of the Japanese and the divsion of the peninsula, the American military government in the fall of 1945 started an aid program with the import of foodstuffs, fertilizer, oil, coal, cotton, medicines, and relief supplies. By the end of 1948, when much of this program was turned over to the Economic Cooperation Administration, the value of the aid had been some $310,000,000. The ECA program was aimed at projects of longer range including technical assistance and basic commodities. The total of military and ECA economic aid for Korea through 1951 (when the ECA responsibilities had been passed on to United Nations agencies) was $280,000,000. During the period 1952-1954, the value of economic aid through military and civilian agencies which reached Korea totaled $520,000,000. The amount of outside assistance was, therefore, of a considerable magnitude. It was a situation quite different from that in North Korea where the economy was not given much outside support by the Soviet Union or by the Chinese but where a certain amount of economic recovery and reorientation was achieved by severely restricting civilian consumption.

The economic recovery in South Korea was thus dependent to a large extent upon outside aid rather than internal financing. Unfortunately, some of the foreign aid was not effectively used because of administrative weaknesses in the Korean government and the necessity of diverting economic strength from economic rehabilitation to military expenditures. Even so, as a consequence of this different economic situation the standards of living in South Korea became appreciably higher than in those in North Korea. Naturally under this system the ratio of imports to exports for South Korea was and is obviously one-sided, about nine to one. Aid programs all call for an increase of exportable commodities and a reduction of imports.

It is, of course, almost impossible to assess the effects the Korean war has had on the economy of South Korea, but some idea can be gained from the study of Table VII-2. The devastation by bombing, by scorched-earth policies, and by disruption of law and order has been staggering. It has been estimated that five million of the 21 million South Koreans were uprooted from their homes. At least 400,000 homes were destroyed. Industrial and transportation facilities were especially hard hit, and villages and cities in the line of battle were severely damaged. The city of Seoul, for example, lost 85 per cent of its industry, transportation facilities, and public utilities and half to three-quarters of its living and office space. In the south 75 to 80 per cent of the textile industry, an important segment of industrial life, was damaged by war and by attempted dismantling on the part of the Communists. War damage in South Korea is

TABLE VII-2

Postwar Production in South Korea

Product	1947	1949	1951	1953	1955
Rice (unpolished) (1,000 bu.)	68,696	73,081	56,291	74,415	—
Barley, wheat, rye (1,000 bu.)	18,421	25,073	15,093	25,553	27,030
Marine products (1,000 M.T.)	302	300	277	258	—
Power generated (million KWH)	274	655	337	737	879
Anthracite coal (1,000 M.T.)	463	1066	129	867	1,307
Lignite (1,000 M.T.)	37	60	6	}	
Gold (Kilograms)	77	106	31	494	1,502
Amor. graphite (1,000 M.T.)	2.6	39.8	21.6	18.7	90.0
Copper ore conc. (4-20%) (1,000 M.T.)	1.8	0.3	1.1	0.7	—
Tungsten ore (64-80%) (1,000 M.T.)	1.0	1.3	1.2	4.99	—
Salt (1,000 M.T.)	71	188.8	83.4	193	354
Cotton yarn (1,000 lbs.)	12.3	28.2	12.6	29.3	58.6
Cotton sheeting (1,000 yards)	30,600	63,700	29,900	60,400	87,800
Bicycle tires (1,000's)	—	482	41	63.6	89.7
Common brick (M.T.)	40,641	112,800	65,600	42,005	71,146
Cement (M.T.)	8,191	24,132	7,319	41,720	56,257
Coal (M.T.)	467,458	1,044,362	323,080	866,705	1,307,504

Sources: Bank of Korea reports.

estimated to have involved $1,500,000,000 worth of productive goods. Internally the crowding of people, the overloading of the transport lines by military traffic, the collapsing financial structure and the inflationary chaos have caused tremendous economic havoc. It has been estimated that the level of total economic production in late 1952, estimated at $44 per capita, was one-third lower than that of the immediate prehostilities period; per-capita consumption was probably one-fourth below that of the pre-invasion year. The raising of the present South Korean standard of living by 1959 to the 1949 level, which was relatively low, will require $1,750,000,000 of outside relief and economic aid, a stupendous sum to raise among the United Nations.

United Nations agencies, such as the Civilian Assistance Command and the Korean Reconstruction Agency, have striven valiantly with the social and economic problems of a nation swept by war. The United States has been the heavy contributor to the United Nations relief work. It has also carried on programs unilaterally. The expressed aim of the United Nations' and United States' economic activities is to help the Koreans plan and build the solid economic foundations necessary for a unified, independent, and democratic Korea.

The key to these goals lies in unity, for the longer the two Koreas are separated by a rigid political barrier the more important will be the role of geographic diversities in their development. If they could be reunited or if the barrier between them could be breached or abolished, these same diversities would make for strength.

SELECTED GEOGRAPHICAL BIBLIOGRAPHY

1. Canada, Department of Mines and Technical Surveys, Geographical Branch. *Korea.* Ottawa: 1951.
2. Fisher, C. A. "The Role of Korea in the Far East," *Geographical Journal,* September, 1954, pp. 282-98.
3. Grajdanzev, A. J. *Modern Korea.* New York: Institute of Pacific Relations, 1944.
4. Kang, Y. *The Grass Roof.* New York: Scribners, 1931.
5. Lautensach, H. *Korea.* Leipzig: Koehler, 1945 (in German).
6. Lee, Hoon K. *Land Utilization and Rural Economy in Korea.* Chicago: University of Chicago Press, 1936.
7. McCune, George M. *Korea Today.* Cambridge: Harvard University Press, 1950.
8. McCune, Shannon. *Korea's Heritage, A Regional and Social Geography,* Tokyo: Charles E. Tuttle & Co., 1956.
9. ———. "Climatic Regions of Korea and Their Economy," *Geographical Review,* January, 1941, pp. 95-99.

10. ——. "The Physical Basis for Korean Boundaries," *Far Eastern Quarterly,* May, 1946, pp. 272-88.
11. SCAP, Natural Resources Section. Report No. 35, *The Mineral Industry of Korea in 1944.* Tokyo: 1946.
12. Shabad, Theodore. "North Korea's Postwar Recovery," *Far Eastern Survey,* June, 1956, pp. 81-91.
13. Trewartha, G. T., and W. Zelinsky. "Population Distribution and Change in Korea, 1925–49," *Geographical Review,* January, 1955, pp. 1-26.
14. United Nations, Food and Agricultural Organization. *Rehabilitation and Development of Agriculture, Forestry, and Fisheries in South Korea.* New York: Columbia University Press, 1954.
15. Zaichikov, V. T. *Geography of Korea.* New York: Institute of Pacific Relations, 1952. (Translated by A. Parry with notes and introduction by S. McCune.)

Comments

The most recent publication covering all of Korea is S. McCune's *Korea's Heritage.* McCune has been the most productive American geographer working on Korea. The above articles are merely a sample of his numerous publications.

A thorough work is in German, Lautensach's prewar *Korea.* Zaichikov is a useful general survey. Fisher gives a stimulating introduction to Korea's role in eastern Asia, and George McCune traces the development of modern Korea through the war. Grajdanzev and Lee are still useful, though dated. Kang's book is an autobiographical account of life in Korea.

The FAO monograph represents a series of studies directed toward the rehabilitation of the South Korean economy and includes the most recent data concerning South Korean agriculture as well as useful descriptions of agricultural techniques and policies. The United Nations Korean Reconstruction Agency and other agencies and commissions have published a great deal of valuable material on Korea. Shabad summarizes recent economic information for North Korea.

China

PHYSICAL DIVERSITY

CHINA LIES IN EASTERN ASIA. YET, ASIA EXTENDS FROM THE EAST-
ernmost part of China, northeastern Manchuria, 55 degrees of longitude
still farther *eastward*, or one-seventh of the way around the world. More
correctly stated, then, China is situated in the central part of eastern Asia,
for the northernmost tip of Manchuria is about the same distance from
the northernmost reaches of the Asian continent as the southernmost tip
of Hai-nan island is from Singapore. When it is added that China lies between latitudes 18° and 57°N., it follows that southernmost China lies in
the subtropics, while northernmost China has the same latitude as northern Labrador and southern Alaska. This gives some clue to the variety
that China exhibits in climates and regional characteristics.

Geographical position not only prescribes certain climatic regimes for
a territory, but also provides commercial and strategical limitations or
advantages. China has access to the Pacific Ocean along some 4,000 miles
of seacoast, with a few excellent harbors both in the north and in the
south. An arterial river provides navigation far into interior China. For
foreign trade purposes, it has the advantage of cheap marine transport
to numerous offshore island chains from Japan through the Philippines to
Indonesia, as well as to adjacent Korea, to the Maritime Provinces of the
Soviet Union, and to Vietnam, Malaya, and Thailand. The east and south

China coast lies along one of the important shipping lanes of the world. Ships plying between western North America and South and Southeast Asia or between Japan and these areas must sail along this lane following the Great Circle route.

In spite of this frontage on the Pacific, China does not have free strategic access to it if the offshore island chains are in the hands of unfriendly nations. These island chains not only hem in and command the gates to the three great seas bordering the China coast—the Japan, East China, and South China seas—but through airpower also may dominate maritime movements. China, therefore, understandably has a vital concern in the character of and relations with the nations that occupy these island chains.

Because China is predominantly a continentally oriented state, her land frontiers have preoccupied her in the past even more than her maritime frontiers. Before the detachment of Outer Mongolia from China, the Soviet Union stretched all along China's north and northwest frontiers. Korea shares about 500 miles of frontiers with northeastern China, joining the Soviet Union in cutting China's direct access to the Sea of Japan except along the shallow Tumen River. India adjoins her in the southern reaches of Tibet. Remote Afghanistan sends a slender finger to touch China in the narrow crack between India and the Soviet Union. Equally remote Nepal and Bhutan share the Himalaya with China's Tibetan territories. Burma bars China's access to the Indian Ocean, while Laos intervenes between China and Thailand.

These neighbors provide opportunity for trade and friendship, but they also present political problems and strategical dangers. These dangers may arise from the direct menace of stronger neighbors, such as the Soviet Union which shares with China a large segment of her land boundaries, or from the situation of weak nations such as Korea, Burma, or Vietnam, which may become a bone of contention between rival powers or may be dominated by a stronger colonial power. Political problems also arise from rivalry for resources and markets. Thus the resources and markets within China, especially in Manchuria, were coveted by Japan to further her own industrial and economic development at the expense of China's development. This rivalry and others between various foreign powers for exploitation of China's resources have several times plunged China into war.

China's immense size, even without her former Outer Mongolian territories, is second in the world to that of the Soviet Union. Area alone, however, does not provide a gauge either for productive agricultural capacity or for the size of the resource base for industrial development. Geographical limitations conspire to restrict China's potentially productive land to the eastern third of her great area. This one-third may be termed China's "net agricultural area," in contrast to her "gross area" of some 3.86 million square miles.

Size of area, nevertheless, is almost certain to provide for variety in land use and agricultural production, which in turn leads to internal regional trade and to self-sufficiency in many aspects of national life. A large area also is more apt to contain greater quantities and varieties of mineral resources, although it does not guarantee all the requisites for modern industrial development. In China's situation, a large land area presents opportunities for the occurrence of all the major types of land forms. Although diversity is the keynote of China's topography, within this diversity is an unusual amount of uniformity from an over-all point of view.

China's radial drainage pattern

The radial character of Asia's rivers indicates that the highest part of Asia is its center (Map 9). China reaches from the Pacific Ocean westward to the sources of some of its greatest rivers in the heart of Asia. These rivers follow the land's slope downhill to the east and south. The Yang-tzu (Yangtze),[1] Huang (Yellow), Lan-ts'ang (Mekong), and Nu (Salween) rivers all originate within the eastern half of the Tibetan plateau. The mouths of these rivers, however, may be over 2,000 miles apart. Thus, the Huang empties to the northeast into the Yellow Sea, whereas the Salween debouches southward into the Andaman Sea.

Although the eastern two-thirds of China slopes generally eastward and southeastward, about a third of the western plateau land of Tibet and Monogolia does not pour the little water it collects into the ocean. Instead, this run-off drains into the numerous salt lakes and marshes or into the sands and rocks of the desert basins. In small areas of the western rim-lands of Tibet and Hsin-chiang (Sinkiang or Chinese Turkestan) the collected run-off of rain and melted snow flows into the neighboring countries of India, Pakistan, or the Soviet Union.

Only three rivers form significant parts of China's international boundaries. The longest and largest is the Hei-lung Chiang (Black Dragon River), called by the Russians the Amur, which encloses the northern bulge of Manchuria. Together with its tributary, the Ussuri, which runs into it from the southeast, the Amur separates China's northeastern provinces from the Soviet Union's eastern Siberian territories. South of these two rivers and smaller, the Yalu river forms most of the boundary with

[1] The Yang-tzu is known also as the Ch'ang Chiang, or "long," river. In the southwest plateau stretches it is known as the Chin-sha or "golden sand" river.

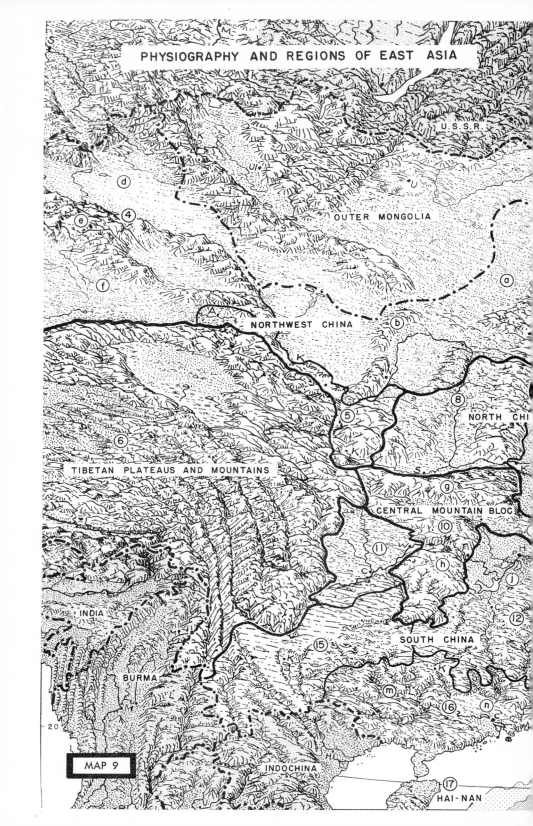

PHYSIOGRAPHY AND REGIONS OF EAST ASIA

U.S.S.R.

OUTER MONGOLIA

NORTHWEST CHINA

NORTH CHI

TIBETAN PLATEAUS AND MOUNTAINS

CENTRAL MOUNTAIN BLOC

INDIA

SOUTH CHINA

BURMA

MAP 9

INDOCHINA

HAI-NAN

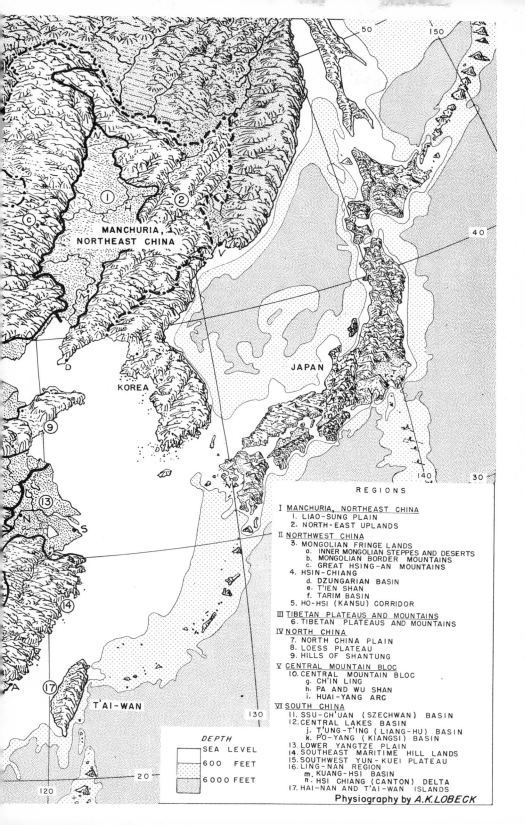

MANCHURIA,
NORTHEAST CHINA

JAPAN

KOREA

T'AI-WAN

DEPTH

SEA LEVEL

600 FEET

6000 FEET

REGIONS

I MANCHURIA, NORTHEAST CHINA
  1. LIAO-SUNG PLAIN
  2. NORTH-EAST UPLANDS
II NORTHWEST CHINA
  3. MONGOLIAN FRINGE LANDS
    a. INNER MONGOLIAN STEPPES AND DESERTS
    b. MONGOLIAN BORDER MOUNTAINS
    c. GREAT HSING-AN MOUNTAINS
  4. HSIN-CHIANG
    d. DZUNGARIAN BASIN
    e. T'IEN SHAN
    f. TARIM BASIN
  5. HO-HSI (KANSU) CORRIDOR
III TIBETAN PLATEAUS AND MOUNTAINS
  6. TIBETAN PLATEAUS AND MOUNTAINS
IV NORTH CHINA
  7. NORTH CHINA PLAIN
  8. LOESS PLATEAU
  9. HILLS OF SHANTUNG
V CENTRAL MOUNTAIN BLOC
  10. CENTRAL MOUNTAIN BLOC
    g. CH'IN LING
    h. PA AND WU SHAN
    i. HUAI-YANG ARC
VI SOUTH CHINA
  11. SSU-CH'UAN (SZECHWAN) BASIN
  12. CENTRAL LAKES BASIN
    j. T'UNG-T'ING (LIANG-HU) BASIN
    k. PO-YANG (KIANGSI) BASIN
  13. LOWER YANGTZE PLAIN
  14. SOUTHEAST MARITIME HILL LANDS
  15. SOUTHWEST YUN-KUEI PLATEAU
  16. LING-NAN REGION
    m. KUANG-HSI BASIN
    n. HSI CHIANG (CANTON) DELTA
  17. HAI-NAN AND T'AI-WAN ISLANDS

Physiography by A.K.LOBECK

Korea. Nevertheless, in terms of international politics, the Yalu boundary is most significant.

With the exception of that of the Amur and its chief tributary, the Sung-hua (Sungari), China's important drainage systems run toward and through the most productive and populous portions of the country. Of these, the largest and most significant is the Yang-tzu River drainage system, which empties into the East China Sea near Shanghai. The Yang-tzu drainage region contains not only the greatest area of cultivated land in China but also the largest of the population segments. The navigable waters of the Yang-tzu and its tributaries comprise transportation arteries of vast significance to China's economic development. Ocean liners of up to 27-foot draft reach Han-k'ou (Hankow), some 585 miles above its mouth. Small river steamers with up to 9-foot draft negotiate the Yang-tzu gorges to reach 150 miles above Ch'ung-ch'ing (Chungking) in Ssu-ch'uan (Szechwan) province. The Yang-tzu system contains the larger portion of China's potential for hydroelectric development (Figure 5).

Second in size to the Yang-tzu drainage basin, the Huang Ho drainage system is completely different in character. Draining a region of low rainfall and little natural vegetation, the river is too highly silted to be of great service for navigation and in fact contributes little to the country's transportation services. Although providing fresh alluvial silts which enrich some areas of agricultural land in the course of its frequent floods, the Huang Ho all too often plays havoc with farmlands, farm houses, and farm people on the vast plain that it has built. Nevertheless, more than 100 million people derive a precarious livelihood on this plain.

The third largest of the river drainage systems running into productive eastern China is that of the Hsi Chiang (West river) which runs past Kuang-chou (Canton) to empty into the South China Sea west of Hongkong. Deriving its source from the eastern part of the Yün-nan plateau, the Hsi taps a labyrinth of small narrow valleys sandwiched among thousands of hills large and small. Although the water channels of its drainage provide useful transport routes in topography difficult for land travel, its silt-laden floodwaters spread out over no such plains as are found in the lower reaches of the Yang-tzu and the Huang Ho. Only in the delta land around Canton is there a significant area of level plain, although many such deltas would fit into the lower plains of the Huang Ho or of the Yang-tzu.

China's topography

China's topography is extremely complex, as will be evident from the discussion of her geographical regions in subsequent pages. Generally speaking, the larger western and northwestern part of China is occupied by plateau land, the smaller eastern part by low plains and hill land. The plateaus are varied. The southwestern quadrant is occupied largely by high plateaus over 12,000 feet above sea level surmounted by the world's highest mountain chains; the quadrant includes the large Tsaidam basin near its northeastern rim. The northwestern quadrant comprises the Mongolian plateau, of which Outer Mongolia now forms a separate state, and the western desert basins of Dzungaria and Tarim, separated by the great T'ien Shan. The Great Hsing-an mountains border the Mongolian plateau on the east. On the southeast the Yin Shan north of the Huang Ho loop and the Ho-lan Shan west of the loop also form part of its bounds.

East of the Tibetan high plateaus are two plateaus 5,000 to 7,000 feet lower in elevation, separated by an east-west mountain range running out of the high plateaus. This range, the Ch'in Ling (Tsinling), carries the general level of the high plateaus into eastern China. To its north is a loess plateau of about 4,000 feet average elevation. Within the loop of the Huang Ho is the Ordos plain at more or less the same elevation. South of the Ch'in Ling the large, mountain-rimmed Ssu-ch'uan basin intervenes between the Ch'in Ling and the Yün-nan and Kuei-chou (Kweichow) plateaus, which in turn form two general levels averaging 7,000 feet and 4,000 feet respectively. East of these plateaus, the land south of the Yang-tzu breaks up into hilly country with limited areas of level plains. Only the central lake plains and the lower Yang-tzu plain offer large areas of level land south of the Ch'in Ling extensions.

North of the Ch'in Ling and its outliers, the Ta-pieh and Huai-yang, are two great plains separated by the bloc of hills in the former Je-ho province (Jehol) along which the Great Wall runs down to the sea. The southern one, the North China plain, surrounds the Shan-tung hill lands and has a comparatively long coastal fringe. The northeastern one comprises the depositional alluvium of the Liao River and the rolling erosional plain of the Sung-hua (Sungari) River. As the divide between them is so low as to be hardly noticeable, the two are known collectively as the Manchurian plain. Mountain ranges bounding this plain to the north, west, and southeast give it a basin-like situation out of which the Sung-hua valley provides a passage in the northeast, and the narrow delta plain of the Liao provides a restricted sea front in the southwest.

Hang-chou Bay divides China's seacoast into two different segments. South of this bay, the irregular coastline with numerous rocky promontories, islands, and inlets, betrays its hilly hinterland. From Hang-chou Bay northward the coastline is little indented. Its long, low, flat beaches are merely the seaward extensions of the great plains. Shallow water and sand flats extend far out to sea, imperiling navigation, and few ports and harbors are found. However, this seascape is altered by the two peninsular hill lands of Shan-tung and Liao-tung, which provide a number of excellent deep-water harbors.

The components of China's climate

The principal components of China's climate include (1) a vast land mass, (2) a west-Pacific Ocean location, (3) a wide latitudinal range, (4) a characteristic orography, and (5) wind systems resulting from all of these.

China's vast land mass is near a great ocean only along her eastern fringe; most of it lies far inland. No large seas indent the land mass here such as moderate the climates of Europe. The rapid and prolonged heat loss through radiation during the winters brings about the development of an unusually intense and persistent high-pressure atmosphere in the regions of Outer Mongolia and eastern Siberia. Cold, dry air masses from the north and northwest push outward to grip much of China during long winters in the north and northwest and cool even southeastern China as far as the Nan Ling. In contrast, when the direct rays of the sun cross the Equator and reach farther north to their northward limit in the summer solstice, heat absorption exceeds radiation. The rising air brings about exceptionally low pressures in interior western China and inner Asia. The inrushing warm, maritime air masses from the south and southeast take the place of the retreating cold air masses of the dry interior, bringing moisture with them to large areas of eastern China. It is this winter and summer reversal of predominant wind directions that defines a so-called monsoon-type climatic regime.

The monsoon effect in China differs in character from the Indian monsoon in that the winter dry season in China is of considerably longer duration than the summer rainy period, whereas in India the reverse is true. The gradual onset of the summer wind system is in sharp contrast to the pronounced "outburst" of the summer monsoon in India. In China the winter air drift also is more pronounced than the summer one. It is because of this dominance of the winter high-pressure belt and of the great extremes of winter and summer weather conditions that the term "continental" is used in describing the predominant climatic characteristic of China.

To China's west Pacific location must be attributed in large part the direction of the seasonal winds. The southwest Pacific waters, including those of the seas bordering China, supply most of China's moisture. The clockwise winds around the north Pacific high-pressure region during the summer send maritime tropical air laden with moisture into China from the southwest Pacific and the South China Sea. These are reinforced by winds from the Australian high-pressure region. In winter, low-pressure centers in the north Pacific and in northern Australia reinforce the outward movement of the Mongolian cold waves.

The effect of latitude on climate in China is obvious. Middle-latitude China stretches such a long distance north and south that the southernmost part always has tropical or subtropical climatic conditions, while the northernmost territory is cold to cool for much of the year.

Orographical effects on climate are no less significant. In general, four great mountain blocs are climatically significant to China. One is the Himalaya and the associated Tibetan high plateau. The Himalaya blocks the entry of much moisture into interior northwestern China from the south. A second bloc, comprising the Ta-hsüeh Shan (Great Snowy mountains) and other high mountains bordering the eastern section of the Tibetan plateau, creates a similar barrier to Pacific moisture moving farther westward. A third is the Ch'in Ling system which runs west to east, with outliers reaching the lower Yang-tzu plain. In its central stretches the Ch'in Ling is high enough to protect the Ssu-ch'uan basin from the Mongolian cold waves. On the other hand, it prevents the entry of much moisture into north and northwest China and thus forms a clearcut climatic divide between dry, cool north China and moist, warm south China. The fourth mountain bloc of major climatic significance in China is the southeast hill-and-mountain complex. Since the prevailing summer air masses come from the south and southeast, these mountains receive much orographic rainfall. This region is the wettest in mainland China. In northeastern China, the east Manchurian mountains also have significant rain-shadow effects.

Four chief types of air movements are involved in China's weather. These are the monsoon-type movements, convectional movements owing to local heating, the large cyclonic storm circulation, and the smaller but more violent typhoons or hurricanes. In the foregoing pages the origin of the monsoon type of air movements has been described. Some further aspects of China's air movements are worth noting.

The winter winds derive from the movement of the polar continental air mass or polar Siberian air mass. The prevailing summer winds are identified with the tropical and equatorial marine air masses invading China at this season. Beginning with April, the latter enter southwest China from the Bay of Bengal and southern China from the Tongking Gulf. By the beginning of June they have reached their limits in Inner Mongolia and northern Kan-su. Usually by the end of October they have entirely withdrawn from China.

In the regions where rainfall is not complicated by cyclonic and frontal activities the rainfall shows a marked increase with the arrival of the prevailing summer winds. Even the little rainfall received by southern Outer

Mongolia is brought in mainly by the southeast winds, which are fore-runners of midsummer thunderstorms and showers. In northern Mongolia, where the rainfall is higher, the sources of moisture are mainly the Atlantic and the Arctic oceans. Rainfall in Outer Mongolia decreases from north to south.

Rainfall associated with the prevailing summer air movement occurs in connection with orographical lifting on the windward side of mountains, with convectional rise of air currents in the moist air masses, and through frontal lifting in the zone of contact between polar Siberian air and maritime tropical air. This latter generally occurs in connection with the so-called extratropical disturbances or cyclonic storms generated around low-pressure centers. As in North America, the low-pressure centers move from west to east, but the China "lows" are much smaller than their American counterparts. Although all parts of China may feel the influence of these cyclonic storms, the southern part of the central Yang-tzu lake basin appears to be their most important generating area. Their paths travel eastward to the coast and then curve northeastward past Japan. In May and June when the polar front remains quasi-stationary the lows stagnate along the Yang-tzu valley. Along the lower Yang-tzu this results in continuous rains called the *mai-yü* or plum rains.[2] The continuous cloud cover has an important effect in keeping down temperatures, which during the month of June often are not as high as those of north China.

In eastern China the classic geographical boundary zone between north and south follows the Ch'in Ling crestlines and the Huai River of An-hui (Anhwei) province. It appears both as a temperature and a rainfall boundary, marking the southern limit of occasional "steppe years" (years when the total rainfall corresponds to the average annual rainfall of the drier grasslands), so that it is a boundary zone of both rainfall amount and reliability. North of this line only the tropical maritime air mass brings in moisture, whereas south of this line humid equatorial air masses are brought in also from the Indian Ocean and the South China Sea.

Typhoon types of tropical atmospheric disturbances occur primarily on the western sides of oceans, so that China, especially in the south, feels their effects. The sea areas east and southwest of the Philippines are important sources for the typhoons affecting China. As the Mongolian-Siberian high-pressure area gradually weakens and finally disappears, an increasing number of typhoons strike the China coast, and in late summer no part of the coastal area is free from the threat.

The greatest typhoon dangers stem from sea swells and destructive waves, and upon occasion these have caused the loss of thousands of lives in the south China coastal area. Fortunately, after traveling westward only a minority of the typhoons reach the China coast. Most of them be-

2 Known in Japan as *baiu*.

fore reaching the coast recurve toward the northeast. Few penetrate far inland; those that enter southeast China usually recurve to leave the China coast between Shang-hai and the Shan-tung peninsula.

China's soil and vegetation associations

In the Manchurian mountain regions, especially in the north and east where the cool climate reduces evaporation, forest growth is the predominant natural vegetation. Farther south in the loess-land valleys and the north China plain an equal amount of precipitation may support a steppe-grass vegetation because of the higher evaporation rates. Still farther south in the humid part of eastern China the much higher rainfall again supports a forest vegetation. On the other hand, in the high altitudes of the Tibetan plateau and many of the higher mountain lands there is a zonation of vegetation in accordance with precipitation, drainage, and temperature characteristics. Steppe grass may cover the lower slopes up to 7,000 or 8,000 feet if rainfall is low, with a zone of forest following above it. Still higher, the forest may again change to the grass cover of the mountain meadow land. Finally, "tundra" mosses and barren rock landscapes appear.

Each of these vegetation types is associated with soil types. In general, forest soils are less fertile than grassland soils, and temperate forest soils are more suitable for agriculture than either the cold boreal forest soils or the subtropical forest soils.

China's more fertile soils, therefore, are found in the plains of Manchuria and north China. Good soils also are found in much of the Ssu-ch'uan basin, in the loess region, and on the alluvium of the river valleys. On the other hand, some poorly drained alluvial and loessial soils, whether near the coast as in Chiang-su (Kiangsu), or inland as in parts of Shan-tung and An-hui (Anhwei), or in the arid northwest, as in Inner Mongolia, may accumulate harmful salts that inhibit cultivation.

Whatever the original character of the soils and natural vegetation cover, the present situation in both respects has changed greatly in most of the agricultural parts of China owing to the activities of men. Denudation of vegetation cover has left little forest in China. Large remnants are found only in the Manchurian mountains, the hills of Che-chiang (Che-kiang) and Fu-chien (Fukien), and the eastern Tibetan plateau fringes, including scattered parts of western Yün-nan and Ssu-ch'uan. Long centuries of cropping, together with fertilization and irrigation practices, have given special characteristics to the agricultural soils. In large areas, especially in the northwest, cultivation of former steppe-grass slopes has resulted in severe sheet erosion and gully formation. Destruction of vegetation cover in the loess plateau has greatly increased the flood menace on north China's "Yellow plain."

Characteristic vegetation of the arid northwest and far west includes drought-resistant shrubs and tall reeds around salt lakes. Short grass grows in the moister steppe regions, sometimes in scattered clumps and sometimes in thin stands. Taller, denser grass also is to be found south and southeastward from the arid parts of Inner Mongolia, but there is no sharp division.

The loess-earth region of the northwest supports a mixed natural vegetation of thorny shrubs such as the "Chinese date" or jujube, and tall and short grasses. Planted trees thrive in the loess hills where they are protected, as in temple enclosures; planted trees include poplars, pines, occasional cedars, and arbor vitae. On the mountains above the loess-line considerable forest growth may be found.

East of the loess-land the mountains of Shan-tung and Je-ho present mostly eroded grassy slopes, with occasional forest remnants among the barren, stony outcrops. Oaks, elms, chestnuts, maples, coniferous pines, and junipers may be found here in small areas. Grass and jujube move in when the trees are cut down.

All of China south of and including the Ch'in Ling and their extensions eastward once was in forest. At present most of this has·been cut down and the slopes carry a cover of coarse grass. The more inaccessible mountain reaches still support spruces, firs, hemlocks, and Cunninghamia. Characteristic trees in the Ssu-ch'uan basin are pines and cypresses and an imported evergreen broadleaf tree, the banyan. On the karst limestone hills of Kuei-chou and Kuang-hsi (Kwangsi) the tree growth is mainly deciduous, while pines predominate on the leached soils of the other hills. The red-earth area, which includes most of China south of the Yang-tzu, where soil denudation has been rapid, mainly supports immature "horsetail pine" and coarse grasses. In the semitropical and tropical regions, camphors and sweet-gums, citrus, bamboo, palm trees, and a great variety of other tropical trees grow.

In the association of cultivated vegetation with soils, climate is a more important determining factor than the character of the soils, although soil character is an important factor in productivity. Soils in China show a general deficiency in nitrogen, more marked in south China than in north China. Calcareous loess soils generally are of high fertility, and their alluvial derivatives in the Yellow River valley resemble them in fertility. Farther southward higher rainfall and resulting leaching decreases the nitrogen available. The reddish brown-earths of Ssu-ch'uan, on the other hand, are moderately high in fertility.

Generally speaking, north of the Ch'in Ling and the Huai river, the farm soils need nitrogen supplements. On the farms of south China, soils are deficient in nitrogen and phosphorus, while the yellow earths of Kuei-chou and Kuang-hsi also lack potash. Because most farmers cut the stalks and leaves of crops for use as fuel or feed, Chinese soils also lack organic matter in spite of the use of nightsoil and animal manures.

SELECTED GEOGRAPHICAL BIBLIOGRAPHY

1. Chang, Chi-yun. "Climate and Man in China," *Annals of the Association of American Geographers*, March, 1946, pp. 44-73.
2. Cressey, G. B. *The Land of the 500 Million.* New York: McGraw-Hill Book Company, 1955. See also Gherzi, E. *The Meteorology of China.* Macao: Serviço Meteorologico, 1951. Two volumes.
3. Lee, J. S. *The Geology of China.* London: Thomas Murby and Company, 1939.
4. Lee, Shu-ching, and Ngan Han. "Forestry in China," *Unasylva*, November-December, 1948, pp. 304-308.
5. Thorp, James. *The Geography of the Soils of China.* Nanking: National Geological Survey, 1936.
6. Tieh, T. Min. "Soil Erosion in China," *Geographical Review*, October, 1941, pp. 570-90.
7. Tu, Chang-wang, and Sze-sung Hwang. "The Advance and Retreat of the Summer Monsoon," *Bulletin of the American Meteorological Society*, January, 1945, pp. 9-22.
8. United States Army Air Forces, Weather Division. Report No. 890, *Weather and Climate of China*, Parts A, B, and C. Washington: 1945.
9. Walker, Egbert H. "The Plants of China and Their Usefulness to Man," *Smithsonian Institution, Annual Report, 1944*, pp. 325-61. Washington: 1944.

Comments

Cressey's book is the only textbook in English devoted solely to the geography of China. It gives all-around physical and cultural coverage and a good regional treatment. Thorp is the standard book on the soils of China, which are covered competently and not too technically for the general student. The Army Air Forces' study of weather in China has an excellent analysis of China's climates. Parts A and B are the only sections of interest to the general reader, however. Numerous graphs and charts of air movements and rainfall patterns are collected conveniently. Father Gherzi's work is a fine source of data and ideas about China's climate. Volume 2 is a climatological atlas.

Regional studies of China's physical geography are noted in the bibliography for the chapters on China's regional geography. Unfortunately, no English-language atlas is available that gives good topographic coverage for China. These must be sought in Chinese-language atlases. Serviceable maps are found in Goode's, Bartholomew's, and the Oxford atlases.

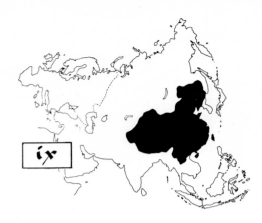

ix

China

AGRICULTURE AND FOOD SUPPLY

CHINA'S CULTURE HAS AN AGRARIAN BASE THAT IN IMPERIAL DAYS was epitomized by the annual plowing ritual performed by the emperor on the marble altar of agriculture at Pei-ching (Peking). Farm people still make sacrifices at local shrines to the God and Goddess of Agriculture, their most significant deities. In the five-rank hierarchy of China's traditional social classes, the farmer occupied second place after the scholar-officials. The thesis that the greatest virtue of the universe is fecundity, in Chinese "sheng," reflected the emphasis upon agriculture.

All cultures and civilizations impress certain of their features upon the landscape. It is not surprising, therefore, that the Chinese landscape clearly reflects the intense agricultural drive of the Chinese people (Figure 31). This is seen in the utilization of virtually every square yard of arable alluvial land in some form of crop production, in the terracing of slopelands for paddy fields in the moist south and for dry crops on the loess plateau, and in the race for a harvest on river beaches or lake beds before the annual flood inundates the land. The fragmentation of the agricultural surface into tiny fields not only is an indication of the great population pressure that necessitates intensive hand tillage, but also of the traditional custom of the equal division of family farms among the sons at a farm-owner's death. Finally, the farm landscape reflects the relative absence of direct land use for animal husbandry and the preponderance of cereal cultivation. Pasture lots are non-existent, although non-arable hill slopes are grazed by plow animals, goats, and some sheep.

Fig. 31 · The intensity of the usage to which agricultural land is put in China is illustrated by the settlement and cultivation patterns along the east bank of the Yang-tzu near Wu-ch'ang in Hu-pei. Almost all land, most of it fertile alluvium, is ultilized for crops. The general area is the Central Yang-tzu plain region. The river is flowing away from the island. Near the lower edge of the photograph the width of the river is about 1.2 miles.

Paralleling the riverbank is a levee constructed to protect the fields from flood; atop it runs a road. Settlements in the area are of the *strassendorf* or shoe-string type and are located on old beach ridges slightly higher than the adjacent farmland. The fields themselves are minute and tend to run, long and narrow, at right angles to both stream and village axis. Most are between 35 and 40 feet wide. Wet-rice and winter wheat are the common crops; some tobacco and cotton also are grown. (*Herold Wiens.*) The photo shows pre-collectivization patterns.

Grazing animals are closely watched by herdboys, for no fences divide fields or property. The fragmentation of farms into numerous scattered plots results in wasteful boundary strips which, together with the practice, especially in the north, of having cemetery plots on family farmland, waste almost 3 per cent of the arable land. Nevertheless, this is made up for in part by planting even the sides of boundary levees with crops such as beans, and cultivation gradually nibbles away the grave mounds.

The Chinese farmer lacks the mechanized farm implements that have enabled American farmers to cultivate huge areas of land with few or no hired hands. As in the case of the early American pioneers, an individual Chinese farmer with crude implements and draft animals can cultivate only a few acres. In the dry-farming north, this physical limitation generally restricts him to cultivating less than 12 acres even where he has more land to use. In the wet-paddy areas of the south, with their traditional cultivation of a more intensive type, the farmer's limited capability may restrict the maximum area of land he can cultivate to three acres or less (Figure 32). However, a large percentage of Chinese farmers lack even draft animals to help them pull the plow, and in some wet-paddy areas the field may be too small for the use of buffalo-drawn plows. In such cases, the farmer's dependence entirely on his own muscular energy further reduces the area that he can cultivate.

The farmer, therefore, must cultivate the crops and adjust his family's diet to foods that yield the maximum number of calories upon the minimum land area. This means cereals and starchy root crops such as sweet potatoes. Livestock are limited to necessary work animals and to others that scavenge farm and household wastes for feed, such as pigs and fowl.

Fig. 32 • The Chinese farmer depends upon animate energy in his farming, sometimes that of water buffalo or oxen; often his own. Here in northern Taiwan in late March a farmer harrows one of his minute fields with the aid of a water buffalo. The bench terraces occupy the former course of a small stream. Notches in the edges of the fields carry the overflow down from one to another. In the right background is the dense subtropical forest that occupies much of the lower highlands of Taiwan, intermixed with bamboo and fern. *(Norton Ginsburg.)*

The result of this intense system of farming is a dense population on the better arable land. This land has become densely filled with a population unable to find enough room for expansion. It is, therefore, a population pressed often by poverty and hunger and susceptible to disease, despair, and early death. Traditional Chinese cultivation has arrived at an impasse. It has in effect created a vicious circle composed of an excessive density of rural population which in turn blocks the raising of agricultural productivity.

The availability and distribution of arable land

Since about 75 per cent of China's gainfully employed population is engaged directly or indirectly in agricultural activities and some 80 per cent of China's population lives in farm villages and small market towns, it is important to know how much agricultural land there is, where it is located, and how it is being used. Unfortunately, statistics for large areas in China are unreliable, especially in the cases of population and land use.

With this reservation, it can be said that only from a quarter to a third of China is humid enough, warm enough, and possessed of good enough soils and gentle enough slopes to be considered of value to agriculture. This compares with about half of the total area of the United States under the same classification. However, the United States has from four to five times as much arable land per capita as China. Utilization presents an equally sorry picture. One Chinese economist in 1948 has quoted an official but undated Chinese estimate of about 200 million acres in 25 provinces under cultivation, or about 10 per cent of the same area's total land surface.[1] Communist sources gave the estimated cultivated acreage in 1932 as 206 million acres and in 1957 as 278 million acres.

If it is assumed that China has 278 million acres under cultivation and a 1957 population of about 643 millions, as claimed by the communist regime, the cultivated land available per person would be only 0.39 acres. Although the communist agricultural program probably will add certain new agricultural land to provide a total of over 300 million acres, this still means only 0.5 acres per person. The intense pressure of population on land is obvious. It is equally obvious that the uneven distribution of land among the people, while creating social problems, is not the fundamental problem. Ownership and an equal distribution of land still mean poverty unless the farmer can produce more food.

Not being able to increase the acreage of land he can cultivate under

[1] D. K. Lieu, *China's Economic Stabilization and Reconstruction* (New Brunswick: Rutgers University Press, 1948), p. 8.

traditional Chinese methods, the farmer must resort to the most intense methods of hand cultivation. The man-hours of labor input per acre of cotton crop in China thus have amounted to five and a half times as much as in the United States. For corn or maize crops, the labor input has been 14 times as much, while for winter wheat, for which United States' mechanization is more thorough, it has risen to 23 times as much per unit of crop land. Productivity per man, therefore, is very low. Yet, in spite of this great labor expenditure, crop yields for cereals other than rice on the average are about the same as they are in the United States. Average yields could be much higher if more effective insect and disease controls and better seed strains were introduced. The addition of commercial fertilizers to the organic fertilizers (such as nightsoil and compost) already in use also would raise productivity. Some progress has taken place.

The obvious question, in the face of the limited area of China's great surface in agricultural use, is why Chinese farmers have not expanded the farm area. Elevation and steep slopes impose fundamental restrictions. If we arbitrarily set 6,500 feet as the upper limit for agricultural enterprise, then 60 per cent of China's land surface is removed from farming considerations. Moreover, a sizable portion of the land below this altitude also is unsuitable because of steep slopes and leached soils, as in south China, or because of aridity, as in much of Hsin-chiang and the Inner Mongolian region.

On the other hand, traditional methods did not concentrate much effort on many slope lands which presumably are usable for fruit, nut, or vine crops. The intensive form of hand labor of Chinese farming limits the area that can be cultivated by an individual. This limited area produces enough for his family's livelihood only if he concentrates on producing high-calorie crops. Each farmer thus has striven to obtain as fertile land as possible, since cereal crops are exacting in their soil demands. Because his energy must be concentrated on this best land, he has neglected poorer land. Moreover, a farmer who would have to depend upon cash for buying food on the market instead of upon his own production would feel highly insecure because of the small surpluses that reach the market and the high prices that often are demanded. Specialization in non-staple crops, therefore, has been avoided if good land could be had for basic food crops. The utilization of slope soils, too, has been limited, casual, and supplementary.

Where is China's cultivated land? If Tibet and Manchuria are not considered, over 97 per cent of China's farm lands are found south of the Great Wall and east of the Tibetan plateau. The addition of the central valley region of Manchuria would bring the percentage close to 99 per cent. In all, there are seven principal regions where the percentage of the land in cultivation is especially high (Maps 9 and 10). In order of size, these are:

(1) The Huang Ho, Huai, and lower Yang-tzu Chiang plains area.
(2) The Ssu-ch'uan basin lowlands.
(3) The central lowlands of Manchuria.
(4) The central lake plains.
(5) The Wei Ho and Fen Ho plains in the loess plateau.
(6) The Hsi Chiang valley and delta.
(7) The Han Chiang valley of Hu-pei province.

It is understandable that the provinces associated with the great river plains rank first. In the provincial divisions of China during the last century, Chiang-su (Kiangsu) ranked first with 52.4 per cent; Shan-tung had 46.5 per cent, Ho-pei 46 per cent, and Ho-nan 37.6 per cent. Although Ssu-ch'uan ranks high in the total acreage of cultivated land, the cultivated land density is only 15 per cent because of its large area, most of which is topographically unsuitable. Hsin-chiang has a density of only 0.5 per cent, not because of rough surface, but because of lack of rainfall and water for irrigation. In terms of the area of cultivated land per person, the drier lands of the north and northwest come first; there is a decrease southward in the area available per person. The following table is representative of the period before World War II.

Province	Cultivated acres per person	Predominant crops grown
Hei-lung-chiang	1.8	wheat, millet
Sui-yüan	1.4	kao-liang, millet
Ho-pei	0.5	wheat, millet, kao-liang
Chiang-su	0.39	rice, wheat
Kuang-tung	0.21	double-cropped rice

These data show great pressure of population upon the land, although in Hei-lung-chiang the real pressure is less. In Sui-yüan and Ho-pei, however, in spite of the greater acreage per person, livelihood may be more precarious than in Kuang-tung because of the greater climatic hazards faced by agriculture.

Agricultural land use

Land use may be divided into two major regional divisions by the Ch'in Ling-Huai River line. The northern realm is the wheat realm, with about 57 per cent of all cultivated

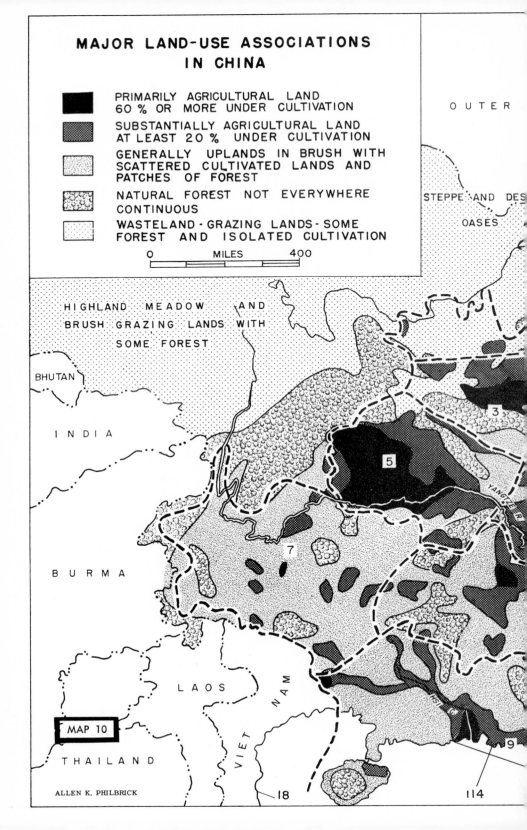

MAJOR LAND-USE ASSOCIATIONS
IN CHINA

- PRIMARILY AGRICULTURAL LAND 60 % OR MORE UNDER CULTIVATION
- SUBSTANTIALLY AGRICULTURAL LAND AT LEAST 20 % UNDER CULTIVATION
- GENERALLY UPLANDS IN BRUSH WITH SCATTERED CULTIVATED LANDS AND PATCHES OF FOREST
- NATURAL FOREST NOT EVERYWHERE CONTINUOUS
- WASTELAND - GRAZING LANDS - SOME FOREST AND ISOLATED CULTIVATION

O   MILES   400

OUTER

STEPPE AND DES

OASES

HIGHLAND MEADOW AND
BRUSH GRAZING LANDS WITH
SOME FOREST

BHUTAN

INDIA

3

5

YANGTZE R.

BURMA

7

LAOS

MAP 10

VIET NAM

HSI

9

THAILAND

ALLEN K. PHILBRICK

18

114

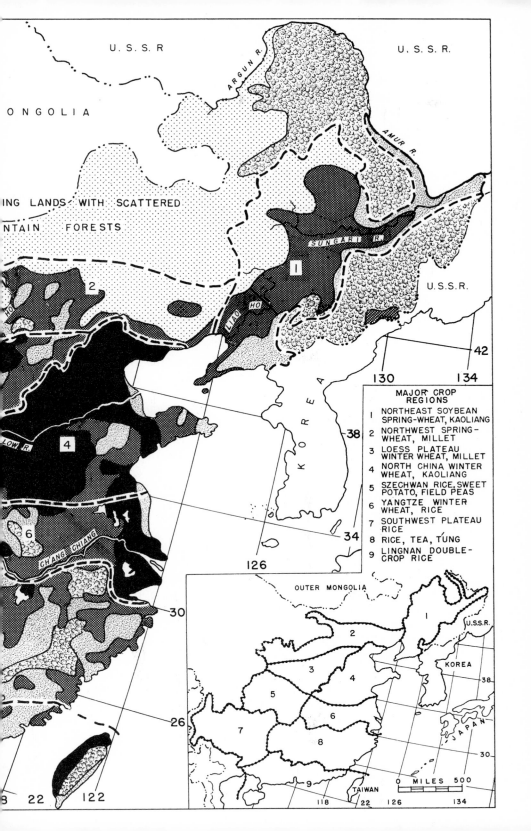

U.S.S.R

ONGOLIA

U.S.S.R.

ARGUN R.

AMUR R.

ING LANDS WITH SCATTERED
NTAIN FORESTS

SUNGARI R.

1

U.S.S.R.

LIAO HO

42

130   134

KOREA

38

HO

2

LOW R.

4

34

126

6

CHANG CHIANG

30

26

30

8   22   122

MAJOR CROP REGIONS

1 NORTHEAST SOYBEAN SPRING-WHEAT, KAOLIANG
2 NORTHWEST SPRING-WHEAT, MILLET
3 LOESS PLATEAU WINTER WHEAT, MILLET
4 NORTH CHINA WINTER WHEAT, KAOLIANG
5 SZECHWAN RICE, SWEET POTATO, FIELD PEAS
6 YANGTZE WINTER WHEAT, RICE
7 SOUTHWEST PLATEAU RICE
8 RICE, TEA, TUNG
9 LINGNAN DOUBLE-CROP RICE

OUTER MONGOLIA

1

U.S.S.R.

2

KOREA

3

4

38

5

JAPAN

6

7

30

8

9

118   22   126   134

TAIWAN

0   MILES   500

land. The southern realm is the rice realm, with about 43 per cent of the cultivated land. Agricultural subregions are shown in the map of land uses (Map 10). The inset at the lower right of the map shows the divisions indicated by the dotted lines on the larger map. These subregions may be characterized briefly under the following corresponding numbers:

(1) *The northeast soybean, spring-wheat, kao-liang region* occupies the drainage basins of the Sungari and Liao rivers of Manchuria. It supports over 40 million people and with less density than other agricultural parts of China, owing to the recency of settlement over the northern two-thirds of the area. Kao-liang (a grain sorghum) is concentrated mainly in the south; soybeans are more prevalent in the north. Spring wheat is found throughout. Subsidiary crops are millet, corn, barley, and some rice along the Korean frontier.

(2) *The spring-wheat millet region* has more land in pastoral use than in cultivation, since it has a steppe climate, and a large part of the area is hilly. Chinese farmers in this Mongolian fringeland gamble against heavy climatic odds in plowing up the short-grass lands and exposing them to wind erosion. Safer cultivation is in the irrigated lands adjacent to the northeastern bend of the Huang Ho. Much of the Great Wall passes through this region, indicating the marginal character of agriculture here. Low yields and low living levels prevail.

(3) *The loess plateau winter-wheat, millet region* has much of the cultivation concentrated in the valleys of the Fen and Wei rivers, although the terraced dry slopes of the loess hills add large areas of crop land. Most of Shan-hsi (Shansi) and Shen-hsi (Shensi) and the southeastern part of Kan-su provinces are included in this region. Millet predominates on the drier slope lands, whereas winter wheat and kao-liang are grown in the valley lowlands. Cotton is a specialty of the warmer Fen and Wei valleys. Although soils are fertile, rainfall is low, erratic, and concentrated. Sheet and gully erosion has damaged much farm land in this region.

(4) *The north China winter-wheat, kao-liang region* takes in all the north China plain in Ho-nan, Ho-pei and Shan-tung provinces, as well as the adjacent Shan-tung hills. This is the most important wheat region. Kao-liang and millet are summer crops along with lesser crops such as corn, soybeans, and sweet potatoes. Cotton and tobacco also are important crops. The largely calcareous soils support a great diversity of crops, including a large variety of vegetables, especially around the cities. The chief hazards facing the dense rural population are flood and drought.

(5) *The Ssu-ch'uan rice, sweet potato, and field-pea region* supports over 62 million people, according to the 1953 communist estimate, the largest provincial population in China. It is the only individual province constituting a crop region. Crop varieties and per-unit yields are among

the greatest in China. An almost year-round growing season is found in the southern valleys. Rice is the dominant summer crop; wheat, rapeseed, and broad beans are important winter crops. Sweet potatoes are an important food, and sugar-cane production here is surpassed in China only by T'ai-wan. Tobacco, t'ung oil, and citrus fruits are produced in large amounts. Irrigated rice terraces are characteristic landscape features.

(6) *The Yang-tzu winter-wheat, rice region* lies south of the Ch'in Ling - Huai river climatic divide, but it is an agricultural transitional zone between north and south China. Most of the region lies north of the Yang-tzu, although in the east it includes a large delta area south of the river. Most of Hu-pei, An-hui, and Chiang-su provinces lie within the region, which contains the most important cotton- and silk-producing parts of the country, providing raw material for China's leading industry, textiles. Rice is the leading crop, but wheat is more prevalent here than in other parts of south China.

(7) In *the southwest plateau rice region* a sparse population is concentrated mainly in a few small lake basins and river valleys. Here, rice and some wheat and broad beans are raised intensively, and the population density reaches 2,600 people per square mile of cropland. Most of the land, however, is in mile-high dissected slopes cultivated sparsely by mountain farmers, many of whom are non-Chinese tribesmen who engage in shifting agriculture and grow corn, barley, and millet. A semitropical climate in the low-lying valleys permits the growth of fruits and vegetables. Most of the region is found in Yün-nan and Kuei-chou provinces.

(8) *The rice, tea, and t'ung region* comprises a wet, semitropical dissected hill land rising in the west, south, and along the Wu-yi range in the east to 5,000 or 6,000 feet. Intensely cultivated rice lands occupy the central parts of the two provinces of Hu-nan and Chiang-hsi as well as the river valleys and deltas of the coastal provinces of Che-chiang and Fu-chien. Tea is grown everywhere in the hill regions, but especially in the eastern sections where Che-chiang and Fu-chien teas have long been famous in the export trade. T'ung-nut trees also are widespread hill crops, with the largest concentrations in the northwest part of Hu-nan.

(9) *The Ling-nan double-crop rice region* is almost tropical in climate, and its year-round growing season permits two crops of rice in succession. The hilly topography restricts the cultivated area mainly to the valleys of the Hsi River and of its tributaries in Kuang-hsi and Kuang-tung and the lowlands of T'ai-wan and Hai-nan. Western T'ai-wan and the Hsi River delta have extremely high population densities. Both are noted for cane-sugar production and for sweet potatoes, while Kuang-tung is a large silk producer. Citrus and tropical fruits, tea, tobacco, and other crops suitable to a hot, wet climate are grown, although soils require heavy fertilization to restore leached-out plant foods.

By far the larger proportion of the cropping systems, of which there
are hundreds for the non-paddy farmlands, contain the following essentials of a rotation system: a shallow-rooted crop, a deep-rooted crop, a
cultivated (vegetable) crop, and a leguminous crop. Since there is no
real animal industry as a specialized aspect of farming, there is little
place in the cropping systems for hay or pasture. By-products of crops,
such as stalks and straw, are used for fuel, as fodder for work animals,
and as raw material for handicraft industries.

Whereas the Chinese farmer, like farmers elsewhere, carries on farm
practices destructive of soil, he has some major conservation achievements to his credit. The maintenance of soil fertility over large areas for
3,000 years is the result of knowledge acquired by the trial-and-error
method. Chinese fertilization is primarily organic, utilizing the natural
wastes of humans and animals alike in a composting process. Characteristically, these wastes are collected in odoriferous pits where they are
thoroughly rotted. When fields are prepared for crops, the mixture is
spread over the fields. Mixed with urine and water, it also is ladled out by
hand around the roots of growing vegetables.

The widespread practice of irrigation, which involves 69 per cent of the
cultivated land of the rice realm and 15 per cent of such land in the wheat
realm, helps replenish the soil with silt from streams and canals except
where wells or ponds are the chief water source. Moreover, terracing,
which adds to the crop area for wet-rice in the south and is practiced also
on dry fields in the loess-plateau region, retards erosion by catching the
run-off. Since 1955 irrigation has expanded considerably.

In his attempt to maximize production, the Chinese farmer characteristically engages in multiple-cropping wherever the growing season permits this practice. In the extreme southern lowlands where a year-round
growing season exists, one paddy crop after another is grown on the same
field with little interruption, and three such crops may come to maturity
within a single year. Where seasonally dependable water is not available
for a second or third paddy crop, dry cereals, such as winter wheat or
barley, or vegetables may be planted as a second crop following summer
rice. This is common in the Yang-tzu valley.

The growing of rice seedlings for the first three weeks in small densely
planted plots permits the plowing, harrowing, and puddling of the larger
fields for the next crop after a harvest of paddy or wheat. After gaining a
head start in the seedbeds, the sprouts are transplanted in well-spaced
rows in the soft mud of the prepared paddy fields.

Where the frost-free season is short, the farmer often resorts to inter-
planting in order to bring a second or third crop to maturity. For instance, a few weeks before the winter-wheat crop is ready for the sickle,
beans may be planted in between the rows of wheat. When the wheat is

cut, the young beans are well under way. Where paddy land is poorly drained and the winter is not warm enough for a second crop of rice, the farmer may heap the soil into ridges that stand dry above the water. A hardy dry cereal or legume crop may then be planted on the ridges within the same 12-month period as the paddy crop. By the above various techniques of multiple-cropping, the Chinese farmer has managed to harvest a large yield of food from his small area of farm land, although his man-hour productivity may be low.

China has more land in grass than in cultivated crops. Large areas of short-grass ranges are to be found in the northwestern provinces of Ch'ing-hai (Tsinghai), Hsin-chiang, Kan-su, Shen-hsi, and Shan-hsi, and the Mongolian fringelands (Figure 33). In the humid south the hills are covered mainly by a coarse type of subtropical grass rather than by forest. Owing to their high silica content the southern grasses are rather unpalatable to animals, but research has shown that it is possible to produce abundant forage crops in south China. Grazing will continue to be a minor aspect of the southern rural economy, however, until the large-scale introduction (from other parts of the world) of new grasses suitable to the south China soils and climates.

In spite of the small part that animal food plays in the Chinese diet,

Fig. 33 • Camels graze on the short grass of northwest China near Lan-chou, Kan-su. These are the two-humped Bactrian camel, used widely in Asia. It is not uncommon to see caravans of these beasts on the outskirts of Peking to which they come eastward across the Gobi. (*Wellington D. Jones.*)

there are large numbers of domestic animals and fowl. Horses are found mainly in north China and southwest China; donkeys and mules chiefly in north China. Water buffaloes are characteristic mainly of the warm lands; the vast majority are in and south of the Yang-tzu valley. Sheep and goats are found principally in north China. Chickens are raised everywhere, but ducks and geese are concentrated mainly in the southern provinces, although substantial numbers also are found in the north China plain.

Food yields per animal in China are relatively low. Body weights are low for all types of animals compared with corresponding domestic animals in Occidental countries, because animals are prevented from competing for food with human beings, and grains are used sparingly as feed. Winter is especially hard on animals in the north, since virtually no natural forage is available. The fertility of hens also is low, and since the farmer sells most of his eggs, they figure little in his diet. In the period 1933-1937, however, eggs and egg products ranked third in value in China's agricultural exports.

The Chinese diet

Although the Chinese eat the flesh of many animals, they, like the Japanese, appear to be unaccustomed to dairy products, which commonly are used only in the pastoral realms of the Tibetans and Mongols. Butter and cheese are absent from the diet of the ordinary Chinese, and milk is considered a tonic for the sick. Only in the cities have a few Chinese acquired a taste for milk and milk products.

The Chinese diet varies from region to region, but 85 to 95 per cent of the calories in it are derived from cereals, and 5 to 10 per cent from starchy tubers. By Occidental standards, proteins are likely to be deficient or less digestible. Vitamins A and D also tend to fall short of Occidental standards. Moreover, the per-capita calorie intake for China averaged only about 2,534 in 1937 as compared with 3,300 for the United States in 1953. (Japan's in 1953 was only 2,020). This is attributable partly to differences in body size, although lower protein standards in turn contribute to smaller body size, especially in south China. Since most food is consumed locally, the kinds of local agricultural products strongly influence local diets, and there is not the uniformity generally prevalent in a country such as the United States where products of distant regions are readily available.

Rice acreage in China amounts to only 21 per cent of the crop-producing land. In provinces north of the Yang-tzu valley only 2 per cent of the cultivated land is used for rice, as compared with 42 per cent of such land used for rice in the south. Rice in the Chinese diet varies largely with the percentage of the local crop in rice. Thus, the yearly per-capita consumption in Chiang-su before the second World War was about 271 pounds of rice; in Hu-nan it was 458 pounds; and in provinces of north China from zero to only 77 pounds. In most of rural north China the leading element in diet is represented by millets and kao-liang, followed by such crops as wheat, maize, barley, and oats.

Farm and household handicrafts

The agricultural process varies with different crop systems and different geographical regions, but common to all are periods of intense activity when work in the fields is carried on from dawn to dusk. These periods are followed by slack seasons while the plants grow and mature or while the fields are dormant during the winter season. In the aggregate, the slack periods are the equivalent of several months of idle time each year. It has been estimated that in the pre-Communist economy the idle manpower during these periods for all China was equal to the full-time unemployment of 55 million people between the ages of 15 and 54. Only occasional outlets have existed in productive enterprises to supplement inadequate farm incomes. These outlets had been in the form of home industries of the handicraft type. In much of mainland China today, commune-organized handicraft work has taken their place.

There are numerous types of handicrafts catering to the ordinary needs of the people. Spinning and weaving, fiber working, basketry, food processing, brewing, paper making, tanning, quarrying and mining, pottery making, and all types of service and construction activities are included in such occupations. For the most part, raw materials must be available locally, except in the cotton textile handicrafts where yarn may be transported long distances.

As in much of Asia, private handicrafts and home industries perform important functions of an economic and social character, but many rural industries have declined rapidly or even disappeared owing to the competition of cheaper imports or the development of large-scale manufactures before World War II. This has not only deprived many poor farmers of needed supplementary earnings, but also has made them as a whole more dependent upon a money economy. The latter in turn has resulted in the extension of commercial acreages, thereby tying the farmer to the price vacillations and insecurities of the commercial world.

> ## Commercial farming and
> ## food supply

Chinese farming, therefore, has not been entirely subsistence or self-sufficient, as is often thought. Farm products in reality have constituted important items of commerce. Buck found that agricultural products sold amounted to 53 per cent by value of total production. For north China (exclusive of Manchuria) the amount was a little over 40 per cent, while for the lower Yang-tzu plain it was more than 60 per cent of the total. In north China, farmers ate millet and sold their wheat.

No definitive conclusions may be drawn on the subject of food supply and consumption until more accurate population and agricultural statistics are gathered. That minimum demand has nearly been met by the native supply, however, is indicated by the small net annual imports of principal foods in the period 1934-38 (in metric tons):

Milled rice equivalents	558,000
Wheat and flour, in wheat equivalents	317,000
Sugar	186,000[2]

In addition, there was an annual export during this period of 130,000 metric tons of eggs and 200,000 metric tons of edible vegetable oils. Probable food shortages are indicated by the annual food-production figures which had shown no increase over several decades, although the population may be assumed to have increased at a rate of several millions per year. However, exact data about food production in China are not available. Estimates for average annual production between 1931-37 placed it at about 142 million tons. Minimum food requirements for a population of 450 million people was estimated at 141 million tons.

Communist estimates give production in 1949 as 112.5 million tons, with tremendous increase rates thereafter to 160 million tons in 1952 and with convenient 5-million ton leaps annually during the next two years to a record 170 million tons in 1954. Official figures for 1955 and 1956 "grain" output were 184 million tons and 194.5 million tons respectively. "Grains" included soybeans and potatoes, so these figures may not be comparable with pre-communist statistics. If the official population estimate of about 582 million people in 1953 be accepted, the minimum food requirement for 1954 on the basis of the 1931-37 standard would have been 188 million tons. Thus, it would appear that the food situation was no better than in the 1930's, in spite of the reported great increase in food production. In fact, in 1954, the communist *Ta Kung Pao* stated that 150 million farmers were suffering food shortages. Moreover, the reported

[2] Exclusive of exports from Formosa, which then belonged to Japan.

figures for steady food production increases appear highly dubious, particularly for 1954 when the Peking government admitted that the worst flood in a century had inundated 10 per cent of the nation's entire crop land. In 1959 the official communist estimate of 1958 output was a fantastic 525 million tons, but it later was revised downward to 270 million, still an impressive gain. Continued food rationing, however, appeared to belie even this statistic.

The communist transformation of agriculture [3]

The Chinese communists contend that the "productive potentials" of agriculture are stifled by the traditional organization of Chinese agriculture based upon individual ownership of land. Transformation of the traditional system, therefore, is viewed as necessary in the "liberation of the productive potentials of agriculture." According to Mao Tse-tung, the Chinese villages have to undergo two revolutions to achieve this. The goal of the first revolution is to "smash the feudal production relations," meaning the destruction of the landlord class and the redistribution of landholdings. The goal of the second revolution is "the socialist transformation of agriculture," meaning the change from the production relations of individual ownership and economy to those of collective ownership and economy.

Since the goal of the first revolution appealed to the peasants' land hunger and appeared to resemble historical land reform revolutions, it had wide support among the poorer peasants. They were unaware that the first revolution was intended merely to prepare the way for the second revolution which was designed to destroy their individual ownership and control over land. The first revolution was quickly achieved, therefore. The second has met with much resistance.

The Chinese communists learned from the Russian experience in which the abruptness of the Russian peasant liquidation and collectivization measures shocked the Russian peasants and brought farm chaos and heavy losses in livestock and production. The Chinese communists, therefore, adopted a more gradual program, introducing preparatory phases to condition the peasants to "getting organized." The first phase in the form of temporary and seasonal "mutual aid teams" was not so different from the rural cooperative societies of traditional China, except that communist cadres did the organizing. Stage Two was the organization of perennial mutual aid teams. Stage Three was the formation of the agricultural producer cooperatives.

[3] For a detailed analysis see: American Consulate General, Hong Kong, *Current Background*, No. 373, January 20, 1956.

All of these were started in 1951 but were not fully underway until 1952. By 1954 there were almost 10 million mutual aid teams comprising 58 per cent of all peasant households. However, the cooperativization movement met with increasing resistance. Nevertheless, the communists decided to press forward and set 1958 as the goal for basic completion of the program. The speed in carrying out the program plus a series of natural disasters in 1954 followed by famine conditions in 1955 brought, in the words of the State Council, "misgivings and misunderstanding about cooperativization." Confusion was evident in the widespread dissolution of cooperatives by regional communist leadership. The Minister of Agriculture, in defending the program, denounced a noncommunist member of the People's Political Congress and others who "had repeated such absurd views as 'the peasants are living in hell'." The program then was pushed so successfully that at the end of 1956 the cooperative stage was completed and superseded by collectivization.

While under the mutual aid team system the peasant retained direct ownership and control of his land and its production; in the cooperative the land is entered as a share of investment so as to make unified operation possible. The peasant retained nominal ownership but was made to relinquish direct control over his land. He receives dividends from the production according to the amount of land and capital equipment he contributed. This stage, therefore, is considered semi-Socialist in character.

The final stage transforms these relatively small-sized cooperatives into large agricultural collectives wherein land sales are banned, the land becomes the common property of the collective, and there is a gradual reduction of the dividends which may then be proportional to the labor contribution of the individual peasant. This final collectivization phase was scheduled to be completed in the spring of 1961; but by the end of 1956, 92 per cent of China's 110 million peasant householders were reported on collective farms, indicating a startlingly rapid completion of the collectivization program. The completion of this phase means that the traditional Chinese farm landscapes of tiny fields with numerous boundary strips will disappear from the plains of China and will be preserved only in the terraced slopelands.

Associated with the collectivization program is the so-called technical reform of agriculture, i.e., the introduction of large-sized machinery and the development of general mechanization. Since this technical reform is a matter of industrial development rather than of organizational effort, it cannot be achieved so readily. Moreover, haste in this program may result in such bad planning as that in which the central government at

Peking initially approved the manufacture of 5 million double-wheeled, double-bladed plows, only to have to make successive reductions in this order and to suspend production after the manufacture of 1.5 million plows. About one million of these were rusting in disuse in 1956 because peasants refused to buy them. The plows were found too heavy for single animals to pull or for a single man to handle.

In 1955, there were only some 100 "mechanized farms." There also were 2,310 state farms equipped with "new animal-drawn plows." In 1956, in Manchuria which probably accounted for a large percentage of the mechanization, there were only 19 tractor stations with a total of 659 tractors. This means approximately one tractor for each 52,000 acres of crop land in Manchuria, as compared with the United States nation-wide average of about one tractor for each 18 acres of cultivated land (assuming that the farms having tractors were limited to one each). The beginning of "full development" is projected during Communist China's Third Five-Year Plan (1963-67), with "basic completion" of whatever the plans envisage in mechanization during the Fourth or Fifth Five-Year Plans.

In another technical aspect of agricultural transformation, irrigation, much has been done. It is asserted that 17.2 million acres of farm land were newly brought under irrigation during the First Five-Year Plan to provide China with 75 million acres of irrigated land. This is said to be a quarter of China's crop area, so that the China mainland's crop area in 1956 must have been about 300 million acres. How much water the newly irrigated land is supplied per season, however, is not revealed. Some of this irrigation may be very limited. Much of it is derived from wells. During 1956 it is reported that 900,000 wells were sunk in the north China provinces of Ho-pei, Ho-nan, and Shan-tung. The *Peking People's Daily* on March 13, 1956 also reported plans for building a major canal joining the Yang-tzu River's chief tributary, the Han, with the Huang Ho near Cheng-chou. The route presumably would run through the Nan-yang gap between the Ch'in-Ling and Ta-pieh mountains in western Ho-nan. This canal would provide Han River water to irrigate the Huang and Huai river plains.

The incorporation of grasslands of the less humid Mongolian fringe-lands into the cultivated area has been made possible by the use of tractors and modern implements. In 1956, for instance, some 1.5 million acres of new land were plowed in Inner Mongolia, while 370,000 acres of new land were plowed in Hei-lung-chiang. There is danger of eolian erosion in plowing up these areas, but the Chinese communists may be taking a calculated risk, like the Russians in plowing up the steppes of Kazakhstan.

| Marine food production

Although China's seacoast is relatively short compared with her huge area (only 4,000 miles, compared with Japan's 16,000 miles), her coastal waters and numerous inland waters provide important fishing grounds as yet only partially developed. Numerous varieties of fish, from salmon in the northern streams to tuna in the southern seas, live in abundance in these waters. Shen estimates that China's fishing areas cover more than 186,000 square miles of rivers and lakes and 414,000 square miles of waters above the continental shelf.[4] In addition, there are thousands of fish ponds. Assuming an average yield of 25 metric tons per year on each square mile of water over the continental shelf, a reasonable production goal, the possible yield in marine products from China's sea waters may be estimated at over 10 million metric tons. Before 1937, however, the annual production of China's fisheries was estimated at only 1.36 million metric tons, of which two-thirds were marine and one-third were fresh-water fish. The 1956 catch was estimated at 2.6 million tons. It is obvious that a large potential addition to China's food supplies exists in the development of fisheries.

China's fisheries production nevertheless gave her fourth rank in the prewar world, and fish consumption provides an important nutritive element in meat-poor China. Fishing operations before 1937 directly or indirectly involved the employment of about one million people, of whom about 600,000 were fishermen.

China's fishing fleet comprises mainly nonmotorized sailing junks with capacities averaging only 5 to 10 tons each. Before 1937 an estimated 63,000 fishing junks sailed out of Chinese ports, mostly from 34 chief centers. Probably a smaller number were in operation after the second World War owing to the heavy destruction of junks during the preceding eight years of war in China. More than two-thirds of the junks operated in the waters south of Shang-hai. Fishing traditionally has been most active in southern coastal waters where ports are numerous (Figure 34).

Chinese mainland fisheries are lacking in new-type equipment and motorized craft. In 1951 only about 170 fishing vessels in communist China were motorized, as contrasted with over 1,500 in T'ai-wan fishing operations. T'ai-wan also had 7,685 nonmotorized fishing junks. Hongkong, 60 per cent of whose fish production formerly was marketed in mainland China, in 1958 had a fishing fleet of over 7,000 vessels, mostly sailing junks.

Fish culture in ponds is a significant farm sideline. The lower five provinces of the Yang-tzu drainage system and the Che-chiang and Kuang-tung lowlands are the most important producing areas. In 1958 the fresh

---

[4] T. H. Shen, *Agricultural Resources of China* (Ithaca: Cornell University Press, 1951), pp. 300-304.

Fig. 34 • Wholesale fish market in Hongkong. Fish are an indispensable part of the Chinese diet in southern China, and thousands of junks based at innumerable south Chinese ports scour coastal waters for fish of all kinds. Markets, however, are usually in larger coastal cities, especially Canton and Hongkong in the far south. In Hongkong, fish in baskets are carried in from the wharves, bought by wholesalers (at fixed ranges of prices in Hongkong), and dumped into huge vats before being carried into retail market areas. Weaving baskets is an important handicraft industry in some nearby villages. *(Norton Ginsburg.)*

water fish-breeding areas of China were reported to cover 4,940,000 acres. From them the 1956 fish-catch was 850,000 metric tons. By intensified breeding measures it was hoped to raise this by 1958 to 2,500,000 tons. An additional 11,560,000 acres were believed suitable for this use.

That there is no lack of demand is indicated by the fact that before 1937 China annually imported aquatic products valued at (United States dollars) $8,000,000. The demand for fish is so keen that after the communist prohibition of fish imports from Hongkong and Macao in 1950 the smuggling of fish into China along the coasts of a few districts in the Hsi River delta was estimated at over 50 metric tons daily. A limiting factor on the expansion of the fisheries is the lack of refrigeration facilities. Fresh fish are consumed within only a few miles of where they are landed, so that in the case of salt-water fish, consumption is restricted to a narrow band along the coast. Only about one-tenth of the total catch is processed.

SELECTED GEOGRAPHICAL BIBLIOGRAPHY

1. Adolph, W. H. "The Protein Problem of China," *Science,* July 7, 1944, pp. 1-4.
2. Baker, O. E. "Land and Food in China," *Far Eastern Review,* March, 1928, pp. 121-125.
3. Buck, J. L. *Chinese Farm Economy.* Shanghai: Commercial Press, 1930.
4. ———. *Land Utilization in China* (3 vols.). Chicago: University of Chicago Press, 1937.
5. Chao Kuo-chün. "Current Agrarian Reform Policies in Communist China," *Annals of the American Academy of Political and Social Science,* September, 1951, pp. 113-123.
6. Dawson, Owen L. "China's Food Problem," *Foreign Agriculture,* May, 1944, pp. 99-109.
7. Gourou, Pierre. "Notes on China's Unused Uplands," *Pacific Affairs,* September, 1948, pp. 227-238.
8. Lee, Shu-ching. "The Pattern of Land Utilization and Possible Expansion of Cultivated Area in China," *Journal of Land and Public Utility Economics,* May, 1947, pp. 142-152.
9. Moyer, Raymond T. "China's Agricultural Improvement Program," *Foreign Agriculture,* October, 1947, pp. 130-140.
10. Nuttonson, M. Y. *Ecological Crop Geography of China and Its Agroclimatic Analogues in North America.* Washington, D.C.: American Institute of Crop Ecology, 1947.
11. Rossiter, Fred J. "Agriculture in China," *Foreign Agriculture,* October, 1939, pp. 431-498.
12. Shen, T. H. *Agricultural Resources of China.* Ithaca: Cornell University Press, 1951.
13. Trewartha, Glenn T. "Ratio Maps of China's Farms and Crops," *Geographical Review,* January, 1938, pp. 102-111.

14. Tsou, P. W. "Modernization of Chinese Agriculture," *Journal of Farm Economics,* August, 1946, pp. 773-790.
15. Winfield, Gerald. *China, the Land and the People.* New York: William Sloane, 1948.

Comments

Buck's *Land Utilization in China* is the most comprehensive work on agricultural land use in China and is the standard reference work in this field. Volume 1 comprises statistics; Volume 2, the atlas of maps showing crop and other distributions. Volume 3 is a text accompanying both. His *Chinese Farm Economy* is of greater interest to the general reader and gives an intimate statistical account of the economic aspects of the Chinese farmer's life, diet, expenditures, and poverty. Shen presents a rather cut and dried description of China's crop agriculture, animal husbandry, fisheries and general resources, with a good many up-to-date figures, but relying mainly on Buck's work or similar sources. Winfield's study has an excellent chapter describing the farm cycle and the occupational diseases of the Chinese farmers. Gourou points out some possible uses for presently unused slopelands. For the reader who wishes to know about aspects of land reform in Nationalist and Communist China, the articles by Tsou, Moyer, and Chao are worth consulting.

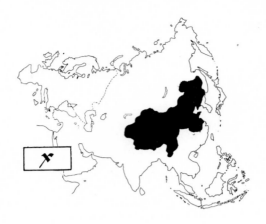

China

THE NORTH AND FAR WEST

THE REGIONS SHOWN ON THE PHYSIOGRAPHIC DIAGRAM OF CHINA
(Map 9) are generalized from divisions devised by Frederick Hung. The
complexity of China's geography is illustrated by the fact that Hung has
divided China into 34 regions subdivided into 145 subregions. For convenience these have been modified to encompass six major divisions divided into 16 regions, under which further subdivisions may be described.
The six divisions are (1) Northeastern China, (2) Northwestern China,
(3) the Tibetan High Plateaus, (4) North China, (5) the Central Mountain Bloc, and (6) South China.

In general, *Northeastern China* is set apart by its large agricultural
plains, its northern frontier location, its strategic political situation as an
international crossroads, and by its more advanced industrial development. *Northwestern China* is characterized by its aridity, its large desert
basins, an extremely continental climate, a sparse population, its oil potential, oasis agriculture surrounded by nomad pastoralism, and predominantly Mongol and Turkic ethnic groups. The *Tibetan High Plateaus*
are marked off by high altitude and dry rarified atmosphere, a boreal-like
climate in southerly latitudes, a long identification of Lamaism with the
Tibetan state, and a sparse population of Tibetan inhabitants. *North
China* specializes in nonirrigated dry-farming, with wheat, kao-liang,

190

millet, and soybeans as chief crops. Horses, donkeys and oxen are used as draft animals, and carts and wagons are the important means of transport. The language is uniformly the "Mandarin" tongue now adopted as *kuo-yü,* or the "national speech."

By contrast, *South China* specializes in irrigated rice and sweet potatoes, with the water buffalo the characteristic field animal. River boats (junks and sampans), pack animals, and human carriers provide the traditional transport for the area. The south also shows important linguistic and dialectical differences, especially in the southeast and southwest where local cultural differences also become prominent. The *Central Mountain Bloc* marks the climatic divide between subhumid, cool North China and humid, warm South China; it is a transition zone in climate and land use. It also acts as an important barrier to communication between Ssu-ch'uan and northern and eastern China.

Northeastern China

The Western name for northeastern China is Manchuria, but it has long ceased to be the land of the Manchu. This region comprises a large central plain bordered by mountains to the west, north, and east. The Great Hsing-an mountains on the west are part of the Mongolian fringe lands. The Lesser Hsing-an to the north are on the Siberian frontier, while the east Manchurian hills form a common border with Korea.

Northeastern China (*tung-pei,* the "northeast") is the land of promise for the Chinese. It has a large productive agricultural base in its central plains. Population densities and pressures are low as compared with other parts of China. The movement of Chinese settlers into the northern half of Manchuria has been relatively recent, except in the Liao River valley, because the last dynasty of China, the Manchu, tried to bar Chinese from its homeland during the earlier part of its reign. Today, the less than one million Manchu not only have lost their cultural heritage, but have been submerged by the nearly 50 million Chinese who have swarmed into Manchuria in search of farmland. There may be sufficient farmland on the Manchurian plains for nearly double this number before densities reach the marginal levels of the north China plain. Moreover, soils are relatively fertile.

Although the northeastern provinces have the disadvantages of long, cold, continental winters, the climate of the Liao plain is not much different from that of North Dakota, and the climate of the Sung-hua plain is similar to that of Saskatchewan, Canada. The Manchurian plains are China's prairies. The growing season is long enough for one crop to mature even in the far north, while rainfall is adequate for dry-farming.

This rainfall, which is over 28 inches in the south, diminishes northwestward, so that before the Great Hsing-an mountains are reached, it amounts to less than 15 inches, and farming is no longer an important activity. Grazing of sheep and other livestock takes its place. In the southern part of the plains, diversified crops are produced with the emphasis on kaoliang, millet, soybeans, corn, and wheat, and considerable surpluses of these crops are exported. In the more restricted farming of the north, wheat and soybeans are most prominent.

The great expanses of plain are well adapted to mechanized farming. The Chinese communists in 1956 had most of their large "state farms" (averaging about 8,500 acres each) in this area, but only about 1 per cent of the cultivated area of Northeastern China was in such mechanized farms.

Manchuria's northern and eastern mountains also provide the Chinese with one of the more important timber stands in nearly denuded China. The best forests are in the central parts of the east Manchurian hills. The Hsing-an mountains have smaller, scrubbier trees because of the longer winters and shorter growing seasons. In the east Manchurian hills the Sung-hua and Yalu rivers provide important logging streams. Moreover, the higher rainfall in these mountains also furnishes the raw material of water power, and hydroelectric plants developed by the Japanese during their occupation of Manchuria provide much of the electric power for the northeast.

Northeastern China also contains China's greatest industrial complex, based in large part on substantial mineral resources. Some 60 per cent of China's iron-ore reserves are found in southern Manchuria, as well as huge reserves of magnesite and aluminum ores. Although only a small percentage of China's coal is found in the region, the actual tonnage of reserves in southern Manchuria is very large. Thus the foundations for both heavy- and light-metals industries exist (Figure 35). The occurrence in close proximity to each other of fuel and raw materials further strengthens industrial potentials.

Another advantage of northeastern China is its excellent network of railroads. However, highways are poor, the dirt-surfaced roads acting mainly as feeders for the railroads. The rail net has half of China's rail mileage. Through-connections tie the network to the railroads of Korea and Siberia, as well as to China south of the Great Wall. The main southern line, the former South Manchurian railroad, terminates at two excellent ports in the mountainous Liao-tung peninsula: Lü-shun (Port Arthur), a naval port at the extreme end; and Ta-lien (Dairen), a fine commercial harbor 20 miles northeast of Lü-shun. A railroad leading from Harbin in the heart of the Sung-hua plain to the north Korean port of Najin (formerly Rashin) provides a nearby maritime exit for the prod-

Fig. 35 • Cooling towers at the An-shan steel works in southern Manchuria. These towers were modeled after German designs by the Japanese who built them. Manchurian steel production by 1952 is reported to have exceeded the midwar peak production after severe deterioration due to fighting, neglect, and Russian withdrawals of tools and machinery in 1946. *(Lt. Col. David R. Longacre.)*

ucts of the north. Moreover, the Sung-hua is navigable by large steamers as far as Harbin, so that during the summer half-year, water transport is available for trade northward with the Soviet Far East.

Northeast China may be characterized also as a strategic crossroads for northeastern Asia. Its key international importance is found both in its situation as a Chinese spearhead surrounded on three sides by the territory of foreign countries, and in its historical situation as the object of rival imperialisms. Because of the southerly location of the Russian port of Vladivostok compared with the northern bulge of Manchuria, the so-called Chinese Eastern railroad through Harbin, connecting the Trans-Siberian railroad with Vladivostok, is 300 miles shorter than the all-Russian route beyond the Amur River. Russian interest in this line, therefore, always has been extremely keen. Strategic interest in the all-year, ice-free port of Ta-lien also has led to Russian interest in this railway, since for several months of winter Vladivostok harbor is only with difficulty kept free of ice by ice-breakers. Japanese interest in Manchuria was motivated not only by her desire for Manchurian food and industrial resources and for a continental empire, but also by her desire to use it as a counterbalance to any strategic threat that Russia might apply against Japan. Moreover, the key command that the naval port of Lü-shun exercises over sea entry to the Gulf of Chih-li (Po Hai), added to Lü-shun's nearness to the west-coast ports of Korea and to Shan-tung, makes the Liao-tung peninsula of utmost military value to its possessor.

Finally, northeastern China is the meeting ground of many major cultures. During earlier times Manchu, Mongol, Korean, and Chinese groups and cultures struggled for dominance in various sectors of Manchuria. The Mongols had easy access, for the Great Hsing-an mountains are significant barriers to communications with Mongolia only in their northern and central reaches. In the south they change to rolling steppes that provide easy routes of travel and invasion between the Manchurian plains and the Mongolian plateau. In more recent times Russian and Japanese cultural influences have been most marked. Russian influence is evident especially at Harbin, the most Russianized city of China. Japanese cultural influences have become weaker with the postwar repatriation of most Japanese. The Japanese heritage is manifested mainly in the economic and industrial development that took place under Japanese control, and this reflects more Occidental than Oriental cultural diffusion. The Korean cultural intrusion is noticeable mainly in several districts in eastern Manchuria near the northern Korean frontier in which Koreans represent over two-thirds of the population. The western fringes of Manchuria, especially the steppes of the northwest and the western part of the Liao drainage basin, are part of the Mongol culture region.

Northwestern China

The *Mongolian fringelands,* the first great region of northwestern China to be discussed, are part of Greater Mongolia. They include the Inner Mongolia steppes and deserts, the southern and western parts of the Great Hsing-an mountains, the Mongolian border mountains on the south, and the Ordos steppes and desert. The great Gobi spans both Outer and Inner Mongolia. In most of this area economic activity is confined mainly to livestock herding by Mongols. Although politically Outer Mongolia is separated from the Mongolian fringelands, the entire southern boundary of the Mongolian Peoples Republic of Outer Mongolia was still undefined in 1958. Culturally, the differentiation of the Mongols in the fringelands from those in Outer Mongolia is one of tribal groupings and dialects, with each occupying traditional pasture lands. A further differentiation may be made on the basis of the predominant Soviet Russian interest and control in Outer Mongolia as contrasted with the predominant Chinese interest and control in the Mongolian fringelands. These fringelands, therefore, may be characterized as "Chinese Mongolia."

"Chinese Mongolia" is a cultural and environmental transition zone, confined mainly to the eastern part of the fringelands, where climate and water make dry farming possible and the grasses are at their best. On the one hand, the felt tents of the horse-riding Mongols form small round domes over thin grasslands dotted with large flocks of sheep or goats and smaller herds of horses, cattle, and camels. On the other hand, in the east and southeast where the rainfall rises to 12 inches or more, wretched adobe-type hovels at infrequent intervals once indicated dwellings of poverty-stricken Chinese farmers who have been forced by land hunger in China proper to gamble against odds in this agricultural pioneer zone. Westward of the great northern bend of the Huang Ho, even grasses in most areas fail to find enough water; only a scrubby vegetation of drought-resistant weeds and shrubs interrupts vast reaches of sand dunes and barren flats. The desert regime is within as well as without the great northern Huang Ho bend, for this bend encloses the great Ordos, a desert a thousand feet below the elevation of the Mongolian plateau to the north and west (Figure 36). Here along the northern and western reaches of the river are the first irrigated oases of the Mongolian fringelands. They constitute rather dense Chinese population enclaves in

Fig. 36 • The Ordos is a great middle-latitude, rocky desert. Through it wend camel caravans like this one, stopping at the widely spaced oases where Chinese farmers have attempted to transfer Chinese agriculture to a hostile environment. *(Wellington D. Jones.)*

Mongol-land, where close-packed villages stand surrounded by fields of grain. Because of the long, dry, and extremely cold winters, crops are not planted here in fall. Spring wheat and drought-resistant millets are the main crops in this region, although there is considerable variety in the irrigated crops.

The Mongolian fringelands are the "dust bowl" of China. In most of the vast area the less than five inches of precipitation do not provide enough water for vegetation to hold down the soil before the gale-strength winds of the dry winters. Blowing out of the north and north-west, these winds blast rolling clouds of dust out of the ground and carry them for distances up to several hundred miles. Over many millenia this dust has settled in a heavy mantle over the loess plateau and parts of the north China plain, smoothing over rough topography and choking valley bottoms. The removal of virtually all the soil in many areas such as the Ordos has left only a barren desert "pavement" covered in large patches with coarse sands and pebbles. Of no value to man or beast, these desolate wastes merely create obstacles to communication and economic development.

The "dust bowl" is not restricted to the desert areas, however, nor is it limited to natural causes. In the pioneer fringe of dry farming, the temptation is ever to plow up good grassland for the planting of cereals. Without the anchoring effect of grass roots, soil begins to drift and blow. In a short time the steppe becomes a desert. Not only is farming no longer possible, but the old grass cover is slow to reestablish itself after the destruction of its seed stock, so that the thin grass patches are now useful only for nomadic grazing. Similar effects come about through long periods of drought. Chinese farming shrinks back toward China proper, and the nomad herds follow.

Historically, the region has been a zone of conflict between the nomad Mongols and the sedentary Chinese. The dessication of grasslands often has driven the nomads into China proper for plunder. To protect themselves, the ancient Chinese constructed the Great Wall that "marks the desert from the sown." In the last century, however, the sedentary farmers have gradually pushed back the nomads and plowed up the dry sod more than a hundred miles beyond the Great Wall in the eastern sectors of the Mongolian fringelands. Here, limits have been reached for traditional Chinese dry-farming methods. The efficiency of mechanized farming may extend these limits, but it also may bring disaster, for mechanization would destroy the grass cover where it is needed most to prevent the development of further Chinese dust bowls.

A second major region within northwestern China is *Hsin-chiang*, "The New Frontier." Far from being new, this province has been a frontier region for China ever since the Han emperor in the second century B.C.

extended China's might as far westward as the T'ien Shan. Chinese garrisons have been in the chief cities of the region for 2,000 years. The organization of this area as a political province, however, dates from very "recent" times in China, only a few decades before the American Revolution.

The traditional Occidental name of the province, Chinese Turkestan, provides a better ethnic characterization for the region, because 70 to 80 per cent of the population is Turkic in origin and language and Islamic in religion.[1] Although most are sedentary farmers like the Chinese, the cultural and economic clash between the Mohammedan peoples and the Chinese has resulted in some of the bitterest internal warfare of the last century in China. The Turkic and Mongol peoples of central Asia have been squeezed in a political vice between Russian imperialism on the one hand and Chinese imperialism on the other. Although their national independence has been destroyed, the cultural identities of the Mongols and Turkic peoples remain.

Hsin-chiang is divided into two great basins by a mighty bloc of mountains, the T'ien Shan. The northern basin of Dzungaria functions as a main thoroughfare for communications between China and Soviet Middle Asia. Although the Pamir, T'ien Shan, and Altai ranges form massive barriers along most of China's western borders, two low, broad valleys lead through the barrier mountains here. These passages have been called the Dzungarian Gates. Through them went old caravan routes, followed later by branches of the present Northwest Highway. The Turkestan railroad northwest from Lan-chou (Map 4) also follows this route. Near the Sino-Soviet frontier in this region in 1957 a huge lake was reportedly being formed by a hydroelectric power and irrigation dam on the upper Irtysh which was being built on the Soviet side. The basin of the Tarim River to the south has no such easy routes leading across the international border, which is crossed only by high passes. The Tarim, thus, is a more isolated, drier, and hotter basin, the central heart of which contains one of the more desolate great deserts in the world, the Takla Makan. Life is confined to the rim of the basin, along which ran China's ancient Silk Road to Persia and the Roman Occident. In ancient times the desert wastes that cover most of Hsin-chiang shared with the desolate Tibetan high plateaus and mountains responsibility for China's isolated cultural development. In time, however, the lines of oases flanking the T'ien Shan and the K'un-lun formed the links for cultural and commercial channels through this great barrier.

The T'ien Shan is lifegiver for most of the people of the province. It reaches 23,000 feet in the west and over 17,000 feet in its eastern exten-

---

[1] In late 1955, Hsin-chiang was renamed the "Hsin-chiang Uighur Autonomous Region" after the largest of the Turkic ethnic groups in the province.

sions southeast of Ti-hua (Urumchi). Although most of Hsin-chiang receives an average annual precipitation under 5 inches, parts of the mountains may receive as much as 30 inches. Melting snows and glaciers send
water to the desert feet of the range. Broad areas at middle altitudes offer
fine meadows, open forests, and steppe grasses for the grazing herds of
the Mongols and Kazakhs. The chief oases line its southern flanks along
the edge of the Tarim basin; a few important oases also are found along
the northern flanks in Dzungaria. Greater atmospheric moisture in the
western half of Dzungaria has led to the development of steppe grasslands and with it a grazing economy.

The T'ien Shan thus divides predominantly pastoral Dzungaria from
the predominantly agricultural Tarim basin. This functional division is
reflected in the ethnic character of the population. Dzungaria is populated largely by Mongols of the Lamaistic faith,[2] although some Moslem
Kazakh pastoralists also are distributed on the T'ien Shan and Altai
slopes. The Tarim oases are cultivated chiefly by Islamic Uighurs of
Turkic origin, who form 70 per cent of the province's population. Chinese,
who are alien to most of the region, form only 10 per cent of the entire
population and are concentrated mainly in the oasis towns as merchants,
artisans, administrators, and garrison troops. In recent years they have
been augmented by communist technicians and labor battalions.

Oasis agriculture and the pastoral economy are complementary aspects
of livelihood in Hsin-chiang. The oasis artisans, merchants, and farmers
require the wool, hide, meat, cheese, and butter products of the pastoralists for clothing, felts, leather crafts, and food. The pastoral nomads find
convenient and desirable the manufactured handicrafts of the oases and
the grain and tea that form staples in their simple fare.

Although the chief crop of the region is wheat, oasis farming here displays the patterns characteristic of irrigated farmlands with hot summer
climates. Almost all the crops that are grown in such a region as California are common in the Hsin-chiang oases, although the greater necessity for self-sufficiency makes for greater emphasis on staple food crops.
The Tarim climate is generally similar to that of northern Arizona, whereas
colder Dzungaria has a climate like that of Wyoming.

Hsin-chiang may be regarded as a "new frontier" with respect to mineral and industrial development. Both the Chinese and the Soviet governments have shown great interest in Hsin-chiang's relatively unknown
mineral resources. Many of the rarer minerals are known to occur. Although known petroleum deposits have not been considered important,
great areas are "petroliferous" in nature and may yield significant amounts
of liquid fuel to oil-poor China. The communist Ministry of Petroleum
asserts that there are proven reserves of over 100 million tons in China.

[2] A derivative of Mahayana Buddhism.

Estimated production in 1959 was to be 2.5 million barrels, almost half from the Yü-men field in Kan-su adjacent to eastern Hsin-chiang. Hsin-chiang is an important arena for the large-scale search for economic minerals that has been launched by the communist regime. Industrially, the province is still in the handicraft stage. However, at Ti-hua, the main Chinese center in Hsin-chiang, the communist regime has established a large modern cotton mill and a new and larger electric power plant. Far-reaching changes are being inaugurated by the in-coming railroad.

The Ho-hsi (Kan-su) corridor is third among the major regions of northwestern China. The term *ho-hsi* means "west of the (Huang) Ho," but for the Chinese it does not mean just any place west of the Huang, but only the "Chinese" part of this west—in short, the protected corridor between the Tibetan high plateaus and the Mongol desert lands, which for some 2,000 years has channeled Chinese communications with Hsin-chiang. It is less than 50 miles wide but runs for over 600 miles between the Huang Ho valley west of Kan-su and the edge of the Tarim basin. Its 5,000-foot elevation is bordered to the north and south by ranges rising more than 10,000 feet. In early history even this was not enough to protect the Chinese garrisons along the route from the desert nomads, so a great earthen wall was built paralleling half the corridor, forming a western extension of the Great Wall of China. The significance of the route lies not only in its function as a transportation channel but also and even more importantly in the series of productive oases at the base of the Ch'i-lien Shan, which have supported as many as a million people at one time.

The Ho-hsi corridor formed an important segment of the ancient Silk Road, but lost much of its significance after the development of sea transport between China and Europe. With the Manchu conquest of Hsin-chiang it again became important. New significance was gained during the second World War when the great Northwest Highway was built along this route to bring in supplies from the Turk-Sib railroad in Soviet Middle Asia.[3] With the increased exploitation of Hsin-chiang mineral resources and the development of a modern steel plant at Lan-chou, the Ho-hsi corridor will play a greater role than ever before in the development of China's west. Engineering developments also may well add enough land to the irrigated farm area to support double the present population. Although ethnically this population is partly Islamic, and although Ho-hsi is part of the northwestern desert lands, its historical ties to eastern China have led to its inclusion with eastern Kan-su as part of China proper.

[3] The Yü-men oil field in the northwest sector of the corridor in 1956 yielded 520,000 tons of petroleum, and 42,000 of the total of 112,000 workers in China's oil industry were located here in the same year. In 1957, a large, high-grade iron-ore deposit was reported in the Ch'i-lien mountains.

The Tibetan high plateaus

The Tibetan high plateaus form the roof of Asia. Down its gutters and from its eaves run the torrents of water that become such mighty rivers as the Huang, Yang-tzu, Mekong, Ganges, and Indus. The entire eastern portion rises 12,000 feet above sea level, and vast parts of the west reach to barren, lifeless heights averaging over 16,000 feet. It is rimmed in all of its four cardinal directions by giant, snowbound, glacier-gouged ranges rising over 20,000 feet—the Karakorum in the west, the K'un-lun and Altyn Tagh in the north, the Amne Machin and Ta-hsüeh Shan in the east, and the Himalaya in the south.

This largest of all the earth's rockpiles has constituted one of the most nearly absolute isolating factors in history. For thousands of years, two of the world's greatest civilizations, the Indian and the Chinese, evolved on opposite sides of this great barrier with only minor influences upon each other. When mutual influences finally materialized, they traveled by devious routes around the barrier, via Burma, or by sea to the south, or via the desert oases of central Asia, bringing about the establishment of lasting routes of trade.

The high altitudes of the western portion of this plateau, and its central Asiatic situation involving a desert climatic regime, internal drainage, and lack of fresh water and vegetation, have made it unattractive to both man and beast. Vegetation, animal life, and human settlements are restricted chiefly to the lower eastern and southern plateaus and valleys of this region. In the south, the chief population centers are found in the 12,000-foot valley of the Tsang-pu (Brahmaputra) River in which Lhasa is situated. This is the populated part of Tibet proper. In the east the population is distributed mainly in the eastern halves of Hsi-k'ang (Si-kang, now largely incorporated into Ssu-ch'uan) and Ch'ing-hai, chiefly along the borderlands of Ssu-ch'uan, Yün-nan, and Kan-su (Figure 37). The isolation of these segments of the Tibetan high plateaus has produced a cultural and political fragmentation of the Tibetan peoples, which has been accentuated by their historical relationships with the Chinese. In the centuries of struggle by the Tibetans to retain independence or autonomy, the western Tibetans of Tibet proper have been most successful because of their greater consolidation in the Tsang-pu valley, and because of their greater geographical isolation from China proper.

The population of the eastern part of the high plateaus has been divided up into numerous groups ruled by hereditary chieftains. This fragmentation has been facilitated by great topographic complexity, which has made political unification difficult. Here is found the chief zone of contact and conflict between Tibetans and Chinese. Chinese farmers have

Fig. 37 • The high plateaus and mountains of what was southern Hsi-k'ang province form the eastern margins of the Tibetan high plateaus. Near Lu-ku Lake, visible in the far background, are seen the north-south ranges divided by deep gorges that characterize the high highlands. The lake itself lies along the former Hsi-k'ang border with western Yun-nan province at an elevation of about 9,600 feet. Beyond the lake, snow-capped mountains rise several thousand feet higher. Past the lake runs an ancient caravan trail connecting Hsi-ch'ang with Li-chiang, two Chinese towns in this Lolo-Tibetan sector of southwestern China.

Many of the higher slopes are in virgin timber, saved from early destruction by their relative inaccessibility. Grassland, such as that in the right foreground, is grazed by the herds of the Ku-tsung tribes of Tibetans. Tibetan cultivation also is to be observed in the stream valley at the lower left around a small settlement. Population throughout the area is sparse. *(Herold Wiens.)*

Fig. 38 • Monks in the Kumbum monastery courtyard near Hsi-ning in Ch'ing-hai province. This monastery was the seat of the Panchen Lama before the communist conquest of Tibet proper restored him to his palace at Zhikatse in Tibet. The boys shown are donated to the monastery by their parents to enter upon a long apprenticeship to the older monks before themselves becoming monks. *(Lt. Col. David R. Longacre.)*

taken over and settled many of the lower-lying valleys of the southeast, such as that of Hsi-ch'ang, and Chinese and Moslem Tung-kan [4] farmers occupy most of the good lands around Hsi-ning (Sining) east of Koko Nor.

The Tibetan high plateaus are dominated by Lamaism, a form of Buddhism, which is the catholic church of the Tibetans and the Mongols. Traditionally, the church and state have been one in Tibet proper, administered in spiritual and secular affairs by the Panchen and Dalai Lamas respectively. The influence of the spiritual head reaches strongly into the monasteries of the eastern high plateaus where since 1923 the Panchen Lama has had his headquarters at Hsi-ning, owing to a schism with the Dalai Lama (Figure 38). His return to Tibet proper in 1952 under the auspices of the invading Chinese communist armies indicates his utility to the Chinese as a tool to further their control over Tibet.

The Tibetan high plateaus are characterized by monastic aggregations and isolated self-sufficient villages. The few large urban centers are

[4] Chinese-speaking Moslems, also known as Dungans.

monastery towns. Half of Lhasa's 60,000 population in 1952 were monks. Most of the population of Zhikatse, seat of the Panchen Lama, are monks at the Tashi Lumpo monastery. Although the monasteries have been corporately rich in lands and livestock, donations from the pious, church taxation, and trading operations all help to support the priesthood. In general, however, livelihood is on a subsistence level. Settlement most often is in small valleys containing a few two- or three-storied flat-roofed houses made of rock and clay, with high adjoining stone defense towers. Livestock may be kept in enclosures or may occupy the ground floor of the houses.

The economy may be expressed in terms of the food staples—butter, tea, and *tsamba*. *Tsamba* is a rough-ground flour of roasted wheat or barley, the chief crops of the farmlands, and is the mainstay of the population. Tea forms the chief item of the import trade, and the competition between Chinese and British Indian teas for the Tibetan market had such strong political repercussions that in 1906 it resulted in the organization of Hsi-k'ang as a Chinese province so as to prevent the invasion of Indian tea. *Tsamba* is stirred into hot tea in which clarified butter has been melted. The butter may be taken to represent the pastoral aspect of Tibetan livelihood. Although dry farming supports most of the population, it is confined to small, scattered areas, in contrast to the extensive grassland pastures of rolling plateau surfaces or mountain slopes. The yak, acclimated to high altitudes, provides strength for the plow and serves as the chief pack animal. Sheep, cattle, and horses also thrive in parts of the plateau, especially in eastern Ch'ing-hai which annually exports 13,000 tons of wool to north China and some 20,000 horses to Tibet. Tibet exports large amounts of wool to India and through India to China.

The Tibetan has shown a remarkable ability to live within a harsh and demanding environment. He has survived the rarified atmosphere of his steppe-like mountain climate for over a thousand years. He accepts its variable rainfall (from 10 to as much as 160 inches yearly) and temperature extremes (−43° to over 90°F.) with the calmness of familiarity. Like the Mongol, he makes the most of his animals. Their hides and skins furnish him with clothing and shelter, their meat and milk with food, their dung with fuel, and their bones with implements. His clothes of felt are conveniently made to shuffle on and off with temperatures that change sharply from day to night, from shade to sunshine, or even with the passage of a cloud. He has a bold, self-assured manner, but when events occur for which his experience has not prepared him, he twirls his prayer-wheel, mutters incantations to the clay image of a deity in his pouch, and trusts to his amulets to preserve him as best they can.

In Tibet, as in other parts of China, great changes are going on. A motor highway crossed its high ranges to connect Lhasa with Ssu-ch'uan in

Fig. 39 • The loess highlands in western Shen-hsi province display massive bluffs produced by water erosion through the thick loess, which may be hundreds of feet in depth. The loessal soils are fertile, but must be terraced and dry-farmed. The terraces are formed in part by cutting into uphill slopes and spreading the soil materials downslope to form the bench. Virtually the entire area is put into cultivation in this fashion. *(Wellington D. Jones.)*

1954, while highways in Ch'ing-hai province now form connecting links between the Ho-hsi corridor in southwest Kan-su and the two regions of Tibet and Ssu-ch'uan. Over 1,800 miles of main highways and some 800 miles of secondary motor roads connect the few cities and the chief agricultural and pastoral areas of Tibet. The round trip from Ssu-ch'uan to Lhasa formerly required two seasons. Now it takes two months. The strategic importance of this in the domination and exploitation of Tibet by the Chinese is obvious. In addition to facilitating the movement of heavy military and economic equipment and machinery into the heart of Tibet, the roads make possible the settling and exploitation of various parts of Tibet by political prisoners and civilian workers who are being sent westwards from eastern China by the thousands. By the end of 1956, 500,000 Chinese were reported to have been brought into Tibet, and this number was planned to reach some 5 million in five years. Because of climatic limitations on food production, the latter goal appears highly unrealistic.

North China

The three major regions of north China form the most ancient hearths of Chinese civilization. Among these, the *loess plateau* forms at once one of the more distinctive and significant regions of China. True loess soil is formed only in relatively dry climatic regions and preserves its character only under a climatic regime similar to that at its formation. Loess possesses a columnar structure that differentiates it from ordinary clays. Vertical channels created by decayed grass roots allow loess to absorb moisture rapidly, while its high calcium content cements the soil to prevent easy collapse of the earth structure. At the same time, erosion of loess under the attack of running water is rapid because of its unconsolidated nature. These characteristics evidence themselves in the form of steep-walled gulleys and canyons and in the defile-like roads, which have been worn tens of feet below the surface of the surrounding loess (Figure 39). In many places also the cultivation of steep slopes has led to serious sheet erosion.

A peculiarity of the loess country is the practice of dry terracing by cutting into the uphill slope and spreading the soil on the downhill slope. This not only slows down erosion from heavy rains, but also spreads a fresh layer of soil over the field surface. Unlike soils in wetter climates, loessal soils are fertile in what normally would be the "subsoil" layers. Moreover, because of the tendency of loess to maintain vertical faces, many Chinese farmers unable to afford or obtain materials for surface house construction simply burrow their homes out of the loess. The earth provides insulation from the heat of summer and the numbing cold of the long continental winters. Unfortunately, the western part of this area lies in a seismic belt, and occasional earthquakes may collapse these underground dwellings and suffocate the inhabitants.

The fact that loess covers most of the slopelands has made for a high degree of slope utilization in crop growing and for a relatively dense population. Moreover, the two large rift valleys of the Wei and Fen rivers in Shen-hsi and Shan-hsi respectively provide level lands of fertile alluvium on which population is especially dense. The Huang Ho flows south from its great northern loop through the middle of the loess plateau in narrow, rapidly dropping gorges and thus forms no large flood plain there. However, it carries a large volume of sediment to add to the Yellow plain. The loess plateau, rather than the desert lands of the upper Huang, is the source of the alluvium of the Yellow plain, for the silt content of the Huang in the Ordos is only a small per cent of what it is in Ho-nan province.

The region's low rainfall, averaging less than 20 inches, is offset somewhat by its concentration during the summer growing season. However, it is among the least dependable rainfall regimes in China, and rain often occurs too late during the growing season or comes in too heavy downpours between long intervals of drought to be agriculturally useful. Thus, the agricultural venture in the loess region is one of the most precarious in

China. Winters are shorter and less severe than in the Mongolian fringe-lands, so that winter wheat is the chief crop, together with drought-resistant millet. Where irrigation water is available, especially in the Wei River plain, cotton comes into prominence.

The Wei River plain was the cradle of Chinese civilization (Figures 40 and 43). The birthplace of this civilization is lost in the mists of antiquity, but for the first millennium of recorded Chinese history at least, this plain was the heartland of China. Hsi-an (Ch'ang-an) and its vicinity was the site of the Chinese capital for at least 900 years. From here Chinese culture and the Chinese state spread eastward and southward. The naturally strategic situation of the Wei valley, with its command over communications northwestward and southwestward from eastern China, has given Hsi-an lasting geographical advantages, and the passage of the trunk line of the Lung-hai railroad through it provides added significance.

Finally, the loess plateau forms China's great coal reservoir. Although industrial development in this region has lagged because of poor communications, the 80 per cent of China's enormous coal deposits found on both sides of the Huang Ho ensures a high industrial potential for the region. Although only moderate quantities of iron ore are present near the coal deposits, rail hauls can bring additional amounts from the Mongolian fringelands at the northeast end of the loess plateau, while coal is the foundation for a host of chemical industries. Thermoelectric power can be developed easily, and coal liquefaction may well supply the deficit in

Fig. 40 • The raised embankment of the railroad between T'ien-shui and Lan-chou in Kan-su crosses the western end of the Wei River flood plain. Cultivated loess terraces like those in the background are responsible for the relatively dense population of the loess region. Note the deep gullies cutting into the hills; also the scarcity of trees. *(Lt. Col. David R. Longacre.)*

Fig. 41 • The north China plain, the largest unbroken stretch of arable land in China, rises for the most part only a few feet above sea level. Cutting across the plain are shallow, braided streams useful in short stretches for shallow-draft barges and sampans (literally: "three planks"), as shown here some 20 miles southeast of Pei-ching (Peking). Small groves of willow and aspen provide wood for construction and furniture-making. Soybeans, one of the primary crops of north China, are growing to the left of the stream. *(Herold Wiens.)*

China's petroleum resources. Iron and steel industrial complexes, machine plants, arsenals, and cotton mills are found at T'ai-yuan in Shan-hsi and at Lan-chou in Kan-su where there also is an oil refinery.

In April, 1957, the communist regime announced the start of construction of a 394-feet high dam six-tenths of a mile long across the Huang Ho at San-men gorge (111° 25′ E.). Designed to control floods, provide irrigation water and generate electric power, it is but one of a series of projects planned for the middle course of the great river. Communist engineers claim that completion of the dam will reduce the maximum flow through the San-men gorge from a possible 46,000 cubic yards per second to a little less than 8,000 cubic yards per second, thus protecting the lower reaches of the Yellow plain. The electric power generating capacity projected at this site is 1.1 million kilowatts, the largest in China. This construction is scheduled to be completed in 1967. Many more years will be required for the entire Huang Ho project to be completed, but the plan envisages the six-fold increase in irrigated area in the Huang Ho drainage basin and the opening of the river to navigation for 500-ton boats from Lan-chou to the Yellow Sea.

East of the loess plateau is the *north China plain,* the largest unbroken surface of arable land in China, some 125,000 square miles, or equal to Kansas plus two-thirds of Oklahoma. The agricultural climates of these two states are similar to that of the north China plain. The near-level plain stretches southward from the Great Wall at Shan-hai-kuan to the Huai-yang hills north of the Yang-tzu Chiang. The northern part is formed by the alluvia of the Hai Ho and other Ho-pei rivers (Figure 41). The southern part consists of the lower Huai River drainage system. By far the largest part is covered by the plain of the Huang Ho or Yellow River, so that the term "Yellow plain" often is equated loosely with the area of the entire north China plain.

With a density of over 650 people per square mile of area and more than 15 times the total population of Kansas and Oklahoma combined, the north China plain is one of the world's most overcrowded regions. Moreover, the high percentage of its population finding a livelihood in rural activities makes for a density of about 1,000 people per square mile of cultivated area. Prior to the collectivization of private farms, individual farm sizes reached only about five acres while the farm family averaged six persons. The fact that the communist "redistribution of land" to the farmers here in 1949-50 brought an average addition of only from one-third to one-half acre to a farm indicates clearly that a basic cause of poverty on the north China plain, as in other parts of China, is an actual shortage of crop land. No amount of "land reform" can circumvent this deficiency.

The term "land of famine" applies to no other part of China so aptly as to the north China plain where the chief causes of famine may be attributed to the whim of climate and to the physiographic regime of the Huang Ho. The northern portion of the plain has little more rainfall than the loess plateau, and precipitation is almost as unreliable. Although near the Huai River precipitation rises to an average 30 inches per year, the plain has a steppe climate. Drought often plagues the farmers.

The plain has been built by Huang Ho sediments, and the great river runs along a self-created ridge which rises to 50 feet above the level of the surrounding flood plain. When in summer exceptionally heavy rains occur for an unusually long period, the river may rise and burst through weak places, along its hundreds of miles of dikes, flooding immense areas and bringing misfortune to millions of farmers. The completion of the San-men dam should reduce these flood dangers.

In good years, the harvests furnish enough food for a marginal livelihood for the people, but there is little surplus that may be turned into savings for years of calamity. Winter wheat is the most distinctive crop, although kao-liang also is an important staple. In the last half century, however, commercial crops such as tobacco, cotton, and peanuts have come to fill the need for cash that developed when home handicraft industries declined owing to competition of modern manufactures. Crop rotation is carried out everywhere to spread the farming risk and to maintain soil fertility.

In most of the north China plain there are few nonagricultural resources. In the northeast near Tientsin coal is important, and some of the highest-producing mines in China are found west of Chin-huang-tao.[5] Large amounts of salt are produced by evaporation from the coastal flatlands. The scarcity of natural forest growth causes many farmers to plant quick-growing willows and aspens for domestic fuel and building use.

Two of China's seven cities with over a million population as of 1957 are found in the northern end of the plain. One is the communist capital, Peking (properly Pei-ching), traditional political and cultural heart of China. Prior to the second World War Peking contained five important universities. The second, Tientsin, or T'ien-ching, with a poor harbor site 40 miles above the mouth of the Hai Ho, nevertheless has geographical advantages of situation that make it the port of entry and exit for the northern half of the plain, for the loess plateau east of the Huang Ho, and for much of Mongolia and the Mongolian fringelands. It is the commercial center of north China and is second to Shanghai in cotton and wool textile manufactures. As the crossroads of major railroads and the gateway to the land route to the northeastern provinces and to Peking, it has the utmost military significance.

Third among the regions of north China are *the hills of Shan-tung*. The hilly Liao-tung peninsula projects southwestward from Manchuria into the Yellow Sea to stand opposite the hilly, northeastward-thrusting Shan-tung peninsula. Together, they form the pillars of the marine gate leading to the Gulf of Chih-li. Between them are stretched the small Ch'ang-shan islands that point to the genetic geological connections between the two peninsulas. Southwest of the Shan-tung peninsula, a larger and higher hilly mass rises to the 5,000-foot elevation of T'ai Shan, separated from the peninsula by a low alluvial corridor. With a climatic regime that also is not far different from that of the Liao-tung peninsula, the hills of Shan-tung are similar in many ways to the Liao-tung hill mass (Figure 42). Both have rocky coastlines with several excellent harbors strategically located. Ch'ing-tao (Tsingtao), on the southern peninsula, rivals Ta-lien on the northern peninsula for excellence and spaciousness of harbor accommodation. The numerous smaller havens on the coast of each have led to important fishing activities off Shan-tung as off Liao-tung. Similar coal and other mineral resources form the backbone of industrial activities in both areas.

Both hilly extensions are backed by large hinterlands of agriculturally productive plains. Easy railroad communications in each case have led from these hinterlands to the best port of the area, Ta-lien in the north and Ch'ing-tao in the south. Each of these ports has become the chief commercial gateway to the immediate hinterlands of the plains, and each

[5] For decades these mines have supplied Japan with her imports of coking coal.

is an important coal-export terminal. Ch'ing-tao is situated at the eastern end of the alluvial corridor separating the two hill masses of Shan-tung, so that it is provided with a natural route for the highway and railroad that lead inland to Chi-nan (Tsinan), one of the largest cities of the north China plain and a strategic crossroads of communications on this plain.

Because much of the hill land is rolling, a surprisingly large percentage of the surface is under crops, with corresponding high population densi-

Fig. 42 • The edge of a village in the hills of Shan-tung province northeast of Ch'ing-tao, the chief city of the province. The village walls are made of adobe brick with some local stone used for corner posts and foundations. Roofs are thatched. Though November nights are cold, the dry air permits intense insolation near south-facing walls, and during the day light clothing is worn; some very young children wear none, in part through poverty. Note the completely barren hillslopes beyond. *(Norton Ginsburg.)*

ties, but climatic limitations like that of the north China plain make farming in the Shan-tung region as precarious as on the plain. Ch'ing-tao, third in cotton-textile manufacturing after Shang-hai and Tientsin, also draws on the hill land and adjacent plain for wheat, tobacco, and peanut supplies for its important food industries. Besides being the most significant commercial port between Tientsin and Shang-hai, Ch'ing-tao also is a major naval port for China.

SELECTED GEOGRAPHICAL BIBLIOGRAPHY

1. Barbour, G. B. "Recent Observations on the Loess of North China," *Geographical Journal*, July, 1935, pp. 54-64.
2. Chang, Chih-yi. "Land Utilization and Settlement Possibilities in Sinkiang," *Geographical Review*, January, 1949, pp. 57-75.
3. Chu, Coching. "The Aridity of North China," *Pacific Affairs*, June, 1935, pp. 206-17.
4. Clapp, F .G. "The Hwang Ho, Yellow River," *Geographical Review*, January, 1922, pp. 1-18.
5. Ginsburg, Norton S. "Manchurian Railway Development," *The Far Eastern Quarterly*, August, 1949, pp. 398-411.
6. ———. "Manchuria," in *Encyclopedia Britannica*, 1957 edition.
7. Hanson-Lowe, J. "Notes on the Climate of the South Chinese-Tibetan Borderland," *Geographical Review*, July, 1941, pp. 444-53.
8. Hung, Fu (Frederick). "The Geographic Regions of China and Their Subdivisions; a Study in Methodology," *The International Geographical Union, 17th International Geographical Congress, Publication No. 6*, pp. 28-29. Washington: National Geographical Society, 1952.
9. "Imperial and Soviet Russia in Manchuria," *The World Today*, September, 1946, pp. 414-30.
10. Kaulback, R. "A Journey in the Salween and Tsangpo Basins, Southeast Tibet," *Geographical Journal*, February, 1938, pp. 97-122.
11. Kingdon-Ward, F. "Tibet as a Grazing Land," *Geographical Journal*, July-September, 1947, pp. 60-75.
12. Lee, Shu-tan. "Delimitation of the Geographic Regions of China," *Annals of the Association of American Geographers*, September, 1947, pp. 155-68.
13. Li, An-che. "Dege, A Study of Tibetan Population," *Southwestern Journal of Anthropology, Winter*, 1947, pp. 279-93.
14. Liu, En-lan. "The Ho-hsi Corridor," *Economic Geography*, January, 1952, pp. 51-56.
15. McLean, N. L. D. "Sinkiang Today," *International Affairs*, July, 1948, pp. 377-86.
16. Moyer, R. T. "The Agricultural Potentialities of Manchuria," *Foreign Agriculture*, August, 1944, pp. 171-91.
17. Rodgers, Allan. "The Manchurian Iron and Steel Industry and Its Resource Base," *Geographical Review*, January, 1948, pp. 41-54.
18. Thorp, J. "Colonization Possibilities of Northwest China and Inner Mongolia," *Pacific Affairs*, December, 1935, pp. 447-53.

19. Todd, O. J. "The Yellow River Reharnessed," *Geographical Review,* January, 1949, pp. 38-56.
20. Todd, O. J., and S. Eliassen. "The Yellow River Problem," *Proceedings of the American Society of Civil Engineers,* December, 1938, pp. 1921-1991.

Comments

Except for the two studies of regional delimitation by Lee and Hung, the foregoing bibliography has to do with limited areas of China. Certain articles, such as Chu's study on the aridity of north China, are more general, while the studies of the Huang Ho or Yang-tzu river problems also cover large areas. Articles of geographical interest pertaining to different Chinese regions are very numerous, and only a selection can be offered here. Periodical guides, indices of journals dealing with Far Eastern or East Asian affairs, and the *Current Geographical Publications* published by the American Geographical Society of New York are useful bibliographies for consultation.

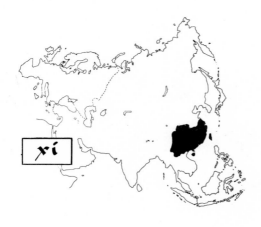

China

THE SOUTH

AS A TOPOGRAPHIC OBSTACLE, THE CENTRAL MOUNTAIN BLOC (MAP 9) extends the highlands of the Tibetan fringe eastward into the heart of densely settled agricultural China. The northern segment of this bloc, the west-east 11,000-foot Ch'in Ling and its lower southeastward extensions along the north bank of the Han and Yang-tzu rivers, separates north from south China. The southern segment, with the Ta-pa Shan turning south from the Ch'in Ling into the Wu Shan knot, cuts off the Ssu-ch'uan basin from the central lakes plains.

The central mountain bloc

In the early history of China, the Ch'in Ling permitted the isolated development of the Thai cultural center in the Ssu-ch'uan basin and the Chinese cultural center in the Wei River valley (Figure 43). In subsequent times, the Ch'in Ling often formed the boundary zones of independent rival states. The southern segment of the central mountain bloc served a similar though less important function, locking in Ssu-ch'uan from eastern China. The strategical protection afforded by the central mountain bloc, both in the north and in the east, made Ssu-ch'uan an ideal base for the Chinese government's resistance to Japan in the Sino-Japanese War after 1938.

213

Fig. 43 • The east-west running Ch'in Ling (mountains) act as a major climatic divide between north and south China and have been a barrier to communications between north and southwest China. The Ch'in Ling mark a great fault scarp zone and rise dramatically from the Wei Ho plain on the right or north, reaching a height of 13,392 feet at T'ai-pai Shan, the snow-covered mountain seen in the distant background. The mantle of loess that blankets the plateau region north of the Wei Ho valley also covers the northern face of the Ch'in Ling. Originally, these slopes were well forested, but wanton cutting and burning destroyed the forests and prevented natural reforestation. Barren slopes and young V-shaped valleys are the rule in the Ch'in Ling. From the lower slopes northward intensive cultivation and compact walled villages become apparent. (*Geographical Review.*)

Although the Ch'in Ling remains a major topographical obstacle to communications, its larger significance lies in its more permanent role as a climatic divide. Stretching as it does athwart China's prevailing seasonal air movements, the northern sector of the central mountain bloc robs northwestward-moving maritime air of most of its moisture, while blocking and diverting southeastward-moving, cold, continental air masses. North of the Ch'in Ling system, therefore, the climate is characterized by low precipitation and cold, long winters. Only 10-15 per cent of the cropland is irrigated, and dry-cereal crops are dominant. South of the Ch'in Ling, warm moist air predominates; precipitation is ample, and the growing seasons are long. More than 40 per cent of the farm land is under irrigation. Wet-rice everywhere is the dominant crop. The irregularity of the rainfall regime becomes less, so that widespread crop failures occur seldom, and the danger of famine from natural causes decreases.

The southern sector of the central mountain bloc also has some singular attributes aside from its character as an obstacle to communications. These pertain chiefly to the Yang-tzu, which courses its way through tortuous rocky gorges 1,000 to 2,000 feet deep. The rough topography makes the Yang-tzu the sole natural gateway to the Ssu-ch'uan basin. It by no means forms an easy or safe route, for upstream boats must buck a current that in places reaches 13 knots, and the rapids and sharp turns in the gorges bring about high annual losses of boats, men, and cargoes.

A second major attribute of the gorges is their hydroelectric potential. The site a short distance upstream from I-ch'ang alone could supply three times the combined kilowatt capacity of the Hoover, Shasta, and Grand Coulee dams in the United States (Figure 5).

South China

South China may be divided into seven major regions:

(1) The Ssu-ch'uan basin,
(2) The central lakes basins,
(3) The lower Yang-tzu,
(4) The Yün-kuei plateau,
(5) The southeast maritime hills,
(6) The Ling-nan hills and Hsi Chiang delta, and
(7) Hai-nan and T'ai-wan islands.

Westernmost of these, and most isolated, is the *Ssu-ch'uan basin.* Ssu-ch'uan is a large rice-bowl containing within its rim virtually all the ingredients of the varied topography, climates, vegetation, crops, and human activities that are found in South China, with the exception of a coastline.

Fig. 44 • Paddy terraces in eastern Ssu-ch'uan province. Terraced paddy farming is almost universal in the Ssu-ch'uan basin, although the level Ch'eng-tu plain does not require such practices. A surprisingly high proportion of the land in the basin is thereby brought under cultivation. This cultivation takes place on purple-brown soils derived from sandstone, with a fair amount of clay content and watered by abundant run-off fed from one level to another by an intricate irrigation system. The great pressure of population is indicated by the planting of terrace walls with beans. The characteristic cloudiness of the basin is well illustrated in this view. *(Herold Wiens.)*

Its estimated 1953 population of 62 million people outranks that of Great Britain. It is large enough, rich enough in resources, productive enough in agriculture, and isolated enough to constitute a state within a state. In fact, although not so populous in an earlier time, it was the core area of one of three chief contending dynasties of China for about half a century after the Han Empire broke up in A.D. 220.

The productiveness of this province is based upon the lime-enriched purplish-red sandstone bed of an ancient inland sea. When the Yang-tzu, which drained this sea, gradually cut down into the mountain rim to form the present gorges through the Wu Shan, erosion of the consolidated seabed cut up the basin plain into an intricate pattern of meandering river valleys. Flat-topped remnants of the old seabed remain to give much of the basin a horizontal skyline, although the basin floor is characterized by rough terrain. The fertility of the soil and the density of the population have led to an unusual degree of slope cultivation and terracing (Figure 44). In some places slopes on which a man cannot stand erect without losing his balance are cultivated by farmers who garden-till on hands and knees. Elsewhere, water from higher levels is led to fill and spill over tier on tier of paddy terraces. From the air, the association of terraced slopes, level-topped elevations, and alluvial valley bottoms resembles a contour-model made of cardboard sheets.

Ssu-ch'uan literally means "four rivers" and refers to the four chief streams of the province. Most of the lower parts of the basin are connected by river channels navigable for native flat-bottomed boats or steam launches (see boat in Figure 45). Larger steam vessels navigate virtually the entire length of the Yang-tzu in the basin. Until the second World War, motor highways and air transport were not important in the basin, which then contained no railroad. A railroad completed in 1952

Fig. 45 • Beach agriculture in Ssu-ch'uan. The intensity of cultivation in the Ssu-ch'uan basin is illustrated by this scene along the banks of the Yang-tzu River. In late winter and early spring enormous areas of river beaches are left exposed. Farmers with insufficient land adjoining the river use the beaches to plant beans, gambling upon their ripening before the beaches are flooded. The planting procedure consists of dropping small amounts of manure, seen in the dark heap at the right center, into holes scooped into the sand. Then seeds are dropped and the sand smoothed over. The high groundwater of the beaches provides ample moisture. (Herold Wiens.)

connects the provincial capital of Ch'eng-tu in the west with the commercial and industrial center of Chungking in the eastern part of the basin; the northwest trans-Ch'in Ling highway also has been paralleled by a railroad. For communication with eastern China, however, the Yang-tzu remains primary.

Humidity averaging 75 to 80 per cent the year around is the key feature of the warm basin climate. The protection afforded by the Ch'in Ling gives the basin a growing season of up to 350 days; in the larger part of the cultivated land frost is virtually unknown. Relatively higher winter temperatures are found in Ssu-ch'uan than in eastern China down the Yang-tzu. These higher temperatures may be attributed to the overhanging pall of mist, which, however, makes winters gloomy, especially over the lower eastern parts of the basin. Ample rain occurs in winter as well as in summer, although heavy summer maximums aided by the melting snows in the high western mountains may bring flood stages on the Yang-tzu at Chungking 90 feet higher than the winter low-water level. If this coincides with heavy rains in the central lake basins, destructive floods may result all along the Yang-tzu from I-ch'ang to the sea.

The Ch'eng-tu plain in the west forms an exception to the general landscape pattern in the Ssu-ch'uan basin. Nearly equal in area to the state of Delaware, its surface of 2,300 square miles, except for built-up areas, is almost entirely occupied by cultivated fields. In summer from 50 to 100 per cent of the fields are in paddy; rape and wheat dominate the fields in winter. China's model irrigation system is situated here, developed in the third century A.D. and operating with little change under the original principles. Streams dammed at the feet of the western mountains fan out into multiple channels over the alluvial plain. Productivity is high and is associated with the densest population distribution in the basin. In the midst of this plain is Ch'eng-tu, a city that is supposed to have reached half a million population almost 2,000 years ago, and which has held the seat of cultural leadership for the region since even earlier times.

There has been a traditional dichotomy in provincial leadership, however, which in ancient times derived from the situations of Ch'eng-tu and Chungking as the capitals of rival kingdoms. Political rivalries between Ch'eng-tu and Chungking divided the natural unity of the province. In modern times the former has derived its influence from its position as the seat of administration and learning, and the latter has asserted its dominance on the basis of its commercial and industrial leadership. Chungking, or properly Ch'ung-ch'ing, which in 1952 had three times the 400,-000 population of Ch'eng-tu, is strategically situated at the point where most of the drainage of the basin converges. It has lasting geographical advantages commercially, just as Ch'eng-tu has a prosperous base in the productive plain around it. Moreover, the most productive coal and iron mines in the varied mineral realm of the province occur near Chungking, giving it industrial advantages furthered by a large labor market. For these reasons it was chosen instead of Ch'eng-tu as the temporary capital of China during the second World War.

Of the variegated products that since early history have given Ssu-ch'uan fame, two stand out in national economic importance and in contrasting taste—sugar and salt. The bountifully watered southwestern valleys around the third largest city of the basin, Nei-chiang, often boost the provincial cane-sugar production to half the national total, exclusive of T'ai-wan. A short distance southwest of Nei-chang are the 4,000-foot deep salt wells of Tzu-liu-ching from which the Ssu-ch'uanese had been pumping brine by ingenious methods for centuries before the Western world discovered how to tap such subterranean depths.

The lack of industrialization of the basin is shown by its low degree of urbanization. In 1953 besides the three cities mentioned only I-pin had more than 50,000 people. Although modern industries are being established slowly, the Ssu-ch'uan basin still is predominantly a rice bowl.

The region of the *central lakes basins* lies immediately east of the Ssu-ch'uan basin. As the Yang-tzu boils out of the gorges west of I-ch'ang, it widens and flows eastward through the basin lands of China's two great central lakes, the T'ung-t'ing and the P'o-yang. The region as a whole has a common northern boundary in the Ta-pieh and Huai-yang ranges and a common southern boundary in the Nan Ling. The eastern basin of the P'o-yang extends only southward of the Yang-tzu and is much the smaller of the two subdivisions of the region. It comprises most of the area of Chiang-hsi province. The more important T'ung-t'ing basin, however, spans all the territory of the two provinces of Hu-pei and Hu-nan on both sides of the river and is known to Chinese, therefore, as the Liang-Hu ("the two-Hu") basin. The ranges of hills separating the two great lake basins do not form serious obstacles to land communications, and the basins are linked by highways and by a railroad. The Yang-tzu flood plain forms an integral connection about 30 miles wide between the basins.

Topographically and climatically, Hu-nan and Chiang-hsi are very similar. The 600-mile north-south stretch of the Liang-Hu basin, however, shows in winter some marked climatic differences between the northern and southern extremities, although the uniformly hot, humid summers show differences mainly in the longer growing season of the south. Winters along the Yang-tzu in the basin are considerably cooler than in more highly protected Ssu-ch'uan, but here again the summer climates are very similar.

A contrast between northern and southern landscapes emphasizes the importance to agriculture of the large alluvial plains in the lower parts of the Han and Yüan river valleys and around P'o-yang Lake. The more than 14,000 square miles of plain betwen Ch'ang-sha and Han-k'ou are broken up by the long irregular fingers of dozens of lakes in addition to the T'ung-t'ing. Isolated individual small hills here and there rise above the level alluvium. By contrast, southward of the two great lakes that serve as flood reservoirs for the Yang-tzu, the land surface becomes increasingly higher and hillier, and the broad valleys narrow and become hardly more than ravines as the Nan Ling is approached. To the east and west the hills also soon shut out the lowland. Although intensive land use makes the lower parts of the southern hill land a mosaic of lowland paddy fields surrounding upland islands of green shrubs and grass, the agricultural heart of the region is in the north in the vicinity of the lakes (Figure 31).

The Hu-pei area north of the Yang-tzu is a wheat-rice transition zone, but the wetter provinces of Hu-nan and Chiang-hsi are more specialized in rice. Hu-nan is a heavy surplus producer. There is a local saying: "When the Hu-nan harvest arrives, the sky itself does not provide enough storage space." The cities of Ch'ang-sha and Chang-te in Hu-nan and Nan-ch'ang in Chiang-hsi are among the leading rice markets of China. North of T'ung-t'ing Lake the land between the Yang-tzu and its chief tributary, the Han, is one of the three chief cotton regions of China, contributing raw material to the important textile industries of Han-k'ou. Ramie production south and southwest of T'ung-t'ing often ranks first in the country. Occupying little land but constituting an important farm sideline, tea growing becomes important in the hills, and the t'ung tree is widespread. A specialization of the southeastern part of the P'o-yang basin is pond-fish culture and fish-fry production.

The southern hill lands of the central lake basins have two unique mineral monopolies. About 88 per cent of China's antimony is found west and south of Ch'ang-sha, while 90 per cent of China's tungsten ore occurs in the vicinity of Kan-chou, the largest city of southern Chiang-hsi province. The production of each satisfies an important percentage of world demand for these metals and brings large amounts of foreign exchange to China. Moreover, the iron ore of the Ta-yeh mines and the nearby coal southeast of Han-k'ou provide materials and fuel for an important center of heavy industry in China at the Han-yang iron-and-steel works and at the iron works southeast of the mines. China's leading sulfur, lead, zinc, and silver mines also are found in Hu-nan, and the gypsum production 60 miles northwest of Han-k'ou is the most important in the country. Fine kaolin [1] clay near the northeastern end of P'o-yang Lake early made famous the porcelain and earthenware center of Chin-te city (Chin-te-chen), which produces about a third of China's fine ceramics.

---

[1] The term kaolin derives from the characters for *kao ling t'u,* literally "high-range clay," from a mountain where the clay was obtained.

Fig. 46 • The tomb of Sun Yat-sen near Nan-ching along the hilly margins of the lower Yang-tzu plain. Rolling hills characterize the terrain, while reforestation has again covered the denuded slopes of the lower Yang-tzu in the area. To the east (the right), the low hills disappear into the plain itself. The mausoleum is a shrine revered by the revolutionary followers of the founder of the Republic of China, whether they be Nationalist or communist. (Herold Wiens.)

Of some 85 million people inhabiting the central lake basins, over four-fifths are in the Liang-Hu basin. In the center of this basin, dominating the commercial, economic and political life of the entire region, is the Wu-Han metropolitan area, which includes the triplet cities of Han-k'ou, Wu-ch'ang, and Han-yang. Wu-ch'ang is the ancient political and cultural heart of Hu-pei. Han-k'ou is the more recently developed commercial and industrial center and the most important city in central China. Its eminence has arisen from situational advantages similar to those that have given importance to other cities of the region such as Ch'ang-sha, Nan-ch'ang, and Chiu-chiang. Among these factors, the most significant is that of command by inland-water transport over large hinterlands. During the last half century, the position of the Wu-Han area as the crossroads of water channels with strategic highways and railroads has greatly enhanced the importance of its situation. A major project to bridge the Yang-tzu and Han rivers for highway and railroad use was finished in 1957. This will add further to the importance of the Wu-Han industrial and commercial complex.

Easternmost of the middle-China regions is *the lower Yang-tzu plain*. Northeastward of the P'o-yang basin, the Yang-tzu flood plain continues to be constricted by hills in the north and in the south (Figure 46). The numerous drowned side valleys here give the river the aspect of an embayed seacoast. Fingers of the plain reach along these valleys, providing routes for highways and railroads. The main flood plain widens just before Wu-hu city is reached, spreading into the so-called Yang-tzu delta. Strictly speaking, however, the river does not have the numerous distributaries of the classic delta such as are exhibited by the Hsi Chiang southeast of Canton. Nevertheless, the close-knit river and canal network covering the lower Yang-tzu plain emphasizes the fluvial character of this coastal lowland. South of the river, the plains form a triangular area enclosing Lake T'ai and dozens of smaller lakes, with Shang-hai, Hang-chou, and Chen-chiang at the points of the triangle. Several thousand miles of irrigation canals and waterways criss-cross this triangle, so that within a 100-mile radius of Shang-hai it is possible to travel by small boats from any settlement to any other settlement. The traditional Chinese bridges here all are of the camel-backed variety so as to provide mast-clearance for sailing craft. Few of the older roads in the triangle, therefore, are open to wheeled vehicles.

The continuity of the coastal plain from Hang-chou to the Shan-tung hills is broken only by streams. The Yang-tzu is three miles at its widest here, so that in the past it has formed a cultural barrier leading to a linguistic break between the northern "Mandarin" dialect and the Wu tongue of Shang-hai.

Although no elevations interfere with atmospheric flow in the coastal plain, average annual rainfall drops off rapidly in the northern half of Chiang-su beyond the latitude of the Huai River mouth, and the change to north China climate is achieved. Agriculturally, the north-bank lands form a rice-wheat transition zone, with local cotton specialization near the river mouth. The south-bank lands are heavy rice producers, with important mulberry-tree stands that make this the leading silk region of China. Hill slopes are often planted with tea bushes. Near lakes, streams, and coastal waters about 50,000 households depend on fishing for their livelihoods. Pond-fish culture and duck raising in the wet-paddy fields are everywhere part of the farm scene.

The number and density of the population indicate the productiveness of this well-watered plain, although its slight elevation above sea level leads to frequent flooding. The triangular area of about 20,000 square miles of almost level land has an estimated population of 40 million, giving an average density of some 2,000 people per square mile. This contrasts with the state of Mississippi, which is in the same latitudes, which is more than twice as large, but which has only about one-tenth the population. The greater and denser population of the lower Yang-tzu Plain does not derive from the greater fertility of its alluvium, but from the intense hand cultivation, fertilization, and multi-cropping of Chinese agriculture that results in higher unit-area yields.

The population density derives also from the degree of urbanization, higher here than in any other part of China of comparable size—roughly 30 per cent in the triangle as compared with about 15 per cent for China as a whole. This is one of China's significant industrial regions and contains numerous large cities. Hang-chou, Su-chou, and Nan-ching (Nanking) all have been imperial capitals in the past. Among them, Nan-ching has occupied the most recent role as a national capital before the second World War. The former two and Wu-hsi are famous for silk reeling and weaving. Wu-hsi, with the largest population after Nan-ching and Shanghai, also is a noted rice center.

The extraordinary significance of this region, however, must be sought in the situation and functions of Shang-hai, one of the largest cities of the world (reported to have 7,100,000 people in 1957) Shang-hai is 13 miles up the Huang-p'u (Whangpo) River which joins the Yang-tzu at Wusung. It is sited upon unconsolidated alluvium 1,000 feet deep, the surface of which lies only a foot above spring high tide. The city suffers from difficulties with regard to fresh water supply, drainage, and building foundations. Sandbars obstruct both the Yang-tzu and the Huang-p'u, which must be dredged often for navigation. Larger ocean-going vessels usually anchor off Wu-sung. In spite of these and other serious disadvantages of site, the advantages of its situation have triumphed to make Shang-hai the most important commercial and industrial city of all China.

Basic to Shang-hai's situation is the fact that it stands at the mouth of the entire 750,000 square miles of the Yang-tzu drainage basin, containing the productive services and market demands of 200 million people. Half or more of China's foreign and domestic trade in the past has been handled by this great entrepôt. Estimates made before the second World War indicate that nearly half of China's large-scale Western-type industries were concentrated in Shang-hai, which then contained some 43 per cent of the country's industrial labor force. Textile industries were in first place and accounted for more than half of this labor, followed by food processing in which flour milling and tobacco manufacturing led. Virtually every type of light industry catering to the China market is found in Shang-hai. It is the center of the nation's printing industry and has important shipyards and arsenals as well as steel and machinery plants.

With the exception of silk and cotton and some wheat, most of the industrial raw materials for the city are not available in the immediate hinterland. The city's power supply depends upon coal brought from north and northeastern China. Shang-hai is highly vulnerable to blockade, for its commercial and industrial activities depend largely upon free access to raw materials, fuels, and manufactures brought by sea, as well as upon access to foreign markets. However, the long-run advantages assured by its geographical situation operate to maintain the industrial and commercial primacy in China of this gateway to middle China.

The southeast maritime hills are among the least-developed regions in South China. Interior isolation and external contacts epitomize the effects of the geography of this region. Small alluvial plains at the mouths of short rivers reach inland from an irregular coastline. Narrow valleys rise to the northeast-by-southwest Wu-yi range which separates the P'o-yang basin from the Pacific watershed. Each alluvial plain has its own restricted hinterland, and communications among them are difficult. Separation and isolation have produced strong linguistic differences. Ning-po, Fu-chou, Hsia-men (Amoy) are the centers of mutually unintelligible, spoken dialects; in the interior there are other linguistic groups.

By contrast, the numerous sheltering harbors have facilitated external contacts; and interest in marine activities has been enhanced by the factors that limit agricultural opportunities. Men of the southeast coastlands account for a large percentage of China's ablest naval officers, merchant seamen, and fishermen, as well as for some of her more notorious pirates. Harbors, such as those of Amoy and San-men Bay, act as excellent naval bases as well as fishing ports. The hundreds of islands along the coast are surrounded by rich fishing grounds, the full productivity of which awaits more modern fishing boats and equipment. The production around the Chou-shan islands in Hang-chou bay gives Ning-po national fame as the leading fishing market of mainland China, although all the leading ports of this coast are significant fishing centers. Che-chiang is mainland China's biggest source of marine products. Aquatic products from this province in 1955 were estimated at 386,000 tons.

Valuable mineral resources are to be found in the region, although exploitation still is limited. The iron-ore reserves of southern Fu-chien are third-ranking among those of China's provinces. Eighty per cent of China's fluorspar production comes from central Che-chiang province. Large alunite resources are located in the hills on the border between these two provinces. Salt evaporation from sea water is especially important along the southeast shores of Hang-chou Bay where large tidal

Fig. 47 • Shang-hang city, in southwestern Fu-chien province. The city's walls are over five centuries old, having been renewed from time to time, but this is young for Chinese cities. According to records of the existence of walled cities, Fu-chien is one of the younger provinces in the sequence of occupance by Han-Chinese (replacing the ethnically non-Chinese who formerly occupied and still live in numbers in southern China). The city walls initially included agricultural land, but this has gradually been covered by buildings, although even in Nan-ching there are large areas of cultivated land within the walls.

Level land for farming is scarce in Fu-chien and is utilized intensively. The bamboo grove on the river bank is a characteristic component of the subtropical vegetation of southeastern China. This variety produces prized edible shoots. Ripe paddy stands ready for harvest next to elevated rows of sweet potatoes, the two major staple crops of the region. Most of the hills have been denuded of forest, leaving coarse grasses, ferns, and shrubs often cut for fuel. From the hinterland up river, pine logs are cut and floated down the river in rafts; small boats like those on the far bank carry passengers and goods. The river is the Han, which enters the South China Sea near Shan-t'ou (Swatow). (*Herold Wiens.*)

flats occur. A large hydro-electric plant lies southwest of Hang-chou.

The subtropical coastal climate of the region is similar to that of Florida and Georgia. The destructive forces and torrential rains of the southwest Pacific typhoons are felt often, just as the two states suffer from east Caribbean hurricanes. Virtually no freezing temperatures occur in winter near the coast, although in the higher inland regions light frosts are known. Rainfall is heavy and averages over 60 inches yearly. A great variety of semitropical fruits are grown and exported. Wet-rice is overwhelmingly dominant, and two crops a year may be grown on the same land. The sweet potato is a highly important crop and a staple food. Nevertheless, the restricted areas of arable land and the poor leached soils have produced a relatively sparse population that in the entire region totals only 40 million (Figure 47). The effect of these agricultural limitations has been to increase the economic role of home industries, especially in village settlements, although nationally noted handicrafts are produced mainly in the large cities. Fu-chou fine lacquers, silks, fans, and umbrellas, Han-chou and Shao-hsing satins and embroideries, Ning-po reed mats, and Shao-hsing rice wine are some examples. Ning-po saw-lumber and boards are other noteworthy products of the region, for some of the few remaining important timber-producing lands of China are found in the hills here, often as a plantation crop.

The agricultural limitations of the region not only have spurred men to engage in foreign and domestic trade, but also have driven many of the impoverished among them to seek their fortunes and livelihoods overseas as settlers, traders, small entrepreneurs, and laborers. T'ai-wan was settled largely by immigrants from this region, and it supplied also a large percentage of the 10-14 million Chinese in the Southeast Asian countries. Historically, the southeast coast has long been important in foreign trade, and it contains some of the earliest "Treaty Ports" open to Western commerce. Although major economic development is unlikely, many natural resources, including minerals and water power, remain to be developed along with improvements in communications and technology. Railroad connections with the Yang-tzu valley came to this coast for the first time in 1957 when the line from Amoy to Ying-t'an on the Hang-chou to Ch'ang-sha railway was completed. A branch connects with Fu-chou.

In contrast with the coastal southeast, southwestern China is identified with *the southwest Yün-Kuei plateaus.* Southwest of the central lake basins, the hill lands rise to merge into eroded plateau lands of two general levels. The Kuei-chou plateau is the lower level, averaging 4,000 feet. Rising to the second level southwest of it and averaging about 7,000 feet is the Yün-nan plateau. Slope lands comprise over 70 per cent of the land surface, and the chief agricultural lands are found in small lake or river basins. The plateau aspect is most clearly preserved in the northeastern sector of Yün-nan and the adjacent lands of the Kuei-chou border. In Yün-nan south of Ta-li and the central lake cluster around K'un-ming, the plateau aspect is lost in the mountain chains that fragment the landscape. West of the Lan-ts'ang (Mekong) River is the Burma frontier zone, where great longitudinal ranges of mountains are separated by deep, narrow gorges. Virtually no alluvial plains have been built by the upper Salween and Mekong rivers, which also are useless for navigation. They serve mainly as obstacles to communications between China and Burma. Only short reaches of navigable rivers flow through the plateau land.

The climate of Kuei-chou contrasts sharply with that of the Yün-nan

Fig. 48 • The southern Kuei-chou plateau near the Kuang-hsi border and the town of Lo-tien. This is an outstanding example of contrasting geological formations coupled with contrasting types of land uses. The remarkable band of limestone formations running diagonally across the photograph from middle right to upper left is eroded erratically and intricately dissected. In contrast to the cultivation on the broad, sweeping, and relatively gently sloping sandstone formations in the foreground, the darker limestone hills appear virtually devoid of cultivation and are characterized by precipitous slopes, caverns, and disappearing streams. Similar topography appears in Kuang-hsi to the south.

To the north toward Kuei-yang, the Kuei-chou provincial capital, numbers of Miao and Lolo tribesmen live in the hills, engaged in shifting cultivation. In this sparsely populated area, however, the tribesmen are fewer, and they decrease in numbers toward the Kuang-hsi border. *(Herold Wiens.)*

plateau. Summer heat becomes oppressive in the humid basins of Kuei-chou. Fog occurs often, as it does in adjacent Ssu-ch'uan. On the higher slopes this produces a damp and acid soil. Cloudy weather prevails a large part of the year. The higher Yün-nan plateau, however, bears out its name, which means "south of the clouds." Winters have bright, sunshiny, dry weather; summers are wet but not oppressive. A spring-like climate reigns the year around in the plateau levels, but in the southwestern valleys below 4,500 feet the climate assumes the mantle of the hot tropics, and they are rife with malaria and fevers.

Kuei-chou is the most impoverished province of the south. Hence the local saying: "No one has three ounces of silver." Its sterile soils provide a bare subsistence for most of the population (Figure 48). Some rice grows in the basin lowlands, but the main crops are maize and kao-liang, much of it grown on slopes. The only large areas of good paddy land in the southwest plateaus are found in the alluvial fringes of lakes, such as that of Ta-li and K'un-ming in Yün-nan. Here, enough rice, wheat, and maize are produced in good years for self-sufficiency. Large amounts of tea are grown in Yün-nan and exported to the Tibetan high plateau region. The 1956 consignment to Tibet by the communist trade agency amounted to 3,750 tons from Yün-nan and Ssu-ch'uan. Formerly, much opium was produced in both Yün-nan and Kuei-chou, because its light weight and high value could outweigh high transport costs to market areas. Although the private opium traffic has been suppressed by the governing authorities, the opium poppy still is grown for official use in clandestine world traffic.

Yün-nan is the chief tin-producing area of China and is part of the Southeast Asian tin belt. The tin is produced mainly near the Laotian border in an area connected by meter-gauge railroad with K'un-ming and Hanoi. Copper and silver deposits in Yün-nan form about half the national total. Exploitation of tin has progressed furthest, but production is by primitive methods. Nevertheless, Yün-nan tin is important in the world market.

The southwest Yün-Kuei plateaus form a great ethnic frontier of China. Of the more than ten million people in Kuei-chou in 1952, about 40 per cent were non-Chinese tribesmen, the most numerous of which were the Miao mountaineers and Chung-chia valley farmers. In Yün-nan the Chinese are the largest single group, but are a minority in a total population divided into 60 different ethnic groups. Foremost among the tribesmen in Yün-nan are the Thai groups related to the Chung-chia as well as to the founders of modern Thailand, followed by Lolo, Miao, and Moslem groups.

These southwestern plateau lands have retained their frontier character because of their rough topography, poor communications, unsuitability for Chinese-type agriculture, and isolation from the heartland of Chinese civilization, as well as because of the hostility of the non-Chinese tribesmen. Although the Kuei-chou tribesmen have been suppressed ruthlessly during the last two centuries, Chinese control in the southwest near the Yün-nan-Burma frontiers has been very restricted and has centered in "oasis"-like basins like that of T'eng-ch'ung (Figure 49). Large areas were autonomous under feudal-type overlords as late as 1950. The communist regime has recognized the special status of these minority ethnic groups by organizing their territories into so-called "autonomous regions." Their situation in the Burma frontier zone is highly significant in the international relations between the two countries.

Between the southwestern plateaus and the coastal southeast lies *the Ling-nan hills and Hsi Chiang delta region*. The term Ling-nan, the reversal of the Chinese characters for "Nan Ling," indicates the position of this region south of the "Southern Range." The Ling-nan region stretches from the Yün-nan plateau to the South China Sea and is composed of two major physiographic parts, the Hsi Chiang basin, mostly included within Kuang-hsi province, and the coastal drainage of the maritime province of Kuang-tung. Like most of the territory south of the Yang-tzu, Ling-nan primarily is a hilly country in which narrow alluvial river valleys form the chief farmlands. However, owing to the large drainage and volume of the Hsi Chiang and the heavily eroding rainfall of summer, the river carries a great volume of sediment and has built up a delta in Kuang-tung, 2,900 square miles in area. It is only a little larger than the Ch'eng-tu plain, but it is the largest plain south of the central lake basins and contains the largest population concentration in Ling-nan. The political, cultural, and economic focus of Ling-nan thus has come to lie in the Hsi Chiang delta with its great city of Canton, or properly, Kuang-chou.

Except on the higher interior hills, there is no winter in Ling-nan. On the other hand, its coasts bear the main brunt of westward-moving summer typhoons from the tropical Pacific. The January average in the region is over 50°F., although along the coast it is much higher. Rainfall averages the highest in China, more than 60 inches, and is abundant the year around, with heavy summer maxima. There is no pause in the growing season, therefore, so that growing two rice crops a year on the same land is common; a third crop may be rice or a dry crop such as wheat, sweet potatoes, or maize. This multiple-cropping has permitted the Hsi Chiang delta to become the most densely populated agricultural area in China, with over 3,100 persons per square mile of cultivated land. Nevertheless, the food needs of the population of Kuang-tung have exceeded the production of the land, and Kuang-tung has had to import one-fourth of its food supplies. Abundant tropical fruits and other tropical crops are grown in eastern and southern Kuang-hsi and everywhere in Kuang-tung,

but most of Kuang-hsi has a subsistence agriculture. Sugar cane is a specialty of the delta, and mulberry growing and silk production are important subsidiary—and sometimes primary—farm activities.

Kuang-tung has the longest coastline of any province and has some of China's most productive fisheries. Pisciculture is especially important in the delta and engages the activities of more than a million people. Annually some 226,000 metric tons of pond fish are produced.

A variety of minerals occur in Ling-nan, but none is outstanding, and production is limited by antiquated methods. A large number of modern light industries are concentrated mainly in the vicinity of Canton, which is the most important industrial center south of Shang-hai. In 1947 silk and cotton textiles led in the number of workers employed, although the porcelain-and-earthenware industry and boat-building led in value of products. Sugar-processing mills are situated in the delta and in the northeastern lowland around Shan-t'ou (Swatow).

Although not as important industrially as several northern parts of China, Canton prior to communist control was second commercially only to Shang-hai. On a smaller scale than Shang-hai, it nevertheless commands a large hinterland, most parts of which can be reached by navigable streams and for which it is the sole gateway. Railroad connection with the Liang-Hu Basin has enlarged its market area. Although its riverine harbor prevents access by larger ocean-going vessels, the nearness of Hongkong gives it some advantages as well as detracting from some of its commercial prosperity. Historically, Canton was the first port of China open to Western trade, so that its overseas ties are among the strongest of any port of China. Its population is about 1,600,000.

Ethnic and linguistic diversity characterize these southlands. Southwest Kuang-hsi is inhabited largely by the non-Chinese Thai ethnic groups who comprise one-third of the 15 million people of the province. They are highly sinicized, however, and intermarry freely with the Chinese. Another million are from other ethnic groups, almost half being Yao mountaineers. The former non-Chinese peoples of Kuang-tung largely have become acculturated into Chinese civilization and are mixed with Chinese immigrants from the north. Four mutually unintelligible Chinese dialects are spoken by large population groups. In northern Kuang-hsi, the "Mandarin dialect" predominates; Cantonese prevails in

Fig. 50 • Hongkong is the great port for southern China and one of the world's important entrepôts. It stretches along part of the northern coast of Hongkong island and rises up the slopes of the island toward the peak, seen here in the background, the highest point on the island. At the right is the terminal of the Kowloon ferry connecting the island with Kowloon, the urbanized area on the mainland one mile distant, which also forms part of the Crown colony. The buildings along this sector of the waterfront are labelled with the names of companies that help make the city a great commercial center and illustrate its port functions. These structures date from the period of Hongkong's greatest building boom, the last few years of the nineteenth century and the beginning years of the twentieth. Other parts of the city are occupied by Chinese shophouses or by Victorian or modern Western structures. *(Norton Ginsburg.)*

southern Kuang-tung and eastern Kuang-hsi; northeastern Kuang-tung is mainly Hakka-speaking; but around the Shan-t'ou lowland the so-called "Swatow dialect" is spoken. The latter is a variant of Hsia-men (Hoklo) speech.

The British Crown Colony of Hongkong occupies a unique situation some 60 miles southeast of Canton. It is composed of the 32-square-mile island of Hongkong, the mainland Kowloon peninsula, several lesser islands (all of which belong to Great Britain), and the 355-square-mile New Territories, leased from China until 1997. Its sheltered harbor can accommodate the deepest-draft vessels, and its huge warehouse facilities signify its primary function as the main entrepôt between Shang-hai and Singapore (Figure 50). In addition, it is a free port, and to facilitate trade the free exchange of currencies is permitted.

232

Although about 50 square miles of arable land in the New Territories aid in providing food for Hongkong, the 2,250,000 population (in 1955), mostly Chinese, depend primarily on food supplies from Chinese-controlled areas. The colony's commercial existence also depends chiefly upon trade with China, although since 1950 there has developed an increasing trade with Southeast Asia. A variety of light industries, developed especially since 1949 by refugees from Shang-hai, as well as shipbuilding and repair, form an important part of Hongkong's economic life,[2] and its fishing fleet is the largest in the British colonies.

The last of the regions of China consists of two quite distinct parts: *Hai-nan and T'ai-wan islands.* China possesses numerous islands, especially along the south and southeast China coast, and has two small clusters of islands, the Spratleys and Paracels, far south in the South China Sea. Only two of her islands, Hai-nan and T'ai-wan, are of large size. Hai-nan geologically is an extension of the southeast Kuang-hsi hills, parted only by a shallow 20-mile channel from the Liu-chou peninsula. It has a forested, mountainous south rising to a slightly over 6,000-foot core, known as the Li-mu mountains (Mother of the Li) from the fact that they are inhabited by the Li tribes. The northern third is occupied by a low plain where the majority of Chinese settlements and farms are found.

Hai-nan is the only large, tropical part of China, with annual average temperatures of about 77°F. A wet season and a drier season characterize the moist climate, but local wet seasons depend upon the exposures to the prevailing winds. The southwest has a relatively dry season during the winter, while the north gets rain the year around. Crops are similar to those of Kuang-tung, but coffee, cocoa, and rubber also are produced. Hai-nan has some large deposits of high-quality iron ore in the southwest, originally developed by the Japanese, which are tapped by a narrow-gauge railway. Industry is insignificant on the island, the primarily agricultural activities of which support only about one-third as many people as are in T'ai-wan. Hai-nan has a commanding situation in the Gulf of Tongking, and the fine naval base of Yu-lin is strategically situated at the southern end of the island.

T'ai-wan, by contrast, is part of the high, west-Pacific chain of volcanic islands. It has a mountainous eastern side rising precipitously from the Pacific to slope gradually westward to a narrow coastal plain composed of coalescing alluvial fans and only 25 miles at its widest. Most of the 13,885 square miles of surface is occupied by the mountain chain, 48 peaks of which rise over 10,000 feet above sea level. T'ai-wan is roughly one-third the size of Cuba, or the size of Connecticut and Massachusetts combined.

[2] As a result of this rapid industrial expansion, Hongkong probably exceeds Canton in importance as an industrial center.

Although less than a quarter of its surface is arable, it supports a population twice that of Cuba in virtually similar latitudes.

T'ai-wan was not settled by the Chinese in substantial numbers until the middle of the seventeenth century when Ming refugees from the Manchu invasion fled there. Primitive Malay peoples then were the chief inhabitants. These indigenes number some 200,000 and occupy most of the hilly part of the island, while Chinese immigrants from Fu-chien Province have taken over the fertile lowlands. Much of T'ai-wan's economic development and population growth took place during the 50-year period of Japanese occupation between 1895 and 1945. T'ai-wan became Japan's chief source of sugar and, next to Korea, her major source of imported rice, sending a million tons of sugar and two-thirds of a million tons of paddy to Japan each year. The island assumed major international importance when Japan used it as a base for her invasion of the Philippines at the start of the Pacific War; when the war ended it returned to Chinese sovereignty. In 1949 it became the fortress home of the refugee Nationalist government of China, its armed forces, and a large refugee population from the mainland. Its population in 1957 was estimated at 10 million exclusive of the armed forces.

The strategic role of T'ai-wan stems from its position only 100 miles off the China mainland. T'ai-pei (formerly Taihoku), the capital in the north, is 418 miles from Shang-hai; the port of Kao-hsiung (formerly Takao) in the south lies 360 miles from Hongkong. Only 250 miles of water separate T'ai-wan from Luzon island, and Okinawa is closer than Shang-hai. Strategically, T'ai-wan lies within easy air-reach of the southern half of the China coast, and offers air and naval forces on the island potential control of the west-Pacific sea lanes. The Straits of Formosa provide an obstacle to communist conquest that has enabled Nationalist China to evolve here a miniature state.

As in the case of Hai-nan, T'ai-wan's island situation and its mountain core provide a climatic regime that varies from place to place with the direction of prevailing winds. Northeast winds from October through March bring heavy rainfall to the northeast part of the island, but most of the southwest then has clear skies. Southwest winds prevail from the beginning of May through September when the south and southwest are very wet and the north has somewhat lower rainfall. The northeast winds of winter often are of gale strength and do so much damage to crops in the north that bamboo fences or tree shelter belts must be provided to protect exposed fields. During late summer, typhoons are especially destructive in the south. In the southwest coastal plain the average rainfall is lowest, between 40 and 60 inches. Elsewhere it reaches 80 inches and in the mountains may be as high as 200 inches. Disastrous floods sometimes bury parts of the fertile alluvial plains under cobblestones, gravels, and sand, especially on the steep east coast.

Fig. 51 • The southeastern edge of the T'ai-pei basin in northern T'ai-wan, one of the chief agricultural areas of the island. Its level-to-gently-undulating surface and the sloping margins of the surrounding hills are in terraced, double-cropped paddy fields, watered in part from streams impounded behind irrigation dams of the sort seen in the background. The water is diverted into the large canal that runs from the right middleground to the center foreground. An agricultural village occupies the middleground, on the margin of the plain, surrounded by small vegetable gardens, fruit trees, and bamboo groves, omnipresent in subtropical China. In the background are the northern hills and mountains of the mountain mass that extends north-south along the axis of the island. The slopes are heavily forested, but most of the forests in this area are second growth, the aftermath either of logging or of the shifting cultivation practiced by aborigines who live in the uplands. Hydroelectric installations were constructed upstream by the Japanese, the high-tension wires from which may be seen extending into the distance at the left. *(Foreign Operations Administration.)*

During the Japanese occupation, T'ai-wan specialized in producing rice and sugar (Figure 51). These remain the two major crops, although since 1949 a somewhat more balanced agricultural economy has been established. In spite of its large population growth, T'ai-wan remains self-sufficient in foodstuffs and can export a modest surplus of rice, sugar, tropical fruits, essential oil, and tea. In 1956 the rice crop reached 1.78 million metric tons, while even higher goals were being planned. Rice in 1952 accounted for about 42 per cent of the total value of agricultural products. Sweet potatoes in 1952 followed rice with 20 per cent of the total agricultural value. Hog production, with 14 per cent of the total value, is the leading animal industry. The productive fisheries around T'ai-wan bring employment to over 107,000 people. In 1956 the fish catch had risen to a record high of 190,000 metric tons, with a planned production increase by 1960 to a total of 250,000 metric tons.

Forestry is active in the mountain area, about 70 per cent of which is covered with forests. Camphor production from these forests provides three-fourths of the world's natural camphor, although it has diminished in importance with the development of synthetic camphor.

In contrast to mainland China's 70 per cent agrarian population, only about 53 per cent of T'ai-wan's population is directly engaged in agriculture for a livelihood. However, the primarily agrarian character of the island is emphasized by the fact that almost half of the 14,392 factories in operation in 1954 processed food products from T'ai-wan farms. The next four leading types of industry were ceramics, textiles, chemicals, and machines and appliances, each with about 1,300 factory units.

T'ai-wan is highly mineralized, but is poor in minerals available in commercial quantities. Coal is the chief mineral product. In 1955 about 2.36 million metric tons of coal were produced, and a small surplus over domestic needs was exported. A petroleum refinery at Kao-hsiung imports crude oil; and the aluminum refinery, also at Kao-hsiung and based upon hydroelectric power, depends upon ore imports largely from Southeast Asia and partly from Quemoy island, near Hsia-men. Extensive hydroelectric development took place under the Japanese, and in 1954, after some additions to capacity had been made, installed hydroelectric capacity reached some 330,000 kilowatts out of a total of 392,000 kilowatts. By the end of 1957 vigorous expansion of both hydroelectric and thermoelectric facilities was reported to have increased total installed capacity to about 800,000 kilowatts. This provides major support for further industrialization.

Sugar refining is the leading industry, centered in the west and southwest coastal cities, and T'ai-wan in 1953 produced over 900,000 metric tons of sugar of all kinds. Of this amount, over a third was exported to

Japan. The port of Chi-lung (Kiirun or Keelung), with the only outstanding natural harbor, also has some shipyards.

A relatively good rail net—Cape gauge, except for the 2'6" gauge east-coast line—and highway net cover the western plain,[3] while T'ai-wan's steam shipping in 1953 was about twice that of the communist mainland. Foreign commerce is highly important to the economy of the island. Exports in 1957 totaled $148,300,000 in United States dollars, while imports amounted to $128,800,000, but the island also "imported" substantial quantities of fiscal support from the United States to keep its basic needs supplied. Sugar accounted for almost 64 per cent of the exports in 1957, followed by rice. Imports were mainly chemical fertilizers, metals, and machine parts. By 1950 Japan had regained her former position as chief supplier and customer for T'ai-wan, if American-aid imports are excepted. In spite of improvements in both agricultural and industrial production, the island's economy is far from self-sufficient, and outside aid will be necessary until such time as one of the two Chinese governments becomes sovereign over all of China.

SELECTED GEOGRAPHICAL BIBLIOGRAPHY

1. Canada, Department of Mines and Technical Surveys, Geographical Branch. *Taiwan (Formosa), a Geographical Appreciation*. Ottawa: 1952.
2. Chen, C. S. "The Agro-Climate of Formosa, Taipei, Taiwan," *National Taiwan University, Memoirs of the Faculty of Agriculture*, Vol. II, No. 1 (January, 1948).
3. Chen, Han-seng. *Frontier Land Systems in Southernmost China, a comparative study of agrarian problems and social organization among the Pai Yi people of Yünnan and the Kamba people of Sikang*. New York: International Secretariat, Institute of Pacific Relations, 1949.
4. Cressey, George B. "Land Forms of Chekiang, China," *Annals of the Association of American Geographers*, December, 1938, pp. 259-276.
5. Davies, H. R. *Yunnan, the Link Between India and the Yangtse*. Cambridge: 1909.
6. "Formosa," *Focus*, April, 1955.
7. Gage, Eugenia. "The Industrial Development of Formosa," *Economic Geography*, July, 1950, pp. 214-222.
8. Ginsburg, Norton S. *Economic Resources and Development of Taiwan*. New York: Institute of Pacific Relations, 1953.
9. Hanson-Lowe, J. "The Structure of the Lower Yangtze Terraces," *Geographical Journal*, January, 1939, pp. 54-65.
10. Harbour, G. B. "The Physiographic History of the Yangtze," *Geographical Journal*, January, 1936, pp. 17-34.

[3] There are about 2,500 miles of railways on the island, of which all but 590 miles are lines, chiefly of 2-foot gauge, used on sugar plantations and in the foothills. The road system is about 10,000 miles in length, but less than 2,300 miles are main roads.

11. Harland, W. B. "On the Physiographical History of Western Szechwan with special reference to the Ice Age in the Red Basin," *Journal of the West China Border Research Society*, Vol. 15 (1945), Series B, pp. 1-19.

12. Hsiang, C. Y. "The Mountain Economy of Szechwan," *Pacific Affairs*, December, 1941, pp. 448-462.

13. Hoh, Chih-hsiang. "Southwest China, A Political, Social, and Economic Survey," *China Quarterly*, Autumn, 1938, pp. 415-430.

14. Hu, C. Y. "Agriculture and Forestry Land Use of Szechwan" (Ph.D. dissertation, Department of Geography, University of Chicago, 1946).

15. Hu, Huan-yong. "A Geographical Sketch of Kiangsu Province," *Geographical Review*, October, 1947, pp. 609-617.

16. Jen, M. N. "Agricultural Landscape of Southwestern China: A Study in Land Utilization," *Economic Geography*, July, 1948, pp. 157-169.

17. Ladejinsky, Wolf I. "Land Reform in Formosa," *Foreign Agriculture*, June, 1950, pp. 130-135.

18. Liu, Hans. "Hainan, the Island and the People," *China Journal*, November, 1938, pp. 236-246, and December, 1938, pp. 302-314. See also Murphy, R. *Shanghai: Key to Modern China*. Cambridge: Harvard University Press, 1953.

19. Richardson, H. L. *Soils and Agriculture of Szechwan*. Chungking: 1942.

20. Taiwan, Provincial Government, Department of Agriculture and Forestry. *Taiwan Agricultural Yearbook* (annuals 1949 onwards). Taipei, Taiwan.

21. Tang, T. Y. "Land Utilization in South China," *Proceedings of the Sixth Pacific Science Congress*, California, 1939, Vol. 4 (1940), pp. 933-940.

22. Trewartha, G. T. "Field Observations on the Canton Delta of South China," *Economic Geography*, January, 1939, pp. 1-10.

23. Wang, Sheng-tsu. "The Agricultural Regions of Taiwan," *The Science Reports of the National Tsing Hua University*, Series C, Vol. 1, No. 3 (April, 1948), pp. 175-195.

Comments

As a continuation of the selected regional bibliography begun in the preceding chapter, these references pertain to South China. Regional discussions of the various parts of South China are found in George Cressey's *Land of the 500 Million* as well as in his *Asia's Lands and Peoples*. Davies' early book on Yün-nan still forms a valuable reference book for the complex landscape and ethnic composition of this frontier land. Ginsburg's study and the Canadian Department of Mines and Technical Surveys' geographical description of T'aiwan both are useful as references to this strategic island's varied geographical character and economic development in recent times.

China

INDUSTRY AND COMMERCE

ALTHOUGH HER RESOURCES ARE NOT PLENTIFUL OR CONVENIENTLY distributed, China has the foundations for a moderate degree of industrial development. She has enough workers available to make up an industrial labor force: an estimated 83 million Chinese live in urban areas and depend upon nonagricultural pursuits for livelihood. Winfield [1] suggests that China's farms could dispense with another 180 million and continue the same or increased food output, with a more efficient farm size per family. Collectivization and increased use of machine power either under private or state auspices would reduce the number of people required to operate the present farm area and consequently reduce rural job opportunities, thus releasing men for industrial labor.

Human resources and social organization

In 1930 an estimated 20 per cent of China's manpower was engaged in transport activities, compared with only about 5 per cent in industrially advanced countries. This situ-

[1] Gerald Winfield, *China, the Land and the People* (New York: William Sloane, 1948), p. 313.

ation has changed little. A better system of roads and railroads, together with the necessary fuel, vehicles, and rolling stock, would release large numbers of people for new work.

A major problem, of course, would be the training of these novices to the point where they would form a skilled industrial labor force. But many of the handicraft and home-industry artisans are highly skilled in their traditional operations. Rural cottage-industry workers in pre-communist China numbered an estimated 22,660,000, and in urban areas were another 2,000,000. These, plus an additional 1,200,000 workers in small-scale mining, made a total of 25,000,000 part- or full-time workers in small traditional industries and mining.

Before 1937 there probably were fewer than 2,000,000 persons employed in modern industrial activities. In 1951 the communist regime classified 3,000,000 persons in China as industrial workers (excluding those in T'ai-wan). The labor-union membership of about 5,000,000 was about the same under the Nationalist government in 1948 as it was under the communist regime in 1953. The membership, however, included seamen, highway workers, postal workers, and others, as well as factory workers. All told, the total number of people engaged in manufacturing (and mining) in China comes to some 30,000,000, or about 11 per cent of the estimated labor force. This compares with about 30 per cent for the United States, and about 23 per cent for Japan.

In Chinese civilization itself lies the explanation for China's laggard industrial development. China developed philosophy and literature to a high degree, but the method of science, of acquiring knowledge by testing hypotheses under experimental conditions, did not develop until after its introduction from the Occident. Social prestige also encouraged the intelligentsia to avoid those types of manual labor with which engineers, for instance, necessarily are associated. Moreover, efficiency and precision did not acquire high status in traditional Chinese society. The superabundance of so-called "cheap" labor and the social obligation of kinship inhibited the discharge of superfluous labor, encouraged nepotism, and promoted economic inefficiency. The tightly knit family and clan system handicapped the mobilization of capital resources from small potential investors, who invested in agricultural land at inflated prices. Individual initiative also was stifled by the family system, and state industrial enterprise was not developed significantly owing to both tradition and lack of capital. Further, understanding the need for precision work and for the care of machines that involve small tolerances comes hard to people accustomed to crude implements and to a lack of standards of uniformity.

Western Europe, Russia, and Japan during the nineteenth and early twentieth centuries sought to keep China a reservoir of raw materials and

Fig. 52 • The wheelbarrow is one of the prime movers in China's land transportation system. Its use illustrates the degree to which China depends upon the direct use of human energy for the movement of its produce. The barrows shown here are characteristic of those in Shan-tung province—this November scene having been photographed in the Lao Shan of eastern Shan-tung. Note the treeless eroded hills and the lines of neglected terraces in the background. At the right are small rock-bordered fields in which winter wheat, the chief grain of the region, has been planted. The road itself is better than most in the hilly areas of northern China, though unsurfaced and poorly graded. *(Norton Ginsburg.)*

a noncompetitive market for their own industries. Then when the Chinese system of autocratic government that had lasted for thousands of years broke down—precisely at the time when revolutionary Western science, technology, and thought were thrust upon the scene—China was thrown into convulsions from which she still had not recovered when the Japanese invasion occurred. This invasion blossomed into the Pacific war and brought havoc to China's society and economy, and despair to the intelligentsia, softening it for the penetration of communist ideology. Under a chaotic economic system, industrial development had been so ill-organized that long before the communist regime came into power the Nationalist government had taken the initiative in and control of a wide range of industrial activities in order to accelerate economic development. However, state control of almost every aspect of the economy began only with the communist accession to power in 1949.

Transportation and communications

The inadequacy of its land communications has seriously retarded the development of modern China (Figure 52). China has only two miles of railways per 100,000 population, as compared with 250 miles for the United States or 50 for northwestern Europe. The poorest American laborer commands about 200 times as much transportation as a Chinese laborer relying on transport by manpower. This reflects not merely the higher real wages of the American workman, but also the cheaper transport that serves him.

The belief that "coolie" transport is cheap is erroneous. A sedan-chair carrier during the 1930's earned the equivalent of about 75 cents U.S. money per day, but he could travel slowly and only for short distances. Charges for human carriers amounted to more than eight times the 2-3 cents (in Chinese currency) per mile by train. High-cost transport of this type acts to restrict the radius of trade as well as the variety of market goods. Even in coal-rich Shen-hsi province, Chinese cannot afford to use much coal except in the vicinity of the mine because of high transport costs.

The damper on the interregional exchange of products caused by slow and expensive transportation in China has been effective in making many regions practically dependent on local resources alone. Between B.C. 108 and A.D. 1911 there were 1,828 famines important enough to be registered in different parts of China, or an average of about one per year. That they were unnecessarily serious was due chiefly to an inability to bring relief shipments in time from food-surplus areas within the country.

The relative costs of transport in China vary with differences in transport methods. If 100 was the cost of river-steamer transport in China in 1937, then railroad transport cost about 112, river junks 175, pack animals 425, handcarts 450, and "coolie" carrier 890. Horse-drawn carts in 1937 probably rated between the native boats and pack animals in cost per ton-mile.

North China, with its large plains and relatively level surface, traditionally relies upon carts drawn by animals and men. Because of the dry climate, seasonal drought, and shifting river channels, few rivers in north China are navigable, except seasonally by small boats. In southern China, "coolie" carriers and pack animals furnish transport on routes not paralleled by navigable rivers. The mountainous topography makes land transport slow and difficult, but almost every stream with over a foot of channel depth carries boat traffic. These traditional forms of transport, whether in north or south China, are inefficient compared to mechanized transport.

The first real work on motor highways in China was a project of the American Red Cross to provide relief work for famine sufferers in 1920-21, when 850 miles of dirt motor roads were constructed in north China. It was only in 1931 that the central government began a concerted plan for building new highways. The civil and international wars slowed construction of roads or destroyed them in some parts of eastern China, while stimulating construction in parts of the west. Motor highways in 1954 reached only 96,000 miles, exclusive of 2,300 miles of highways in Outer Mongolia. The majority of these highways are dirt-surfaced, although the main routes are macadamized. Although China thus is being provided with a network of motor highways, their use is limited mainly to strategic and official purposes. Only a few tens of thousands of motor vehicles, mostly trucks, are found in all China. Most of these are for military use. Moreover, because China produces little petroleum, fuel is expensive and scarce. Rehabilitation of motorized transport was undertaken by the communist regime after 1949. In 1950 the index of highway transport capacity, compared with an index of 100 for 1941, was only 65. By 1951 this reportedly had been increased to 119.[2]

Railroad construction in China, as in the West, preceded modern highway construction. It was initiated by foreign interests desiring to carve out commercial domains in China and interested in profitable investments. There was no coherent plan of development. Each foreign power used political and economic pressure to force the Manchu government and the succeeding republican regimes or the controlling warlords to give it rights of investment in particular railroad lines. Although many Chinese officials saw the advantages of railroads and sought to finance their construction without foreign capital, to which undesirable economic or political commitments often were tied, they seldom were able to raise sufficient capital of their own.

The northeast has the best rail network in China, largely as a result of Japanese development, with nearly half of China's 16,800 miles of rails in 1956. The Soviet Union successfully reasserted its dominant interests in and joint control of the main Manchurian lines in 1945 with the ousting of Japan. However, by 1953 full control reportedly was turned over to communist China.

[2] The reported imports of only 13,863 trucks and passenger cars (together with some spare parts and extra tires) during the period from August, 1950, to March, 1953, indicates how modest this progress actually has been.

Fig. 53 • Construction of a railway embankment for the Lung-hai railroad near Lin-t'ao, Kan-su province, 1947. Although this segment of the railroad was completed by the communists, it was begun under Nationalist direction. No machinery is employed, only hoes, baskets, and carrying poles backed by the muscles of men. While the efficiency of this labor is low, there is no shortage of it. Note the bare and eroded loessal hills in the background. *(Lt. Col. David R. Longacre.)*

South of the Great Wall, the rail net is most dense in north China east of the Huang Ho loop. The chief east-west line is the Lung-hai railroad running from the port of Lien-yün through Hsi-an in Shan-hsi to Pao-chi. From here an extension has been constructed by the communists to Lan-chou (Figure 53), and further construction is extending it westward through Dzungaria eventually to join the Turk-Sib railroad at Alma Ata in the Kazakh S.S.R.[3] The completion of this route will shorten considerably eastern China's rail ties with European Russia. A shorter connection (by 721 miles) between the Soviet Trans-Siberian railway and Inner Mongolia is provided by the Trans-Mongolian railroad (completed in 1955) between Ulan Bator, already connected with Ulan Ude on the Trans-Siberian to the north, and Ch'i-ning on the Peking-Pao-t'ou railroad. At Ch'i-ning there is a break-of-gauge between the broad-gauge Trans-Mongolian line and the Chinese network, and cars are shifted by cranes from one set of car frames to another. From Pao-t'ou, a rail extension is to follow the outside of the Huang Ho loop westward and southward to connect with Lan-chou. While the Trans-Mongolian and Trans-Turkestan

[3] At 1957 rates of construction, however, this railroad cannot be completed much before 1970.

railroads will provide better connections with Soviet Russia, long-run economic and political gains for China may be derived from the improved communications with Outer Mongolia and Hsin-chiang.

In south China, railroads are more widely spaced, and many areas are as much as 200 miles from the nearest rail line. No railroad parallels the Yang-tzu River, the chief east-west transport artery in China, into which, however, a number of railways feed.[4] But north-south lines connect the northern Siberian and Korean borders with Vietnam and the Kuang-tung coast. The lack of railroads in south China is made up in part by the navigable rivers. In southwest China railroad construction has made little headway, although the line from Liu-chou in Kuang-hsi was being extended to Kuei-yang, and a railroad eastward from Liu-chou was being planned to connect with Canton. The lack of railroads in the southwest is a particular handicap, since most rivers in the Yün-Kuei Plateau region are not navigable. In Ssu-ch'uan significant rail-laying did not occur until 1952, when the Chungking-Ch'eng-tu line was completed and the Trans-Ch'in Ling railroad to Pao-chi was begun. This 415 mile line was completed in 1956. In the southeast coastal region a rail line was completed in mid-1955 from the port of Chan-chiang (formerly the French Kuang-chowan), not far from Hai-nan island, inland to connect with the Kuang-hsi-Vietnam railroad at Li-t'ang. Farther north, construction was completed in 1957 on a railroad to the port of Hsia-men (Amoy) from the interior town of Ying-t'an on the Che-chiang - Chiang-hsi railway, thus providing connections with Shang-hai and Han-k'ou. In 1960 a railroad was to be built to Lhasa from Hsi-ning in Ch'ing-hai.

Although 24,200 miles of inland waterways are considered navigable by different sizes and types of craft in China, about two-thirds are usable only by flat-bottomed junks and sampans. Large steamers can use only 2,000 miles, mostly on three rivers: the Yang-tzu in central China, and the Amur and the Sungari along the northeastern frontier. Shallow-draft steamers operate on another 1,200 miles. Additional mileage is currently being added through dredging operations.

Although China has besides her rivers some 4,000 miles of coastline, her prewar steam shipping amounted to only 570,000 gross tons. Foreign-owned shipping brought the total in her waters to 1,280,000 gross tons. By 1947, after the second World War, reparations from Japan, lend-lease, and purchases brought China's steam-shipping tonnage to about 1,000,-000 tons. Much of this was withdrawn by the Nationalists to T'ai-wan, and the communist mainland in 1956 had under 500,000 tons, an esti-

[4] Until 1957 the Yang-tzu was not crossed by a railroad. In 1955, construction was begun on a railway bridge to span the river at Han-k'ou. This was preceded by a bridge across the Han river finished in 1956. The Yang-tzu bridge is 5,600 feet long with two decks, the upper for a multilane highway and the lower for a double-track railroad. A second bridge now spans the Yang-tzu at Chungking.

Fig. 54 • Junks and sampans carry enormous quantities of goods over China's rivers and along her coasts. These in the harbor of Hongkong illustrate the differences in size among them. The sampan in the foreground moves goods from one part of Hongkong harbor to another and is similar to those that ply the waters of the Hsi River and the streams of the southeast coastal region. In the background are ocean-going junks of about 100 tons capacity, mostly sail-driven although some are motorized, which carry goods for hundreds of miles in the coastwise trade and penetrate well up the great rivers such as the Yang-tzu. Similar vessels are employed in fishing, although the fishermen use even smaller sampans, and in southeastern China they also use bamboo rafts. The people who man the vessels are the so-called "boat people," who number over 100,000 in Hongkong alone and live aboard their junks. (Norton Ginsburg.)

mated 500,000 tons short of minimum needs. These figures do not include the thousands of junks plying China's inland and coastal waters, which may possess up to a million tons capacity (Figure 54).

Mineral and power resources

Although traditional social organization, chaotic political developments, and poor communications have hindered industrialization in China, these retarding influences may be changed or manipulated, particularly where government has power to promote industrialization. More rigid limitations become evident when one considers the availability and distribution of resources, but even these limitations must be regarded as applying more to the type and scope than to the over-all level of industrial development. Moreover, one must differentiate between short-term and long-term potentials.

China has the only substantial coal reserves in eastern Asia, excluding Siberia. In 1947, the National Resources Commission of China estimated her reserves at 444 billion metric tons, more than four times that of Germany prior to the second World War, about twice that of Great Britain, but less than 7 per cent of that of the United States. The per-capita reserves, therefore, are about equivalent to those of Germany before the war. In 1957, however, Peking estimates of 1,200 billion tons were announced. Coal measures in China are for the most part of high grade. Bituminous coal amounts to 78 per cent of the total reserves. The quantity suitable for coking is considerable, at least some six billion tons, and most of it is close to sources of iron ore. Although coal is scattered widely in China, and 14 provinces each have reserves of over a billion tons, there is a marked localization of reserves. Four-fifths of the total are found in the loess-region provinces of Shen-hsi and Shan-hsi. Southern China is relatively poorly endowed, although there are sizable reserves in Ssu-ch'uan.

Paradoxically, China's coal production is chiefly from areas with small reserves. Southern Manchuria and Ho-pei Province, with only about 2 per cent of the reserves,[5] contributed 56 per cent of the production in 1931, whereas the loess-land provinces contributed only 9 per cent of the total. In south China, of the four leading provinces, only Hu-nan produced as much as 900,000 tons, or less than 4 per cent of the total. The annual production prior to 1937 was about 32 million tons. Under the stimulus of war and the westward movement of industries, production in Ssu-ch'uan, Yün-nan, and Kuei-chou provinces reached more than three million tons

[5] A communist news report in 1955 asserted that new surveys have increased estimates of Fu-shun coal reserves by one-third.

in 1939. Free and Occupied China, including Manchuria, in 1944 produced 62.5 million tons of coal. In 1956, however, production was reported at 95 million tons, and the planned production annually by 1967 is 300 million tons.

Development and prospecting in Manchuria, Hai-nan island, Hu-pei and western Ssu-ch'uan provinces, and elsewhere have in recent years raised estimates of China's iron-ore reserves. This emphasizes the fact that, although the important mineral resources of China are reasonably well known, future exploration may change the picture, especially in the more remote regions. However, China has only moderate supplies of iron ore, although a 1952 U.N. report gives estimates of 4-5 billion tons and the Peking government claims 12 billion, four to five times earlier estimates. Most of the ores have a low iron content, so that utilization of them must wait cheaper methods of extraction and reduction. About 76 per cent of China's known iron ore in 1956 was found in southern Manchuria. Some high-grade iron ores are found south of the Great Wall, of which those on Hai-nan may be the most important. The former Cha-ha-erh province (included chiefly in the Inner Mongolian Autonomous Region) has deposits of high-grade ores estimated at 92 million tons. In recent years a deposit of over 100 million tons of ore with 65 per cent iron content was located in eastern Hsi-k'ang. The Ta-yeh mines in eastern Hu-pei are the most important in middle China. In late 1956 there were reports of two new deposits along the Yang-tzu in Hu-pei, totaling 600 million tons with other large deposits in Kan-su and Ssu-ch'uan.

China south of the Great Wall had an annual production during 1930-34 of only some 140,000 tons of pig iron, and production in Manchuria amounted to 647,000 tons in 1936. Japan's vigorous drive for production after her invasion of China brought the total iron ore production in 1942 to 9,727,000 tons, of which less than 1,000,000 tons were produced outside of Japanese-occupied areas. Half the total was produced in southern Manchuria. Here the steel works at An-shan and Pen-ch'i together had a capacity for producing over 2,500,000 tons of pig iron in 1944, but actual production did not reach 2,000,000 tons. After Japan's collapse in Manchuria, production was brought to a virtual standstill by neglect, civil war damage, and Russian looting. By 1958, however, production of pig iron reportdly reached 13 million tons, and steel, 8 million tons. Plans for 1960 envisaged an increase of steel ingot production to about 18 million metric tons, through the rehabilitation and expansion of the facilities in Manchuria and at Ta-yeh, as well as in Tientsin, T'ai-yüan, Shang-hai, and Chungking, and the construction of a new installation at Pao-t'ou.

Oil reserves of China still remain largely unknown. Earlier estimates based upon superficial field surveys indicated that large parts of the northwest showed sedimentary rocks of a petroliferous character, and oil seepages were observed. However, limited drillings did not provide an optimistic forecast of reserves. Pre-communist estimates on the basis of known reserves indicated a total of only some 1.6 billion barrels. By 1956 the vigorous search by communist geologists disclosed proven reserves of at least 100 million tons. In 1957 over half the annual production came from the Yü-men field in northwest Kan-su. This amounted to 800,000 tons. Great hopes have been aroused by prospecting at Karamai in northern Hsin-chiang, and in the Tsaidam basin of Ch'ing-hai province. Other oil-bearing structures are found in Ssu-ch'uan, Shen-hsi, and Manchuria. Total crude oil production, including oil from shale, in 1956 amounted to 1.2 million tons. Estimated 1957 production was 1.5 million tons, and by 1962 the Chinese hope to produce over 5 million tons or about half of China's planned needs annually.

Large deposits of oil shale are present in Manchuria, Ssu-ch'uan, Shen-hsi, Hu-nan, and Ling-nan. The largest accumulation is in southern Manchuria. In 1957 the shale-oil extraction plant at Fu-shun, where the great open-pit coal mine is located, produced 600,000 tons of oil reportedly at full capacity. Both oil shale and coal, from which oil can be derived through hydrogenation, represent large potential oil sources for China. Techniques developed in the United States have demonstrated that oil extraction from shale can compete economically with natural petroleum.

China has no important natural sulfur deposits, but obtains sulfur, basic to the chemical industry, from pyrite. Production has not met industrial needs, so that sulfur has been imported from Japan. Copper is widespread in China, but, as in the case of lead, zinc, and silver, which in China show a similar pattern of distribution, the domestic supply in the past has not been sufficient—the reasons being the lack of refining plants and the fact that most deposits have been developed only partially. Manchuria has about half the known deposits of lead and zinc, which are not abundant. The southwestern provinces of China have about half the known reserves of copper and silver. China has some very substantial quantities of certain ferro-alloys. Manganese reserves are adequate for her needs, and supplies of tungsten, tin, and antimony are far in excess of needs. As noted in a preceding chapter, antimony and tungsten both exhibit a striking concentration. Tin is most important in Yün-nan, but adjacent provinces also produce it.

China has in southern Manchuria one of the world's largest reserves of magnesite. Reserves of 882 million tons of bauxite are distributed mainly in southern Manchuria, Shan-tung, the Yün-Kuei Plateau, and Kan-su. Alunite, a subsidiary aluminum ore, is found in An-hui and the east-coast provinces of Che-chiang and Fu-chien.

In the nonmetallic field, China has abundant resources for the glass and ceramic industries, and ample quantities of salt, gypsum, and talc for cement and chemical uses. Asbestos, mica, quartz, saltpeter, soda, and phosphate all are to be found.

China's potential water power amounts to over two-thirds that of the United States and about 3.3 per cent of the world total. In 1957 it was estimated to be 300 million kilowatts. Unfortunately, much of the potential lies in the remote, sparsely populated, and undeveloped mountain areas fringing the eastern approaches to the Tibetan plateau. The seasonal factor also causes undesirable fluctuations in the water volume. Several magnificent sites for hydroelectric development, however, are situated in south and west China. Most of the potential lies in the south. North China's rivers carry so much silt (as much as 40 per cent by weight of the liquid volume of the Huang Ho in flood) that reservoirs are apt to have a relatively short useful life before they become silted full. Moreover, in winter ice formation restricts water movement. Nevertheless, as noted previously, the communist regime has ambitious plans for a series of 46 dams to help control the Huang and to produce 110 billion KWH of electricity a year.

The most significant hydroelectric developments, however, have taken place (under the Japanese) in eastern Manchuria, partly along the upper Sungari and Mu-tan rivers and partly on the Yalu River, shared with Korea. In 1944 the total installed capacity of both hydro and thermal power facilities in Manchuria was estimated at 1,790,000 kilowatts as compared with 1,350,000 kilowatts in all the rest of China. The Sui-feng (Sup'ung) plant on the Yalu is one of the largest in the world. Situated 40 miles up the river from the port of An-tung, the dam is 525 feet high and 2,530 feet long (Figure 28). In 1952, its capacity was said to have been 700,000 kilowatts. Entirely within Manchuria, the Hsiao-feng-man hydroelectric plant on the Sungari River has a dam 3,510 feet long and 330 feet high, which backs up a large body of water known as Sung-hua Lake. The installed capacity was as high as 567,000 kilowatts; in 1954 most of this capacity had been restored following civil-war destruction and Russian looting. The Mu-tan River, also in Manchuria, has a potential of 200,000 kilowatts, but in 1952 the hydroelectric station at the mouth of Ching-po Lake had a developed capacity of only 46,000 kilowatts. In 1957 work started on a hydroelectric station in Che-chiang province on the Hsin-ah territory of the Ch'ien-t'ang River. This plant is to have 580,000 kilowatts capacity.

Industrial regions and production

The competition of modern industry has made serious inroads into Chinese home and handicraft industries, but during the prewar period much of this competition came from foreign imports or from industries in China owned by foreign capital. China as a whole still depends upon home handicrafts and traditional industries for about 75 per cent of its manufactured commodities. In certain lines, however, home industries have long been largely superseded, and supply depends almost entirely upon modern factory output, and often upon imports. Cotton cloth and cotton yarns represent the most important commodities of this type. Home weaving has almost disappeared from the Chinese scene.

Before 1937, modern industrial development was confined to six areas, which were relatively accessible to foreign intercourse. All except one were located along or near the eastern coast. These were:

(1) Liao-ning province in southern Manchuria, with iron-and-steel mills at An-shan (Figure 35) and Pen-ch'i, the shale-oil reduction plant at Fu-shun, and the largest railway shops, shipyards, and cement factory in China, as well as important chemical plants. At Ch'ang-ch'un an automobile plant was completed in 1956, capable of producing 30,000 trucks a year.

(2) The lower Yang-tzu plain within the triangle south of the river, where two-thirds of China's textile industry were found. Shang-hai occupies a position with respect to China somewhat like that of New York in relation to the United States. It is the commercial and industrial headquarters of the country.

(3) Northeastern Ho-pei province from Peking through Tientsin to the Great Wall. Here are the K'ai-lan coal mines, China's second largest, and the three industrial centers—T'ang-shan, with its large cement factory; Ch'in-huang-tao, the coal export port and the site of the largest glass factory in China; and Tientsin, port as well as the chief cotton textile and flour-milling center for north China. The region also has steel plants.

(4) Eastern Shan-tung along the railway from Ch'ing-tao to Chi-nan, with coal mining and iron industries, cotton textile mills, flour mills, and vegetable-oil plants. Ch'ing-tao has a locomotive factory.

(5) The Liang-Hu Basin in the triangle between Han-k'ou, P'ing-hsiang, and Ch'ang-sha, with the iron-and-steel works at Wu-han based upon the Ta-yeh iron mines, the largest outside of Manchuria. Here in the Wu-Han metropolitan area also are large textile mills and factories preparing tea, eggs, cotton, t'ung oil, and vegetable oils, and in Ch'ang-sha are textile and flour mills and refineries for antimony. A new Ta-yeh iron-and-steel plant was being constructed in 1956 with Soviet aid.

(6) The Hsi River delta along the Canton-Kowloon railroad, with silk filatures, factories for ceramics, rubber goods, light bulbs, and electric fixtures, as well as sugar refineries and small shipyards. Although Hongkong is British territory, it belongs industrially to this area and has

a great number and variety of light industries, as well as considerable shipbuilding capacity.[6] Textiles are of particular importance.

The loss to Japan of these industrial areas during the Sino-Japanese War and the second World War forced a shift of some of Free China's industries to the northwest and southwest provinces, largely neglected prior to 1937. The two principal areas that developed into industrial centers as a result of the westward flight were Chungking, with its small steel and cement plants, and southwest Ssu-ch'uan, centering around Lo-shan south of Ch'eng-tu city. Industries here produced sugar, salt, paper, silk, matches, pottery, and cotton textiles, using bituminous coal and hydroelectricity as power sources. Lo-shan is not far from the recently discovered deposits of high-grade iron ore at Lu-ku on the Ta-tu River. In the loess region the capital of Shan-hsi province, T'ai-yüan, long had an arsenal and light industries, and after 1953 heavy industrial development was pressed forward with the construction of a large thermoelectric plant and a major steel and machinery complex. Lan-chou also has expanded.

During 1954 a Sino-Soviet agreement provided Soviet aid for the development of two new iron-and-steel plants in China, aside from the rehabilitation of certain industries in Manchuria. One is the plant at Ta-yeh already mentioned. A second is an iron-and-steel combine blueprinted by the Russians for Pao-t'ou in Inner Mongolia based upon local iron and coal resources. The population of this former capital of Inner Mongolia reportedly had increased tenfold to 500,000 since 1949. Pao-t'ou is not far west of Chi-ning, the terminus of the Trans-Mongolian railroad to Soviet Siberia. In 1956, a new Sino-Soviet agreement was signed, providing Russian capital equipment for these and other heavy industries in return for Chinese "agricultural, mineral, and handicraft products."

China's industrial production by no means satisfies the needs of her people for consumer goods, which are in gravely short supply. In commodities supplied by the light industries, especially, China has advantages of raw materials and abundant labor for large-scale development. The chief difficulty encountered in pre-communist industrial development was the lack of capital accumulation to finance new enterprises under a free-enterprise system. This was largely the result of poverty and lack of savings for investment, but partly also because of a social psychology that distrusted the impersonal Western-type stock companies based upon small investors, partly because of political insecurity, and partly because of the traditional feeling that farmland provided the safest and most valuable form of investment. With the state now having unrestricted access

[6] The industrial labor force in Hongkong in 1956 was estimated at 100,000 persons, more than in any other city in southern China. Hongkong's postwar industrial development, especially in textiles, light metal, and plastics manufactures, was greatly stimulated by the flight of Chinese capital and entrepreneurs from Shanghai after 1949.

to capital as well as labor, industrial development may be rapid where raw materials or plant equipment do not depend upon imports from the West. Imports from other than Soviet-bloc countries are restricted both by political factors and by domestic need for China's own exports.

Trade [7]

The traditional attitude toward foreign trade was expressed by the Ch'ien Lung emperor in the eighteenth century when he wrote to the King of England: "Strange and costly objects do not interest me. As your ambassador can see for himself, we possess all things. I set no value on objects strange and ingenious and have no use for your country's manufactures." Originally, the difficulty that faced the commercial West was in finding something the Chinese wanted in exchange for their merchandise. The answer was Indian opium, until China herself began to produce large amounts. In contemporary times, China has been the party seeking to satisfy the market demands of the West, while she has been eager to obtain Western manufactures. The resultant trade in bulky utilitarian commodities is a comparatively recent phenomenon, for the earlier trade had been mainly in luxury goods.

The last four or five decades have seen great changes in the total volume of imports and exports, as well as in the chief types and values. There has been a notable decline in the once-flourishing tea trade, from which China has been ousted by more aggressive and adaptable rivals. In 1913 tea accounted for 8 per cent of the total value of exports. In 1928 it amounted to only 4 per cent, and in 1947 only 3.6 per cent. From 1913 to 1928 silk exports rose from 17,500 tons to 25,400 tons, but China's world position was lower, and silk's position among the total exports fell from 24 per cent to 16 per cent. In 1947 silk exports had fallen to about 2.5 per cent of total exports by value. Here again, as in the case of tea, competition of better-grade silks from Japan and other countries, as well as the development of synthetics, were important factors in the decline.

In exports, China came to rely more on bulky items such as foodstuffs and raw materials. Over many years these bulky materials supplied 50 per cent of the total exports, with foodstuffs alone running from 17 to 33 per cent by value. Beans, for instance, made up 6.8 per cent of exports in the period 1909-13, but in 1923-29 they averaged 12.2 per cent. The drop to 1 per cent in 1935 reflected the Japanese conquest of Manchuria and its detachment from the Chinese customs. A reported export of 640,-

[7] The trade of China is difficult to assess because of the lack of both adequate data and meaningful norms for comparative purposes. China has been in a state of revolutionary convulsion for about a century. Political changes in territory control such as that involved in Japan's occupation of Manchuria and the divided control over China have confused statistical analyses.

000 tons of soybeans from Hei-lung-chiang province went to Soviet bloc countries in 1956. In 1936, t'ung oil accounted for 10.4 per cent of all exports, although previously it had accounted for only 2.4 per cent. In 1947 it accounted for 15.2 per cent for all exports in value. Although accounting for only a small percentage of China's "normal" exports, minerals became an increasingly important export during the first half of the present century. Modest quantities of coal and salt were sent to Japan from Manchuria during the Japanese occupation. From China proper, coal exports also were sent to Japan from Shan-tung and Ho-pei and iron ore from the Ta-yeh mines in the Yang-tzu valley. An agreement was signed with Pakistan in May, 1956, to ship 300,000 tons of coal to that country in exchange for cotton. South China's exports of surplus antimony, tungsten, and tin during the Sino-Japanese War added significant foreign exchange to Free China's treasury.

There have also been marked changes in the relative importance of major import items. Food imports increased from 17 per cent in 1913 to 25 per cent in 1927. However, in 1947 wheat flour amounted to only 3.3 per cent of the imports in value. During the earlier period there was an increase of raw material imports from 12 to 24 per cent, and a drop in manufactured imports from 62 to 43 per cent. Both of these reflect the increasing degree of industrial development, especially of the textile industry, within China. Among the raw material imports, raw cotton, cotton yarn, and thread headed the list in 1947, amounting to 18.5 per cent of all imports, although after 1950 the Communists claimed that domestic raw cotton production satisfied all domestic needs. Nevertheless, China's 1954 trade included imports of 32,000 tons of cotton. In 1909-13 cotton goods averaged 30.8 per cent of all imports, but by 1930-34 they were down to 6.9 per cent, although still among the leading imports. In 1947 they are not even mentioned as important imports. The decline of textiles and foodstuffs was associated with increases in metals and machinery imports. Machinery, tools, metals, and metal manufactures together amounted to 19.7 per cent of total imports in 1947. In 1956 the communist Chinese were beginning to boast of exports of textile machinery to Egypt and Southeast Asian countries presaging possible future competition with Japan in these markets. However, food still leads exports to the USSR.

During the first four decades of this century, the trend of trade was away from Great Britain and toward the Pacific powers, especially Japan and the United States. Between 1913 and 1929, Great Britain's percentage dropped from 11.4 to 8.5, Japan's share increased from 19 to 25.4 per cent, while the percentage for the United States increased from 7.5 to 16.1. In 1953, 75 per cent of the mainland trade was with the Soviet Union and its satellites, the embargo imposed by the West on China in

1950 having greatly decreased the non-Soviet oriented trade. In 1957, this embargo was partially lifted by the western European countries, though not by the United States. Trade with Japan has been small.

Such dependence upon the Soviet Union and its satellites is highly undesirable, both from the Soviet and from the communist Chinese viewpoints. Aside from political considerations, the Soviet Union is unable to supply much that China needs for industrialization, and increased Chinese communist trade with the outside world would aid the Soviet Union in obtaining more of what it wants from China. Strenuous efforts are being made by the Chinese communists, therefore, to enlarge their trade with the free-world countries and to surmount the restrictions and embargoes placed upon this trade by unfriendly countries.

The communist regime in 1955 announced that since 1949 it had concluded trade agreements with 17 countries and had had trade with 60-odd countries. Its 1954 trade amounted in value to 8,486 million communist yuan.[8] The reported foreign trade in 1957 was $4.2 billion.

In general, the communist system of barter agreements on a governmental basis with foreign countries or foreign trade delegations appears to be the prevailing method of commercial interchange. A barter agreement with Ceylon in 1954 resulted in the exchange of 270,000 tons of Chinese rice for 50,000 tons of Ceylon rubber. A barter agreement with Burma involved Chinese purchase of 150,000 tons of Burmese rice and Burmese purchase of steel materials, textiles and the like, while 60,000 tons of Egyptian cotton. In 1955, British trade with China, restricted by the embargo, amounted to only £20 million, in real value a mere fraction of the prewar trade at its peak. It has risen greatly since.

China's chief commercial ports are Ta-lien for Manchuria, Tientsin and Ch'ing-tao for north China, Shang-hai and Han-k'ou for central China, and Hongkong and Canton for south China. Shang-hai by far ranks first, and in the 1920-36 period it was the sixth or seventh ranking world port. In the 1870's it handled 62 per cent of the total foreign trade. By 1920 this position had dropped to 45 per cent as the north Chinese ports developed. In 1947, however, it accounted for 75 per cent of the entire import trade and 60 per cent of the exports. This marked an abnormal situation, for trade in Manchuria was almost at a standstill. However, in 1956 the Chinese press reported that exports via Shanghai reached their highest peak in the city's history in the first six months of that year.

In the long view, there have been significant increases in the volume of trade during the last century, especially during the first decades after

[8] Depreciation of communist currency by 1954 resulted in its replacement at a rate of exchange of 10,000 yuan old currency to one yuan in the new currency. Further depreciation makes uncertain what the above cited value of the 1954 trade actually means.

1900. Nevertheless, although China's huge population represents a large market in total, the per-capita trade of China remains among the lowest in the world.

SELECTED GEOGRAPHICAL BIBLIOGRAPHY

1. Arnold, J. "Commercial Problems of China," *Annals of the American Academy of Political and Social Science*, November, 1930, pp. 142-159.
2. "The Electric Power Development in China," *The Third World Power Conference, 1936, Transactions*, Vol. II, 1938, pp. 105-130.
3. Fong, H. D. "The Postwar Industrialization of China," *National Planning Association*, Planning Pamphlets Nos. 12-13, June, 1942.
4. Ginsburg, N. S. "China's Railroad Network," *Geographical Review*, July, 1951, pp. 470-474.
5. Howard, Harry Paxton. "Transportation in China, New and Old," *China Journal*, May, 1939, pp. 299-304.
6. Juan, V. C. "Mineral Resources of China," *Economic Geology*, June-July, 1946, No. 4, Part 2, Supplement, pp. 399-474.
7. Lieu, D. K. *China's Economic Stabilization and Reconstruction*. New Brunswick: Rutgers University Press, 1948.
8. Murphey, Rhoads. "China's Transport Problem and Communist Planning," *Economic Geography*, January, 1956, pp. 17-28.
9. Ou, P., and F. Wang. "Industrial Production and Employment in Pre-war China," *Economic Journal*, September, 1946, pp. 426-434.
10. Rostow, W. W., and Associates. *The Prospects for Communist China*. New York: John Wiley, 1954.
11. Read, Thomas T. "Economic-Geographic Aspects of China's Iron Industry," *Geographical Review*, January, 1943, pp. 42-55.
12. Smith, A. Viola. "Mineral Resources, Production, and Trade of China," *Foreign Minerals Quarterly*, October, 1941, pp. 1-31.
13. Stables, F. H. A. "Present Conditions of Road Travel in China," *Journal of the Royal Central Asian Society*, April, 1948, pp. 144-150.
14. Wang, Kung-ping. *Controlling Factors in the Future Development of the Chinese Coal Industry*. New York: King's Crown Press, 1947. See also article by the same author and title in *Pacific Affairs*, June, 1946, pp. 165-181.
15. "The Water-Power Resources of China," *The Third World Power Conference, 1936, Transactions*, Vol. II, 1938, pp. 93-96.
16. Wu, Yüan-li. *An Economic Survey of Communist China*. New York: Bookmans Associates, 1955.

Comments

The economic and industrial development of China is conditioned not only by the natural resources of the country, but also by social and political factors which change with time. Studies by economists, geographers, and other scholars have been predicated upon the social and political systems of the time. Some of their observations necessarily become invalid with a communist political economy wherein the state takes the initiative and control in many fields hitherto left to private enterprise. Nevertheless, the practical operation of the Chinese economic system in mainland China has not altered as drastically as might be supposed, and things are much the same in techniques, underproductivity, and underdevelopment. The general pattern of resource availability and distribution remains much the same, so that the basic conditioning factors of development as described by pre-communist writers generally are still valid. In any case, the exposition of the pre-communist situation on the mainland is essential to the understanding of the historical development of economic and industrial resources. Little bibliography is available of reliable studies of the developments occurring in mainland China under communist rule. The best source is Wu, Yüan-li's study, based primarily on Chinese sources. Another valuable study is that edited by W. W. Rostow, which applies the economist's analytical tools to Chinese data. Much valuable statistical data, including many more recent figures used in the preceding chapters on China, are to be found in the translations from Chinese communist newpsapers and publications made by the American Consulate General at Hongkong. The most important of these are the two series entitled: *Survey of China Mainland Press* and *Current Background*.

China

POLITICAL ORGANIZATION, POPULATION, AND PROSPECTS

THE TERRITORIAL BOUNDARIES OF POLITICAL CHINA HAVE FLUCTU-
ated widely in the course of her 3,500 years of history, but as early as
B.C. 100 all of present-day agricultural China south of the Great Wall was
under the unified rule of the Han (Chinese). The Great Wall then extended into southern Manchuria to enclose most of the Liao river valley
and the Liao-tung peninsula. The larger part of the northern half of the
Korean peninsula also was one of China's provinces, while in the south
its boundaries ran halfway down the Vietnam coast to enclose Annam and
Tonkin as another. Until after A.D. 100, however, the southeast maritime
hill lands managed to resist absorption. By the tenth century Annam
had shaken off the Chinese grip, while the Yun-nan-Kuei-chou plateau
region had come under the control of the independent Thai kingdom of
Nan-chao. A united kingdom of Korea, then known as Kao-li, broke away
about the same time as Annam, but both continued to pay tribute to
China until the nineteenth century.

Political divisions and boundaries

In Manchuria, China's terri-
tory under the rule of the Manchu Ch'ien Lung emperor (1736-96) en-

compassed all the drainage of the Amur River and theoretically included Sakhalin island. However, the area north of the Amur was lost to the advancing Russian Empire in 1858, and the coastal region east of the Ussuri two years later.

About 2,000 years ago, China embarked upon her first military actions in the territory of present Hsin-chiang province. The Great Wall system reached out almost to the 98th meridian, roughly guarding the Ho-hsi corridor. The incorporation of Hsin-chiang as a province of China did not occur until the eighteenth century, and the "New Frontier" was given civil provincial status only near the beginning of the twentieth century.

While Tibet sent tribute missions to China as early as the T'ang dynasty, China did not exercise political control over Tibet until after 1700. Even thereafter, the internal affairs of Tibet continued to be controlled by the Tibetans. The boundary between Tibet and China was settled by the Manchu emperor and the Tibetans in 1727. When the Republic overthrew the Manchu dynasty, the Tibetans considered their ties with China ended. However, Chinese leaders refused to recognize Tibetan independence, and years of desultory warfare followed between Chinese and Tibetan forces. Although the Nationalist government eventually succeeded in forcing two resident commissioners and their staffs upon the Tibetans at Lhasa, direct control in Tibetan affairs was not imposed until the communist military conquest. In 1950, the march of the Chinese communist armies into eastern Tibet integrated Tibet into China once more. The Tibetan uprisings have been since repressed.

In the north, China's outer boundaries coincided with those of Outer Mongolia along the frontiers of the Russian, and the later Soviet, empire until 1945. Outer Mongolia's formal independence was then recognized by Nationalist China, although in 1953 this recognition was withdrawn by the Nationalist government on T'ai-wan. The international boundary of communist China here crosses the Gobi in an undefined zone. In the far west and the Tibetan outer boundaries, the border is disputed at the strategic passes commanding gateways into and out of the country. Between the passes, the line follows the unmapped snows and rocks of the high ranges. Along the Assam frontiers of eastern Tibet and in northern Burma no boundary settlement has been recognized by the Chinese. Between Burma and China the defined boundary runs only as far northward as the Chien-kao mountains east of Myitkyina. Southward from here the boundary down to the Nan-ting River was finally fixed in 1941 by the Chinese Nationalists and the British in Burma. The Chinese communist regime does not accept this boundary, however. The line of the Nan-ting south to the border of Laos was fixed in treaties with Great Britain in 1898, while the border with Laos was settled by a treaty with the French in 1895. Neither of these have been satisfactory to China. In the southern sections, unwilling cessions of territories were made under what Chinese consider unfair pressures. In northwest Yün-nan and northern Burma, China has claimed all the territory in the drainage basin of the upper Irrawaddy as well as the Hukawng valley east of Assam. However, in 1956 Premier U Nu of Burma and Foreign Minister Chou En-lai of communist China agreed to Chinese recognition of Burma's right to all the northern Irrawaddy drainage basin except for three Chingpaw (Kachin) districts, including the strategic Hpimaw tract, which were to be ceded to China. The Namwan Assigned Tract, for which a perpetual lease of 100 square miles of Chinese territory had been negotiated by the British half a century earlier, was to be returned, and Chinese troops occupying the Kachin and Wa states in Burma were to be withdrawn.

Within China proper, administrative divisions have changed with every dynasty to suit the whims, conveniences, or strategical ideas of the court. In many instances, administrative boundaries have followed water partings, or provincial units have been formed on the logical bases of drainage basins. Until communist China came into being, the provincial divides of the last century had changed little except in the eastern Tibetan plateau frontiers of Ssu-ch'uan, Hsi-k'ang, and Yün-nan.

As organized by the Nationalist government, China had 35 provinces (sheng) subdivided into 208 administrative regions (chü), further subdivided into a total of 2,059 districts or counties (hsien), of which 36 were in a provisional stage of organization.

The accession of the Communists to power in 1949 brought many changes that are altering the familiar pattern identified with China for decades and even centuries past. New maps for the new administrative divisions must be used in studying any geographically distributed data given by the communist regime. The administrative hierarchy in communist China has the "People's Government" at the apex in the new capital at Peking, with the newly formed communes at the base. The great gap between central government and the provinces was bridged by six so-called "administrative areas," but these were abandoned in June, 1954, as encouraging undue regional autonomy. Inner Mongolia has officially shifted northeastward to include the steppe regions of the Great Hsing-an mountains, and in 1954 the Mongols of former western Inner Mongolia were included in the Inner Mongolian Autonomous Region when Sui-yüan Province became part of the region. Two other so-called autonomous regions exist: Tibet and Hsin-chiang; and in mid-1957 the creation of two additional autonomous regions was proposed, one for the Tung-kan ethnic group in the northwest and a second for the Thai-related Chuang people in Kuang-hsi near the Vietnamese border.

On the provincial level there also have been marked changes. Almost every province in northern and western China has undergone some changes in boundaries. Cha-ha-erh was divided between the Inner Mongolian Autonomous Region and Ho-pei; Je-ho was partitioned between Ho-pei, Liao-tung, and Inner Mongolia; Ning-hsia was joined with Kan-su; chiefly out of southern Ho-nan, a new province was created, P'ing-yuan, which was re-merged with Ho-nan and adjacent provinces in 1953; and Hsi-k'ang was divided in 1954 between Ssu-ch'uan and Tibet. Thus, in 1957 there were reported to be 22 provinces in China, exclusive of T'ai-wan and 5 autonomous regions. As under the pre-communist government, certain important cities are under the direct control of the central government—Peking, Tientsin, and Shang-hai. In addition, the several provinces also have direct rule over certain cities within them.

In spite of an apparent trend toward more diverse political divisions and the creation of ethnic "autonomous regions" for many minorities within China, the communist regime has imposed a system of centralized control completely unparalleled in the 3,500 years of known Chinese history. This includes outlying area once loosely held, such as Hsin-chiang, Tibet, and Inner Mongolia.

Population numbers, characteristics, and distribution

China has long had a large population. Historical records show that as early as the turn of the Christian era China already had a population of more than 60 million ethnic Chinese listed in official registries. How many millions more there may have been cannot be ascertained, since the early censuses presumably were inexact. In 1761 the estimate ran over 143 millions. By 1800 it had doubled, and by 1851 reached 432 millions. Four separate estimates made by different Chinese government agencies in 1931 show differences of as much as 46 million in the total count. The highest of these estimates was 485 million. In 1953 the communist government began the organization of a new registration which gave a population of 582,603,417. In addition, it reported 11,743,320 Chinese overseas, not including an estimated 8,438,000 people on T'ai-wan.

China sometimes has been called a "land of children," as though this were a simple reflection of the love of children among the Chinese. Actually, China's population is young because of short life expectancies. Only about 60 per cent of the infants born alive survive their tenth year. The youthful population also reflects the relatively high annual birth rate of about 40 per thousand population. This birth rate is explained partly by the high fertility of Chinese women and partly by the universality of early marriage in the traditional society of China.

Fig. 55 • Famine refugees from Ho-nan province on a flatcar of the Lung-hai railway travelling across the plain near Lo-yang. These migrants illustrate the pressure of population on productive land in China and suggest the degree to which the population of China has been kept in check by famine and its economic efficiency reduced by malnutrition.

The low hills around the Lo-yang plain share the loess cover of the loess plateau region, although these extensions of the Ch'in Ling are near the edge of the Yellow plain. The loess cliffs under the terraces in the background have been dug out by the local farmers for use as cave-dwellings. *(Lt. Col. David R. Longacre.)*

Males have been a majority in the Chinese population. In rural areas in the 1930's there were between 108 and 110 men for every 100 women, although this differential may have reflected underenumeration of females, and the ratios may have changed with the incidences of war, famine, and migration. In the larger cities, the differential has been much higher. In 1947, for instance, Shang-hai had 128 men to every 100 women, while the proportion for Peking was 142 to each 100 women. This type of sex distribution probably is undergoing change as a result of the communist social revolution. The existence of a large and relatively young male population means a large labor force and an abundance of able-bodied men for military service, provided their health matches their youth and numbers.

While the birth rate is high, the death rate also is high. Sampling estimates placed the death rate at about 30 per thousand population in the

1930's during times without famine or warfare conditions (Figure 55). If the "normal" birth and death rates be accepted at 40 and 30 per thousand population respectively, the annual rate of increase amounts to 10 per thousand. For a population of 582 millions this means an annual increase of 5.82 million. However, in 1954 the Chinese Communists estimated the annual increase at 12 million. If this be fact, then the death rate must have dropped to about 20 per thousand. This still would be double the Japanese death rate. The reduction of the death rate still further through disease control and health measures to the level of that of the West, as was achieved in Japan after the Allied occupation, without a corresponding reduction in the birth rate would not only thwart the raising of living standards, but might well result in further lowering of the already marginal levels of living. Even a doubling of the nation's grain output, great as such an achievement would be, might not be enough to cope with the "population explosion" that would result.

For a time, the communist regime officially refused to recognize the population problem, as shown by denunciations of Western scholars for having stressed China's overpopulation. However, a leading communist official in 1954 reported to the National People's Congress: "It is a good thing to have a large population, but in an environment beset with difficulties it appears that a limit should be set." Moreover, the revolutionary social changes being made in China, should they persist, may in themselves bring about considerable long-run reductions in the birth rate. In 1957 official instructions were issued to the public on birth control. Chinese were urged not to marry early. As a result of manpower dislocation in 1958, this attitude was reversed to favor a larger population.

How is this enormous population distributed? (See back end paper.) A line following the eastern edge of the Great Hsing-an mountains south to the Great Wall and then following the Great Wall to the vicinity of Lan-chou, if then extended southward along the eastern edge of the Tibetan high plateau would enclose east of it all except about ten million of the people in mainland China. These ten million are found sparsely scattered in the larger half of China west of the line, while the rest of China's people are densely packed in the agricultural lowlands to the east. Within this eastern section there are six great concentrations of population and several minor ones, the pattern of distribution generally following the distribution of farmland. The greatest area of dense population lies in the lower Yang-tzu plain. This is followed by the north China plain, the central lake basins, southern Manchuria, the Ssu-ch'uan basin, and the Hsi Chiang delta. Smaller concentrations are in the Wei and Fen river valleys in the loess plateau, on the coastal river deltas of the southeast, and in western T'ai-wan.

Ethnically, 90 per cent of China's population is Chinese. Nevertheless, the 40 million non-Chinese peoples occupying over 50 per cent of China's territory form significant minorities. The western peripheral territories of China are the least well integrated into Chinese civilization and have the largest percentages of non-Chinese populations. In the Tibetan high plateaus until recently there have been only handfuls of Chinese in the towns and markets, except for the military garrisons in strategic centers and in the fringe towns of western Ssu-ch'uan, eastern Hsi-k'ang, and northeastern Ch'ing-hai. News reports in 1956 and 1957, however, indicate that the Chinese communists plan to settle large numbers of Chinese in Tibet, so that within a short time Chinese may outnumber Tibetans. In the northwestern desert regions, the Islamic Turkic and Tung-kan (Dungan) peoples total about six million. The largest single group are the Uighurs of Hsin-chiang who in 1956 numbered 3.9 millions. The 1953 Communist Handbook puts the whole population of the Inner Mongolian Autonomous Region at 2.3 million. In a note to this figure, it indicates that 80 per cent of the population of this region was engaged in agriculture. Since virtually all of these agriculturalists are Chinese, this points to a Mongol population of only about 500,000. Estimates based on earlier Nationalist figures indicate from 800,000 to a million Mongols in Inner Mongolia and up to almost twice this number if those in other northwestern territories be included. Northeastern China contains approximately one million each of Korean immigrants and Manchus, although most of the latter have become wholly sinicized.

In southern and southwest China are scattered considerable numbers of the non-Chinese tribesmen once dominant there. Many southern Chinese also are related through blood mixtures with or are descended from early Thai or other tribal peoples, but have become thoroughly assimilated within Chinese culture. Nevertheless, 20 to 30 million people in the southwest continue to exist as distinctly non-Chinese ethnic groups with their own languages and cultures. The Chinese have tended to regard them as barbarians. The tribesmen in their turn have viewed the overwhelming mass of incoming Chinese much as the American Indians looked upon the white man, as intruders and interlopers robbing them of their land and heritage. They are in all stages of sinicization. Those that have adopted Chinese ways are no longer registered as non-Chinese.

The movement of the Han (Chinese) into south China is a part of the general southward shift of population masses in eastern Asia, which does not stop at the political borders of southern China. The importance of Southeast Asia to China can be judged by the fact that in 1955, of the total of some 13,129,000 Chinese emigrants living abroad (in places other than T'ai-wan), an estimated 10,000,000 were to be found in Southeast Asia. The Americas had only 244,289; Europe had only 11,640, as compared with 54,000 in 1948; and Africa had 32,441. Another 2,000,000 were in Hongkong, while Japan had 44,000 and South Korea 22,000. An unknown number of Chinese were in the Soviet Union and in North Korea and North Vietnam.

This outward migration has been part of the search for economic opportunities for a better livelihood, not only for the migrants concerned, but also for the families at home. In some prewar years, remittances home from these expatriate Chinese have amounted to the equivalent of U.S. $300,000,000, an important item in helping China balance her international payments. Within her own territory, too, there have been migratory shifts apart from the shifts forced by combat during the Sino-Japanese war.

While the southward and overseas migrations have come largely from the overcrowded parts of Fu-chien and Kuang-tung provinces, the densely populated parts of Shan-tung and Ho-pei provinces have sent great numbers of people to Manchuria. Some of these went as annual migrant laborers during the 1930's, but up to a million a year remained as permanent settlers. Migratory shifts in the precarious agricultural regions of Kan-su and Shen-hsi have been directed to newly reclaimed agricultural lands along the northern bend of the Huang Ho. Immigrants also poured into the Inner Mongolian fringe after the railroad was built from Peking to Chang-chia-k'ou (Kalgan) in 1906.

The wartime migratory movement after 1937 was on a vast scale, an estimated 30 to 40 million people being displaced from their homes as a result of military operations. Most of these were temporary movements, with return shifts when conditions permitted. One result, however, was the economic development of the west, for the eyes of the Chinese leaders had opened to its unexploited resources.

International relations and prospects for progress

Without international contacts Russia would not have become Sovietized, Japan would not be industrially important, and China probably would still be living serenely in the past. International relations mean the introduction of new ideas, social changes, and new technology, while they provide for possible credits and economic aid from the wealthier, stronger nations to less developed and weaker nations. The beginning of the revolution that is still going on in China started with the introduction of Western science to China by the Jesuits in the seventeenth century; the democratic ideas of the American and French revolutions paved the way for the rise of the radical Kuomintang and communist movements in the twentieth century. Both Western commercialism and Christianity were disrupting influences to the tradi-

Fig. 56 • The impact of the West on China was greatest in the coastal cities. Here were concentrated the Western banking and commercial houses, which drew upon great hinterlands for their livelihoods. In these cities also developed a Chinese entrepreneurial class, bridging the gap between Western and Chinese systems of exchange. This crowded, narrow commercial street in Hongkong illustrates the great variety of commercial enterprise that came to characterize these cities. It is similar to many similar streets in Canton, Amoy, Shanghai, and other former treaty ports in central and southern China.

Note the various signs in Chinese and English. The buildings themselves are examples of Chinese "shophouses" found in southern China and in many cities of Southeast Asia —for example, Singapore—where southern Chinese form significant elements in the population. The ground floors and some of the upper stories are in shops, offices, restaurants, and service occupancy; the remainder of each building is divided into cubicles wherein live Chinese families under conditions of exceptional crowding. Note also the open sewer at the right covered in part with stone slabs, a reflection of the high rainfall that characterizes southern China during the rainy season. In some cities these channels carry raw sewage and other waste. *(Norton Ginsburg.)*

tional Chinese social structure, and the industrial revolutions in the West and in Japan pointedly emphasized to China that the way to national power required a transformation of her old way of life.

China's early trade with the West was mainly in luxury items. With the introduction of steamships, the building of the Suez Canal, and the expanding demand of Western industry, China's trade changed increasingly to cheaper bulk products and raw materials, particularly in the export sphere. Foreign trade became a mainstay of the Chinese national treasury, which in 1937 derived from it 54 per cent of its total revenue.

This trade also had unfortunate effects. It destroyed many of the traditional cottage industries with which the farmer supplemented his meager income. It brought an increasing commercialization of agriculture, so that former self-sufficient farmers now had to face the fluctuations of an uncertain market. In the period before the second World War there also was an unbalanced commercial and industrial development because of the heavy foreign investments in the coastal cities (Figure 56). Here capital glutted the market, while farmers in the rural areas suffered from usurious interest rates. The interior region also lagged behind in the development of communication and transportation facilities. Thus, the dependence upon foreign raw materials, which might have been supplied domestically if transport costs had permitted, steadily increased.

In the political sphere, although China has suffered severely from foreign aggression, her political integrity has depended upon the rivalries of foreign powers in the East Asiatic realm. History has taught the Chinese that military weakness made China a pawn in international affairs. Nationalism in China, regardless of ideology, seeks to create a strong China; but strength demands a thorough-going industrialization with many accompanying social changes, whether this be accomplished in the Soviet manner or by democratic means. Progress, however, is hindered when military development and interventions take precedence over social and economic improvement. Thus, the military intervention in Korea during 1950-53 had serious effects on the Chinese economy. Excessively heavy taxes were imposed on farm and industrial producers alike, and excess capital was collected by forced donations and loans. Living standards were adversely affected. The war also provided a convenient excuse for tightened controls on the economy.

While on the one hand trade with non-communist countries was greatly restricted by Nationalist China's blockade and by economic sanctions imposed by Western countries, trade with the "Soviet Bloc" countries increased. In 1950 the Soviet Union and communist China signed agreements of alliance and mutual friendship, part of which set the pattern for the long-run economic penetration of Hsin-chiang by the Soviet Union. In 1951 agreements permitted through passage of railroad traffic across the Manchurian-Siberian borders. They also provided details for the supply of equipment and material to China under the $300,000,000 Soviet loan of the preceding year. China's foreign trade, which previously had been overwhelmingly oriented toward the Pacific countries and Western Europe, shifted overwhelmingly toward the "Soviet Bloc." China's dependence on the Soviet Union was increased by her need for war materials; and Soviet advisers appeared to play an important role in helping to direct communist China's domestic policies.

The pattern of planned development undertaken by the communist regime, as exemplified by the First Five-Year Plan of 1953-7, is designed to ensure a continual growth of the state sector of the economy at the expense of the private sector. At the same time the private capitalist sector is induced to develop along the lines of the state enterprises, and petty commodity enterprises are encouraged to develop along cooperative lines. These two lines of development are designed to lead to the complete nationalization of industry and commerce and the collectivization of agriculture, thus ultimately eliminating private enterprise.

Socialization of industry has been rapid. In 1957, state industry accounted for 54.5 per cent of the total industrial output, and private industry for only 1.3 per cent, the rest being accounted for by cooperatives and joint public-private enterprises. Through state control of transport, credit, and raw materials, however, the government role is actually greater than the percentage indicates. In the field of distribution, government and cooperative trading companies by 1954 handled 50 per cent of the retail trade and 80 per cent of the wholesale trade. That such control over internal trade had not worked out satisfactorily was indicated in an official proposal at the 8th National Party Congress for a "free market under state leadership." It was admitted that strict control of the rural market especially produced some ill effects. The policy prescribed, therefore, was to have the state control the trade in essential commodities with supply and demand in the open market governing trade in lesser commodities.

The First Five-Year Plan began in 1953. The investment allocations indicated the concentration on the development of heavy industry. Consumer-goods production had much less emphasis. Thus, the plant-construction plan provided for 21 metallurgical and chemical factories, 24 large machine-building plants and 24 thermo- and hydroelectric plants, in contrast to only four cotton mills, two flax-processing plants, four rubber plants, and 12 paper mills. The intense effort devoted to mineral discoveries is indicated by the nine-fold increase in the number of geological prospectors between 1953 and 1956.

According to the communist regime's statistical bureau in Peking, index of output was said to have tripled during the first Five-Year Plan, implying as much as a 24 per cent annual increase. Production of coal went from 63.5 to 128 million metric tons between 1953 and 1957, of steel from 1.35 to 5.2 million tons, of electric energy from 7.26 to 19 billion KWH. Chinese communist thinking in the first Five-Year Plan follows the Stalinist model of economic development:

(1) The rapid expansion of producer goods and the defense industries;

(2) A modest rate of growth in textile manufacturing;

(3) Agricultural development through better organization rather than through capital investment;

(4) Creation of capital by underemployed labor in mass water conservation and other labor-intensive projects;

(5) The financing of industrialization through net transfers out of agriculture, largely at the expense of agriculture; and

(6) The gradual collectivization of the peasantry so as not to disrupt output drastically or damage farm capital.

However, it is argued that this policy faces a vicious circle whereby industrialization is accelerated at the outset by keeping agriculture on short investment rations. Thus, agricultural development is sluggish, although accompanied by a growing demand for farm products arising out of increased population, urbanization, and the need for exports. This forces the regime to extract a rising proportion of farm output in order that demand be met, thus further interfering with agricultural development. This in turn means that the screws must be tightened on the peasantry. The cumulative effects of the peasants' expectations of imminent collectivization and hence the disinclination to make farm improvements, the more or less permanent state of tension in the countryside, and the disruption that is bound to occur in the collectivization process, all may discourage the farmer from taking measures to raise output. In fact, the establishment of the communist system may have been in response to these difficulties.

The fulfillment of the import requirements of the Five-Year Plan, however, depend upon greatly increased agricultural production for export estimated at a rate of 11 per cent increase over 1952 by 1957 and 25 per cent by 1962. The difficulties in reaching these goals are numerous. In the first place, increased political stability accompanied by public health control on a large scale was resulting in a rate of natural increase in population claimed as high as 2.5 per cent, or, in 1958 alone, an increase of some 15 million people. Communist China claims that it will have added about 30 million acres to the cultivated area between 1950 and 1960, for an average increase of about 1.2 per cent. The amount of cultivated land per person, therefore, seems still to be decreasing despite strenuous efforts. In order to raise farm production in China, main reliance must be placed upon increasing unit yields. To raise unit yields by 25 per cent, however, would require the application annually of some 6,500,000 tons of ammonium sulphate fertilizer, 3,800,000 tons of calcium superphosphate, and 300,000 tons of potassium sulphate, according to the Chinese National Agricultural Research Bureau. However, production of chemical fertilizers in 1958 reached only about 1,000,000 metric tons.

Natural calamities add to the difficulties of agriculture. Although the much publicized Huai River flood-control project of 1949-50 was said to have virtually freed the area from future flood danger, the people in the Yang-tzu and Huai river valleys suffered in 1954 the worst floods of the past hundred years. About one-tenth of China's farmland, totaling 24 million acres, was submerged. The Peking government in March, 1955, admitted that 200 million people were receiving food relief from the communist regime; and communist publications in May conceded that serious famine conditions still existed in almost half of agricultural China. Because of conditions on the farms and the loss of incentive owing to collectivization measures, so many farmers had left their farms for the cities that the Peking regime in 1954 had to issue a directive calling a halt to what was termed the "blind drift" of the peasants into the cities. Observers in Hongkong attributed the 1955 food shortage in China to the disastrous flood of 1954, the abnormally cold winter that followed, the communist-forced grain purchases at lower prices, and confiscatory taxation. Communist publications admitted that farmers deserting their fields had left large areas uncultivated, while draft animals were being slaughtered. Since then droughts and floods have continued to affect millions.

The difficulties described must be considered in any evaluation of the optimistic trends indicated in statistics issued by the communist regime. China still has a long way to go in industrialization. Winfield has estimated how far China must progress by the year 2000 to attain a level of living for an estimated 650 million people equivalent to one-sixth that of the United States during the period 1926-29. The following table outlines some of the levels of achievement in production and development in 1944 and the necessary goals for the year 2000: [2]

Category	1944 level	Required level by 2000
National income	U.S. $9 billion	U.S. $85 billion
Coal production	50 million tons	750 million tons
Pig-iron production	2 million tons	50 million tons
Railroads	18,000 miles	150,000 miles
Trained doctors	12,000	150,000
Trained nurses	5,000	1,000,000
Secondary schools	4,000	124,000
College students	110,000	3,500,000

[1] Late in 1956, however, two rich deposits of phosphate were discovered in Ssu-ch'uan and Yün-nan. The latter is said to be the largest in the country and one of the largest in the world. A 500-million ton deposit of peat valuable for nitrogenous fertilizer use also was discovered not far from Ch'eng-tu.

[2] Gerald Winfield, *China* (New York: Wm. Sloane, 1948), chap. 8.

Considering the inherent difficulties, the picture presented by this estimate is not optimistic—especially when one remembers that this estimate depends on the population's not exceeding 650 millions.

What has been most lacking in China is industrial capital. The greatest obstacle to its accumulation has been the uniformly low income levels of the predominantly rural population. Although a state controlled by totalitarian methods can create certain forms of capital through its command over labor, there are limitations to the substitution of labor. The most serious problem confronting communist China in 1957 still was that of securing sufficient capital to finance industrial construction. The chief sources of revenue were taxation and state enterprises, but in spite of heavy tax exactions, the communists in 1954, for example, found it necessary to float Economic Construction Bonds amounting to eight billion *yuan,* of which a quota of 53 per cent was assigned to the urban middle class.

Even were there sufficient domestic capital to carry through the necessary program of industrialization, many kinds of capital goods cannot be produced in China at her present stage of development. Technicians and teachers also need to be trained abroad or else imported to train students for operating the new technology. Such imports may be bought by increased exports, as in the Soviet Union in the late 1920's, but the possibilities for this under existing circumstances are few. China's chief sources for such training and teachers now are the Soviet bloc countries.

China's natural resources are sufficient for a moderate scale of industrialization. Even though iron-ore reserves are not large, further exploration may bring more to light. If Japan, with only 4 per cent of China's reserves, could create basic industries, the chances for China appear even better, provided her access to foreign ores can be assured.

Both the Russia of 1921 and Japan of the Meiji era are comparable with China in the mid-1950's stage of economic development. However, both of those had more favorable international settings. They were faced with lesser difficulties in importing capital goods, technology, and know-how from the West. Soviet Russia also had a relatively low density of population and a relatively large amount of high-quality natural resources conveniently located. Japan did not have the difficult transportation problem that faces China and, moreover, was able to export her labor in the form of manufactured products, and able also to find a lucrative market for high-priced raw silk. With her greater problems, China faces enormous difficulties in industrialization as compared with either the Soviet Union or Japan. The pace that the Chinese communist regime has set for its subjects and the manner in which it is carrying out the industrial transformation involve immense sacrifices of cultural values and personal freedom.

SELECTED GEOGRAPHICAL BIBLIOGRAPHY

1. Alexander, John W. "The Pre-War Population of China: Distribution and Density," *Annals of the Association of American Geographers*, March, 1948, pp. 1-5.
2. Bain, H. Foster. "Manchuria, A Key Area," *Foreign Affairs*, October, 1946, pp. 106-117.
3. Barclay, George W. "China's Population Problem," *Pacific Affairs*, May, 1950, pp. 184-192.
4. Chang, Chih-chung. "Dilemma in Sinkiang," *Pacific Affairs*, December, 1947, pp. 422-428.
5. Chen, C. S., and C. H. Tuan. *The Population of Taiwan*. Taipei: Institute of Agricultural Geography, 1951.
6. Chen, Ta. *Population in Modern China*. Chicago: University of Chicago Press, 1946.
7. De Riencourt, Amoury. *Roof of the World: Tibet, Key to Asia*. New York: Rinehart Book Company, 1950.
8. Eckstein, Alexander. "Conditions and Prospects for Economic Growth in Communist China," *World Politics*, January and April, 1955.
9. Herrmann, Adolph. *A Historical and Commercial Atlas of China*. Boston: Harvard-Yenching Institute, 1937.
10. Ho, Franklin. *The Population Movement to the Northeast Frontier in China*. Shanghai: China Institute of Pacific Relations, 1931.
11. Lattimore, Owen. "Chinese Colonization in Manchuria," *Geographical Review*, April, 1932, pp. 177-195.
12. ———."At the Crossroads of Inner Asia," *Pacific Affairs*, February, 1950, pp. 34-44.
13. ———. *Inner Asian Frontiers of China*. New York: American Geographical Society, Research Series No. 21, 1940.
14. Mills, J. P. "Problems of the Assam-Tibet Frontier," *Journal of the Royal Central Asian Society*, April, 1950, pp. 152-161.
15. Strausz-Hupé, Robert. "Manchuria and Mongolia: Red and White Imperialism," *Current History*, August, 1950, pp. 73-77.
16. "A Survey of Chinese Emigration," *International Labour Review*, September, 1949, pp. 289-301.
17. Teichman, Eric. *Travels of a Consular Officer in Eastern Tibet*. Cambridge: Cambridge University Press, 1942.
18. Trewartha, Glenn T. "Chinese Cities: Numbers and Distribution," *Annals of the Association of American Geographers*, December, 1951, pp. 331-347.
19. ———. "Chinese Cities: Origins and Functions," *Annals of the Association of American Geographers*, March, 1952, pp. 69-93.
20. Wiens, Herold J. *China's March Toward the Tropics*. Hamden, Connecticut: The Shoe String Press, 1954.
21. Yuen, Ren-chao. "The Languages and Dialects of China," *Geographical Journal*, August, 1953, pp. 63-66.

Comments

Chen, Ta, is one of the foremost authorities on the population of China and has the most up-to-date thorough study of population trends. Trewartha's study of Chinese cities and urban development, largely confined to Chinese language sources, suffers the same defect as many of his sources: the lack of accurate censuses in China. Lattimore's *Inner Asian Frontiers of China* is a valuable study of the historical geography of northwest China. Wiens' book discusses the historical relationships between Chinese and non-Chinese groups and the latter's cultural geography in the south and southwest China frontier region.

Eckstein's work and that of Wu, Yuan-li, cited in the previous bibliography, are excellent analyses of communist China's current and projected economic developments seen with objectivity. Herrmann's atlas is the only good recent atlas of China in English, but is mainly historical. The geographical field lacks a good atlas of China in English, but those who know the Chinese language can find a number of good reference atlases, including one published by the communist *Ta Kung Pao* in 1952.

Mongolian People's Republic

THERE ARE THREE WAYS OF LOOKING AT "MONGOLIA": (1) AS THE great physical region called the Mongolian plateau; (2) as the area in which Mongol ethnic groups and culture predominate; and (3) as the political divisions known as Inner and Outer Mongolia in which Chinese and Soviet political control respectively are dominant. Physical Mongolia changes little; ethnic Mongolia changes relatively slowly; but political Mongolia reflects more rapid rates of change. The political organization of Inner Mongolia has undergone significant revison under Chinese communist control in terms of both administrative area and administrative structure. This chapter, however, is limited to the northern portion of the Mongolian plateau occupied mainly by the Khalkha tribe of Mongols. The area has long been known as Outer Mongolia, organized politically in 1921 as the Russian-supported Mongolian Peoples Republic (MPR).

Encompassing an area of over 600,000 square miles, Outer Mongolia stretches 1,400 miles from east to west and has a latitudinal spread of generally 300 to 500 miles. Its continental situation is emphasized by its great distance from the sea. To the west, 4,000 miles away, is the Atlantic. The Indian Ocean lies 1,500 miles to the south. In the north lies a 1,000-mile-wide strip of Soviet Siberia. The arm of the Yellow Sea, the Gulf of

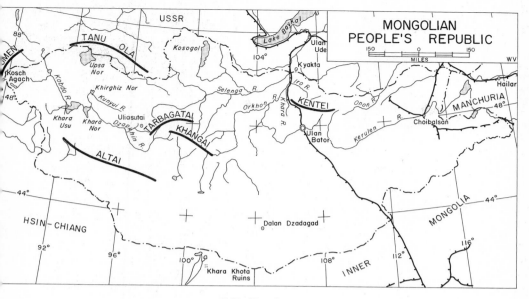

MAP 11

Chih-li, 500 miles to the southeast is the part of the Pacific nearest south-eastern Outer Mongolia.

Surface configuration

Most of Outer Mongolia lies at elevations between 3,000 and 6,000 feet. Its plateau character is unmistakable in terms of both general elevation and the vast rolling-to-level plains that cover most of the region. Only in the extreme northeast, in the extreme west, and in the southeastern part of the Gobi are there small areas under 3,000 feet. The term *Gobi* refers to the great basin-like depression between the 40th and 45th parallels, which lies largely outside of the Mongolian Peoples Republic. It coincides, however, with the most arid parts of the Mongolian plateau and is predominantly desert. Through the Gobi runs the boundary (still undemarcated in 1958) between the Peoples Republic of China and the Mongolian Peoples Republic.

The rock surface of the Gobi is interrupted by broad, shallow depressions in which sediments have accumulated. Numerous depressions extending between Chang-chia-k'ou (Kalgan) in Inner Mongolia and Ulan Bator, the capital of the Mongolian Peoples Republic in the north, are parted by low broad mountain masses. In the far west lies the great basin that has been given the name of the chief western settlement, Kobdo. Numerous salt lakes here accumulate waters from the high Sailjumen and Altai mountains in the west and southwest, the Tanu Ola mountains to the north of the basin, and the Khangai and Tarbagatai in the central part of the country.

Except for the Sailjumen range in the far west, which runs in a north-south arc and connects the Altai with the Tanu Ola, most of the mountain chains of Outer Mongolia trend generally east-west (Map 11). The effect of this trend on precipitation and drainage patterns is significant, especially since the moisture falling on the Mongolian Peoples Republic comes from across the northern borders.

The westcentral Khangai and Tarbagatai ranges are particularly important. Lacking a precipitous character but rising to almost 10,000 feet, the broad Khangai mountains, north and northeast of the Altai, are maturely dissected and gently sloping. Their gentlest slopes run toward Siberia, forming what has been described as a huge plain. The western slopes drain into the salt lakes of the Kobdo basin. From the more arid southern slopes flow only small, scattered streams which disappear into the desert sands. The slopes facing north, however, experience much greater precipitation and feed the principal river system of the country. This is the drainage basin of the Selenga River which, fortified by its lower tributary, the Orkhon, empties into Lake Baykal in Siberia. Small steamers navigate 197 miles up the Selenga from its mouth and 194 miles up the Orkhon from its mouth.

In the northeast, the Kerulyen River draws water from the southern slopes of the northern frontier range, the Kentei, and runs off northward as one of the major headwaters of the Amur River. The easternmost tongue of the Mongolian Peoples Republic reaches the foothills of the Great Hsing-an mountains which lie in the newly formed Inner Mongolian Autonomous Region of communist China.

In the west the Altai ranges rise in a long chain of latitudinal-trending fault blocks, with their steeper fronts facing the Irtysh basin in Dzungaria. Gaps in the eastern stretches provide gateways to the lowlands of Dzungaria and the Tarim basin. The highest elevations in the country are found in the western parts of the Altai, which form the political and physical divide between the Mongolian Peoples Republic and China's Hsin-chiang province. In 1957 a major earthquake shook the Altai.

Climate and vegetation patterns

Since northern Mongolia is the center of the continental high-pressure area of winter, and since the center for the summer low is near its southern borders, it follows that Outer Mongolia is a region of continental extremes. The climate resembles that of Montana in the United States and Alberta in Canada. January averages are between −7° and −9°F., while absolute minima at Uliassutai at an elevation of just over 6,000 feet may reach −52°. Ulan

Bator has an equally low January average, and almost as extreme absolute minima. July averages for Ulan Bator are only 63°, while July minima may drop to as low at 45°. On the other hand, maxima may rise to 94°. The growing season in northern Mongolia is a little more than 100 days.

Moisture is the critical climatic element. Since northerly winds bring in most of the moisture for the country, and since higher areas are in the north and west, precipitation is highest in the north and diminishes toward the south, from an average of about 12 inches in the higher mountainous north to less than 2 inches in the southwestern Gobi. At Ulan Bator the annual average is 8 to 9 inches. Fortunately, about 75 per cent of the precipitation comes during the three summer months that comprise most of the growing season. Between October and April gale-strength winds drive southward out of Mongolia to carry cold waves far into China, bringing winter drought to all of North China.

Although moisture is sufficient to provide a forest cover of larches, aspens, and birches in the higher northern slopes as far south as the Khangai mountains, trees are seldom seen in most parts of Mongolia. Only near running water will be found such tree growth as willow, osier, and tamarisk. Much of Outer Mongolia is one vast, tall-grass land, which in the northern half of the country provides luxuriant fodder during the growing season. The tall grass grades into short grass and sparse bunch grass southward of the 46th parallel and in the Kobdo basin, and then gradually into desert steppe and wastelands (Map 12). Only about 15 per cent of the country is true desert, although considerable areas furnish very poor grass for grazing.

Pastoralism and the Mongol way of life

Cultivation has never been of importance in Outer Mongolia and holds small promise of becoming significant in the national economy. Herding has been the Mongols' chief source of livelihood in the past, and from it they derive 80 to 90 per cent of their food. Only about 10 per cent of the Mongol diet is derived directly from cultivated crops, a large part of which has been imported in the form of cereals, chiefly from China and the U.S.S.R. The Mongols traditionally looked on cultivation as degrading, not only because the farmer works dismounted instead of riding masterfully on horseback or camel, but also because from the Mongols' point of view it distorts the landscape. Their attitude is somewhat like that of the early Western cowboy toward the homesteading farmer. Work with the hoe and plow is regarded by them as below the dignity of the self-respecting Mongol. Only the poorer Mongols, such as those along the western borders of Man-

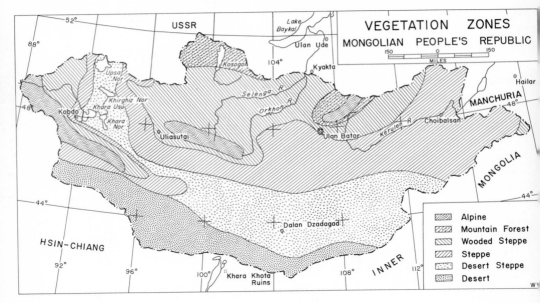

MAP 12

churia and the southern borders of Inner Mongolia, have felt compelled
by Chinese encroachment and by lack of pasture and animals to resort to
a miserable existence based on cultivation.

To the Mongol, his herds are vital elements of his life. From them he
derives meat, milk, butter, and cheese (he milks all his animals except
his dogs). They furnish him with a high-protein diet that has made him
relatively large of stature and physically strong. From them he also derives the skeepskins, wool, and hides for his clothing, felt boots, and bedding, and for his heavy felt-covered, dome-shaped *yurt* or tent (Figure
57). Horsehair is woven into the lariat-like loop that he ties to the end of
a long pole to lasso his animals. The dried dung of all animals furnishes
him with fuel, and great heaps are gathered for use at his winter camps.
His horses, camels, and yaks furnish him with transport. In short, the
Mongol grazing economy is virtually self-sufficient. Tea is imported from
China, and Tibetan *tsamba,* a cereal gruel made of rough-ground barley
or wheat mixed with hot tea and melted butter, is an important dietary
supplement. *Tsamba* also is carried as a kind of short ration for emergency use.

The Mongol is noted for his mobility, an attribute that helped Genghis
Khan conquer a large part of the medieval world. This mobility is a
direct outgrowth of his dependence upon grazing animals which in turn
must be driven in search of fresh pastures. Sedentary existence for some
of the population came only with the adoption of Lamaism, the Tibetan
form of Buddhism patronized by Genghis Khan.

Because of the Mongol dependence on nomadic herding, the people,
with the exception of the sedentary population, are distributed in much

278

Fig. 57 • A Mongol encampment in the Gobi. The circular dome-shaped *yurts,* made of heavy felt stretched over a collapsible frame of light wooden poles, provide adequate protection against the worst blizzards, but they also are easily portable. Horses are hobbled nearby ready for use. A camel-drawn cart stands near the *yurt* at the right. Little vegetation growth covers the seemingly endless plains of southern Outer Mongolia. Winters especially present a bleak landscape; in summers for short periods and after light rains the landscape turns green, until seared again by drought and heat. Water in most of this desert region comes from shallow and often brackish wells in slight depressions in the land surface. *(Alonzo W. Pond.)*

the same pattern as their livestock, especially since the very large holdings of the great princes and church nobles have been abolished or reduced during the last few decades. However, the grazing circuits of individual tribes and clans have traditionally circumscribed limits, so that nomadic movements tend to be localized. Livestock, on the other hand, being dependent upon grass and water, are distributed in accordance with grasslands, streams, and potable well-water. Thus, livestock numbers as a whole are greater in the better-grassed portions of the north and in certain mountain slopelands where higher precipitation provides better forage and more abundant water. In summer, when sheep, for instance, must drink daily, livestock become restricted to the vicinity of water holes, streams, or wells. In winter, grazing can be extended out onto the plains where snow can be substituted for water.

Some indication of the extent of the available grasslands may be had from Table XIV–1 (p. 280), which shows vegetation types.

In some areas, even where grasses are abundant, there has been too little water for the Mongol herds. Such lands mainly support herds of antelope, which are able to travel much farther than the domesticated herds for water or can derive sufficient water from the vegetation. The tapping of groundwater through wells is one way of extending the capacity of the Mongolian rangelands, and before 1930 there were an estimated 10,000 wells scattered about Outer Mongolia. The water table is relatively high in most parts of the country; water generally is reached from 10 to 30 feet below the surface, in some places only a few feet below.

TABLE XIV–1

OUTER MONGOLIAN VEGETATION

Vegetation type	Percent- age of total area	Sq.mi. of area	Acres	Average annual precipitation (inches)
Alpine	3.0	18,180	11,630,040	Under 15
Forest mountain	4.1	24,846	15,901,440	" 15
Wooded steppe	25.2	152,712	97,735,680	" 11
Steppe	26.1	158,166	101,228,240	" 11
Desert steppe	27.1	164,226	105,104,640	" 8
Desert	14.5	87,870	56,236,800	" 4
Total	100.0	606,000	387,840,000	

However, the utility of the water varies according to its salt content. Much of it is brackish, but still usable for watering stock. From 1932 to 1945, 22,000 additional wells are said to have been dug under the auspices of the Mongolian government, and another 20,000 wells were to have been dug during the First Five-Year Plan completed in 1952.

In 1941, the Mongolian livestock population was estimated at 27,500,-000 head of all types—15,900,000 sheep, 5,500,000 goats, 2,800,000 cattle, 2,600,000 horses, and 700,000 camels.[2] The preponderance of sheep is characteristic of most nomadic grazing in northwest China as well as in Outer Mongolia. Together with goats, they constitute about three-fourths of the total domestic livestock. Although the number of animals is estimated to have doubled since 1920 and further efforts are being made to increase livestock numbers as well as the carrying capacity of the range, the latter is 70 per cent overstocked, according to conservative standards of sustained grassland utilization. In 1957 livestock numbered 24,185,000.

The increasing of production and the improvement of livestock depend on overcoming obstacles such as initially poor breeds of animals; game and rodent competition for use of the range; destruction by wolves, zootics, and pests; climatic hazards and lack of winter fodder; and the limitations imposed by lack of water resources and by deteriorating rangelands. Selective breeding and cross-breeding to improve stock have been furthered by Russian experts sent by the Soviet government. Rodent damage involves the hoarding of grass seeds as well as the cutting of grasses, decreasing the natural reproduction of the grasslands, especially during and after drought years. The 1.5 to 2 million marmot pelts exported by Outer Mongolia account for the destruction of only a small percentage of the rodents, but they are economically of value, as they

[2] The reliability of this estimate is questionable, since the Russian newspaper *Izvestia* on June 17, 1954, referred to a 1957 *goal* of 27.5 million animals at the end of the Second Five-Year Plan.

account for about 70 per cent of the fur exports of the country. Antelope hunters supply some supplementary food, but do little to reduce the range competition for grasses. The 13,000 wolf pelts taken annually indicate the number of wolves that cause great damage to livestock, especially to sheep. More serious than the wolves are the cattle plagues which in some districts and years have almost wiped out horned livestock. To combat these diseases, Soviet veterinarians have organized dipping stations and control measures and given elementary veterinary training to Mongol assistants, who in 1950 manned a reported 632 stations supplied with locally produced vaccines and serums.

As natural fodder is scarce in winter, livestock may suffer great weight loss or die of starvation. Freezing blizzards often form a hard ice-crust over the snows, so that the animals, especially sheep and goats, are unable to break through to get at the dried grass beneath. However, in 1940 winter fodder from planted forage was reported grown on 250,000 acres, and in 1950 there were 55 horse-drawn, hay-mowing stations with 1,100 mowing machines. The production of hay on state-owned grazing areas was sufficient to provide close to 300 pounds per state-owned animal. On private grazing grounds hay production was sufficient to provide about 100 pounds per animal (wet or dry hay not indicated). Covered sheds or shelters have been built by the tens of thousands to be used by livestock during severe storms and extreme cold, adding a new element to the Mongolian landscape, although traditional open shelters of dung blocks are common, especially in the south (Figure 58). In the north they are constructed of wood, but in other places mainly of stone. In the Gobi region, construction materials are brought from the north.

Despite these measures, livestock cannot be expected to greatly increase, although growing survival rates and weight improvement will add to the food output. The carrying capacity of the range, already overburdened, remains the limiting factor.

Agriculture in Outer Mongolia

Fifty years of effort by Russian and Chinese farmers, and more recently by Mongol cultivators under Soviet direction, have not added materially to the area under cultivation in Outer Mongolia. The largest acreage under cultivation appeared before 1912, when Chinese influence was strongest. Most of this cultivation was carried on adjacent to the only three large settlements then existing, Ulan Bator (then called Urga), Uliassutai, and Kobdo. Some scattered Russian farms also were found on the route between the capital and the Russian frontier, where rainfall is high enough to permit marginal dry-farming.

The principal change in agricultural activities appears to be a contraction in intensive irrigated truck and grain farming of the Chinese type but with some increase in extensive dry grain farming. This change has been accompanied by the introduction of horse- and tractor-drawn machinery and farm tools, with increasing participation by Mongols.

The reported cultivated area in 1952 did not exceed 112,000 acres. About a third was in state farms, while the remainder was operated by private cultivators, in large part by Chinese and Russians. Cooperative farming by the private cultivators is encouraged by the state. The main crops are wheat, oats, barley, millet, and spring rye. Yields vary greatly from year to year, owing to variances in precipitation. From 1943 to 1947, average yields were about 6.4 bushels per acre, but in 1950 the yield on the state farms was reported to be 9.3 bushels per acre.

The possibilities for extending cultivation are limited and may be judged from a comparison with northern Montana and southern Alberta where a similar climatic regime prevails. Experience has indicated that in this area 12.5 inches of rainfall yearly and 7.5 inches during the growing season are critical requirements for wheat production. Where rainfall is less, wheat growing has not been economical, and grazing has been the chief form of land use. In the Mongolian Peoples Republic, however, only the higher regions north of Ulan Bator average 12 or more inches of precipitation; thus they lie in the marginal zone for wheat cultivation. Profit-

Fig. 58 • A Mongol winter encampment often includes a sheep corral, such as this one, for protection from cold winter winds and wolves. The corral walls are made from animal dung, with felt, the chief building material of the pastoral Mongol. Dung is used also as fuel. In the background are dung "chips," similar to the buffalo "chips" of the American West, which are burned directly as fuel. (*Alonzo W. Pond.*)

able extension of cultivation could occur mainly through the development of irrigation in parts of the Selenga and Orkhon lowlands. Plans called for the cultivation of 494,000 acres by 1960.

Industry, transport and trade, and mineral resources

The growth of Mongolian industry, still in its initial stage, has been associated closely with the processing of animal products and is concentrated at Ulan Bator and Choibalsan. Of a population of perhaps one million in 1950, 5,000 were classed as "industrial workers" in the loose Soviet terminology. Of these, 3,500 are Mongols and the remainder Russians and Chinese. Engineers, foremen, and skilled workers tend to be Russian. The leather combine, situated at Ulan Bator, is the largest industry, with 1,500 workers, of whom 80 per cent are said to be Mongols. Modern machinery reportedly is used for making shoes and leather articles and sheepskins. A meat combine processes animal by-products as well. Aside from food processing, such as butter and cheese making (most butter and cheese still is homemade for home consumption), a small proportion of labor is engaged in mining and lumbering. The 100,000 tons of coal (some estimates are as high as 300,-000 including output from all other mines) derived annually from coal mines at Nalaykha east of Ulan Bator are used for running the electric power plant at the capital and for railroad and other uses. Several machine shops, a wood-working shop operating in conjunction with a sawmill utilizing lumber from the mountains north of Ulan Bator, and a cement plant also are in operation at the capital.

Commodities manufactured or processed by Mongolian industry constitute about one-third of all manufactured commodities required by the country. A small flour mill at Ulan Bator processes most of the wheat production of the Mongolian Peoples Republic. Numerous cooperatives are reported to have been formed for more efficient processing of butter and cheese products. The importance of the food industries in the nation is seen in the fact that the value of the 1950 production of food was reported to be 78 million *tugrik* (Mongolian monetary unit at parity with the rouble), as compared with 47 million *tugrik* for other domestic industries and crafts.

Before 1921, 90 per cent of Outer Mongolia's foreign trade was with China. Chinese wares were more suited to the tastes and demands of the Mongols, especially in such items as cooking vessels, ready-made clothes, tea, tobacco, silks, and jewelry. Moreover, Chinese merchants were well-organized into guilds and held a virtual monopoly of the Mongol market. A significant change in the direction of trade came with increasing Soviet influences and control. From 1924 to 1927 China's share dropped from 86 to 64 per cent, while the share of the Soviet Union rose from 14 to 36 per cent. Subsequently, the Chinese merchants were increasingly squeezed out, while Stormong, the Soviet trade agency, began to monopolize the trade. By 1945 the wholesale and export-import trade in the Mongolian Peoples Republic had been made state monopolies, so that the ordinary Mongol was in no better position than before in getting the benefits of competitive price biddings. In 1940 more than 96 per cent of the internal trade was carried on by the government trade agencies and a "network" of cooperatives.

Except for local camel and horse transport, all transport in the country is state-owned, and the government also controls and operates all banking and credit facilities, telephone and telegraph systems, newspapers, and theatres. Until 1959 about 50 per cent of the Mongol animal economy still was privately run. Thereafter, measures discouraging private nomadic enterprises and inducing the joining of "cooperatives" were reported to have eliminated most private nomadic activity. A loose type of collectives was formed, serviced by state veterinary and dipping stations.

Communications improvements have made significant progress in limited parts of the country. Old forms of transport were slow and costly. However, a special Mongol courier with the right to change to the best horses at all post stations once made the 1,800-mile trip from Uliassutai to Peking in nine days, averaging 200 miles a day by horseback. Ordinarily, camels require 30 to 50 days for the 660-mile trip between Ulan Bator and Chang-chia-k'ou. Between Ulan Bator and Ulan Ude in Siberia a freight train (a relatively recent phenomenon) now carries in one trip as much as 7,000 to 8,000 camels used to do (Figure 59). Aside from the Ulan Ude connection, a rail spur near the Manchurian border extends via Choibalsan to the southeast of the Kerulyen River from the Trans-Siberian railway. Both lines serve to bind the Mongolian Peoples Republic more closely to the Soviet Union economically as well as politically. In late 1955 a broad-gauge railroad line was completed between Ulan Bator and Chi-ning near the Inner Mongolian capital at Chang-chia-k'ou which is connected by rail to Peking. This link may help strengthen Outer Mongolian ties with communist China.

All the administrative centers of the country, of which there are only a few, and various stations along the motor routes between Ulan Bator, Uliassutai, and Kobdo, as well as stations along branch roads, are connected by a network of telephone and telegraph lines. In the larger centers the state operates radio stations. Several air routes carry regular passenger and freight traffic between the Soviet Union and a number of cities in the Mongolian Peoples Republic. Highways are only dirt-surfaced.

Mineral deposits occur in considerable variety in the country. As early

Fig. 59 ◦ The contrasts between old and new forms of transportation in Outer Mongolia are seen here in a view along the broad-gauge rail line which connects Ulan Bator, the capital, with the Siberian city of Ulan Ude, capital of the Buryat Mongol A.S.S.R. The chief form of transport prior to the construction of the railroad in 1949 was the camel train, which still remains important in areas away from the railroad despite the increasing use of motor transport. In late 1955 the railroad was extended southeastward to China to provide a shorter route between Peking and the U.S.S.R.

The camels are hairy, two-humped Bactrian camels each weighing about 1,000 pounds. They yield about seven pounds of camels wool (and the females about 900 pounds of milk) each year. A camel can carry about 500 pounds for some 25 miles in a day.

The two engines of the train indicate the difficult terrain across which the line runs in northern Mongolia near the town of Sukhe Bator where this photograph was taken. Note the snow cover typical of most of northern Mongolia in the winter months, and the heavily padded garments worn by the camel driver. The complete lack of trees documents another characteristic of most of the Outer Mongolian landscape. *(Sovfoto.)*

as 1920 the Russian observer Maiski reported deposits of lignite, coal, magnesite, iron ore, and chrome ore, while in the foothills of the northern border mountains gold had been worked in a small way for many years by Russian and other settlers. Copper is found in several places, especially around Kosogol near the Siberian frontier, where one field is said to be 35 miles long. Coal is found not far from Ulan Bator and near Choibalsan. Large deposits of lead, graphite, sulfur, mercury, ochre, and antimony also have been reported. Since the Mongol aversion to mining as an occupation is certainly as great as the Mongol aversion to cultivation, lack of a labor force is a serious handicap to the development of mineral resources.

The cities of Outer Mongolia

Until recently, only three towns have been significant in Outer Mongolia: Ulan Bator (Urga), Dzhibkhalantu (Uliassutai), and Dzhirgalantu (Kobdo). Ulan Bator (Red Hero) formerly called Da Khure (Great Monastery), is situated more than a mile from the Tola River. It was primarily a religious center, with which was associated a market quarter. The business section has been rebuilt and expanded with Western-type buildings along the main street to house government agencies. It also has a number of manufacturing plants, a power station, and a railroad station. The religious center is at some distance from the rest of the city. The population of the capital had risen to an estimated 150,000 in 1958.

Uliassutai in 1899 was the political capital and garrison fortress of the Manchus. As early as 1734 it is mentioned as the seat of the Manchu Governor-General; under Manchu rule it was populated chiefly by soldiery. Its monastery was built in 1787. At Uliassutai began the great postroad to Urga (now Ulan Bator) and to Kalgan (now Chang-chia-k'ou). In 1958 its population was estimated over 10,000.

West of Uliassutai in the lake-basin country lies Kobdo. This also was the site of a Manchu fortress to which a small commercial town eventually became attached. In 1958 its population also was estimated at about 10,000. Choibalsan, a new town in the eastern part of the Mongolian Peoples Republic, is named after the first premier of the Republic. In 1958 it was estimated to have a population of almost 20,000.

Population and new social forces

Estimates of population for the Mongolian Peoples Republic during the last decades generally have been between 750,000 and 885,000. These figures are by no means reliable and undoubtedly are too low. It seems safe to believe that the population of the Mongolian Peoples Republic is over a million.

Moreover, changes in social organization provide a basis for more rapid population increases than hitherto. In the prerevolutionary era (pre-1921) the social structure was compounded of four main elements: nobles or feudal lords, the lama priesthood, a relatively small number of serfs, and a majority consisting of free nomads or *arats*. The noble families numbered about 700, of whom only 100 possessed great wealth in cattle and palaces. Some 120,000 lama priests and novices, comprising an estimated one-sixth of the population, were attached to the lamaseries. A large percentage of these were mere servants of the higher lamas, tending the lamasery herds and waiting upon their superiors.

The revolutionary regime under Soviet direction at first proceeded cautiously in attempting to change the social and economic life of the Mongols. Feudal rights were cut gradually. After 1929, under various pretexts, the property of the feudal nobles was confiscated, and by 1945 this class was virtually eliminated. The power of the lamaseries was curtailed even more gradually. In 1938 there still were 82,000 priests and novices. After 1930, lamasery schools, which had had a virtual monopoly over schooling, were prohibited from enrolling children under 18, but in 1934 there still remained some 16,000 novices under 18 years of age. Since that time the lamaseries have steadily declined in wealth and influence. Many of their flocks have been confiscated, and their serfs have been freed.

The "free" nomads or *arats* formerly were bound by tradition and Mongol law to join responsibility for family, tribal, or regional debts to the feudal lords and were obligated to present frequent gifts to overlords upon special occasions. This type of bondage has been eliminated, but taxes and fees to the new regime must be paid. They receive in return veterinary and medical aid, some secular education, and some of the indirect benefits that result from improved communications and industrial development. Today, the Mongol is no longer completely nomadic.

The decline of the lamasery population probably has resulted in a greater proportion of family units, while increases in livestock per family, improved health measures, and medical and veterinary aids pave the way for a lower death rate. All indicate a more rapid rate of population increase.

Strategical significance of the Mongolian Peoples Republic

Before the thirteenth century the Mongols were divided into numerous quarreling tribes of nomads. At the beginning of the thirteenth century Genghis Khan succeeded in welding them into a powerful, mobile military force which conquered an empire stretching from the Pacific to the Black Sea and from Siberia to Burma and Vietnam. However, under his grandson, Kublai Khan, the empire was restricted largely to what is now China and Outer Mongolia, excluding Tibet. Ultimately the Mongols were driven out by a resurgent Chinese nation which held them in check until the rise of Manchu power in the early seventeenth century.

The Mongols helped the Manchu tribes of what is now northeastern China gain the Dragon Throne, but under conditions that assured Mongolia a semi-autonomous position within the empire. When the Manchu Empire was overthrown in 1911, the Mongols declared their independence. The Chinese through force of arms managed for a time to suppress the abortive rebellion. Internal wars in China, however, weakened China's power in the north, while Soviet influence was on the rise. By 1931, Chinese power was eliminated in Outer Mongolia, which had by then come within the Soviet sphere of influence. In 1945 Nationalist China recognized the *de facto* separation of Outer Mongolia from China.

In recent decades Outer Mongolia has been a buffer and zone of contention between China and the Soviet Union. Whether communist China can regain its influence in Outer Mongolia depends upon Sino-Soviet relations as well as the reactions of the Mongols to both their neighbors. Historically, the Mongols and the Chinese have regarded each other with suspicion or hatred. Attempts by one to gain control over the other have involved intrigue and ruthless slaughter. Yet there have been strong economic ties binding Outer Mongolia to China. In production and trade they are perhaps more complementary than are Soviet Siberia and the Mongolian Peoples Republic.

Soviet interest in the country is understandable for several reasons. The Soviet Far East and Trans-Baykalia have been food-short regions, and the Soviet desire to make these regions logistically independent makes imperative Soviet command over what food products Outer Mongolia may be able to supply. Moreover, the Trans-Siberian railroad lies only a short distance from the north Mongolian border and would be endangered were an unfriendly power in control of Outer Mongolia. The plains of Outer Mongolia, centrally located with respect to Soviet Siberia and Central Asia, North China, Korea, and Japan, can harbor airfields of high strategic value to any occupying power. Topographically, there is little obstacle to the movement of mechanized armies out of Outer Mongolia eastward into Manchuria or southward into China's Shan-hsi Province. The southwest Gobi and the low eastern passes of the Altai mountains furnish routes that lead quickly to the Ho-hsi corridor, the gateway between eastern China and Hsin-chiang province.

For all of these reasons, Outer Mongolia has a long-term importance that will have a great bearing upon future relations between China and the Soviet Union, for Outer Mongolia not only is a buffer between the two, but is also a political prize of the first order.

SELECTED GEOGRAPHICAL BIBLIOGRAPHY

1. De Francis, J. *Chinese Agent in Mongolia.* Baltimore: Johns Hopkins University Press, 1949.
2. Friters, G. M. *Outer Mongolia and Its International Position.* Baltimore: Johns Hopkins University Press, 1949.
3. Haslund-Christensen, Henning. "In the Mongol Encampment, 1937," *Journal of the Royal Central Asian Society,* April, 1938, pp. 175-193.
4. Kislovsky, O. "Domestic Animals of Mongolia," *Journal of Heredity,* January, 1938, pp. 27-32.
5. Lattimore, Owen. *Inner Asian Frontiers of China.* New York: American Geographical Society, 1940.
6. Mandel, Wm. "Outer Mongolia's Five-year Plan," *Far Eastern Survey,* June 15, 1949, pp. 140-141.
7. Obruchef, M. "Orography of Central Asia," *Scottish Geographical Magazine,* February, 1896.
8. Serebrennikov, I. I. "The Soviet Satellite Outer Mongolia Today," *Foreign Affairs,* April, 1931.
9. Wiens, Herold J. "Geographical Limitations to Food Production in the Mongolian Peoples Republic," *Annals of the Association of American Geographers,* December, 1951, pp. 348-369.

Comments

A thorough geographical study of the Mongolian Peoples Republic has yet to appear in English, although several studies of the state have appeared in Russian, notably two volumes by E. M. Murzaev, one discussing physical geography, the other dealing with economic geography. These were published in 1948. De Francis' book is a translation of a Chinese book relating to travels in Mongolia in 1921 of a Kuomintang Chinese official. Friters' is a useful work emphasizing mainly historical and political events and interpretations, although a considerable amount of economic data is contained in the beginning chapters. Wiens analyzes the present rangeland capacity for support of livestock and the possibilities of agricultural land use. Lattimore's book is a valuable historical geographical interpretation of such areas as Mongolia, Hsin-chiang, and Manchuria in their interrelated situations along China's frontiers.

Southeast Asia

AN INTRODUCTION

SOUTHEAST ASIA IS THE NAME APPLIED TO THAT GROUP OF COUN-
tries—Burma, Thailand, Vietnam, Cambodia, Laos, the Philippines, Malaya, Indonesia, and British Borneo—lying between the mass of China on
the one hand and India on the other and occupying the southeastern
corner of the Asiatic continent (Map 13). Its gross area, including seas,
is comparable roughly to that of the United States, although its land area
is only slightly over half that of the United States, some 1,750,000 square
miles. From east to west Southeast Asia spans a distance approximating
that between Boston and Seattle; from north to south it covers 37 degrees
of latitude, approximately the distance between Miami, Florida, and
Lima, Peru.

Within that vast realm there are so many variations in natural and cultural forms that until very recent times Southeast Asia was considered to
be without regional integrity. Also, most of its countries have been colonial dependencies oriented toward other parts of the world. In fact, the
term "Southeast Asia" has come into common use only since the second
World War.

Historically, Southeast Asia has been a zone of convergence for Indian
and Chinese cultures and a crossroads between the European West and
East Asia. This role has been furthered by its position astride an inter-

ocean bottleneck, the Straits of Malakka, which Fisher has likened to the man-made Suez and Panama canals. Although it is possible for ocean shipping to bypass the straits corridor more easily than either Panama or Suez, the net effect of this constriction in the route between the Indian and Pacific oceans has been to make Southeast Asia more a zone of passage than a focus of developmental concentration—until very recent times. The realm also lies midway between Asia and Australasia. The long spinning out of archipelagoes and islands on its peripheries gradually merges into the Pacific and Austral world, and over the steppingstones thus provided peoples have moved outward from Asia.

Southeast Asia also has acted as a giant funnel into which peoples from the southern regions of East Asia have migrated southward under the pressure of long-continuing Chinese expansion into southwestern China. These migrations into and through Southeast Asia have left their mark in an enormous variety of ethnic, linguistic, and religious differences. The borders between the mainland states and between them and China run through rugged, sparsely settled areas populated by numerous minorities. These peoples often straddle the international boundaries and provide constant points of international friction. Within each country, also, sizable minorities present problems of internal administration that have yet to be fully solved: the Karens, Shans, and Talaings in Burma; the Karens, Lao-Thai, and Cambodians in northern and the Malays in southern Thailand; the Thai, Chams, and Moi [1] in Indochina; the negrito peoples and Moslems in the Philippines; and the primitive groups in Indonesia.

Linguistic differences are even more significant since not only does each ethnic group have its own tongue, but also local or regional dialects may be so distinct as to be incomprehensible. Especially is this true in Indonesia and the Philippines, where national languages have been promoted, Bahasa Indonesia in Indonesia and Tagalog in the Philippines. Throughout insular Southeast Asia bazaar Malay has been used as a commercial *lingua franca*, and European languages, especially English, Dutch, and French, also have been used widely.

Religious differences add further variety to the already variegated scene. Nearly half of the 183 million people in Southeast Asia are Moslems, but most are concentrated in Indonesia, which has, therefore, a notable interest in the affairs of predominantly Moslem Southwest Asia (Figure 60). Burma, Thailand, and Cambodia are predominantly Hinayana or Theravada Buddhist (Figure 61); the Philippines are predominantly Catholic; and Vietnam is eclectically Confucian with a large Christian minority. Amidst all of these concentrations, however, are aberrational minorities, such as Hindu Bali in Indonesia, and underlying the dominant religious structures is an often deep-rooted layer of animism.

[1] A collective term for the diverse preliterate tribal groups in Indochina.

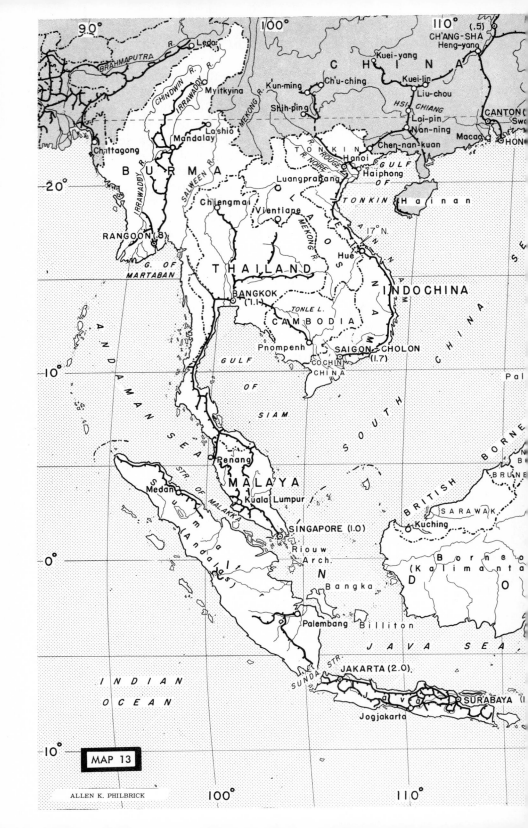

MAP 13

ALLEN K. PHILBRICK

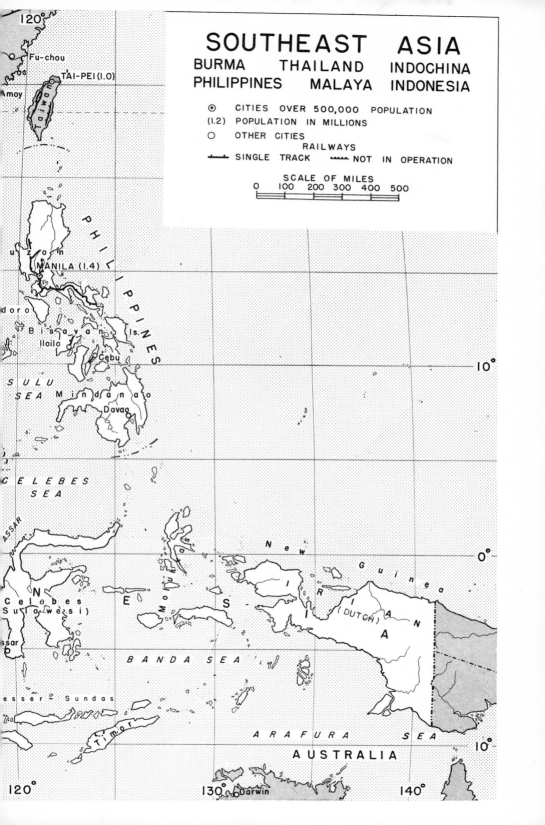

SOUTHEAST ASIA
BURMA   THAILAND   INDOCHINA
PHILIPPINES   MALAYA   INDONESIA

⊙   CITIES OVER 500,000 POPULATION
(1.2)   POPULATION IN MILLIONS
○   OTHER CITIES
RAILWAYS
├──┤ SINGLE TRACK   ┅┅┅ NOT IN OPERATION

SCALE OF MILES
0   100   200   300   400   500

120°

Fu-chou

Amoy

TAI-PEI (1.0)

120°

Taiwan

PHILIPPINES

u z o n

MANILA (1.4)

doro

Bisayan Is.

Iloilo

Cebu

SULU

SEA   Mindanao

Davao

CELEBES
SEA

10°

MASSAR

N

Celebes
(Sulawesi)

ssar

E

Moluccas

S   New

I   R   I   Guinea

A   (DUTCH)   N

A

BANDA SEA

esser Sundas

Timor

ARAFURA   SEA

AUSTRALIA

130° Darwin

140°

0°

10°

A special minority problem centers about the ten or more million Chinese in Southeast Asia, some of whom migrated to the region centuries ago, although most have arrived within the last century seeking economic opportunities. Relatively unassimilated, they form an alien element in every country, of an importance beyond mere numbers because of the Chinese function as middlemen in commerce. In Malaya, however, exclusive of Singapore, they form no mere minority, since they are barely outnumbered by the Malays. Singapore itself is largely Chinese. The Chinese also are numerically important in Thailand, where one out of every five persons is said to have Chinese blood (Figure 62). Even where they are a small minority, however, as in the Philippines and Indonesia, anti-Chinese animosity has taken the form of both official and unofficial persecutions. The importance of the Chinese in Southeast Asia makes China of greater importance in economic and political affairs than they otherwise would be, and part of the distrust of the Chinese stems from a fear of Chinese cultural, economic, and more recently political imperialism.

Fig. 60 • Interior of a mosque near Palembang, Sumatra, Indonesia. Most of the people of Indonesia are Moslem, and they, with other Moslems in British Borneo, Malaya, and the Philippines, account for about half of the population of Southeast Asia. Although it is said that Islam is not practiced so faithfully in Southeast Asia as in Pakistan, Southwest Asia, and North Africa, the rise of nationalism in Indonesia has been accompanied by a notable rise in the strength of Islam as both a social and political force. Note in the picture the mats on the floor, of straw or bamboo rather than cloth; the bare light bulbs hanging from the ceilings; the whirling fan also suspended from the roofbeams; and the latticed door. All these are characteristic of urban housing in many parts of Southeast Asia. (Standard Oil Company, N.J.)

The pattern of lands and seas

The simplest expression of diversity in Southeast Asia is observed in the areal arrangement of its lands and seas (Map 14). In brief, Southeast Asia can be divided conveniently into two major parts: a continental component and an insular component.

The continental division, sometimes termed in its entirety the Indochinese peninsula, is composed of Burma, Thailand, and Indochina, with Malaya a southern peripheral appendage which belongs more properly in the second of the major divisions. This mainland unit is itself by no means monolithic. Its character resides chiefly in its several major river

Fig. 61 • The entrance to a Buddhist monastery in Rangoon. Dormitories for the monks are in the foreground, and a great statue of Buddha looms in the background. Similar structures, including temples and elaborate tomb markers called *stupa*, are found in all of the countries of Southeast Asia that profess Hinayana or Theravada Buddhism as their primary religion—Burma, Thailand, Laos, and Cambodia. These countries originally received their indoctrination from Ceylonese monks, and Ceylon is the remaining Asian country the larger part of whose population is similarly Buddhist. The abundance of vegetation—banana plants, palms, and larger evergreen and deciduous trees—is characteristic of much of Southeast Asia, even in many of its cities. The women in the foreground wear the traditional *longgyi*, a variant of the sarong. (*John E. Brush.*)

Fig. 62 • A group of Chinese rice-mill workers on the outskirts of Bangkok in Thailand. The Chinese dominate Thailand's rice marketing and milling industries, although most of them are employed workers and not mill owners. Chinese are prominent in all aspects of commerce in Southeast Asia, but only in a few areas are they engaged in rice agriculture, the main occupation of the Southeast Asian realm. *(Norton Ginsburg.)*

valleys and deltas; these are separated from each other by larger inter-fluves of meridionally trending mountain and hill ranges, splaying south-ward from the eastern margins of the Himalayan mountain core. The most important of these valleys, each densely occupied and intensively cultivated, are the focal regions of the countries that compose the unit. the Irrawaddy in Burma; the Menam Chao Phya in Thailand; and the Mekong in southern and the Red in northern Indochina.

In general, these corelands lie well off the established shipping lanes that pass through Southeast Asia. The western part of the division, Burma, faces the Bay of Bengal and the Indian Ocean; the eastern part of the division faces the South China Sea and the Pacific. On both sides of the mainland division, however, the configuration of the shoreline is sufficiently irregular so that most of the major national cores front on lesser arms of the major seas: the Gulf of Tonkin in the case of the Red River delta region; the Bight of Bangkok and the Gulf of Siam in the case of the lower Chao Phya valley; and the Gulf of Martaban and the Andaman Sea in the case of the Irrawaddy system.

The second major component consists of the archipelagoes that rim the southeastern margin of Asia, which are divided primarily between the Philippines and Indonesia. In addition, it is customary to include the

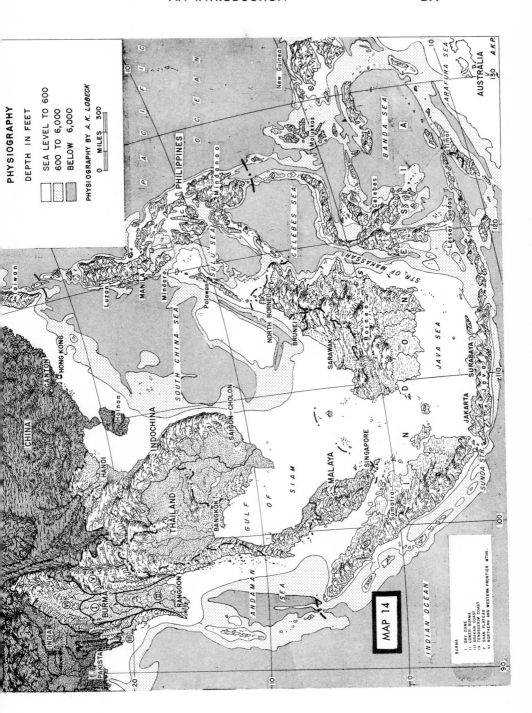

PHYSIOGRAPHY

DEPTH IN FEET

SEA LEVEL TO 600
600 TO 6,000
BELOW 6,000

PHYSIOGRAPHY BY A. K. LOBECK

0   MILES   300

MAP 14

BURMA

I   DRY ZONE
II   LOWER BURMA
III ARAKAN COAST
IV   TENASSERIM COAST
V   SHAN PLATEAU
VI   NORTHERN AND WESTERN FRONTIER MTNS.

Malayan peninsula, which extends from the mainland well into the complex of islands and seas known as Malaysia. The relations between Malaya
and the rest of archipelagic Southeast Asia are further established on
ethnic and linguistic grounds. The peoples of Indonesia are predominantly
Malay, as are those of the Philippines, and the languages of all are
closely related.

The islands of the division are characterized by highland cores out of
which flow short rivers which cross the often narrow coastal plains, usually
densely occupied. In cases where exceptionally fertile upland soils have
attracted settlement and assisted agricultural development, as in Java
and certain of the western intermontane basins of Sumatra, the uplands
also are characterized by dense populations. Demographic contrasts are
even more striking than in the continental half of the realm, and certain
large alluvial coastal regions are as yet little occupied—eastern Sumatra
and coastal Borneo, Mindanao, and New Guinea.

In terms of geologic structure, the western half of the realm consists of
an extension of the continental mainland, the so-called Sunda Platform,
a stable and ancient land mass which has been likened to the Deccan of
India and the Laurentian Shield of Canada. The continental shelf extends
southeastward from the Indochinese peninsula, crosses the southern half
of the South China Sea, and connects Borneo, northern Java, and eastern
Sumatra—the Great Sunda islands—with the continent. A similar, stable
land block protrudes from Australia and underlies much of Australia,
southern New Guinea, and the Arafura and Coral seas between. The
mountains, which run generally north-south across the continental countries through Malaya and the islands of Riouw, Lingga, Bangka, and Billiton, are extensions of the Himalayan system of folded sedimentaries
underlain by granite cores. Under conditions of high rainfall and temperatures these mountains have become maturely rounded, in contrast to the
rugged Himalaya which are of about the same geological age.

Through western Sumatra and southern Java, however, run extensions
of the Burmese Border ranges, which can be traced southward through
the Andaman and Nicobar islands into Indonesia. These are young mountains still characterized by a high degree of volcanic activity. A similar
arc, part of the circum-Pacific system of volcanic ranges, runs through the
Philippines and northern New Guinea, with extensions into Celebes and
northern Borneo. Between the two stable continental platforms and the
two major arcs of volcanic instability lies a complex knot of mountainous
islands and deep seas, within which are included the eastern Sundas, the
Molukkas, and Celebes, together with the deep Celebes, Molukka, and
Banda seas, and the Straits of Makassar.

The seas that lie over the Asiatic continental shelf are shallow and of
uniform depth—no more than 140 feet. Into them pour the great mainland

rivers and the lesser streams of the islands or parts of islands that face them. Their waters are in general warmer and fresher than the deeper seas to the east. The southern coast of Java and to a lesser degree the western coast of Sumatra front on the deep waters of the Indian Ocean itself. Along these coasts there are only narrow and discontinuous coastal plains; marine and fluvial deposition is less significant than on the coasts opposite, which front on the shallow seas.

Extra- and intra-realm connections

The physical atomism in Southeast Asia created by intervening seas and barrier mountain ranges is reflected in the transportation facilities that link the realm with the outside world, the various countries with each other, and their internal regions among themselves. Of equal importance, however, in the development of international transport channels has been the colonial status of all of the countries but Thailand. Extra-realm transportation facilities tend to be oriented toward the actual or former mother country, although the postwar assumption of political freedom has modified this pattern somewhat. These external connections substantiate the description of the Southeast Asian countries as facing the world, and "turning their backs to one another."

Southeast Asia's chief connections with the outside world are maritime. Until 1952 there was only one railway connection, and that temporarily inoperable, with the outside world, the meter-gauge Yün-nan railway from Hanoi. In that year a second connection was made, also from Hanoi, but towards the northeast where a break-of-gauge connection was made with the Chinese Kuang-hsi line. The only road connections are via roads paralleling these railway lines, by the largely deteriorated Burma Road between the Shan States of Burma and southwestern Yün-nan province, by the so-called Ledo Road which was built during the war to connect northern Burma with Assam, and by the lesser route through Manipur state on Burma's western border.

The great focus of shipping is Singapore, guarding the Straits of Malakka, the passage between the Indian Ocean and the Pacific. Regularly scheduled services connect Singapore with all the regions of the world and with each country in the realm (Figure 63). Each of the Southeast Asian countries also has at least one major port that acts as its chief point of contact with the outside world: Rangoon for Burma, Bangkok for Thailand, Saigon and (through Haiphong) Hanoi for Indochina, Manila for the Philippines, and Jakarta and Surabaya for Indonesia. These cities are basically Western in form and function, if not in origin, and provide economic and political leadership for the various countries, as well as port facilities. In terms of shipping services, they still tend to maintain their prewar politically-induced orientations: for Rangoon toward India and Great Britain; for Saigon toward France; for Manila toward the United States; for Jakarta toward the Netherlands. Singapore has been characterized by a greater diversification of areal interests than the others, owing to its entrepôt function and crossroads situation. In the ports of each nation the flags of the former or present colonial powers dominate the shipping scene, but for the realm as a whole British shipping centered upon Singapore is most prominent, with Dutch, Scandinavian, American, French, and Japanese vessels following in that order.

Shipping also serves an important regional and local function, especially in archipelagic Southeast Asia where shipping services perform functions equivalent to roads and railways elsewhere. Regional shipping companies, such as the Koninklijke Paketvaart-Maatschappij in Indonesia and the Straits Steamship Company in Malaya, bind the major national ports together. Each port in turn acts as an entrepôt for lesser ports within each country, which are served by local services or by native craft, especially in Indonesia and the Philippines (Figure 64).

Fig. 63 • Singapore is one of the world's great ports, as well as being the major port for Malaya and a regional entrepôt for archipelagic Southeast Asia. Along the main wharves in Singapore, just west of the heart of the city, are moored five great freighters of the British Blue Funnel Line, one of the larger shipping companies in the Orient. The port of Singapore has efficient port facilities, extending along the southern shore of Singapore island for over a mile. Similar installations may be observed in Tanjong Priok, the port of Jakarta, and in Manila, and to a degree in the other major ports of Southeast Asia, but most ports in the realm have no such modern facilities. (Norton Ginsburg.)

Fig. 64 • A sailing outrigger with a skiff across its bows, another tied astern, and a cargo of oil products and lumber prepares to move out to sea in the waters of Luzon, the Philippines. Boats like these carry huge amounts of cargo in cabotage and inter-island trade in Southeast Asia. For the most part they are the distributors of goods from local entrepôt and the collectors and gatherers of produce to be exported from the larger ports. Unfortunately, statistical records concerning the movement of these craft are few and incomplete. Since many of them also move in international trade, they represent a gap in the knowledge of trade movements in Southeast Asia. Note the larger vessels moored in the open roadstead in the left background. *(Standard Oil Company, N.J.)*

In the postwar period air transportation has assumed a major role in the movement of passengers, though not of goods. At least eight major international air lines serve the realm, and the airfields of the larger cities, which usually also are the metropolitan ports, have been enlarged to handle the largest aircraft in commercial service. Although Singapore retains much of its strategic crossroads function as an air-route hub, Bangkok, with a more northerly location, has become the major junction for extra-realm services between Europe, the Far East, and Australia. Intrarealm connections also have been strengthened by air services. Each country has an air line of its own that services both domestic and regional demands. The result has been increased mobility and a great diffusion of ideas and practices from the great cities.

Land communications between and even within the countries remains restricted. Total railway mileage in Southeast Asia, 11,650 miles in 1938,[2] was less than that in Japan alone. No operational railway links Burma with Thailand, although the Japanese-built line between Bangkok and Moulmein still exists in part (Map 13). One line links Bangkok with Pnom Penh, the capital of Cambodia. Another, more important, runs the length of the isthmus of Kra to link the Thai and Malayan railway systems on both the east and west sides of the Malay peninsula. Road connections (poor ones) exist at several points, but in general they are of little international commercial significance.

Internally, each country has developed a railway network peculiar to the nature of national demands. Indonesia possesses the largest rail system, although it is concentrated primarily on Java. All lines are metergauge, except those of Indonesia and the Philippines which are Cape gauge (3 feet 6 inches). The railways have begun to face serious competition from highway transportation, especially since the war. Although by American standards road facilities are poorly developed, least so in Malaya, Java, and Indochina, in each densely settled area mobility has been greatly increased by bus services since 1946. The result is a rapid breakdown of local isolationism.

Inland waterways are especially significant in the mainland areas. In Burma, the Irrawaddy is navigable for river vessels drawing 3.5 feet for 1,000 miles from its mouth, and its major tributary, the Chindwin, is navigable for smaller craft for another 500 miles. The Chao Phya is navigable for launches for many miles, and, like the Irrawaddy, its delta is laced with navigable canals over which sail- or pole-propelled country boats move much of the country's produce (Figure 65). Similar canals navigable by barges and launches as well as by country boats and sampans lace the deltas of the Red and Mekong rivers, and the Mekong is navigable for over a hundred miles above Pnom Penh for small river steamers.[3] In general, the rivers of the insular regions and Malaya are navigable only for small native boats, sampans, and bamboo rafts; this is true also of the upper courses of the larger mainland rivers.

[2] In 1952 operational mileage had decreased to 10,230 miles, primarily because of disturbances in Burma, Indochina, Malaya, and Indonesia.

[3] The middle Mekong also is navigable for river steamers along so-called "reaches" which are separated from each other by rapids and shallows.

The natural triune:
climate, soils, vegetation

The diversities reflected in Southeast Asia's physiographic, ethnic, and transport patterns are found also in its varieties of climatic, edaphic, and vegetative phenomena. Just as the former, however, by their very differences place an identifying stamp upon the realm, even more do the associations of these three natural conditions place a comprehensible regularity upon the face of Southeast Asia.

Climate:—Climatic variations depend mostly upon the fluctuations in rainfall and not upon temperatures. Plate B (P. 376) shows this clearly. The temperature lines on the diagram digress very little, whatever the season

Fig. 65 • A canal in Lower Siam just northwest of Bangkok. Roads in the area are few and unimportant. Most carriage of passengers and goods is by water taxis or sampans. Note the houses of bamboo, rattan, and thatch on piles well above the water level. During the rainy season, the canal level rises several feet and laps at the floors of the houses. The building on the left is a tea house; the sign in front of it advertises a Siamese motion picture. The profuse vegetation is characteristic of most settled or *kampong* areas in Southeast Asia where houses are surrounded by "gardens" of bananas, coconut palms, and other fruit trees. Similar scenes may be observed in the densely settled deltaic lowlands of several of the other Southeast Asian countries. (*Norton Ginsburg.*)

of the year, from a range of 80 to 85°F. Temperatures tend to be higher on the average in those areas farther from the equator, especially during the spring, the driest part of the year in the marginal regions. All of the stations shown are marine-oriented, however, and none reflect the wider temperature fluctuations found in the interior uplands. Yet, except for the highest highlands, frost is virtually unknown in Southeast Asia, and all of the densely occupied lowland regions possess year-round growing seasons.

In contrast to the relative constancy of temperatures throughout the realm, rainfall varies radically from season to season and from place to place. At Singapore, virtually on the equator, rainfall varies little from month to month. It is an equatorial station, with an annual average rainfall of 95 inches and with an even seasonal rainfall distribution similar to that in much of Malaya, Sumatra, Borneo, Celebes, and the Molukkas. Both north and south of the equator, however, rainfall takes on a marked seasonal quality, in general with very wet summers and dry winters. At Jakarta, 6 degrees south of the equator, total rainfall averages 72 inches a year with a notable maximum in January-February, the middle of the southern-hemisphere summer. In the northern hemisphere, each sample station is characterized by a lengthy dry season in winter and a longer summer rainy season. At Saigon and Bangkok, which receive only 55 inches per year, the maximum monthly precipitation comes in September, but in Rangoon and Iloilo, and indeed in most of the area removed from the equator, the maximum comes in mid-summer, July or August.

Seasonal rainfall variability is primarily a reflection of the play of air masses across Southeast Asia. In the northern winter the northeast trade winds (a northern tropical air mass), reinforced by an outflow of cool air from the northeast Asian coast, sweep down over most of the realm, taking on a northwesterly component according to Ferrel's Law as they cross the equator. Just south of the realm, they meet the southeast trade winds (a southern tropical air mass) moving northward from Australia. Between the two is formed a fluctuating zone of rising air traditionally known as the Doldrum Belt and more properly as the Intertropical Front. The frontal zone tends to migrate with the sun and the seasons and is characterized by high convectional rainfall which tends to fall in sudden and intense thundershowers. The equatorial zone, roughly between 5 degrees north and south of the equator, receives most of its rainfall in this way. Although there are variations from place to place, in general there is no dry season of note near the equator.

In the northern summer the wind system is reversed. The low-pressure areas in India and northwest China and Mongolia provide such an attraction to the air masses from the south and southeast that the southeast trades sweep across the equator, thereby taking on a southwesterly component, and bring rain to India, most of Southeast Asia north of the equator, and much of East Asia. Meanwhile, the northeast trades have withdrawn northward and tend to move northwestward toward the attracting lows in East Asia. For this reason, the otherwise latitudinal Intertropical Front becomes occluded, and southern-hemisphere winds sweep over all of Southeast Asia and southern East Asia. The most rapid and marked transition from winter to summer is experienced by Burma, which may be considered within the sphere of the true Indian monsoon. Changes are less rapid and extreme in Thailand, Indochina, and the Philippines, which are associated more with the moderate East Asian monsoon effect.

Climatic extremes are modified by marine influences, which penetrate well in each country. Temperature and rainfall variations are encouraged, however, by altitudinal differences. Hill stations, for example, provide relief from the sultry heat of the coastal lowlands. Or again, as an example of orographic rainfall, the eastern Annamese coast experiences a winter rather than a summer maximum because the prevailing northeasterly winds of winter rise over the Annamese coastal ranges after crossing the South China Sea. On the other hand, a conspicuous example of a rain-shadow region is the Dry Zone of Burma, which is virtually surrounded by high physiographic barriers. In the equatorial zone, as at Singapore and over Borneo, cloudiness perennially is heavy, and the ability of certain cultivated plants to thrive under such conditions is limited. In addition, north of latitude 10°N., tropical cyclones or typhoons develop over the Philippine or South China seas between July and November. These violent storms bring downpours, tidal waves, and 100-mile-an-hour winds as they break against the northern Philippines and the east coasts of Annam, Tonkin, and South China.

Soils. Climate is the primary soil-producing element over much of Southeast Asia. High temperatures, humidities, and generally abundant rainfall have resulted in the rapid chemical decomposition of complex minerals within the soil and in the rapid leaching out of organic matter and plant nutrients. The major soil-forming process is laterization, whereby rapid decomposition and removal of silicates takes place, leaving a fine reddish topsoil that is friable, porous, low in organic matter, and composed primarily of alumina clays and iron oxides. Three to five feet below the surface, sometimes associated with shallow, fluctuating water tables, impermeable iron pans often appear. On slopes these may form a concretized surface layer when erosion has removed the topsoil.

Lateritic soils usually are infertile. The lush forest growth that appears naturally over many of these soils seems to belie their infertility. However, this growth is the result of a delicately balanced cycle in which the soil acts primarily as a retainer or medium to which the protecting forest constantly returns as much fertilizing material as it takes out. When the forest

Fig. 66 • The alluvial soils of Southeast Asia are the most fertile and the more intensively utilized. Here a small herd of water buffalo struggle through a flooded paddy field in Brunei, British Borneo. They are homogenizing the soil under hoof prior to the transplanting of paddy. The surface probably will be smoothed with a board or fine harrow immediately before transplantation. Note the seedbed in the middleground and the light shelter from which watch is kept against birds as the grain ripens. *(British Information Services.)*

is removed, this cyclical equilibrium is broken, and the soil, exposed to the elements, quickly loses its small reservoir of nutrient materials through leaching and run-off. In areas removed from the equator, the laterization process with its concomitant leaching is delayed during the drier seasons of the year. The result is soils that are more fertile than those in the perennially rainy equatorial areas.

The highly limited and localized fertile soils of Southeast Asia are those that, in contrast to the "mature" lateritic soils, are "young." Such soils are composed of alluvium, which is deposited along the lower courses of most of the Southeast Asian rivers. These alluvial materials are often so recently deposited that they may be regarded as reservoirs of fertility into which the eroding soils of the rest of a given river basin drain (Figure 66). Such are the soils of most of the great agricultural regions of Southeast Asia: the Irrawaddy central dry zone and delta, the lower Chao Phya basin, the Cambodian flats and Cochin-Chinese delta of the Mekong; the central valley of Luzon; the Red River delta of Tonkin; and the lower courses of innumerable lesser streams. Not all of these soils are renewed periodically by flooding, but, in some cases, as in the lower Chao Phya basin, flooding takes place annually, and the inundation of fields is regarded as a blessing *á la Egyptienne*.

Another type of young and fertile soil is found over recently deposited basic volcanic materials. It is soils of this type that have provided the basis for Java's agricultural development into one of the most productive and densely populated areas on earth.

Vegetation. The original vegetation over most of Southeast Asia was forest, and more than 60 per cent of the land area of Southeast Asia still is in forest and woodland (Figure 67). The two major forest types are (1) the tropical rainforest, which is found in the lowland equatorial areas and elsewhere where climatic conditions tend to resemble those near the equator, and (2) the monsoon forest, which is associated with areas of marked seasonal precipitation. The tropical rainforest is predominantly broadleaved and evergreen. It is characterized by numerous heterogeneous species of trees and plants, and by relatively clean, shaded forest floors, a closed canopy, and many auxiliary plants, such as lianas and ferns. In commercial terms, the tropical rainforest is known chiefly for its rare tropical hardwoods, rattan, and gums and resins, and not for a mass production of timber.

The monsoon forest is predominantly tropophilous and deciduous, although some evergreen species persist. Teak is perhaps the most famous of the monsoon forest trees. In general, the monsoon forest, as found in Burma, Thailand, and parts of Indochina, is characterized by larger stands of single species than the tropical rainforest, by a more open appearance and incomplete canopy, by somewhat denser ground cover especially in the wet season, by thickets of bamboo and tropical grasses, by fires set either by men or nature, and by a greater commercial importance. Between it and the tropical rainforest lies a continuum of mixed forest which partakes of the characteristics of both.

Within both the tropical rain- and monsoon forests, but especially in the latter and along its drier margins, there exist localized grasslands, apparently the result of widespread and repeated burning of the forest either by men or by natural means. These grasslands—known as *cogonales* in the Philippines, *lalang* in Malaya, and *alang alang* in Indonesia—are dominated by such species as *Imperata Cylindrica,* a pernicious, deep-rooted grass, impervious to fire, and, except when very young, unsuitable for pasture. The areas under grass are considered lost to the native cultivator, since deep-plowing, perhaps the only means of bringing the grasses under control, is beyond indigenous technologies. Where clearings are restricted in size, the forest eventually replaces itself. In its early stages of replacement it is characterized by a dense undergrowth, and becomes the "jungle" of common usage. Actually, much of Southeast Asia's forest land is believed to be second-growth forest that gradually has restored itself to its primate state. Especially in northern Southeast Asia, bamboos have replaced the original forest and form almost impenetrable thickets swept frequently by fires; bamboos, like the grasses and teak, can survive (Figure 67).

In addition to these dominant vegetation types, there are three others of significance. One consists of beach woodland in which casuarinas and coconut palms are conspicuous along sandy, well-drained shorelines. Secondly, where tidal fluctuations on gently shelving shores are important, fringing mangrove forests are found. These act as anchors for coastal marine sediments and help build out the shoreline. They provide valuable firewood and charcoal for the coastal communities. The third type of forest appears at 2,000 to 3,000 feet, is primarily deciduous, and resembles temperate forest growth. Above 5,000 feet pine forests also may appear, and in the most humid areas dense moss forests are found.

Fig. 67 • A road running through a grove of giant bamboo in northern Thailand. Groves like these may be found throughout Southeast Asia, although the species of bamboo vary from place to place. The stems of these giants may measure eight inches across and are used, among other things, as water pipes in irrigation works. These plants are grasses rather than trees and often replace monsoon forest or tropical rainforest vegetation after fires. Bamboos also are cultivated around villages and along communal property lines. *(Norton Ginsburg.)*

Fig. 68 • The intensity of cultivation in parts of Southeast Asia is suggested by these paddy fields in northern Vietnam in the Tonkin lowland. Some of the fields are double-cropped and have been placed in vegetables planted on small ridges raised about the moist ground level. In the background is a Vietnamese village, with houses directly on the ground in Chinese fashion rather than elevated on stilts as is common in most of Southeast Asia. A road is being built by hand of clay and sand along the canalized river in the background. Since most of the area is under water during the rainiest season, the road must be elevated several feet above the plain if it is to be usable throughout the year. The mound at the left is a grave mound, again a reflection of Chinese cultural influence. Most of the land utilization in Southeast Asia is not so intensive, with exception of small areas of Chinese horticulture and much of densely settled Java. *(MSA, Saigon.)*

Livelihood and the functions of Southeast Asia

As in most of Asian Asia, the basis for livelihood in Southeast Asia is agriculture. About three-fourths of the total working population is engaged in agriculture, in the direct processing of agricultural products, in fishing, or in elemental forest exploitation. The pattern of population distribution shows the heaviest concentrations in the more fertile alluvial lowlands and in the few uplands, as in

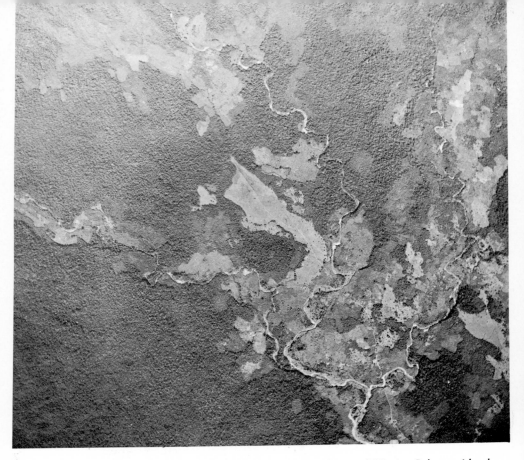

Fig. 69 • An area of shifting cultivation, Aborlan Municipal District, Palawan island, the Philippines. In general, the lightest patches represent the most recently cleared areas. The darkest areas, as in the lower left, indicate the tropical rainforest which covers most of the island. The patches of greys between the lightest and the darkest are clearings that have been abandoned and are growing back into forest. Not infrequently these clearings when abandoned are invaded by pernicious tropical grasses, and are known in the Philippines as *cogonales*. The shifting pattern of cultivation is widespread throughout Southeast Asia, and the smell of clearing fires before the beginning of the rainy seasons is a noncommensurable characteristic of the countries of the realm. *(U.S. Air Force.)*

Java, where basic volcanic ejecta has enriched the soils. With few exceptions, the distribution of agricultural land use coincides with that of population, almost perfectly so far as food-producing agriculture is concerned. The high degree of localization of agriculture is suggested in Table XV-1 which shows that only 8.5 per cent of the total land area of Southeast Asia is under cultivation. Insofar as there are large areas in the realm that are not yet under cultivation, Southeast Asia represents one major Asian agricultural frontier. This concept is supported by the relatively low densities of population in most of Southeast Asia, the gross

310

density per square kilometer being only 107, as compared with Japan's 619. However, in the intensively cultivated ecumenes of the various countries densities of population may be as high as anywhere in Asia.

Wet-rice is the dominant crop, grown on small holdings primarily for subsistence purposes. In Java and the Red River delta of Tonkin, extremely intensive cultivation is practiced (Figure 68). Transplantation, irrigation, double-cropping, and hand cultivation are the rule. Over the realm as a whole, however, these practices are only partially employed. With the exception of Tonkin, a highly sinicized region, controlled or technical irrigation and heavy fertilization are not widely practiced. Most of Southeast Asia's rice is grown without a controlled water supply and for the most part depends on frequently variable rainfall.

Where wet-rice agriculture is not possible, maize and other crops—sesame in the Dry Zone of Burma, for example—are important food crops. Root crops, especially the sweet potato and cassava, are also important. Table XV-1 tends to understate these strictly subsistence crops, since many are raised under systems of shifting cultivation and fail to appear in statistical compilations. The significance of shifting cultivation—called *caiñgin* in the Philippines, *tamrai* in Thailand, *ray* in Indochina, *ladang* in Malaya and Indonesia, and *taungya* in Burma—is difficult to measure, but it is common to all of Southeast Asia (Figures 69 and 92). For example, it is estimated that 90 per cent of the farmers in the outer islands of Indonesia (those areas other than Java, Madura, Bali, and Lombok) practice some form of shifting cultivation over an area that has never been measured. The effects of shifting cultivation, however, are seen in the destruction of valuable forest lands, in the erosion of soils, and in the destructive flooding of permanent agricultural lands in valley bottoms downstream from the forest clearings. Every government in the realm is concerned with limiting this practice.

Over the past 75 years the impact of a money economy on the peoples of the realm has resulted in an increasing percentage of foodstuffs and other farm products being sold for cash. The zenith of this trend was the creation of a surplus rice reservoir for Asia out of the three countries—Burma, Thailand, and Indochina. Before the Pacific war they accounted for most of the world's rice exports and made up food deficits in India, Ceylon, Hongkong, and China, as well as in Malaya, Java, and to a lesser degree the Philippines and Japan. The average exports for the three countries between 1935-9 was 5.6 million metric tons of cleaned or milled rice.

In 1954 the three countries exported only 3 million metric tons to a world demanding more rice than ever before. Rising internal consumption, internal disturbances, especially in Burma and Indochina, and declining yields were among the causes of the export decline. However, as Dobby suggests, the costs of producing rice have risen, and the hidden

TABLE XV–1

LAND UTILIZATION IN SOUTHEAST ASIA (1951)

Country or area	Population[a] (millions)	Total land area (000 ha.)	Population density (per km.)	Cultivated land[a] (000 ha.)	Land area cultivated (%)
Burma	18.8	67,802	28	7,000[h]	10.3
Thailand	19.2	51,352	37	6,000[d]	11.8
Indochina	30.0	70,540[e]	43	6,000[h]	8.5
Vietnam	22.6[b]	32,960[e]	76	—	—
Cambodia	3.2[b]	13,900[e]	27	—	—
Laos	1.2[b]	23,680[e]	5	—	—
British Borneo	1.4	20,379	5	1,000[d]	4.9
Philippines	20.6	29,968	68	4,200	14.0
Malaya	6.6[c]	13,200[c]	41[d]	2,100[c]	16.0
Indonesia	78.2	190,435	51	11,000[i]	5.8
Java Madura	53.0[d]	13,197	401	8,300	62.9
TOTAL	174.8	443,676	39.4	37,300	8.5

TABLE XV–1 (Cont.)

Country or area	Area in major food crops (000 ha.)	Cultivated area in major food crops (%)	Pop. per ha. of land in major food crops	Forests and woodlands (000 ha.)	Land area in forest and woodland (%)
Burma	5,015	72	3.75	39,094	57.5
Thailand	5,541	92	3.63	32,600[d]	63.4
Indochina	5,645	94	5.31	31,000[d]	50.0
Vietnam	–	–	–	–	–
Cambodia	–	–	–	–	–
Laos	–	–	–	–	–
British Borneo	318	32	4.40	16,178	79.4
Philippines	3,122	74	6.60	15,875	53.4
Malaya	384	18	17.19	9,737[e]	73.5
Indonesia	–	–	–	121,000[d]	63.5
Java Madura	7,097	86	7.47	3,000	23.0
TOTAL				269,484	60.8

TABLE XV–1 (*Cont.*)

Country or area	Area in rice (000 ha.)	Cultivated area in rice (%)	Arable land under technical irrigation (%)	Rice double-cropping ratio[d] (%)	Yield (100 kg./ha.)
Burma	4,931	70.0	7.0[h]	100	14.4
Thailand	5,500	91.6	12.0	115	12.7
Indochina	5,000[h]	83.0	15.0	125	11.6[h]
Vietnam	3,000[d]	–	–	–	–
Cambodia	1,100[d]	–	10.9	–	12.2
Laos	–	–	–	–	–
British Borneo	318[k]	9.2	7.0[d]	100	–
Philippines	2,000[l]	47.6	7.7	110	11.5
Malaya	368[k]	17.5	5.5	101	19.1[k]
Indonesia	4,300[i]	39.1	–[m]	–	–
Java Madura	3,400	41.00	15.9[n]	117	15.4
TOTAL	22,417	60.0			

TABLE XV–1 (*Cont.*)

Country or area	Production of paddy (000 m. tons)	Area in maize (000 ha.)	Cultivated area in maize (%)	Area in cassava, sweet potatoes, yams (000 ha.)	Cultivated area in cassava, sweet potatoes, yams (%)
Burma	6,971[h]	84[h]	1.0	–[q]	–[q]
Thailand	6,782[p]	41	0.7	–[q]	–[q]
Indochina	6,498[h]	500[h]	8.3	245[h]	4.7
Vietnam	—	—	—	—	—
Cambodia	—	—	—	—	—
Laos	—	—	—	—	—
British Borneo	163[p]	–[q]	–[q]	—	—
Philippines	2,831	950[i]	22.6	172	4.1
Malaya	714[p]	–[q]	—	16	0.8
Indonesia	9,286[g]	3,000[i]	27.3	—	—
Java Madura	6,125	2,000[i]	24.1	1,110	13.2
TOTAL	33,245	4,575	12.3	1,553	4.3

TABLE XV–1 (*Cont.*)

Country or area	Area in coconuts (000 ha.)	Area in coconuts (%)	Area in rubber (000 ha.)	Cultivated area in rubber (%)	Production of rubber (000 long tons) (1952)
Burma	–	–	46[a]	0.6	–
Thailand	61[k]	–	272[a]	4.5	110[d]
Indochina	–	–	93[a]	1.6	57[d]
Vietnam	–	–	–	–	36
Cambodia	–	–	–	–	14
Laos	–	–	–	–	–
British Borneo	25	–	158	15.8	66[r]
Philippines	965[k]	23.0	–[q]	–[q]	2
Malaya	206[d]	9.8	1,350	64.0	584
Indonesia	1,180[d]	10.7	1,490[d]	13.5	738
Java Madura	–	–	240[d]	2.9	–
TOTAL	2,437	6.5	3,413	9.1	1,553

NOTES: All data should be regarded as approximate. Published statistics fail to distinguish clearly between areas cultivated, cropped, or in farms; between areas under natural and technical irrigation. Indeed, major discrepancies exist even in data for land areas of various countries. In all such cases estimates have been made on the basis of the best available information. Basic sources are U.N. or F.A.O. publications.

a. 1952 estimate.
b. From census of 1946.
c. Includes Singapore.
d. Very rough estimate.
e. U.N. estimate; F.A.O. statistic for 1952, 63,780 square km.
f. Excluding Singapore.
g. Estimated land area actually under cultivation, exclusive of double-cropping, uncultivated land on farms and estates, and shifting agriculture.
h. Prewar estimate.
i. Land under a shifting cultivation at any one time is estimated at about 2,000,000 hectares additional.
j. Includes some double-cropping.
k. 1949 estimate.
l. 1950 estimate. Total cropped area was 2,215,000 ha. In addition rice competes with sugar cane (150,000 ha. in 1950) for better land.
m. No reliable data. F.A.O. gives 30% of cultivated area for 1949, but this is far too high.
n. Prewar estimate. Postwar estimates up to 40%, an unrealistic percentage.
p. 1950 estimate.
q. Negligible.
r. 1951 figure.

costs of production, which were obscured by the family and communal systems of social organization, are beginning to appear. At the same time rice prices have risen as demand has increased. As a result, American rice has been able to compete successfully with regionally grown rice in Southeast Asian and other world markets, and Burma and Thailand in particular have been faced with rice surpluses which they have not been able to market in Asia. The problem demands an expanded and more efficient agriculture on the one hand, and greater employment opportunities on the other. Two possibilities with regard to agriculture are (1) the expansion of rice production into eastern Sumatra and coastal Borneo by mechanized rather than indigenous means, and (2) the increase of yields and lowering of production costs by enlarging the controlled irrigated areas, expanding the use of fertilizers, making available improved seeds and agricultural tools, and reducing waste.

Southeast Asia also exports specialized agricultural products grown principally on large estates. Although accounting for only a small portion of the total agricultural area, these foreign-controlled estates or plantations have been the focus for foreign investment and for large receipts of foreign exchange in the Southeast Asian world. Rubber has been the most important product, but quinine, abaca, kapok, sugar, tea, sisal, palm oil, tobacco, and copra also are significant. In fact, Southeast Asia produces most of the world's rubber, abaca, and natural quinine, and a very large percentage of its copra. Rubber and the coconut palm fit especially well into the tropical Asian scene and do not compete on the whole with rice for land. With the exception of copra and sugar, these products were imported and promoted by foreign enterprise, which until about 1930 maintained firm control over their production. Since that time, however, native smallholders have begun to supply increasing percentages of rubber, for example, as well as copra and tobacco, until they supplied about half of all the rubber produced within the realm in 1955. Plantations of teak, usually under government control and leased to foreign and native concessionaires, also are widespread.

In addition to the dual functions of supplying rice to deficit areas in Asia and estate products to the Western world and Japan, Southeast Asia is a source of other raw materials. Tropical hardwoods are one, although on the whole the realm is an importer of wood and paper products. Mineral raw materials are of exceptional importance, and Southeast Asia supplies about 60 per cent of the world's tin from alluvial deposits principally in Malaya, Indonesia, and Thailand. Iron ore from lateritic deposits in the Philippines and Malaya also is mined for export. Chromite in the Philippines, bauxite, lead, zinc, copper, and gold all are exploited, though in modest quantities.

More striking is the location in Borneo and Sumatra, and to a lesser degree in Java and Burma, of the only major oil deposits, other than those of Sakhalin and Hsin-chiang, east of the Persian Gulf in Asian Asia. In 1955 these produced less than 3 per cent of the world's production, but they are of great significance in an Oriental world notably deficient in petroleum. Coal reserves are restricted, however, although Indochina is a major producer, and some coal is mined in almost every country in the realm. Additional coal is imported from Japan, North China, and India, or is brought occasionally as ballast from western Europe.

In sum, Southeast Asia is characterized by a noteworthy degree of homogeneity of form and function, in spite of its great variations from place to place. In terms of the gross patterns of occupance and liveli-hood, similarities among countries are evident in the types of agricultural systems and the ways in which land is utilized. In terms of climate, soils, and vegetation there is a distinct and regular pattern characteristic of the realm. Furthermore, in its relations with the outside world, each coun-try within the realm has functioned, and still functions, as a specialized supplier of raw materials and foodstuffs.

In addition, the economic and social problems that face the formerly, or still, colonial Southeast Asian countries are remarkably similar for all. In addition to an almost universal problem of internal political and social disorganization, each country is faced with feeding a rapidly expanding population and diversifying its specialized colonial economy so as to pro-vide greater livelihood opportunities and means for raising low levels of living. All wish to lessen dependence upon uncertain world markets for a few raw material exports. Each is attempting to rationalize agriculture, to raise yields, to develop nonagricultural resources, to develop manufactural industries. In these terms, greater regional cooperation and integration appear necessary in order to solve problems common to all.

SELECTED GEOGRAPHICAL BIBLIOGRAPHY

1. Broek, J. O. M. "Diversity and Unity in Southeast Asia," *Geographical Review*, April, 1944, pp. 175-95.
2. Dobby, E. H. G. "Food and Changing Functions of Southeast Asia," in Thayer, P. W., ed., *Southeast Asia in the Coming World*. Baltimore: Johns Hopkins University Press, 1953.
3. ———. *Southeast Asia*. New York: John Wiley and Sons, 1950.
4. ———. "Winds and Fronts in Southeast Asia," *Geographical Review*, April, 1945, pp. 204-18.
5. Fisher, C. A. "Southeast Asia," in East, W. G., and O. H. K. Spate, eds., *The Changing Map of Asia*. London: Methuen, 1950.
6. Fryer, D. W. "The Million City in Southeast Asia," *Geographical Review*, October, 1953, pp. 474-94.

7. Ginsburg, N. S. "The Great City in Southeast Asia," *American Journal of Sociology,* March, 1955, pp. 455-62.
8. Pelzer, K. J. *Pioneer Settlement in the Asiatic Tropics.* New York: American Geographical Society, 1945.
9. Pendleton, R. L. "Laterite and Its Structural Uses in Thailand and Cambodia," *Geographical Review,* April, 1941, pp. 177-202.
10. Purcell, V. *Chinese in Southeast Asia.* Oxford: University Press, 1951.
11. Swemle, I. "Indonesia, British Borneo, and Burma," in Pratt, W. E., and D. Good, *World Geography of Petroleum.* New York: American Geographical Society, 1950.
12. Unger, L. "The Chinese in Southeast Asia," *Geographical Review,* April, 1944, pp. 196-217.
13. Zelinsky, W. "The Indochinese Peninsula: A Demographic Anomaly," *Far Eastern Quarterly,* February, 1950, pp. 115-45.

Comments

The basic geography text on Southeast Asia is Dobby. Fisher's shorter statement places Southeast Asia well within its historical geographical setting, as does Broek's short article. Pelzer compares the pioneering aspects of settlement in the Philippines and Indonesia, and provides a valuable discussion of agriculture in general. Useful geographical descriptions are found also in the several textbooks on Asia noted in the bibliography following Chapter II.

The University of Malaya began publication in October, 1953, of *The Malayan Journal of Tropical Geography,* which deals primarily with Southeast Asia. Valuable information also can be found in the U.N. Economic Commission for Asia and the Far East publications.

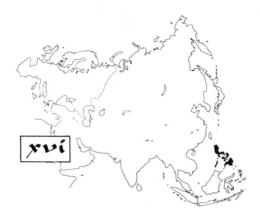

The Philippines

THE PHILIPPINE ISLANDS LIE ON THE EASTERN MARGINS OF SOUTH-east Asia, so far removed from the central axis of the realm, which runs through Singapore, that they are sometimes said to belong more properly in East Asia than in Southeast Asia itself. Certainly there is some justification for questioning the placing of the Philippines within Southeast Asia. Their northernmost islands are separated from T'ai-wan by Bashi Channel, less than 100 miles in width. Manila is nearer to Hongkong than to any other major city. In the past, and to a large extent in the present, Manila has acted as a co-terminus with Hongkong of trans-Pacific shipping services that originate in North America and link that continent with Japan and China. Also, for some 50 years the Philippines were a dependency of the United States oriented eastward across the Pacific, whereas the other countries and colonies in Southeast Asia looked primarily westward to Europe via Suez, to the metropolitan powers that maintained political control over them, provided important markets, and were their chief sources of imports. In much of Southeast Asia the end of the war saw burgeoning nationalisms, followed by complete or partial independence from foreign domination in Burma, Indonesia, and the countries of what had been French Indochina. This nationalism was manifest also in the Philippines long before the war, but its consequence has not been a violent withdrawal from the former colonial power, as in Indonesia, and the United States remains influential in Philippine economic and military affairs. Lastly, the Spanish left a cultural heritage of which one of the chief expressions is Catholicism, the dominant religion of the Philippines, another factor in differentiating the Philippines from their neighbours.

In spite of these centrifugal forces, there are a sufficient number of centripetal influences at work to justify placing the Philippines in the Southeast Asian realm. Basically, the Philippine economy is agricultural and in large part is centered upon the cultivation of rice. Climate and soils, though differing radically within short horizontal and vertical distances, are similar to those elsewhere in the realm. Racially and even culturally, most Filipinos are related to the Indonesians and may properly be termed Malaysians. Above all, the Philippines share with the other areas in the realm the problem of more efficiently utilizing similar resources so as to balance the pressure of an increasing population on the land.

The physical basis for agriculture

Only Indonesia in Southeast Asia can match the Philippines in its variety of natural elements and qualities; these make for an extreme fineness of landscape pattern. There are over 7,000 separate islands in the Philippine archipelago, most of them, however, being bare rocks unnamed and too small to be inhabited. About 95 per cent of the total land area of the country, some 115,000 square miles, is composed of 11 islands—in order of size, Luzon, Mindanao, Samar, Negros, Palawan, Panay, Mindoro, Leyte, Cebu, Bohol, and Masbate. Luzon and Mindanao are the giants of the group, and it is on these that regional differences are most easily recorded. However, the typical pattern for most of the islands is a mountainous core, generally below 9,000 feet and trending longitudinally,[1] rimmed by foothills and interspersed by rolling uplands. On the seaward margins of the foothills and the uplands are relatively narrow riverine and coastal lowlands, sometimes ill-drained and marshy. In few cases, however, is this idealized pattern displayed uniformly, since tectonic structure lines converge on the Philippines from several directions, and volcanic activity, especially from southern Luzon southward, has made for special irregularities. The major lowland areas are those of central Luzon (the largest), the Cagayan valley in northeastern Luzon, the Bicol plain in southeastern Luzon, the

---

[1] In northwest Luzon the highest point is 9,600 feet; in Mindanao, there are several peaks over 8,000 feet topped by volcanic Mount Apo, 9,690 feet; in general, the mountains rise to no more than 5,000 feet on the other islands.

southeastern plain of Panay, and the western plains of Negros, all highly developed. In Mindanao are two major lowlands which are as yet less highly developed—in the northeast the Agusan lowland and in the southwest the Cotobato-Koronadel plain. These lowlands, together with the Bukidnon plateau in Mindanao, are the major actual or potential foci of agriculture and settlement in the Philippines,[2] although the percentage of the total land area included within them is relatively small.

Climatically, the Philippines are characterized by freedom from frost the year around. The range of temperatures is roughly between 75° and 85°F. with few marked differences among the seasons, and the temperature differentials between north and south are minimized by the seas that surround the islands. Altitude rather than latitude is the important temperature differentiator. The chief distinguishing feature of climate is precipitation, which almost everywhere is above 60 inches and varies seasonally in different ways in different parts of the country. In general, the westernmost areas are characterized by a rainy season in the summer and fall, when the southwest monsoon is blowing, and by a notable dry season in the winter and spring. The easternmost areas have no dry season, but experience a period of maximum rainfall in winter when the northeasterly trades blow strongly across the islands. Between these two extremes are, first, an irregular zone of moderate rainfall with no pronounced rainfall maximum, but with a short dry season, as in northern Luzon; and a second discontinuous zone of heavy precipitation with no rainfall maximum and no dry season, as in southern Mindanao. Where rainfall is both highly seasonal and variable within seasons, as in the central Luzon lowland, agriculture is geared in large part to the rainier seasons; even so, a reliable supply of moisture for cultivation can be assured only through controlled irrigation facilities.

An important climatic phenomenon is the typhoon, which occurs about 20 times a year, most commonly between August and November, although its occurrence as early as June is not unusual. Typhoons rarely hit Mindanao and are most frequent and destructive north of latitude 11°N. Since they invariably move in a WNW direction, it is the eastern coasts of the central islands and Luzon that bear the brunt of their onslaught.

Generally abundant rainfall and high temperatures and humidities have encouraged the growth of forest vegetation, common to most of Southeast Asia, which covers about 60 per cent of the land area of the Philippines. Mangrove and nipa palm stands are common along the coasts, and tropical

[2] A major exception is Cebu in the Bisayan group of the central Philippines, a densely populated island given over almost entirely to agricultural occupance, although it is largely in slope and possesses only a narrow coastal plain. Here corn, not rice, is the major subsistence crop. Neighboring Negros also is densely populated, rice and corn sharing the subsistence crop acreage, and sugar dominating the commercial sector of agriculture.

rainforests prevail along the lower coastal plains and foothills except where they have been cleared for agriculture. Along higher slopes mixed tropical evergreen and deciduous forests appear, and on the very highest and wettest slopes moss forests are found. Where the dry season is lengthy or where shifting cultivation has resulted in widespread fires, the forests may have been replaced by bamboo and tall grasses called *cogon,* the *lalang* of Malaya. The resulting bamboo thickets and *cogonales,* as the grass-covered areas are called, are estimated to cover 15 to 20 per cent of the Philippines. They serve only to impede productive use of the land either for crop cultivation or for animal husbandry, since the grasses are in general not suitable for grazing except when new. Restricted areas of freshwater swamp are not uncommon; and these also have impeded agricultural expansion in the lower Pampanga valley on Luzon and in the Agusan and Cotabato valleys on Mindanao.

In general, Philippine soils are not fertile. Fertile soils appear in the alluvial lowlands, but even these, except in the few instances where they are renewed by periodic inundation and silting, have been leached of much of their fertility by the heavy rainfall and by continuous monocultivation practices in which fertilizers are insignificant. Many soils in the uplands are formed over acidic volcanic materials and are both thin and infertile; others, less common, are formed over more basic and fresher ejecta and are proportionally richer in plant nutrients. On the slopes of the mountains soils tend to be thin and easily eroded. Along the coasts of some of the central and southern islands, soils have formed over uplifted limestone reefs, as in Cebu, and are quite fertile, although the problem of keeping water on the land for paddy cultivation appears insurmountable. All soils are characterized by lateritic weathering, except where immature, but maturely developed laterites are rare.

Agriculture and food supply

Upon these elements of natural endowment has been established an agriculture that has failed to make the Philippines wholly self-sufficient in foodstuffs, although the level of food consumption is as low as in any area in Southeast Asia and is considerably lower than that in Japan. Moreover, it is an agriculture heavily biased toward export crops.

It is estimated that only 10.5 million acres (4.2 million hectares), about 14 per cent of the surface area, are actually under cultivation,[3] although

---

[3] However, 12.4 million acres of land are believed to be *cropped.* This means that the double-cropping ratio for all crops is about 115 per cent, but the multiple-cropping index certainly is undervalued.

the addition of fields which are part of the *caiñgin* or shifting agricultural system may add another 1 per cent. This is approximately the percentage of total land area under cultivation in Japan and about four-fifths of the total acreage cultivated in Japan. Yet, Japanese agriculture succeeds in supplying 80 per cent of the food requirements of a population of over 86 millions. Philippine agriculture, on the other hand, barely supplies the requirements of a population of about 21 millions, although it produces large quantities of agricultural products for export, and these can be traded for foodstuffs consumed internally (Table XVI–1).

TABLE XVI–1

PHILIPPINE EXPORTS AND IMPORTS OF AGRICULTURAL FOODSTUFFS

	Millions of pesos value				
	1934-38 av.	1939	1941	1952°	1953°
Exports					
Coconut oil and copra (est. 10% edible)	5.1	4.5	3.9	21.1	25.7
Desiccated coconut	8.3	8.8	7.4	19.1	31.5
Pineapple, tinned	—	3.4	5.0	23.5	24.4
Sugar	107.3	98.7	94.5	187.8	193.8
Totals	120.7	115.4	110.8	251.5	275.4
Imports					
Grains and grain prepartions				73.9	46.2
Dairy products				35.1	45.7
Coffee, tea, cocoa				6.3	8.8
Other foodstuffs †				49.6	57.8
Totals	33.8	40.3	28.9	164.9	158.5
Excess of exports over imports	86.9	75.1	70.8	86.6	116.9

° 1952 and 1953 figures from *Amer. Chamb. Comm. Journ.*, May, 1954; other data from various *Annual Rpts. of the High Commissioner to the Philippines*. Data supplied by Mr. E. D. Hester.

† On the import side the *Amer. Chamb. Comm. Journ:* data leave about 12 per cent of total imports unclassified. Although import controls have greatly restricted imports of meat, vegetables, and fruit and their products, the amounts allowed to come in must have been material. These figures represent 50 per cent of the value of the unclassified imports.

The basic grains consumed by the Filipinos are rice and corn (Map 15). Rice is grown throughout the archipelago, but it does not dominate either land uses or the diet as it does, for example, in Thailand or southern Burma. About 40 per cent of the cultivated area in the Philippines (4.2 million acres) is in rice, of which about one-fifth is dry or upland rather than wet rice. By far the major rice region is the central lowland of Luzon, a surplus area which produces some 40 per cent of the national output

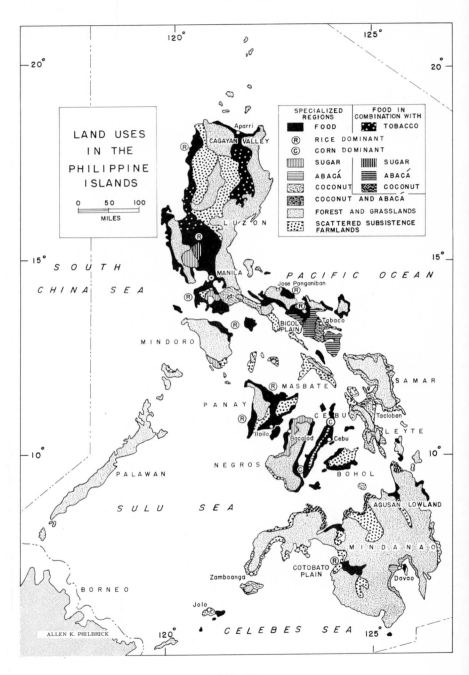

LAND USES
IN THE
PHILIPPINE
ISLANDS

0   50   100
MILES

SPECIALIZED REGIONS	FOOD IN COMBINATION WITH
FOOD	TOBACCO
® RICE DOMINANT	
© CORN DOMINANT	
SUGAR	SUGAR
ABACÁ	ABACÁ
COCONUT	COCONUT
COCONUT AND ABACÁ	
FOREST AND GRASSLANDS	
SCATTERED SUBSISTENCE FARMLANDS	

MAP 15

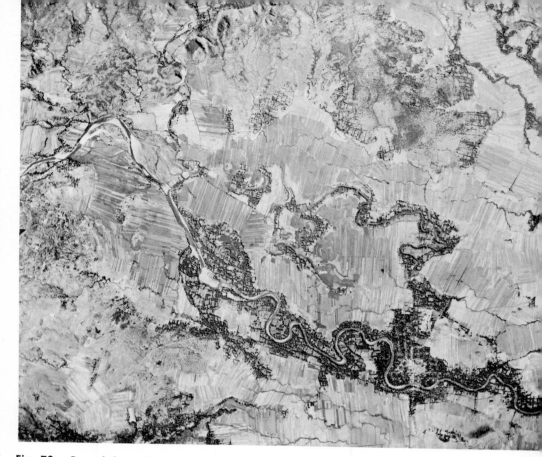

Fig. 70 • Part of the northwestern sector of the central Luzon plain. The intensity of land use in the plain is indicated by the prevalence of long narrow field strips in irrigated rice. Settlement tends to follow drainage courses; the stream is a tributary of the Agno River. From the town of Camiling stretches an almost continuous belt of settlement along the river's edge. Houses are surrounded by tree gardens which stand out plainly in contrast to the level paddy fieds. A former course of the river is suggested by the secondary grouping of settlements along bayous and ox-bow lakes. In general, irrigation in the area is not controlled. The uplands support only a scanty population and for the most part have been cleared of what must have been a heavy forest vegetation. The pattern of occupance in this, one of the more densely settled areas in the Philippines, should be contrasted with that shown in Figure 69. (U.S. Air Force.)

and from which rice is exported to deficit regions such as the Bisayas, southern Luzon, and the area about Davao in Mindanao. Here the rice landscape bears a marked resemblance to that in the other rice-oriented regions of Southeast Asia, and cultural practices including transplantation are similar to those elsewhere (Figure 70). Fertilizers are little used, and Philippine average yields are low; before the war they were the lowest in Southeast Asia at 11 bushels of cleaned rice per acre. These averages include upland rice yields, however, which are unduly low; yields in the

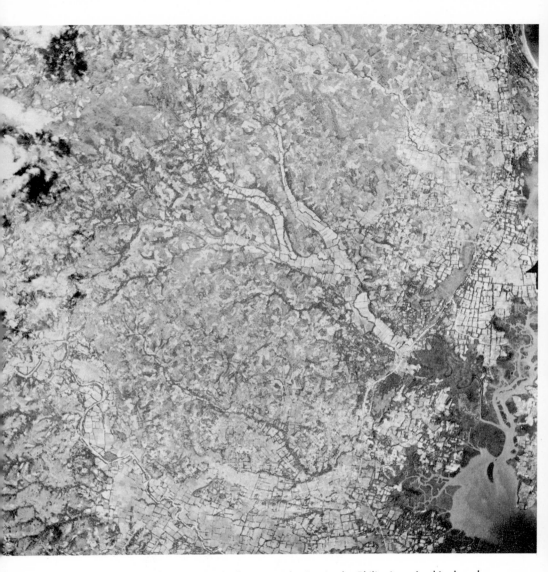

Fig. 71 • Cebu is a center of corn production in the Philippines. In this densely populated area just north of Cebu city almost all of the land is under cultivation, and most of it is in corn. In contrast to the motley and irregular arrangement of the corn fields is the relative regularity of the tree-like bands of irrigated paddy fields which occupy the drainage bottomlands or the reclaimed coastal lowlands where water is available. The paddy fields for the most part are gently terraced as they rise upstream, the streams themselves being channeled from one field to another on the resulting downward gradient. Most of the corn fields are on sloping land covered by relatively poor soils residual over reef limestones. Since these soils are droughty, water scarcity is a major agricultural problem. Soil erosion is another. Though multiple-cropping is practiced, and perhaps because of it, yields are conspicuously low. Note the swamp area cut by tidal channels at the lower right of the photograph. *(U.S. Air Force.)*

better portions of the central Luzon wet-rice region may reach 20 bushels per acre, approximately the average yields in Korea.

Another factor that handicaps wet-rice cultivation is the lack of controlled irrigation facilities. Although 1,300,000 acres are said to be under irrigation in the Philippines, only 260,000 acres of paddy are under controlled irrigation, about 5 per cent of the total rice area. Much of the irrigated acreage is under sugar cane. Controlled irrigation is characteristic also of the magnificently terraced slopelands of northern Luzon, but these amount in all to only 70,000 acres, and their expansion is considered uneconomic. In general, the Filipino rice farmer depends for his water supply upon rainfall. The double-cropping of rice, so common in south China, T'ai-wan, and Tonkin, is restricted almost entirely to the lands under controlled irrigation. In 1953-4, 3,180,000 metric tons of paddy were produced, a yield considerably higher than that in 1940, but on a very much larger acreage.

Corn, introduced by the Spanish from Mexico, occupies 14 per cent of the cultivated area (1.47 million acres) and provides a major proportion of the caloric intake for many poorer Filipinos, who eat it in the form of gruel, pounded and boiled like rice, or in small cakes. Although it is widely grown throughout the country, the center of corn production is in the Bisayan group. About a quarter of the total acreage is on the island of Cebu, where rainfall is variable and soils are derived in part from porous coral-reef materials (Figure 71). Yields are very low; in all, about 750,000 tons were produced in 1952. Double-cropping, however, is very common, and in some cases third crops are raised, but the second and third crops are much less productive than the first. As a rule, the predominance of corn in the Philippines indicates a food-deficit region.

Other subsistence food crops center about tubers and legumes. The originally imported sweet potato has become an increasingly important article of diet, especially in the mountain country, and the terraced-rice agriculturalist of northern Luzon is expanding his cultivated slopelands, unterraced, into sweet potatoes, not rice. Cassava (also called manioc) is another foreign root crop that has become an important source of food; it is most common in the Sulu archipelago. Beans and peanuts are important supplementary crops, of which the mungo, or meng, bean is the most important. It is associated generally with wet-rice cultivation and is grown as a second crop or on the bunding of paddy fields. Green vegetables are of little importance, except near the larger cities where Chinese market gardens appear or in the uplands as near Baguio, but fruits are raised in abundance; bananas, pineapples, mangoes, citrus fruits, and papayas are among the more important. Protein is provided by poultry, particularly chickens, which are associated with every farm unit; by hogs, which average two to a farm; and by primarily work animals, carabao and

TABLE XVI–2

APPROXIMATE PERCENTAGES OF STARCHY FOODSTUFFS
IN THE FILIPINO DIET

(by region and class) °

(Eighty-five per cent of the total population is in the poor class; 10 per cent in the middle class; 5 per cent in the wealthy class—estimates which vary substantially by regions.)

	Rice	*Corn*	*Wheat* †	*Others* ‡
Ilokos, Cagayan valley:				
Poor	55	15	xx §	30
Middle	65	10	5	20
Wealthy	80	xx	10	10
Mountain province, also Sulu-Palawan:				
Poor	40	xx	xx	60
Middle	65	xx	5	30
Wealthy	90	xx	5	5
Other Luzon Areas:				
Poor	70	5	xx	20
Middle	80	5	5	10
Wealthy	80	xx	15	5
Bisayas and parts of Mindanao (Misamis, Agusan, Surigao):				
Poor	10	70	xx	20
Middle	45	40	5	10
Wealthy	70	15	10	5
Other Mindanao areas (Bukidnon, Lanao, Cotabato, Davao, Zamboanga):				
Poor	60	15	xx	25
Middle	70	15	5	10
Wealthy	80	10	5	10

° This table consists of crude estimates based upon an imperfect series of data. It is published through the courtesy of Mr. E. D. Hester.

† Wheat flour (imported) and wheat products (imported and domestic).

‡ Sweet potatoes, bananas, beans, *mungo*, cassava, millet (not sugar), in this order.

§ xx = negligible.

cattle, which are slaughtered in small numbers each year. Especially along the coast, however, fish provide the bulk of the animal protein. An estimated 344,000 metric tons were caught in 1954, and 140,000 acres (56,000 hectares) of fish ponds in association with flooded paddy fields may have provided an additional 25,000 tons.

The importance of the Philippines in world commerce depends largely upon the production of export crops, of which coconuts, sugar cane, and abaca (manila hemp) are the most important. Sugar-cane production is concentrated in the central Luzon plain north of Manila and in northern and western Negros Island. In the former area production is largely from sizable holdings (200 acres or more), which use migrant labor from other islands and other parts of Luzon during the planting and harvesting seasons. The cane occupies the land for about 14 months, although on Negros rationing may be practiced for a second crop year. In 1951 the area in cane was about 375,000 acres (150,000 hectares), less than 4 per cent of the total cultivated area and about 60 per cent of the area planted to cane in 1940. Sugar production, however, has exceeded the prewar averages of a million metric tons a year, (production in 1953-4 reached 1.22 million tons) as land used for food crops during the war is being put into food production and more effective cultivation techniques are being applied to the better lands.

Coconuts occupy more land than any crop other than rice, almost 2.4 million acres (965,000 hectares) or 23 per cent of the cultivated area. They are distributed widely along the margins of the islands especially to the south where typhoon frequencies are less, but the major producing area is in southern Luzon. In general, production is a small-scale operation, although large plantations are becoming increasingly important. Most of the nut meat is converted to copra, some 730,000 metric tons a year, and the Philippines is the world's largest exporter of coconut products.

Abaca, or manila hemp, is highly localized in two regions: southeastern Luzon and southeastern Mindanao. A third region of lesser significance is that of Leyte-Samar. Localization is explained in part by the inability of the plant to withstand drought and waterlogged soils, and these two areas have well drained soils and no pronounced dry season. Both acreage and production since the second World War have been below prewar standards of 725,000 acres (290,000 hectares) and 170,000 tons, owing to damage and neglect during the war and to declines in world demand thereafter. Tobacco also is an important commercial crop, though of declining relative significance owing to decreases in the consumption of cigars and increases in the use of the American-made cigarettes. Luzon contains the major tobacco areas, and the Cagayan valley produces about half of the total crop.

Some problems of agriculture

In some respects the basic problem of Philippine agriculture—to raise productivity per acre and per man—is similar to that which faces the rest of Southeast Asia and indeed the Orient as a whole.

Soil erosion is a serious problem, as it is elsewhere in Southeast Asia,

despite the plasticity of lateritic soils. It is accelerated by shifting cultivation which depends upon forest clearance by fire. Preliminary figures indicate that 30 per cent of the country suffers from soil erosion in one form
or another, the problem being much more serious in areas of steep slope
where corn and sweet potatoes are the key crops, rather than in the more
level and terraced rice-centered lowlands. Although terracing of an
elaborate nature is practiced in some areas, by and large new lands
brought into cultivation in the hill and mountain country are not being
terraced.

Tropical grasses, which cover 15 to 20 per cent of the land surface and
which tend to follow shifting cultivation, are another problem. Since the
root systems of the grasses are deep and fire-resistant, native methods of
land clearance cannot compete with the spread of the grasses, and deep-
plowing with tractors is necessary. Once the grasses take hold, forest regeneration is impeded, and the loss of good timber is significant. Also,
when natural shorter grasses are overgrazed, the *cogon,* generally unpalatable to animals, tends to move in, thereby reducing the areas of good
grazing land.

Lack of fertilizers is yet another problem, easily remedied in theory but
difficult to deal with in practice, except in the cases of commercial crops
such as cane, abaca, and tobacco. A farmer must be able to sell much of
his crop in order to buy commercial fertilizers, but surpluses are few in
the Philippines after rents are paid. Farm-produced fertilizers and nightsoils are little used, except for the manure of the carabao that graze over
stubble in the fields. Some crop rotations are practiced, as when mungo
beans follow rice or corn, but in general rice follows rice on the best lands,
and corn follows corn on the poorer.

Controlled irrigation facilities also are limited, as indicated previously.
About half of the irrigation systems were built under Spanish rule by
church and nongovernmental institutions and individuals. About 220,000
acres are parts of national projects administered by the government, and
the other projects in the 1.3 million acre total are small, local, and of
limited effectiveness. Irrigation and flood-control projects are planned by
the government, especially in the Pampanga River valley of the central
Luzon plain where floods associated with the typhoon season cause substantial annual damage.

Tenancy and associated problems also complicate the difficult agricultural situation and tend to reduce the possibilities for expanding production. Tenants occupy about a third of the farms and cultivate about
27 per cent of the land; part-tenants account for some 15 per cent of the
land cultivated. Tenancy conditions vary enormously, however, and are
most serious in the wet-rice and sugar-cane areas of central Luzon where
tenants and part-tenants may operate over 80 per cent of the farms. Most

of the tenant-operated farms, which operate under a system of share-tenancy, are part of large estates or *haciendas*, inheritances of Spanish rule, which are divided by their owners into smaller production units. In the cases of some of the larger *haciendas*, blocks of land may be leased to tenants who in turn sublease smaller units to other farmers. Although the average size of farms in the Philippines is approximately 10 acres, the averages are misleading since they include those large estates and sugar plantations that are operated as single units. More meaningful is the fact that over half the farms in the Philippines are less than 5 acres, and in the more crowded areas of northwest Luzon and Cebu the average is about 4 acres. Since rural credit facilities are limited, it is customary for the farmer to go into heavy debt, and this intensifies his relative immobility and helps explain the farmers' failure to move in large numbers to the agricultural frontiers.

Another unusual aspect of Philippine agriculture is the *partial use of the farm area for cultivation*. About 40 per cent of the total area in farms in the Philippines is *not* in crops. The percentage of farmland idle is highest in the frontier regions of Mindanao, for example, and in the mountainous regions where shifting cultivation may be practiced from a fixed residential base. However, even in the central Luzon rice-and-sugar-cane region, 20 to 30 per cent of the farm area is not in cultivation. In certain more densely populated regions of the Orient, however, only 2 to 5 per cent of the farm area is in uses other than cultivation. Explanations involve the occurrence of sterile or stony soils, land fallow for want of fertilizer, reserves on large estates, and the use of some land for pasturage and the gathering of forest products.

Population, settlement, and transportation

The population of the Philippines was estimated to be over 21.8 million persons in 1955, slightly larger than that of Thailand or of Burma. The over-all density of population, 180 per square mile, is two and a half times that of Burma and nearly twice that of Thailand, but is less than a third that of Japan. The physiologic density (i.e., the ratio of population to cultivated land), 1,186 per square mile, also is considerably higher than that of Burma, Thailand, and Indochina, although it is well below that of Java and Malaya, including Singapore. Locally, physiologic densities are as high as anywhere in Southeast Asia and even in the Orient as a whole. Population increase is becoming more rapid, and the natural growth rate is estimated at 1.9 per cent annually.

Population distributions are closely related to the distribution of cultivated land, and in general the cultivated lowlands are associated with major nodes of population. Thus, central, northwestern, and southeastern Luzon and the Bisaya group, except for Samar, are the most densely populated regions. Cebu, in the center of the Bisayas, with about 600 persons per square mile, is the most densely populated of the provinces, apart from Rizal in which several large suburbs of Manila are located. Population outside of these concentrations is strung out along the coasts or is distributed more densely in the intermontane valleys where opportunities for cultivation are more numerous.

Ethnic, linguistic, and religious differences are characteristic, though to no greater degree than in Indonesia. The official languages of the republic are English, Spanish, and Tagalog; the language spoken by the greatest percentage of people, however, is Bisayan, related to Tagalog but substantially different from it and mutually comprehensible only with difficulty. The Philippines are primarily Christian, a noteworthy differentiation from the rest of Southeast Asia, but many of the hill tribes are pagan, and in parts of Mindanao and the Sulu archipelago Islam is the dominant belief. These differences provide major handicaps to resettlement from the more densely populated areas, since the Christian Filipinos are in general still reluctant to move into what is regarded as Moro (Moslem) territory, although the Moro population may locally be small. Many of these differences, however, are modified by the rising nationalism, which is channeled through the press, radio, and educational systems. English acts increasingly as the commercial *lingua franca* and is the language of instruction in the public schools.

Two important minorities should be noted, the Chinese and the Spanish. The Chinese, 120,000 in number, are active in trade, especially the retailing trade which they dominate, and have been the object of much distrust and occasional persecutions on the part of the Filipinos, as in Indonesia. In the Philippines, also, the Chinese have so intermarried that the number of racially identifiable Chinese remains obscure. Many of the leaders in the Philippine government and business have Chinese blood, although they have otherwise completely assimilated into Philippine society. The Spanish community is much smaller than the Chinese and is of declining economic significance. It retains, however, a special prestige status derived from the period of Spanish suzerainty.

Occupationally, the population is primarily agricultural; about 70 per cent is rural. There is only one great city in the Philippines, Manila, with an estimated population of over a million,[4] and it is one of the great multifunctional cities of the world, encompassing in its hinterland all of the country. Therefore, lesser cities of size are few, and there are none over 200,000 population. Commercial and political centers of size are either in

[4] The 1948 census gave Greater Manila a population of 1,180,611.

Fig. 72 • Although the development of modern highway transportation has been rapid in the Philippines, much of the road traffic consists of two-wheeled wooden carts like this one in the streets of San Fernando, Luzon, drawn by a *carabao*. Note that the road, although in town, is not surfaced. Although the cart frame is of wood, the body is made of bamboo sections and woven bamboo strips. On the wooden and corrugated iron-roofed building in the background gleams an omnipresent Coca-Cola sign, in striking contrast to the carabao below. Similar two-wheeled carts, drawn by water buffalo or oxen, and often elaborately carved, are widely characteristic of the countries of Southeast Asia. *(U.S. Army.)*

Mindanao, far removed from Manila—so sited are Zamboanga and Davao —or they are in the Bisayas, a traditional cultural center of the islands— here are Cebu, Bacolod, and Iloilo. Each of these cities has a population between 100,000 and 200,000.

Rural settlement varies with the kind of occupance limits set by tradition. In those subsistence areas little affected by the large Spanish land grants, traditional villages (*barrios*) surrounded by fruit and shade trees are characteristic. Similar villages of post-Spanish origin also appear on the larger estate lands, but here groups of scattered farmsteads also are found. In many cases the former reflect the Spanish desire to bring together "under the bells" of the church widely scattered and minute native settlements. Almost every town has its cathedral dominating the local skyline, or sharing it with the smokestacks of a sugar mill. In the frontier areas and in the mountainous regions where dry crops are raised or shifting cultivation is common, scattered dwelling units are typical. In some areas, as in western Negros, sizable villages are located about the central focus of the sugar mill in which many of the villagers may be employed.

The traditional settlement pattern, which tended to follow closely the rivers of the country, also has been modified by the extension of a highway system already greatly extended and modified during the American occupation. New settlements, and even some of the older villages, have been located near or relocated from riversides to sites more convenient to the roads. Surfaced highways, which in 1950 measured over 10,000 miles, also have stimulated migration from the overcrowded areas and in general have greatly increased the mobility of the population (Figure 72). Regular bus services connect the larger towns and cities with their hinterlands, and the growth of highway transportation since the second World War has been phenomenal.

The Philippines also possess a 3 foot 6 inch railway network, which, however, is restricted to one extensive line in Luzon, owned by the government, and two short privately-owned lines in Panay and Cebu (the Cebu line has been abandoned). Mileage has declined from a prewar total of 840 miles to a 1954 mileage of about 700 miles, and traffic, both freight and passenger, remains depressed. Ton-kilometers in 1954 were 143 million as compared with 162 million in 1938. The line on Panay is used primarily to carry sugar from the producing areas to the ports. The government line in Luzon carries sugar cane, centrifugal sugar, rice, and copra for relatively short distances either to Manila or to the nearest open port. On Luzon, highway transportation has cut severely into the passenger traffic of the railway, and the railway, never a financial success, is heavily subsidized.

The traditional method of transportation in the Philippines, as in much of Southeast Asia, is by water. Although none of the short swift Philippine rivers are navigable by modern vessels for any distance, considerable quantities of native produce are rafted downstream to markets and transshipment centers. More important is the coastal traffic, partly in native-type vessels that carry locally produced foodstuffs and raw materials to small ports for transshipment abroad or distribute goods from Manila down through the hierarchy of lesser ports and roadsteads (Figure 64).

Manila is the giant among Philippine ports and is the center of the shipping web that binds the island republic together. Regular services are operated by shipping companies between Manila and the outlying ports. About 150,000 tons of shipping are employed, and 6 million net tons of coastal shipping entered the port. In general, cargoes outgoing from Manila are larger than those going in by sea from the other parts of the country. Manila is the great entrepôt for the islands, and imported goods almost invariably are distributed through it. Bulky Philippine exports of agricultural products and mineral ores, however, tend to by-pass Manila, unless they are produced nearby; usually agricultural products are trans-shipped to the outside world via the nearest ports open to foreign ship-ping—Aparri, Jose Panganiban, Tabaco, Iloilo, Cebu, Tacloban, Davao, Zamboanga, and Jolo.[5] Lumber and ores, however, tend to move directly from mill or mine docks to ocean shipping which carries them abroad.

In international shipping as a whole, however, Manila, with one of the best harbors in the Orient, is clearly dominant, and few ships touching at other Philippine ports fail to touch at Manila as well. Several shipping companies use Manila as the western terminus of their trans-Pacific serv-ices, and the port marks the western border of what has become since the war a primarily American sea, the north Pacific; west of it British and other flags predominate. Manila does not compete to any large degree with Singapore and Hongkong as an entrepôt for Southeast Asian trade because of its peripheral situation in relation to the realm, but the 6 to 7 million net tons of international shipping that annually enter Manila har-bor rank it as one of the realm's major ports.

Manila also is the focus for numerous air services linking the Philippines with the outside world and Manila with the rest of the archipelago. In 1956, four major international airlines called at Manila.

Nonagricultural resources

The Philippines are far from wealthy in nonagricultural resources, but possess certain major resource assets that can contribute to the diversification and development of the economy.

About 60 per cent of the total land area of the country is in forests, al-most all government-owned and exploited under government-supervised systems of licensing. Forest products not only include construction timber and lumber, among which *lauan* or Philippine mahogany is conspicu-ously important, but also fuelwood, rattans, and gums and resins. Not all of the forested areas are suitable for commercial exploitation, however, since many of them are covered by second-growth forests of highly mixed species with relatively dense undergrowths. The destruction of valuable forests continues with the practice of shifting cultivation, and the grant-ing to settlers of forest lands that should not be broken by the plow (Fig-ure 69). Conservation measures are necessary if the forest heritage is to

[5] A similar situation exists in Singapore and Malaya. Most of Malaya's imports are imported at and distributed from Singapore. Much of Malaya's agricultural ex-ports, however, go out through those smaller west-coast ports nearer than Singapore to the producing areas.

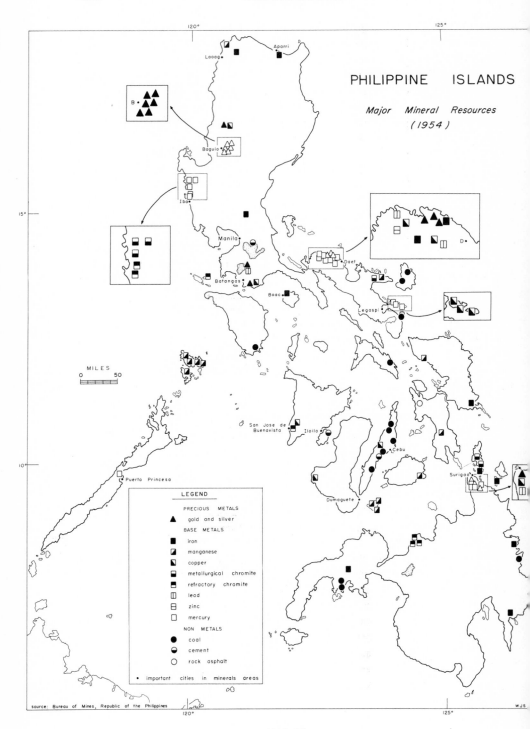

PHILIPPINE ISLANDS

Major Mineral Resources
(1954)

MILES
0   50

LEGEND

PRECIOUS METALS
▲ gold and silver
BASE METALS
■ iron
◨ manganese
◪ copper
⬓ metallurgical chromite
⬒ refractory chromite
▣ lead
⊟ zinc
▢ mercury
NON METALS
● coal
◓ cement
○ rock asphalt
• important cities in minerals areas

source: Bureau of Mines, Republic of the Philippines

MAP 16

be maintained, but there appears to be an abundance of wood for domestic uses, and the prospects for exports, which were important before
the second World War, are excellent. In 1951, about 1.6 billion board feet
of lumber and timber were produced, of which a small percentage was
exported. A high growth rate in the frost-free Philippine climate, moreover, may well make possible the cropping of trees for timber both from
large planted stands under government supervision and from woodlots
exploited as a cash crop by small farmers.

Power resources, however, are limited. The Philippines possess a reserve of some 40 million metric tons of lignitic coals, found chiefly in
Cebu, Polillo and Batan islands off the southeastern coast of Luzon, and
in southeastern Mindanao (Map 16). The production of 160,000 tons in
1950 was nearly three times higher than prewar.[6] Petroleum is not produced commercially within the country, although some favorable formations have been observed. Water-power resources have only begun to be
developed, and the bulk of electrical production is thermoelectric. However, the ample rainfall of the island and the numerous short swift rivers
offer opportunities for future development on the model of Japan. Three
hydro plants are in operation in central Luzon, and a third is nearing
completion. In Mindanao, a site at Lake Lanao, roughly comparable to
that at Sun Moon Lake in Taiwan, is believed to have a potential capacity
of 400,000 kilowatts. It is being developed, and the first unit of 25,000
kilowatts was completed at Maria Cristina in 1953 in association with a
fertilizer plant.

Of the nonpower mineral resources, iron ore, chrome, manganese, copper, and gold are most significant.[7] The medium-quality lateritic iron ore
reserves of northeastern Mindanao measure about a billion tons of ore
with 48 per cent iron content. Unfortunately these ores contain quantities
of nickel, chrome, and aluminum, which make refining difficult, and the
reserves remain little exploited, although among the largest in the Far
East. Lenticular deposits of much higher grade ores have been the chief
sources of Philippine iron-ore production, which amounts to a million and
a half tons a year (811,000 metric tons of iron content in 1954), almost
all exported to Japan. The chief producing areas are in southeastern
Luzon, northeastern Samar, and Marinduque Island. Chrome and manganese are found in many sites, and the reserves of chrome ore in western
Luzon, though of low quality, are among the world's largest. In 1953 about

[6] Before the war, the Philippines consumed about 400,000 tons of coal, imported chiefly from Japan. Postwar demand has been more limited, owing to the
conversion of the larger thermoelectric plants to imported fuel oil and the gradual
transfer to oil from coal by the Manila railway.

[7] A so-called "basement complex" of crystalline rocks underlies the prevailing
Tertiary sedimentary formations which appear over most of the country. Outcrops
are common owing to the intensive folding and fracturing that characterize the
Philippines' geological structure.

Fig. 73 • Salt pans at Paranaque, on Manila Bay, southwest of Manila. The squares are paved with impervious tile. During the dry season between February and May each square produces one bag of salt per day, each bag weighing 110 pounds. Although the dry season is short, the Philippines are able to produce enough salt to satisfy domestic requirements, and salt pans are a not uncommon sight along the islands' shores. Similar pans also are found in eastern Java and the Lesser Sundas and near the mouths of some of the great rivers of the Southeast Asian mainland. Outside of the realm, coastal salt pans are characteristic of the drier coasts of Pakistan, Ceylon, and India in South Asia, and of northern China and the Inland Sea of Japan in East Asia. (U.S. Army.)

556,000 tons of chrome ore were produced; some 25,000 of manganese also ore were exported. Southeastern and western Luzon produce over 12,000 tons of copper in ore annually for export. Gold, which was long the focus of mining enterprise in the Philippines, is mined chiefly in northern Luzon, southeastern Luzon, and northeastern Mindanao. Salt evaporated from sea water also is an important mineral product (Figure 73).

| **Industry, trade and development**

The chief industry in the Philippines is agriculture, and the commercial relations of the republic with the outside world depend in large part on the production and export of agricultural surpluses, some of which are processed in whole or part within the country. Less than 10 per cent of the prewar labor force was engaged in manufacturing, and many of these workers were occupied in what might best be classified as handicrafts. (At least one of these crafts, embroideries, was significant in the export trade.) Such industries as are not concerned with agricultural processing are localized largely in and about Manila. Most of the electric power production also is consumed in Manila, but the large government-owned cement plant, which produced over 300,000 metric tons in 1954, is located on Cebu where local coal and limestone are available. A second large government plant at Batocan was opened in 1954.

Trade has for many years been oriented toward the United States, and more than three-fourths of the trade is with that country. There are few indications of a gradual shift away from the United States; the countries of Asia account only for about 15 per cent of Philippine postwar trade. Exports are for the most part consistently agricultural and mineral, with sugar, copra, abaca, and lumber the most important commodities. Imports are far more diversified and consist of a great variety of manufactures, among which textiles, petroleum products, metal manufactures, and food-stuffs (especially wheat flour, canned fish, and evaporated milk), are of special importance.

The trade problem that faces the Philippines stems from the United States' planned imposition of tariff duties on Philippine produce after 1974. This means that certain Philippine products, especially sugar, will no longer receive the preferential treatment that since the turn of the century has guaranteed them a market in the United States. Other markets must be found, of which the more promising appear to lie in eastern Asia, with Japan the prime focus. At the same time, the Philippines will be competing with other Southeast Asian and subtropical regions for markets in a constricted world arena of commerce. However, many of the Philippines' export products, such as copra, abaca, and tropical hardwoods, are little affected by the American tariff, and American strategic interests in the Philippines cannot help but lead to special consideration for their economic difficulties.

In terms of agriculture, the Philippines must proceed toward goals of (1) greatly increasing domestic food production so as to diminish a partial dependence on foreign food sources, and (2) increasing the efficiency of commercial crop production, so as to compete more effectively with other nations producing similar products. The first goal demands both the increase of yields per acre and the expansion of cultivated land. Increases in yields demand the expansion of irrigation facilities, greater use of fertilizers, diversification of subsistence crops, and in general improved agricultural practices on the part of the average farmer. Increases in the cultivated area and the opening of the frontier demand programs of soil, hydrologic, topographic, land-use, and cadastral mapping; the construction of transportation and communications facilities in the frontier regions; and encouragement to migrants in the form of improved credit facilities.

The second goal demands at a minimum a concentration of sugar-cane cultivation on better lands and the conversion of marginal sugar lands to other uses, improved processing of coconut products, and higher-quality products in all spheres. For both goals soil- and water-conservation practices must be encouraged and agricultural extension services more adequately developed.

As in other countries in Southeast Asia, increasing pressure of a rapidly expanding population on the land makes desirable a diversification of the national economic base through the development of nonagricultural resources and industrialization. Here the Philippines' mineral, forest, and water-power reserves will make major contributions, although the absence of large supplies of mineral fuels may hamper development. However, the Philippines possess a "time cushion" in the form of unoccupied arable lands and prospects for rapidly increasing yields, which will permit a more gradual diversification of the economy and will tend to minimize the great pressures that bear, for example, upon Java and northern Vietnam.

SELECTED GEOGRAPHICAL BIBLIOGRAPHY

1. Cutshall, Alden. "Problems of Land Ownership in the Philippine Islands," *Economic Geography*, January, 1952, pp. 31-36.
2. Dawson, O. L. "Philippine Agriculture: A Problem of Adjustment," *Foreign Agriculture*, July, 1940, pp. 383-456.
3. Hainsworth, R. G., and R. T. Moyer. *Agricultural Geography of the Philippine Islands*. Washington: Office of Foreign Agricultural Relations, 1945.
4. King, P. B., and Edith McKee. "Terrain Diagrams for the Philippine Islands," *Bulletin of Geological Society of America*, December, 1949, pp. 1829-36.
5. Kolb, Albert. *Die Philippinen*. Leipzig: K. F. Koehler, 1942.
6. McIntyre, W. E. "The Retail Pattern of Manila," *Geographical Review*, January, 1955, pp. 66-80.
7. Pendleton, R. L. "Land Utilization and Agriculture of Mindanao, Philippine Islands," *Geographical Review*, April, 1942, pp. 180-210.
8. Pelzer, Karl. *Pioneer Settlement in the Asiatic Tropics,* chaps. 4 and 5. New York: American Geographical Society, 1945.
9. Philippine Bureau of Public Works. *Philippine Highways*. Distributed by U. S. Bureau of Public Roads, 1950.
10. Spencer, J. E. *Land and People in the Philippines*. Berkeley: University of California Press, 1952.

11. ———. "Abaca and the Philippines," *Economic Geography,* April, 1951, pp. 95-106.

12. ———. "The Philippines," in *The Development of Upland Areas in the Far East.* New York: Institute of Pacific Relations, 1949.

13. ———. "Abaca Plant and Its Fiber," *Economic Botany,* July-September, 1953, pp. 195-213.

14. U. S. Army Service Forces. *Civil Affairs Handbook: Philippine Islands.* Washington, 1944.

15. Van Valkenburg, S. "The Philippine Islands: Part X of Agricultural Regions of Asia," *Economic Geography,* July, 1936, pp. 231-49.

Comments

Spencer's book is the most complete work in English on the rural geography of the Philippines. Kolb's German-language book is more complete in that it contains more detail and maps and treats the Philippines as a whole. The Army Service Forces Manuals, though based on prewar data, are valuable for statistical data and analyses. Both Pendleton and Pelzer deal primarily with problems of resettlement and the agricultural frontier in Mindanao.

The Philippine government publishes an annual *Yearbook of Philippine Statistics,* of which the latest available in 1956 was the 1946 edition. The last complete published census figures are for the 1939 census. Partial data are available for the last census in 1948. Trade statistics are published by the Philippine Bureau of the Census and Statistics. The several departments of the Philippine government publish frequent pamphlets dealing with their specialties.

xvii

Indonesia

INDONESIA IS ONE OF THE WORLD'S LARGER NATIONS. IT IS AN IN-
tegral part of Asia, but its insular location on the fringes of the continent
has given it, like the Philippines and the rest of Malaysia, a measure of
detachment from Asia. Long a colonial possession of the Dutch, it was
occupied by the Japanese during the second World War. In the chaotic
postwar period, the anticolonial and nationalistic movement throughout
Asia was evidenced in Indonesia, and in 1949, after four years of conflict,
Dutch sovereignty over the Indies was transferred officially to Indonesia.

The newly independent country has an enormous developmental potential, but it faces many problems, many of them rooted in geographic
backgrounds that merit analysis. Throughout is a regional diversity unparalleled in Southeast Asia. Some parts of the island of Java are very
densely populated, with a farming economy that is delicately balanced
with natural conditions; other areas, in Borneo, for example, are virtually
unoccupied because of their isolation and physical character (Map 17).
These great contrasts between highly developed and underdeveloped
areas within a single country are responsible for some of the severe problems confronting the Republic.

The physical basis
of Indonesian life

Indonesia is the largest country in Southeast Asia. The island empire contains some 3,000 islands; these stretch for a distance of 3,000 miles, or equivalent to the distance from New York to San Francisco. Six islands make up the bulk of the total area of 575,895 square miles. (Western New Guinea, or Irian, now in the possession of the Dutch though claimed by Indonesia, has an area of 159,375 square miles and a population of about one million people, largely primitive tribes.) Some of the islands are small and virtually uninhabited; others, though small, such as Bali, are intensively cultivated. This diversity is occasioned in part by their differing capacities, in part by their different accessibilities to migratory peoples and foreign influences, and in part by a variety of contrasting cultural developments. Indonesia's insularity has served as an isolating influence; approaches to the islands and interisland contacts have been maritime. One of the major problems facing the young republic is that of overcoming the handicaps of isolation and fragmentation.

There are three major geologic regions within Indonesia: (1) the Sunda Shelf region, (2) the Sahul Shelf region, and (3) the areas between (1) and (2). Borneo and the area south and west of it, including eastern Sumatra, are the emergent parts of the Sunda Shelf, a relatively stable block of the earth's crust related to Malaya and parts of the mainland of Southeast Asia. Far to the east, New Guinea is a part of another "shelf," the Sahul Shelf, of which Australia is the largest component. These shelves are covered in part by shallow seas which are bordered by large alluvial flats. Above the shelves rise mountain and hill lands made up of old geologic materials that have gone through successive cycles of uplift and denudation. They are composed of rocks of complex character—granites and metamorphic rocks in which patches of sedimentary rocks have been enfolded, the stumps of once-large mountain ranges. In part because of their inaccessibility and in part because they contain only small areas of fertile soil, the uplands are sparsely inhabited by primitive tribes.

Around and between the two shelves are geologic structures of younger age, generally folded sedimentary rocks grouped in parallel festoons. These mountain systems are separated and broken by deep trenches. Earthquakes denote that they are unstable, rising portions of the earth's crust. The welling up of molten material through weaknesses in their structures has given rise to volcanic peaks. From these peaks and caldera have come great lava flows and explosions of ash which in some cases form the basis for rich soils. Though the lines of weakness may be traced

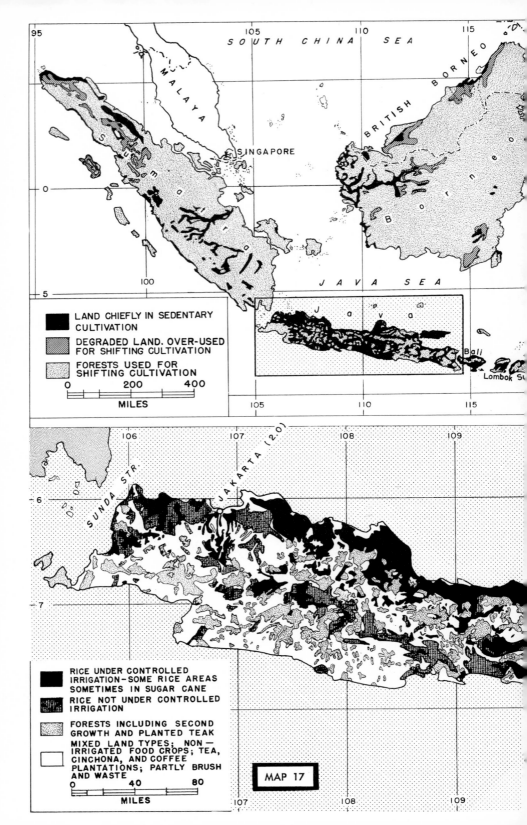

95 105 110 115
SOUTH CHINA SEA
MALAYA
SINGAPORE
S U M A T R A
BRITISH BORNEO
B o r n e o
0
JAVA SEA
5
J a v a
Bali
Lombok St.

LAND CHIEFLY IN SEDENTARY
CULTIVATION

DEGRADED LAND, OVER-USED
FOR SHIFTING CULTIVATION

FORESTS USED FOR
SHIFTING CULTIVATION

0   200   400
MILES

105 110 115

106 107 JAKARTA (2.0) 108 109
SUNDA STR.
6

7

RICE UNDER CONTROLLED
IRRIGATION—SOME RICE AREAS
SOMETIMES IN SUGAR CANE

RICE NOT UNDER CONTROLLED
IRRIGATION

FORESTS INCLUDING SECOND
GROWTH AND PLANTED TEAK

MIXED LAND TYPES; NON—
IRRIGATED FOOD CROPS; TEA,
CINCHONA, AND COFFEE
PLANTATIONS; PARTLY BRUSH
AND WASTE

MAP 17

0   40   80
MILES

107 108 109

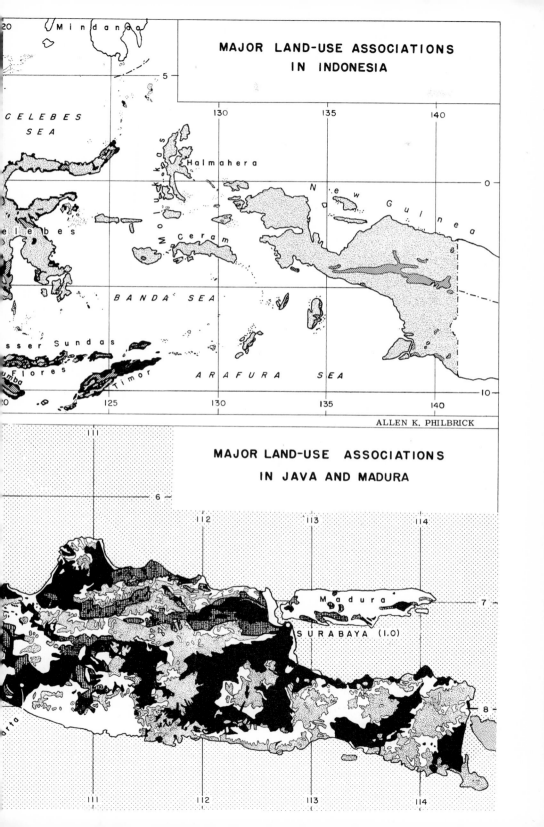

MAJOR LAND-USE ASSOCIATIONS
IN INDONESIA

MAJOR LAND-USE ASSOCIATIONS
IN JAVA AND MADURA

ALLEN K. PHILBRICK

for long distances by a series of volcanic cones, these lines are not continuous, and they vary in direction. Some of the 300 or more volcanoes are beautifully symmetrical and have gently sloping lava flows; others have blown themselves out of existence, leaving only the scars of the cataclysm.[1] Some 60 volcanoes are active in Indonesia. The types of sedimentary rocks and volcanic ejecta differ greatly, and the landforms that develop are variegated. The drainage that develops in this mountainous landscape may be symmetrical down a lava cone or, in contrast, be irregular or angular in an area of folded sedimentaries. There are some volcanic crater lakes, such as Lake Toba in Sumatra.

Thus, in geomorphological terms, a sharp distinction is made between (1) the old stable blocks—Borneo, eastern Sumatra, and the islands between on the Sunda Shelf in the west; and New Guinea and some of its offshore islands in the east—and (2) the relatively young lands—western Sumatra, Java, and the Lesser Sunda Islands, which stretch in one magnificent arched archipelago, and Celebes, Halmahera, and the Molukkas which are formed along twisting lines that appear to go almost at right angles to one other. Within each of the two great divisions are found great contrasts in landforms depending upon basic rock structures.

The stable Sundra block regions possess at least one major handicap insofar as economic development is concerned—the relative infertility of their highly laterized soils. In a tropical climate such as that of Indonesia the nutrient elements and humus in the soil leach out rapidly. In upland areas, where the soils may not be maturely developed because of rapid erosion, the land actually may be more fertile, for the top, infertile layers have been removed. The resulting immature soils are not so rich in nutrient elements as are volcanic soils, but they can be used temporarily for agriculture, usually losing their fertility after two or three years. When this occurs, the farmers clear new patches, usually by burning the forest cover, as part of a cyclical process of shifting cultivation. These uplands are well drained. In contrast, along the coasts of Borneo and eastern Sumatra are extensive alluvial plains with sluggish rivers, swamps, and tidal flats. For the most part these areas of poor drainage also are sparsely settled, except where elaborate drainage projects have been completed by native technologies, as in the Pontianak region of western Borneo.

The better lands for agriculture lie on the lava and ash slopes of the geologically younger lands on the western and southern periphery of the Sunda block. In general, western Sumatra, the Lesser Sundas, and especially Java, have soils capable of supporting large numbers of people. Earthquakes and volcanic activity are as much a blessing as an evil, for they indicate the relative youth of the land-forming processes. Thus, soils are immature, are relatively little leached, and are enriched by recent lava flows and ash deposits.

[1] The most notable explosion in recent times was that of Krakatoa, a small island between Sumatra and Java, which "blew up" in 1883.

The lands of recent age have varied relief, and much of the land is in slope. The industrious Indonesian farmers through the centuries, recognizing the fertility of these lands, have overcome the handicap of slope by terracing (Figures 7 and 74). Men seemingly have been the chief erosive agents in parts of Bali and Java where ingenious primitive engineers have carved the hillsides into intricate steps and terraces. By trial and error, these improvisers have created fields and have led water to them in just the right amounts. It is on these immature but fertile soils that the highest densities of agricultural population—sometimes as high as 3,000 to 4,000 per square mile—are found in Indonesia.

Within the areas of relatively young geologic formations also are found areas of older folded or faulted limestones and other sedimentary rocks,

Fig. 74 • The agricultural landscape of Java, as seen here in the vicinity of Bandung, is dominated by arrays of terraced paddy fields, carefully tended and jewel-like. Usually these fields depend on direct rainfall for their water supply; controlled irrigation is practiced for the most part only in the larger lowlands where Dutch irrigation works were constructed. Around the fields are rows of banana trees. In the right background are hillsides in brush and small trees from which firewood is gathered. Farther back, the cleared hills are almost completely covered by upland fields or *tegalan*, chiefly in maize and other dry grains. In the far distant background, the mountain slopes are in forest, possibly planted stands of teak, a valuable estate crop in Java. The house at the left is atypical of Javanese village housing and probably was built for Europeans. *(Standard Oil Co., N.J.)*

Fig. 75 • The mild climate throughout most of Indonesia is reflected in the degree to which Indonesian activities take place outdoors. Street cafes like this one in Jakarta are common even in the largest cities. In the foreground is an ambulatory vendor of food; in the background a more permanent restaurant. The shelters are made of bamboo poles and strips of the atap palm leaf. Woven bamboo matting also is used. Although dishes are in use here, in the rural areas banana leaves take their place. Note the variegated costumes worn by the men, except for the standard black cap characteristic of most of Indonesia; the sarongs of the women; the fly whisk of the little boy in the right middleground; the ubiquitous chicken; and the giant banyan tree in the right background. *(Standard Oil Co., N.J.)*

which do not have such fertile soils. Along the shores, sometimes lifted quite high, are patches of coral. On these less fertile areas agricultural occupance is less dense, and crop associations differ from those in the volcanic soil regions.

The climate of the islands also is important to the potential and actual development of agriculture. Most of Indonesia has high temperatures throughout the year and abundant rainfall with a decided maximum during a "rainy" season.

The constancy of temperatures is, of course, a direct reflection of an equatorial location (Plate B). The angle of the sun's rays does not vary to a great degree during the year. The annual range of average monthly temperatures at Jakarta, for example, is only a matter of 2 or 3 degrees; the difference between temperatures at night and those during the day is at least five times as much as the differences between "winter" and "summer" (Figure 75). Though the temperatures are high the year around, they are not excessively high; the highest ever recorded in Jakarta was 96°F.; the lowest, 65°.

The greatest variations in temperature reflect differences in elevation. To escape from the tropical heat in the lowlands, foreigners unused to the climate often spend time at "hill stations." For example, the yearly average temperature at one hill station, Bandung (2,200 feet), is 72°, while at Jakarta, close to sea level, the yearly average is 79°. Differences in temperature are reflected by differences in natural vegetation cover on mountain slopes. They also may be reflected in crop patterns; for example, the lower limits of the tea gardens are often like contour lines circling the hills.

Rainfall throughout Indonesia generally is ample for agriculture, but it varies greatly from place to place, depending on the elevation and exposure to rain-bearing air masses. Except for equatorial eastern Sumatra and Borneo, there is a decided seasonality in rainfall, though the "dry" season might better be described as a "drier" or "less wet" season. Jakarta has an average yearly rainfall of 80 inches, but the average for the month of August is 2 inches, in contrast to 13 inches in January. Rainy seasons also differ markedly over short distances. On one side of a mountain range—for example, in Celebes—the rainy season may be exactly the opposite of that of the other side of the range.

Rainfall usually comes in the form of heavy convectional showers in the late afternoon. In mountain and hill areas of uneven slopes and consequent variation in convection, thunderstorms are common. At Bogor, Java, thunder is heard on the average of 322 days a year, usually in the late afternoon, never in the early morning. At Jakarta on the plain only a few miles away, thunder is heard on the average only 133 days in the year.

The major causal agents for the seasonal variation in rainfall are the Asian monsoonal air drifts and the convergence of tropical air masses along an intertropical front. The climate of Indonesia has long been explained rather simply in terms of the attraction for air masses from a high-pressure area over Australia of a continental low that develops over Mongolia in May to September; during the northern winter a reverse situation prevails, with the monsoon air drifting out of Asia toward Australia. However, more recent data indicate that the air-mass movement is much more complex. Though there are monsoonal air drifts, the convergence of air masses from both north and south of the equator and their meeting along an intertropical front appear to be important causal agents of precipitation and tropical storms and winds. This intertropical front of low pressure shifts from just south of the equator in the northern hemisphere's winter months to far north of the equator (as a discontinuous zone, however) during the northern summer. As warm maritime air flows toward the frontal zone of convergence, it rises and cools, and the consequence is precipitation. Variations in precipitation are associated with the location of the intertropical front and with orographic factors.

Though most of Indonesia is said to have a tropical monsoon climate, there are variations from year to year and season to season. In some years the rainy season may be delayed or may be very pronounced, and serious crop damage by drought or floods may occur. Eastern Java and the Lesser Sunda islands experience greater variations from normal and are characterized by lengthy dry seasons of varying durations during the southern "winter."

The climatic variations, particularly the cooler temperatures at higher elevations and the differences in rainfall, which ranges from some 20 inches in protected valleys to over 300 inches on exposed mountain slopes, are matched by variations in vegetation. In parts of Indonesia where the

dry season is pronounced, savanna grasses and monsoon forests of varying densities are found; in areas of heavy rainfall with no long dry season, luxuriant tropical forests predominate. Particularly along the rainy equatorial margins of the shallow southern South China Sea and Java Sea, lengthy stretches of mangrove swamp extend out to sea, as in eastern Sumatra and Borneo, and dense fresh-water swamps lie inland on the alluvial lowlands where drainage is poor.

The historical development of the Indonesian state

The Indonesians are not a unified ethnic group, although the struggle for independence united them remarkably under the rallying cry of "Merdeka," Freedom. However, with independence won, inherent cultural, economic, and social diversities are tending to create grave problems in the administration of the newly independent state.

The diversity of ethnic groups and activities in Indonesia has resulted in part from the waves of migratory peoples and ideas that have swept over the variegated islands. Three major waves of outside influence have played decisive roles in shaping modern Indonesian culture upon its Proto-Malay base.

The first outside force was Indian. From the first century A.D. the Indies were visited by Hindu traders and priests, followed by some permanent migrants. These people founded a large number of scattered kingdoms and principalities, some of them grouped into confederacies, and brought with them new religious ideas, both Hindu and Buddhist, with associated forms of social organization. The chief centers of contact were in the coastal areas of Sumatra and Java. A strong empire, Sri Vijaya, based on naval power, became established on Sumatra. This kingdom, strongly Indian in character, controlled a large area including most of Malaya and parts of Cambodia, and trade was carried on with other parts of Asia. During this period there occurred a flowering of Hinduized culture, and magnificent temples were constructed. Another Indonesian-Hindu empire, Majapahit, arose in eastern Java. By the thirteenth century it was able to challenge the power of the Sumatran empire and by 1377 had overthrown its rival. For the first time, nearly all of modern Indonesia was under one political power, though many islands and interior highlands remained virtually untouched, and life in the agricultural villages was little affected.

Islam, the second foreign influence, came to Indonesia in the wake of Moslem Indian and Arab traders during the latter part of the Hindu period. The new faith was propagated by mass conversions, often by force, and spread quickly through the islands. Finally, in 1478 the Majapahit empire was overthrown, but the victory of Islam was not complete, for places like Bali kept a form of Hinduism as their religion, and animistic beliefs continued to be held by many peoples outwardly professing Islam. No united Islamic empire was formed; rather, a number of sultanates of varying size and strength came into being, related only by a common religious belief.

The most profound impact of recent times on Indonesian society has been that of the West. However, the Chinese also have come to attain a strong position in the commercial life of the country. Thus, the term "the West" is not wholly correct in epitomizing this last, and present, invasion. Apart from the Chinese, the Portuguese were the first to gain access to Indonesia in 1521. Soon other European trading nations and companies came to seize a share in the fabled riches of the Indies. Finally, the Dutch East India Company was able to gain ascendancy. Eastern Timor and nearby enclaves and islands still remain in the possession of the Portuguese. Power passed from the Dutch company to the Dutch government in 1799. For a brief time, roughly 1803-1816, the British held Java, but after the defeat of Napoleon in Europe the Dutch regained control over the Indies.

Dutch policies varied in different parts of the archipelago. In the isolated parts of the islands of Sumatra, Borneo, and Celebes where primitive shifting cultivation prevailed, there was little contact and change. Some of the sultans were allowed to continue in control of their states or long evaded the imposition of Dutch sovereignty. Even in the more accessible parts of the islands where Dutch administration was more direct, policies were variable. In general, the villages were allowed a considerable degree of autonomy, though under complicated and varying systems, and the inhabitants had to pay heavy taxes in kind or services. In the eastern islands, the Molukkas and the other islands, where cultivation of the sago palm was the basis of agricultural activity and was combined with fishing to provide a livelihood, Dutch control was little evidenced. These islands were a source of cloves and nutmeg; later coconut palms were introduced as a cash crop.

It was in the heart of the Indies—Java, Madura, and to a lesser extent Bali and the Lesser Sundas—where rice cultivation dominated the agricultural economy that Dutch control was established most firmly. Here, the important estate crops, coffee, and later tea, quinine, rubber, and coconut palms, were introduced. Some forest products, notably teak, were an added source of wealth. Sugar cane and to a lesser extent tobacco were grown by native cultivators on a share basis. The commercial crops were also produced on newly developed land held by foreign companies under lease from local rulers. Though the Dutch were in political control, they exercised indirect rule through the Indonesian aristocracy. Meanwhile,

Fig. 76 • Early Jakarta (Batavia) developed around a small Javanese fishing port in west Java at the mouth of a small river. The area has come to be known as Old Batavia. The Dutch built warehouses and business offices, and their commercial activities came to be sited near the harbor itself, shown here. In effect, Old Batavia was a river port, in part because of the shallowness and lack of protection for the waters offshore. As vessel sizes increased the old harbor became increasingly inadequate, and the Dutch completed a great modern port several miles east of the city, Tanjong Priok. The old port is now used for smaller native shipping, but some of the old warehouses still stand as material evidences of Dutch rule. *(Norton Ginsburg.)*

most local commercial enterprise was carried on by Chinese merchants.

Java became the heart of the colonial system. The physical transformation of Java was most marked by the building of new roads (and later railroads) and ports. The city of Batavia (now Jakarta) grew rapidly from its inauspicious start in a swampy marsh in 1619 (Figure 76). In eastern Java another great commercial port city, Surabaya, was developed out of an old Javanese rice port. The changes in Java were accompanied by great increases in population.[2] Before 1800 the population of Java had been rather stable, and in 1815 it was estimated that some 5,000,000 people lived on the island. By 1895 the population had increased fivefold, and by 1945 it was estimated at 50,000,000. This population explosion naturally created severe pressures upon the land. Though new land was cleared and planted to food and commercial crops, increases in agricultural production barely kept pace with population growth.

There were less spectacular changes in the other islands, the so-called Outer Islands. This was due in part to difficulties of access and in part to their less favorable potentialities for the production of products desired in world trade. A major exception was the spice trade of the Molukkas, but the spice trade could be, and was, controlled from Java. Notable was the increase of certain commercial crops, such as tobacco in northeastern Sumatra and rubber planted in foreign-owned estates and later by native smallholders. Mineral production was especially important in the Outer Islands. Oil fields were developed in Sumatra and Borneo, where production was much greater than in the fields of eastern Java. Bauxite deposits in the islands of the Riouw archipelago near Singapore have been more recently exploited. Tin dredges were active on Bangka and Billiton islands, off southeastern Sumatra.

The development of the Indies was of vast benefit to the Netherlands. The economic development of the islands provided career opportunities for a large number of Dutch. Originally traders, government officials, and soldiers, they became managers of estates, mines, factories, and commercial enterprises. As health conditions improved, many Dutch families settled in the Indies, though commonly they maintained ties with the Netherlands and retired there. The flow of funds back to the Netherlands by the government, business concerns, and individuals was very large, though difficult to estimate. Many of the profits derived from development in the Indies were, however, reinvested in the islands. On the eve of the second World War, Dutch and other foreign holdings in Indonesia were measured in billions of guilders.

The effects of the Pacific war on Indonesia were earthshaking. The

---

[2] Particularly as a result of the Culture System (see page 359), which placed a high premium on a large family-labor supply, and of the decline in the death rate with the Dutch introduction of improved sanitation practices.

Dutch government-in-exile in London was unable to prevent the Japanese invasion and conquest of the Indies early in 1942. Many Indonesians welcomed the Japanese as fellow Asians who had defeated the European overlords. Some Indonesian nationalists who had been put in exile or under detention by the Dutch were freed and took an active role in support of the Japanese, but became disillusioned as the Japanese regime instituted increasingly harsh methods of control.

Upon the surrender of the Japanese in August, 1945, Indonesian leaders declared the independence of the Indies. To the Dutch, the new republic was simply a Japanese creation. For several years the Indonesians sought to preserve their new freedom against Dutch so-called "police actions." Eventually the Dutch were forced to relinquish their hold over all of the Indies with the exception of western New Guinea, or Irian. On December 27, 1949, sovereignty was transferred to the Republic of the United States of Indonesia, a loose federation which was "voluntarily associated" with the Netherlands in a union of which the Dutch Queen was the symbolic head. After only nine months, the United States of Indonesia gave way to the Republic of Indonesia, and in 1956 the "association" with the Dutch formally was renounced.

The young Republic has been confronted with many problems associated with the centrifugal regionalisms that characterize so highly fragmented a state. The stabilizing of government has been impeded by the existence of many political groups split along regional, religious, political, and economic lines. One militant Moslem group, the Darul Islam, has held portions of western and central Java. A communist attempt to seize power during the struggle of the Indonesians against the Dutch was put down successfully, although by 1952 the communists had become a potent force once more. The military has taken an active political role, and military leaders control portions of the Outer Islands. There have been rebellions against the central government in Sumatra and in Celebes.

In the economic sphere, the Indonesian Republic has been faced with the problem of converting a dualistic colonial economy to an independent economy, meanwhile expanding production to match both the growth of population and the desire for higher levels of living. In the fervor for independence, many Indonesians appear to have forgotten that one of the major assets of the islands is their ability to produce goods valued in world markets. European commercial concerns and Chinese middlemen have been an obvious target for chauvinistic discrimination, despite the inability of Indonesian entrepreneurs to replace them. Smuggling between Sumatra and Singapore and between northern Celebes and the Philippines of government-controlled products such as rubber and copra has reflected the regional complexity of Indonesia's economic problems.

Fig. 77 • The Javanese countryside is bursting with life and activity, despite the deceptive slowness with which many Javanese appear to move. Here in West Java women are washing clothes, their children, and themselves in what serves as both a drainage ditch and an irrigation canal. Canals like these appear everywhere men have settled in lowland Java, over most of the island. Mud from the bottom of the ditch is drying on the right bank and will be used as field dressing. Like most Malayan peoples, the Javanese are preoccupied to an unusual degree with water, particularly flowing water. Even in the canals that run through cities like Jakarta and Surabaya, countless people bathe, launder, brush their teeth, and relieve themselves, with an air of modest innocence that surprises the foreigner. Note here the small terraced paddy fields, the banana trees, the evidences of Dutch rule in the paved highway on the left, and the delicate poles and wires with which the Dutch laced Java. (Standard Oil Co., N.J.)

Java: The core of Indonesia

Java is the hub of the Indonesian universe (Figure 77). The volcanic mountain chains that form the backbone of the island have renewed the land with rich volcanic flows and ash. On gentle slopes, well watered by radial drainage from the mountain summits, terraced fields have been constructed. As estate crops —coffee, tea, rubber, cinchona—were developed in the last century, the population spread up the mountain slopes. With economic development other commercial crops, such as sugar and tobacco, were introduced into the native smallholding pattern. New lands were cleared, and more intensified agricultural practices were introduced. Java thus has come to account for better than two-thirds of all the cultivated land in Indonesia. The population doubled again and again until more than 50,000,000 people crowd the island. This population explosion has been accompanied by the construction of a transportation network of roads and railroads and the growth of large cities.

Within the island are many differences in landscapes because of variations in geologic structure and relief. Belts of limestone hills look decidedly different from the slopes of volcanoes or the plains along the north coast. Within the mountain areas, basins, some of them former lake beds formed by the damming action of lava flows, contrast with the abrupt slopes of active volcanoes. Much of Java is in slopes, some of which have been terraced into paddy fields; on others, unterraced, dry crops are grown. Differences in soil also may be noted by the contrasts in crops and natural vegetation.

Climatic variations also are factors in the development of contrasting geographical landscapes within Java. One study of rainfall in Java identifies more than 40 distinct types of rainfall on the basis of the different seasonal patterns and amounts of precipitation. The eastern third of the island is apt to have more pronounced dry seasons. As a consequence, agriculture is more precarious, for even a short period of unpredicted drought at critical times will result in crop failures. Differences in temperature because of variations in altitude are significant climatic differentiators in Java.

The Javanese are predominantly farmers. The rural villages, or *kampong*, have had closely knit social structures now becoming more diffuse under Western influence. Islam is the dominant religon. Linguistically, differences between Sundanese in the west, Javanese in the center and east, and Madurese in the northeast have been sharp, though all are Malay dialects. The government-sponsored Bahasa Indonesia, a standardized Malay, should in the long run override these differences.

Java is a rice-dominated island; in fact, an early name of Java meant "rice island." Over 40 per cent of the cultivated land is in paddy fields, or *sawah*. The major areas of rice are along the north coastal plains, the intermontane basins, and up the valleys along the mountain slopes. Rice is grown throughout the year, and in some years as much as one-fifth of the *sawah* is double-cropped with rice. Though it would appear that more double-cropping might be carried on, this does not happen, since water for irrigation is lacking, and many lowland fields are not easily or quickly drained. The major season of rice harvest is in May and June at the beginning of the dry season in most of Java, although where water supplies are more regular, paddy may be raised the year around. Nearly 20 per cent of the paddy fields are irrigated by modern large-scale irrigation systems developed by the Dutch, but many of the fields are dependent upon the simple diversion of running streams and more directly upon rainfall (Map 17).

In drier central and eastern Java, corn ranks as an important crop along with rice. Some corn may be found also on the higher hillslopes in western Java. On Madura, the small island just to the north of eastern Java (and which is administratively a part of Java), corn is grown on three-fourths of the planted area. Corn often is double-cropped and occasionally triple-cropped. With both corn and rice other crops, such as sweet potatoes, cassava, and peanuts, commonly are rotated. The Javanese farmers follow the common South and Southeast Asian practice of having vegetable plots and fruit trees near their homes to provide supplements to their diets. These gardens coalesce into almost continuous islands of green rising above the level, flooded paddy fields in the plains and basin areas.

In contrast with the subsistence food-crop agriculture in Java is the estate and smallholding commercial crop agriculture. In part because of legal restrictions the Dutch imposed, little land was alienated from the native farmers in Java. Thus, the ratio of the land in estates to that in individual farms is less in Java than in some of the Outer Islands. Most of the estates in Java are in the uplands. Rubber is grown in the lower elevations from 500 to 1,500 feet; tea is grown at higher elevations, although both may be grown together. Other plantation crops, such as kapok and cinchona, are grown in the highlands also. Some commercial crops, such as tobacco and sugar cane, are grown on leased lands or on smallholdings in areas where soil or climatic conditions are favorable, usually in central and eastern Java. Under the so-called "Culture System," which was put in practice in 1834 and lasted for decades, farmers were virtually forced to grow certain export crops—tobacco and sugar

Fig. 78 • Unloading salt from Madura and copra from Makassar at Tanjong Priok, the port of Jakarta. The vessel is one of the great fleet of the Dutch-owned Koninglijk Paaketvaart Maatschapij, better known as KPM, one of the largest shipping companies active in Asia. KPM has a virtual monopoly of the movements of goods over long distances within Indonesia, and in Dutch days monopolized the government mail, goods, and officials' travel. The company is the equivalent of a major railway system in a non-insular country and, being foreign-owned, is a constant reminder to Indonesians of their dependence, at least in substantial part, on the technology, experience, and capital of the Western countries. Although the Indonesians have not yet been able to develop a modern merchant marine able to compete with KPM in the interisland trade, they have taken control of the former Dutch airline in the country, which is managed, however, by the Dutch KLM. *(Norton Ginsburg.)*

cane in the basins and coffee on hillslopes. This system provided revenues for the Dutch regime but was abandoned eventually as being too exploitative. It did serve, however, to introduce commercial crop production among the Javanese farmers.

The predominance of Java in the economic life of Indonesia has been enhanced by the development of modern transportation facilities. An excellent network of roads was developed, in part by the use of a *corvée* system. These roads were coordinated with a trellis-shaped railroad net developed to make more efficient the movement of export products. Two large ports, Surabaya in the east and Tanjong Priok (the port of Jakarta) in the west, served as export centers and as import centers for the manufactured products that were sold throughout the island. These ports also were the foci for the shipping routes that tied the Indies together and connected them with the world of commerce (Figure 78). In these cities were the main headquarters of the large export-import companies and the banks. Manufacturing facilities were developed in these and certain other towns. Jakarta (the Batavia of the Dutch) was the site of the Netherlands East Indies government and is the administrative center of the Republic of Indonesia. Other important centers are Jogjakarta and Surakarta in central Java. The Dutch developed Bandung, in a mountain basin in western Java, as a healthful hill station and a railroad and manufacturing center. The Dutch governor-general established his summer capital at the hill station of Buitenzorg (now Bogor), also famed as the site of an excellent botanical garden and research institute.

The Outer Islands

In contrast to Java where population increased rapidly and population densities are very high, the Outer Islands have had a spotty, irregular history of development. They have little regional coherence, and Java dominates them. Dutch colonial policy was to some extent one of indirect rule, allowing considerable local autonomy to outlying areas, although all key decisions were made in Batavia. The Indonesian Republic, however, after a few months of experimentation as a federation, has moved more and more toward a centralized administrative control—not, however, with complete success, since regional identification remains strong and divisive tendencies continue.

Sumatra (Andalas) was not developed to the same degree as Java for numerous reasons. Dutch control over the island actually was not complete until 1908, when the resistance of the Achinese in the north finally was quelled. Only certain areas have been intensively developed by native farmers or by foreign interests—such as the agricultural settlements in the Padang highlands in central Sumatra, the tobacco region of Deli in the north, and the oil fields near Palembang in the south (Figure 79).

In Sumatra, and even more commonly in other of the Outer Islands, sedentary rice farming is not nearly so significant as in Java. Ladang, or shifting cultivation, is widely practiced. This method of tillage has many harmful consequences: fires may get out of control; soils quickly become exhausted as forest cover is cleared; forests may be replaced permanently by pernicious coarse grasses. Nevertheless, ladang cultivation may be regarded as an economical method by which land that would not otherwise be productive can support a sparse population. Of course, it covers a greater area than does the sedentary agriculture; the average ladang farmer uses 12 times as much land as the rice cultivator. Ladang cultiva-

Fig. 79 • In Sumatra, as in much of Indonesia, settlements are located near or on the banks of streams used from ancient times as means of transportation. Houses are erected on piles, even in the larger cities, or on their outskirts where most of the *kampong*-type areas are located. Palembang, in southern Sumatra, extends along the banks of the Musi River. At one end are refineries associated with the foreign-owned petroleum industry of the region; at the other and along the short streams and canals tributary to the Musi are scenes such as these. Note the stilted yet relatively substantial buildings, using the canal as a street as is customary throughout the Malaysian world. The boatman carries fuelwood faggots. In areas where there is a conspicuous dry season, as in eastern Java, the water level in the canals tends to fall and the water becomes stagnant and malodorous, but the washing, bathing, and toothbrushing continue. *(Standard Oil Co., N.J.)*

tion is found throughout Sumatra, but is mainly of significance in the central and western plains and hill lands of the island.

The development of estate and other commercial crops has been quite localized within Sumatra. In prewar days over half the acreage in estates in the Indies was found in Sumatra. The east coast of northern Sumatra became a rich center for tobacco, rubber, palm oil, and sisal production. In the hills to the west of this area, tea and coffee plantations were started. Near the southern tip of the island an area was developed for pepper cultivation. In Sumatra smallholders have been increasingly important producers of commercial products. During the second World War, with the loss of foreign markets, many estates were abandoned or converted by squatters to food production. Squatters still occupy these lands and lands that were earmarked for future estate development.

Sumatra is one of the islands to which it has been hoped that Javanese farmers, crowded in their home island, would emigrate. Under the Dutch, programs were developed for migration, particularly to settlements in southern Sumatra. However, the number of Javanese who came as permanent settlers was disappointingly low. These programs have been continued by the Indonesian government. Though there are no comparably extensive areas of fertile lands in Sumatra, as in Java, there are many localities that are not intensively cultivated and that could absorb a considerable population.

Resources, other than agricultural, have been developed in Sumatra. Sumatran petroleum supplies Indonesia with much of her foreign exchange. The oil fields in northern Sumatra, however, are still being rehabilitated after their wartime decay and destruction, and the Indonesian government questions the legal status of the leases under which they were operated. In central Sumatra new fields were being developed during the years just before the war; these developments have been continued. The major oil fields are in southern Sumatra; crude oil is piped to the refineries at Palembang. These operations have been developed by foreign capital—chiefly Dutch and American—and under agreement with the Indonesian government have been allowed to continue, though they turn over a large share of their revenues to the Republic in the form of lease rents and taxes. In 1954, about 11 million metric tons of petroleum were produced in all Indonesia, chiefly in Sumatra. Tin dredges are used in the alluvial tin deposits on the east-coast islands of Bangka, Billiton, and Singkep. About 35,000 metric tons of tin-in-ore are produced annually, making Indonesia the world's second most important tin producer. Bauxite deposits in the Riouw archipelago, especially on Bintan island near Singapore, also have been exploited; the best-grade deposits were mined during the days of Japanese control, but significant reserves remain and are being mined by a Dutch-controlled company operating under a lease arrangement with the Indonesian government. Coal also is mined in western Sumatra and exported from the port of Padang. In 1954 about 900,000 metric tons were produced.

Sumatra's proximity to the Malayan peninsula has been an important factor in its development. Northern Sumatra especially has long been oriented economically toward Singapore. In fact, the Japanese administered the two areas as one political unit, and there remain many economic and cultural ties between the two areas. The Republic centered in West Java faces the possibility of strong separatist movements developing in Sumatra, for the island differs markedly from Java in economic development and geographic character.

Borneo (Kalimantan) has undergone less economic development than Sumatra. It is a very large island,[3] of which the northern part is under British control. Most of it is mountainous and forested; there has been relatively little intensive agricultural development. Penetration into the interior has been handicapped by the ill-drained lowlands of the coastal region, the swampy lands of which, with slow meandering rivers, have made an inhospitable base for penetration. The city of Bandjarmasin, built on piles and protected by dikes at the mouths of two rivers which join to form a delta, is in part isolated by its location. In the lower valley of the Kapuas River near Pontianak, however, Chinese paddy cultivators have brought an extensive area of marshland into cultivation. Within the mountain lands, primitive shifting cultivation prevails. Soils are poor, and a subsistence economy based on rice, corn, and cassava is the basis of life for the isolated tribal folk. Some rubber and copra plantations have been developed, and there has been some increase in smallholders' production of rubber. The forests of the interior have tropical hardwoods of value, though it is difficult to transport the logs from the isolated mountain and hill lands. Some attempts have been made to drain the swampy coastal lands and develop more modern agriculture, but this is handicapped by the reluctance of Javanese farmers to migrate to Kalimantan (Indonesian Borneo). Oil fields at Tarakan and Balikpapan on the east coast were developed by foreign companies during the latter period of Dutch control, and they account for most of Borneo's exports to the outside world.

The other islands of the Outer Indies reveal the same diversity in their geographic character and economic development as do the three large islands. Celebes (Sulawesi) is the largest of the remaining outer islands, and it is only patchily occupied. In the northern peninsula permanent rice cultivation provides a livelihood for locally dense populations. The people of Celebes have derived much of their livelihood from the sea, for harbors are plentiful and the adjacent waters have rich fishing grounds. Lake Tempe produces fresh-water fish which are dried and salted for export. Some commercial crops—notably coffee and copra—are produced in Celebes, although estates have not been developed notably on the island. One extraordinary feature has been the growth of Christianity in the

[3] Next to Greenland and New Guinea the world's third largest, covering about 290,-000 square miles.

northern peninsula, with headquarters at Menado, and the Menadoese maintain close ties with the Christian Philippines. The major city, however, is Makassar in the south, around which are permanent agricultural settlements. *Ladang* cultivation prevails in the mountainous interior. There are possibilities for development of mineral resources, such as nickel and iron, which could be extremely significant as industrialization proceeds within Indonesia.

In the *Molukkas* separatism has been strong, in part as a result of the unique historical geography of these fabled Spice Islands. The early spice trade which attracted European traders was dependent upon forest gatherers; an estate economy did not develop, and the spice trade declined long ago. On the coral atolls and along the shores of the larger islands, coconut palms have provided some basis for livelihood; many people are dependent upon the sago palm. From this region come the Christian Amboinese, upon whom the Dutch relied for their native troops and who at least once have rebelled against the Indonesian government since independence.

The *Lesser Sunda* islands, which extend eastward from Java in a long chain, have a great deal of local diversity. The most famous of these islands undoubtedly is Bali. Rising from the sea in Bali are gentle slopes of volcanic lava flows which have been carved into terraces by generations of Balinese. It is a land of intensive rice cultivation, of vegetable plots and fruit trees around villages located near small streams, of Hindu temples and village dancers. The eastern islands of the Sunda group are much drier; corn replaces rice as a staple food; and settlement is much less dense than in the western islands near Java. There are decided differences also in natural vegetation. Cattle and horses are grazed on grasslands cleared by fires. Portuguese Timor, occupying the eastern end of that island and a small enclave in the center, is politically not a part of Indonesia, but has the same geographic character as the rest of the eastern Sundas.

A major area of political dispute is western New Guinea or *Irian*,[4] which was not included in the transfer of sovereignty to Indonesia and is still under Dutch control. Its possession is disputed by Indonesia and has been under long and involved negotiation. Irian is a mountainous, forested region with a sparse and scattered population of primitive tribespeople, ethnically distinct from the basically Malay Indonesians. Its chief mineral resource is petroleum, already under modest exploitation by Dutch and American interests (Figure 4).

[4] The term Irian refers to all of New Guinea, and the Indonesians claim an interest in the eastern half of the island, which is controlled by Australia.

Problems of development

Indonesia often has been termed a "storehouse of natural wealth," but the development of its fragmented resource base is no easy task. In the "native" sector of the economy, subsistence agriculture prevails in the form of rice, corn, fruits, and vegetables. Great efforts have been made to increase the cultivated land for these crops. In recent years, as the limits of new land for cultivation have been approached, particularly in Java, efforts have been made to increase productivity on already cultivated land, but yields remain low relative to Japan and other East Asian countries. Commercial fertilizer is used mainly on commercial crops from which monetary returns are expected and not so commonly on the subsistence food crops. Other improvements may be made, particularly in farm management, irrigation, and crop diversification, but these will be accepted only gradually by the conservative Indonesian peasant.

Under colonial control certain resources were exploited for specialized world markets. One consequence has been economic dependence upon uncontrollable events in distant places with different economic systems. Thus, changes in the demand for rubber or tin in the United States and Europe cause violent fluctuations in their price in Indonesia and sharply affect production and the national economy.

It was from the estate and commercial crops (in addition to minerals) that the Indies under the Dutch obtained their foreign exchange to buy consumer goods other than food. Coffee, tea, rubber, palm oil, cinchona, sugar, tobacco, and other crops were produced on a large-scale, scientific basis on land owned or leased by largely non-Indonesian management. This estate system was modified drastically under the Japanese during the second World War when worldwide markets were cut off. Subsequently, internal unrest further curtailed or disrupted the production, still below its prewar levels. The situation is complicated by the development of substitutes and synthetics that may reduce the demand for the estate crops.

Many of the estates and the facilities for processing the commercial crops grown on leased lands are Dutch- and foreign-owned. Particularly in Sumatra and parts of Java, the "open door" policy of the Dutch attracted American, British, and other investors, so that the estate economy should not be thought of as solely a Dutch creation. On many of these Dutch- and foreign-owned or -leased holdings during the second World War, Indonesian farmers (most of them former estate workers) squatted and produced subsistence food crops. In many cases these farmers remain as squatters, delaying the restoration of production.

However, rubber production has increased because of the increased output of the smallholders, who operate with a minimum of overhead costs. These may own only a few rubber trees, often planted in former *ladang* patches, which they tap only when prices are high. In times of low prices they raise subsistence crops, often as part of a shifting cultivation pattern. Thus, smallholders' rubber production in Indonesia increased from 268,073 metric tons in 1949 to 529,687 tons in 1950 as a result of the Korean war; at the same time, estate production increased from only 170,-678 metric tons to 174,147 tons in 1950. Generally, the quality of the rubber from the smallholders is not nearly so high as that from the scientifically managed estate. The extent of the Indonesian smallholders' rubber acreage is estimated to be between 2.5 to 3 million acres. Production from these holdings is difficult to control, and production controls to keep prices under regulation are almost impossible to apply. The flow of rubber from Indonesia in both regular and irregular channels in recent years has been of great value to the economy, and Indonesia has come to be the world's leading rubber producer. In 1950 rubber constituted 42 per cent of Indonesia's total recorded value of exports.

As in the case of estate crops, the exploitation of mineral resources has been largely in the hands of foreign interests. Here also recent Indonesian government policy has followed nationalistic lines, though it has not moved toward outright nationalization. The minerals of importance for export are tin and bauxite; coal is used for local consumption. Some refining of petroleum is done for local demands of kerosene and gasoline, though most of the production and refining is done for export purposes. All of the mining enterprises are operated by companies or concessions which in one way or another contribute heavily to the Indonesian treasury. There is potential mineral wealth that has not yet been exploited; it awaits a clearer definition of Indonesian national policy toward minerals and the mining industry.

In short, an underlying problem of Indonesia is the duality of its economy. On the one hand is the vast agricultural population, living on a simple basis of self-sufficient food production, carrying on a limited amount of handicraft industries and commercial activity; on the other is the commercial crop, estate, and mineral economy, highly developed in the past, generally in the hands of outsiders, including Chinese. Under a colonial regime, the commercialized economy is apt to receive advantages and the "peasant" economy may be depressed. At the same time, the creation of a commercial, highly industrialized economy out of a subsistence base is extraordinarily difficult. Some of the handicaps are the lack of modern technical training, conservatism in the villages, and the general lack of capital formation by people who have a very small per-capita income.

Yet, the Indonesian economy is changing rapidly. Though it has been considered dual, it might better be characterized as a plural economy undergoing rapid transformation. The economy of a primitive migratory agricultural folk in Borneo is vastly different from that of the long-settled Javanese rice farmer; both of these economies differ from those of the estate worker or the urban dweller. The challenge for the new Republic of Indonesia thus lies not only in the diversity of its islands, but in the diversities of its peoples' economies.

SELECTED GEOGRAPHICAL BIBLIOGRAPHY

1. Alex L. Ter Braake, *Mining in the Netherlands East Indies.* New York: Institute of Pacific Relations, 1944.
2. Boeke, J. H. *The Evolution of the Netherlands Indies Economy.* New York: Institute of Pacific Relations, 1946.
3. Bowie, Beverly M. "This Young Giant, Indonesia," *The National Geographic Magazine,* September, 1955, pp. 351-92.
4. Bro, Marguerite Hermon. *Indonesia: Land of Challenge.* New York: Harper & Bros., 1954.
5. Broek, Jan O. M. *Economic Development of the Netherlands Indies.* New York: Institute of Pacific Relations, 1942.
6. ———. "Indonesia," *Focus,* December, 1956, pp. 1-6.
7. Douwes-Dekker, N. A. *Tanah Air Kita; A Book on the Country and People of Indonesia.* The Hague: W. van Hoeve, 1950.
8. *Economic Development and Cultural Change* (Issue on Indonesia), January, 1956.
9. *The Far Eastern Quarterly* (Special Number on the Netherlands Indies), February, 1946.
10. Higgins, Benjamin. "Indonesia's Development Plans and Problems," *Pacific Affairs,* June, 1956, pp. 107-25.
11. Koninklijk Nederlandsch Aardrijkskundig Genootschap (with the Topographischen Dienst). *Atlas van Tropisch Nederland.* Batavia: Topographische Dienst, 1938.
12. Metcalf, John E. "The Agricultural Economy of Indonesia," *Agriculture Monograph 15.* Washington: U.S. Dept. of Agriculture, July, 1952.
13. Mohr, E. C. J. *Soils of Equatorical Regions with Special Reference to the Netherlands East Indies.* Ann Arbor: Edwards Bros., 1944. (Original edition, 1933–38; translated by R. Pendleton.)
14. Ormeling, F. J. *The Timor Problem, A Geographical Interpretation of an Underdeveloped Island.* Djakarta, Groningen: J. B. Walters, 1955.
15. Pelzer, Karl J. *Pioneer Settlement in the Asiatic Tropics.* New York: American Geographical Society, 1945.
16. Terra, G. J. A. "Mixed Garden Horticulture in Java," *Malayan Journal of Tropical Geography,* October, 1954, pp. 33-43.
17. "Transportation and Communications in Indonesia," *Transport and Communications Review,* April-June, 1952, pp. 20-42.

18. Van Bemmelen, R. W. *Geology of Indonesia*. The Hague: Netherlands State Printing Office, 1949 (2 volumes).
19. Van der Kroef, Justus M. "Population Pressure and Economic Development in Indonesia," *The American Journal of Economics and Sociology,* July, 1953, pp. 355-71.
20. Van Kleveren, F. F. *The Dutch Colonial System in the East Indies*. Rotterdam: Drukkerij Benedictus, 1953.

Comments

For many decades scholarly geographic work on Indonesia was almost completely carried on by Dutch scientists. A government research bureau, under the direction of competent geographers, prepared maps and research monographs and reports. Unfortunately, most of this valuable material is available only in Dutch. In recent years, the geographic bureau under the topographic service has been continuing some of this research work, and maps and reports are prepared in Indonesian and in English. However, the professionally trained Indonesian geographers are few, and some of them are doing non-geographic service.

American students of the geography of Indonesia have as a consequence limited source materials at their disposal. They must depend on the works of non-geographers and general summaries, often prepared for intelligence rather than research purposes. Karl Pelzer, one of the few American geographers able to carry on field research and who carried on field work before Wold War II, has recently completed another year of research on pioneer settlement in Indonesia. Several Dutch geographers, for example, Ormeling, Ver Stappen, and Van Artzen, also have done field work in recent years.

For general coverage the Embassy of Indonesia in Washington published a useful *Report on Indonesia*, some background booklets, and a colorful map by Covarrubias. There are some active research centers, for example at Cornell and M.I.T., where monographs and reports are being published. Official documents and publications, such as the *Indonesian Economic Review* or the reports of the former Javasche Bank, provide economic data, but their reliability may be questioned. Travellers' accounts, and photographic essays, such as *Tanah Air Kita*, give some of the color and detail which is so significant in gaining an understanding of Indonesia. The *Atlas von Tropisch Nederland* is particularly valuable as a source of information on landforms, settlement, and communications. The monograph by Metcalf and the article by Terra provide useful analyses of aspects of Indonesian agriculture. Ormeling's case study of Timor is one of the few detailed regional studies available, and the only one available in English. There are no recent census data on Indonesia.

Malaya and British Borneo

MALAYA MAY BE DESCRIBED IN TERMS OF ITS TWO MAJOR ECONOMIC functions: the first as a primary producer of rubber, tin, and lesser minerals and tropical agricultural produce; the second as a trade and shipping center for the Southeast Asian realm. These functions operate under circumstances that distinguish Malaya in its regional setting: (1) like many other countries in the realm, it has recently (1957) received its independence in part; (2) like the others, it is characterized by a society of multiple ethnic strata, but it is the only area in which the native population is not a majority of the whole; (3) unlike the other countries, it is not basically self-sufficient in foodstuffs; (4) like Indonesia, it is a major producer of rubber and tin, but, unlike Indonesia, it is largely dependent for its gross livelihood on their production; (5) it lies not off the major trade routes of the world as do Burma, Thailand, Indochina, and to a lesser extent Indonesia and the Philippines, but athwart the major ocean route connecting western Europe, India, and East Asia via the Straits of Malakka.

Malaya has been a center of British influence in Southeast Asia. Its importance as a Western outpost increased after the conclusion of the second World War, following the withdrawal of Burma from the British Commonwealth, the withdrawal of the Dutch from Indonesia, the diminution of French power in Indochina, and the granting of freedom to the Philippines by the United States. The British government recognized this strategic position by maintaining in Malaya a High Commissioner for Southeast Asia, who has overseen British interests within the realm wherever they may be. Rising Malay nationalism and interest in greater autonomy were associated with the unification of all the peninsula into a Federation of Malaya under a commissioner appointed by the British Crown.[1] Singapore, however, like Hongkong, remains a British Crown Colony, but economically and politically it is integrated into the Malayan unit. In 1955, both Singapore and the Federation were granted extensive powers of democratic self-government, and in August, 1957, the Federation was granted independence.

Political autonomy on a democratic basis is made difficult, however, by the complexity of the demographic structure of Malaya, in which the largest single ethnic group is not Malay but Chinese. The Chinese account for 45 per cent of the population; Malays and other Malaysians, chiefly Indonesians, 43 per cent; and Indians, 10 per cent. Of the total estimated population in 1955 of 7,200,000, Europeans and Eurasians accounted for less than 1 per cent. In the Federation itself Malays and Malaysians constitute 49 per cent, and the largest single group. It is partially because of Malay desires *not* to be swamped by a Chinese majority that Singapore, with its 850,000 Chinese, has not yet been integrated politically into the Malaya of which it is so important an economic part.

The presence of large non-Malay groups is primarily the consequence of the development of rubber and tin production. South Indians, chiefly Tamils, were brought in as laborers on the rubber plantations, and Chinese from Kuang-tung and Fu-chien provinces were brought in as tin miners.[2] In addition, thousands of Chinese came to Singapore as that city grew rapidly after 1850 into one of the major ports of Asia and the world. The Chinese are localized primarily in the larger cities of the peninsula, where they form the basis of the local commercial community, and in settlements that are associated with tin mining. The Indians are more widely dispersed and are settled both in the cities and in the tin-and-rubber belt of the west coast. The Malays are found throughout the country and form the majority of the rural population, but they are most highly localized in the coastal regions of Kelantan and Trengganu in the far northeast, and

[1] The states included in the Federation are Johore, Pahang, Negri Sembilan, Selangor, Kedah, Kelantan, Trengganu, Perlis, and Perak. The former Straits Settlements of Malakka and Penang (including Province Wellesley) also are included. The Crown Colony of Singapore is not, but the term "Malaya" is commonly used to include both the Federation and Singapore.

[2] Whereas the Indians were brought in by European planters, Chinese tin miners were numerous in Malaya shortly after the middle of the nineteenth century, long before rubber had made its appearance.

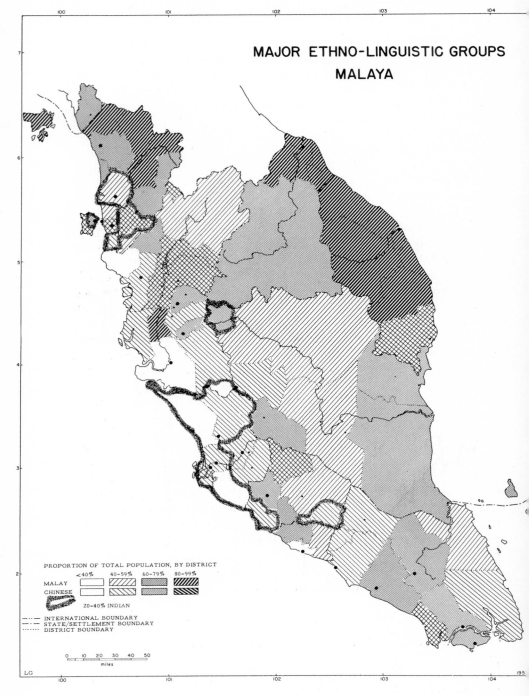

MAJOR ETHNO-LINGUISTIC GROUPS
MALAYA

PROPORTION OF TOTAL POPULATION, BY DISTRICT

	<40%	40-59%	60-79%	80-99%
MALAY				
CHINESE				

20-40% INDIAN

---·--- INTERNATIONAL BOUNDARY
--·--·-- STATE/SETTLEMENT BOUNDARY
········· DISTRICT BOUNDARY

0 10 20 30 40 50
          miles

LG   195

MAP 18

372

Perlis, Kedah, and Perak in the far northwest. Neither Indians nor Chinese are found in large numbers along the relatively less developed and sparsely settled east coast (Map 18).

Examination of the settlement pattern of Malaya reveals that three-quarters of the country's 51,200 square miles are still in forest and woodland; that the east coast is identified by a narrow ribbon of shoreline settlements, often separated from each other by lengthy stretches of swamp and forest; [3] that the main centers of occupance are found in a belt some 45 miles wide paralleling the west coast, and on Singapore island at the southern tip of the peninsula. The western belt of settlement, which developed only toward the end of the last century, is composed of a number of multifunctional urban centers connected with each other and their rubber- and tin-producing hinterlands by an effective network of railways and roads. In addition, there is along the west coast a line of port towns that act as outlets for the produce of the interior—Malakka, Port Dickson, Port Swettenham, Telok Anson, Port Weld, and as a special case Penang—each the terminus of a branch from the railway main line (Map 19).

The railway system itself is more highly developed relative to total population than any other in Southeast Asia. Meter-gauge, as are most of the railways in Southeast Asia, it has just under 1,000 miles of trackage. The basic pattern is Y-shaped, with the base of the Y standing on Singapore in the south and the knotch of the Y in southern Malaya at the border of Johore and Negri Sembilan. The base of the Y and the western arm, extending northwestward to the Thai border, form the main line, along which Kuala Lumpur and to a lesser extent Ipoh are key junctions. The so-called East Coast line, which forms the eastern arm of the system, also extends to connections at the Thai border, and was planned as a device for stimulating economic development along the east coast. However, since its completion in 1931 it has not paid its way, and not until 1954 had it been fully restored from the damage inflicted upon it during the Japanese occupation. Since bulky raw materials tend to move to the nearest ports, most of the freight traffic along the main line is northward from Singapore, which has its immediate hinterland of domestic produce only Johore, although its distributional hinterland is Malaya-wide. Highway transportation competes conspicuously with the railways for both passengers and freight over a highway network of 6,000 miles, of which

[3] The traditional Malay settlement pattern was one of villages near the mouths of the rivers, which tend to run at right angles to the sea. Communications customarily were by sea from river mouth to river mouth rather than overland. To some extent this pattern still prevails on the east coast and in the other predominantly Malay-populated areas.

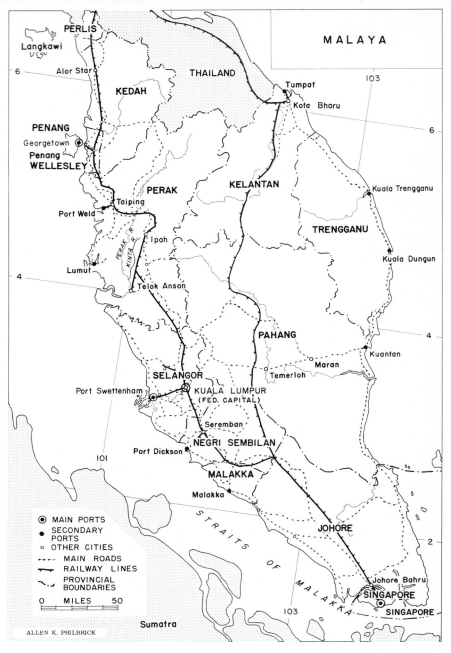

MAP 19

4,000 are metalled.[4] Except in the south, however, only one road links western and eastern Malaya, and this is subject to inundation; one recently completed road parallels the east coast.

[4] In 1951, 83,000 motor vehicles were registered in Singapore and the Federation, as compared with, for example, 15,000 in Thailand.

The natural basis
for development

Most of Malaya is in slope, and only Singapore and the southernmost part of the peninsula are out of sight of mountains. Yet the mountains rise no higher than 7,200 feet and display the maturely rounded contours of a landscape evolved under conditions of high temperatures and high precipitation. The backbone of the country is the arced central range that runs from the southeastern tip of Thailand southward and then southeastward through the peninsula to Johore. To the northwest of this range, which itself lies west of center, is a complex of hills and valleys also originating in Siam, rising to a height of 6,000 feet. To the east is a ridged upland, the Trengganu highlands, which forms the eastern bulge of Malaya, generally lower than the central range but containing the highest peak in the country. The mountain structures in simplest form consist of meridional cores of granite, exposed over large areas by weathering and paralleled by uptilted limestones, shales, and quartzites.

Around the peninsula are lowlands, narrowest in the east and broken often by mountain ridges which extend into the sea. On both coasts the lowlands are associated with mangrove swamps and tidal marshes. These, combined with winding silted estuaries (partially the result of rising sea levels), and granitic forelands, have made for a singularly inhospitable eastern coast. On the western side of the peninsula, however, the coastal plain is wider, and inland from it is a piedmont much broken by foothills and outliers of the central range. Except for considerable areas of freshwater swamp between the coastal lowland and the piedmont, most of this region is occupied, and it forms the economic heartland of the country.

All of Malaya is frost-free. Almost all of it receives more than 70 inches of rainfall, and most of it far more. Since it lies within 7 degrees of the equator, ranges in temperature are small, except as it varies with altitude. Similarly, rainfall does not vary seasonally as much as it does in the countries to the north where a marked monsoon effect and seasonal rainfall are characteristic. At Singapore (Plate B) rainfall is well distributed throughout the year, with minor maxima during the passage of the doldrum belt north and south, but wind shifts and major rainfall maxima are strongly evident farther north on the peninsula. Penang, with a total rainfall of 104 inches, has a major rainfall maximum in the late summer and fall associated with southwesterly winds; Trengganu, on the east coast, receives an average of 119 inches and displays a marked late fall and winter maximum associated with strong northeasterly winds. In all areas, however, rainfall is erratic, and short periods of drought alternate with tor-

PLATE B

MEAN TEMPERATURE AND PRECIPITATION FOR SELECTED SOUTHEAST ASIAN STATIONS rential convectional rains from a cloud cover which is most prolonged in the south. Humidities are uniformly high, to a lesser degree in the uplands, and hill stations at four and five thousand feet provide relief from the steaming lowlands.

High rainfall also has made for rivers carrying enormous quantities of water. Vague drainage inland, a consequence of rapid erosion of the gross drainage basins, has resulted in large fresh-water swamps underlain by thick deposits of peat. In the lower courses, however, the rivers have built up natural levees over wide flood plains, along which Malay settlement has tended to align itself, but rapidly extending deltas are exceptional, since tidal currents have tended to spread sediment laterally along the coasts.

In general, soils that have formed directly upon the exposed granites, quartzites, and shales are, like most mature tropical soils, highly laterized and relatively infertile. The transported soils, those formed over alluvial materials, are in their immaturity often very fertile, and it is on these valley and lowland soils that food production particularly is centered.

Most of the country is or was covered with a dense tropical rainforest varying in character somewhat with altitude and merging into deciduous hill and moss forest above 4,000 feet. Mangrove forests rim the coasts and are backed often by fresh-water swamps with casuarina along their margins. These supply fuelwood and charcoal; nipa palms, which appear where water is fresher, supply thatching and weaving materials. However, exploitation of the forests has barely begun, and much of the construction timber for the country is still imported.[5]

Malayan mineral resources are limited, but not insignificant. Low-grade subbituminous coal is mined in quantity in Selangor at Batu Arang by open-cast methods, and 225,000 long tons were mined in 1954, as compared with 782,000 in the peak year 1940. Railways and power stations are the big consumers, and some coal is imported to satisfy demand. No petroleum has been discovered, although the nearness of Indonesian and British Bornean supplies make this deficiency of little importance. Hydroelectric development however, is limited to one major installation of 27,-

[5] Lumbering is increasingly significant, and railway ties and much construction timber are domestically supplied. Fuelwood, of course, comes from the forests, as do valuable gums, resins, rattan, and fruits which enter into local and foreign trade. In 1950, 120,000 tons (each comprising 50 cubic feet) of timber were exported, an eightfold increase over 1947, and fuelwood went in sizable quantities to Hongkong. Of the total land area of Malaya 22.4 per cent is in reserved forest.

The primary forest is not impassable, and its underbrush is moderate, but the secondary forests, which are omnipresent and blend into the primary growth, generally contain dense thickets of bamboo, harsh grasses (lalang, or cogon, as it is known in the Philippines) and thorn shrub, the result of burnings associated with shifting cultivation.

000-kilowatt capacity on the Perak River east of Taiping, although possibilities for such development are considerable.

Lateritic iron-ore deposits are found in Johore, Kelantan, and Trengganu. Ore amounting to almost two million metric tons was sent to Japan in 1939. Production in 1955, again for export to Japan, primarily from the Trengganu deposits, reached 1,466,000 metric tons. Bauxite also was produced from deposits in Johore before the second World War; production in 1953-4 had risen to 170,000 tons, as production soared also on Indonesia's Bintan island south of Singapore in the Riouw archipelago. Some manganese, wolfram, and, as a by-product of tin-mining, ilmenite, source of titanium, also has been produced. Granites for building stones and clays for brick making are available.

Tin is the major mineral resource of Malaya, normally accounting for 25 per cent by value of the internally-originated exports of the Federation and nearly one-third of the world's production. Production is primarily from alluvial deposits of cassiterite (75 per cent tin) derived from the decomposition of the contact-metamorphosed granite rocks by which most of Malaya and peninsular Thailand are underlain. The 1955 output of 71,000 metric tons of tin-in-ore exceeded 1931-9 levels, but not the 1940 peak of 84,000. The deposits in the Kinta valley near Ipoh and those about Taiping, both in Perak state, account for three-fifths of the output. The deposits about Kuala Lumpur account for most of the remainder, but other deposits are known and exploited. Two techniques are utilized primarily, dredging and hydraulic mining. The former demands high capitalization and is chiefly in European hands; the latter is less demanding of capital and is chiefly in Chinese hands. Labor in both instances is largely Chinese. Scars from tin mining are locally conspicuous on the Malayan landscape, but more serious problems have arisen from the dumping, now restricted by government regulation, of the coarse mining wastes downstream from the mines, with consequent silting of river channels, flooding, and destruction of paddy fields. Tin is exported as a refined product, together with Thai and some Indonesian tin, from smelters at Singapore and Butterworth, on the mainland opposite Penang (Figure 80). Yet, tin must be regarded as a wasting asset, and the exhaustion of known deposits is predicted by 1980.

Agriculture

Agriculture provides a livelihood for the vast majority of Malayans outside of Singapore, but only 16 per cent of the total land area of the country is under cultivation. Agricultural patterns are broadly of two types: (1) those characteristic of the traditional Malayan subsistence economy, centering about the cultivation

Fig. 80 • Tin ingots on the wharves at Penang. The tin is of both Malayan and Siamese origin and was refined at Butterworth. The tin ingots are brought to Penang (to the port of Georgetown) for transshipment to the outside world, chiefly to Europe and the United States. Some of these ingots on the rail trucks used on the wharves are stamped "New Orleans," their destination. The laborers are chiefly south Indians—Tamils—brought in under the British administration as contract laborers not only in the cities but also and especially in the rubber industry. Penang is a standard port of call on the Suez route between Europe and the Orient, and tin is one reason for its significance, although it is also a major entrepôt for Malaya, peninsular Thailand, and northern Sumatra. *(Norton Ginsburg.)*

of wet-rice, and (2) those related to commercial agriculture for export, centering about estates, chiefly of rubber.

Paddy cultivation is highly localized in those alluvial areas where the Malay population is most prominent, as in the far northwest and the far northeast of the country (Map 20). Cultivation practices generally involve transplanting and closely resemble those found throughout Malaysia. Rural settlement associated with paddy cultivation is linked with drier sites on levees and along the marginal uplands, although rather more dispersed than elsewhere in Southeast Asia. Stilted houses with bamboo frames, siding of woven pandanus and nipa fronds, and thatched roofs are typical in all villages. Characteristically, these settlements possess a barter rather than a money economy, although usually some cash exchanges take place.

The total area under paddy in Malaya was 930,500 acres in 1950, less

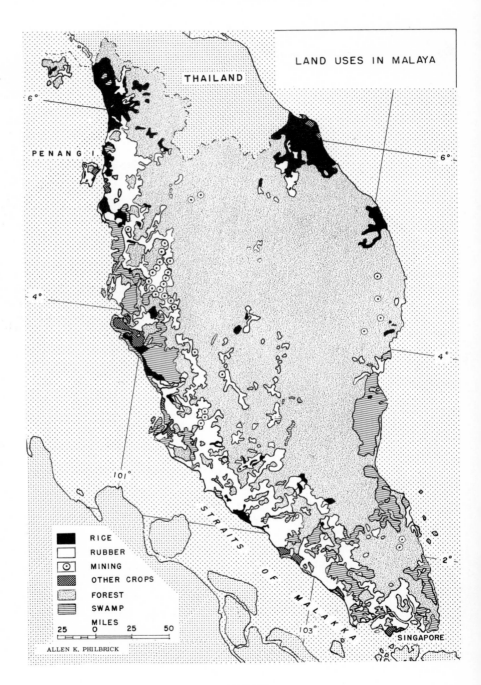

LAND USES IN MALAYA

THAILAND

PENANG I.

RICE
RUBBER
MINING
OTHER CROPS
FOREST
SWAMP
MILES
25   0   25   50

ALLEN K. PHILBRICK

STRAITS OF MALAKKA

SINGAPORE

MAP 20

than 17 per cent of the total cultivated acreage of 5,700,000 acres, but about one-fifth more than the rice acreage in 1939. Yields are low compared with those in Japan and China, but are, at 16 bushels to the acre, somewhat higher than in the rest of Southeast Asia. Total production in 1952 had risen substantially above the prewar figure to some 700,000 metric tons of rough rice (443,000 tons of cleaned rice at a milling recovery rate of 63 per cent), about 43 per cent of the gross consumption in Malaya as a whole. Rice, therefore, must be imported in large quantities —600,000 tons (in milled rice equivalents) in 1951, chiefly from Thailand —to feed the urban population of the country. The expansion of rice production forms a major part of British developmental planning. Although postwar emphasis on rice production has resulted in significant production gains, only 20 per cent of the wet-rice acreage is subjected to controlled irrigation, very little fertilizer is used, and double-cropping, which is permissible under prevailing temperatures, is seldom practiced.[6] Because as recently as 1941 non-Malays were not permitted to purchase paddy land, Chinese and Indians have not been wet-rice producers, and the shortage of Malay labor is an additional factor in weighing the possibilities for increased production. Much land remains avalable, particularly on the east coast, but the costs of reclaiming it seem prohibitively high. On the west coast relatively little suitable land remains available, since rubber competes with rice on well drained land, and the remaining peat soils also are costly to reclaim.

To the world at large, however, Malayan agriculture does not mean rice, but rubber (Figure 81). The coastal and piedmont zone of western Malaya, with a few outliers in the east, produces about 38 per cent of the world's rubber, and 65 per cent of Malaya's cultivated area is occupied by it. Stands of rubber trees appear in an almost continuous band in western Malaya from the island of Singapore itself northward to Penang. For a near-equatorial country rubber provides an excellent and remunerative crop which duplicates to some extent the natural vegetation cover, although the rubber tree (*Hevea brasiliensis*) is a native of Amazonia and was not introduced into Malaya until shortly before 1880. High continuous humidities with high even temperatures and abundant precipitation are demanded for optimum growth. Well drained lateritic soils, as found in the western Malayan foothills, provide a satisfactory foundation for the crop.

The growth of the rubber industry demanded the importation of a cheap labor supply. Thus, the present labor force on rubber plantations consists of some 300,000 workers, of whom over half are Indian and a quarter are Chinese. In recent years Malaysians have moved into this field and now account for about 20 per cent of the total labor force.

[6] The continual cloud cover and the frequently excessive precipitation also militate against double-cropping.

However, recent years have witnessed a marked shift from the domination of the Western-run or -operated estate to the smallholding of less than 100 acres, which is owned chiefly by Malaysians and Chinese and which often produces rubber in conjunction with food crops such as cassava, sweet potatoes, sago, bananas, and the like. In many ways these small-holdings represent a compromise between the largely subsistence, food-producing Malay agriculture and the basically foreign commercial agriculture of the estates. Of the total long tonnage of rubber produced in 1950, 693,000 tons, as compared with 544,000 tons in 1940—approximately 46 per cent—came from smallholdings; of the total acreage of 3,358,000 acres, 42 per cent were in smallholdings. The smallholder, who operates with little overhead and in relative independence of major market fluctuations, threatens the supremacy of the plantations, which, however, can be expected to maintain their control of the market for higher-grade rubber.

Fig. 81 • The rubber estate is characteristic of parts of the landscape in Malaya, Indonesia, peninsular Burma and Thailand, southern Vietnam, and Cambodia. Plantations of young trees like these are most common in Malaya, Sumatra, and Java. In Sumatra, where this picture is taken, tea may be planted beneath the trees as a second crop. Until their seventh year or later, when the trees begin to produce large quantities of latex, the forest floor is free of the paths that the tappers follow in making their rounds from tree to tree on an established course. In Malaya, the largest number of hired laborers are Indian. Chinese are next. Smallholdings both in Sumatra and Malaya have become increasingly important in recent years, and in Sumatra they produce considerably more rubber than is produced on the estates. Estate rubber in general is of higher quality than that from the smallholder, and yields from selected clones are higher, but the smallholder has the advantage of no overhead costs and the flexibility of a reversion to subsistence agriculture when rubber prices fall. *(Indonesian Information Office.)*

Coconut and oil palms also are important estate products, each accounting for some 100,000 acres. However, another 500,000 acres of coconut palms are estimated to be growing in small patches in and around Malay *kampong* in association with fruit trees and vines which, though not fully recorded statistically, provide a noteworthy addition to the food supply of the country. These smallholdings were the source of 75 per cent of the 150,000 long tons of copra produced in 1950 and of a substantial proportion of the 73,000 tons of coconut oil produced in that year. Over 50,000 tons of palm oil are produced from the estates, about the same as in the prewar period. Pineapples, a lesser estate crop, accounted for 60,000 acres in 1940, but only 28,000 in 1950. Johore is the main producer, and production is largely on smallholdings operated by Chinese. Tea, another plantation crop, is restricted to some 9,000 acres mostly in the uplands of the central range in the Cameron highlands southeast of Ipoh, where vegetables for the European markets in Singapore and the other large cities also are grown. Arecanut (or betel-nut) palms are produced on 55,000 acres, mostly in small lowland plantations or groves for both domestic consumption and export.

In addition to these two major forms of agriculture and their combinations, shifting agriculture, though outlawed by the English, has long been practiced by primitive hill tribes in the sparsely settled forested uplands. Moreover, during the war the practice was greatly expanded by some 500,000 Chinese who fled from the Japanese into the forest and carved out clearings upon which they raised vegetables and root crops, chickens and pigs. These squatters, many of whom settled on the margins of the great rubber estates, provided a nucleus for the unsettled rural conditions that have characterized Malaya since the end of the war. The British have attempted to remove this sore spot by resettling the squatters into "new villages," which provide residences for Chinese who work in rubber and other plantations and in mining. Each village has enough arable land so that it can become relatively self-sufficient in foodstuffs. The consequence in terms of rural occupance has been the introduction of nucleated Chinese settlements into what had been largely Malaysian or estate-occupied countrysides.

Singapore and the trade of Malaya

The value of Malaya's trade is greater than that of any other Southeast Asian country. The trade pattern, however, is divided into two separate but interrelated and overlapping parts: (1) the trade of the Federation itself, and (2) the trade of Singapore. The Federation pattern is the simpler of the two and concerns about 60 per cent of the total trade by value. It is characterized almost entirely by exports of rubber, tin, copra, and vegetable oils, and by the import of a lesser value of manufactures of great variety, with textiles prominent, and of foodstuffs. The direction of the export trade is in general toward the United States, Great Britain, and the other European countries, with a lesser export to Asian countries, especially India and Japan. The sources of imports are more varied: the European countries, the United States, and Japan supply the bulk of the manufactures; foodstuffs come from Hongkong (specialties for Malaya's Chinese) and Thailand (rice). About half of the Federation's trade moves through Singapore, the balance entering and clearing chiefly through Penang and Port Swettenham.

Of the total trade of Malaya (the Federation and Singapore) about one-third consists of entrepôt trade, that is, of commodities that are collected and then re-exported without entering the internal trade structure of the country. The entrepôt trade moves through the ports of Penang and Singapore, of which Singapore is overwhelmingly the more important. Singapore's trade, *both* entrepôt and direct, amounts to about 70 per cent of the *total* Malayan trade.[7] Thus, Singapore possesses two major trade functions: (1) to act as the major port for the Federation of Malaya, and (2) to act as an entrepôt for other countries and regions in Southeast Asia.[8]

[7] In other words, this 70 per cent is composed of about 30 per cent entrepôt trade, 30 per cent Federation trade, and the balance the trade of Singapore itself. These percentages are very rough estimates.

[8] "The entrepôt trade of Singapore is a question of economic not political geography. One glance at the map will show that Singapore is an obvious distributing and collecting center. The radius of the circle in the past varied very considerably. Political factors do arise, naturally, but these do not depend primarily on the political administration of our neighbours, but rather on their political stability. . . .

One might say that Singapore's traditional entrepôt trade is divided into three circles, of which the widest is the one in which we expect to operate only when the security and stability we offer is considerably greater than that of any neighboring administration, whereas the narrowest is the one we shall always keep. The same Malayan race lives on both sides of the Straits of Malacca and the same Chinese traders operate businesses both in Sumatran ports and in Singapore, while Dutch merchants, bankers, and shipping firms are firmly established without discrimination in Singapore . . . and the Straits dollar is the recognized currency of the Rhiouw Archipelago. This narrow-circle entrepôt trade we anticipate always keeping, unless either we ourselves adopt a suicidal restrictive control policy and virtually blockade ourselves or unless outside agents erect artificial barriers which make re-export trade impossible. . . .

The important middle circle is one which Singapore is making every endeavor to retain. Our free-port status means more than freedom from customs duties; it includes optional freedom from harbour dues, since vessels which choose not to go alongside the Harbour Board wharves pay nothing. The absence of any trade discrimination either against ships or traders also is important. . . . The greatest advantage, of course, is the simple geographic one, which makes us the obvious main store of consumer's goods from which all our neighbours in British Malaya, Thailand,

Singapore traditionally has offered a fine harbor with a free anchorage; a stable currency; a free-port organization; a highly developed commercial establishment of an international nature which is equipped to handle trade matters in any of the Oriental countries; political stability; and ethnic connections with the producers and traders within the realm.[9]

The more important commodities in the entrepôt trade are rubber, chiefly from Sumatra but also from Thailand, Borneo, and Burma;[10] tin from Bangka and Billiton, Thailand, and Indochina; vegetable oils and copra, from Indonesia especially; rice from Thailand; foodstuffs from Hongkong and China for the Chinese populations within the realm; timber from Borneo and Thailand; and petroleum from Sumatra and Borneo. Singapore itself and the Federation consume most of the imported rice and other foodstuffs, as well as some of the petroleum products, but most of the petroleum that is held in storage near Singapore and that is handled by shipping based on Singapore does not appear in Malayan trade statistics. Two of the three major storage depots in the area are in British territory, but do not issue records of their traffic; the other is in the Riouw archipelago, in Indonesian territory, and its traffic also is not reported.

The other aspect of the entrepôt trade consists of commodities from well outside the realm: textiles and both consumer and producers' goods from the West and from Japan, which are stocked in and distributed from Singapore. Unlike Hongkong, also an entrepôt, Singapore tends to emphasize the re-export of consumer rather than producers' goods, in order to attract raw materials into the colony and buttress its tenuous hold on regional trade.

Singapore possesses the best natural harbor and port facilities in Southeast Asia. Its chief competitors are Hongkong, Rangoon, Manila, and Tanjong Priok (Jakarta). However, Hongkong is strongly oriented towards China and also maintains a major trade with Singapore; Manila and Rangoon lie on the peripheries of the realm and tend not to compete in a broad entrepôt trade; and Tanjong Priok possesses none of the advantages of a free port and no financial and political stability. Although each of

---

Indochina, Indonesia, Borneo and Sarawak draw their supplies at short notice. Our chances of losing this middle circle rest mainly, not on political grounds but on high overhead handling and processing charges." Mr. Andrew Gilmour in Great Britain, Board of Trade, "Malaya," *Overseas Economic Surveys*. London: His Majesty's Stationery Office, 1952.

[9] Since the second World War, however, Singapore has maintained rigid currency controls and limits imports from hard-currency countries. Thus, Hongkong, Singapore's rival on the northern edge of the South China Sea, possesses a significant comparative trade advantage in its free money market, and the Philippines, a hard-currency country, have moved farther out of Singapore's orbit.

[10] As an example of the entrepôt trade, in 1950 Malaya exported 1,106,000 long tons of rubber, of which 449,000 tons had been imported, largely through Singapore and Penang.

these places has repair and maintenance facilities, Singapore has the advantage of a greater traffic, with concomitant demands for services and a correspondingly greater growth of them. Customarily, Singapore handles about five million tons of cargo and 24 million net registered tons of shipping. The latter figure is more than twice that of any competitive port other than Hongkong and is raised by the considerable number of ships that call twice, once on their outbound voyage from Europe to the Far East and once on their return voyage, and by trampers that are attracted by the vast amounts of goods accumulated in Singapore's godowns.

The port of Singapore [11] is divided into two main parts: the Harbour Board wharves, which charge a small fee (Figure 63), and the Roads, which are free, although lighterage fees are charged. Of the two, the latter part handles a far greater amount of shipping tonnage, but the wharves account for three-quarters of the recorded cargo movements. There are additional facilities for small craft which come from all around the Java Sea and from the Malayan and Sumatran coasts.[12]

The city of Singapore is located on the southeast shore of Singapore island, 26 miles in length and 14 in breadth, upon which live over a million persons. The city most closely resembles one of the southern Chinese treaty ports; three-fourths of the population is Chinese, but the remaining quarter is highly varied, with substantial Malay, Indian, Indonesian, and European minorities. Commerce and the port provide the major *raison d'être* of the city, but light and service industries have developed which employ almost 20 per cent of the working population. The industrial function centers about the processing of raw materials such as tin and copra, repair facilities for shipping, and the manufacturing of consumer goods such as carbonated beverages and beers,[13] cigarettes, soap, shoes, clothing, plastic ware, battery cells, rubber goods, glass, and the like. Bricks and tiles are produced in large quantities, but cement is imported. Singapore also is the site of the University of Malaya and acts as a sophisticated cultural center for the country. In terms of amenities, it is modern, and its water supply comes from across the mile-wide Johore Strait which separates it from the mainland, although emergency reservoirs are located on the island itself.

[11] The harbor lies on the south shore of Singapore Island and is protected from strong southerly and southwesterly winds by two small islands directly to the south.

[12] Since Singapore is a free port, except for a few commodities, trade records often are lacking. The cargoes handled in the Roads and in the native craft from other parts of Malaysia can only be estimated.

[13] A Singapore-brewed beer was judged the best beer in the British Commonwealth at the 1950 Brewers' Exhibition in London.

British Borneo

The British-controlled areas in Borneo—British North Borneo, Brunei, and Sarawak—are closely associated economically and (less closely) administratively with Malaya. Most of their trade moves through Singapore, though to a somewhat lesser degree now than in the past, and the British High Commissioner for Southeast Asia maintains general supervision over their affairs. North Borneo and Sarawak have been colonies since 1946, the latter having been a protected state under a British rajah, the former having been administered until that date by the British North Borneo Company. Brunei, the smallest of the three, after which Borneo was named, is a sultanate, but it is administered by the Sarawak Civil Service, which is responsible to the governor of Sarawak, who acts as Commissioner for Brunei and adviser to the sultan.

The 80,000 square miles of British Borneo rim the northern and northwestern margins of Borneo and account for about one-fourth of its total area. It is in many ways an archetype of an undeveloped region. Most of the population of about a million consists of interior forest dwellers engaged in hunting, fishing, and a primitive shifting agriculture. The coastal Malays, who formerly controlled most of the island of Borneo, are primarily fishermen and wet-rice cultivators. The second most numerous people next to the aborigines, however, are the Chinese, concentrated in the towns or on small holdings about them; through their hands a large part of the local commerce passes. On the fluvial lowlands where swamps have been drained, wet-rice is cultivated on some 100,000 acres (Figure 66) but none of the three territories is self-sufficient in rice, which forms one of the major imports. Rubber is the chief commercial crop on 380,000 acres, largely smallholdings, and exports to Singapore have been the second most important source of foreign exchange. Pepper is another growing agricultural export, largely in Chinese hands.

The chief significance of the area as a whole is its petroleum. In 1955, nearly 5.2 million tons of crude oil were produced,[14] largely from fields at Seria in the southwest corner of Brunei and secondarily from Miri in Sarawak to the southwest of Seria. Crude oil from the two fields is piped to a refinery with 38,000 barrels-per-day capacity in Sarawak at Lutong, the Brunei oil crossing an "international" boundary in the process. Miri is the chief port of export for crudes and refinery products, mostly for Singapore and to a lesser extent for Labuan. British Borneo has quintupled production since 1940 and seems destined to rival Sumatra in importance as the leading petroleum producer in the Orient.

[14] The conversion factor in use in Sarawak is 6.655 U.S. barrels to a metric ton of crude oil.

Fig. 82 • The interiors of the three countries in British Borneo remain little-developed wildernesses. Communications for the most part are by river craft such as the long sampan in this Sarawak photograph. Overland communications are limited to the coastal areas; even there they are segmented and short. Where trails cross sizable streams, bamboo bridges similar to the one shown are constructed by the tribal peoples, using rattan from the surrounding tropical rainforest as binding material. *(British Information Services.)*

The possibilities for balanced development of the area's resources, using proceeds from petroleum royalties and exports of rubber, copra, sago flour, and tropical hardwood forest timber and derivatives, have yet to be fully explored. Communications are poor (Figure 82); the beach along great stretches of the Sarawak coast is used as a highway at low and middle tide. Coastwise shipping has developed considerably, although port facilities as a whole are poor except at Jesselton, Sandakan, and Kuching. Labuan retains a long-term function as entrepôt for the Borneo coast. Air services to Hongkong, Malaya, and Indonesia also are regular and reliable from the major cities. Poor soils, fresh- and salt-water swamps, heavy cloud cover, and retarded technologies have severely impeded the development of agriculture, as in eastern Sumatra, but soil and geological surveys by means of aerial photography, especially in Sarawak, suggest that further enquiries into the developmental possibilities of the region may be well rewarded.

SELECTED GEOGRAPHICAL BIBLIOGRAPHY

1. Allen, D. F. *Report on the Major Ports of Malaya.* Kuala Lumpur: Government Printer, 1951.
2. Blaut, J. M. "The Economic Geography of a One-Acre Farm on Singapore Island," *Malayan Journal of Tropical Geography,* October, 1953.
3. Dobby, E. H. G. "Agricultural Questions of Malaya,"' *Malayan Questions* (pamphlet series). Cambridge: University Press, 1949.
4. ———. "North Kedah Plain," *Economic Geography,* October, 1951, pp. 287-315.
5. ———. "Settlement and Land Utilization, Malacca," *Geographical Journal,* December, 1939, pp. 466-78.
6. ———. "Settlement Patterns in Malaya," *Geographical Review,* April, 1942, pp. 211-32.
7. ———. "Singapore: Town and Country," *Geographical Review,* January, 1940, pp. 84-109.
8. ———, et alia. "Padi Landscapes in Malaya," *Malayan Journal of Tropical Geography,* October, 1955.
9. Firth, Raymond. *Malay Fishermen.* London: Kegan Paul, 1946.
10. Fisher, C. A. "The Railway Geography of Malaya," *Scottish Geographical Magazine,* December, 1948, pp. 123-36.
11. Fraser, J. M. "Town Planning and Housing in Singapore," *Town Planning Review,* January, 1953, pp. 5-25.
12. Ginsburg, N.S., and C. F. Roberts. *Malaya.* Seattle: University of Washington Press, 1957.
13. ———, ed. *Area Handbook of British Borneo.* Preliminary edition, Chicago: University of Chicago, Dept. of Geography, 1955.
14. Great Britain, Board of Trade. "Malaya," *Overseas Economic Surveys.* London: HMSO, 1952.
15. Harrisson, Tom. "Explorations in Central Borneo," *Geographical Journal,* October-December, 1949, pp. 129-50.
16. International Bank of Reconstruction and Development. *The Economic Development of Malaya.* Baltimore: Johns Hopkins University Press, 1955.
17. Lim, J. J. "Tradition and Peasant Agriculture in Malaya," *Malayan Journal of Tropical Geography,* October, 1954, pp. 44-47.
18. Ooi, Jin-bee. "Mining Landscapes of Malaya," *Malayan Journal of Tropical Geography,* January, 1955, pp. 1-58.
19. Roe, F. W. *Natural Resources of Sarawak.* Kuching: Government Printer, 1952.

Comments

Dobby is the recognized authority on the geography of Malaya, and his articles provide a major detailed addition to the discussion of Malaya in his *Southeast Asia*. Firth's book, together with articles not noted above, is the result of extended anthropological field work along the eastern Malayan coast. The British Board of Trade publication is a valuable storehouse of information about Malaya's economic conditions. The World Bank's report is a thorough economist's analysis of the Malayan economy, and the Ginsburg and Roberts volume is the most complete analysis of the organization of Malayan society in its broadest sense.

Information on Borneo is limited. The *Annual Reports* of the British Colonial Office on Brunei and North Borneo are the most useful official sources of information. The government of Sarawak also published an *Annual Report* in Kuching. Most available information is summarized in the handbook on British Borneo edited by Ginsburg.

An *Annual Report for the Colony of Singapore* also is issued by the Colonial Office, and certain government departments in Singapore publish special reports of their own. There is an *Annual Report for the Federation of Malaya* published in Kuala Lumpur. Monthly *Malayan Statistics* of a general and economic nature are published by the Government Printer in Singapore, and the December volumes are cumulative.

Thailand

THAILAND, OR SIAM, IS UNIQUE AMONG THE COUNTRIES OF SOUTH-
east Asia in at least one respect: it has not within modern times been
under the domination of a foreign power. In the struggle between France,
England, and Holland for control of Indochina, Burma, and the East Indian archipelago, Thailand acted as a buffer between conflicting interests,
particularly those of France and England, although its territory steadily
was cut into by the British in Burma and Malaya and the French in Cambodia and Laos.

The significance of this fact is illustrated by the course of resource development that has been pursued. Emphasis has been almost entirely on
non-estate agriculture. Rice, the main agricultural product, is even more
important than it is in Burma and in Indochina. The great rubber, tea,
coffee, sugar, tobacco, cinchona, coconut palm, oil palm, and other plantation units of Indonesia, Malaya, and the Philippines are conspicuous by
their absence, despite some rubber and coconut plantations in the south
and southeast, as is the European and American capital behind such enterprises in these other countries. Most of the capital in agricultural enterprises has been Thai; a substantial portion of it has been Chinese, usually
from Thai nationals of Chinese ancestry; little has been European.

As for nonagricultural development, the forests of the country have been exploited by Thai and by foreigners, but a government agency now accounts for a third of the gross production of teak, and miscellaneous forest production is solidly in Thai hands. In the exploitation of the alluvial tin deposits of the peninsula, however, European investment has been significant.

Thailand also lacks much of the veneer of industrialization that centers in most of its neighbors' major port cities. Thus, modern industrial output, even of consumer goods, is less in Thailand than in these other countries. However, the purpose of railway development there has been much the same as that in the rest of continental Southeast Asia: to consolidate the control of the governing authority and to open up sparsely settled regions to settlement and exploitation. On the other hand, the intent was not to impose foreign conditions upon a native population, but to strengthen the indigenous regime.

Siam was neglected by the West for many years partly because its known resources were seemingly of little consequence to the European powers, partly because these powers were occupied elsewhere, and partly because it lay so far off the beaten paths of commerce as they were developing in the latter half of the nineteenth century. Even today Thailand lies off the chief maritime trade routes intersecting at Singapore. Bangkok is situated almost 700 miles off the main shipping lane between Singapore and Hongkong. A vessel calling at these two ports en route to or from Europe is not likely to call at Bangkok; this was as true a hundred years ago as it is today. Also, the food and forest products of Thailand were known to be duplicated elsewhere, as in Burma, Malaya, and Indochina, and when estate agriculture began to develop in Southeast Asia, plenty of land was available for it without adding Thailand to the developmental area.

Natural resource endowment

Thailand's nonagricultural resources are clearly limited, according to the inadequate inventories that have been made. Tin, normally second or third among Siam's exports, is found in alluvium derived from the granite-cored mountains that form the backbone of peninsular Siam and of Malaya, with its important tin-mining industry, to the south. Siamese production in 1955 was about 11,-300 metric tons, 6 per cent of the world total, and about one-fifth of the Malayan production for that year. Other minerals are believed to be lacking; neither coal nor oil has been discovered in commercial quantities, although some lignite is available. Water-power potentials remain unknown. Among the metals, tungsten is produced in conjunction with tin, but none of the metals basic to modern industrialization (iron, manganese, aluminum, copper, zinc, lead, and the like) appears to be available in commercial quantities.

Perhaps 70 per cent of the country is under some kind of forest cover. Most of the forest may be classified as semideciduous monsoon forest, except in the Kra region (peninsular Siam) and in southeastern Siam, where tropical rainforest is more characteristic. There are some pine and moss forests in the higher mountains of the west and the northern border regions. Along the coasts, especially those of the southeast and of the peninsula, mangroves cover the tidal areas. In the northeast (the Korat region) the forest cover is composed of relatively slow-growing hardwoods, entirely deciduous, and rather widely spaced except where local water supply is unusually favorable. In places, the forest blends off into a kind of tropical savanna or thorny scrub, or it may cease abruptly at the margins of great barren flats, or *tung*, which are seasonally and alternately either flooded or parched. The central valley of the Menam Chao Phya, is largely under cultivation, although each village is associated with a grove of bamboo and mixed broadleaved evergreen and deciduous trees (Figure 2).

The mixed, semideciduous monsoon forest begins at the margins of the central plain and covers most of the northern and western parts of the country. This forest is generally composed of varieties of Dipterocarps (long-boled trees of magnificent aspect), teak, and bamboo with intermixtures of evergreens, the evergreens being most plentiful on the rainier mountain slopes. Thus the forest is by no means homogeneous in appearance; in the dry season especially it is characterized by patches of green scattered over a predominantly greyish, bare-branched background. Unlike the rainforest, there is no closed canopy, and thorn shrubs and grasses cover the forest floor. In the drier regions, as in the rain-shadow of the western mountain ranges, thorn and bamboo scrub forest predominates.

The bamboos, grasses, and shrubs are highly inflammable during the dry season, and periodic fires sweep the forests. The bamboos, certain of the Dipterocarps, and, above all, teak, possess seeds that are fire-resistant and act to maintain the identity of the forest types. Much of the forested area is secondary forest, therefore, if not because of these natural burnings, then because of the fires that provide the clearings necessary for the shifting agriculture practiced in the uplands. Solid stands of teak, some planted, are found throughout the northern forests and provided some 75,000 to 100,000 logs a year before the war when teak ranked fourth among Siam's exports. In almost all regions of the country the forests provide fuel not only for routine household purposes and for heating when necessary, but also for steam locomotives, mill machinery, and electric power plants, though other fuels may be used for each of these purposes

(Figure 83). The forests also provide a number of other products—rattan, gums and resins, cutch, torches, thatch, and the invaluable bamboo itself, the plant of a thousand uses.

Both the predominantly forest vegetation of Thailand and its agriculture are dependent upon the *topographic, climatic,* and *edaphic associations* that together comprise its physical geographic foundation.

It is difficult to say how much of Thailand's land surface (200,000 square miles) is in slopes too steep for normal agriculture, since no topographic survey of the country has been completed. Nevertheless, it appears that only 40 per cent of the land surface is in slopes of less than 15 degrees. About a quarter of the relatively level land is found in the great central valley of the Chao Phya, about a half is found in the northeast, and the balance is distributed in relatively small patches in northern, peninsular, and southeastern Thailand.

Fig. 83 • Wood is the chief fuel on the meter-gauge Thai railway system. Stacks of wood are here awaiting transfer to the tenders of the Japanese-built locomotives purchased from Japan in 1949-50. Some of the wood is of relatively high quality, but most consists of cuttings from second-growth stands that were not exploitable as timber. Nevertheless, the dependence of the country upon wood for fuel has resulted in notable inroads on its forest resources. To this end, the railway system is initiating the use of diesel locomotives, and the government is urging the use of lignite from northern Thailand in locomotives, thermoelectric plants, and tobacco drying sheds. The women along the track are refreshment vendors who sell through the windows of the cars. Note the omnipresent homeless dogs. *(Norton Ginsburg.)*

The central valley is surrounded on three sides by mountains. To the west are a series of old mountain ranges, rising to altitudes of 7,000 feet and formed largely of granitic intrusives rimmed by upturned limestones and shales. These north-south ranges form the border between southern Burma and Thailand and trend southward into the Kra region and Malaya. To the north is a high dissected plateau, an extension of the Shan plateau of Burma, which is composed also of meridionally trending ridges of ancient granite and complexes of shales, schists, and limestones. To the east are low mountains reaching to 3,000 feet which rim the Korat plateau on its west and south, and in the southeast is an extension of the Cardamom mountains of southwestern Cambodia, which rise well over 3,000 feet and extend almost into the sea.

Northeastern Thailand covers about a third of the country and contains about half of the land *topographically* suitable for agriculture. It consists of a low platform topped with horizontally bedded sandstones and clays, with some limestone in the west, which slopes gently eastward at no great height toward the Mekong River, boundary for much of eastern Thailand. However, less than 7 per cent of the total area is in cultivation since most of the sandy soils are infertile if not sterile, and much of the region is characterized by water shortages.

The central trough or valley of Thailand is the true heartland of the kingdom, and within it is well over half of the total cultivated land of the country. The valley is that of the main river of Siam, the Menam Chao Phya, known simply as the Menam, which means The River. The Menam is formed by the confluence of several lesser streams which flow southward from the uplands of the north and join finally just south of latitude 16°N. Above that point the valley extends northward another degree or so. Through this northern sector flow the several streams that contribute to the Menam, separated from each other by rolling interfluves which in the east are of some height.

The near-level southern part of the valley, or Lower Siam, below the confluence at 16 degrees, is of greater significance to the country than the upper valley. Almost all of the region, some 12,000 square miles, is subject to flooding as the Menam and its several distributaries rise in the spring (Map 21). The average depth of flooding ranges between one and five feet, but in about 30 per cent of the region flooding occurs only when flood level is inordinately high; in almost 40 per cent of the region, chiefly in the depressions that parallel the natural levees of the main streams, flooding occurs normally to a depth of ten to 13 feet and deeper when floods are higher. Most of the region's soils are deep clays enriched with silt from the floodwaters of the rivers and canals that criss-cross the plain.

Thailand is characterized by frost-free conditions and warm-to-hot

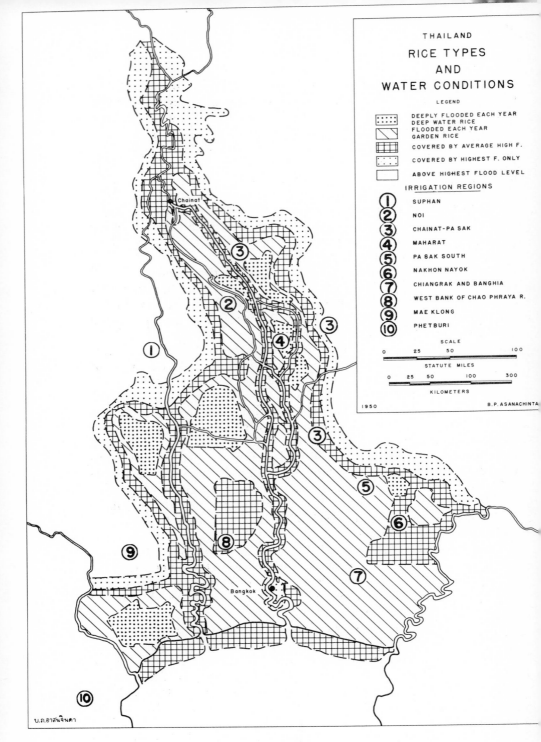

THAILAND

RICE TYPES
AND
WATER CONDITIONS

LEGEND

DEEPLY FLOODED EACH YEAR
DEEP WATER RICE
FLOODED EACH YEAR
GARDEN RICE
COVERED BY AVERAGE HIGH F.
COVERED BY HIGHEST F. ONLY
ABOVE HIGHEST FLOOD LEVEL

IRRIGATION REGIONS

1 SUPHAN
2 NOI
3 CHAINAT-PA SAK
4 MAHARAT
5 PA SAK SOUTH
6 NAKHON NAYOK
7 CHIANGRAK AND BANGHIA
8 WEST BANK OF CHAO PHRAYA R.
9 MAE KLONG
10 PHETBURI

SCALE

0   25   50   100
STATUTE MILES

0 25 50   100   300
KILOMETERS

1950   B.P. ASANACHINTA

Chainat

Bangkok

บ.ภ.อาสนจินดา

MAP 21

396

weather the year round, and by a dry winter and rainy summer. Most of the country receives 40 to 60 inches of rainfall annually, largely between May and October. The annual precipitation at Bangkok is 55 inches; at Chiengmai in the far north, 46 inches. However, the amount of precipitation varies greatly with relief; the higher western and northern mountains, the mountains of southeastern Thailand, and the edges of the Korat plateau receive more than 120 inches. The areas in the rain-shadows of these barriers receive as little as 30 inches. Rainfall is associated with the prevailing winds which in turn reflect the monsoon-influenced climate of Southeast Asia. At Bangkok, wind direction in·January is predominantly from the north and northeast; in July it is overwhelmingly from the southwest and south in association with the southwest monsoon. The general pattern, therefore, is one of a relatively dry zone surrounded by rain-catching slopes and protected by these barriers from the occasional weak cyclones or violent typhoons off the South China Sea that might otherwise alter the rainfall regimen.

Almost all of peninsular Thailand, however, receives rainfall of over 80 inches, rather better distributed throughout the year than in the north. The west coast receives more rainfall than the east. The rainy period on the west coast coincides with that in the rest of the country, but that on the east coast occurs in the late fall and early winter, when the northeast monsoon winds, having crossed the Gulf of Thailand, drop their newly acquired moisture orographically.

Most of the country is affected by extreme annual variations in rainfall. Over a 30-year period there occurred in central Thailand three years of severe drought, nine years of superabundant rainfall, and only 18 years of near-normal rainfall. The effects upon agriculture directly and, through varying flood levels, indirectly are considerable during deviant years. The Chao Phya with its numerous tributaries customarily has only one period of flood, and this tends to come on gradually. In the northeast, however, where the effect of typhoons from the South China Sea is felt and where the river systems tap a less extensive drainage hinterland, more than one flooding often occurs. Equally significant are seasonal variations in stream flow. In many cases the lesser streams dry up completely during the dry season, and even the larger rivers, with the exception of the Chao Phya itself, bare their sandy bottoms and braid their channels through bars of shifting silt and sand. With the onset of the rains the smaller streams, like the gulches and arroyos of the American West, fill rapidly with water and cause local floods, which take their toll of soil and property.

In general the soils of Thailand are not fertile. The soils of the northeast, formed residually over sandstones, are thin, laterized, sandy, and of low productivity, except in scattered depressions and parts of the valleys of the Mun and Chi rivers. In the north, soils are generally thin, except

in the fertile river basins of the rivers that later join to form the Chao
Phya. In peninsular and southeastern Thailand, soils are either thin slope
soils or heavy lateritic clays of indifferent fertility. Erosion usually is a
serious problem and often causes excessive silting of canals in the lowlands. Yet, as Pendleton points out, in much of the northeast too little
surface erosion may take place, and the soils, formed *in situ,* are leached
of their plant nutrients which then lie too far below the surface for most
cultivated plants to make use of them. The largest area of fertile soils is
in the central valley, especially in Lower Siam, its southern portion, for
here the soils are young, are little leached, and are renewed each year
with alluvial silts spread by the floodwaters of the Chao Phya system.

Agriculture and land utilization

Thailand is rare among the
countries of Asia; it produces more food than it consumes. As one of a
trinity with Burma and Indochina, it shared a virtual monopoly of the
world's prewar export trade in rice.

Agriculture in Thailand is overwhelmingly associated with rice cultivation. Only about 11 per cent of the total land surface of the country (14
million acres) is cultivated, but 92 per cent of the cultivated area is in rice
(Map 22). About half of the cultivated land is localized in Lower Siam,
where alluvial soils are most extensive and where the floodwaters of the
Menam provide water for irrigating the fields and fertile silt for maintaining soil fertility. The major rice region is that part of the lower plain
that is flooded every year, except under conditions of major drought. In
addition, there are considerable areas, which are flooded to much greater
depths, where so-called "floating" rice is cultivated. In these latter areas
the rice is sown broadcast after the first spring rains and then grows at a
pace approximating that of the rise in river level until the stalks reach
over 12 feet, more than the flood depth. In some parts of the plain flooding occurs only at times of highest flood; here there is a larger quantity of
land not under cultivation, although water is often pumped from canals
or distributaries onto the paddy fields. About three quarters of the lower
plain is under cultivation at any one time; the remaining quarter is occupied by other land uses, or is too high above flood level to be easily irrigated, or is possessed of soils unusually poor.

The most common cultivating procedure for wet-rice [1] is to begin
plowing, using water buffaloes as motive power, shortly after the beginning of the spring rains when the hard-baked soil begins to soften. Mean-

[1] In Thailand, normal wet-rice, as contrasted with floating rice, is known as
"garden" rice.

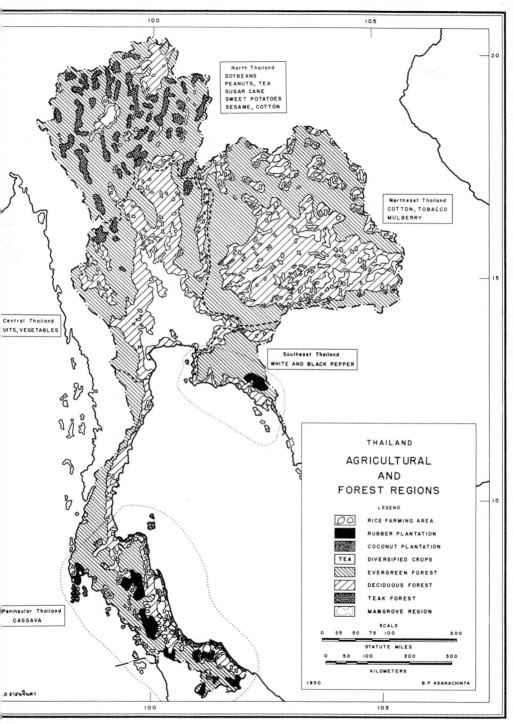

North Thailand
SOYBEANS
PEANUTS, TEA
SUGAR CANE
SWEET POTATOES
SESAME, COTTON

Northeast Thailand
COTTON, TOBACCO
MULBERRY

Central Thailand
UITS, VEGETABLES

Southeast Thailand
WHITE AND BLACK PEPPER

Peninsular Thailand
CASSAVA

THAILAND

AGRICULTURAL
AND
FOREST REGIONS

LEGEND

	RICE FARMING AREA
	RUBBER PLANTATION
	COCONUT PLANTATION
TEA	DIVERSIFIED CROPS
	EVERGREEN FOREST
	DECIDUOUS FOREST
	TEAK FOREST
	MANGROVE REGION

SCALE

0   25   50   75   100   200

STATUTE MILES

0   50   100   200   300

KILOMETERS

1950   B.P. ASANACHINTA

ภ.อาสนจินดา

MAP 22

399

Fig. 84 • In areas where drainage is poor and the paddy fields cannot be drained before the harvest, or when late rains flood the fields immediately before the harvest, the wet, lodged grain is hurriedly gathered, dried in the sun, and threshed. Late rains and floods throughout rice-growing Asia cause substantial damage to rice crops every year, and excessive moisture late in the growing season tends to reduce yields in any case. The tree groves in the background hide a road and settlement surrounded by palms and fruit trees. *(Konrad Kingshill.)*

while, rice is planted in small nursery beds and carefully tended for about a month. The young rice plants then are trimmed and transplanted to the paddy fields, which by then have been plowed and puddled several times until the soil has a mushy consistency and have been flooded to a depth of several inches. Fertilizers are seldom used except in the nursery bed. The rice is harvested by hand in late fall after the flood waters have gone down, and the field stubble is grazed over by water buffaloes and cattle during the dry season (Figures 84 and 85).

Since few parts of Thailand receive enough rainfall to permit wet-rice cultivation without irrigation of some sort, the agricultural calendar is geared closely to the availability of river water, especially in the central valley. When the Menam and its tributaries rise to abnormally high flood levels, large areas are inundated to too great a depth for normal rice to grow; when the rivers do not rise far enough, considerable areas of productive land produce small crops, or none at all. At lower water, various pumping devices, manually operated water-scoops or foot-operated "dragon-bone" pumps, are used to bring water to the fields. Only 13 per cent of the total cultivated area of the country is watered by modern, controlled-irrigation facilities, and most of these are in the northeastern part of Lower Siam, the Rangsit area, where a complex system of canals, distributaries, locks, and weirs has been constructed.

Where water for irrigation is particularly uncertain or frequently super-abundant, as in the "floating" rice areas, or where labor is especially short, rice may be sown broadcast on puddled fields at the time of the early rains, which are then flooded on a catch-as-catch-can basis. In the northeast, most of the rice is transplanted, but yields are lower on the whole than in the central valley, and the variations in water supply are much greater. The northeastern farmer, however, raises a different kind of rice than his equivalent elsewhere—glutinous rice—which is especially suited for rice confections and pastries, is better liked by the local consumer, and brings high prices on the domestic market. Considerable rice in the northeast also is upland rice, which is raised on dry fields and of which the yields generally are substantially lower than those of irrigated rice. In the south and southeast, where relatively little land is under cultivation but where rainfall is quite high, wet-rice is raised on paddy fields that are irrigated by rainfall alone.

In most of Thailand the standard farm unit is small, averaging three to four acres; but larger units are characteristic of Lower Siam, which averages 11 acres per farm and, despite its overwhelming importance in the national economy, is the most recently developed rice region in the coun-

Fig. 85 • During the extensive Siamese dry season, occurring for most of the country between October and April, fields are in fallow, except in areas where controlled irrigation facilities are available. The paddy-field stubble is grazed over by cattle and water buffalo, each of which is accompanied by its buffalo birds which maintain a symbiotic relationship with the animals, eating insects that infest their hides and keeping flies away. The manure from the animals as they graze is usually the only fertilizer that the fields receive during the year. In some cases the animals will be tethered to a tall, flexible bamboo pole, which limits their grazing (and their droppings) to one field at a time. (Norton Ginsburg.)

try, having doubled its cultivated acreage since 1930. In the controlled irrigated northeastern region of Lower Siam, large estates, hundreds of acres in size and owned by absentee landlords, are divided into operating units of up to 40 acres. These are cultivated by tenants on a yearly basis, most of them insecure, propertyless and rightless, and in considerable debt. The tenancy problem, with its ramifications of political and social unrest and deleterious effect on per-unit-area productivity, is restricted largely to the central valley. In the uplands, permanently cultivated fields are not common, and shifting cultivation characteristically occupies some half a million acres each year.

Among the more significant features of Thai agriculture, then, are these:

(1) The monocultivation of rice is most characteristic. Rice is the chief article in the diet and is raised everywhere, although the major producing area is in Lower Siam. Rubber occupies about 300,000 acres in peninsular Siam, and exports of 50,000 tons a year, moving down to Penang and Singapore, rank rubber second among Thailand's exports. Coconuts are important, and tobacco, cotton, sugar cane, sweet potatoes, mulberry, cassava, sesame, peanuts, soybeans, and tea also occupy significant acreages.

(2) Rice cultivation is largely on a commercial and export basis, especially in Lower Siam. Out of a total harvest of almost 3 million metric tons before the war, up to 2 million metric tons were exported.[2] The normal postwar export tonnage, however, from a 40 per cent larger acreage, has been between 1 and 2 million tons.

(3) The major agricultural areas of the country do not normally have sufficient rainfall to permit wet-rice cultivation, and water is obtained from the natural flooding of paddy fields by the rivers. Only a small percentage of the land possesses controlled-irrigation facilities, and the harvests vary as nature varies.

(4) Rice yields normally are low,[3] but, more important, in the past decades yields per unit area have remained stagnant or even have declined. The increases in total production, which have resulted in a doubling of output during this period, have depended upon a rapid expansion of paddy acreage.

(5) Fertilizers are little utilized. Soil fertility is maintained primarily by the addition of mineral and humus-bearing silts carried in suspenson by irrigation water, which thereby serves two purposes—irrigation and fertilization. Additional fertilizer is obtained from the manure of water buffaloes and cattle, which graze through the dry season on the field stubble. Nightsoil, however, is little used.

(6) Although the climate is frost-free, little double-cropping of rice or of rice and other crops is practiced. The key factors here are the availability of water and soil fertility. Only in parts of the northern intermon-

[2] In terms of cleaned rice.
[3] In 1952, about 1,150 pounds per acre. Compare with Japan's 3,680 pounds.

tane basins, such as that of the Ping River about Chiengmai, is there sufficient water available during the dry season for the irrigation of a second crop of rice. Here also a first crop of rice may be rotated with peanuts or soy beans as second crops. In the vicinity of Bangkok, Chinese truck gardeners raise two or more crops of vegetables on soil enriched by nightsoil from the city and with water brought laboriously from the main canals.

(7) Finally, as in the rest of Southeast Asia, animals play a major role in the agricultural structure, but primarily as draft animals rather than as a source of food. However, in the northeast, cattle provide a major source of cash income, as do swine and poultry, and all are shipped to the central market at Bangkok. But even in the northeast, cattle raising is auxiliary to crop raising. In the central plain duck farms are a common riverside occupance unit.

Population and settlement

Thailand, with an estimated population in 1955 of about 20.3 millions and a gross density of over 90 per square mile, may well be considered underpopulated in relation to the much higher densities in Java, the Philippines, eastern China, Japan, and most of the western European countries. Nevertheless, the population has been increasing at an extremely rapid rate and has exhibited a 100 per cent increase since 1920.

The distribution of population shows that the greatest densities are in Lower Siam, where the average approximates 250 per square mile and where individual rural areas may have densities of over 1,000 per square mile. At the other extreme, a province in the far northwestern part of the country has a density of only 11 per square mile. Over one-third of the population is in the central part of the country; another third is in the northeast; and the larger part of the remainder resides in the valleys of the north. The large population in the northeast seems to be an anomaly, since livelihood opportunities in that part of the country are less favorable than those in the central heartland. Indeed, it is customary for the Korat farmer not only to export his cattle as draft animals and his pigs as food for the people in the plain, but also for him to seek employment in the central region during the planting and harvesting periods. Furthermore, as Dobby has pointed out, the pressure of population on cultivated land seems to be much greater in northern, northeastern, and southeastern Siam than in the central valley. The explanation is by no means clear, but appears to be twofold: (1) land that is under shifting cultivation is not recorded as cultivated land and is most common in the peripheral regions of the country, thus suggesting that pressures may be less than the data indicate; and (2) large minorities of non-Thai peoples live in these areas and despite considerable hardship cannot or will not attempt to make a living in the central valley.

Nutritionally, the Thai depend heavily on rice, to the extent of about 70 per cent of their daily caloric intake. The balance of their diet, which like most in Southeast Asia is low in fats and animal protein, is acquired through spicy sauces of shrimp and fish paste and peppers, accompanied by vegetables and occasionally fish or meat. Fishing is an important auxiliary industry, and in 1954, 250,000 metric tons of seafood were produced. Most are salt water in origin, but about a quarter come from freshwater streams and swamps and from flooded paddy lands during the wet season. Since the bulk of the population is Buddhist and cattle are valued most highly as draft animals, meat is not a prominent article in the diet, and even fish food may be regarded with some aversion. The greater numbers of the swine that enter the Bangkok market from Korat and elsewhere are destined for consumption by the Chinese in Bangkok and by the more westernized Thai. Although the average diet is low and ill-balanced by Western standards, it is above the Southeast Asian average, and there is no indication of a food shortage in the near future.

Despite the minorities referred to above, Thailand is conspicuous in Southeast Asia for its relative ethnic homogeneity. The Thai themselves—divided into the Central, Northern, Southern, and Eastern Thai, who possess basically the same language and culture—acount for about 85 per cent of the total population. Ethnic minorities of Karens in the north, Khmer (Cambodians) in the east, and Malays in the south are significant, and there are lesser hill peoples in all the mountain areas.

The most important minority are the Chinese, estimated to number 2,500,000, but intermarriage between Chinese and Thai has been so great that it is impossible to trace clearly the ancestral blending of the two peoples. Many of the Chinese live in Bangkok, which is remarkably Chinese in appearance, but every town of size, and even most of little size, has Chinese shopkeepers or traders. The Chinese are the businessmen of Thailand and have virtually controlled the largest industry, rice milling (Figure 62). They also have been the major rubber producers in the Kra region and possess major interests in tin mining. As entrepreneurs and aliens, the Chinese have incurred the overwhelming dislike of the Thai, and the Siamese government has attempted to break the Chinese control of rice milling by regulating prices and establishing competitive government mills.

Settlements in Thailand are highly localized along streams and canals, over which a large proportion of traffic moves during the rainy season and in the central valley all year round (Figure 65). Bangkok is without challenge as the largest city in the country and is the political, economic, and cultural capital. It is a relatively modern city, built largely in a Western and south Chinese manner, with a population estimated at just one million; its canals, flowing to and from the Chao Phya on the banks of which it lies, carry much of the traffic of the city (Figure 86). The older cultural centers of the kingdom, however, lie to the north, at Ayuthia and farther

Fig. 86 • Water taxis on the Menam at Bangkok. Although the river is crossed at the city by one large bridge, much transfer of goods and passengers takes place by water taxi. These are workers, most of them white-collar workers in businesses or government offices, on their way home; a kind of "rush hour" scene. The river is less than a quarter of a mile wide at this point, and gives the impression of being a much less significant stream than it actually is. A river steamer is anchored in midstream. In the background is a former military barracks, now used as part of the state University of Moral and Political Science. *(Norton Ginsburg.)*

at Chiengmai, somewhat neglected witnesses to the march of Thailand's development southward into the flooded delta country of Lower Siam. Rural settlements rise out of the paddy fields like islands in the sea during the rainy season or like tree-fringed oases in the dry season (Figures 2 and 87). Houses resemble those in Malaysia in that they are generally elevated on log stilts as protection against floods, animals, and marauders and so that smudge fires against mosquitoes can be built under the matting floor. Bamboo and thatch are the most important building materials, except for the numerous and beautiful *wat* or temples, with their soaring rooftrees and eaves, which are built more substantially of stone, brick, stucco over wood, or more rarely of quarried laterite.

The centers of population in Lower Siam, in the northern valleys, in the northeastern river lowlands and basins, and along the southern coastal plain are connected by an efficient railway system which centers upon Bangkok. All lines, 5,236 miles of them, are meter gauge, equipment is increasingly Japanese, and the major fuel still is wood, although some Swiss diesels are in service. Only two of the lines reach international boundaries: the southern line, which bifurcates north of the border and joins with the Malayan railway system on both the east and west coasts,[4] and the eastern line, which crosses into Cambodia and terminates at Pnom Penh. A railway to Moulmein, constructed by the Japanese with Allied prisoner-of-war labor, has fallen into disuse, and is unlikely to be rebuilt.

[4] The southern line was designed primarily to link Malayan-populated south peninsular Siam to Bangkok. In fact, however, it also serves to link peninsular Siam more closely with the Malayan entrepôts.

Fig. 87 • On the edge of a village in northern Thailand, within the Chiengmai basin. The stilted houses of the villagers are buried among the tall *yang* trees, coconut palms, and other fruit trees behind the woven bamboo fencing on the right. Banana trees also grow luxuriantly within the compound. The pond is artificial, resulting from a small log dam barely visible at the right. Since this is the dry season, the pond waters are shallow, and the children play in them and in the dammed stream which parallels the short dirt road into the background. The pond may also be used for fish-raising. The shaded coolness of the compound is in marked contrast to the intense heat over the parched fields without (See Fig. 82). *(Norton Ginsburg.)*

Competition against the railways is chiefly from the waterways of central Siam, down which most paddy moves after the harvest, and teak logs often travel for years at a single voyage. Short-run passenger traffic also moves by water, but there is little competition from highways, since the Thai road system remains underdeveloped despite recent and rapid construction. A government airline serves all of the major towns, and international services touching at Bangkok have made that city's airport the fulcrum of the Europe-Orient-Australia air-traffic region.

Industry, trade, and development

Agriculture is the economic mainstay of Thailand. Nonagricultural industry is as yet of minor significance in the country, although light industries producing consumer goods on the one hand and service industries such as the railways on the other indicate possible courses for immediate industrial expansion. The trade pattern is characteristic of a nonindustrialized region, with foodstuffs and raw materials moving outward and manufactures moving inward. Exports of rice account for half of the total exports by value, rubber for about 20 per cent when world demand is high, and teak and tin together for about 10 per cent. Exports are oriented to an outstanding degree toward other areas in Asia, in part because Singapore, Indonesia, the Philippines, China, Hongkong, and Japan are major importers of rice; in part because most of Thailand's tin and rubber finds its way either to Singapore or to Penang, although since the war the United States has appeared as a major trade figure. Just as Singapore acts as entrepôt for Thai goods to Southeast Asian countries, Hongkong serves the same function for the East Asian countries, although both cities are major consumers of Thai exports in their own right.

Imports, consistently lower in value than exports, are extremely varied and include, in addition to textiles and a host of manufactures, specialized foodstuffs for the Bangkok market. Here again, Singapore and Hongkong, as the two major entrepôts, dominate the import trade, with Great Britain and the United States playing lesser but important roles. Japan, formerly a major supplier of Thai imports, is only gradually assuming prominence on the postwar scene.

International trade is largely by sea, primarily through the port of Bangkok, which in 1951 became accessible to deep-water vessels, although most larger ships still anchor in the lee of a small island (Kao-hsi-kang) in the Bight of Bangkok and unload their cargoes by means of lighters and junks.

The facts of resources, trade, and population indicate clearly the necessity for two courses of development in Thailand: (1) toward a rapid increase of agricultural production, and (2) toward a general diversification of the nation's economic base.

The aim of *increasing agricultural production* is to keep pace with, and if possible exceed, the rises in internal consumption of foodstuffs occasioned by a rapidly increasing population and a rising level of living. It aims also at maintaining, and if possible increasing, the volume of agricultural exports which are to a large extent financing the economy. Continuing world food shortages, though unfortunate in other respects, would act as a stimulus to Thailand to increase its volume of rice exports.

Plans for increasing production thus far center about improving the control of water resources; projects under construction or planned for Lower Siam anticipate the controlled irrigation of 3,500,000 acres or 60 per cent of the present cultivated acreage. Improvement in water control should permit double-cropping over much of the area and a marked rise in gross production. Further increases in production must come from increases in the per-unit-area productivity of agriculture, which is low. Fertilizers, improved cultivation techniques, better-quality seeds, all fit into a standard developmental pattern, as does the supplying of motivation for increased investment and production through the supplying of security, land reform, credit, and marketing facilities. Mechanized rice cultivation is a possibility on the level stretches of the delta, but technological, financial, and social aspects of mechanization have only recently come under examination.

The *diversification of the economic base* means (1) the diversification of agricultural production itself, (2) the increased exploitation of non-agricultural resources, and (3) industrialization.

The first of these will be of relatively low priority so long as rice retains its dominant place in domestic food-consumption patterns and so long as a major market exists abroad. Inertia along present commodity lines is also encouraged by the fact that other Thai agricultural products, rubber for example, can be and are produced elsewhere just as cheaply in the face of a possibly stagnating world market.

The second offers possibilities in that forest resources can well be utilized more efficiently, and mineral resources such as tin can be exploited more intensively. However, as noted at the beginning of this chapter, Thailand's nonagricultural resource base is singularly limited, and the prospects for major increases in the production of nonagricultural raw materials, other than forest products, are few.

The third is perhaps the most significant, although Thailand cannot expect to enter upon a program of heavy industrial development on a base lacking sorely in mineral fuels and basic metal ores. However, seasonal, if not perennial, underemployment is the rule in the country, and capital is available if it can be deflected into productive investment rather than religious edifices and consumption goods. This, of course, is the problem of most lesser-developed regions of Asia, for which Japan tends to stand out as an example of what can be done. Whether her experience can be transferred to the Southeast Asian realm is a question of unparalleled importance.

SELECTED GEOGRAPHICAL BIBLIOGRAPHY

1. Credner, W. *Das Land Der Tai*. Stuttgart: J. Engelhorns, 1935.
2. deYoung, J. E. *Village Life in Modern Thailand*. Berkeley: University of California Press, 1955.
3. Fisher, C. A. "The Thailand-Burma Railway," *Economic Geography*, April, 1947, pp. 85-97.
4. Food and Agriculture Organization of the United Nations. *Report of the FAO Mission for Siam*. Washington: 1948.
5. Pendleton, R. L. "Land Use in Northeastern Thailand," *Geographical Review*, January, 1943, pp. 15-41.
6. ———. "The Agriculture of Siam," *Foreign Agriculture*, November, 1946, pp. 154-67.
7. Thompson, V. *Thailand: The New Siam*. New York: Macmillan, 1941.
8 U. S. Army Service Forces. *Civil Affairs Handbook: Thailand*. Washington: 1944.
9. Zimmerman, C. C. "Some Phases of Land Utilization in Siam," *Geographical Review*, July, 1937, pp. 378-93.

Comments

Credner's German-language volume is the most complete and authoritative work on Thailand as a whole, although somewhat dated for the postwar world. However, no major postwar studies have appeared to replace it. Pendleton also has published several monographs in Thai government journals, but these generally are not available in the United States. His prewar study on northeastern Thailand provides excellent insights, however, into the social and economic geography of the country as a whole. One valuable postwar study is that of deYoung on a northern Thailand village, but it should not be regarded as covering village life in all of Thailand. In addition, the Army Service Forces Manuals, which are available in many universities about the country, contain a wealth of data about Thailand, all prewar.

The FAO report deals directly with agricultural problems on the basis of postwar surveys and contains much useful information. The bulk of the report, however, consists of discussions of detailed recommendations for developing Siamese agriculture.

The basic Thai government statistical report is the *Statistical Yearbook, Thailand*. As of early 1957 the latest issue is 1939/40-1944, published, however, in 1951. Trade statistics are found in the *Annual Statement of the Foreign Trade and Navigation of the Kingdom of Thailand*. In addition, there are published the *Current Statistics* of the Bank of Thailand, but these are generally not available in the United States.

Indochina

THE TWO VIET, CAMBODIA, AND LAOS

BETWEEN 1862 AND 1907 FRANCE CARVED OUT OF THE EASTERN portion of the Indochinese peninsula the largest unit of its Asian empire. From the first, French Indochina, as it was called until after the close of the second World War, consisted of a series of loosely integrated political-economic units displaying a conspicuous physical, ethnic, and economic diversity. The centrifugal forces associated with this diversity were greatly strengthened by the Japanese occupation (which came into being after the fall of France to Germany in the spring of 1940) and by the rise of rampant nationalisms, especially among the majority ethnic group in Indochina, the Annamese or Vietnamese.[1] Under these pressures France was unable to maintain her hegemony over Indochina, and after the war granted partial autonomy to the three major units within the area—Vietnam, Cambodia, and Laos. By 1954 these states acquired their independence from France and joined the long list of former colonial territories that had become free in the decade after 1945. The defeat of the French in 1954 by the Viet Minh, a communist-dominated nationalist party in northern Indochina, resulted in the division of Vietnam into two parts,

[1] The term *Annamese* will be used in this chapter for the majority ethnic group in eastern Indochina. These also are known as *Vietnamese* and as *Annamites*.

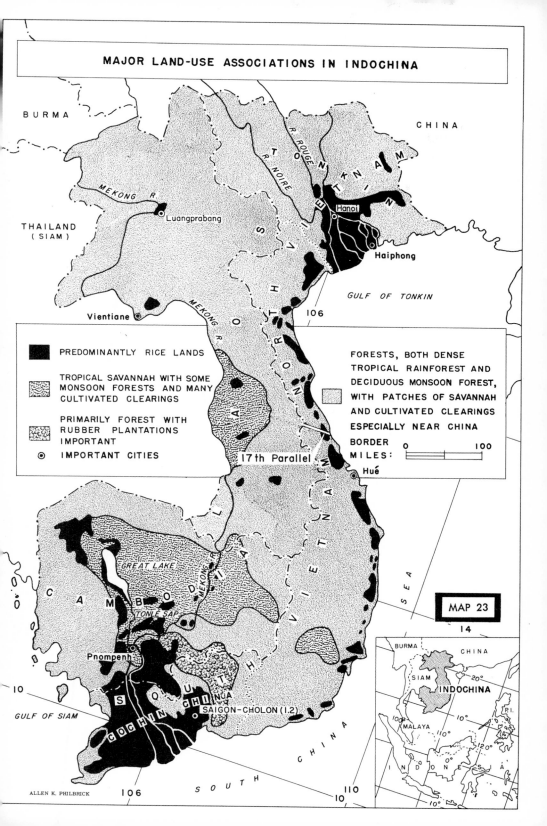

MAJOR LAND-USE ASSOCIATIONS IN INDOCHINA

BURMA

CHINA

THAILAND
(SIAM)

MEKONG R.

Luangprabang

R. NOIRE

R. ROUGE

TONKIN

VIETNAM

Hanoi

Haiphong

GULF OF TONKIN

Vientiane

MEKONG R.

106

NORTH

LAOS

VIETNAM

17th Parallel

Hué

PREDOMINANTLY RICE LANDS

TROPICAL SAVANNAH WITH SOME
MONSOON FORESTS AND MANY
CULTIVATED CLEARINGS

PRIMARILY FOREST WITH
RUBBER PLANTATIONS
IMPORTANT

⊙ IMPORTANT CITIES

FORESTS, BOTH DENSE
TROPICAL RAINFOREST AND
DECIDUOUS MONSOON FOREST,
WITH PATCHES OF SAVANNAH
AND CULTIVATED CLEARINGS
ESPECIALLY NEAR CHINA
BORDER
MILES: 0   100

GREAT LAKE

CAMBODIA

MEKONG R.

TONLE SAP

SOUTH

VIETNAM

SEA

MAP 23

14

Pnompenh

COCHIN   CHINA

SAIGON-CHOLON (1.2)

10

GULF OF SIAM

106

SOUTH   CHINA

110

10

BURMA   CHINA

SIAM   20°

INDOCHINA

10°

100°   110°

MALAYA   P.I.

120°

I N D O N E S I A

10°

ALLEN K. PHILBRICK

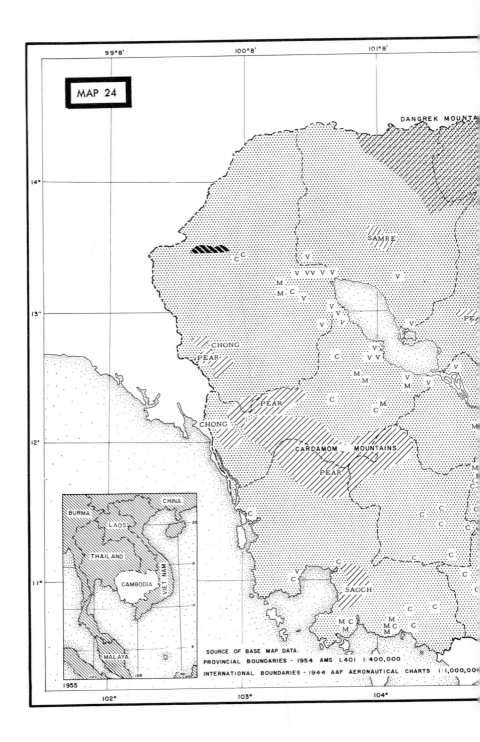

MAP 24

99°8'   100°8'   101°8'

DANGREK MOUNTA

14°

SAMRE

C C

V
V VV V V
M
M C
C V

V
V V

13°   PE/

V

V
CHONG   C   V V
PEAR   V V
M M
V
V M
PEAR   C   V
CHONG   C   M
C

12°
CARDAMOM MOUNTAINS

PEAR

C   C   C
C   C
C   C

CHINA

BURMA
LAOS
THAILAND
VIET NAM   V   SAOCH   C   C
CAMBODIA   C   M C

MALAYA   M C   M   M C C
M   M C   M
M

1955

SOURCE OF BASE MAP DATA:
PROVINCIAL BOUNDARIES - 1954 AMS L401 1:400,000
INTERNATIONAL BOUNDARIES - 1944 AAF AERONAUTICAL CHARTS 1:1,000,00

11°

102°   103°   104°

412

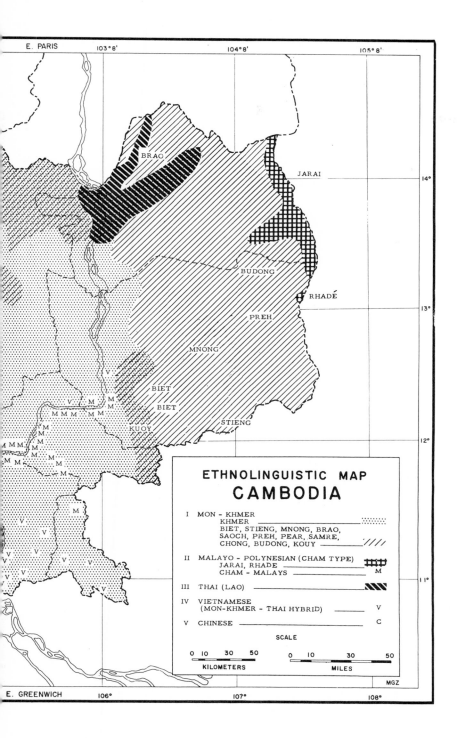

E. PARIS 103°8' 104°8' 105°8'

14°

13°

12°

BRAO

JARAI

BUDONG

RHADÉ

PREH

MNONG

BIET

BIET

STIENG

KUOY

V

M M M M M M M

M M M M M

M

V V

M V

V V V V

V V

V V

ETHNOLINGUISTIC MAP
CAMBODIA

I MON - KHMER
    KHMER _____
    BIET, STIENG, MNONG, BRAO,
    SAOCH, PREH, PEAR, SAMRE,
    CHONG, BUDONG, KOUY _____ ////

II MALAYO - POLYNESIAN (CHAM TYPE)
    JARAI, RHADE _____
    CHAM - MALAYS _____ M

III THAI (LAO) _____

IV VIETNAMESE
    (MON-KHMER - THAI HYBRID) _____ V

V CHINESE _____ C

SCALE

0 10   30   50   0   10   30   50
KILOMETERS   MILES

14°

13°

12°

11°

MGZ

E. GREENWICH 106° 107° 108°

413

the state of Viet Minh or North Vietnam and the southern state, the Republic of Vietnam, or South Vietnam. Thus, what had been one political unit became four (Map 23).

These four states merit separate treatment as sovereign units, but their association under French rule in modern times, and the problems of economic rehabilitation and development that all share, encourage their description as a convenient unit. Their grouping is justified also by the fact that many of the data concerning them deal with the larger unit as it existed under French rule.

In general the policies of the French in Indochina were oriented less toward the full development of the resources and potentialities of Indochina than toward its integration into the economy of the French empire and toward the advancement of French interests in East and Southeast Asia. The French first obtained control of Cochin China in southern Vietnam in 1862; control over the two other major political units (cy) of the then Empire of Annam, Annam and Tonkin, was solidified by 1885; most of Cambodia meanwhile had come under French domination in 1867; Laos followed in 1893; western Laos and northern Cambodia were ceded by Thailand in 1904; and finally, the western portion of modern Cambodia was acquired from Thailand in 1907. The French aim was as much to extend French influence into southern China as it was to dominate Indochina itself. The French were stimulated by the gradual extension of British power in Burma and by fear of British penetration into China's Yün-nan province. Both powers were interested in Thailand, but their rivalry tended to balance out their influences, and Thailand remained the only country in Southeast Asia free of direct foreign domination. British influence, however, particularly in fiscal matters, moulded the course of Thailand's economic life until the second World War.

In general, the French policy in Indochina, unlike that in North Africa, was static rather than dynamic until after 1930 when concerted efforts were directed toward the economic development of the territory. Until that time, the major French contributions to the development of the Indochinese economy were associated with improving the cultivation of rice, the overwhelmingly dominant agricultural product of the country. These contributions were in themselves no small achievement, but the results had little effect on the ways of life and levels of living of the residents of Indochina. Indochina assumed the character of a plural society, similar to that in other South and Southeast Asian countries, in which a great mass of peasantry labored under the ultimate direction of a small European administrative and entrepreneurial elite, but separated from direct contact with the latter in economic matters by a stratum of Chinese middlemen.

Indochinese society is plural also in the sense that it contains within it a multitude of ethnic groups. Among these the Annamese or Vietnamese are the most numerous; in 1950 they were estimated at 21,000,000. Second are the Cambodians or Khmer, whose ancestors had possessed a great empire extending over southern Indochina, Thailand, and even parts of Burma; they numbered an estimated 3,500,000 in 1950 (Map 24). Third are the Lao-Thai, of Laos, numbering less than 750,000 persons and closely related to the Thai of Thailand by whom they had periodically been dominated for the previous several centuries. In addition to these major ethnic groups, primarily lowland-oriented, are about three million upland-dwelling tribesmen—the Hill Thai (the Black Thai and the White Thai), the Man, Muong, and Meo (or Miao) all of whom originated in southern China and migrated southward in relatively recent times; the Cham and the Moslem Cham-Malays of southern Indochina whose ancestors had contended with the Khmer on the one hand and the Annamese on the other for control of southern Indochina; and the tribes of so-called Indonesian aborigines, variously known as *kha* or *moi,* unrelated to the other ethnic groups. Finally there remain the Chinese, concentrated particularly in the larger cities of the south and playing the roles common to them in the rest of Southeast Asia, that of middlemen, skilled craftsmen, and specialized horticulturists.

The cultural diversity of Indochina has resulted not only from its multiplicity of ethnic groups, but also from the civilizations that have influenced it. At an early date, from perhaps the first century A.D., southern and western Indochina particularly came under Indian influence, both Hinduistic and Buddhistic. The great empires of Fu-nan, of Champa, and of the Khmer, as evidenced by the great twelfth-century temple ruins at Angkor, were cultural outliers of Indian civilization. Modern Cambodia and Laos, furthermore, together with Burma and Thailand, remain predominantly Theravada Buddhist nations. The second major influence was that of the Chinese who established effective control over Tonkin and Annam during the Han dynasty and retained a kind of tenuous feudal suzerainty over the empire of Annam until the period of French domination. The Annamese themselves are believed to be partly of Chinese descent. An aggressive people, the Annamese inexorably pushed down the coast of Annam into Cochin China and wrested effective control of that rich country from the Khmer. There in the south the two great traditions of India and China competed for permanency of occupance. Until slowed by the French, the Annamese (and the Chinese tradition they carried with them) seemed destined to dominate the whole of Indochina, and Annamese cultural imperialism is feared by Khmer and Laotian alike.

| The physical basis
| of livelihood

Surface configuration and drainage. Indochina displays the characteristic physical diversity of the mainland regions of Southeast Asia, and this physical differentiation has facilitated the development of distinctive patterns of occupance. The physiographic core of Indochina is the highland mass that extends southward from Tonkin and the delta of the Red River to the delta of the Mekong in Cochin China. This rugged highland, known as the Chaine Annamitique, reaches heights of 8,000 feet, but properly should be considered a series of west-tilted high plateaus rather than a continuous mountain chain. North of about latitude 17°N., the sandstones that cover the plateaus to the south have been stripped away by erosion leaving ancient crystalline rocks, granites, gneisses, and schists. In the far south is an ancient crystalline massif through which outflows of basalt have poured and overlain the ancient rocks. The highland tends to step down gradually via sandstone and limestone tablelands to the Mekong valley in the west, but it rises precipitously in the east, making access from that direction difficult and leaving only a narrow and discontinuous coastal plain. In several places, however, the chain is cut by several gaps or *cols* no more than 3,000 feet above sea level, which provide access across the mountain barrier.

The sandstones and limestones that cover much of the central and northern portions of the Chaine Annamitique extend northwestward and form an extensive dissected highland between the Red and Mekong rivers, embracing most of northern Laos and characterized by northeast-southwest trend lines at between 4,000 and 6,500 feet, similar to those in Yünnan, northern Thailand, and northeast Burma. North of the Tonkin lowlands are the mountains separating Tonkin from China proper, which are composed of igneous formations overlain by partly eroded sandstones and limestones. In this region fluvial erosion has cut fantastic patterns in the heavy limestone formations, similar to those in China's Kuang-hsi and Kuei-chou provinces, and extending into the sea as the dreamlike islands of the Baie d'Along east of Haiphong. The other mountains of Indochina are the Cardamom and Elephant mountains of southwestern Cambodia, which rise abruptly out of the Gulf of Siam—and only somewhat less precipitously from the Cambodian plains to the east—to heights of over 5,000 feet. In northern Cambodia, the 1,000- to 2,500-foot and 200-mile long Dangrek escarpment marks the upturned edge of the sandstone Korat plateau of northeastern Thailand.

Although the highlands account for perhaps 85 per cent of the land

Fig. 88 • The Tonkin delta is flat. It is criss-crossed by a network of canals that act as drainage ditches, irrigation ditches, and means for navigation, especially in the summer when the water table rises and many of the canals and distributaries of the Red River system overflow. Villages rise like green islands from the paddy-field covered plain. Houses in the village, tile-roofed or thatched, are constructed directly on the ground despite hazards from floods. Note the bamboo footbridge across the canal in the right background and the road under construction just parallel to it. *(Foreign Operations Administration.)*

surface of Indochina, it is the plains that define the Indochinese ecumenes. There are two major lowlands in Indochina, the Tonkin lowland in the north and the deltaic plains of the Mekong in the south. The former is by far the smaller, with an area of some 6,000 square miles (Figure 88). The

Red River, parent of the Tonkin delta, flows through a great northwest-southeast rift from its headwaters on the western plateau of Yün-nan and joins with its major affluents, the Black River to the south and the Clear River to the north, before it debouches upon the near-level delta and fans out in a series of intricately meandering and interlaced distributaries. These distributaries flow on elevated beds as much as 40 feet above the level of the flood plain proper. Most of the distributaries are diked, and many originated as canals dug by Chinese or Annamese engineers for flood control, irrigation, or drainage purposes, but over time they have become so "natural" in appearance that they cannot be distinguished from the true stream channels. The discharge of the river varies enormously between summer and the remainder of the year, and much of the delta, though protected by dikes, is threatened by destructive floods between June and September. The river also carries enormous quantities of silt, estimated at 130,000,000 metric tons a year, and the river owes its color to these materials, just as the Yellow River of north China derives its name from the loessial silts it carries. The silt tends to be deposited within the channels of the distributaries and especially at their mouths in the southern portion of the delta; it rapidly is extending the delta into the sea.

The Mekong is one of the great rivers of Asia. It rises within the eastern Tibetan plateau and flows some 2,600 miles into the South China Sea, forming most of the boundary between Laos and Thailand. In its upper course it is deeply incised, but patches of cultivable flood plain are found, such as that around Luang Prabang, the traditional capital of the Laotian kings. Sizable patches of flood plain appear also along the middle course of the river, separated by stretches of rapids and falls. The river is navigable in so-called "reaches" of considerable length for most of the year between Vientiane and Savannakhet and from Pak Sé to the Khone Falls at 14°N. From the Khone Falls to Kratié at about 12°30′N. the river course is broken by rapids, but south from Kratié the river is navigable by large craft and from Pnom Penh to the sea by vessels drawing up to 20 feet. From Kratié to well below Pnom Penh the river flows on an elevated bed bordered by natural levees and paralleled by low-lying strips of flood plain known as *beng* which flood every spring.

Below Pnom Penh the river divides into two major distributaries, the Mekong proper to the east and the Bassac River to the southwest. A multitude of lesser distributaries and interlaced canals, most of which were dug under French direction, criss-cross the great delta of the Mekong, which covers some 14,000 square miles. Most of these canals are large drainage ditches designed to drain the virtually level deltaic plain of the flood waters that flood it seasonally. The floods of the Mekong, however, are not as violent and destructive as the dimensions of the

Fig. 89 • An aerial view of the western shore of the Great Lake in Cambodia, the area of which fluctuates dramatically from wet season to dry season. Here in the dry season, the lake is contracted to about one-third its maximum size. During the rainy season the floodwaters of the Mekong back into the lake reservoir through the Tonlé Sap River. The waters of the lake itself are not visible in the photograph. In the upper right corner is the freshwater swamp forest that covers the dry-season margins of the lake and which is flooded when the lake expands in the spring. Next is an area of mud flats partly in temporary, dry-season cultivation permitted by the high water table beneath the flats; then a broken arc of tree growth on a beach ridge marking the outer limit of the lake shore in time of flood. Behind this arced boundary are the roughly rectangular paddy fields of the Cambodians, which tend to be flooded shallowly during the rainy season. Note the temporary roads and paths leading to the fish-rich lake across the flats. *(U.S. Air Force.)*

stream might suggest. There are two reasons for this: (1) relatively fewer people live in the flooded areas as compared with the Tonkin delta, for example, and life is geared to the seasonal floods, as in Thailand's central lowlands; (2) the Tonlé Sap River and the Great Lake into which it flows act as a safety valve for the river in time of flood (Figure 89).

The Tonlé Sap River flows northwestward from Pnom Penh when the Mekong is in flood. The floodwaters back into the lake and expand its area from 1,100 square miles to 3,900 square miles and its depth from just a few feet to over 30. The 24 to 32 million acre feet thus stored markedly alleviate the flood downstream. As the river subsides, the Tonlé Sap River reverses its flow back into the main stream and the Great Lake drains into the Mekong once more. The mechanism is similar to but more effective than that which characterizes the Yang-tzu and the lakes of T'ung-t'ing and P'o-yang in China. The deltaic lowland also is drained along its northeastern margins by several lesser rivers such as the East and West Vaico and the Saigon rivers, which are not directly a part of the Mekong system.

The Mekong delta and its associated areas of new alluvium account for only a part of the southern Indochinese lowland. Considerably larger than the delta, the plains of Cambodia consist of relatively flat expanses of old alluvium and horizontally bedded sandstones, similar to those in the Korat plateau of northeastern Thailand and ending in the north at the upturned edge of that plateau, the Dangrek escarpment.

Finally, between the northern and southern lowlands are a series of tiny alluvial enclaves along the coast of Annam, wedged between the Chaine Annamitique and the South China Sea.

Climate. Southern Indochina has a tropical monsoon climate in which the most marked characteristic is a strong contrast between dry winters and rainy summers. As is the case in neighboring Thailand, the coming of the summer monsoon with its prevailing southerly winds is gradual. At Saigon the annual range of monthly mean temperatures is less than 4 degrees; it is about as warm in January as it is in July (Plate B). Rainfall is conspicuously seasonal, however. Almost all of Saigon's 80 inches of annual rainfall occur between April and October. Twin precipitation maxima in June and September are associated with the passing of the sun northward and southward. Humidities are high throughout the year. In general these patterns characterize the lowlands of Cochin China and Cambodia, although there is a decline in annual precipitation westward and northward toward the Siamese border. The western plains of Cambodia receive less than 50 inches of rainfall annually. In the highlands, however, precipitation is markedly higher, and on the western slopes of the Cardomom and Elephant ranges, precipitation of over 120 inches is common. The dryness of the winter season is accentuated by the barrier of the Chaine Annamitique in the lee of which southern Indochina lies during the winter months.

The climate of northern Indochina also is monsoonal, but it more nearly resembles that of southern China. The range of mean monthly temperatures between midsummer and midwinter is marked, about 20 degrees near Hanoi where the July average is 83°F. and the January average 62°. Temperature ranges are greater with distances inland and higher altitudes, and temperatures in the low thirties have been recorded in the mountains of northern Laos. Occasionally in winter, thin wedges of cold air extend over the Tonkin delta region, but these never are prolonged enough to break a year-round growing season in the lowlands. Rainfall is concentrated between May and September, and near Hanoi it averages about 72 inches annually. Cyclonic lows cross the area frequently enough, especially in winter, to bring drizzly winter rains known as *crachin* and lessen the contrast between the rainy and less-rainy seasons of summer and winter respectively. Wide ranges in rainfall occur from year to year, especially in the north, and these strongly effect agricultural production. West of the Tonkin delta, precipitation remains high and even increases in the highlands, but it drops sharply at the protected valley of the Mekong, and much of occupied Laos receives less than 50 inches of rainfall each year.

The coast of Annam presents a different picture. Trending from southeast to northwest, it lies athwart the strong northeast monsoonal winds of winter which have picked up moisture in crossing the warm South China Sea. Thus, Hué, the ancient capital of imperial Annam, receives 116 inches of rainfall per year, much of it orographic and received during the fall and winter months. The period of maximum rainfall, however, is in the autumn when the coast experiences damaging tropical typhoons which bring with them torrential rains. In contrast, the sheltered coasts of Annam lying to the south and curving westward toward the Mekong delta are comparatively dry and receive as little as 30 inches annually.

Soils and vegetation. The soils of Indochina resemble those of the other countries of mainland Southeast Asia and of southern China. The major process of soil formation is laterization in which high temperatures, humidities, and rainfall have combined to encourage not only the leaching of soluble materials but also chemical processes that result in an accumulation of aluminum and iron oxides near the surface. Most of the residual soils of Indochina, almost all the upland soils, are lateritic and infertile. In areas underlain by limestone, soils are thin, porous, and droughty where they exist at all. On the sandstone plateau and plains areas of Laos and Cambodia, weathering has produced grey soils also of low fertility. On the basalt highlands north of Saigon, weathering has produced the famous *terres rouges,* or red soils, which are of relatively high fertility. In general, however, the most fertile areas in Indochina, as in most of Southeast Asia, are covered by freshly deposited alluvium relatively rich in humus and plant nutrients. These areas are the deltas of the Red and Mekong rivers and the flood plains of the middle Mekong and the lesser streams along the Annam coast.

Most of Indochina is in forest (Map 23). Where rainfall is sufficiently high, this forest resembles tropical rainforest; where rainfall is somewhat

Fig. 90 • The plains of Cambodia reach from horizon to horizon, covered with sparse tropical grasses in the dry season or with the scattered scrubby trees of the savannah. The ground is baked hard and dry throughout the winter, and in the spring and summer huge plains areas are flooded. Here a dike is under construction across a slight depression in the plain. Behind it floodwater will be stored long enough to permit the irrigation of second crops sown at the beginning of the dry season and to regularize somewhat the water available during the rainy season of summer. Very little of Cambodia is supplied with controlled-irrigation facilities. Thus, double-cropping of paddy is rare. With water available under controlled conditions, the rice output of Cambodia could be increased enormously. *(Foreign Operations Administration.)*

lower and markedly seasonal, the forest becomes a monsoon forest in which evergreens and deciduous species are intermixed. Except in Laos, teak, so common in the forests of northern Burma and Thailand, is uncommon. Much of the original forested area has been cut or burned over, and the resulting secondary forest cover is characterized by denser undergrowth and poorer timber. Over large areas, estimated by some to be as much as 50 per cent of the originally forested area, clearing and burning has resulted in a park-like savannah and open forest called by the French *forêts clairiére* (Figure 90). In other areas are found huge tracts of tropical grasses, chiefly *Imperata cylindrica*, called *tranh* in Indochina, which have taken over formerly forested regions, as has been the case elsewhere in South and Southeast Asia. Around the shores of the Great Lake are found fresh-water swamp forests, and mangrove stands rim the coasts of the southwestern Mekong delta, parts of the Tonkin delta, and the southern coastal tip of the Cardamom Mountains. The economic potential of this forest cover is high, although it is lessened by the typical handicaps of most tropical and subtropical forests—heterogeneous stands, inaccessibility, and lack of predictable markets for forest products other than fuelwood.

Land utilization and settlement

Most of Indochina is unoccupied (Map 23). Most of that which is permanently occupied, about 15 per cent of the whole, is devoted to agricultural uses and the settlements associated with them. In Indochina the primary use of agricultural land is the raising of wet-rice. Rice accounts for about 87 per cent of all the cultivated area in the country. In 1934-8 rice production averaged 6.5 million metric tons on about 14 million acres. Although production in 1955 still was about 25 per cent below this quantity, rice is still far and away the most valuable product of the Indochinese states, and it plays a role in the lives of the peoples of Indochina that places it at the heart of their cultures. For this reason, it is reasonable to define land utilization and settlement regions in Indochina primarily in terms of rice cultivation. These regions are (1) the northern Annamese rice region; (2) the southern Annamese rice region; (3) the Cambodian-Laotian rice region; and (4) the highlands.[2]

The northern Annamese rice region. The northern Annamese rice region includes the major lowlands of Tonkin and the string of isolated lowlands that rim the South China Sea coast of Annam. The heart of this region is the Red River or Tonkin delta with an area of some 2,700 square

[2] These regions are modified from Gulick's regional system.

miles.[3] The Tonkin delta is one of the earth's more densely populated regions. Its average population density approximates 1,500 to the square mile and more. Settlement consists primarily of compact villages often only a few hundred yards apart and surrounded by a continuous mosaic of paddy fields (Figure 88). The agricultural landscape thus bears a striking resemblance to that of the lower Hsi River valley of southern Kuang-tung Province in China. Population densities tend to be somewhat less in the lowlands of Annam where the average is about 500 to the square mile, but the patterns of occupance are virtually identical with those in the Tonkin delta.

In general, settlement patterns and cultivation practices resemble those of southern China. Rivers are diked and flow in channels elevated well above the delta floor. Irrigation is partially controlled, and water is lifted from a maze of distributaries of increasing fineness into the fields themselves. The availability of water from streams and from the winter rains which provide additional moisture and, through cloudiness, restrict evaporation, makes double-cropping possible. Of the estimated 2.6 million acres of riceland cultivated in the region, about 50 per cent are double-cropped. Fertilizers are used intensively, and yields, though not as high as those in south China or Japan, are the highest in Indochina. In fact, the northern Annamese rice region supports, though barely, about twice as many people from about half as large a cultivated area as the southern Annamese rice region. Where drainage permits, second crops of dry crops also may be raised on paddy fields, and the intensity of cultivation is reflected in the use of field bundings and road shoulders for the cultivation of dry crops such as beans, mulberry, fruit trees, maize, sweet potatoes, and vegetables.

As is the case in south China, farm units and fields are small. In the Tonkin delta region about 85 per cent of the farm units are under 4.5 acres in size, and about 61 per cent are under nine-tenths of an acre. Individual fields are minute, and there are estimated to be about 16 million separate fields in the delta. Both farm and field sizes are somewhat larger in the Annam rice areas to the south.

Densities of population tend to decline at the margins of the deltaic lowlands. In the Tonkin lowland region there are considerable areas of older alluvium and diluvial terraces which for the most part also are in rice, but they are not under controlled irrigation and must depend upon rainfall for water.

The southern Annamese rice region. The southern Annamese rice region consists primarily of the delta of the Mekong. It contrasts markedly

---

[3] The true delta of the Red River accounts for about half of the area of the Tonkin lowland. The rest of the lowland is composed of diluvial terraces and the valleys of lesser streams marginal to the Red River.

with the northern Annamese rice region in the following respects: (1) it is a relatively sparsely populated area; (2) cultivation practices are much less intensive than those in the north; and (3) it is a great surplus rice region, in contrast with the north which often experiences rice shortages.

The average population density in the southern region is only about 100 to the square mile. In central Cochin China where rice cultivation is most highly developed, population densities reach 450 per square mile, much less than the average in the north.

In general the patterns of cultivation that characterize the north also characterize the south, but the intensity of cultivation is much less. Almost no double-cropping of rice is practiced. There are substantial areas of land not under permanent cultivation. These expanded as a result of postwar rural insecurity and the flight of population to the cities, but by 1955 some were being placed into cultivation once more. Transplantation is practiced, in some places as many as three times in order to keep pace with the rising floodwaters of the lower Mekong and Bassac rivers which flood most of the delta each year.

In general, irrigation, in contrast with the north, is uncontrolled or virtually so, and harvesting is handicapped by water that remains on the usually ill-drained fields. Fields are surrounded by bunds which retain rain and flood water, but water is brought to the fields primarily by natural, and therefore irregular, mechanisms. They are flooded for the most part by the rising waters of the rivers, but in a zone nearer the sea, fields may be flooded as the result of high tides pushing back the fresh waters of the streams onto the low delta surface. In this zone ground water is brackish particularly in the dry season, and salt-resistant varieties of rice must be grown. Drainage is assisted by a system of large canals cut through the deltaic alluvium, chiefly under French direction. Upstream, near the Vietnamese-Cambodian border, floating rice is grown in the *beng* paralleling the main rivers, where floodwaters may rise over a dozen feet each year. Fertilizers are used only sparingly, and yields are only about two-thirds of those in the north, averaging about 1,050 pounds per acre, or about 30 per cent those of Japan.

Settlement in the southern rice region is much less compact than that in the north. Villages tend to follow routes of water transportation, and almost continuous ribbons of settlement parallel the stream banks and canals. Whereas houses in the north are built on the ground, in the south they tend to be raised upon stilts so as to avoid the floodwaters. This is true particularly of the areas of Cambodian settlement in the southwestern part of Cochin China.

Properties in Cochin China are much larger than those in the north. Large landholdings of over 50 hectares account for nearly half of all the cultivated land. Most of the *landholders* in the region, however, own less

than 5 hectares. The larger estates, owned primarily by wealthy Annamese, are divided into units of about 5 hectares and cultivated by tenant
farmers who form roughly two-thirds the population and are provided
with little security of tenure and even less capital. This is in contrast with
the north where tenancy itself is relatively low, although many of the
farmers may be deeply in debt even so.

Despite low yields, the southern region is the major source of rice surplus in Indochina. Before the war the region produced about 750,000
metric tons of rice each year for export. In addition, frequent exports of
rice to the northern Annamese rice region were necessary, especially in
time of poor Tonkinese harvests. The great rice mills of the region are at
Cholon, the Chinese twin city to Saigon, to which great strings of barges
bring the paddy from the rural collection and distribution centers in the
delta.

The Cambodian-Laotian rice region. The Cambodian-Laotian rice
region includes the lowlands of Laos and Cambodia, or about 36,000
square miles out of a total area of Laos and Cambodia of some 161,500
square miles. Part of the region consists of the alluvial banks and lowlands associated with the Mekong, its tributaries, and the Great Lake; the
greater part consists of plains covered by savannahs and grasslands in
which both shifting cultivation and livestock raising are practiced, and
there are huge areas with population densities under 3 to the square mile.
In general, people cluster in the alluvial lowlands. The density of population in the more densely settled area paralleling the banks of the rivers is
relatively high, but the average for all of Cambodia for example is only
172 per square mile. The total population in the region may be estimated
at 4.5 million persons.

The total area under rice in the region is estimated at just under 3.5
million acres, of which nearly two-thirds are within the political confines
of Cambodia. Rice is overwhelmingly the major crop, accounting for over
80 per cent of the cultivated area. Maize is an important second crop in
both Laos and Cambodia, but its importance has been decreasing rather
than increasing since the war, partly because of declines of exports of
chicken feed to France.

For the most part rice is cultivated even less intensively in the Cam-
bodia-Laotian rice region than it is in the southern Annamese rice region.
Fields are about the same size, and irrigation is almost entirely uncontrolled in areas characterized by nearly the lowest annual precipitation
in all Indochina. The only major irrigation works are around Battambang.
For the most part uncontrolled irrigation is supplied by the overflowing
rivers and the flooding of the low flood plains beyond the river levees
(Figure 91). Where the *beng* are deepest, floating rice is grown. Almost
no fertilizer is used, other than the droppings of cattle grazing over the

Fig. 91 • The natural levees of the Mekong in Cambodia are lined with almost continuous rows of settlement known as *chamkar* villages. The villages are backed by fields elongated at right angles to the river in this area south of Kratié. On the right bank above, the *beng* or depressions immediately beyond the levee are not utilized and are usually under water, although fields cover the levee where settlement does not already occupy it. The sinuous stream-courses across the marshy *beng* flow toward the Mekong in the dry season and away from it during the rainy season. An artificial cut through the levee on the left bank permits water to flow in and out of the *beng* off the photograph below more easily. The island in midstream is devoted primarily to rice, although there are plantings of tree crops, perhaps kapok, as well. During high-water season most of the island is flooded. Permanent settlement on the island is sparse because of flooding, although houses are built on stilts, as they are along the levees. *(U.S. Air Force.)*

rice stubble after harvest. Double-cropping of rice is not practiced, although in some areas rice and maize may be double-cropped. Fields have rounded corners which are labor saving but wasteful of land, and they tend to be discontinuous, indicating relatively little pressure of population on agricultural land (Map 25). Livestock are relatively numerous.

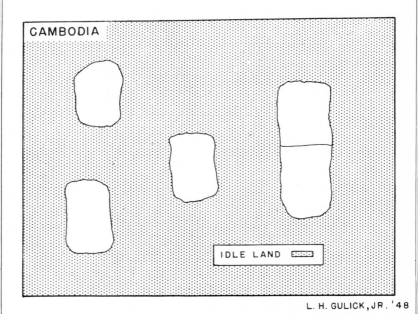
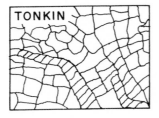

RICE REGIONS OF FRENCH INDOCHINA

COMPARISON OF RICE FIELD
LAYOUT AND PARCELLING
IN TONKIN AND CAMBODIA

TONKIN

1000 FEET

1:10,000

CAMBODIA

IDLE LAND

L. H. GULICK, JR. '48

MAP 25

Yields of rice are low. The average in Cambodia is even less than in the southern Annamese rice region. Yields on the better alluvial soils are higher, but many of the soils formed from older alluvium or from sandstones are inherently of low fertility. Nevertheless, the possibilties for greatly increasing production remain, especially in Cambodia, either through increased yields per acre or through a vast expansion of cultivated area. However, the great Khmer empire based at Angkor is believed to have declined because the fertility of the soils around it, utilized mainly in a system of shifting cultivation, declined to the point where the empire was no longer able to feed itself.

Almost all of the rice grown in Laos is of the glutinous type. Much of the rice grown in Cambodia likewise is glutinous, although the surplus of about 200,000 tons of rice exported each year from Cambodia presumably is common rice milled with that of Cochin China in the mills of Cholon. Laos on the other hand exports no rice and at times requires rice imports.

Additional food supplies come from the invaluable fisheries of the Great Lake, which provide about half of Cambodia's fresh-water fish catch and are worked most intensively in February after the lake contracts and the dense fish population becomes concentrated in the narrowing water body. The Khmer fish primarily for subsistence, and their stilt villages may be found along the high-water margins of the lake. Most of the commercial fishing activity is in the hands of Chinese and Annamese who market the dried product in the markets of Pnom Penh or Saigon-Cholon or manufacture the catch into one of the nutritious, putrefied fish sauces widely used as condiments in Southeast Asia called *nuoc mam* in Annamese and *prahoc* by the Cambodians. The lake yields about 50,000 tons each year, and about 25,000 tons is exported to other parts of Southeast Asia.

The highlands. The highlands of Indochina are sparsely populated, largely by about 3,000,000 tribal peoples who practice primitive shifting agriculture known as *ray* in much of Indochina. Many of these people are malarial, and the malaria zone in Indochina tends to be localized in the upland foothills up to 3,000 feet, rather than in the lowlands which are relatively malaria free. Expansion of Annamese settlement into the lower highlands, therefore, has tended to be restricted by fear of malaria. Although upland rice is the major crop over most of the highlands, maize, cassava, cotton, sesame, sugar cane, beans, and poppies (for opium) are among the major associated crops. In some areas along the border between the highlands and the lowland rice region, irrigated and sedentary rice cultivation on terraced fields is practiced by some of the Thai tribes and the Muong who learned the technique from the Lao-Thai, the Annamese, or the Chinese (Figure 92). In many instances an individual farmer will permanently cultivate small paddy fields and at the same time clear, burn, and plant patches of nearby slope and forest land.

Most of the highland peoples in the north, such as the Black and White Thai, the Man, the Meo, and the Muong are relatively recent migrants from southwestern China, and their kinsmen still live within Chinese territory. In the southern highlands most of the highlanders are of Malaysian origin.

Fig. 92 · The borderland between northern Tonkin and southwestern China is rugged and high. Most of its steep-sloped hills have been cut over, and their soil washes down into the rivers below. Where limestone underlies the hills, erosion has created fantastically shaped spires, much less impressive in the background here than they are in other nearby areas. On some of the steep slopes, clearings are devoted to shifting cultivation. In the middleground are the paddy terraces of highland tribesmen, who learned the art of terrace cultivation from the Chinese. In general, terracing is little practiced in Indochina, except along the margins of the Tonkin delta and nearer the China border. *(U.S. Army.)*

In the southern basalt highlands north and west of Saigon the French have established great rubber estates which are among the higher-producing in Asia. The total acreages are modest, 400,000 acres, and Indochina has competed successfully only in the French market with the primary plantations in Malaya and Indonesia, in part because rubber did not become a major cash crop until relatively late. Since 1940 there have been some rubber plantings made in western Cambodia, especially in the grey-soil areas near the margins of the Cardamom and Elephant mountains. Pepper is another important crop in Cambodia on the margins of the plains and highlands, again at the feet of the western Cambodian Mountains. The industry is run almost entirely by Chinese of Hainanese origin.

Nonagricultural resources, industry, and commerce

Resources. The forest, mineral, and hydroelectric resources of the Indochinese states are virtually unexplored. Except for fuelwood, the *forests* of Indochina are little exploited, and softwoods from the higher latitudes are imported in the form of construction timber or paper. In fact, it is reported that more French capital was invested in the teak forests of northern Thailand and Burma than in the forests of Indochina. Shifting cultivation has destroyed vast areas of virgin or old secondary forest, and it is possible that the development of forest resources must await not merely interest and accessibility, but also the clearing of jungles and the planting of homogeneous stands of marketable timber.

Indochina appears not to be especially well endowed with *mineral resources,* but mineralogical exploration has been too retarded to permit a conclusive generalization. Most of the exploration has taken place in Tonkin, and it is here that major mineral resources have been discovered. Overwhelmingly the most important of these are the coal deposits, which lie in an east-west trending arc, convex to the south, along the northeastern rim of the Tonkin delta. The major basin is that of Quang Yen. Formerly only open-cast mining was practiced, but the exhaustion of the more easily accessible surface beds have necessitated pit mining on an increasing scale. Most of the coal is a relatively high-grade anthracite, though rather brittle, and reserves have been estimated as high as 20 billion tons, roughly comparable to those of Japan. Production reached 2,500,000 metric tons in 1940, about 1.5 million tons of which were exported chiefly to Far Eastern markets, but production declined markedly after the war. The coal is exported primarily through the ports of Hongay and Campha on the Gulf of Tonkin.

All the electrical energy generated in Indochina comes from coal, or in uncommon instances from imported oil. The extensive water-power resources of the country are undeveloped.

Of the nonfuel mineral deposits, tin and zinc are the more important. Tin is mined close to the Chinese border in northern Tonkin and near Nam Patene along the middle Mekong in Lower Laos. Production from the latter and more important mines has amounted to about 1,200 tons of cassiterite annually, most of which was concentrated at the mines and transported down the Mekong for refining at Singapore. Zinc ore in the form of calamines also has been mined in northern Tonkin. About 10,000 tons of ore of 50 per cent metal content were mined annually before the war, but production dropped markedly after the war. Salt, gold, iron, wolfram, and antimony ores among others have been mined in Tonkin and in the highly mineralized mountains of northeastern Laos, but production has been small and the dimensions of deposits are not known. In addition, phosphates are mined in small quantities.

Manufacturing industries. Modern manufacturing in the Indochinese states is restricted to the vicinities of the larger cities. The French established cement, glass, textile, and other light manufacturing industries chiefly in Hanoi, Haiphong, and Saigon-Cholon. Cement production reached 235,000 metric tons before the war. The chief industries concern the processing of agricultural products. Rice mills, owned largely by Chinese, partly by French, tend to be concentrated in Cholon. The manufacture of alcohol from rice was regulated strictly by the French, and major distilleries were located in the cities of Tonkin and in Pnom Penh and Saigon. The residue was used as pig food. Cane sugar also is produced in small modern mills in Cochin China.

Agricultural products also are processed in native establishments of small size. Rice and sugar for local consumption are prime examples. In addition, silk and cotton textiles have long been manufactured as cottage industries, and Annamese and Chinese have produced glass, china, pottery, tile, lime, mat, basket, lace, and tobacco products for hundreds of years.

Most of these industries have faced unsuccessfully the competition of imported manufactures. In this respect Indochina has resembled the other countries of Southeast Asia, and its handicraft industries have tended to decline. However, the relatively slow pace of colonial economic development in the area as compared with India, for example, has resulted in greater local self-sufficiency and thus greater temporary viability for handicraft and other small industries.

Trade. The prewar foreign trade of Indochina was oriented primarily toward the mother country, France. Slightly over half of all foreign trade was with France or French dependencies. Trade was regulated carefully by the French, and most of it was in French hands; the larger part of the remainder was handled by Chinese. Per-capita trade, however, was low, far below that of Indonesia, Malaya, and even the Philippines.

Imports consisted of that great diversity of manufactured goods, with textiles predominating, that characterizes the import schedules of most underdeveloped and colonial territories. Exports consisted almost entirely of agricultural and other raw materials. In 1932-6 rice accounted for about one-half of all exports by value. Maize, rubber, coal, dried fish, pepper, and hides followed in value. The volume of rice exports, chiefly from the southern Annamese rice region, fluctuated widely from year to year, but averaged close to 1.5 million metric tons of cleaned rice annually. On the average, about a third of all rice exports went to Hongkong and China; about 40 per cent went to France; the remainder was widely distributed throughout Southeast Asia. Since the quality of Indochinese rice is low because of discoloration, lack of standardization, and high content of broken grains, Indochinese rice has failed to command high prices on the world market. Rubber was exported primarily to France, and exports reached 60,000 metric tons in 1937.

Since the close of the war the trade pattern has altered remarkably. Exports of rice have declined greatly; tonnage in 1954 reached only 240,-000 metric tons, about half of which came from Cambodia. On the other hand, high rubber prices stimulated rubber production, which rose to 79,300 metric tons in 1954. However, coal exports, which averaged 1.5 million tons immediately before the war, remained depressed at about one-fifth that figure in 1952. This depression characterized other previously significant exports. Imports, however, rose as military and economic aid from France and the United States poured into Indochina after the war.

The direction of postwar trade has seen France still in a position of dominance, but with the transfer of sovereignty to the several states a diversification of trade relations can be anticipated.

The several states of Indochina

French Indochina was a mélange of peoples and territories among which the unifying bond was French domination. The major political unit prior to the French occupation was the Empire of Annam, centered at Hué, and including the three *ky* of Tonkin (which means "eastern capital" and in both Chinese and Japanese is written with the same characters as those for Tokyo), Annam, and Cochin China. The Annamese empire was nibbling steadily away at Cambodia. Cambodia was a political unit, but its western provinces were occupied by Siam (Thailand), and it paid tribute to both the courts of Hué and Bangkok. Laos did not exist as a political unit. It was in effect

Fig. 93 • Vietnam possesses a huge underemployed labor force which can be brought to bear upon the construction of major public works in the place of labor-saving machinery. Here, southeast of Saigon, a road is under construction. Although a steamroller is used, most of the energy utilized comes from laborers who carry the crushed stone for the road in wicker baskets and strew it over the road surface. Note the flat plain with scattered tree growth in the background and the fortified strongpoint which suggests the rural insecurity in the area. *(Foreign Operations Administration.)*

Siamese territory; the northern kingdom of Luang Prabang was a vassal state; the area about Vientiane on both the right and left banks of the Mekong was a Siamese province; and Lower Laos, notably Bassac in the far south, was a fief of the Siamese crown.

After the second World War the French created the Associated States of Indochina, which were joined by a customs union, by common foreign relations through France, and by common partnership in the French Union of nations. By 1949 the idea of an Indochinese Federation was abandoned, and each of the three Indochinese states, now named Vietnam, Cambodia, and Laos, was permitted to open diplomatic relations with other countries, by-passing France. A common customs union and currency issue remained. By the time of the Geneva Conference in August, 1954, the independence of the three major political units was recognized by France. The Conference also brought into being the communist state of Viet Minh, separated from South Vietnam at the 17th parallel and including northern Annam and Tonkin.

South Vietnam.   The heart of South Vietnam is the delta of the Mekong and the former colony of Cochin China. By 1957 postwar unrest in rural areas had greatly diminished, and the republican government in Saigon had established firm control over most of the territory in which it claimed sovereignty. The population of the new state is estimated at 11,-000,000 and its area about 65,400 square miles. Population is swollen by an influx of 800,000 refugees, chiefly Christians, from Tonkin, and the economic problems of the state have been exceptionally severe (Figure 93).

The nodal focus of South Vietnam is the twin cities of Saigon and Cholon, with a combined population of 1.6 millions. Saigon lies on the banks of the winding Saigon River about 50 miles from the South China Sea. Although the approaches to it are difficult, the river depth of over 30 feet is maintained in part by a tidal bore which flushes out the debris and silt that otherwise would clog its mouth. Saigon is one of the great cities of Southeast Asia. It is relatively new, built for the most part by the French after 1860 in the fashion of a large French provincial city, so that like many of the cities of Southeast Asia it presents a substantially European facade. Its population is almost wholly Asian, and increasingly Vietnamese. Cholon immediately to the west was settled by Chinese as early as 1778. Gradually, the two cities have grown together until they now form one metropolitan area, and they have come to share the functions of capital, commercial center, and cultural center of South Vietnam. Saigon has not been a major trading center for Southeast Asia in the manner of Singapore; it lies off the main oceanic trade route that connects Singapore and Hongkong. However, it has acted as the major port not only for southern Vietnam but also for Cambodia.

Saigon is connected by meter-gauge railroad with the coastal settlements of Annam and the cities of Binh-Dinh, Tourane, and Hué. This railroad was constructed by the French and named the Trans-Indochina line. Another connection is with Dalat, the former summer capital of Cochin China, on the eastern margins of the basalt highlands of the Chaine Annamitique. The French never completed the proposed rail connection with Pnom Penh, and communications between the two cities have been primarily by the steamships and barge lines that traverse the network of canals dug by the French in the Mekong delta and along its margins.

South Vietnam possesses in its agricultural surpluses a "time-cushion" for development, but these surpluses have been decreased as a result of internal conflict, and it is upon their restoration that the economic future of the country depends. Resettlement of thousands of Tonkinese in the delta region is proceeding, and with American assistance plans are in being to greatly expand the area of rice by the restoration of previously cultivated land and the draining of potentially rich rice areas such as the marshy Plaine des Joncs between the Mekong proper and the West Vaico River to the east.

Cambodia. Cambodia has been less affected than any of the other Indochinese states by the postwar chaos in Indochina. With an area of 71,000 square miles and a population estimated at only 4,100,000 persons, Cambodia faces few short-run economic problems. Rice production, up to 1.5 million metric tons, somewhat exceeds the prewar figures, and rubber production continues high.

Relations between Cambodia and South Vietnam remain far from easy, however. The Khmer have long harbored ill-will toward the Vietnamese (Annamese) who took over Cochin China two centuries ago and have been infiltrating southeastern Cambodia in more recent times (Map 24). Cambodia also resents the need to reach the commercial world through the Vietnamese port of Saigon. As a result, she plans the expansion of the port of Pnom Penh, the capital on the Mekong, and has encouraged foreign shipping companies, such as the Straits Steamship Company of Singapore, to provide direct services between Pnom Penh and the outside world via the Mekong which has become an internationalized stream. Pnom Penh itself is an ancient city, much modernized by the French, with a population of about 375,000. The Cambodians also are enlarging Ream, one of their ports on the Gulf of Thailand, and a new highway between Kampot, a second port on that coast, and Pnom Penh has been completed across rugged and sparsely populated hill country. Cambodia also is connected with Thailand by a meter-gauge railroad which runs westward from Pnom Penh via Battambang through the so-called "Cambodian gateway" to Bangkok.

Laos. Unlike Cambodia, which possesses a high degree of ethnic homogeneity, Laos is torn with centrifugal forces resulting from her ethnic heterogeneity and from the lack of a tradition of statehood for all of her territory of 90,500 square miles. Only about half of the total population of Laos, some 1.4 million persons, consists of Lao-Thai, a lowland-dwelling people closely related to and speaking the same language as the Siamese. There is constant friction between the Lao-Thai of the lowlands and the highland peoples, some of whom also speak languages of the Thai family. There also is rivalry between Upper Laos, formerly the kingdom of Luang Prabang, and Lower Laos which was joined to the former by the French. In addition, as of late 1957, two provinces of northern Laos, Phong Saly and Sam Neua, were not under control of the capital at Vientiane, but were dominated by Laotians sympathetic to and supported by the communist regime in Viet Minh.

These centrifugal forces are accentuated by Laos' unique location and historical relations in Southeast Asia. It borders China on the north, and the Lao-Thai themselves, like the Thai of Siam, had their origins within

Chinese territory. Many of the minority peoples living in the Laotian Mountains have kinsmen on the Chinese side of the border, and the Chinese themselves have established a Thai Autonomous Region in southwestern Yün-nan province to indicate their friendly interest in Thai affairs and in the possibility of a Thai federation friendly to the communist cause. The communist threat to Laotian independence has been increased with the establishment of neighboring Viet Minh. Although movement across the north Laotian Mountains into Yün-nan and eastward to the Tonkin delta is difficult, there are two good highways eastward from Lower Laos into Annam.

The traditional outlook of Laos has been toward Bangkok, and Siamese influence has increased in Laos since the war. Extension of the Siamese railway system to the Mekong across the river from Vientiane will make communication with Bangkok much easier than with Saigon. Laos also shares a common frontier with Burma. Thus, Burma, Thailand, Laos, and Cambodia form a solid bloc of countries culturally related through their common following of Theravada Buddhism.

Viet Minh (North Vietnam). The most densely populated of the states of Indochina is Viet Minh. Covering an area of 64,000 square miles it has a population estimated at 13 million persons. Although there are over a million highland tribesmen in the Tonkinese hills and the Chaine Annamitique, the overwhelming majority of the population is composed of Annamese, resident in the Tonkin lowland and the smaller lowlands of Annam. The permanent Chinese population is small, about 60,000, less than one-tenth the number in South Vietnam.

Viet Minh inherited the bulk of France's investments in industry in Indochina. The valuable coal mines and varied mineral resources, the great cement plant, textile mills, and various light industries, all fell into Viet Minh hands. They also inherited a relatively highly developed transportation system. This includes the northern half of the Trans-Indochina line to Hanoi; the branch line eastward to the port of Haiphong; a northeastern branch to the China border at Lang Son, which ties in with the standard-gauge Chinese railway system; and a northwestward line, the famous Yün-nan railroad, which extends into Chinese territory to K'unming, the capital of Yün-nan province.

Thus, Viet Minh is connected with China by two main overland routes. Both played important roles in assisting the Viet Minh to defeat the French during the civil war. However, it was not until 1952 that the Chinese completed their connection with the northeast branch; and portions of the Yün-nan railroad just north of the border, as well as much of the line in Indochina itself, in 1956 had not yet been restored after wartime destruction. Both routes are single-track and meter-gauge. The Yün-nan railroad was designed as a means for extending French economic and political influence into Yün-nan. Thus, its original function had little to do with Indochina as such.

The southern boundary of Viet Minh is the 17th parallel north of Hué. The boundary cuts across some of the more rugged and least known parts of the Chaine Annamitique. It is, therefore, a boundary difficult to protect and subject to infiltration at night. Although the boundary is closed officially, a considerable movement of people and goods continues at night off the main coastal roads.

The chief cities of Viet Minh are Hanoi and its port to the southeast, Haiphong, with populations of 298,000 and 189,000 respectively. Hanoi is, like Saigon, constructed in the manner of a French provincial town. All transportation routes in the Tonkin delta region focus upon it—railroads, roads, canals, and air services. Haiphong is located about 20 kilometers from the open sea on the River Cua Cam, one of the outlets of the Thai Binh River at the northern edge of the delta region, which is connected with the Red River by canal. Silting in the dredged channels leading to the port has made Haiphong a relatively poor port, but, like Shanghai, Haiphong has maintained itself through the locational inertia of a going concern. Several lesser cities act as local market centers in the delta region, and each of the Annam lowlands along the coast has a sizable town that acts as a local economic and political capital.

The economic problems faced by the Viet Minh government resemble those of most newly independent states looking toward economic development, but they are made more acute by the enormous pressure of population on the land of Tonkin and by the inflexibility this pressure imposes upon the economic system. For this reason, the short-run economic status of South Vietnam may be considered stronger than that of Viet Minh, although the variety of nonagricultural resources available to the latter in the long run may make for a stronger economy than that of the south. Viet Minh also is handicapped by its isolation from most of the Western world, since it is recognized only by countries of the Soviet bloc, and the assistance it can expect from Chinese and Russian sources is far less than South Vietnam can expect from the United States.

SELECTED GEOGRAPHICAL BIBLIOGRAPHY

1. *Area Handbook on Cambodia.* Chicago: University of Chicago, Department of Geography, 1955 (limited edition).
2. *Area Handbook on Laos.* Chicago: University of Chicago, Department of Geography, 1955 (limited edition).
3. Brodrick, A. H. *Little Vehicle: Cambodia and Laos.* London: Hutchinson, 1949.

4. "French Indo-China: Demographic Imbalance and Colonial Policy," *Population Index*, April, 1945.
5. Gourou, Pierre. *L'utilisation du Sol en Indochine Française*. Paris: Centre d'etudes de politique etrangere, 1940 (later translated and published in a mimeographed edition by the Institute of Pacific Relations in New York, 1945).
6. ———. "Land Utilization in Upland Areas of Indochina," in the *Development of Upland Areas in the Far East*. New York: Institute of Pacific Relations, 1951 (mimeographed).
7. Gulick, Luther H., Jr. "Rice Regions of French Indochina." (Unpublished masters thesis, the Department of Geography, University of Chicago, 1948).
8. *Indo-China: A Geographical Appreciation*. Ottawa: Geographical Branch, Department of Mines and Technical Surveys, 1953.
9. McCune, Shannon. "The Diversity of Indochina's Physical Geography," *Far Eastern Quarterly*, August, 1947, pp. 335-44.
10. Miller, E. W. "Industrial Resources of Indochina," *Far Eastern Quarterly*, August, 1947, pp. 395-408.
11. Pendleton, R. L. "Laterite and its Structural Uses in Thailand and Cambodia," *Geographical Review*, April, 1941, pp. 177-202.
12. Robequain, Charles. *The Economic Development of French Indo-China*. New York: Oxford University Press, 1944.
13. Sion, Jules. "Indochine" in "Asie des Moussons," *Geographie Universelle*, Tome IX, Part 2. Paris: Librairie Armand Colin, 1929.
14. U. S. Department of Agriculture. *The Agriculture of French Indochina*. Washington: Government Printing Office, 1950.
15. "Vietnam," *Focus*, February 15, 1951.
16. Zelinsky, Wilbur. "The Indochinese Peninsula: A Cultural Anomaly," *Far Eastern Quarterly*, February, 1950.

Comments

Indochina is one of the lesser known areas in Southeast Asia. It never has had a modern census of population, agriculture, or industry, and its customs data are admittedly subject to question. Most of the literature about it is in French. The better-known works are those of Sion and Gourou, the latter more nearly up to date and translated into a mimeographed English-language edition. A more general economic analysis is found in Robequain. Both Gourou and Robequain have written extensively in French about Indochina, and students who can read French are urged to consult their works. The Canadian handbook on Indochina is a useful factual outline. The handbooks on Laos and Cambodia are preliminary editions available from the Department of Geography, the University of Chicago, and are on file in the country's major research libraries. They are studies of available and current sources on the geography and ethnography of the two countries. Gulick's thesis is an able appraisal of rice in Indochina's economic and social structures.

The French authorities in Indochina published an annual statistical volume for the entire area, *Annuaire Statistique de l'Indochine*, from 1913 on. A handbook covering the three states extant in 1953 also is available, *Annuaire des Etats Associés, Cambodge, Laos, Vietnam, 1953*. In addition, both Laos and Cambodia publish statistical volumes, usually appearing irregularly and covering more than one year. A particularly valuable source of economic geographic information has been the French journal, *Bulletin Economique de l'Indochine*.

Burma

AS SIAM IS THE LAND OF THE MENAM CHAO PHYA, SO BURMA IS THE land of the Irrawaddy. The delta and interior plains of the Irrawaddy and its tributaries form the bulk of the good agricultural land, the centers of population, and the real home of the Burmese-speaking people. The Union of Burma includes a belt of mountains and plateaus bordering the plains and enclosing them on the east, west and north, which is sparsely inhabited by non-Burmese tribal peoples (Map 26). Burma's 261,610 square miles of territory also include the west-facing coasts of Tenasserim and Arakan along the Bay of Bengal, inhabited in part by the Burmans.

Burma is a new country by comparison with India or China. Its authentic history dates only from the eleventh century A.D., when King Aniruddha of Pagan brought central Burma under his rule. Mongoloid in race and speaking a language akin to Tibetan, the Burmese people are believed to have moved into the Irrawaddy plains from the northeast between A.D. 200 and 800. They owe their civilization more to India than to China. It was the ancient Indian expansion overseas to Southeast Asia that brought writing, Hinayana (Theravada) Buddhism,[1] and other elements of civilization by way of the Talaing (Mon) people, whose flourish-

[1] Hinayana (Little Vehicle) is one of the two great divisions of Buddhism and encompassed the southern Buddhist countries, Ceylon, Burma, Siam, and Further India, in contrast to Mahayana (Great Vehicle) which spread from India to Central Asia, Tibet, China, and Japan.

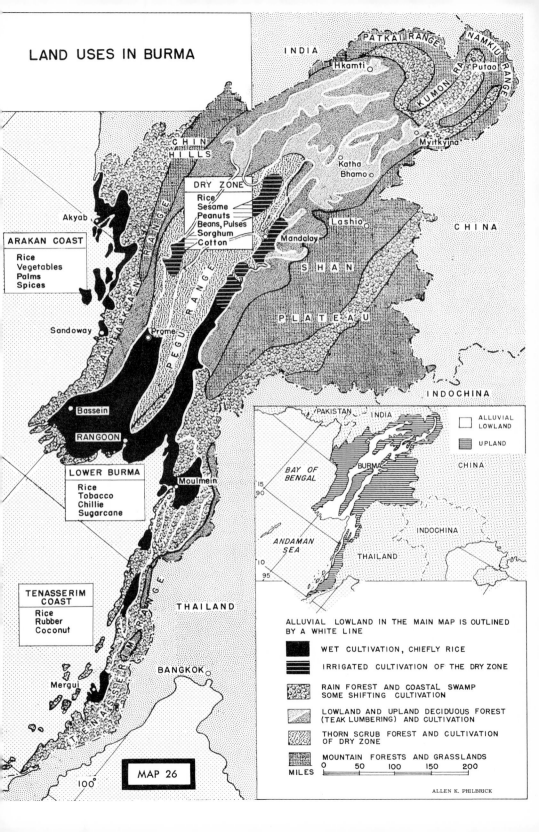

LAND USES IN BURMA

INDIA

PATKAI RANGE

NAMKIU RANGE

Hkamti

Putao

KUMON RA

CHIN HILLS

Myitkyina

Katha
Bhamo

CHINA

Akyab

DRY ZONE
Rice
Sesame
Peanuts
Beans, Pulses
Sorghum
Cotton

Lashio

Mandalay

SHAN

ARAKAN COAST
Rice
Vegetables
Palms
Spices

ARAKAN RANGE

PLATEAU

Sandoway

Prome

PEGU RANGE

INDOCHINA

Bassein

RANGOON

PAKISTAN

INDIA

ALLUVIAL
LOWLAND

UPLAND

BURMA

CHINA

BAY OF
BENGAL

LOWER BURMA
Rice
Tobacco
Chillie
Sugarcane

Moulmein

15
90

ANDAMAN
SEA

INDOCHINA

10
95

THAILAND

TENASSERIM COAST
Rice
Rubber
Coconut

TENASSERIM RANGE

THAILAND

ALLUVIAL LOWLAND IN THE MAIN MAP IS OUTLINED
BY A WHITE LINE

WET CULTIVATION, CHIEFLY RICE

IRRIGATED CULTIVATION OF THE DRY ZONE

RAIN FOREST AND COASTAL SWAMP
SOME SHIFTING CULTIVATION

LOWLAND AND UPLAND DECIDUOUS FOREST
(TEAK LUMBERING) AND CULTIVATION

THORN SCRUB FOREST AND CULTIVATION
OF DRY ZONE

BANGKOK

Mergui

MOUNTAIN FORESTS AND GRASSLANDS

0   50   100   150   200
MILES

100°

MAP 26

ALLEN K. PHILBRICK

ing kingdom centered at Thaton and who were conquered by Aniruddha. Though not differing from the Burmese in racial traits, the Talaing have ties by language to the ancient Mon of Siam and Khmer of Cambodia.

The colonial status of the Burmese people under Great Britain was of relatively short duration, ending in January, 1948, when all ties to London were severed. British annexation began in 1826, with the conquest of the Arakan and Tenasserim coasts, and was extended in two stages to include Lower Burma in 1852 and Upper Burma in 1886. For administrative convenience the country was governed as a British Indian province until 1937, but thereafter it was separated and had partial self-government under a special constitution.

Burma was known as a model colony, clearly one of the more secure of the many jewels in the King-Emperor's crown. It became a prime exporter of rice, timber, and minerals, and contributed a large revenue to the central government of India. A fourfold increase of population [2] and the clearing of new land in the alluvial plains of Lower Burma enabled the country to become the world's major rice exporter. There was a normal surplus of more than 3.4 million metric tons before the second World War, amounting to more than half of the total annual exports of all Southeast Asia, or nearly two-fifths of the volume of international rice trade in the world. During most of the period of British rule, the prosperity of the Burmans, together with that of immigrant laborers and merchants from India and China, seemed assured.

Yet, Burma was beset during the 1930's by economic maladjustments and political unrest, and after the second World War it achieved precarious independence without economic recovery. The country was strained by the collapse of world rice prices, and the problems of agricultural credit and absentee land ownership became aggravated. Burma emerged from the war in 1945 with its transport and trade disrupted, its political life disorganized, and its productive capacity reduced about one-third below prewar level.

The basic problems confronting the country today are (1) political integration of non-Burmese minorities; (2) suppression of multiple rebellions of both Burmese and non-Burmese groups; (3) recovery of prewar export trade in rice, teak, and petroleum; and (4) nurture of mining and manufacturing industries of modern type without foreign control. Solution of these problems hinges upon governmental policy in regard to public or private land ownership and to the role of Burmans and foreigners in trade and industry. But their solution also relates to the quality of the land and the skills and distribution of the people.

[2] The population of all Burma in 1826 is believed to have been 4.0 million; in 1941, the year of the last census, it was 16.8 million. In 1956 the population was estimated at 19.9 million.

Drainage and terrain

The master stream of Burma, the Irrawaddy (Elephant River), surpasses all other resources in natural benevolence. Not only does it provide through depositional action the best soils, but also its channel is navigable for 1,000 miles, and its distributaries form the country's chief outlets to the sea.

Another Burmese river, the Salween, rises in Tibet north of the Irrawaddy, traverses Yün-nan province of China, the Shan state and Karenni state in eastern Burma, and ends in the Gulf of Martaban, but the drainage area of the Salween is very much restricted. It flows deep within narrow gorges covered with malarial jungles in its lower course. It does not carry large craft because of several rapids, and the single important city on its banks, Moulmein, is located in the relatively small alluvial deposits that fringe its estuary.

The basin [3] of the Irrawaddy, comprising the entire valley of the Chindwin, the Sittang, and the main river below Katha, is an ancient (Tertiary) gulf filled with river-borne and marine sediments. The gulf is now divided by a series of longitudinal central ridges resulting from unfolding of the sedimentary rocks such as the Pegu range and from outpouring of volcanic lavas. The highest point is the cone of Mount Popa, 4,981 feet.

The twinned pattern of the present-day rivers reflects these geologic changes and shows evidence of river capture. On the west, the ancestral Chindwin has captured the headwaters of the proto-Sittang (Upper Irrawaddy), which once flowed directly southward from Mandalay past Toungoo to the Gulf of Martaban in the valley now occupied by the much-diminished Sittang. As a consequence, nearly all drainage of Burma north of the 22nd parallel collects in the combined Chindwin-Irrawaddy near Myingyan.

The Irrawaddy's 1,400-mile course begins in the snowfields and glaciers of the 15,000 to 19,000-foot mountains standing near the junction of the Chinese, Indian, and Burmese boundaries. At the confluence of the Mali and Nmai sources, a few miles above Myitkyina, the river is one-quarter mile wide and 30 feet deep in the dry season and is navigable from this point downstream, although narrow defiles with swift water occur at three places. Bhamo, between the first and second defile, 874 miles from the sea, is normally the terminus of steamer service. Below the third defile, 50 miles above Mandalay, the river has a gradient of about 4 inches to the mile and flows in a meandering course on a flood plain 3 to 10 miles

[3] The term "basin" is used here in the structural sense and includes low hills of sedimentary rock and volcanic materials as well as an alluvial veneer.

wide, flanked on each side by terraced hills which surmount the stream level by from 30 to 400 feet. The formation of these terraces appears to date from pluvial periods, contemporaneous with the Pleistocene ice ages in Europe and America, which alternated in Burma with dry inter-glacial stages of downcutting. There are also lines of hills marking the anticlinal ridges with which are associated Burma's main oil fields.

The width of the delta is 150 miles, and its apex lies about 180 miles from the sea. Altogether there are nine mouths, including the Bassein River and the Rangoon River. These two rivers, the only ones used by ocean-going vessels, are not true mouths of the Irrawaddy because they have separate sources and receive only a small flow from the main stream. Most water is discharged by the Eya mouth, and the bulk of the silt is carried to the Gulf of Martaban. The delta is almost entirely new alluvium, having been formed since the ice ages in recent times. Land is observed to have grown three miles seaward in 100 years. One-third of the delta is a foot or less above spring tides, and most of its area would be subject to flooding were it not for protective dikes.

The mountain frame of Burma consists of two major structural elements: a group of eastern block-faulted massifs and a western folded belt. The eastern massifs comprise largely the Shan plateau and the Tenasserim coast ranges. The western mountains form a series of ridges along the Indian and Pakistan borders, called the Patkai hills in the north, the Chin hills in the midportion, and the Arakan range in the south. Both units converge in the northern mountain knot from which the Kumon range, one of the eastern massifs, extends southward between the Irrawaddy and Chindwin valleys.

The eastern uplands are of older geologic age than the other parts of the country and are made of several contrasting rock complexes which extend eastward into Thailand. In the west, along the great fault scarp that rises sharply 3,000 feet above the Sittang and Irrawaddy valleys, there are gneisses, schists, and marbles. With these rocks are found the precious stones of the Mogok (ruby) district, the vast ore deposits· of Bawdwin (silver and lead), and scattered occurrences of tin (near Tavoy in Tenasserim), tungsten (at Mawchi in Karenni), and antimony. The second rock complex is represented by thick deposits of limestone and dolomite. In these formations, as in the metamorphosed marble, there has developed typical karst topography, with sinkholes, caverns, and underground streams. Two other rock formations present in the region are folded red shales and certain lake-basin deposits containing low-grade lignite.

The upland exhibits an undulating plateau-like surface at 3,000 to 4,000 feet, but is broken into gorges carved by the Salween and its affluents and by those of the Sittang and Irrawaddy. In Tenasserim, granitic massifs give rise to long ridges, arranged *en echelon* and separated by valleys where the weaker sedimentary rocks outcrop.

The mountains that stand along Burma's western frontiers are of simple folded structure, forming ridges of 3,000 to 5,000-foot elevation. Numerous streams flow from north to south, parallel to the ridges and connected through gorges cut at right angles across the ridges, thus forming a lattice system analagous to that of the North American Appalachians. Drainage is partly eastward into the Chindwin, which has a long course through an alternating series of basins and narrows and is navigable to Hkamti, 510 miles above its confluence with the Irrawaddy.

Climate and vegetation

More than any other single factor, the rain-bearing southwest monsoon controls the climate of Burma. As much as 120 to 200 inches of rain are received in Arakan and Tenasserim, where orography intensifies summer convectional precipitation, and even the low-lying Irrawaddy delta receives 60 to 110 inches. During May the rains begin, somewhat less abruptly than in India. Greatest intensity is reached during June, July, and August, when the precipitation is between 20 inches and 50 inches per month. During September the rain lessens, and it ends during October. The coastlands in Burma are in fact among the rainiest regions of the earth and are clothed in broadleaf, evergreen rainforest composed of large trees of the Dipterocarp family, with bamboo and palms as an understory. Salty coastal marshes are the habitat of mangrove, and freshwater swamps in the delta favor other evergreen species.

Height of land and exposure cause important local modifications of the amount of moisture precipitated from the tropical equatorial air coming across the Bay of Bengal from the Indian Ocean. On the leeward side of the western mountains, on both slopes of the Pegu range, on the Shan plateau escarpment and in the northern mountain valleys, the rains are less intense, averaging between 40 and 80 inches annually. A tall tropical deciduous or monsoon forest thrives in these regions. The leaves are shed in the months from January to March but begin to grow again before the rains set in. A greater variety of plants than in the rainforest is found here. Two outstanding species are ironwood (*Zylia dolabriformis*) and the commercially important teak (*Tectona grandis*) (Figure 94).

In the middle Irrawaddy valley from Mandalay to Prome, rainfall is diminished to as little as 40 inches, creating a truly dry zone.[4] There is a

---

[4] Where rainfall is less than 33 inches and prevailing mean annual temperatures are 80-81°F., as in this region, the climatic type is low-latitude steppe, BSh in the Koeppen classification.

Fig. 94 • Teak logs being pulled from the Irrawaddy River at Mandalay by a double team of water buffalo. In the background are the rafts under which these logs were tied to be floated downstream. The rafts, which must be constructed of bamboo or other wood lighter than teak, which does not float, are used repeatedly and serve as dwelling places for the raftsmen. In Thailand similar rafts, less elaborately constructed, are used to float teak logs down the Menam to Bangkok where the rafts are broken up and abandoned or else sold for their construction materials. *(Robert E. Huke.)*

narrow belt that receives only 20 to 25 inches, extending 80 miles downstream from the confluence of the Chindwin. The cause of this moisture deficiency is the rain-shadow effect of the western mountains and the progressive loss of moisture from air traveling into central Burma by way of the Irrawaddy or Sittang valleys. In the driest part of the area the wild vegetation is thorny scrub of low-branching acacia trees, and *Euphorbia* cactus with a ground cover of *Andropogon* grass. Dry scrub forests of deciduous hardwoods are found on the borders of this dry zone.

Seasonal temperature variations are not pronounced in lowland Burma. Maximum monthly temperatures of 85 to 90°F. occur in April or May before the rains arrive. The mean temperature at the coolest month on the plains within tropical latitudes is over 65° and in subtropical northern Burma about 60°. Vegetation in the lowlands is not influenced significantly by temperature differences.

Modified types of vegetation appear above 3,000 feet because of reduced temperatures. In the Shan plateau mixed temperate forests of broadleaf species and pines, adapted to light winter frost, are interrupted by wide areas of rolling grassland. Still higher in the northern mountains, silver fir or rhododendron forest prevails and above this alpine tundra up to perennial snow at 14,000-15,000 feet.

Central Burma:
The dry zone [5]

It is a well known but unexplained fact that the dry zone of central Burma was the earliest center of true Burmese civilization. Until the British conquest, this region was more often than not the seat of the Burmese state and contained the majority of the people. Seven former capitals are situated here. Of these, the most famous are Pagan, Ava, and Mandalay; the last-named is now the second city of Burma. This semi-arid region of the middle Irrawaddy basin must still be regarded as the true heart of Burma, although its population of some six million has fallen behind that of the lower Irrawaddy basin.

The dry zone may be defined as the area with less than 40 inches annual rainfall. Because of moisture deficiency, agriculture is carried on either by irrigation or by special methods of dry farming. Water is obtained for irrigation from small reservoirs in the hilly areas or from canals that tap the streams descending from adjacent mountains. The largest canal systems are government-maintained, many of them dating from the eleventh century and others from the British period. One and one-half million acres under irrigation are devoted almost entirely to rice. No use whatever for irrigation is made of the Chindwin and Irrawaddy. Alluvial land exposed as the rivers fall after the end of the rains may be planted in maize, tobacco, or vegetable crops. Clearly an abundant water supply is available for the time when Burma is ready to invest in the necessary dams and canals, though the terrace topography limits possible irrigation to 20 per cent of the total area with less than 40 inches rainfall.

Dry farming accounts for an aggregate acreage two to three times that of rice in the dry zone. This method depends upon soil moisture stored by fallowing after two to five years of cropping. Soil is plowed following harvest and it soaks up water from the scanty, erratic showers. Several other practices help to ensure returns from such marginal land. Mixed plantings of two crops give a better chance of one of the crops yielding well. Every year about one-sixth of the dry-farming acreage is planted with two successive crops to gain second harvest where first yields are low. Crop rotations, including legumes, to restore fertility also are practiced. The chief crops are, in the order of prewar acreage: sesamum, grain sorghum, peanuts, cotton, and various kinds of beans, pulses, and pigeon peas.

The staple food of the Burmese is common starchy rice; glutinous rice is used primarily for sweetened rice cakes. In the dry zone the supply of rice often is deficient. Widespread drought and crop failures occur about

[5] For generalized land-use associations in the various regions of Burma, see Map 26.

once every ten years; previously they caused famines, but now rice can readily be brought in from lower Burma. Sorghum has long been an alternative food here for poor people and is very useful as fodder. Oil from sesamum and peanuts is vital to the Burmese diet. The dry zone supplies most of the country's requirements for edible oil, though in pre-war times small imports were necessary. Oilseed cake (after oil extraction), beans, and cotton fiber are the chief exportable surplus items of dry-zone agriculture.

Strict Buddhists are vegetarians; but nearly every Burmese consumes some animal protein. All eat fish, and fishing is the most important non-agricultural pursuit. Indeed, fish are a major item in the diet, being consumed fresh or in the form of a pungent fermented fish paste. Few Burmans are so strict as to refuse eggs. Many eat pork and poultry as well as beef, though pigs and cattle are never kept primarily for food. Poultry are ubiquitous in Burmese villages, but are bred for the sporting qualities of the fighting cocks.

Cattle of the zebu (Indian) variety and water buffaloes are kept by Burmese farmers chiefly as draft animals for plowing and for pulling carts. In Burma as a whole before the war, the ratio was four head of cattle and one buffalo to every 16 persons. Buffaloes are used primarily in the wet-rice zone, an aquatic habitat well suited to their requirements. About one-third of the cattle are normally in the dry zone which is constantly called upon to supply draft bullocks for the humid areas of Lower Burma, where the death rate of bullocks is high.

Dry-zone farmers live in nucleated village settlements, the dwellings grouped erratically in a maze of dusty lanes and shaded by groves of mango or tamarind trees and clumps of cultivated bamboo. The typical house is about one-third verandah and is built on piles that raise the floor five feet or so above the ground. The space beneath is used as a stable for livestock, a tool shed, and as a workshop or a play yard. The frame of the house structure is of timber; the walls are of bamboo woven in colored geometric designs; and roofs are generally thatched with palm leaves or grass. Small but significant portions of the diet are provided by the fruit trees and gardens planted around the houses and by betel-nut (areca) palms and toddy palms planted where ground water is adequate.

Nearly every village has a Buddhist pagoda which dominates the scene with its tapered white spire. Often there is more than one pagoda, and grouped nearby around a courtyard are several large wooden buildings set on piles and decorated with curved gables. These house the brotherhood of monks who have renounced ordinary life and taken Buddhist vows of poverty and simplicity. Every boy is taught the alphabet and elements of religion by the monks and, according to Burmese tradition, is expected to spend at least a few weeks as a novice in the monastery.

The principal towns of the dry zone are the river ports which act as collecting stations for agricultural products. The largest oil fields of Burma, found in a 90-mile belt from Yenangyat south, have given rise to barge and pipeline shipping towns. In prewar times all these river points were served by the steamers of the Irrawaddy Flotilla company, which was founded in the 1860's to convey troops, stores, and mail in British Burma and to provide general service to Mandalay, then the capital of independent Upper Burma. Before 1942 the company had over 600 vessels and formerly carried 8 million passengers and 1.2 million tons of cargo in a year. During the war 40 per cent of the craft were destroyed. Service has been restored under government ownership, and the company renamed the Inland Water Transport Board, Irrawaddy Section (Figure 95).

Other important towns of the dry zone are served by the meter-gauge Burma railway system, the main line of which parallels the Irrawaddy from Rangoon northward to Mandalay (population 173,000 in 1952), the largest river and rail center of the whole region. The railway runs up the Sittang valley, sending out two spurs westward to the dry zone; then it crosses the river at Ava near Mandalay and, after sending out a third spur line, continues northward to Katha and Myitkyina outside the dry zone.

Fig. 95 • A river steamer operated by the Inland Water Transport Board at a wharf in Bassein on the Ngawin River in the eastern Irrawaddy delta. Note the small river launches at the left and the native-style craft, hand-propelled by crossed oars. The Irrawaddy and its tributaries form the basis for one of the great inland waterway systems in the world. Especially in Lower Burma the river steamers constitute the main lines of communications, augmented by countless native craft ranging from large country boats carrying several hundred tons of cargo to small sampans carrying a few sacks of grain or several passengers. (Robert E. Huke.)

| Lower Burma:
| The wet-rice zone [6]

If it is true, as Sauer [7] believes, that the Indochinese peninsula was the prehistoric hearth area of the Old World fishing and planting culture, then the early nineteenth-century villages of the lower Irrawaddy perhaps represented a modified survival of this ancient way of life. The scattered settlements here were primarily dependent upon fishing carried on by means of weirs, nets, and hooks. The rights of fisheries were jealously guarded, but attachment to agricultural land was loose. Mere temporary fields were cleared in the flood plains for subsistence rice growing.

In 1850 Lower Burma was inhabited by less than a million Burmans and Karens, the latter then a preliterate non-Buddhistic ethnic group which had entered the country before the Burmans. It is possible that Lower Burma had not always been so empty, because there is record of the destruction in 1756 by Burmans of the second Mon (Talaing) kingdom, abandonment of land, and the subsequent decline of its capital, Pegu. With the decay of Pegu, an old port on a small river near the Sittang, owing mainly to silt deposition, Rangoon in the eighteenth century became the chief port, but it was hardly more than a fishing village when Lower Burma fell to the British in 1853.

When the opening of the Suez Canal (1869) put European markets within reach, a wave of agricultural settlers swept into the lower Irrawaddy and Sittang valleys. Supported by the increasing Indian and other Asiatic markets, agricultural expansion continued until 1930. Rice cultivation in Lower Burma increased from 1.4 million acres in 1865 to 9.9 million acres in 1930. During the same period, population grew from 2.2 million to 8.9 million in Lower Burma. The vast majority of these pioneer settlers were Burmans from the dry zone, but some were Karens from the hills. Others, who came as seasonal farm laborers, traders and transport workers, were Tamils, Telegus, and Bengalis from India proper.

Under a system closely approaching rice monoculture in the rich delta lands, the country has become one of the world's foremost low-cost rice producers. After clearing, the land is diked, planted, and allowed to be inundated by the natural rainfall of 60-100 inches received in four months

[6] "A vast area of thick jungle with a secure rainfall rapidly brought under cultivation by peasant proprietors with seasonal labor and a ready supply of capital producing a single crop for the export market." J. S. Furnivall, *An Introduction to the Political Economy of Burma* (Rangoon: Burma Book Club, 1931), p. 54.

[7] Carl O. Sauer, *Agricultural Origins and Dispersals* (New York: American Geographical Society, 1952), pp. 24-32.

Fig. 96 • Hand sowing of sprouted rice without transplanting. Diked fields such as these in the Irrawaddy delta region of lower Burma are plowed and puddled after the onset of the summer monsoon. Controlled irrigation is not practiced, except insofar as dikes have been constructed to protect the land from inundation at the time of the high spring tides. Note that the size of the fields is much greater than in East Asia and most other areas in Southeast Asia. Transplantation is practiced in Burma, but more in the irrigated areas of the dry zone, where water is scarce, than in the delta region. The laborer's appearance suggests that he is not a Burmese but an Indian employed at the time of planting. The size of landholdings in the delta region has made the use of migrant labor necessary. His presence suggests also the diversified composition of the delta population, primarily Burmese, but also partly Karen and Indian. *(Robert E. Huke.)*

(Figure 96). No irrigation is needed; indeed, the fields are protected against flooding from the main rivers and the sea. Deep-water varieties of rice are grown here without fertilization.

Burma's average rice yield per acre during 1935 to 1940 was about a third of Japan's yield and about half of China's. Though yield is low, the ratio of land per farmer is high. Typical farms vary from 8 to 10 acres, which is about all that one farm family can plant and harvest with the aid of neighbors, a single yoke of oxen, and simple implements. Before the second World War additional labor and capital were required to produce surplus. Burmans from the middle Irrawaddy and transient Indians supplied much of the extra labor needed. The cash outlay for wages, for seed and tools, and for land improvement was obtained at a high rate of interest from rice brokers and moneylenders, many of whom were Chettiars, a South Indian banking caste.

Postwar Burma has been in the anomalous position of contracting instead of expanding its agricultural production in the midst of a rice-

hungry Oriental world. From 1930 to 1940, rice production did not increase because of the decline in world markets, but after the second World
War and until the early 1950's market demands exceeded Burma's
rice supply. Its failure to resume its prewar output is due to political and
economic factors within the country, where two million acres of rice land
have reverted to jungle. In part, the cause has been destruction of sea
dikes and damage to crop land. Other causes have been political anarchy
and guerrilla warfare, shortages of labor and capital, and discrimination
against absentee landholders. The crux of the matter is that the previous
agricultural system was unsatisfactory to the peasants because they too
often found themselves in debt, received little return for their labor, and
lost their land to the moneylenders. Evidently, the peasants now cultivate
less land, securing a smaller surplus above subsistence requirements.

Rangoon

The rise of Rangoon from a
population of less than 50,000 one hundred years ago to 500,000 on the

Fig. 97 • A view of downtown Rangoon. Sule Pagoda is in the foreground, one of
the major Buddhist shrines in the city. The Independence Monument in the middleground
commemorates the independence of Burma from British rule. In the background are
public buildings, and beyond them is the Rangoon River with its wharves and warehouses.
Rangoon is one of the great Asian cities developed by foreigners that act as centers for
the organization and development of the newly independent Asian nations. (Robert E.
Huke.)

eve of the second World War resulted chiefly from its position as the world's greatest rice and teak port (Figure 97). The site, 20 miles up the Rangoon River at the southern extremity of a ridge running southward from the Pegu range, has the advantage of controlling the rail and road approaches to both the Irrawaddy and Sittang valleys. Although the river is subject to large tidal variations, the water is sufficiently deep (28 feet) for ocean-going vessels. The four deltaic creeks that converge here are used by small craft, and the Twante Canal to the southwest provides access for river steamers to the main streams of the delta and Upper Burma.

Rangoon's population has always been markedly unstable and characterized by ethnic diversity. At the last census in 1941 it was more than half Indian and only one-third Burmese. Chinese (8 per cent) more than twice outnumbered all inhabitants of European or part-European origin. Wartime losses of foreign population and recent crowding of refugees driven by guerrilla warfare from the surrounding rural territory made the population more Burmese in composition (estimated 64 per cent, as compared to 21 per cent Indian or Pakistani and 9 per cent Chinese, according to the sample survey of January, 1950). The number of inhabitants had increased to 613,000 by that date.

As the capital and center for foreign financial interests, Rangoon attracted industry. Rice milling concentrated here because of its close connection with the export trade, although some mills were located in the market towns of the rice districts and in smaller ports of Moulmein, Bassein, and Akyab. The largest sawmills and the only large refinery in the country were attracted to the Rangoon waterfront for similar reasons. Some refining and considerable sawmilling occurred near the sources of oil and teakwood in central Burma.

Outlying coasts and highlands

The populated part of the Arakan coastal lowland from Sandoway north to the East Pakistan border consists of numerous islands and a series of small plains separated by rocky headlands. Prevalence of rice cultivation and of palm groves and gardens around the settlement shows economic as well as climatic resemblances to Lower Burma. Akyab has the largest local hinterland and serves as the chief port for some one million inhabitants of the region. The Arakanese, though kin to the Burmans of the central Irrawaddy, speak a distinct dialect and show racial modification. Burma's intercourse with India for many centuries was through this coast, and there is today a fairly large and distinct Bengali-speaking (East Pakistani) population.

Tennasserim is like Arakan in the north-south alignment of its coastal mountains and of its beautiful island archipelago; but Tenasserim is unlike Arakan in the granitic composition of its bedrock and the associated tin and tungsten mining. As in Arakan, the sea is depended upon for transportation, and settlement is spotty because of concentration on small tracts of flat land. Rice is predominant, especially in the north around Moulmein (1953 population 103,000), the third largest city of Burma and most important town in the region. Because the dry season is shorter than elsewhere in Burma, the climate is suitable for rubber. Estates existed before the second World War near Tavoy and Mergui, but production of rubber never reached quotas set by international agreement. Tenasserim's two million inhabitants are comprised not only of Burmans but also of Karens and Mons in the northern section, and of Tavoyans and Shans in the southern section, with Indian and Chinese traders in the coastal towns.

The population of the sparsely settled uplands east of the Irrawaddy and Sittang is dominantly Shan and Karen, with minor groups also present, such as Palaung, Wa, and Lolo. Chinese from Yün-nan are the largest foreign group. The Shans, related by language to the Thai of Siam, are widely distributed in hill-top settlements, some of which serve as the centers of some 30 small feudal states. Despite their traditional antagonism toward the Burmans, the Shans are organized within the Burmese Union as a semiautonomous unit. The Wa state and Karenni are controlled directly by the central Rangoon government (see page 260, Chapter 13).

The Shan plateau has great potential value to Burma for economic development, as it produces a wide range of tropical and temperate crops and is capable of receiving many settlers. Each of the two railroad terminals—Lashio and Kalaw—is the starting point for roads reaching out to China and Siam. No one can foretell whether these roads, particularly that leading to China, will become main traffic arteries or function only as routes between the local border areas. Mining of lead-silver ore, wolframite, and tin may be revived with the restoration of internal stability in Burma.

The western and northern mountainous borderlands, including the upper Chindwin and Irrawaddy valleys, remain the least developed territories of Burma. Large tracts of dense forest are completely uninhabited. Kachins predominate in the north around Bhamo and Myitkyina; Nagas along the Assam frontier of India; Chins in the west near the Pakistan and Manipur state (Indian) boundaries. The mountain tribal groups live in settlements on the higher slopes and defensible ridges away from the damp, unhealthy valleys and engage in hunting, gathering, and the cultivation of upland dry rice or maize in burnt-over clearings (*taungya*)

Fig. 98 • A Kachin farmer planting in a newly burned *taungya* clearing near Mayan in Kachin state, one of the semiautonomous political units for the non-Burmese minority groups in the Union of Burma. The charred logs and stumps remain and gradually will decay, fertilizing the crops to be planted. The land is never plowed, but is hoed at those places where seeds, usually of upland rice or maize, will be deposited. Burning ordinarily takes place toward the end of the dry season, and the smell of woodsmoke at that time is prevalent not only in upland Burma but also in similar areas in Thailand, Laos, Cambodia, Vietnam, and in much of archipelagic Southeast Asia. Under the British, the destruction of timber resources was countered to a degree by the requirement that the shifting cultivators replant their fields with teak when they abandon them after several years of cultivation. *(Robert E. Huke.)*

(Figure 98). Parts of the territory were unadministered and inaccessible during the British period. Although penetrated by military roads from India during the second World War, the region has lapsed again into obscurity. The Naga and Chin tribes are under special administration by the central government of Burma. Kachins, the most articulate, are organized as a semiautonomous federal state in the Burmese Union.

Political integration and economic development

The most pressing problem of independent Burma is political integration. The slow recovery of the country from the semianarchy that prevailed during the Japanese occupation is rooted in the previous disrespect for the British government, so long regarded as alien and hostile. The Burmans themselves are still in the throes of transformation from a social and political system based on unwritten popular traditions and on the personal authority of leaders to a system based on formal legislation, elected representation, and administration by bureau.

There is also the question of relationships between the several ethnic authorities and the Burmans who constitute only two-thirds of the population of the country. Provision for the rights of frontier peoples such as Shans and Kachins, who predominate in their respective territories, has proven easier than for the Karens. Numbering probably 1.6 million, the Karens are the largest minority (9-10 per cent) and are not restricted to the uplands of Karenni and Tenasserim, but are mingled with the Burmans in the Irrawaddy-Sittang delta region. Indians and Chinese are welcome only if they become citizens and make Burma their homeland.

The economic condition of Burma is an interrelated and perhaps an equally important cause of unrest. The national income of Burma is estimated to be something over one-half of the previous level. This does not mean that the peasants are reduced to starvation, but it does mean that they are reduced very nearly to a subsistence economy. What is desired and is being planned for by the Burmese government is a renewal of export trade, capital investment, and development of local industries without reestablishment of the politico-economic system introduced by the British, whereby foreigners benefited more than Burmans from the enhanced values of land and resources.

SELECTED GEOGRAPHICAL BIBLIOGRAPHY

1. Andrus, J. R. *Burmese Economic Life,* Stanford, California: University Press, 1947.
2. Christian, John L. *Modern Burma: A Survey of Political and Economic Development.* Berkeley: Univ. of California Press, 1942.
3. Collins, Maurice. *Last and First in Burma (1941–1948),* New York: The Macmillan Co., 1956.
4. DeTerra, Hellmut. "Component Geographic Factors of the Natural Regions of Burma," *Annals of Association of American Geographers,* June, 1944, pp. 67-96.
5. DeTerra, Hellmut, and Hallam L. Movius, Jr. "Research on Early Man in Burma," *Trans. American Philosophical Society,* 32 (1943), Part 3, pp. 265-436.
6. Furnivall, J. S. *An Introduction to the Political Economy of Burma,* Rangoon: Burma Book Club, 1931; "Political Reconstruction in Post-War Burma," *Pacific Affairs,* 16 (1943), pp. 277-300; "Twilight in Burma: Reconquest and After," *Pacific Affairs,* 22 (1949), in two parts, pp. 3-20, pp. 155-72; *Colonial Policy and Practice,* Cambridge: Cambridge University Press, 1948.
7. Spate, O. H. K. "Beginnings of Industrialization in Burma," *Economic Geography,* 17 (1941), pp. 75-92; *Burma Setting, Geography,* Calcutta:

Longmans, Green, 1943; "The Burmese Village," *Geographical Review*, 35 (1945), pp. 523-44.

8. ———, and L. W. Trueblood. "Rangoon: A Study in Urban Geography," *Geographical Review*, 32 (1942), pp. 56-73.

9. Stamp, L. D. "The Vegetation of Burma," *Univ. of Rangoon Research Monograph*, No. 1, Calcutta: 1925; "Burma: An Undeveloped Monsoon Country," *Geographical Review*, 20 (1930), pp. 86-109; "The Irrawaddy River," *Geographical Journal*, 95 (1940), pp. 329-56.

10. Welsh, Janet. "Burma's Development Problems," *Far Eastern Survey*, August, 1956, pp. 113-122.

Comments

Brief regional descriptions have been made by Stamp, Spate, and DeTerra. Each has also treated particular aspects of Burma: Stamp, geology, natural vegetation, and drainage; Spate, urban and rural settlements, industrialization; DeTerra, prehistory and the physical environment of the dry zone and the Shan plateau.

The best general studies by American authors are those of Christian and Andrus. Christian is concerned primarily with the historical development of Burma's social and political life; Andrus is more concerned with economic matters. Furnivall is the most sympathetic and perhaps the most understanding observer of Burma. His early classic, not widely available in this country, is supplemented by several articles on current developments in Burma and by his later book comparing colonial policies in Burma and Netherlands India. Collins' book and Welsh's article are examples of the considerable postwar literature covering Burma's political and economic affairs.

South Asia

PEOPLES AND CULTURES

THE GREAT TONGUE-SHAPED PROMONTORY THAT JUTS SOUTHWARD
from the continent of Asia is known to the world as India. This part of
Asia, however, contains Pakistan and a half dozen smaller independent
countries and colonies in addition to the Republic of India (Map 27).
The word India[1] is no longer an accurate designation for the countries
lying south of the Soviet and Chinese boundaries, between Iran on the
west and Burma on the east. This group of countries, including Afghanistan and the Himalayan countries, Nepal, and Bhutan—together with
Ceylon and the smaller islands of the Bay of Bengal and Arabian Sea, and
the coastal Portuguese territories—collectively forms a geographic realm
best described as South Asia, standing as it does between the Southwestern and Southeastern realms of Asia. The realm includes the territory in
the British Indian Empire at the date of its dissolution (August 15, 1947)
and all the adjacent territories, except Burma, which were formerly under

---

[1] There is no word in any of the languages of the realm to properly designate
South Asia. The word *India* is a European corruption of *sindhu* (meaning "river" in
Sanskrit, whence also *Indus*) and was transmitted to Europe through Iranian usage
and the writings of ancient Greek geographers. The term has been applied in the
sense of Greater India to all of South and Southeast Asia since the fifteenth century.
The concept of India as a precise geographic and political entity dates from the
nineteenth century during the period of British rule in South Asia.

TABLE XXII-1

THE NATIONS OF SOUTH ASIA

Name	Political status	Area (sq. mi.)	Population	Capital
Afghanistan	Independent kingdom	c. 260,000	12,000,000 (1952) *	Kabul
Bhutan	Kingdom, foreign affairs controlled by India	c. 18,000	300,000 (1951) *	Punakha
Ceylon	Dominion, member of (British) Commonwealth	25,332	8,098,636 (1953)	Colombo
India	Republic, member of (British) Commonwealth	1,135,141 †	356,691,760 (1951)	New Delhi
North East Frontier Agency	Assam frontier tracts and tribal areas under Indian control	c. 28,200	600,000 (1951) *	———
French India	Administered by India	197	362,100 (1948) *	Pondicherry
Jammu & Kashmir state	Area under Indian control	c. 55,000	3,600,000 (1951) *	Srinagar
Maldive islands	British-protected sultanate	c. 115	87,000 (1950) *	Male
Nepal	Independent kingdom	c. 54,000	8,600,000 (1953) *	Katmandu
Pakistan	Republic, member of (British) Commonwealth	364,737	75,842,165 (1951)	Karachi
Azad Kashmir and Gilgit agency	Area under Pakistan control	c. 27,300	800,000 (1951) *	Muzaffarabad
Portuguese India	Overseas province of Portugal	1,538	637,591 (1950)	Nova Goa
Sikkim	Kingdom, protectorate of India	2,745	137,725 (1951)	Gangtok
TOTAL, South Asia		1,972,305	467,756,977	

* Estimated population.
† Area included in census, 1951, except Sikkim.

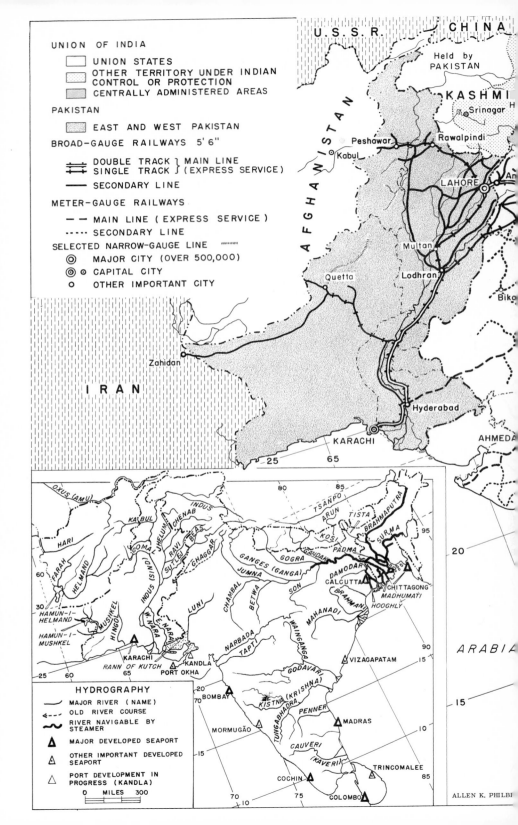

UNION OF INDIA
☐ UNION STATES
▨ OTHER TERRITORY UNDER INDIAN CONTROL OR PROTECTION
▨ CENTRALLY ADMINISTERED AREAS

PAKISTAN
▨ EAST AND WEST PAKISTAN

BROAD-GAUGE RAILWAYS 5'6"
━━ DOUBLE TRACK } MAIN LINE
━━ SINGLE TRACK } (EXPRESS SERVICE)
─── SECONDARY LINE

METER-GAUGE RAILWAYS
─ ─ MAIN LINE (EXPRESS SERVICE)
····· SECONDARY LINE

SELECTED NARROW-GAUGE LINE
◎ MAJOR CITY (OVER 500,000)
◉ CAPITAL CITY
○ OTHER IMPORTANT CITY

U.S.S.R.   CHINA
Held by PAKISTAN
KASHMI
Srinagar
AFGHANISTAN
Peshawar   Rawalpindi
Kabul
LAHORE   An
Multan
Lodhran
Quetta
Bika
Zahidan
IRAN
Hyderabad
AHMEDA
KARACHI
25   65

OXUS (AMU)
HARI   KABUL   INDUS
FARAH   GOMAL   JHELUM   CHENAB
HELMAND   INDUS (SIND)   RAVI BEAS   SUTLEJ   GHAGGAR   TSANPO   TISTA   BRAHMAPUTRA
ARUN   SURMA
KOSI   95
60   GANGES (GANGA)   GOGRA   GANDAK   PADMA
JUMNA   SON   DAMODAR   SURMA
HAMUN-I-   CHAMBAL   CALCUTTA   CHITTAGONG
HELMAND   MUSHKEL   BETWA   BRAHMANI   MADHUMATI
HAMUN-I-   HINGOL   W. NARA   LUNI   NARBADA   MAHANADI   HOOGHLY
MUSHKEL   E. NARA   TAPTI   WAINGANGA   20
KARACHI   KANDLA   VIZAGAPATAM
RANN OF KUTCH   GODAVARI   90
PORT OKHA   BOMBAY   15
KISTNA (KRISHNA)
MORMUGÃO   TUNGABHADRA   PENNER   MADRAS
10
CAUVERI (KAVERI)   TRINCOMALEE
COCHIN   85
COLOMBO

ARABIA
20
15
15

HYDROGRAPHY
── MAJOR RIVER (NAME)
◄-- OLD RIVER COURSE
∿ RIVER NAVIGABLE BY STEAMER
▲ MAJOR DEVELOPED SEAPORT
△ OTHER IMPORTANT DEVELOPED SEAPORT
△ PORT DEVELOPMENT IN PROGRESS (KANDLA)
0   MILES   300

70   75   80   85   10

ALLEN K. PHILBR

SOUTH ASIA

Lhasa

TIBET

SIKKIM
BHUTAN

25

NEPAL

Darjeeling

Katmandu

Moradabad
Bareilly

Dacca

Lucknow

Patna

Chittagong

BURMA

Agra

KANPUR

Benares

CALCUTTA

Allahabad

20

Jubbulpore

Nagpur

MILES   300

0

90

Vizagapatnam

15

BAY OF BENGAL

Sholapur   HYDERABAD

Poona

BAY

Port. Goa

MADRAS

10

BANGALORE

Mysore   Salem

LACCADIVE
IS

Calicut

CEYLON

85

Kandy

MAP 27

Trivandrum

Colombo

5

70   10   75   80

British hegemony.[2] South Asia thus coincides to a remarkable degree with the territory historically associated in our geographic concept of India, though it is more inclusive than the present political entity of India.

South Asia is of nearly continental dimensions. The compact form and broad attachment of this subcontinent to the much larger land mass of Asia might lead one to overlook the fact that its total area is nearly two million square miles (Table XXII–1)—an area that exceeds by 275,000 square miles that of the mainland of Europe west of the Soviet Union. The distance from the extreme western part of Pakistan to the undemarcated eastern border of the Indian Union where it meets Burma and China is somewhat in excess of 2,100 miles; the north-south distance from the Afghan-Soviet boundary to the south coast of Ceylon is approximately the same. Superimposed on North America, the South Asian realm would stretch from the Atlantic seaboard to the Rocky mountains and from Hudson Bay to the Gulf of Mexico.

The inhabitants of South Asia form an aggregate population of 468 million (estimated at 489 million in 1954). This is one-fifth of the world's population, estimated at roughly 2,600 million (1953). Among the major population clusters on the earth, only two others contain more people—Europe and East Asia. The countries of Europe and the U.S.S.R., including the area of primarily European settlement in Siberia, have an aggregate population of some 600 million, surpassing South Asia by a large margin, though the latter exceeds by 85 million the population of all Europe west of the Soviet Union. East Asia (China-Japan-Korea) surpasses all other population clusters with perhaps 712 million inhabitants. Thus, South Asia ranks as the third major concentration of human beings in the world. There are no other population clusters even half as large as that in South Asia. Not merely on the basis of numbers alone, but also on account of its cultural, political and economic importance, South Asia ranks as one of the most important centers of human affairs today.

Population distribution

Within South Asia population is markedly concentrated in the lowlands with adequate moisture for agriculture. The largest region of high density is a belt that begins in West Pakistan and runs across North India into East Pakistan (see Map 27a) occupying the well-watered portions of the vast Indo-Gangetic plain. This 1600-mile belt, which contains over 200 million people, spreads throughout the plain of the Ganges River and its tributaries in India, fills the Bengal delta both in India and East Pakistan, and extends into the Punjab section of the Indus River plains in West Pakistan. Here

[2] See Chapter XXIV.

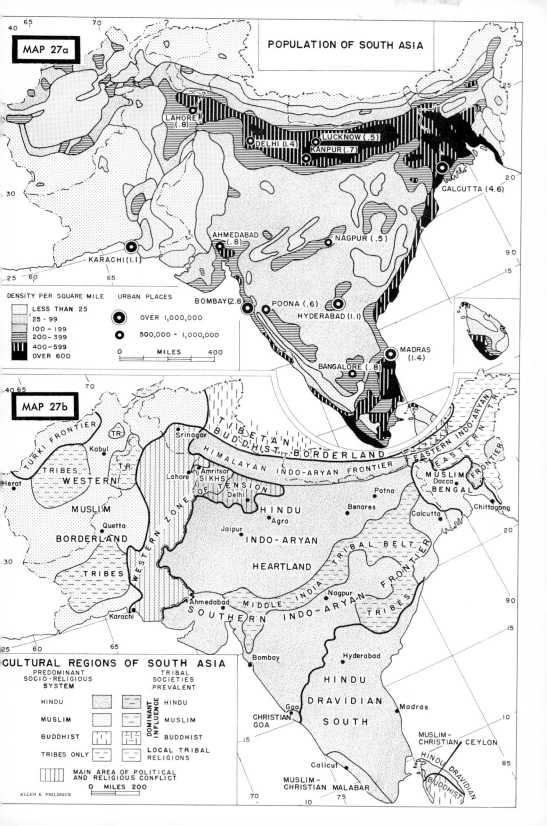

MAP 27a

POPULATION OF SOUTH ASIA

LAHORE (.8)
DELHI (1.4)   LUCKNOW (.5)
KANPUR (.7)
CALCUTTA (4.6)
KARACHI (1.1)
AHMEDABAD (.8)   NAGPUR (.5)
BOMBAY (2.8)   POONA (.6)
HYDERABAD (1.1)
BANGALORE (.8)   MADRAS (1.4)

DENSITY PER SQUARE MILE   URBAN PLACES

LESS THAN 25
25 - 99
100 - 199   OVER 1,000,000
200 - 399
400 - 599   500,000 - 1,000,000
OVER 600

0   MILES   400

MAP 27b

TURKI FRONTIER
TR
Kabul   TR
TRIBES
WESTERN   Srinagar   TIBETAN BUDDHIST BORDERLAND   EASTERN INDO-ARYAN T.R.
Amritsar   HIMALAYAN INDO-ARYAN FRONTIER
Lahore   SIKHS   MUSLIM
Herat   ZONE OF TENSION   Dacca   FRONTIER
MUSLIM   Delhi   Patna   BENGAL
BORDERLAND   HINDU   Chittagong
Quetta   Jaipur   Agra   Benares   Calcutta
WESTERN   INDO-ARYAN   MIDDLE INDIA TRIBAL BELT
TRIBES   HEARTLAND   INDO-ARYAN FRONTIER
Karachi   Ahmedabad   MIDDLE   Nagpur   TRIBES
SOUTHERN   INDO-ARYAN
Bombay   Hyderabad
HINDU
DRAVIDIAN
CHRISTIAN   Goa   SOUTH   Madras
GOA
MUSLIM-
CHRISTIAN CEYLON
Calicut   HINDU DRAVIDIAN
MUSLIM-   BUDDHIST
CHRISTIAN MALABAR

CULTURAL REGIONS OF SOUTH ASIA

PREDOMINANT   TRIBAL
SOCIO-RELIGIOUS   SOCIETIES
SYSTEM   PREVALENT

HINDU   HINDU

MUSLIM   MUSLIM   DOMINANT INFLUENCE

BUDDHIST   BUDDHIST

TRIBES ONLY   LOCAL TRIBAL
                     RELIGIONS

MAIN AREA OF POLITICAL
AND RELIGIOUS CONFLICT

0   MILES 200

ALLEN K. PHILBRICK

the average density is at least 400 persons per square mile, often 600, and in places as much as 1,000 per square mile. The continuous belt of high density ends before the Indus River is reached, but there is an extension with only minor interruptions along the east coastal plain of the peninsula. The tracts of equal density are narrower and discontinuous along the west coast of India.

The main population concentrations of South Asia are peripheral to the peninsular uplands, which appear as a huge quadrilateral of less-densely settled territory interposed between the crowded regions. The general density of the peninsular uplands is less than 200 persons per square mile, and in the most rugged parts less than 100, though in the interior valleys of central India and in the western and southern parts of the Dekkan plateau the density exceeds 200. Northeastern India (Assam) is a minor extension from the main populated area of South Asia. Ceylon shows a striking contrast in density, ranging from over 600 per square mile in the southwestern coast to less than 25 in the southeast and northern interior.

The occupied areas of South Asia constitute a fairly compact zone of close settlement, having an over-all density approaching 300 per square mile, and separated from the other population centers of Eurasia by large areas of thinly settled or empty land. The sharpest decrease of density occurs along the flanks of the rugged Himalaya and the associated mountain ranges on the northern and eastern borders of the realm. Entirely vacant areas exist here at high elevations and beyond are still more extensive areas devoid of permanent settlement in southern U.S.S.R. and western China. There are equally empty areas to the west in the desert plains of India (Rajasthan) and in the arid mountains and basins of West Pakistan (Baluchistan) and southern Afghanistan. But here the vacant spaces are broken at wide intervals by oasis settlements, the largest of which are in the lower Indus plain of West Pakistan (Sind) and in the northern and southern piedmont belts of Afghanistan.

The ecumene of South Asia is, therefore, a well defined region shut off by deserts and mountains on the landward side and fronting on a vast ocean along the shores of which are few other population centers. Here an ancient culture took root and developed in a distinctively Indian way, though not without receiving strong influences from outside, coming at first chiefly by land routes and in the modern period by sea.

Population growth

Far back in history, the Indian subcontinent appears as a region of outstanding population concentration. Buddhist and Greek records indicate that between b.c. 400 and 300 the crafts and commerce of northern India were at a level of development comparable to that of later medieval times in Europe. The population is estimated to have been 100 to 140 millions at a time of unusual prosperity and political stability in the third century B.C., when much of the subcontinent was ruled by the Buddhist king, Asoka.

During the 2,000 years between the ancient and the modern period of India's history, population does not seem to have made permanent gains, though undoubtedly it would increase in times of peace and adequate rainfall and decrease abruptly during wars, famines, or epidemics. In 1650 India is believed to have had at least 100 million people while at that date Europe, including Russia, had approximately the same number. Not until 1800 did Europe as a whole clearly exceed India. This means that for most of recorded history India has been more densely settled than Europe.

During the 79-year span up to 1951 [3] the population of India and Pakistan has grown from 255,166,000 to 437,449,000 allowing for corrections of the first official census returns of 1872 so that the territories included are the same for both dates. This growth of 58 per cent is certainly phenomenal when compared to the slow and erratic rate of India's increase prior to the nineteenth century. But India's modern rate of growth is not exceptional in relation to the rate of growth in Japan or in western countries such as Great Britain, Germany, Russia, or the United States, all of which have exceeded India's percentage increase. Indeed the annual rate of increase in India of 0.60 per cent a year is slightly less than the estimated rate for the whole world—0.69 per cent a year over the past 100 years. Population growth of South Asia thus is only one wave in a worldwide population upsurge set in motion by the commercial and industrial revolutions.

The three most significant facts about the growth of population in the Indian subcontinent are: (a) the huge absolute increases, (b) the continuing high level of natural fertility, and (c) the grinding poverty of the people. Accelerated rate of increase during recent decades has resulted in increments of almost unbelievable numbers in the Indian Union and Pakistan: 1921 to 1931, 32 million (10.6 per cent increase); 1931 to 1941, 51 million (15 per cent); and 1941 to 1951, 48 million (12.4 per cent). Prior to 1920 growth was extremely sporadic, decades of marked increase such as 1881 to 1891 and 1901 to 1911 alternating with decades in which famine or epidemics brought abrupt rises in the death rate. However, from 1921 to 1941 India enjoyed an unprecedented period without catastrophe, and in the decade of 1941 to 1951 when famines in Bihar, Bengal,

---

[3] Since 1872, the knowledge of India's population is more certain because of the censuses taken by the British government each decade and continued by the new governments of India and Pakistan. Ceylon has had censuses at irregular intervals, but true censuses have never been undertaken in Afghanistan or Bhutan, and Nepal's census is not of a high order of reliability.

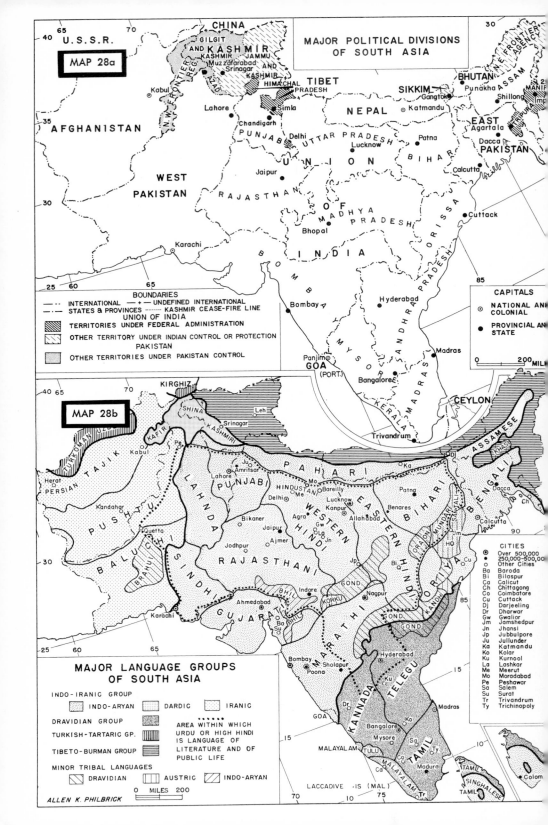

MAJOR POLITICAL DIVISIONS OF SOUTH ASIA

MAP 28a

CHINA

U.S.S.R.

AFGHANISTAN

GILGIT
KASHMIR JAMMU
Muzzafarabad Srinagar
AND
KASHMIR
HIMACHAL
PRADESH TIBET
SIKKIM
BHUTAN
N.E. FRONTIER AGENCY
Punakha Assam
Shillong
MANIF
Kabul
Lahore
Chandigarh Simla
PUNJAB Delhi UTTAR PRADESH
NEPAL
Katmandu
EAST
Agartala
DACCA
PAKISTAN
Jaipur
UNION Lucknow
Patna
BIHAR
Calcutta

WEST
PAKISTAN
RAJASTHAN
OF
MADHYA
PRADESH
Bhopal
INDIA
ORISSA
Cuttack

Karachi

BOMBAY
Bombay
Hyderabad
ANDHRA PRADESH
MYSORE
MADRAS
Madras

BOUNDARIES
- – · – · INTERNATIONAL
- – · – UNDEFINED INTERNATIONAL
- – · · – STATES & PROVINCES
- – · · · KASHMIR CEASE-FIRE LINE

UNION OF INDIA
TERRITORIES UNDER FEDERAL ADMINISTRATION
OTHER TERRITORY UNDER INDIAN CONTROL OR PROTECTION

PAKISTAN
OTHER TERRITORIES UNDER PAKISTAN CONTROL

CAPITALS
NATIONAL AND COLONIAL
PROVINCIAL AND STATE

0   200   MILES

Panjim
GOA
(PORT.)
Bangalore
CEYLON

MAP 28b

KIRGHIZ
SHINA
TURKOMAN UZBEK
TAJIK
KAFIR
KASHMIRI
Leh
Srinagar
PAHARI
ASSAMESE
KHASI

PERSIAN
Herat
PUSHTU
Kabul
Kandahar
LAHNDA
PUNJABI
Lahore Amritsar
HINDUSTAN
Delhi Me
Mo Bareilly
Lucknow
Kanpur
Benares
Patna
BIHAR
BENGALI
Dacca
Ch
Calcutta

Quetta
BALUCHI
BRAHUI
SINDHI
RAJASTHANI
Bikaner
Jaipur
Ajmer
Jodhpur
WESTERN HINDI
Agra
Gw Jn
Allahabad
EASTERN HINDI
ORAON
MUNDARI
HO
ORIYA
Cu

Karachi
GUJARATI
Ahmedabad
BHIL
Indore
KORKU
GOND
Nagpur
GOND
GOND
ORIYA

Bombay
MARATHI
Poona
Sholapur
Hyderabad
TELEGU
Madras

MAJOR LANGUAGE GROUPS OF SOUTH ASIA

INDO-IRANIC GROUP
INDO-ARYAN   DARDIC   IRANIC

DRAVIDIAN GROUP
TURKISH-TARTARIC GP.
TIBETO-BURMAN GROUP

MINOR TRIBAL LANGUAGES
DRAVIDIAN   AUSTRIC   INDO-ARYAN

AREA WITHIN WHICH URDU OR HIGH HINDI IS LANGUAGE OF LITERATURE AND OF PUBLIC LIFE

0   MILES   200

GOA
KANNADA
Bangalore
Mysore
TULU
MALAYALAM
Madura
LACCADIVE IS (MAL)
TAMIL
TAMIL
SINGHALESE
TAMIL
Colom.

CITIES
- ● Over 500,000
- ● 250,000–500,000
- ○ Other Cities

Ba	Baroda
Bi	Bilaspur
Ca	Calicut
Ch	Chittagong
Co	Coimbatore
Cu	Cuttack
Dj	Darjeeling
Dr	Dharwar
Gw	Gwalior
Jm	Jamshedpur
Jn	Jhansi
Jp	Jubbulpore
Ju	Jullunder
Ka	Katmandu
Ko	Kolar
Ku	Kurnool
La	Lashkar
Me	Meerut
Mo	Moradabad
Pe	Peshawar
Sa	Salem
Su	Surat
Tr	Trivandrum
Ty	Trichinopoly

ALLEN K. PHILBRICK

and South India caused uncounted millions of deaths, and several hundreds of thousands died because of religious strife in the Punjab following the partition of India (1947), there was still an enormous increase. These three consecutive decades of rapid growth added nearly 132 million to the population of India and Pakistan—a figure which is 60 per cent in excess of Japan's total population in 1950, or 88 per cent of the whole U.S. population in 1950.

India and Pakistan are still in an early stage of the shift from an agrarian to an urban-industrial economy and show the usual wide margin of births over deaths. The annual death rate has gradually dropped from 40 to 45 per thousand at the beginning of the century to about 30 per thousand, while the birth rate has remained generally in the range from 40 to 45 per thousand, giving promise of still further rapid population increases of 10 to 15 per cent per decade. The growth trend has yet shown little evidence of stabilization, following the cycle of rapid growth, as in the countries of northwestern Europe where the full social effects of the urban-industrial economy have been felt.

The teeming masses of India and Pakistan, who owe their increases to the reduction of warfare, famine, and disease, have not enjoyed the economic benefits of modern scientific and technological advances and have remained a poor, underfed, agrarian people. Overseas emigration is not a potential outlet because of political factors and the future millions will have to find their livelihood within the territory of the subcontinent. How long can the people of South Asia keep up their present rate of increase? How long can the resources of South Asia support their increasing numbers? Eventually the birth rate must fall or the death rate must rise in order to establish a new equilibrium. The questions of when and how the increase will diminish or stop have profound meaning for Asia and the rest of the world.

Cultural origins

In the northwestern mountain borderlands of South Asia there is archaeological evidence of cultures with food-producing technology sufficiently developed to support sedentary population some 5,000 to 7,000 years ago. Being near the Middle Eastern centers of Neolithic culture India was early to receive and doubtless contributed to the invention of pottery and polished stone tools, and the domestication of plants and animals. Following this Neolithic period which, perhaps, lasted until B.C. 5,000, Bronze Age farming villages existed in the mountain basins of Baluchistan between B.C. 3,000 and 4,000, linked to the ancient cultures farther west in Iran, Iraq, and Egypt.

Then two different peoples appeared in South Asia: the city builders of Mohenjo-daro and Harappa in the Indus plains, who were very likely the ancestral Dravidians, in B.C. 2,500; and the pastoral and agricultural Indo-Aryans (Sanskrit-speakers) who entered the Punjab and the Upper Ganges Plain between B.C. 1,500 and 1,000. It is from the blending of these two peoples that the peculiarly Hindu culture of India has evolved. The conquest of India by the Greeks under the leadership of Alexander in the fourth century B.C., and subsequent invasions by the Sakas and Kushans about the first and second centuries A.D., are events of secondary significance as compared to the synthesis of Dravidian and Indo-Aryan cultures that was going on. It was during this period before A.D. 1000 that there came into being a vaguely defined geographic entity recognizable as a kind of Indian homeland, stretching from the Himalaya to Cape Comorin and cradling not only Hinduism but for a time its offspring, Buddhism.

During the last millenium, the Persian-Afghan invasions and the European colonial expansion in South Asia have penetrated and modified Indian culture. The invaders fought with India, traded with India, and taught India. They tried to destroy Hindu civilization and to implant their own political and religious systems. While some of India's indigenous culture was altered or lost, most of it survived.

Thus, India's cultural and political evolution during most of recorded history has been characterized by an irregular succession of external contacts which have ultimately enriched Indian civilization. Today India and the adjacent countries in South Asia show as much if not more variety of racial composition and ethnic groupings than the continent of Europe.

Racial stocks

The bulk of the inhabitants of South Asia are of the same racial stock as the Caucasoid inhabitants of Europe and southwest Asia (Figure 99). In India and West Pakistan, Caucasoids with Mediterranean and Alpine or Nordic traits are similar though not identical with these subraces in Europe and show the strongest resemblances to kindred peoples in southwestern Asia. The bulk of the population belongs to the Mediterranean branch of the Caucasoids, the chief difference between this type in India and elsewhere being in the darker pigmentation. The palae-Mediterraneans with dark skin color, long, deeply-vaulted heads and slight build are dominant in the extreme southern peninsular region. The modern Mediterraneans, likewise long-headed but of olive-brown color and taller stature, are prevalent in the Gangetic plain, whereas the Irano-Afghan Mediterraneans of still lighter complexion and long convex noses are concentrated in the upper Indus valley and in the highlands of Afghanistan. Broad-headed Alpines with

Fig. 99 • The diverse racial composition of India's people is illustrated by these Hindu holy men who lead a life of contemplation and religious study in Uttar Kashi along the upper Ganga (Ganges) River in Uttar Pradesh, India. The man at left, holding a begging bowl, is probably of mixed Alpine racial stock, being round-headed (brachycephalic or mesocephalic) and displaying facial traits that may result from Mongoloid or proto-Australoid admixture. The handsome, curly-haired man in center represents the racially Mediterranean long-headed (dolichocephalic) stock. (*John E. Brush.*)

certain variations form an important element in the population of Baluchistan and Sind, the west coast near Bombay and the interior of the Indian peninsula, Ceylon, Bengal, and the central and the western Himalayas. Admixture of a tall long-headed Nordic race with light skin and hair colors, and with blue-gray eyes, is evident in the Hindu Kush and western Himalaya, but elsewhere these traits are rare.

The darker pigmentation of the Caucasoids in South Asia could be due to natural selection for its survival value in the intense sunlight of these latitudes but is more likely due to intermarriage with earlier black-skinned peoples: the Negritos and the Australoids. The Negritos, who are kin to the pygmy tribes of Malaya, the Philippines, New Guinea, and perhaps Africa most probably were the earliest humans in South Asia. Nothing more than the merest trace of this very dark, short, frizzly-haired race with infantile facial features appears among the forest tribes of the southern and northeastern highlands of the Indian mainland. Only among the dwindling Andaman islanders of the Bay of Bengal were pygmy traits, including steatopygia and tightly spiraled "peppercorn" hair, preserved

Fig. 100 • This peasant standing beside his bamboo-framed mud and thatch dwelling is spinning twine for fishnet weaving. He is an Oriya-speaking Hindu who lives in Balasore district, Orissa state, India. His features suggest a partial ancestry of the aboriginal tribes of middle India, who commonly have proto-Australoid traits such as broad noses, everted lips, and coarse facial features. Intermixtures of the aboriginal stock with Alpine and Mediterranean racial stock are particularly marked in Orissa and Madhya Pradesh where contacts between the races have been prolonged. *(John E. Brush.)*

Fig. 101 • The Bhotias of Tehri-Garhwal, Uttar Pradesh, are a farming and pastoral people, who live in India and customarily cross into Tibet on trading expeditions during summer when the mountain passes are open. The woman in center with braided hair and silver ornaments is spinning wool from which most of the clothing she wears is woven. The man at right is smoking tobacco in a water-pipe. The Bhotias are of medium or short stature with round heads, broad flat noses and prominent cheekbones, and they display the narrow Mongoloid eyes. None of the peoples of South Asia outside the Himalayan region and Assam show such clear-cut Mongoloid racial traits. *(John E. Brush.)*

unmixed until the twentieth century. Another dark-skinned stock, the proto-Australoid, was spread across the subcontinent before the arrival of the Caucasoids and enters deeply into the ancestry of the lower castes and poorer classes of Indian society today. Its members are characterized by medium stature, very wavy hair, broad noses, and rather coarse facial features (Figure 100). The purest survivals of this race are among the hill tribes of middle India, who exhibit strong affinities to the primitive Australians and certain aboriginal groups in the Australasian archipelago.

Peoples of Mongoloid racial stock are located on the peripheries of the realm to the north of the Hindu Kush and the main Himalayan range, in the foothills of the eastern Himalaya and in the Assam-Burma frontier mountains (Figure 101). Only in East Pakistan and Assam do Mongoloid traits appear in the plains population. There is present in the Himalayan foothills and the Indo-Burmese border region an old long-headed Mongoloid racial type that contrasts with other round-headed Mongoloid racial type, which has lighter skin and marked obliquity of eyes (owing to well developed epicanthic folds) and is found in the areas immediately adjacent to Tibet. In general the boundary of the Mongoloids marks an abrupt change in physical traits along the northern and eastern margins of the dominant Caucasoid stocks in South Asia.

Languages

Language even more than racial kinship influences the cultural grouping of South Asia's peoples. In many instances, cultural ties developed through the use of a single medium of communication bridge across racial differences. At first glance the linguistic differences within the realm would seem even more confusing than the racial differences; 179 official languages and 544 dialects were recognized in the former British Indian Empire alone. But more than 100 of these languages are insignificant speeches on the northern and eastern borders in the Tibeto-Burman tribal areas, and several scores of others are small tribal speeches in middle India and the western highlands in Pakistan and in Afghanistan. Speakers of these minor languages must of necessity learn the language prevailing in their respective territories, and in order to participate in public life they must become bilingual or even trilingual. For education, local government, and literature only about 15 regional languages are important, and for national affairs in India and Pakistan there are only four important languages: English, Hindi, Urdu, and Bengali.

In India and Pakistan the Indo-Aryan speech family is the most important both numerically and culturally. Languages belonging to this family are the mother tongue of at least 310 million people, more than 70 per cent of South Asia's population. All derive from the original Sanskrit of the prehistoric Indo-Aryan invaders and have probably been used in the subcontinent some 3,000 years. Sanskrit, the sacred language of Hinduism, and its later modification, Prakrit, the sacred language of Buddhism, became the vehicles of ancient Indian cultures, spreading their influence over much of India and beyond into Southeast Asia, and for a time even to Central Asia. Sanskrit has been the natural source of new words and its script, in various modified forms, is most widely used in India today.

The 12 modern Indo-Aryan languages now have a wide distribution (Map 28b) throughout the densely settled Indo-Gangetic plain. They spread from the south slopes of the central Himalaya to the lower Indus plain (Sind) in the west, to the Assam plain in the east, and across the Dekkan plateau about as far south as to a line running from Goa north of Hyderabad city to Puri on the coast of Orissa state.

Within this Indo-Aryan language region Hindi or its modified form, Hindustani, has come to be the modern *lingua franca* for trade and travel. Hindi, which stems from the local dialect used in the vicinity of Delhi, because of close affinities in grammar and vocabulary has readily spread to the Eastern Hindi, Bihari, Rajasthani, and Pahari areas. Hindi shows a tendency also to spread into the areas of Punjabi and Eastern Marathi. In this interior region, which might be called the Indo-Aryan heartland, it has become the language of literature, education and public life.

The peripheral languages of Indo-Aryan origin show divergences in script, grammar, and vocabulary; and they have developed more or less independently as the regional cultural media—especially Bengali, Marathi, and Gujarati. These "outer-band" languages (see Map 28b), including also Assamese, Oriya, and Sindhi, are being penetrated by Hindustani in its function as the language of commerce. Hindustani developed from Hindi in the courts of the Moslem Mughal emperors who ruled in Delhi and Agra before the British conquest. It uses many Arabic and Persian words and can be written either in the Urdu script (derived ultimately from Arabic) or in the Nagari script (derived from Sanskrit).

It would seem that either Hindi or Hindustani might satisfy India's need for a national tongue. Simple bazaar Hindustani is understood in the cities and towns of the whole Indo-Aryan region in both India and Pakistan; and it is intelligible to users of either Hindu or Urdu. Hindi's Nagari script and its associations with Hindu religious literature (written in Sanskrit) peculiarly suit it to predominantly Hindu India. Yet neither Hindi nor Hindustani is universally known or accepted in the Indian Union, owing chiefly to resistance in the south peninsula by a large Dravidian block of about 87 million people who comprise about 21 per cent of India's total population. The Dravidian languages are unrelated to the Indo-European tongues of the north. Long literary traditions characterize the four major Dravidian languages—Tamil, Telegu, Kannada, and Malayalam.

Urdu might seem suited to be Moslem (Muslim) Pakistan's national language by reason of its Perso-Arabic script and its association with the Arabic words of the sacred Koran. Yet, although Urdu is spreading into the non-Indo-Aryan, Pushtu-speaking northwest frontier, it meets with no small resistance among literate Bengalis, who not only possess a rich literature of their own but also are more accustomed to English or even Hindi as a second language.

English is therefore the only language common to all India, or to all Pakistan, and it is still the language of the central legislative bodies of both countries. The passing of the British Empire from the subcontinent has not been followed by a quick abandonment of the English language because of its practical advantages in national administration of government, post and rail services, and business affairs. English continues to be used widely in higher education, but it must always remain a speech of the intelligentsia. It seems likely to recede to the status of the major foreign language, being gradually replaced by the languages whose roots are closer to those of the speech of the masses.

Afghanistan has no single national language. The two official languages are Persian and Pushtu, both written in modified forms of the Arabic alphabet. The Tajik dialect of Persian, spoken in Afghanistan, differs in vocabulary and pronunciation from the Persian of Iran and is not native to as large a proportion of the inhabitants as Pushtu, which is preferred because it is the mother tongue of the ruling Afghan clan. Both Tajik and Pushtu are closely related members of the Iranic language group (Map 28b) as is also the Baluchi language in Western Pakistan. Another distantly related language group—Dardic—is found in eastern Afghanistan as well as in northern Pakistan and Kashmir. In extreme north Afghanistan are heard languages such as Uzbek and Turkmen, branches of the Turkic-Tartaric family of languages, which are completely unrelated to the country's dominant Iranic tongues.

All other states and territories in South Asia are also multilingual. In the public affairs of Ceylon, English provides at present the best compromise amongst a population divided between Dravidian Tamil (about 23 per cent) and Indo-Aryan Sinhalese (over 70 per cent). In the Portuguese territories the European tongue is the language of the government and of the educated classes, though the vernaculars are Indo-Aryan Marathi in Goa and Gujarati in Damão and Diu. The language of the Maldive Islands is akin to Sinhalese, but many Arabic words have been introduced. In Nepal, local Pahari dialects of Indo-Aryan prevail, and the official Nepali language is closely related to Hindi; but Tibetan (Newar and Bhotia) dialects are used in the center, north, and east. Sikkim is similarly divided between Tibetan and Indo-Aryan. Bhutan with its dominant Tibetan Dukpa dialect has more nearly achieved linguistic unity.

Religious communities

In South Asia religion is a powerful determinant of social relationships. It fixes certain items of dress and diet and even influences the choice of livelihood. People of identical racial stock, speaking the same language and sharing a culture otherwise similar, find themselves separated by religious differences. Comparatively, religion is as significant a factor in the affairs of South Asia today as it was in Europe at the time of the Reformation.

The separation of Pakistan from India on the eve of Britain's relinquishment of the Empire was brought about by socio-economic conflicts associated with religious differences between Moslems and Hindus. In the initial stage of the growth of modern nationalism, leaders of both Hindus and Moslems cooperated in anti-British agitation. However, as nationalism stirred the masses of people in the subcontinent, consciousness of differences in belief and custom attained such proportions that the political and economic unity developed throughout the subcontinent under British rule broke asunder.[4]

The unique socio-religious system known as Hinduism is an amalgam of traditions from Indo-Aryan, Dravidian, and pre-Dravidian sources. By reason of its variations in beliefs and customs it is more correctly described as a *Brahmanical civilization* than as a single religious creed. If all castes and sects be included, Hinduism may be said to be the religion of almost two-thirds of the inhabitants of all South Asia. In 1941 Hindus made up 66 per cent of the population of the undivided Indian Empire; in 1951, after partition and refugee movements, they formed 85 per cent in the Union of India and 13 per cent in Pakistan. Hindus are absent in Afghanistan but are dominant in Nepal and constitute 22 per cent of Ceylon's inhabitants. The two regions with largest Hindu concentration and high relative predominance (80 to 90 per cent of the population) are: (a) the great population belt of the Gangetic plain in Bihar and Uttar Pradesh, and (b) the southeastern peninsular lowland in Madras state.

The social institution of caste is the most distinctive aspect of the Hindu system. Caste regulations prevent the taking of marriage partners outside the caste or subcaste, though marriage is forbidden also between closely related families—these form exogamous units within each caste.

---

[4] Analysis of this recent conflict and of the formation of Pakistan will be found in Chapter XXVII.

Taking of food cooked by persons of lower caste also is forbidden. All castes are ranked in a socio-religious hierarchy, in which the local order of castes varies, but always Brahmins are at the top. Certain occupations traditionally are associated with each caste, although adherence to these rules is much less strict than to rules on marriage and food. There are "untouchable" castes with which are associated menial and ritually unclean occupations and of which the lowest class of Hindu society is formed. Birth determines a Hindu's caste for life—unless he be expelled for violation of its rules.[5]

It is true that in the anonymity of Indian cities, rules pertaining to food and occupation have weakened. The exclusion of "untouchables" from the use of temples, schools, and other public facilities has been outlawed, but urban neighborhoods tend to develop into religious and even caste groupings. Among most Hindus who remain rural, caste retains its strength in social organization. Hinduism thus can be described best as an assem-

[5] So pervasive is the influence of social castes that the system exists in modified forms among the Moslems and Christians in India, and it even extends to Buddhist Sinhalese of Ceylon.

Fig. 102 • The stairs descending to the bank of the sacred Ganga (Ganges) River at Banaras are occupied by Hindus engaged in ritual bathing or in meditating and reciting prayers while seated in the shade of huge umbrellas. Funeral pyres burn on platforms from which the ashes are cast upon the waters. Many small Hindu temples, one of which is slipping gradually down the bank into the river, are overlooked by the towering minarets of Aurangzeb's mosque, seen in the background at right. (*Wellington D. Jones.*)

blage of caste and outcast groups—some 2,300 main castes in all—insulated in social strata and also subdivided regionally because no single endogamous caste is spread over all India.

Nevertheless, some aspects of Hinduism do provide a basis for national unity among Hindus. Deference to Brahmins, practice of rituals in honor of one or another of the five principal deities, belief in reincarnation and in the sacredness of cattle, participation in folk festivals to commemorate legendary heroes and gods, pilgrimages to sacred rivers (Figure 102) and mountains; these things set apart Hindus from persons of other faiths. From the viewpoint of political integration these common Hindu traditions are of utmost significance because they provide in part the symbolism for the incipient Indian national state. These things can waken the loyalty of every caste and subcaste amongst the Indo-Aryan-speaking Hindus of Mediterranean or Alpine race in the north and amongst the palae-Mediterranean Dravidian-speaking Hindus in the south.

The cleavage between Moslems and Hindus is rooted in the period from the eleventh to the sixteenth centuries, when the Islamic creed of the invaders and conquerors from South Asia's western borderlands assumed political meaning. In Southwest Asia for some 1,300 years Islam with its monotheism and brotherhood, its veneration of the prophet Mohammed and of the holy city of Mecca, and its Arabic scriptures, has dominated and permeated political and cultural development. Here originated the Islamic civilization, which clashed with Hindu civilization in South Asia as earlier it had clashed in Spain with Christian Europe. In Southwest Asia Moslem religious leaders have worked hand in hand with the rulers or have themselves been the rulers. Islam has provided the basis for laws and customs. It has strictly controlled art and architecture and influenced education and literature.

Islam's political impact was not felt in the major population centers of South Asia, however, until A.D. 1000, though the faith had been brought previously by Arab traders to settlements in the Indus delta and along the Malabar coast of peninsular India. The western mountain borderlands of South Asia had been conquered by Arabs and Turks during the first three centuries of Islam's expansion; but it was the Turki King of Ghazni (in present-day Afghanistan) who began raiding the Punjab settlements about A.D. 1000, thus starting the waves of overland Moslem expansion that during the next 600 years so deeply altered the political. and religious structure of north India. Other Turkis, Afghans, and later Mughals extended the domain of Islam to Delhi, which became their capital, and down the Gangetic plain to Bengal as well as southward into the interior Dekkan plateau, the Mughals (A.D. 1556 to 1764) building the greatest empire seen in South Asia since Asoka's time.

The spread of Islam into the subcontinent may be likened to the flowing of a tide from the northwest, its depth still discernible until 1947 in terms of percentage distribution of adherents. The highest percentage of Moslems (virtually 100 per cent) is found today in Afghanistan and Baluchistan. The tide flooded the Sind and Punjab plains (50-90 per cent) and passed through the eastern Punjab gap, a strip of land bounded on the north by the Himalaya and on the south by the Thar desert (25-50 per cent), and flowed with diminishing force down the Ganges valley (10-15 per cent) or turned southward across the Vindhya hills into the Dekkan (10-15 per cent). The delta region of Bengal stands out with its anomalous preponderance of Moslems (50-80 per cent) at a great distance from the source of the tide. In the upper Gangetic plain and the Dekkan, the two chief strongholds of Moslem political power, their proportions nowhere are more than 25 per cent and probably never were larger than this. In Bengal the spread of Islam seems to have occurred during the thirteenth century through wholesale conversion of the semi-Hinduized Buddhist populace.

The vast majority of Moslems in all parts of the subcontinent are in fact descendants of converts; there is no racial difference between them and their Hindu neighbors. Only among the Moslem aristocracy do families trace lineage to Arabia or to the invading Turkis, Persians, or Afghans who settled and intermarried. The threat of the sword was not unknown as an aid to conversion, though Moslems used it much less in India than in Arabia, Persia, Turkestan, and Indonesia. The head tax levied by Moslem kings on their non-Moslem subjects exerted economic pressure. In the main, the most powerful attraction offered by the foreign creed to low-caste and outcast Hindus, or to Buddhists and animistic tribal peoples faced with the alternative of being absorbed into Hinduism, was social freedom. Among the higher castes, political advantages sometimes favored the change.

There are in South Asia over 116 million Moslems, more than a quarter of all Moslems in the world. Pakistan alone with nearly 65 million, comprising 86 per cent of the country's inhabitants, is the world's most populous Islamic state, excepting perhaps Indonesia (Figure 103). The Indian Republic retains about 36 million Moslems, 10 per cent of its total population, even after partition and minority transfers, and ranks third in the world in numbers of Moslems. In Afghanistan almost the entire population of about 12 million adheres to Islam, and in Kashmir about three millions of the population of some four millions are Moslem. Elsewhere in the northern mountain borderlands, Moslems are insignificant minorities, if present at all. In Ceylon the so-called Moors of mixed Arab-Sinhalese origin form a significant minority of 9 per cent.

Other religious groups are also important in South Asia; in the Indian Republic are found followers of a greater variety of religious creeds than anywhere else in the world. There are small numbers of Jews and Parsis (Zoroastrians) whose ancestors migrated here from Southwest Asia. Jains of indigenous Indian origin are numerous, but Buddhism has died out almost completely in India proper. The Lama form of Buddhism prevails today only among the Tibetan-speaking peoples of Nepal, Sikkim, and Bhutan, and the western Himalaya. Southern (or Hinayana) Buddhism is the religion of nearly six million Sinhalese, and Ceylon has the largest concentration of Buddhists in South Asia. The largest articulate religious minorities in India are Christians (over eight million) and Sikhs (over six million). Only the Sikhs have assumed an important political role because of their geographic concentration in the Punjab where they opposed the Moslems at the time of Pakistan's separation from India. They migrated *en masse* to the eastern Punjab, and scarcely any Sikhs now remain in Pakistan. Although Christians exceed the Sikhs in numbers, they are widely scattered and divided by creedal differences into various Syrian, Roman Catholic, and Protestant sects. Christians are found largely in the Indian Union, nearly two-thirds of them being in the Dravidian south, concentrated principally in the Kerala and Andhra coasts. There are minorities of Christians also in Ceylon (7 per cent) and in Goa (43

Fig. 103 • The entrance to the Royal Mughal Mosque in Lahore symbolizes the Islamic character of Pakistan, the most populous Moslem state in the world, though rivalled closely by Indonesia. Beyond the door is the large, open, paved courtyard in which, at the hour of prayer, the worshippers assemble and bow towards Mecca. In the background at right is a minaret from which the call to prayer is given, and at left appears one of three giant domes of the mosque proper, the whole built in the sixteenth century in the Mughal dynasty's Perso-Indic style. *(Stanley E. Brush.)*

per cent). The adherents of tribal religions of middle India and the northeastern Indian frontier region number over two million, according to the latest census and estimates. Actually there are in all about 25 million persons belonging to tribal communities, some of whom are Christian converts and most of whom are in the process of assimilation into Hinduism. However, the tribes form an amorphous, largely inarticulate grouping except in the northeastern frontier region where the Nagas and other Tibeto-Burman tribes exhibit strong social integration and seek to maintain control of their own political affairs.

Cultural regions

The seemingly disparate linguistic and religious patterns outlined above are integrated in cultural regions (Map 27b) which are in many ways the most meaningful geographic groupings among the people of South Asia. These cultural regions have a direct bearing on the current efforts towards political integration within the several countries and hence exert an indirect, yet significant influence upon economic development in South Asia. Certain general observations emerge from the foregoing analysis of population distribution, ethnic relationships and political organization.

(1) The two regions of dense population, (a) the upper and middle Ganges plain in the Indo-Aryan north, and (b) the southeastern coastal plain in the Dravidian south, have been persistent centers of cultural enrichment and political integration. Both of these culture hearths are predominantly Hindu, and, though they lack the bond of common linguistic roots, both have shared in the development of the Hindu socio-religious system. The Dravidian south is secondary to the Indo-Aryan north, which appears always as the heartland of India. The north was the cradle of Buddhism, which was superseded by the Hindu Brahmanical code of caste. In turn the latter has resisted the intrusion of Islam. Whenever a single government gained control of the subcontinent prior to the coming of the British, the capital and center of its power invariably was in the Gangetic plain. It is no accident that Delhi is now again the capital and that Hindi, or Hindustani, has spread widely from this region and most nearly achieves the status of a national language for India.

(2) The outer band of Indo-Aryan speaking people fanning out from Sind to Bengal, lies athwart the great diamond-shaped quadrilateral of Hindu India. This southern Indo-Aryan frontier is predominantly Hindu but shows divergences in religious composition. At the extremities in the Indus and Ganges delta it has become dominantly Moslem. It is here also in the central Indian uplands that the bulk of the preliterate aboriginal tribes, speaking Munda-Kol or Dravidian languages and practicing primi-

tive animistic religion, are found. They tend to be assimilated gradually into the Hindu system. With the exception of Sind and Bengal, the Indo-Aryan frontier has become politically integrated with the Indo-Aryan heartland, though there has been a tendency toward separatism in the Marathi and Bengali territory.

(3) Within the Indo-Aryan language area lies the northwestern zone of Hindu-Moslem tension and political conflict—an area which has felt deeply the impact of the Moslem invasions and from which came the main drive for Pakistan. The population centers of West Pakistan are in this zone of tension. The zone of tension also extends across the eastern Punjab plains through Sikh territory into the heart of Indo-Aryan India.

(4) The northwestern and northeastern mountainous borders have been peripheral to the evolution of Indian civilization and harbor tribal groups not culturally or politically integrated with Pakistan to the west or India to the east. Passes through the western borderland have served as routes of invasion and migration that repeatedly destroyed the ancient states of the Gangetic plain and brought new blood and cultural stimulus. However, the dominant traits of this thinly populated western borderland bear closer resemblances to Persia and the southwestern realm of Asia than to India proper. The northeast border, which contains the Mongoloid Tibeto-Burman and Khasi (Austric) tribes, has had a very minor role in India's history and became incorporated into India only during the British period. It is partially Hinduized in areas such as the Assam valley and Manipur. The central Himalayan region including Nepal is dominantly Hindu and Indo-Aryan and has long been under the influence of the northern culture hearth of the Ganges plain, though Nepal has political independence.

(5) Migration and cultural diffusion in South Asia have progressed generally from west to east and from north to south through the lowlands and along the coast. Movement is from dry climatic zones to wet zones, the two main hearths of civilization being situated in the semi-arid borders of the humid climates. The drift from west to east and from dry to wet climates is also observed in external contacts. India's chief racial affinities and most important cultural connections have been with the peoples inhabiting Southwest Asia and more recently with the peoples of western Europe. On the other hand, India has been a source of colonization and cultural stimulus to the peoples of Southeast Asia. Ceylon clearly shows this dependence upon settlement and stimulus from India. The earlier Sinhalese Buddhist culture emanated from the northern hearth. Subsequently, the Sinhalese (Ceylonese) retreated before Hindu Tamil (Dravidian) settlers, who brought their culture from the southern hearth on the nearby mainland.

SELECTED GEOGRAPHICAL BIBLIOGRAPHY

1. Brush, John E. "The Distribution of Religious Communities in India," *Annals, Assoc. Amer. Geogs.*, June, 1949, pp. 81-98.
2. Davies, C. Collin. *An Historical Atlas of the Indian Peninsula*. London: Oxford University Press, 1953.
3. Davis, Kingsley. *The Population of India and Pakistan*. Princeton, N.J.: Princeton University Press, 1951. See also *Geographical Magazine*, August, 1957 (entire issue).
4. Hutton, J. H. *Caste in India* (2d ed.). London: Oxford University Press, 1951.
5. Moreland, W. H., and A. C. Chatterjee. *A Short Cultural History of India*. New York: Longmans, Green & Co., 1945.
6. Piggott, Stuart. *Prehistoric India*. Harmondsworth, Middlesex, England: Penguin Books, 1950.
7. Smith, Vincent A. *The Oxford Student's History of India* (15th ed.), rev. H. G. Rawlinson. Oxford, England: Clarendon Press, 1951.
8. Smith, W. C. *Modern Islam in India, A Social Analysis*. London: Victor Gollancz, 1946.
9. Sopher, David. "India's Languages and Religions," *Focus*, February, 1956.
10. Spate, O. H. K. *India and Pakistan: A Social and Regional Geography*. London: Methuen & Co., 1954.

Comments

The volume by Kingsley Davis on population in India and Pakistan is a thorough demographic study of the two countries, although it was published too early to make use of data from the 1951 censuses in both countries. For later statistics on India the reader can refer to the admirable summary and interpretation of the Indian census in 1951 by R. A. Gopalaswami (see the bibliography for Chapter 24). V. A. Smith's history of India, revised by H. G. Rawlinson, treats the political evolution of the subcontinent, giving an exhaustive account of the invasions and wars, the kings and emperors from the time of the Greek conquest of the Punjab. Moreland and Chatterjee give a less detailed historical account, placing emphasis on economic, social, and other cultural developments during the main historic periods. Davies' atlas is a valuable supplement to the two histories listed and, along with many maps, contains a brief compendium of events. Prehistoric development of cultures in the northwestern part of the subcontinent to the time of the Aryan invasions is analyzed from archeological evidence by Piggott. The origins and functions of caste are treated by Hutton. The historical background and the role of Islam in India before partition is interpreted by W. C. Smith. Brush has mapped and analyzed the distribution of religious grouping according to the 1941 census of the Indian Empire in relation to the problems of partition in 1947, while Sopher points out the significance of the post-partition patterns of languages and religions in the Indian Republic alone. Spate's comprehensive book on India and Pakistan is not only an authoritative source of information on the cultural geography of the subcontinent, but it also is a valuable reference for every subsequent chapter dealing with India or Pakistan.

South Asia

THE PHYSICAL BASIS OF LIFE

THREE MAJOR EARTH FEATURES EXIST IN SOUTH ASIA: (1) THE stable massif of ancient crystalline rock that forms the central and southern uplands of the Indian peninsula; (2) the northern mountain belt in which the rocks have been folded, faulted, and uplifted in the Himalayan system ;and (3) the Indo-Gangetic alluvial lowland resulting from the filling of the structural trough between the peninsular block and the extrapeninsular mountain ranges. These three geologic divisions of South Asia, differing in structure and terrain, form the three grand physiographic regions of the subcontinent (Map 29).

The peninsular massif

The peninsular massif of hard igneous and metamorphic rocks presents a surface of generally low, gentle gradients produced by prolonged weathering and erosion.[1] The prevail-

[1] The most ancient rocks in peninsular India are Pre-Cambrian or Archean (before fossil records of life), estimated to be 500 to 2,000 million years old like the rocks of the Laurentian upland of Canada, the Angara region of Siberia, the hills of western Australia, and the plateaus of Africa and eastern South America. Rocks of more recent age, overlying the old crystalline massif, are probably Palaeozoic, 200 to 500 million years old, but because of the absence of fossils in most of the strata they cannot be correlated precisely with the formations of this geologic era in Europe or America.

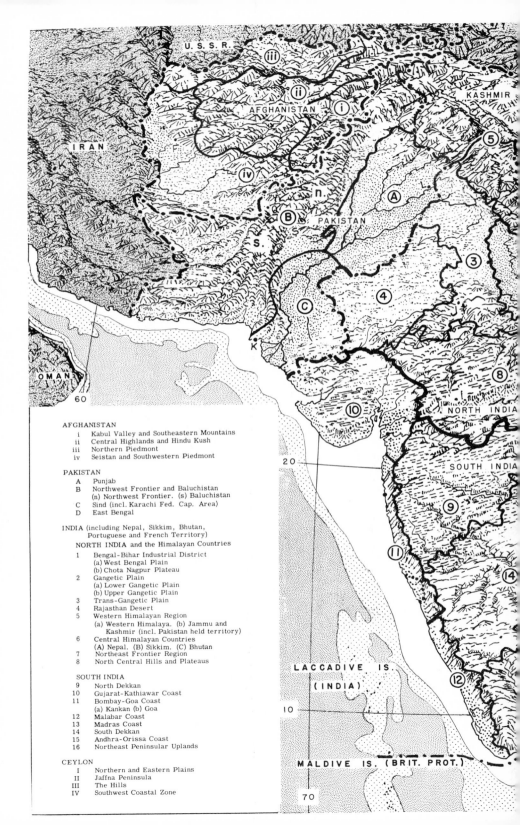

AFGHANISTAN
  i   Kabul Valley and Southeastern Mountains
  ii Central Highlands and Hindu Kush
  iii Northern Piedmont
  iv Seistan and Southwestern Piedmont

PAKISTAN
  A   Punjab
  B   Northwest Frontier and Baluchistan
      (n) Northwest Frontier. (s) Baluchistan
  C   Sind (incl. Karachi Fed. Cap. Area)
  D   East Bengal

INDIA (including Nepal, Sikkim, Bhutan,
       Portuguese and French Territory)
  NORTH INDIA and the Himalayan Countries
  1   Bengal-Bihar Industrial District
      (a) West Bengal Plain
      (b) Chota Nagpur Plateau
  2   Gangetic Plain
      (a) Lower Gangetic Plain
      (b) Upper Gangetic Plain
  3   Trans-Gangetic Plain
  4   Rajasthan Desert
  5   Western Himalayan Region
      (a) Western Himalaya. (b) Jammu and
          Kashmir (incl. Pakistan held territory)
  6   Central Himalayan Countries
      (A) Nepal. (B) Sikkim. (C) Bhutan
  7   Northeast Frontier Region
  8   North Central Hills and Plateaus

  SOUTH INDIA
  9   North Dekkan
  10 Gujarat-Kathiawar Coast
  11 Bombay-Goa Coast
      (a) Kankan (b) Goa
  12 Malabar Coast
  13 Madras Coast
  14 South Dekkan
  15 Andhra-Orissa Coast
  16 Northeast Peninsular Uplands

CEYLON
  I   Northern and Eastern Plains
  II   Jaffna Peninsula
  III The Hills
  IV   Southwest Coastal Zone

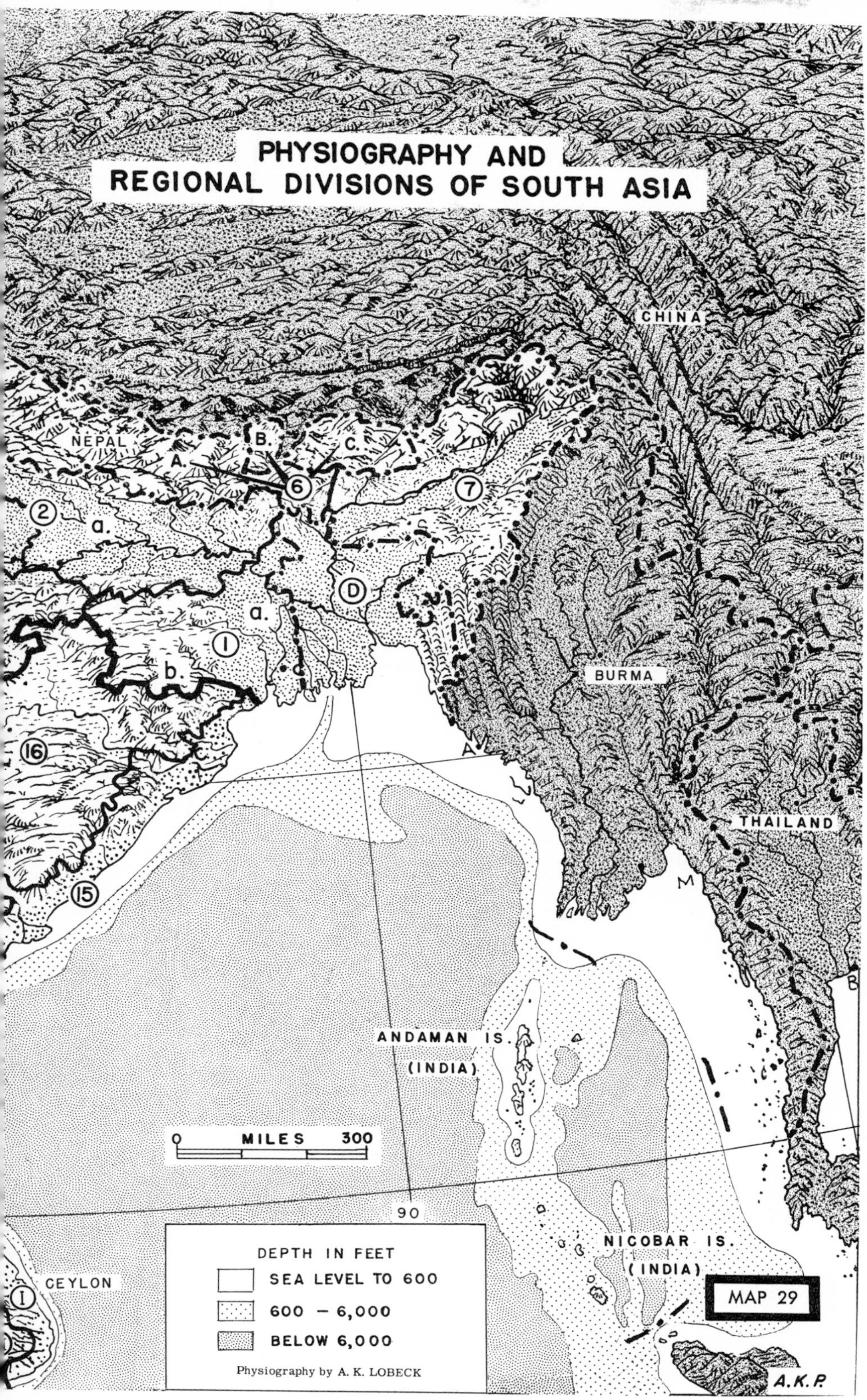

PHYSIOGRAPHY AND
REGIONAL DIVISIONS OF SOUTH ASIA

CHINA

NEPAL

A.   B.   C.

⑥   ⑦

②   a.

D

a.

①

b.

⑯

⑮

BURMA

THAILAND

ANDAMAN IS.
(INDIA)

MILES   300

90

NICOBAR IS.
(INDIA)

MAP 29

CEYLON

DEPTH IN FEET
SEA LEVEL TO 600
600 — 6,000
BELOW 6,000

Physiography by A. K. LOBECK

A.K.P.

ing terrain is made up of plateaus with undulating surfaces or of hills
with broad, rounded summits seldom rising more than 2,000 feet above
sea level. Except along the coasts and in the largest interior valleys the
surface elevation is over 1,000 feet above sea-level. Yet little of the surface
is elevated more than 3,000 feet. Two high granitic massifs are found in
the south—the Nilgiri and Cardomom hills—which rise to heights of 8,000
feet. In the central, western, and eastern parts of the peninsular uplands,
the most prominent hilltops rise only as much as 4,000 to 5,000 feet above
sea level. The one portion of the Indian peninsula that can be accurately
described as plateau is the Dekkan in the northwest, where many successive lava flows spread in Tertiary times over an area 400 miles east and
west by 500 miles north and south in Bombay and Madhya Pradesh. Here
the typical landscape features are the dissected remnants of the high lava
beds, which stand like mesas above the undulating plateau surface. The
lavas are of basaltic composition and were emitted from fissures in the
earth's crust without explosive eruptions, hence without the formation of
volcanic cones.

The configuration and drainage of the Indian peninsula have been influenced by fracturing and tilting of the massif. The part south of latitude
21°N. has been tilted east and presents bold heights to the west. The
major rivers—Godavari, Krishna, Penner, and Cauvery (Kaveri)—start
within 50 miles of the Arabian Sea and flow eastward for distances of 300
to 600 miles across the peninsula to the Bay of Bengal. The entire western margin of the peninsular upland from latitude 20°N. near Bombay to
latitude 12°N. near Calicut (Khozikode) is known as the Western Ghats.[2]
From Bombay south as far as Portuguese Goa the flat-topped ridges formed
is through narrow valleys between the cliffs and flat-topped ridges formed
by differential erosion of unequally resistant layers of lava. The Ghats extend south of Goa to Kerala, and include nonlava uplands which also descend abruptly towards the Arabian Sea. On the eastern side of the peninsula are hills, sometimes called the Eastern Ghats. These east-coast
highlands in some places form steep escarpments, but they are interrupted by large gaps and are known by various local names in Madras,
Andhra, and Orissa states. The east side of the peninsula is bordered
throughout by an alluvial plain, broadest where the deltas of the east-
flowing rivers have been built. On the western side between the sea
shore and the scarp of the Ghats, which is about 50 miles inland, continuous strips of alluvium exist south of Mangalore and north of Bombay.
Between Mangalore and Bombay only small alluvial tracts are found at
the heads of the small bays, separated by spurs of the Ghats coming down
to the shore.

The northern part of the Indian massif is tilted northward and its drain-

2 The word *ghat* comes from the the Sanskrit word meaning mountain pass.

age north of latitude 23°N. is towards the Ganges chiefly by way of the Chambal and Son rivers. The Vindhya range of Madhya Pradesh is the dissected southern edge of this northern block. Close to the foot of the Vindhyas is a narrow east-west valley formed by downfaulting and drained by the Narbada River, flowing west to the Arabian Sea. The Satpura range to the south is a structural uplift, or *horst*, and the valley of the Tapti River is in part another structural trough, or *graben*, parallel to the Narbada and also draining westward. The granite massif, which is here capped by layers of limestone or sandstone and interspersed with metamorphic rocks, ends in a ragged northern border along the margin of the Gangetic plain and the Rajasthan desert. The northernmost part of the peninsular massif is formed by the worn-down Aravalli range, running from *SSW* to *NNE* in Rajasthan and terminating in the ridge at Delhi. In the northeast the undulating surface of the peninsular massif, known as the Chota Nagpur plateau, extends to the lava-capped Rajmahal hills and ends near the great bend of the Ganges, 175 miles north of Calcutta.

Small outlying areas with structure and rock formations similar to those of the Indian massif are separated from it by layers of alluvium or by shallow seas. To the west are the low-lying lava formations of the Kathiawar peninsula and the "island" of Kutch. To the south is the island of Ceylon, where the basement complex of crystalline rocks closely resembles that of the Indian peninsula. To the northeast are the dissected gneissic Garo and Khasi hills of Assam. To the north are the Kirana hills of the western Punjab, small highly eroded outcrops of crystalline rocks closely related to the igneous and metamorphic formations that outcrop 300 miles southeastward near Delhi and southward near Jodhpur. The presence of rocks like those of the peninsular massif here in the Punjab, as well as in Assam, suggests that the bedrock structure of the massif lies buried everywhere beneath the Indo-Gangetic alluvium.

The peninsular massif contains virtually all the mineral wealth of India. The two geologic formations of greatest economic significance are: (a) the rocks of Archean (Pre-Cambrian) origin, highly metamorphosed and containing iron, manganese, copper, lead, and gold ores; and (b) the Lower Gondwana (Palaeozoic) sedimentary rocks, consisting of sandstones, shales, and bituminous coal beds. The outcrops of Archean rocks are scattered in the northeast portion of the Indian massif in Bihar, Orissa, and Madhya Pradesh, where India's most important iron and manganese workings are located; in the south in Bombay, Andhra, and Mysore, where there also are iron and manganese mines and where gold is most abundant; and in the northwest in Rajasthan and Madhya Pradesh, where lead and zinc ores occur. The Lower Gondwana formation, containing almost all of India's supply of coal, occurs in a series of fault basins in the north-

Fig. 104 • Alpine meadows at 12,000 to 14,000 feet above sea level in the western Great Himalaya. The incised stream at the bottom of the U-shaped valley of glacial origin is one of the sources of the Jumna River and is fed by the meltwater of a glacier up the valley to the left. The large rivers of northern India rise within or behind the Great Himalaya and are fed by melting snow or ice, thus somewhat stabilizing their flow, in contrast to the rivers of peninsular India, the flow of which fluctuates enormously with the seasonal variations in rainfall. *(Stanley E. Brush.)*

eastern portion of the massif. The most productive group of coal basins is in the east-west Damodar valley of West Bengal and Bihar. The other coal basins are in two faulted zones located in the Mahanadi valley of Madhya Pradesh and Orissa and along the Godavari River system in extreme eastern Bombay, Madhya Pradesh, and Andhra Pradesh. Aside from the minerals present in these two formations there are others of significance, such as mica and magnetic iron, occurring in areas of Pre-Cambrian gneiss in the eastern and southern portions of the massif. The lava plateau of the northwest is the most extensive area without mineral deposits of economic value in peninsular India.

The Himalayan mountain system

The great mountain walls that rise abruptly on the northern, eastern, and western borders of the Indian subcontinent are in almost every respect the antithesis of the peninsular uplands (Figure 104). The rugged ridges and narrow V-shaped valleys of the Himalayan chains are features resulting from the rapid uplift of the rocks and the vigorous erosion processes prevailing here in contrast to the low relief and stability of most of the peninsula uplands. The unusual height of the peaks in the Himalaya and Karakoram ranges results from the mountain-building forces that have been working here during the recent geologic era (Cenozoic), that is to say, during the last 60 million years, in contrast to the peninsular massif which has been low and relatively stable for at least 500 million years. The folding, uplift, and thrusting of sedimentary strata observed in the Himalaya indicate that horizontal compression has been exerted in the earth's crust, throwing up gigantic rock waves against the buried northern margins of the Indian massif. Fossils of marine origin found embedded in the rocks on the northern flanks of the Himalaya at 14,000 to 18,000 feet elevation prove that these rocks were laid down in a sea called the Tethys over what is now the Plateau of Tibet. The mountains are geologically new and are believed to be rising today, the severe earthquakes of the region being symptoms of this active growth.

Both the rock structure and surface configuration of the Himalaya show trend lines parallel to the margin of the plains and transverse to the direction of tectonic forces. The Great Himalaya range with some 40 peaks between 25,000 and 29,000 feet forms a 1,500-mile arc from the Indus on the west to the Brahmaputra on the east. The core of this range consists of granite and gneiss of unknown geologic age. The Lesser Himalaya range, a belt 50 miles wide, is formed by a series of recumbent folds, overthrust from the north. This belt is composed of metamorphic rocks and unfossiliferous sedimentary rocks which are probably of the same origin as the Pre-Cambrian and Palaeozoic rocks of the peninsular massif and which may actually represent the buckled edge of the massif, itself. Here the surface appears to the observer in the region as an endless maze of interconnected ridges. No single well defined range exists along the axes of folding, but certain prominent ridges 10,000 to 15,000 feet in height are aligned in groups roughly parallel to, or converging with, the Great Himalaya. A distinct part of the Lesser Himalaya is the foothill belt 2,000 to 3,000 feet above sea level, known as the Siwaliks in the west.

The other mountain ranges of extrapeninsular India resemble the Himalayan ranges both in youthfulness and in folded structure. To the north, paralleling the Great Himalaya, are ranges in Kashmir and southern Tibet, rising 10,000 feet above the plateau, which is, itself, 10,000 to 12,000 feet high. The formations here were laid down when the region was below sea level and formed part of the Tethys Sea stretching westward towards southern Europe and the Mediterranean. The Karakoram

range, lying 100 to 150 miles north of the western portion of the Himalaya, is the only range to equal the latter in height. Indeed, the highest
crests of the earth waves in this western portion of the South Asia mountain system are found in the Karakoram. West of the Himalaya the highest crest line is in the Hindu Kush of Afghanistan. The Karakoram and
Hindu Kush, together, form an arc some 700 miles long which is convex
northward towards the Pamir plateau, contrary to the Himalayan arc
which is convex southward. The trend line of the Hindu Kush is prolonged westward in ranges of 10,000-foot height in Afghanistan, the Koh-i-
Baba, and Paropamisus.

Flanking the Himalaya on the east and the west along the India-Burma
and the Afghan-Pakistan frontiers are other rugged folded sedimentary
ranges. On the east is a succession of arcuate ridges, turning southward
to form the Arakan Yoma of Burma from a hinge point in upper Assam
and indicating compressional forces acting from the east towards peninsular India. On the west there are two major arc systems, the Sulaiman
and Kirthar ranges, convex eastward and indicating compressional forces
acting from the west. The hinge points between the consecutive mountain
arcs in the whole extrapeninsular mountain region from West Pakistan to
Assam are thought to be the points where the buried promontories of the
peninsular massif impinge upon the warped, uplifted sedimentary strata
of the extrapeninsular mountain regions.

The rivers of the Himalayan mountain system tend to be entrenched in
narrow valleys, some of which are cut directly between the highest peaks
and transverse to the trend of the ranges and rock structures. The Indus,
Ganges, and Brahmaputra river systems have extended their watersheds
by headward erosion beyond the Great Himalaya into southern Tibet.
Only in the west does the Hindu Kush serve as the water divide between
the Indus headwaters and those of the Amu Darya in interior Asia.

Several intermontane basins exist within the mountain belt, where recent lacustrine and alluvial sediments have been deposited. The largest
basins are in western Afghanistan and in Baluchistan—regions of dry
climate and interior drainage. Smaller basins in the extrapeninsular mountains include the basin of Manipur on the Burma frontier and the Plain
of Kabul in Afghanistan. Other intermontane basins are found in the
Himalaya proper, among which the vale of Kashmir and the valley of
Nepal are notable.

The Indo-Gangetic plain

The third grand division of
South Asia, the contiguous plains of the Indus, Ganges (Ganga), and
Brahmaputra rivers, is of greatest human interest because its cultivated

Fig. 105 • Looking out over the Gangetic plain, the view stretches to the seemingly limitless horizon from a minaret of the great Taj Mahal at Agra, one of the monuments commemorating the dominance of the subcontinent by the Mughal conquerors. The plain is the largest densely occupied alluvial plain in the world. Although much of it is level and unbroken, many small variations in drainage and soil texture are associated with the flood plains and higher interfluves, and in places the streams have incised themselves into the surface, creating local badlands. *(Wellington D. Jones.)*

surface supports nearly half of the entire population of South Asia and forms the politico-economic basis of the two principal countries. Its geologic age is contemporaneous with the building of the Himalaya, and its origin is related to it. As the mountains were uplifted, a long depression was formed parallel to the mountains, where parts of the peninsular massif dropped, or were forced downward under tectonic pressure. At the same time the depression was gradually filled by detritus brought down by streams from the mountains, burying the hard rock except in parts of Assam, Rajasthan, and the Punjab, as noted above.

This plain of 300,000 square miles surpasses in area all other alluvial plains of the earth, exceeding even that of the Huang Ho in northern China. From the Indus delta in West Pakistan it extends in a continuous belt through northern India with an average width of 200 miles and a minimum width of 90 miles for a distance of 1,900 miles to the combined mouths of the Ganges (Padma) and Brahmaputra in East Pakistan. The

total area of the alluvial surface, including the lowlands extending laterally some 300 miles to the Gulf of Cambay in western India and over 400
miles along the Brahmaputra in eastern India, must be at least 420,000
square miles (Map 29). The Indo-Gangetic plain is, of course, smaller
than the structural plains of the Americas and northern Eurasia, but in
none of these continental plains is the continuous alluvia mantle as extensive as in South Asia.

The plains of this vast area, however, are by no means uniform (Figure
105). The stoneless surface appears to the eye to be perfectly flat, going
on endlessly to the monotonous, unbroken horizon until one approaches
the towering ramparts of the northern mountains or the ragged border of
the central Indian uplands, but local variations in relief and drainage of
the surface introduce important modifications. Conspicuous eroded bluffs
occur within a few miles of the major rivers in the Gangetic plain, indicating that alluvial material is now being removed here and redeposited
downstream. Indeed, the rivers of the Indus and the Ganges systems have
become incised below the surface in most parts of the plain and are
capable of freely depositing silt only in the alluvial fans, where they debouch from the mountains, and in the deltas near the sea coast. Most of
the surface, therefore, is old alluvium,[3] not subject to flooding or to deposition of fresh silt. The floods of all the major rivers are confined to relatively narrow belts, except in the submontane and deltaic portions of the
plain.

Although the general gradients of the portions of the plain occupied
by the Indus and the Ganges systems are almost the same, there are differences in detail. The water parting between the two river systems is only
900 feet above sea level at the foot of the Himalaya, 120 miles north of
Delhi. From this point the general gradient is 12 inches per mile southwestward across the Punjab and Sind to the Arabian Sea, 900 miles distant. From the same point the general gradient southeastward across
Uttar Pradesh, Bihar, and Bengal is 11 inches per mile to the Bay of
Bengal, 1,050 miles distant. The Gangetic plain slopes more steeply southward at three to four feet per mile from the foot of the Himalaya towards
the central Indian uplands, and its rivers all flow southeastward obliquely
to the main stream near the southern margin of the plain. The Punjab
plain also slopes away southward from the foot of the Himalaya, and the
five tributaries of the Indus flow obliquely southwestward to the Indus,
which keeps close to the base of the Sulaiman mountains, although the
transverse gradient from the Aravalli hills towards the extrapeninsular
mountains is slight.

[3] *Old alluvium* means deposits laid down at a time when the rivers of the plain
flowed at slightly higher elevations and were capable of carrying larger volumes of
sediment than at present. In northern India these conditions prevailed during the
pluvial periods of the Pleistocene age within the last one million years.

The cause of these differences in transverse gradients and stream patterns is the fact that both river systems receive their largest volumes of
water and sediment from Himalayan sources. The Ganges receives relatively little flow from its southern tributaries. The Indus receives virtually
no flow from the west, south of latitude 32°N., and none at all from the
east, south of latitude 28°N. There is progressive diminution of volume
downstream in the lower Indus in contrast to the increase of volume
downstream in the Ganges.

The Thar, or Rajasthan desert, lies adjacent to the plains of the Indus
and can be considered as being part of the alluvial region, although the
surface is broken by numerous rocky projections of the thinly mantled
massif and by wind-drifted sand ridges. The desert is traversed by a prehistoric river channel (the Ghaggar), traceable for 600 miles from the
Punjab to Sind, by means of which water from either the eastern Indus or
western Ganges affluents once reached the Rann of Kutch. The Indus, itself, during the fourth century B.C. flowed 80 miles to east of its present
course and emptied into the Rann, which was then a gulf of the Arabian
Sea. Today the Rann is a sterile, salt-encrusted marsh, cut off from the
sea and inundated briefly during the summer monsoon season.

The two moonsoons

Everywhere in the eastern and
southern parts of Asia from the Arabian Sea to the Sea of Japan, there is
an inflow of warm, water-saturated air from the tropical oceans in summer and an outflow of dry, cold continental air in winter. This seasonal
shift of winds determines the seasonal rhythm of rains and influences the
climate of South Asia to such a marked degree that the climate is often
called *monsoonal*. The word monsoon (*mausim* = season) comes from
the Arabian coasts of Hadhramaut and Oman where these seasonally re-
versing winds affecting India are also dominant.

The monsoons of South Asia form a separate and distinct system of
winds and air masses, not directly related to the system of East Asia.
The thermal low-pressure center of the Indus plain during summer has
no connection with the Mongolian low-pressure center that dominates
East Asia. The summer monsoon invades India from the Indian Ocean
as a southwest wind and then at the Tropic of Cancer curves towards
the northwest up the Ganges plain towards the Indus plain. Tropical
maritime air is present ordinarily up to heights of 10,000 to 15,000
feet and is dissipated in the valleys of southeastern Tibet and against the
south face of the Himalaya, or loses its identity over the Indus plain
where it meets the dry stream of continental air that is drawn into the
thermal low across the northwestern mountains. The destination of this

shallow wet monsoon is in the regions south of the Pamir and Tibetan plateaus, far from the destination of the East Asian summer monsoon, which originates in the Pacific Ocean or South China Sea and travels on the other side of the Tibetan mountains and plateaus towards Mongolia.

The winter monsoon of India is likewise a phenomenon of the area south of the Himalaya. Dry, cool air travels across the Indo-Gangetic plain from the northwest, coming in part from the plateau basins of Afghanistan and Iran, and in part from subsiding air in the subtropical high-pressure belt. This high is maintained at the margins of the Tropics by the dynamic forces of the atmospheric circulation system—forces present in these latitudes all around the earth. At about the Tropic of Cancer the surface winds of this winter monsoon curve towards the southwest and progress across peninsular India, the Bay of Bengal, and the Arabian Sea towards the equatorial low of the Indian Ocean. The cold, continental air of winter originates in the main Asiatic center of high pressure over eastern Siberia and moves southeastward to the Pacific, never reaching India. The cold continental air masses have no influence in South Asia because they are dammed up in the interior by the plateau barriers of the Pamir and Tibet, which reach up to levels of 12,000 to 14,000 feet, where strong westerly winds prevail in winter. India's winter monsoon, thus, originates in the subtropics and is much less severe than the polar continental monsoon of East Asia.

There are but two monsoons, yet three seasons are recognized in South Asia: (1) the rainy season, (2) the cool season, and (3) the hot season. The rainy season (June to October) is a time of high temperatures and abundant moisture. The cool season (November to February) is a time of the continental monsoon and prevailingly dry weather, except in the northernmost plains and the adjacent mountains and in the extreme southeast coast of peninsular India and eastern Ceylon. The hot season (March to May) is also a time of the continental monsoon and of continued dry weather, except in southwestern Ceylon, southern Malabar, Assam, and East Pakistan. The maximum temperatures of the year are experienced nearly everywhere in South Asia during these three hot season months before the onset of the wet, maritime monsoon.

The rainy season

The arrival of the summer monsoon air after its 2,000-mile trajectory over the Indian Ocean from the Tropic of Capricorn south of the Equator, causes dark clouds to gather and rain to begin abruptly. So distinct is the rise in humidity and fall in temperature that the Indian Meteorological Department officially records the date of arrival of this monsoon at each of its observatories, but the arrival of the monsoon does not automatically bring water to the parched plains of India and Pakistan like the turning on of a garden sprayer. The duration of the monsoon varies from as much as six months in extreme south Madras state to six weeks in West Pakistan or a few days in eastern Afghanistan. The amount and daily frequency of precipitation, furthermore, is influenced by the movement of weak low-pressure centers which travel from east to west between latitudes 20° and 30°N. Variations in the summer rainfall of South Asia may be disastrous if: (1) the monsoon's arrival in June or July is delayed, (2) interruptions of the monsoon are frequent or prolonged in July and August, (3) the monsoon ends earlier than usual in September or October, or (4) the rainfall is so excessive that floods occur where normally they do not occur.

The largest and most reliable precipitation is received on the windward sides of mountains. The western slopes of the Ghats, the Ceylon highlands, and the Burma frontier mountains are all extremely rainy because they stand almost at right angles to the path of the tropical maritime air, coming directly west across the Arabian Sea or southwest up the Bay of Bengal. At least 75 inches of rainfall (June to October) is received throughout each of the exposed areas. The most intense precipitation (100 to 200 inches) does not occur at the seacoast or at the foot of the mountains, but at intermediate elevations where the instability levels are reached in the ascending air—at 2,000 and 3,000 feet in the Western Ghats, and along the ranges east of longitude 88°E. in India at levels between 3,000 and 5,000 feet. Cherrapunji at 4,300 feet elevation south of Shillong in Assam, is perfectly situated for the full orographic effect, receiving an average annual precipitation of 452 inches—one of the two highest recorded averages in the world.

Showers occur in areas of low relief chiefly because of convectional updrafts. A large share of the 30- to 60-inch precipitation (June-October) in the northern plains and the interior valleys and hill country of central and northeast peninsular India is of this simple convectional type (see Calcutta and Hyderabad, Plate C). On the leeward, east-facing slopes of mountains and interior plateaus and valleys of peninsular India precipitation is only 10 to 30 inches during the rainy season. The descent of warm air that has passed over the Western Ghats, for example, works against convection. The maritime air is no longer saturated because of the release of so much moisture on the windward slopes of the mountains and because of adiabatic heating which ocurs as it descends the leeward slopes. Three dry rain-shadow areas exist, therefore, within tropical South Asia: (1) the large area behind the Ghats, which occupies the interior parts of Bombay and Andhra states, as well as much of Mysore state, (2) the

PLATE C

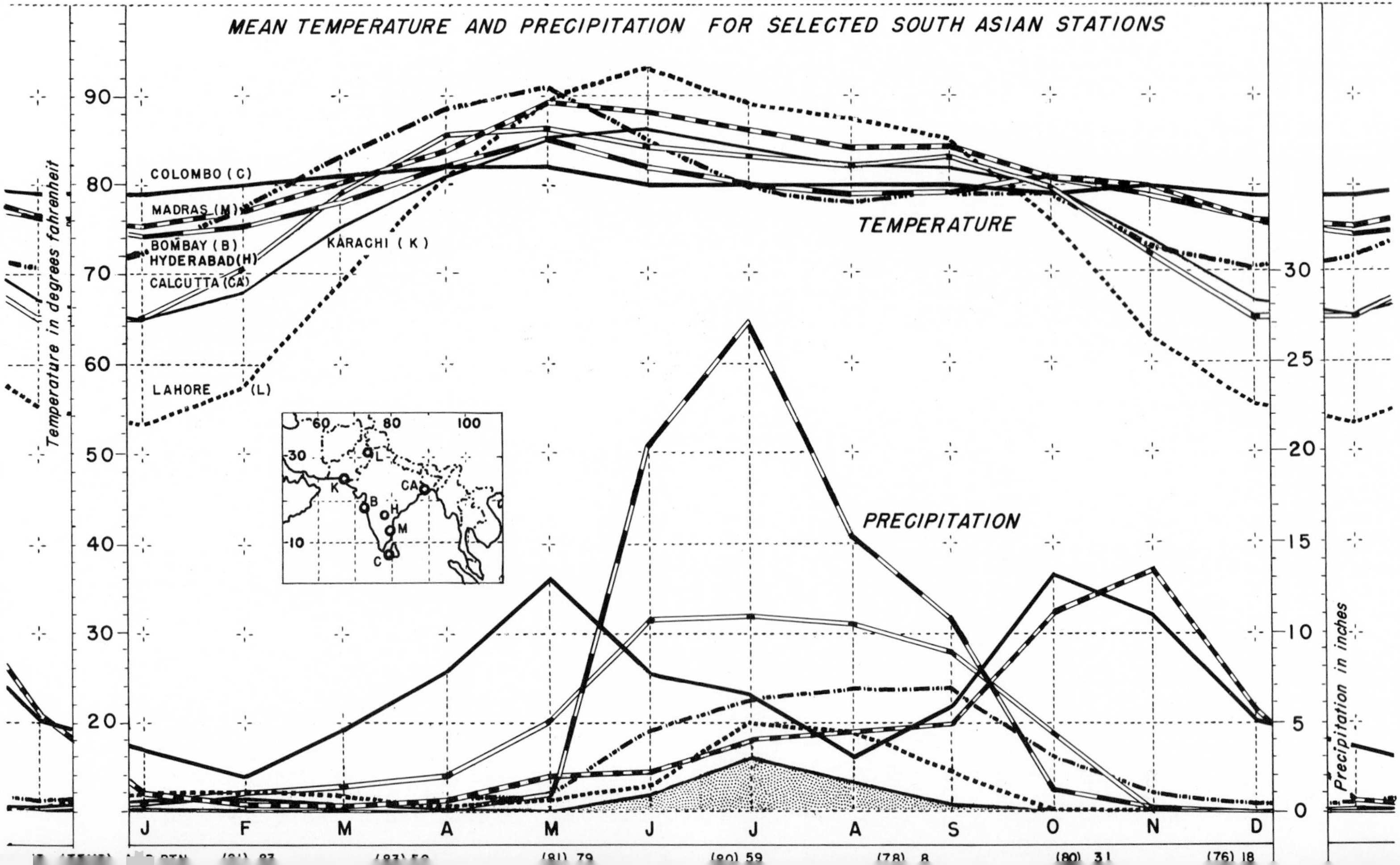

MEAN TEMPERATURE AND PRECIPITATION FOR SELECTED SOUTH ASIAN STATIONS
TEMPERATURE
PRECIPITATION
COLOMBO (C)
MADRAS (M)
BOMBAY (B)
HYDERABAD (H)
CALCUTTA (CA)
KARACHI (K)
LAHORE (L)
Temperature in degrees fahrenheit
Precipitation in inches
90
80
70
60
50
40
30
20
30
25
20
15
10
5
0
J F M A M J J A S O N D
60 80 100
30
10
K B H M C CA L
(81) 79
(80) 59
(78) 8
(80) 31
(76) 18

region east of the Nilgiris and the Cardomom hills in extreme southeastern part of Madras state, and (3) northwestern Ceylon along the Gulf of Mannar.

North of latitude 20°N., however, rain-shadows disappear because of the easterly lows. Winds circulate counterclockwise towards the centers of these lows, which traverse central and northern India three or four times a month from June to September. It is these lows that cause the variations so critical in the summer monsoon rainfall.

The easterly lows appear between latitudes 20° and 25°N. where the southwest winds of the monsoon are recurving as southeast winds at the head of the Bay of Bengal. This returning branch of the monsoon is also fed by air rising over Burma and southwest China. The old maritime air which has crossed the peninsula of India behaves here as a warm air mass with respect to the fresh maritime air, which has just come up the Bay of Bengal. The old maritime air overruns the fresh maritime air that lies south and east of the center of low pressure. Cloud cover is widespread, and there is a drizzle of rain from the old monsoon air which still contains a fairly large quantity of moisture, although less than the fresh, cool monsoon air beneath it. Within the fresh monsoon air stream, converging towards the low-pressure center from the south and southeast, there is squally weather accompanied by heavy rain. This circulation pattern of maritime air currents in these lows accounts for the copious rainfall over the lowlands east of longitude 78°E. and north of latitude 20°N. and adds to the intensity of orographic rainfall in the eastern Himalaya.

As a summer monsoon low migrates to the west, the precipitation gradually decreases because dry, continental air enters its vortex in increasing amounts and the source of the moist air aloft becomes progressively more distant. A tongue of dry, hot air may reach across central India or come down the Ganges plain from the west when the low is still in Bihar or Orissa. Almost invariably continental air from arid source regions is present when the low has moved into Madhya Pradesh or Uttar Pradesh. By the time the low has reached Rajasthan or the plains of West Pakistan, continental air has become dominant. This northwesterly current overruns the shallow southwesterly maritime current and, being extremely dry, gives no precipitation in the western sector of the migrating cyclonic system. Continental air also overruns the old maritime air that it meets to the north of the low-pressure center up to levels of 5,000 or 10,000 feet, but above 10,000 or so the old maritime air is relatively warmer and therefore it now overruns the continental air. Thus, in the northern sectors of the migrating cyclonic system, precipitation is derived where the old maritime air lifted above this peculiar reversed front. When the path of a low is close to the Himalaya, the old monsoon air mass is wedged against the mountain slopes and forced aloft, giving torrential downpours.

Generally, the amount of precipitation decreases progressively as the storm moves on westward. The maritime air that has come up the Ganges plain has lost most of its moisture by the time it reaches the Punjab. It still yields some rain in the Kashmir mountains and the submontane Punjab, where the mean precipitation is 20 to 40 inches from June to October (see Lahore, Plate C). In Rajasthan and Sind there is almost no rain because the hot dry air from the west overrides and stabilizes the fresh monsoon air, which is present below 2,000 or 3,000 feet, coming in directly from the Arabian Sea. At this season in Sind and Rajasthan cumulus clouds are often observed starting to form as a result of intense heating of the maritime air over the land, but they fail to develop into rain clouds because of the stabilizing effect of the warm dry air aloft.

If a low moves west of the Indus River and a deep current of monsoon air flows into Rajasthan and the Punjab, then the convectional updrafts result in thunderstorms and heavy downpours. The plains of the Indus and the adjacent mountains are penetrated occasionally by such deep maritime air masses and the associated rainfall, but this circulation pattern occurs only for very short, irregular intervals during the height of the monsoon. Thus this northwestern portion of the subcontinent, the mean center of lowest atmospheric pressure in summer and the ultimate destination of the maritime air, receives little precipitation. Rainfall is generally less than 15 or 20 inches in the period June to October west of Lahore and north of the Gulf of Kutch. Only four or five inches of precipitation are received in Sind (see Karachi, Plate C) and still less in the intermontane basins in western Baluchistan and southern Afghanistan, which at this time are subject to the violent, dessicating "wind-of-120-days" which blows from the northwest towards the lows of the Indian monsoon (see Chapter 29).

The cool season

Dry continental air masses gradually spread over northern India during September and October and dominate all of South Asia during the ensuing cool season from November to March. Reduced insolation during the northern-hemisphere winter allows the land to cool, and atmospheric pressure rises slightly higher over the land than it is over the adjacent warm seas. The effect of this rise of pressure combined with the presence of the dynamic high-pressure cell aloft, centered during this season at about latitude 15° to 20°N. and longitude 70° to 80°E., is to cause the continental air to drift in anticyclonic fashion over India. The Indian winter monsoon moves from west to east outside the Tropic and then recurves, becoming northeasterly over the peninsula. The combination of cool, dry air at the surface and stable dry air aloft produces the cloudless sunshiny weather of winter in South Asia. The mean January temperature remains above 70°F. in southern India and above 60° in the interior lowlands as far north as Delhi. Beyond latitude 28°N. the monthly mean for January falls to about 55° and light frosts occur on the plains, while in the Himalayan foothills the mean monthly temperatures decrease sharply at altitudes over 3,000 feet.

Not everywhere in South Asia is the weather dry throughout the cool season. During October and the following two or three months, the wet monsoon is recurring in the Bay of Bengal, bringing the year's heaviest rainfall to the Madras coast and the other south Indian uplands east of the Ghats and causing a second rainy season in nearby Ceylon. Weak easterly lows continue to form in the retreating maritime air over the water and move towards the east-facing coasts. Occasionally, violent tropical cyclones of the hurricane, or typhoon, type appear drifting from the east or southeast over the Bay of Bengal or the Arabian Sea and affecting the coasts of Bengal and peninsular India. The retreating monsoon has little effect inland in tropical south India after October because of the semipermanent anticyclone now established here. The rainfall of the retreating monsoon is mostly confined to the east coast of India south of latitude 15°N. and to Ceylon, where November and December are the rainiest months of the year (see Madras and Colombo, Plate C).

Air of land origin passes over the Bay of Bengal from the northeast and becomes involved with these retreating monsoon storms. This continental air gathers moisture from contact with the warm sea, but it is incorrect to ascribe the cool season rains of the coastlands of South Asia to the northeast monsoon alone. Precipitation from the retreating southwest monsoon in the Bay of Bengal diminishes markedly in Madras state after the end of the year, though it continues in Ceylon through January. By February, when the northeast monsoon is dominant in the Bay of Bengal, the rains have ceased.

In extratropical India and the countries to the west, November marks the beginning of a season of westerly lows of the middle-latitude type, the so-called "western disturbances." As frequently as four or five times a month (December to April), these cyclones cross Afghanistan, West Pakistan, Kashmir, and India, generally north of latitude 30°N. Their paths are often traced from the Mediterranean Sea or the Black Sea across Southwest Asia, where they bring most of the annual precipitation. Occasionally such a cyclonic storm passes along the coast of Persia and West Pakistan and crosses India at about latitude 25°N., diminishing in intensity as it continues over Bengal and Assam towards northern Burma.

The cool-season precipitation, which amounts to less than five inches

in the Punjab plain and over five inches in the adjacent mountains, is de-
rived from maritime air brought from the Mediterranean by these lows.
The maritime air is lifted on the mountain slopes or at fronts where it is in
contact with cold air from the plateau basins of Iran and Afghanistan.
The high ranges of the western Himalaya, the Karakorum, and the Hindu
Kush become blanketed under heavy snow and are believed to receive
most of their annual precipitation at this season, but in the plains of the
Punjab and Sind the effect on the annual rainfall curve is merely to produce a secondary maximum which is far surpassed by the summer maximum (see Lahore and Karachi, Plate C). Temperatures fluctuate during the
passage of these westerly lows, rising in the eastern sector of each cyclone
and falling in the western sector as cold, continental air displaces the
mild, maritime air. The frosts on the plains of extratropical South Asia
occur during the nights following the passage of westerly lows, when continental air from the plateaus of Southwest Asia has invaded the plains.
In the interior basins and mountain valleys of Baluchistan, Afghanistan,
and Kashmir, minimum temperatures of O°F. are experienced under clear
night skies and under the influence of local air drainage during the calms
following the passage of cyclones.

The hot season

The northward shift of the
sun's vertical noonday rays and the increasing length of the days during
March, April, and May causes the belt of most intense solar radiation to
move progressively northward over the tropical part of South Asia and
finally by June into the extratropical part. Temperatures, therefore, become higher and occur progressively farther north during the hot season.
In March the highest daytime temperatures of about 100°F. are in the
interior Dekkan of Bombay and Hyderabad; in April the highest daytime
temperatures of 110° are in Madhya Pradesh and northern Bombay state;
in May the highest daytime temperatures of 120° are in Rajasthan and
Sind. Equally high daytime temperatures are recorded in the northern
interior plains of the Punjab and Uttar Pradesh in June and July before
the arrival of the summer monsoon. The afternoon hours at this season
become so intolerably hot that human activity ceases until sunset approaches. Both men and beasts seek shelter from the burning sunlight
and look out upon the dry, brown earth, awaiting the arrival of the life-
giving wet monsoon.

The effect of insolation is less marked on the coasts, particularly in
peninsular India, because of local sea breezes. Thus, the mean monthly
temperatures at Madras and Bombay, which are 74°F. or above in the
cool season (see Plate C), remain below 90° in the hot season, while the

mean at Hyderabad rises from below 65° to above 90° in May and at Lahore it rises from below 55° to almost 95° in June. As a rule, the farther north one goes the cooler is the winter and the hotter is the summer.

It is the persistence of dry, stable air over South Asia from March to May that permits the most intense heating of the land before the summer solstice (June 22-23). Later in July and August the moisture and cloud cover of the wet monsoon reduce the insolation reaching the ground, reducing the mean temperatures a few degrees. From March to May the surface winter anticyclone of India has been disrupted by the onset of the hot season, but the dynamic high pressure and warm stable air persist aloft. The dry stream of air from the Southwest Asia mainland continues to drift across South Asia from west to east and the westerly lows continue to move along latitude 35°N. until May. In the mountain basins of Afghanistan (Kabul) and Kashmir (Srinagar) the maximum precipitation of the year occurs in March and April, evidently as a result of these westerly lows and the associated orographic and frontal rainfall. When fronts pass across the plains of West Pakistan and northern India no rain falls, but instead dust squalls develop. These disturbances, together with local whirlwinds produced by the intense heating of the ground and the resulting convection, raise a pall of dust which remains suspended in the lower atmosphere until the onset of the wet monsoon.

The trajectory of the west winds up to levels of 2,000 or 3,000 feet is deflected southward over tropical India, so that as the continental air comes from the west across the Arabian Sea and from the southwest over the Bay of Bengal, the lower layer is humidified. Such modified continental air drifting onshore again in Malabar, Ceylon, or Bengal may become heated sufficiently to rise and penetrate the layer of dry warm air aloft, resulting in convectional showers. As much as 10 to 20 inches of rainfall is received in these southern and eastern coastal areas and in interior Assam before the arrival of the summer monsoon. Sometimes the local convectional storms in Bengal develop into violent thunderstorms with heavy rain and hail, fed by south winds from the Bay of Bengal and drifting with the westerly winds aloft. There also are violent cyclonic storms (hurricanes) which move from east to west in the Bay of Bengal and the Arabian Sea during April, May, and June, and which originate beyond the latitude of strong westerly winds in stagnant tropical maritime air masses present at about latitude 10°N. before the summer monsoon circulation is established.

The summer monsoon circulation does not become established in South Asia until the equatorial low-pressure belt has been eliminated over the Indian Ocean. The pressure gradient from the sea towards the Indus low is as intense in May towards the end of the hot season as it is in the rainy season months of June or July, but the strong maritime air currents cannot reach India until there is a pressure gradient northward across the Indian Ocean. When the equatorial low-pressure belt reaches a position between latitudes 5° and 10°N. about the end of May, it rapidly shifts northward to 25°N. by June 15, and maritime air moves suddenly into peninsular India and Bengal. This change can be described as a northward displacement of the intertropical front. The winds are southwest over the Arabian Sea and the Bay of Bengal in latitudes where the northeast trade winds exist over most other tropical seas between 10° and 20°N. The southeast trade winds of the southern hemisphere cross the equator and recurve in the northern hemisphere to become the southwest monsoon winds. The equatorial low-pressure belt becomes the "trough of the monsoon" along which weak easterly lows migrate, as elsewhere in the world at the intertropical front.

Climatic zones

The regimes of temperature and precipitation described in the foregoing pages create three broad climatic zones in South Asia—(1) the humid tropical, (2) the humid mesothermal, and (3) the dry zones.[4]

Contrary to popular notion, winterless tropical humid climates do not predominate in the subcontinent (see Table XXIII–1). The *savannah climate* (both Aw and As types) covers less than a quarter of the surface of India and Pakistan below 5,000 feet elevation. The *monsoon rainforest climate* (Am type) prevails along the west coast and western slopes of the Ghats from Alleppey to Bombay (latitudes 9° to 19°N.). This extremely wet tropical climate, which also appears in southwestern Ceylon and in the Tripura and Chittagong hills of India and East Pakistan, respectively, comprises a much smaller percentage of the area. The Aw type of savannah with rains during the summer monsoon period prevails in Ceylon, lower Bengal, and most of peninsular India south of the Tropic of Cancer except in the semi-arid rain-shadows of the Western Ghats. Only the Madras coastal lowland between latitudes 10° and 15°N. and the east coast of Ceylon are savannahs of As type, receiving maximum precipitation during the months from October to January from the retreating wet monsoon.

Nearly one-third of the surface of India and Pakistan below 5,000 feet is in the humid mesothermal climatic zone. The extratropical plains of northern East Pakistan and of India as far west as Kanpur about longi-

---

[4] See the map of the climatic zones in India and adjacent countries (Figure 2, "World Climates," after Köppen and others) in William Van Royen, *Agricultural Resources of the World* (Englewood Cliffs, N.J.: Prentice-Hall, Inc., 1954), p. 2.

TABLE XXIII–1

MAJOR CLIMATIC TYPES OF INDIA AND PAKISTAN

Climatic zone and type	Characteristics	Per cent of Area *
A: Humid tropical zone	Mean temperature of the coolest month over 18°C. (64.4°F.)	
Am: Monsoon rainforest type	Dry season offset by annual precipitation over 80 inches.	4
Aw: Savannah, summer rain type	Rainy months June-October; total annual precipitation usually over 35 inches.	23
As: Savannah, winter rain type	Rainy months November-January; total annual precipitation usually over 35 inches.	less than 1
B: Dry zone	Annual precipitation less than the humid margin.	
BSh: Warm steppe type (semi-arid)	Mean annual temperature over 18°C. (64.4°F.); annual precipitation usually between 18 and 35 inches.	21
BWh: Warm desert type (arid)	Mean annual temperature over 18°C. (64.4°F.); annual precipitation usually less than 18 inches.	23
C: Humid mesothermal zone	Mean temperature of the coolest months under 18°C. (64.4°F.) but over 0°C. (32°F.).	
CW: Humid subtropical, summer rain type	Rainy months May-October.	29

* Exclusive of mountain areas 5,000 feet or more above sea level.

Note: The climatic criteria are from Köppen as modified by Trewartha. See V. C. Finch, G. T. Trewartha, A. H. Robinson, and E. H. Hammond, *Elements of Geography*, 4th ed. (New York: McGraw-Hill, 1957), pp. 123-27.

tude 80°E. form the major portion of the area of humid subtropical climate (Cw type). This climatic zone extends beyond Kanpur in a narrow wedge on the plains at the foot of the Himalaya as far west as the Punjab in West Pakistan, where it terminates in the Salt range near the Indus River. Humid mesothermal climates prevail up to 5,000 or 6,000 feet in the Assam-Burma frontier mountains and in the Himalaya of India and adjacent countries. Above 6,000 feet microthermal and tundra or ice climates are found at progressively higher elevations. The southern limit of the humid mesothermal zone is in the Chhota Nagpur plateau and the crests of the Vindhya and Satpura ranges in the central parts of India, although small outlying areas occur on the crests of the Nilgiri and Cardomom hills in extreme southern India and in the highlands of south-central Ceylon.

The *dry zone* comprises 44 per cent of the area below 5,000 feet in India and Pakistan. It probably amounts to half of the total area of South Asia, including Afghanistan. The limit of arid climate (BWh) is about 18 inches precipitation. The heart of this arid zone lies in Sind and south-western Punjab, where only five inches or less precipitation is received annually. The arid zone extends westward into Baluchistan and undoubtedly into southwestern Afghanistan. It also prevails in the plains of the Punjab south and west of Lahore in Pakistan and in the whole western half of Rajasthan and all of Kutch in India. The *semi-arid climatic type* (BSh) with between 18 and 35 inches annual precipitation extends in a band from the Punjab into India through eastern Rajasthan and extreme northern Bombay state where it reaches the sea in the Kathiawar peninsula. A large semi-arid tract in the Dekkan stretches from the Narbada River to the upper Tungabhadra basin in Mysore; and a smaller tract in south Madras extends from the Cauvery River to the Gulf of Mannar. The upper Indus valley of West Pakistan and Kashmir and nearly all of the mountain and basin region of Afghanistan and Pakistan beyond the Indus, if not arid, are semi-arid. Because of the great extent of dry climates, it is correct to say that the South Asian realm has as much climatic affinity to dry Southwest Asia as it has to humid Southeast Asia.

Vegetation zones

The distribution of wild vegetation in South Asia is manifestly related to climatic conditions, but because of the depredations of man there are few areas where "natural" vegetation exists or where the unhampered growth of plant cover fully reflects climatic potentialities. A high proportion of the area not actually under cultivation or in fallow supports only a scanty growth of low scrub or thin grass because of frequent lopping of branches for firewood and continued browsing by livestock. Much mountain or hill land not under permanent cultivation has been repeatedly cleared by burning for shifting cultivation. Thus, "natural" vegetation is virtually nonexistent except in certain areas of the coastal swamps, the upland rainforests, or the alpine forests. Inferences regarding the general zones of "natural" vegetation elsewhere are based upon observations of the wild vegetation growing with some degree of protection in forest reserves under governmental control. Although 13 climatic forest types have been recognized [5] in India and Pakistan, the three most important forest zones are evergreen broadleaf, deciduous broadleaf, and thorn scrub. The distribution and composition of these forests are controlled chiefly by moisture supply. Temperature has a secondary influence upon vegetation in South Asia except in the mountains above 3,000 or 4,000 feet where the subtropical, temperate, and alpine forest zones exist.

One part of the *evergreen broadleaf zone* [6] is located along the western coastal lowland of India and on the rainy windward slopes of the Ghats. The largest area of this kind spreads over the lowlands of Bengal both in East Pakistan and India (Figure 106) and extends into the adjacent plains of Orissa as well as into the Assam lowlands and hills. The

[5] See H. G. Champion, "A Preliminary Survey of the Forest Types of India and Burma," *Indian Forest Records*, Vol. 1, No. 1 (New Series), 1936. There are six tropical types: wet evergreen, semi-evergreen, moist deciduous, dry deciduous, thorn, and dry evergreen forests; three subtropical types: wet, pine, and dry forests; three temperate types: wet, moist, and dry forests; alpine forest and the edaphic tidal forest of the coastal swamps.

[6] See Map 30 for the distribution of existing forests. Forests are not shown where the land is predominantly under cultivation.

Fig. 106 • An evergreen, broadleaf, banyan tree *(Ficus bengalensis)* seen near Midnapore, West Bengal, India is representative of the semi-evergreen tropical forest zone. It has secondary trunks where aerial roots have grown down from the branches that spread out from the main trunk on the left. Banyan trees grow commonly in and around settlements in the lowlands (note thatched house in background) where most of the vegetation consists of shrubs and young trees, subjected to livestock browsing and firewood cutting. *(Edwin C. Brush.)*

evergreen broadleaf forest zone of Ceylon is located in the lowlands east and south of Colombo and on the wet lower slopes of the central highlands. These forests are closely associated with the monsoon rain forest climate (Am type). In general 80 inches annual rainfall is necessary to support the wet evergreen *climax* forest—a dense stand of large softleaved trees. As little as 50 inches of precipitation will support evergreen growth if the rains are well distributed throughout five or six months from May to October. As much as 200 inches of rainfall are necessary under unfavorable conditions such as steep slopes or dry soil. The fully developed tree canopy consists of a variety of species of large buttressed trees which retain their foliage throughout the year. The dominant species in the wet evergreen type of forest include several belonging to the Dipterocarp family. The understory and shrub growth is scanty, but there are many lianas and epiphytes. Where the rainfall is less than 80 inches annually, certain deciduous broadleaf trees may be present in the top canopy, forming a semi-evergreen forest, which becomes progressively more prevalent towards the dry margins of the zone.

The peculiar *dry evergreen type* of forest with a complete canopy of foliage only 30 to 40 feet high, consisting of hardleaved trees with broad crowns and short boles, is found in the Madras-Andhra coastal lowland. This forest zone is confined largely to the As climatic area, where the annual rainfall of 35 to 55 inches reaches its maximum intensity during October and November. This is the driest climatic condition in which any tropical evergreen forest exists in South Asia.

The *deciduous broadleaf forest* zone is located in the hills and plateaus of central and southern India and in the plains of the Ganges, where annual rainfall of 35 to 80 inches occurs almost exclusively during the four or five rainy months from June to October (Figure 107). The deciduous character of the dominant tree species is a response to the long period (seven or eight months) of dry weather that occurs in both the tropical savannah (Aw type) and humid mesothermal (Cw type) climatic zones. The branches of the trees forming the top canopy gradually become bare as the soil dries and the hot season approaches. The understory is composed of small evergreen broadleaved trees and bamboos in the moist deciduous type of forest, where rainfall is 60 to 80 inches. Teak and *sal* (*Shorea robusta*) are typical species in the moist deciduous forest areas of the uplands in peninsular India (Map 30), where the natural growth is least disturbed by man. Dry deciduous forest is prevalent where the rainfall is as little as 35 or 40 inches. Even the understory trees become bare in the dry season. Shrubby undergrowth is often present and sometimes grass, which tends to become more developed under burning and shifting cultivation. In places a park-like landscape may result, but no tropical savannah type of vegetation is recognized in India. The term "jungle," de-

Fig. 107 • East of Trichur, Travancore-Cochin, approaching the Anaimalai hills, the dry leeward slopes are clothed in a mixed forest of broadleaf evergreen and deciduous trees. Some of the deciduous trees, including teak, lose their leaves by February-March and appear white and bare against the cloudless sky. The valley fields, diked for rice which is grown in the rainy season, are idle in the dry season but provide scanty grazing for the cattle in the middleground. *(Wellington D. Jones.)*

rived from the Hindi word *jangal*, is commonly applied in India to these tropical deciduous forests and to the thickets into which they degenerate under the inroads of woodcutting, shifting cultivation, and grazing.

Thorn scrub is associated with the semi-arid (BSh) climatic areas of West Pakistan, northwestern and peninsular India, and Ceylon, wherever the annual precipitation is between 20 and 35 inches. The fully developed forest under this climate consists of an open canopy of thorny hardwooded species, predominantly of the genus Acacia, which have short boles of 20 to 30 feet and low branching crowns which rarely meet. There is an ill-defined lower story of spiny xerophytic shrubs and sparse grass which does not completely cover the ground even during the rainy season. The thorn scrub forest is replaced by xerophytic shrubs and fleshy cactus where the trees are destroyed by woodcutters and livestock.

The arid (BWh) climatic area of India and West Pakistan, also supports xerophytic shrubs and grasses, but much of the surface is completely barren rock, sand, or salt flats. Some ephemeral grasses and herbs sprout after rain; and in the lowlands there are belts of scrub tamarisk, palms, and other trees along watercourses and near springs. Mountain slopes in the arid climatic zone of Baluchistan and Afghanistan support scrub junipers and small pistachio trees. These slopes become green with grass briefly during the spring after the snow melts.

| Soil zones

The world map of soils [7] shows at least four broad groups of zonal soils [8] in South Asia—(1) sierozems and other desert soils, (2) chestnut and brown soils in dry climates, (3) yellow or red soils and laterites of the humid tropical and mesothermal climates, (4) chernozems and related dark-colored soils of tropics and middle latitudes. An area comprised of nonzonal lithosols and shallow mountain soils also exists.

In the northern mountain belt, which comprises some 15 per cent of the total area of South Asia, lithosols prevail on the steepest and highest slopes, but on the gentler slopes shallow zonal soils exist where the vegetative cover remains more or less intact. Yellow or red soils appear under subtropical forest cover on the lower slopes. Brown or gray-brown podzolized forest soils and mountain meadow soils occur at successively higher elevations. Thus, the soils of the Himalaya and associated extrapeninsular mountains reflect the mesothermal, microthermal, and tundra climatic zones and the subtropical, temperate, and alpine zones of vegetation.

Some 30 to 35 per cent of the total area of South Asia is covered with water- and wind-transported surface materials showing little or no soil-profile development. About 20 per cent of the area of India and Pakistan, together, is covered with alluvial gravels, sands, silts, or clays. The varied characteristics of alluvial soils depend primarily on the texture and fertility of the parent material. Yet on the terraces of old alluvium above flood levels in the warm humid climatic zones (either tropical or mesothermal) there is evidence of leaching and laterization associated with these climates. Effects of soil formation on terraces in the dry climatic zone of northwestern India and West Pakistan tend to produce profiles somewhat resembling the chestnut and brown steppe soils of middle latitudes. The most important effects of soil formation in the arid and semiarid climates are the subsoil lime concentrations, owing to leaching, and the salt encrustations, resulting from evaporation of ground water in low

[7] See "World Soils," Figure 6 in W. Van Royen et al., *The Agricultural Resources of the World* (New York: Prentice-Hall, Inc., 1954), p. 6; and "Soil Regions," Plate VII in V. C. Finch, G. T. Trewartha, et. al., *op. cit.*

[8] In South Asia the numerous local soil types recognized by the peasants on the basis of quality and workability and the various soil productivity classes designated by land revenue officers still await scientific survey and classification according to modern concepts of soil science.

spots. Some alluvial areas are peat-covered where drainage is impeded. An additional 5 per cent of the surface of India, one-fifth of West Pakistan, and at least one-third of Afghanistan are covered by sand dunes and gravelly or clayey materials in which no soil profiles have developed.

In the Indian peninsula, well developed zonal soils are spread over the undulating, rolling, or hilly terrain in a broad area which includes as much as half of the whole territory of South Asia. Here the outstanding zonal soils belong in two groups: (1) dark-colored *regur*,[9] and (2) yellow or red lateritic soils and the true laterite of reddish-brown color.

The *regur* soils are spread over approximately 200,000 square miles of territory between longitudes 73° and 80°E. and latitudes 15° and 25°N., mainly in the northwestern and northcentral parts of the Indian peninsula. These soils also occur south of latitude 15°N. in outlying areas in Mysore and southern Madras, and east of latitude 80°E. in the northeastern peninsular uplands. Soils of this group are composed of dark-brown or black clayey material which expands during the rainy season and contracts during the dry season.[9] *Regur* soils commonly are found over parent material derived from the basaltic Dekkan lavas, or on alluvium derived from the same ultimate source, and their color has often been ascribed to the basic minerals present in the parent rock. But *regur* is also developed from bedrock of sedimentary origin (such as limestone, shale, sandstone), from calcareous clays, and even from metamorphic slates and gneisses. Generally, the rocks upon which all these dark-colored soils are developed are basic in character, low in quartz (silica) content, and upon weathering form clays through which water percolation is slow. The lime content of the *regur* soils also is high. Although the darkness of these soils is now proved to be finely divided organic matter rather than the color of the parent rock, the organic matter content of less than 1 per cent is very low in comparison to the black chernozem and dark-brown prairie soils of middle latitudes. The *regur* soils, thus, cannot be considered as tropical or subtropical chernozems, although much *regur* is in the zone of semi-arid climate (BSh), whence arises the confusion with the chernozems of the middle-latitude grasslands. The natural vegetation of the semi-arid regions is not grass but is either thorn scrub forest or dry deciduous forest, and the precipitation ranges from 17 to 55 inches. Evidently the *regur* soils belong in a distinct soil group, including other dark-colored soils in the tropical and mesothermal climates of Africa and America.

Wherever Ceylon and the Indian Peninsula receive more than 60 inches annual precipitation, there are lateritic soils or laterites. The lateritic

---

[9] *Regur* is made up of 40-60 per cent clay of less than two microns diameter, composed largely of montmorillonite, which has a high water-absorption capacity and gives the soil its high ratio of swelling and shrinking. See R. W. Simonson, "Morphology and Classification of the Regur Soils of India," *Jour. of Soil Science*, July, 1954, pp. 275-288.

soils vary from the deep red clayey soils of the valleys to the light red and yellow gravelly or loamy soils of the hills and lower slopes. Indurated laterite crust is found on hilltops or mountains and on old alluvial or marine terraces. True laterite evidently forms as the end-product of the leaching out of siliceous material and almost all other mineral compounds. Laterite is valuable as building material if cut into blocks, which harden on exposure to air; [10] it is also used for road surfacing. Laterite has even been smelted by the primitive Indian ironsmiths for its iron content, which may be as high as 30 to 35 per cent by weight, although impurities make it undesirable for use in the modern iron-and-steel industry. If the aluminum content is high, the material is mined as the ore of alumina.

Land utilization and agriculture

The interrelationships between man and the land in South Asia are so close and so ancient that it is difficult to conceive of the land without man. Man, himself, has created much of the present landscape, through disturbing natural vegetation, domesticating plants and animals, or introducing foreign species.

One of the most significant features of land utilization in the Republic of India is the large proportion of the area suitable for agriculture that already has been brought under cultivation (Map 30). About 11 per cent of the surface area of India is made up of mountain land over 7,000 feet in elevation, almost all of which is too steep or too cold for agriculture.[11] Another 18 per cent of the surface is hill land between 1,000 and 7,000 feet above sea level, three-quarters of which is too steep to farm. Plateaus of relatively low relief between 1,000 and 3,000 feet form 28 per cent of all land in India, all but a quarter of which is topographically usable. In the lowlands less than 1,000 feet in elevation, which make up 43 per cent of the total area in India, only one acre in 20 is unusable because of roughness of topography. Altogether, 66 per cent of the land in India is topographically usable, but climate imposes limits of aridity which can be overcome by irrigation only in part. Within India 52 per cent of the land area classified is in crops or fallow; although this amounts to only about 0.9 acre per capita, it means that among the large nations of the Orient, India is one of the best endowed with agricultural land. Waste land, land under urban or village settlement, and land put to other nonagricultural

[10] Hence, the term "laterite" (*later* = brick) was coined by the Englishman Buchanan about 1810.

[11] See *Census of India: 1951, Vol. I,* Part I-A Report, (New Delhi: 1953). The land-utilization data are for the year 1949-50 or preceding years and cover only 77 per cent of the total area of India.

uses comprises 16 per cent of the total area; forest land makes up another 15 per cent. The remainder, 17 per cent, is made up of village pastures and firewood groves, jungle scrub and bamboo, private forests and culturable waste. But most of so-called culturable waste is submarginal and can not at present be brought under cultivation.

Pakistan and the smaller nations[12] are less well endowed with agricultural land than India. Only 26 per cent of Pakistan, as a whole, is arable and 10 to 20 per cent more is classified as potentially productive. On account of the severe limits imposed by aridity in the western part of Pakistan, only 3 per cent of the country's total area is forested, and nearly two-thirds is waste land or rough pasture. Little of the island of Ceylon is topographically or climatically unusable, but only 22 per cent of the surface is arable, while 54 per cent is under forest or woodland. About 15 per cent is waste land or devoted to nonagricultural uses, and another 9 per cent is considered potentially productive. Some of the wooded and potentially productive land is used for shifting cultivation, and it is known that much formerly was cultivated. Nepal is hilly or mountainous and most of the surface is under forest or lies in the zone of alpine tundra or perennial ice climate. Yet probably as much as 14 per cent of Nepal is now cultivated. In Afghanistan cultivation is most restricted. Only 2 per cent of this arid mountainous country is at present arable. Irrigation works under construction may increase the arable area to 3 per cent, but less than 2 per cent of the total area is forested and at least 95 per cent is not suited to crop production, although probably half of this nonarable land does provide rough pasturage for Afghanistan's great herds of sheep.

The agricultural land of South Asia may be divided into three major categories on the basis of the crops grown and the methods of farming —(1) wet cultivation, (2) dry cultivation, and (3) irrigated cultivation. It is possible to delineate only the main areas under wet cultivation and irrigated cultivation because of the small scale of the map of India and Pakistan (Map 30), but in Ceylon (Map 31) and Afghanistan (Map 32) more detail is given. Dry cultivation is scattered throughout the zone of thorn scrub vegetation. The proportion of surface arable in the areas of wet, dry, and irrigated cultivation varies from 40 to 75 per cent. The intricate distribution patterns of settlements, fields, and forest or waste land in India and Pakistan are suggested by the large-scale maps of occupance types. (See insets, Map 30.) The proportion of land cultivated is lower, of course, in the areas shown as forest land or mountain land, although innumerable patches of cropland do exist. Permanent cultivation is also

[12] Percentages of land in the various classifications for Pakistan and other South Asian countries are based on statistics for 1948 and 1949 published in the *United Nations' Statistical Yearbook 1951* (New York: 1951).

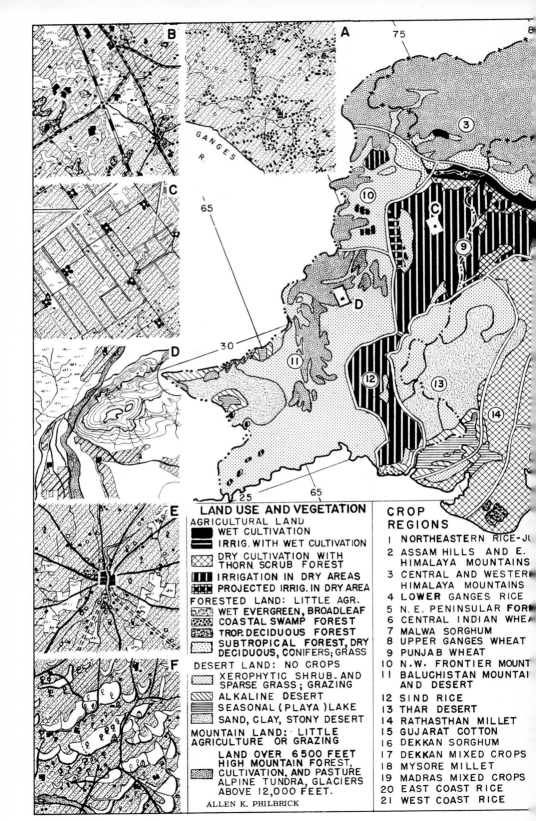

LAND USE AND VEGETATION

AGRICULTURAL LAND
- ▮ WET CULTIVATION
- ▭ IRRIG. WITH WET CULTIVATION
- ⊠ DRY CULTIVATION WITH THORN SCRUB FOREST
- ▥ IRRIGATION IN DRY AREAS
- ▦ PROJECTED IRRIG. IN DRY AREA

FORESTED LAND: LITTLE AGR.
- WET EVERGREEN, BROADLEAF
- COASTAL SWAMP FOREST
- TROP. DECIDUOUS FOREST
- SUBTROPICAL FOREST, DRY DECIDUOUS, CONIFERS, GRASS

DESERT LAND: NO CROPS
- XEROPHYTIC SHRUB. AND SPARSE GRASS; GRAZING
- ALKALINE DESERT
- SEASONAL (PLAYA) LAKE
- SAND, CLAY, STONY DESERT

MOUNTAIN LAND: LITTLE AGRICULTURE OR GRAZING
- LAND OVER 6500 FEET HIGH MOUNTAIN FOREST, CULTIVATION, AND PASTURE ALPINE TUNDRA, GLACIERS ABOVE 12,000 FEET.

ALLEN K. PHILBRICK

CROP REGIONS

1. NORTHEASTERN RICE-JU
2. ASSAM HILLS AND E. HIMALAYA MOUNTAINS
3. CENTRAL AND WESTER HIMALAYA MOUNTAINS
4. LOWER GANGES RICE
5. N. E. PENINSULAR FOR
6. CENTRAL INDIAN WHEA
7. MALWA SORGHUM
8. UPPER GANGES WHEAT
9. PUNJAB WHEAT
10. N.W. FRONTIER MOUNT
11. BALUCHISTAN MOUNTAI AND DESERT
12. SIND RICE
13. THAR DESERT
14. RATHASTHAN MILLET
15. GUJARAT COTTON
16. DEKKAN SORGHUM
17. DEKKAN MIXED CROPS
18. MYSORE MILLET
19. MADRAS MIXED CROPS
20. EAST COAST RICE
21. WEST COAST RICE

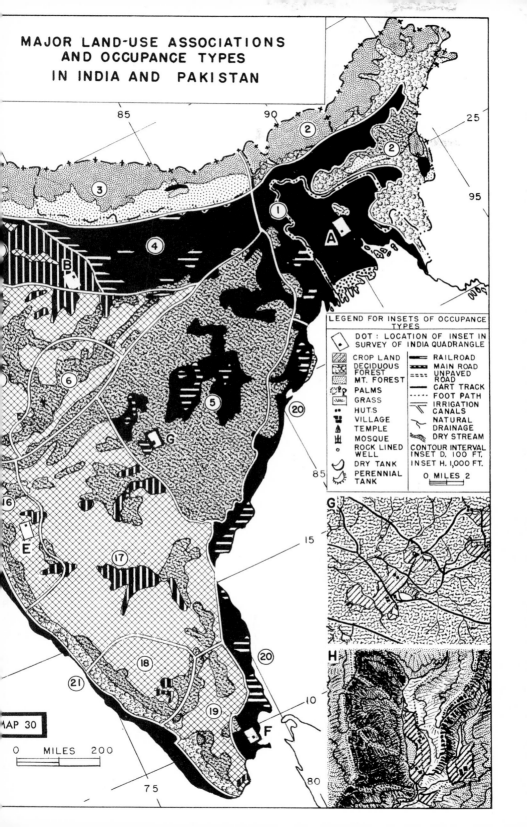

MAJOR LAND-USE ASSOCIATIONS AND OCCUPANCE TYPES IN INDIA AND PAKISTAN

LEGEND FOR INSETS OF OCCUPANCE TYPES

DOT : LOCATION OF INSET IN SURVEY OF INDIA QUADRANGLE

CROP LAND — RAILROAD
DECIDUOUS FOREST — MAIN ROAD
MT. FOREST — UNPAVED ROAD
PALMS — CART TRACK
GRASS — FOOT PATH
HUTS — IRRIGATION CANALS
VILLAGE — NATURAL DRAINAGE
TEMPLE — DRY STREAM
MOSQUE
ROCK LINED WELL
DRY TANK
PERENNIAL TANK

CONTOUR INTERVAL
INSET D. 100 FT.
INSET H. 1,000 FT.

0 MILES 2

MAP 30

0 MILES 200

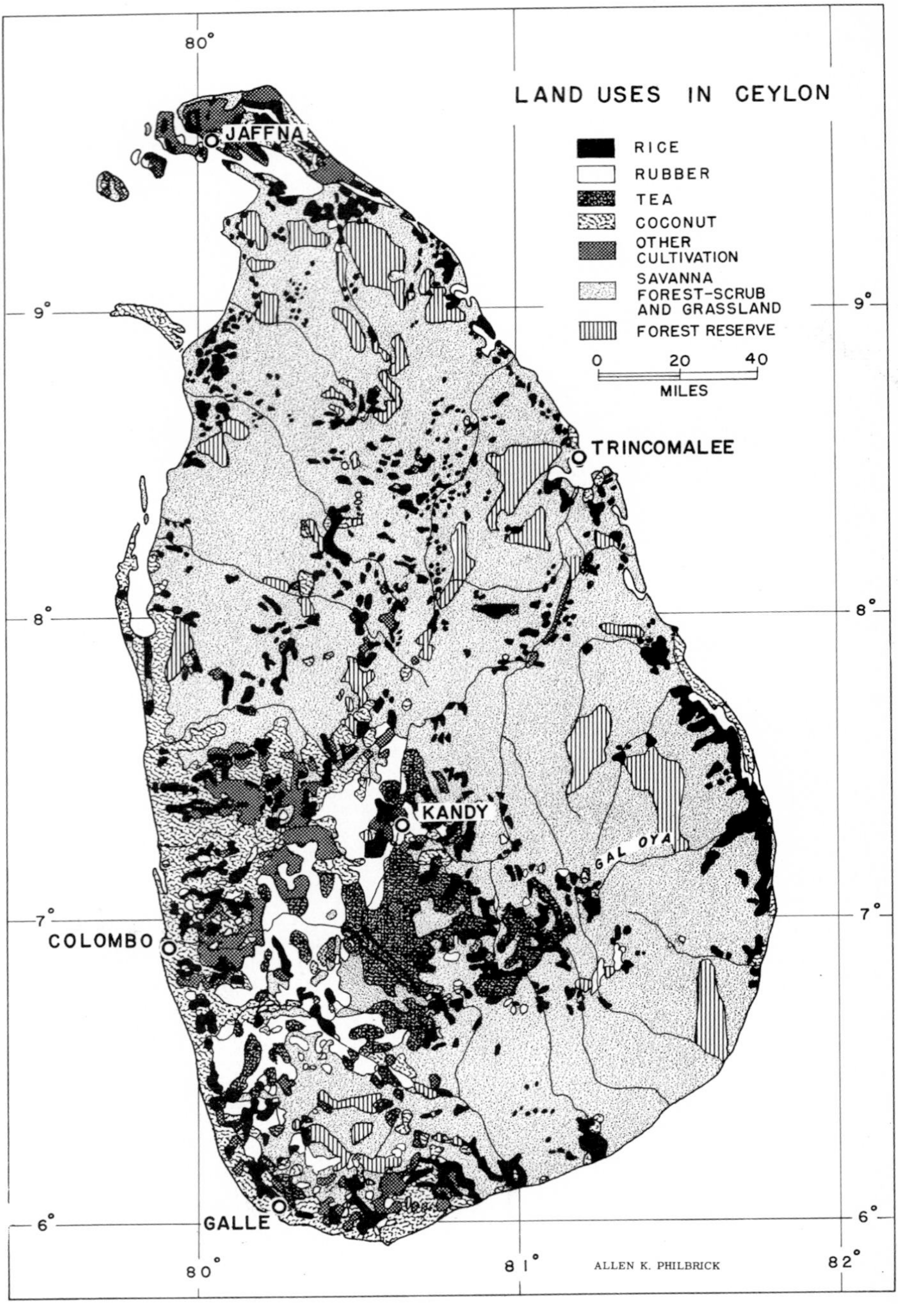

LAND USES IN CEYLON
RICE
RUBBER
TEA
COCONUT
OTHER CULTIVATION
SAVANNA FOREST-SCRUB AND GRASSLAND
FOREST RESERVE
0 20 40
MILES
JAFFNA
TRINCOMALEE
KANDY
GAL OYA
COLOMBO
GALLE
80°
81°
82°
9°
8°
7°
6°
ALLEN K. PHILBRICK

MAP 31

found in irrigated spots outside the few large oases shown in the desert region.

Wet cultivation prevails in the alluvial lowlands within the zones of

LAND USES AND RESOURCES IN AFGHANISTAN

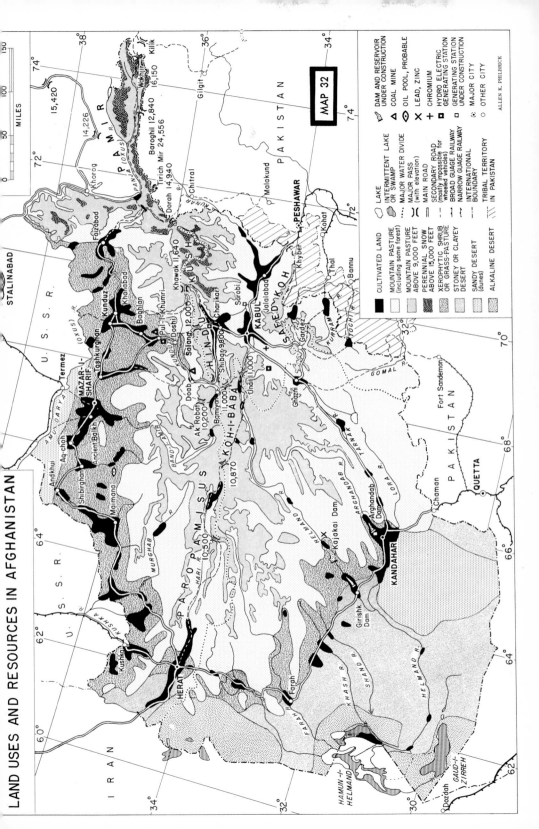

MAP 32

ALLEN K. PHILBRICK

■	CULTIVATED LAND
	MOUNTAIN PASTURE (including some forest)
	MOUNTAIN PASTURE ABOVE 9,000 FEET
	PERENNIAL SNOW ABOVE 15,000 FEET
	XEROPHYTIC SHRUB OR GRASS-PASTURE
	STONEY OR CLAYEY DESERT
	SANDY DESERT (dunes)
	ALKALINE DESERT

- ⬯ LAKE
- ⬯ INTERMITTENT LAKE OR SWAMP
- ‥‥ MAJOR WATER DIVIDE
-)(MAJOR PASS (with elevation)
- ─ MAIN ROAD
- ― SECONDARY ROAD (mostly impossible for wheeled vehicles)
- ╫ BROAD GUAGE RAILWAY
- ╫ NARROW GUAGE RAILWAY
- ─‧─ INTERNATIONAL BOUNDARY
- ▨ TRIBAL TERRITORY IN PAKISTAN

- ◿ DAM AND RESERVOIR UNDER CONSTRUCTION
- ▲ COAL MINE
- ◈ OIL POOL, PROBABLE
- ✕ LEAD, ZINC
- ✚ CHROMIUM
- ▣ HYDRO ELECTRIC GENERATING STATION
- ▢ GENERATING STATION UNDER CONSTRUCTION
- ⊙ MAJOR CITY
- ○ OTHER CITY

Fig. 108 • The rich coastal lowland of Malabar near Trichur in Travancore-Cochin state is occupied largely by rice fields and coconut trees. The second annual rice crop, seen here in the month of February, is planted late on land retaining sufficient moisture from the rainy season, which ends in October. The absence of humans from the picture belies the high density of population in this region of wet cultivation. Thatched dwelling houses of a straggling village are scarcely visible in the coconut grove at the extreme right. *(Wellington D. Jones.)*

tropical and mesothermal climate with 40 inches or more precipitation in eastern and southern India (Figure 108), East Pakistan, and southern Ceylon. Rice is the leading crop. (Note crop regions 1, 4, 5, 20, and 21: Map 30.) It occupies one-half to two-thirds of the area planted annually, except in the Gangetic plain of Bihar and eastern Uttar Pradesh and in the Malabar coast of western Madras, where it occupies about 40 per cent of the planted area. Winter wheat and barley (in the Gangetic plain), maize, and various oil seeds are the commonest secondary food crops in the areas of wet cultivation, but rice, being a fresh-water swamp plant probably indigenous to the Bengal delta or the nearby deltas of Southeast Asia, is ideally suited to the naturally inundated plains wherever rainfall of 60 inches or more is received. Irrigation is necessary for rice in the eastern coastal deltas and the interior lowlands of India where rainfall of only 40 to 60 inches is received. Rice produces an average of 750 pounds of grain per acre in India, more than any other grain, and supports the densest

516

rural population of the subcontinent—600 to 1,000 or more persons per square mile. Sugar cane and jute are indigenous crops, important as sources of cash income in the alluvial areas of eastern India and Pakistan. Tobacco is a locally significant cash crop in East Pakistan and Andhra. Coconuts are produced commercially on the coasts of Malabar and Ceylon. Coffee in Madras; tea in Ceylon, Madras, Bengal, and Assam in India and East Pakistan; and rubber in Madras and Ceylon, are commercial plantation crops produced on the red soils of the terraces and uplands adjacent to the flood plains under wet cultivation.

Dry cultivation prevails in the uplands and interior valleys within the peninsular massif and along the margins of the Indo-Gangetic plains (Figure 109). The climate in general is semi-arid with 18 to 35 inches of rainfall, but dry cultivation extends into the desert zone of Rajasthan where rainfall is as little as 15 inches and into the humid tropical and mesothermal zones of central India where as much as 40 inches is received. The fertile *regur* soils are widespread, but water supply is insufficient to irrigate much land adequately. The necessity of fallowing to conserve moisture in the subsoil withdraws one-tenth to one-third of the arable land from crop production each year. Rice production is unim-

Fig. 109 • The struggle for water is exemplified by this hand-dug well and primitive lifting device, operated by human power, seen in the Gangetic plain near Kanpur, Uttar Pradesh, India. The amount of water lifted by such means is sufficient only for domestic purposes or for irrigating small vegetable plots. The crops of *jowar* (sorghum) and maize in the background are grown typically without natural inundation or irrigation, *i.e.* by dry cultivation, in the rainy season. (Wellington D. Jones.)

portant, although not excluded, and wheat is important within the region
of dry cultivation only in northcentral India (crop region 6: Map 30).
Sorghum and the lesser millets are the dominant subsistence crops (crop
regions 7, 14, 16, 17, 18, and 19: Map 30). Grain sorghum, called *jowar,
durra,* or *cholum* in India, is a major crop throughout the region of dry
cultivation and is the food grain second in rank after rice in acreage and
production in India as a whole. Bulrush millet (*Pennisetum typhoideum*),
called *bajra* or *cumbu* in India, has somewhat lesser moisture requirements
than sorghum and is concentrated in the drier parts of the Dekkan and
Rajasthan. Finger millet (*Eleusine corocana*), called *ragi* or *marua*, and
another millet called *kodo* (*Paspalum scrobiculatum*) are most tolerant
of drouth. Altogether there are nearly three dozen species of lesser millets,
many appearing to be indigenous to India, which will grow under conditions where wheat or rice would fail, but millets are poor substitutes nutritionally for rice and wheat. Oil seeds, particularly peanuts, sesamum,
and castor seeds, are produced under dry cultivation. Cotton growing is
widespread and is the chief source of cash income. Cotton acreage is concentrated on the black *regur* soils of the northern Dekkan, but the yield
and quality are not as high as in the Gujarat coast (crop region 15: Map
30). In general, agricultural production is less intensive under dry cultivation than under wet cultivation, and the population density averages
about 200 to 400 persons per square mile or less.

Irrigated cultivation is the basis of agriculture on the arid plains of the
Indus in West Punjab and Sind and in the piedmont and intermontane
valleys beyond the Indus in West Pakistan and Afghanistan. In semi-arid
plains of eastern Punjab and of the upper Gangetic plain in Uttar Pradesh, where only 20 to 30 per cent of the land is irrigated, it is an assur-
ance of good harvests should the rains fail. These irrigated alluvial plains
of northern India and West Pakistan support moderately dense rural
population, ranging from 100 to 600 persons per square mile, and form the
most prosperous agricultural areas of the subcontinent. Water from the
melting winter snows and the heavy monsoon rains in the Himalaya is
brought to the alluvial terraces through modern systems of diversion
dams, canals, and ditches. The ground water table is close to the surface
and is tapped by means of hand-dug wells or tube wells in order to irrigate the fields not reached by canals. Flood-plain irrigation is commonly
from wells or seasonal inundation canals. Alluvial fans in the West Pakistan and Afghan mountain basins are irrigated by means of diversion
ditches or subterranean channels, dug by hand (Figure 110).

In the irrigated tracts winter wheat is the most widespread subsistence
and cash crop. Barley is a second winter grain, grown for subsistence.
Maize, sorghum, and bulrush millet are the most important subsistence
crops produced in summer—often not in irrigated fields because the water

Fig. 110 • This irrigated tract, seen from the air, is located in the Quetta valley, Baluchistan. Water is brought to the fields several miles in underground channels, known as *karez*, dug out and maintained by means of the rows of holes (wells) which are rimmed with the debris brought up. The water emerges at the lower end of each *karez* tunnel in a small canal from which it is led in ditches to the fields. (See upper center.) Similar tunnels are found in Afghanistan, Iran, Hsin-chiang, and parts of Soviet Middle Asia. Note the walled enclosures around the farmsteads and the contrast between fallow and cultivated fields. *(Stanley E. Brush.)*

must be conserved for rice and cash crops. Rice occupies a prominent place in Sind, both as a subsistence and a cash crop, and also in northern Afghanistan, where it is produced almost exclusively as a cash crop. Cotton of better quality than in peninsular India is grown; and commercial sugar cane is gaining in importance in the irrigated tracts. Oilseeds, especially linseed and rapeseed, are locally significant crops. Legumes and fodder crops are relatively more important than anywhere else in India and Pakistan.

The two greatest problems of agricultural land utilization in South Asia are (1) the low frequency of harvests from arable land, and (2) the low crop yields.

In India, as a whole, 22 per cent of the arable land is in fallow each year while the area sown more than once a year forms 13 per cent of the net sown area. In other words, about two acres of arable land in ten do not yield a harvest, but one other acre yields two harvests in a year. The proportion of idle land is probably not as great in the other countries of

South Asia, but in no country of the realm is there sufficient double crop-ping to raise the annual harvested area to more than the total area under cultivation as is true in China and Japan. The low frequency of harvests in India is astounding in view of the heavy demand for food supplies and the fact that in all parts of India, except the high mountains, temperatures are high enough for plant growth throughout the year. In the words of V. Nath [13] of India's National Planning Commission, "The main limiting factor in the case of India is deficiency of moisture. . . . One of the . . . functions of irrigation in India, therefore, is to make possible production of two or more crops in the year from lands which could produce only one crop otherwise." [14]

The low crop yields that characterize farming in South Asia also may be due in part to insufficient moisture, yet even in the alluvial plains under wet cultivation harvests are smaller than in the humid lowlands of China or Japan. The average rice yield per acre in India is about half of the yield in China and one-third of the yield in Japan. To quote Nath again, ". . . the fertility levels of most of our crop-lands are low, because applications of farm-yard manure are generally inadequate and the use of chemical fertilizers has been practically non-existent." [15]

The future increase of agricultural production in South Asia must come mainly from the extension of perennial irrigation and the application of fertilizers on land already under cultivation. Probably only 15 million acres more, or 6 per cent of the present sown area, can be brought under cultivation. India already has undertaken the construction of large dams and storage reservoirs to capture more river water for irrigation, as well as for power generation. The prospects for expansion of cultivation are proportionately greater in Afghanistan, Pakistan, and Ceylon, where large-scale irrigation works are also under construction, but the basic causes of low and insufficient agricultural production in these countries are similar to those in India.

Another agricultural problem of South Asia, closely related to land utilization, is that of livestock production. India and Pakistan have about 200 million cattle, including water buffaloes and the zebu, or humped, breeds—a number amounting to more than one-quarter of the world's total cattle population. There are also some 100 million goats and sheep in these two countries in addition to the 30 million sheep in Afghanistan. Thus, the farm-animal density in South Asia is higher than in any other Asian realm, and indeed, higher than it is almost anywhere else in the world. This is to say nothing of the camels and donkeys, the horses and mules, and even the elephants, kept as draft animals and beasts of burden.

[13] See his article on "Land Utilization in India," *Jour. of Soil and Water Conservation in India,* January, 1953, pp. 4-18.
[14] *Ibid.,* p. 8.
[15] *Ibid.,* p. 8.

Humped oxen and cows, as well as buffaloes, are used for draft purposes. Oxen, sheep, and goats serve as pack animals. Buffalo cows are preferred to humped cows for milking because their yield is larger and richer in butterfat. Goats are kept for milking because their feeding requirements are small in proportion to their yield. On account of religious taboo, Hindus eat little or no beef. Moslems and others can obtain some beef, but mutton is more generally consumed. Wool is a source of considerable cash income in Afghanistan and the mountainous or dry regions of India and Pakistan.

The problems of animal husbandry are overpopulation and under-nourishment. Little fodder is grown, and the animals have to be supported mainly on unimproved pasturage in the mountains, in the wasteland, in scrub woodland, and on the desert margins. The work animals are nearly always small and underfed. The cows give meager quantities of milk, the average per animal being one-fifth (or less) of the average in Western Europe and North America. There is practically no feed available for sheep and goats, but the larger work and milk animals are given the stalks of grain after harvest and allowed to graze on the stubble. Cow manure is collected and dried for use as domestic fuel, but seldom for use as fertilizer. Most of the livestock in India and Pakistan die of disease or simply of old age. Animals of all kinds are skinned, and their hides form the basis for an increasingly important leather-manufacturing industry. Raw and crudely tanned hides are a major export from both India and Pakistan.

SELECTED GEOGRAPHICAL BIBLIOGRAPHY

1. Aiyar, A. K. Yegna Narain. *Field Crops of India.* Bangalore City: Bangalore Printing and Publishing Co., 1954.
2. Brown, J. Coggin, and A. K. Dey. *India's Mineral Wealth* (3d ed.). London: Oxford University Press, 1955.
3. Champion, H. G. "A Preliminary Survey of the Forest Types of India and Burma," *Indian Forest Records,* Vol. I, No. 1 (New Series), 1936.
4. Nath, V. "Land Utilization in India," *Jour. of Soil and Water Conservation in India,* January, 1953, pp. 4-18.
5. Pascoe, Sir Edwin H. *A Manual of the Geology of India and Burma* (3d ed.). Delhi: Mgr. of Publications, 1950.
6. Ramanathan, K. R., and K. P. Ramakrishnan. "The General Circulation of the Atmosphere over India and Its Neighborhood," *Memoirs,* Indian Meteorological Dept., Vol. 26, Part X, 1937, pp. 189-245.
7. Ramdas, L. A. "The Rainfall of India," *Empire Jour. of Experimental Agriculture,* April, 1946, pp. 85-99.
8. Raychaudhuri, S. P. "Classification and Nomenclature of Indian Soils," *Jour. of Soil and Water Conservation in India,* April, 1955, pp. 92-96.

9. Russell, Sir John. "India's People and Their Food Supply," *Geography*, July, 1952, pp. 125-141.
10. Wadia, D. N. *Geology of India* (3d ed.). London: Macmillan, 1953.

Comments

Wadia's book is the best one-volume treatment of the physical, historical, and economic geology of India and Pakistan. Pascoe's revision of the old *Manual*, previously published by the Geological Survey of India in 1879 and 1893, brings a specialists' reference book up to date in part (only the first of four volumes has been published); the general reader will find useful the introductory chapter on the structure and terrain of the subcontinent. Both authors exclude Ceylon and Afghanistan, but include Burma because of its administrative connection with the former British Indian Empire. Mineral resources in India, Pakistan, and Burma, are exhaustively catalogued and described by Brown and Dey. Among the many publications available on weather and climate only Ramdas' brief article and the monograph by Ramanathan and Ramakrishnan are cited. The reader is directed to the *Memoirs* of the Indian Meteorological Department for interpretation of weather phenomena in terms of modern meteorological analysis and to the annual summary of data in the *India Weather Review*. Champion's survey of forest types remains the best description of vegetation. Conventional descriptions of India's soils are given by Wadia and by Brown and Dey, but Raychaudhuri, who summarizes the problems of nomenclature and classification, notes that no thoroughly integrated study of the effects of climate, vegetation, and topography on the soils of India has yet been done. The excellent articles by Russell on food supply and Nath on land use deal only with the Republic of India. Aiyar's inventory of crops has special reference to Mysore state in south India but the scope of his book includes all of the subcontinent. Two atlases are useful: T. H. Engelbrecht's classic *Die Feldfrüchte Indiens in ihrer geographischen Verbreitung* (Hamburg: Hamburgischen Kolonialinstituts, 1914), and the *Indian Agricultural Atlas* (Dehra Dun, Uttar Pradesh, India; Ministry of Food and Agriculture, 1952). The reader's attention is directed to the maps and appropriate text describing crops and livestock in South Asia in William Van Royen, *Atlas of the World's Resources*, Vol. I, "Agricultural Resources of the World" (Prentice-Hall, Inc., 1954).

South Asia

POLITICAL ORGANIZATION

THE NEW SOUTH ASIAN NATIONS OF INDIA, PAKISTAN, AND CEYLON, which have recently gained their independence, and the old nations of Afghanistan and Nepal, which now are emerging from isolation, provide the political framework through which the people of the subcontinent seek to express their national aspirations and within which they are developing their resources and industries. The political geography of these nations will condition their future development and influence the welfare of the people as much as the historic cultural regions (described in Chapter XXII) or the land-use regions related to physiographic and climatic conditions (described in Chapter XXIII).

The whole area was more or less under British hegemony until August 15, 1947, when Britain's Indian Empire, which had existed from August 2, 1858, was brought to an end. The Empire had been the successor to the British East India Company which gained control of most of the territory during the eighteenth and early nineteenth centuries. Ceylon became independent on February 4, 1948, at the end of 152 years of British rule. Although Portuguese and French India survived the British Indian Empire, the imprint of Britain is far stronger, not only in the formation of political institutions but also in the determination of South Asia's political geography.

The colonial period

At the end of British rule there were three categories of territory in South Asia, in each of which different levels of British jurisdiction existed: (1) the areas administered directly by British officials; (2) the areas in which British control was exercised indirectly, the so-called Native States; and (3) the tribal territories under nominal British rule and the protected states in which little or no control was exercised.

Ceylon, one of the areas directly ruled by the British, was first visited by the Portuguese in 1505, who occupied the coast until they were pushed out by the Dutch in the mid-seventeenth century. The British annexed the island in 1796 and subsequently conquered the interior Kandyan Sinhalese kingdom which had remained independent throughout the Portuguese and Dutch periods. In 1802 Ceylon became a Crown Colony and was administered separately from India.

The areas on the mainland called British India constituted the most heavily populated and productive territory. There were 11 [1] British provinces, administered by governors or commissioners, subject to the authority of the Viceroy in Delhi, who represented the British Crown and the control of Parliament in London. The two oldest provinces (or presidencies) were Madras and Bengal, portions of which were acquired in 1753 and 1757, respectively. The lands around the head of the Bay of Bengal, later known as Bihar, Orissa, and Assam, were annexed to Bengal Presidency during the late eighteenth and early nineteenth centuries. At the same time British control of peninsular India was extended inland from the ports of Bombay and Madras; and by the first quarter of the nineteenth century the two southern presidencies named after these cities had assumed essentially their final outlines. By the middle of the nineteenth century British control was extended to the lower Indus plain, which later became the province of Sind, and to the upper Gangetic plain, subsequently known as the United Provinces of Agra and Oudh. The Punjab was annexed in 1849 after two wars with the Sikhs. Shortly after 1850 the Central Provinces were formed. Thus, a hundred years ago British rule had been extended from the coastline across the Indian peninsula and consolidated throughout the Indo-Gangetic plain. Within 40 years thereafter the British power had pushed beyond the Indus River, where two small provinces, Baluchistan and the North-West Frontier were formed. By the year 1894 the map of British India had been determined.

[1] Burma was another British province, administered as part of India, until 1937.

The Native States under indirect British rule occupied one-third of the territory of the Indian Empire and had one-quarter of the total population. They were located mainly in the peninsular hill and plateau region or in the desert areas and the mountainous borderlands. The rulers of these states, 584 of them, had been recognized by treaty with the British or actually were established by the British. They were subject to the advice, and sometimes to the dictates, of British officials residing in their capitals. Some of the Native States, such as Hyderabad, Bhopal, and Bahawalpur, were ruled by the descendants of invading Moslem conquerors from the Arabian peninsula or the trans-Indus lands, while others, such as Gwalior, Indore, and Baroda, obeyed Hindu Maratha conquerors from the Dekkan. Many of the Moslem and Maratha states had come into existence in the period just preceding the British conquest. The small Sikh states in eastern Punjab actually came into existence during the period of British conquest. Other Native States, for example, those ruled by the Hindu Rajputs in Rajputana, had had a long history before the coming of the British, and their kings were among the few truly indigenous rulers of recent Indian history. Certain large states, notably Hyderabad, Mysore, Baroda, Gwalior, and Indore, maintained armies, built railways and other public works, and in some instances issued their own coinage and postage stamps. Most of the Native States, however, were no larger in area than counties or townships in the United States and their rulers had scarcely any more status or function than feudal landlords paying revenue to the British.

Though British power was recognized as supreme everywhere in the provinces and states in the plains and in the peninsula, it was not equally well entrenched in the frontier mountains. Only in the portions of the United Provinces and the Punjab bordering Tibet and in Baluchistan bordering Afghanistan and Iran had the British extended their direct administration into the frontier mountains. The Native State of Jammu and Kashmir was under fairly close British control, but the Pathan tribal territories of the North-West Frontier, adjacent to Afghanistan, were less closely controlled. Indeed, the Pathan tribes regarded themselves as independent and self-governing, although they lived inside the line demarcating the boundary of the Indian Empire. Manipur was a Native State between Assam and Burma. Most of the remaining area bordering northern Burma and Tibet, and lying between Manipur and Bhutan or China, was unadministered territory occupied by independent Tibeto-Burman tribes. Sikkim, located between Nepal and Bhutan on the border of Tibet, was a Native State, but it enjoyed somewhat more autonomy than the Native States of India proper.

Still a lesser degree of British power was exercised in the mountain

countries of Afghanistan, Nepal, and Bhutan. These countries were protectorates bound by treaty to Britain and were subject to control from
London or Delhi only in regard to their foreign relations. Nepal took its
present boundary lines in 1816 after defeat in war with the British; Bhutan, in 1865. Afghanistan had its origins as a kingdom about the middle of
the eighteenth century, but its present boundaries were determined as
late as 1887-1893 by agreements with Czarist Russia and Britain. The
British officials interfered as little as possible in the political or economic
affairs of these countries and were interested primarily in keeping out
other powers. Afghanistan became an independent buffer state in 1919
after the third Afghan war and its full recognition by London as a sovereign power.

Certain vestiges of foreign rule remain. Portuguese India and French
India (until 1954) were remnants of the period from the sixteenth to the
eighteenth centuries when four European trading nations, including Den-
mark and the Netherlands in addition to France and Portugal, had territorial footholds in India and were competing with Britain for the trade
of the subcontinent. With the exceptions of Portuguese India, the Maldive
islands (a British protectorate in the Arabian Sea near Ceylon), and
Gwadar (a small peninsula on the Baluchistan coast of Pakistan which is
owned by the Sultan of Oman in Arabia), the period of foreign rule has
ended in South Asia. The evolving politico-geographic pattern is being
moulded more and more by forces working within the area than by forces
imposed from outside.

Present international boundaries

The partition of the British In-
dian Empire on the basis of preponderance of Moslems in the west and
the east to form Pakistan has been the foremost event in the series of
boundary changes beginning in 1947 (see Map 27 and Chapter XXVII).
Some details of the Indo-Pakistan boundaries remain uncertain. Pakistan's
claim to the former State of Junagadh in western India seems no longer
in question, but there is in the Rann of Kutch a strip of uninhabited
marshland measuring approximately 20 by 150 miles that is disputed by
India and Pakistan. There was warfare between Pakistan and India for
control of Jammu and Kashmir state from 1947 to 1949. The cease-fire
line of 1949 serves as the temporary *de facto* boundary between Pakistani
and Indian-held territory, but the conflict of claims remains unresolved.
Pakistan controls about one-third of the area and about a quarter of the

population of this former Native State. Aside from a strip 30 to 40 miles in width east of the Jhelum River to the west of the vale of Kashmir, virtually all the territory held by Pakistan is situated in the valley of the Indus and its tributaries and is composed of small kingdoms and districts in Gilgit and Baltistan. India controls the Jammu foothill district and the vale of Kashmir, as well as most of Ladakh in the upper Indus valley beyond the Great Himalayan range. The icy uninhabited heights of the Karakoram range north of the Indus remain undivided; beyond them lies the undefined boundary of Chinese Hsin-chiang.

In the entire Himalayan region the only international boundaries clearly defined and demarcated are those of India with Nepal and Bhutan. West of Nepal the Tibetan (Chinese) boundary has never been defined, and from Nepal eastward the boundaries shown on maps prepared by the Survey of India do not necessarily conform to the boundaries recognized in local usage. Possibly the most significant boundary problem existing is along the Assam frontier of Tibet or China, where the ill-defined tribal tracts extending from the crest of the Himalaya to the edge of the plains are shown on maps issued in Peking as part of China, whereas on Indian maps they appear as part of India. India's claim is based on the previous vague British jurisdiction, never acknowledged by China. The Mongoloid tribes living in the disputed region either are unaware that they are under the jurisdiction of India or they refuse to acknowledge the authority of the troops and civil administrators being sent now by India to secure its claim.

There also are conflicts between the loyalties of local mountain tribes and the boundaries shown on maps along the Burmese frontier of India and the Afghan frontier of Pakistan. The partly autonomous Naga tribes living on both sides of the Indo-Burmese boundary in the mountainous region north of Manipur are accustomed to revolt from time to time against the Indian administration. From Manipur southward to the Bay of Bengal the Burmese boundary of India and East Pakistan had been demarcated long before the termination of British rule and there is no disagreement amongst the nations concerned. On the Afghan frontier of West Pakistan, although the boundary line is clearly defined and much of it was surveyed 50 to 60 years ago, the legitimacy of the line is disputed by pro-Afghan tribesmen and by the Afghans themselves. The remaining boundaries of Afghanistan are clearly defined and demarcated, thanks to the international boundary commissions of the late nineteenth century. The Pakistan-Persian boundary was also defined during the period of British rule but remains undemarcated.

Present political
organization

India. The Union of India, or Bharat,[2] was declared a sovereign independent republic in January, 1950, although it continues to be a member of the British Commonwealth of Nations and recognizes the Queen as a symbol of the free association of nations in the Commonwealth. During the first two years of independence from 1947 to 1949 India was in a process of transition from government according to the Constitution of 1935 in which Parliament had granted limited self-government to the provinces under British control to a new federal system, formalized by the Constituent Assembly which convened in Delhi soon after British rule terminated. Further stages of political reorganization occurred in 1954 and 1956.

From 1949 to 1956 the federation consisted of nine (ten after Andhra was created in 1954) Governor's States, derived from the nine old British Provinces, or parts thereof, not ceded to Pakistan; seven Rajpramukh's States, formed by certain Native States which had acceded to India but were not merged with adjacent Governor's States; and nine small Chief Commissioner's States, which were miscellaneous territories and former Native States directly controlled by the Central Government (see Table XXIV–1a). The Governor's States had elected legislatures with responsible ministries, led by premiers, functioning much as they had under the Constitution of 1935. The Rajpramukh's States, which with few exceptions had the feudal form of government before Indian independence, were reorganized under the supervision of Delhi and the democratic forms of government introduced with universal adult suffrage as in the Governor's States. The titular head of each was called a *Rajpramukh* (prince president), the office being bestowed upon the *Raja* (prince, king) formerly ruling the State, or one of the States, so designated. Five of the Chief Commissioner's States also had elected legislatures and enjoyed adult suffrage. In addition there were five other centrally-controlled annexed or protected territories.

The final phase of India's internal political reorganization was put into effect during November, 1956, when 14 federal states and six centrally-administered territories were established (see Table XXIV–1b.) The distinction between Governor's and Rajpramukh's States was abolished. Many local boundary changes were made in accordance with linguistic

[2] In the Constitution of India, Bharat is used in lieu of the Union of India. It is the Hindi equivalent for India in English. *Bharata-mata* (= Mother India), is a term of Sanskrit origin applied to the whole region of northern and central India. As Hindi assumes the role of the national language the indigenous term, Bharat, will probably replace the foreign term, India.

TABLE XXIV—1a

POLITICAL DIVISIONS OF INDIA

Political units	Area (sq. mi.)	Population (1951)
Governor's States		
Andhra	c.67,000	21,282,000°
Assam	54,084	9,043,707
Bihar	70,368	40,225,947
Bombay	115,570	35,956,150
Madhya Pradesh	130,323	21,247,533
Madras	c.60,768	35,734,002°
Orissa	59,869	14,645,946
Punjab	37,428	12,641,205
Uttar Pradesh	112,523	63,215,742
West Bengal	29,476	24,810,308
TOTAL	737,409	278,802,540
Rajpramukh's States		
Hyderabad	82,313	18,655,108
Madhya Bharat	46,710	7,954,154
Mysore	29,458	9,074,972
P.E.P.S.U.†	10,099	3,493,685
Rajasthan	128,424	15,290,797
Saurashtra	21,062	4,137,359
Travancore-Cochin	9,155	9,280,425
TOTAL	327,221	67,886,500
Chief Commissioner's States		
Ajmer	2,425	693,372
Bhopal	6,921	836,474
Coorg	1,593	229,405
Delhi	574	1,744,072
Himachal Pradesh	11,053	1,109,466
Kutch	8,461	567,606
Manipur	8,620	577,635
Tripura	4,049	639,029
Vindhya Pradesh	24,600	3,574,690
TOTAL	68,296	9,971,749
Other territory controlled by India		
Andaman and Nicobar islands	2,215	30,971
Assam Tribal Areas	c.28,200	600,000°
Pondicherry State (French India)	197	362,100°
Jammu and Kashmir State	c.54,000	3,600,000°
Sikkim State	2,745	137,725
TOTAL	87,357	4,730,796
GRAND TOTAL	1,220,283	361,391,585

Source: *Census of India, 1951,* Summary of Demographic and Economic Data, Paper No. 3, 1953.

° Population estimated as of 1951, except in French India where estimate is for 1948. Areas of Andhra, Madras, Assam Tribal Areas, and Jammu and Kashmir are estimated. Andhra consists of area separated from former Madras state, October, 1954.

† P.E.P.S.U = Patiala and East Punjab States Union.

TABLE XXIV–1b

REORGANIZED POLITICAL DIVISIONS OF INDIA, 1956 °

Political units	Area (sq. mi.)	Population (thousands)
States		
Andhra Pradesh	110,250	32,200
Assam	54,084	9,043
Bihar	67,830	38,930
Bombay	188,240	47,800
Jammu and Kashmir (Indian portion)	c.54,000	3,600
Kerala	14,980	13,600
Madhya Pradesh	171,200	26,100
Madras	50,170	30,000
Mysore	72,730	19,000
Orissa	60,140	14,600
Punjab	46,616	16,000
Rajasthan	132,300	16,000
Uttar Pradesh	113,410	63,216
West Bengal	33,279	26,160
TOTAL	1,169,229	356,249
Territories under central administration		
Andaman and Nicobar Islands	3,215	31
Delhi	578	1,744
Himachal Pradesh	10,904	1,109
Laccadive, Amindive, and Minicoy Islands	10	21
Manipur	8,628	578
Tripura	4,032	639
TOTAL	27,367	4,122
Other territory controlled by India		
North-East Frontier Agency	c.28,200	600
Pondicherry State	197	362
Sikkim State	2,745	138
TOTAL	31,142	1,000
GRAND TOTAL	1,227,738	361,371

° Area of states and other territories controlled by India is estimated. Population is estimated as of 1951, except in French India where the estimate is for 1948. Area and population totals do not conform to totals given in Table XXIV–1a because of rounding of estimates.

distributions, especially in central and southern India. Four Rajpramukh's States and five Chief Commissioner's States were merged with adjacent large states or in the instance of Hyderabad partitioned into three language areas which were attached to the adjacent states using each of the languages. The reorganization of 1956 not only eliminated one-third of the federal units, thus reducing the total costs of governmental administration, but it facilitated the adoption of thirteen major regional languages in the states. The resulting map of India is simpler than any known in history.

There are four predominantly Hindu, Hindi-speaking states in northern and central India. Uttar Pradesh (northern province), essentially the former British United Provinces, and Bihar rank first and third according to population in the Indian Union. Madhya Pradesh (central province) constituted from a portion of the former Central Provinces, the Rajpramukh's State of Madhya Bharat, and the Chief Commissioner's State of Vindyha Pradesh, is second largest in area among the new states, although it does not rank high in population. Certain non-Hindu tribal minorities, speaking non-Indo-Aryan languages, are included in Madhya Pradesh and in southern Bihar. Bhopal has been designated the capital of Madhya Pradesh. Punjab is the eastern portion of the former British Punjab, combined with the Patiala and East Punjab States Union, containing the vast majority of all Sikhs. Both Hindi and Punjabi are established as official languages. Chandigarh, the new capital, is being occupied as construction is completed. In all, a third of the total area of India and 40 per cent of the population are included in the four Hindi-speaking states.

Bombay and Rajasthan, which rank first and third in the Indian Union according to area, are both Indo-Aryan speaking. Bombay state comprises two language areas, distinct from one another and not closely resembling Hindi: (1) Gujarati, having about 17 million speakers in an area extending along the west coast north of Bombay city and including the former Native State of Baroda as well as the many small states of Western India; (2) Marathi, with about 27 million speakers in an area extending from Bombay city as far south as Goa, covering the entire northern Dekkan of former British Bombay, including the Native States, and the Marathi-speaking portions of northwestern Hyderabad and the former Central Provinces as far east as Nagpur. The only territory lost by Bombay was the southernmost Kanarese-speaking portion. Bombay thus gained enormously in area and became the second state in population in the Indian Union. The formation of this large state, with both Gujarati and Marathi accepted as official languages, came about as a compromise between the conflicting interests of the two language groups, particularly in regard to the control of the city of Bombay, the capital. Rajasthan is a relatively sparsely-settled area derived from the merger of former Rajpramukh's State of Rajasthan with Ajmer. The official Rajasthani language and local dialects used in the state are closely affiliated to and mutually intelligible with the adjacent Hindi language.

Three eastern states also are Indo-Aryan. Assam is the most isolated state and smallest in population, save Kashmir. A large non-Assamese-speaking tribal population inhabiting the hills and mountains south of the Brahmaputra plain are included, and the formerly unadministered tribal tracts east and north of the plain form a North-East Frontier Agency in which the central government maintains administrative officers and troops. West Bengal consists of the lowland and northern mountain districts of British Bengal, not ceded to Pakistan, to which have now been added small adjacent Bengali-speaking territories taken from Bihar in the Gangetic plain and the Chota Nagpur plateau. Oriya is the official language of Orissa and is predominant throughout the coastal and interior lowlands of the state, but large tribal minorities inhabit the hill districts which make up most of the inland portion. Cuttack continues to serve as headquarters for Orissa's government, pending construction of the new capital at the historic town of Bhubaneswar.

The four southernmost states are Dravidian-speaking and hence less closely affiliated linguistically with the other states though all are predominantly Hindu. Together, these four states comprise 20 per cent of the area of the Union and 26 per cent of the population. Andhra Pradesh (Telegu-speaking) is the largest Dravidian state. It was formed in two stages: first, by separation from former British Madras in 1954 of the portion extending north of and excluding Madras city; second, in 1956 by the annexation of Telengana section of Hyderabad, including Hyderabad city which now serves as the seat of government for all of Andhra. Mysore is the Kanarese- or Kannada-speaking state, consisting of the former Mysore state, enlarged by the addition in 1954 of a small part of inland Madras and in 1956 by Coorg and the linguistically kindred portions of southwestern Hyderabad, southern Bombay and western Madras. Kerala was formed by the merger of the Malayalam-speaking areas of Travancore-Cochin state and the west coastal district of Malabar in Madras, forming the smallest Dravidian state in terms of both area and population. Large minorities of perhaps one-third non-Hindus exist in Kerala— Moslems in Malabar and Christians in Travancore-Cochin. Madras state, thus reduced by the separation of its non-Tamil northern and western territories, still stands close second in population to Andhra among the Dravidian states. Madras gained small areas near Cape Comorin from Travancore and is now exclusively the land of the Tamils. Madras city is retained as capital.

Kashmir and Jammu form the 14th federated state, officially merged with the Union of India in January, 1957. A war was fought by Pakistan and India during 1947-48 for control of Kashmir, and the territory known as Azad (Free) Kashmir is occupied by the Pakistan army and has an administration appointed by Pakistan, while in the former Gilgit Agency certain powers are retained by the local rulers who acknowledge the authority of Pakistan. Until 1954 the Indian-held portion of the divided state (two-thirds of the total area and three-fourths of the population) had an anomalous status under Indian protection as a partially self-governing state with its own constitution, an elected legislative assembly and chief offices of government in Srinagar. India controlled its foreign affairs, defense and communications, but there was a Kashmiri national movement and the Kashmiri flag flew beside the Indian flag on state occasions. From 1954 to 1957 Kashmir's autonomy was further restricted and its separate citizenship privileges and custom duties abolished. No plebescite has been conducted to ascertain the wishes of the predominantly Moslem population, and Pakistan continues to protest the *de facto* partition of the territory and merger of the Indian-held portion with the Union.

The six centrally-administered territories of India constitute about two per cent of the total area and contain only about one per cent of the people. Delhi, being the federal capital and surrounding rural area, is the most populous, but Himachal Pradesh, essentially the former Punjab Hill States, also has over a million inhabitants. The people of each of these territories are largely Hindu and speakers of dialects of Indo-Aryan languages (Hindi and Pahari, respectively), who enjoy full adult suffrage and local self-government. Manipur and Tripura are located on the southern frontiers of Assam, the former bordering Burma and the latter, East Pakistan. The inhabitants are either Tibeto-Burman or Indo-Aryan speaking tribes who were brought under the political and cultural domination of Hindu ruling classes. Both territories are administered by officials appointed by Delhi, but the hereditary rulers and other vestiges of the old feudal system remain. Manipur is isolated by the mountainous terrain of the Burma frontier and Tripura is accessible by railway only through East Pakistan. The two other administrative territories are the insular possessions of India, inherited from British rule.

The Andamans and Nicobars consist of some 200 to 250 islets and four main islands in a 400-mile chain, located in the Bay of Bengal directly south of Burma. The more southerly Nicobars are inhabited by Mongoloid people of Mon-Khmer and Malay cultural affinities. The Andamans, once used by the British as a penal colony for India and Burma, are populated chiefly by former convicts, their families and descendants who have rapidly displaced the dying aboriginal race of Negritos. The bay islands remain commercially unimportant and the population is small. The Laccadives and neighboring coral islands situated in the Arabian Sea banks off Malabar were transferred in 1956 from Madras to the central government. The few inhabitants are Moslem fishermen of Malayali linguistic affinities.

Sikkim and Bhutan are small Himalayan states bound closely to India. Sikkim, the smaller of the two in area and population, is more closely controlled by the central government of India because of its strategic position on the main trade route between India and Tibet. Sikkim is technically a protectorate of India under the nominal rule of a hereditary *rajah* (king) in Gangtok. Actually, the internal as well as the external affairs of Sikkim are supervised by Delhi, whence the *rajah* receives an annual subsidy. Bhutan is technically an independent kingdom, bound by a treaty of friendship with India which controls its currency, foreign affairs, and routes of access to the sea and from which an annual subsidy is received. The ruling classes in both Sikkim and Bhutan are Bhotia, close kin of the Tibetans, and the state religion in both is Lamaistic Buddhism.

TABLE XXIV–2

POLITICAL DIVISIONS OF PAKISTAN

	Area (sq. mi.)	Population (1951)
West Pakistan *		
Governor's Provinces		
Punjab	62,245	18,828,015
North-West Frontier	13,560	3,252,747
Sind	50,397	4,608,514
Chief Commissioner's Province		
Baluchistan	54,456	622,058
Federal Capital Area	812	1,126,417
States		
Bahawalpur	17,471	1,823,125
Khairpur	6,050	319,543
Baluchistan States Union	79,546	551,978
Other territory		
North-West Frontier Region	25,699	2,647,158†
TOTAL, West Pakistan	310,236	33,779,555
East Pakistan		
Governor's Province		
East Bengal	54,501	42,062,610
TOTAL, Pakistan Federation	364,737	75,842,165
Other territory controlled by Pakistan		
Azad Kashmir and Gilgit Agency	c.27,300	800,000†
GRAND TOTAL	392,037	76,642,165

Source: *Census of Pakistan, 1951*, Census Bulletin No. 3, 1952.

 * The province of West Pakistan was created October 14, 1955. The new province includes all former provinces and states listed under West Pakistan, except the Federal Capital Area.

 † Population estimated as of 1951. In the North-West Frontier Region only 872,369 persons living in 11,852 sq. mi. of Malakand Agency (including Chitral, Dir, Swat, and Kalam states) were censused; population in other Frontier Agencies and the Tribal Areas was not censused. Estimates cover only the area and population in Azad Kashmir and Gilgit Agency, excluding the parts of Jammu and Kashmir held by India.

Pakistan. Pakistan proper is composed of (1) three former provinces of British India—Sind, Baluchistan, and the North-West Frontier, (2) parts of three other provinces—Punjab, Bengal, and Assam, (3) the Tribal Territories of the North-West Frontier, and (4) nine Native States, which acceded to Pakistan following the partition of British India. The capital is Karachi, designated the Federal Capital Area. The new province of East Pakistan, created by the merger of the parts of Bengal and Assam ceded to Pakistan, has Dacca as its capital.

During the first eight and a half years of independence, Pakistan was a Dominion in the British Commonwealth, administered according to the Government of India Act of 1935, the last Constitution given to India by Parliament, as modified by the Pakistan Constituent Assembly in Karachi. Pakistan was a federation of the following: four Governor's Provinces (East Bengal, North-West Frontier, Punjab, and Sind) with elected legislatures and governments responsible to them; Baluchistan Province and the Federal Capital Area with administrations appointed by the Governor-General; and the several semi-autonomous states and frontier territories in which the federal government controlled defense, foreign relations, and communications. In October, 1955, all of the federated units in West Pakistan were merged into one province; their separate legislatures and administrations were thereafter replaced by a single legislature and provincial administration in Lahore, formerly capital of the Punjab only. Thus, Pakistan has become a two-province nation.

Formal inauguration of the new Islamic Republic of Pakistan occurred in March, 1956. The Constitution severs the country's tie to the British Crown and proclaims the President as titular head of state, but Pakistan remains with the British Commonwealth of Nations, following India's precedent. Pakistan had won partition on the basis of Islamic religious principles, but agreement was not easily reached on the place of Islam in the organization of its government. The new Constitution contains the provision that the President shall be a Moslem. In India there is no stipulation that a Hindu must head the nation, although Hindus form the vast majority of the citizens. India has become a secular national state in which Moslems, Indian Christians, Sikhs, Untouchables, Aboriginal Tribes, and various other ethnic groupings and economic classes, with one or two transitory exceptions, no longer have separate electorates and reserved legislative seats as they had during British rule. It is significant that Pakistan also has moved towards the common franchise, irrespective of religious affiliations. Pakistan's parliamentary system in the provincial and federal legislatures, and its concentration of power in the federal government, are further parallels to India.

Ceylon and other territories in South Asia. Ceylon achieved a peaceful transition from Colony to self-governing Dominion. The government is a parliamentary democracy organized on the British model, nurtured under the British from 1931 to 1948 while there was limited self-government. The island maintains its dominion status within the British Commonwealth; and in recognition of its formal tie to Britain has a Governor-General appointed by the British Queen. The economic advantages of preferential trade agreements with the nations of the British Sterling Area are maintained, while in its relations with all nations Ceylon at the same time acts as a sovereign state. Ceylon has a unitary government with the seat of its legislature and administration in Colombo. The major political problem is integration of the various ethnic minorities, chief of which are the Tamil-speaking Hindus, with the Sinhalese speakers who are largely Buddhist and make up three-fourths of the country's some eight million inhabitants.

The status of the French and Portuguese colonies has been in doubt because of the strong political and, at times, economic pressure exerted by the Indian Union to absorb them. In 1950 after a plebiscite the small French enclave of Chandernagore in Bengal was handed over to India. The French territories of Pondicherry, Karikal (located on the coast of Madras state), Mahé (located on the coasts of Kerala), and Yanaon (or Yanam, an enclave near the coast of Andhra) since 1954 have been administered by the central government of India and eventually may be merged with the adjacent states of India.[3] Portugal has lost control of the mainland enclaves of Dadra and Nagar Alevi to India, but still holds the coastal territories of Goa and Damão (Daman), adjacent to Bombay State and accessible from the Arabian Sea, and the island of Diu, just off the coast of the Kathiawar peninsula. Portuguese territories in India are administered together as an overseas province of the mother country. Local governmental headquarters are at the port of Nova Goa, or Panjim, 250 miles south of Bombay in the Goa territory, an area with 600,000 inhabitants which is economically the most important part of Portuguese India.

The Maldive islands, a group of coral atolls in the Arabian Sea located 300-500 miles southwest of Cape Comorin and 500-600 miles from Ceylon, represent another vestige of colonialism. Formerly a dependency of British Ceylon, in 1953 the Maldives became self-governing while remaining under British protection. Some 87,000 islanders, crowded into the small land area of only 115 square miles, make their living largely by the fish and coconut trade.

Within the mountainous interior frontier zone of South Asia, only two countries, Afghanistan and Nepal, are independent states with full sover-

---

[3] French India, known after 1954 as Pondicherry State, still appeared separately on the official *Political Map of India*, issued by the Survey of India after reorganization of the states November 1, 1956.

eignty. Afghanistan now occupies the position of a buffer state between Pakistan and the U.S.S.R.; whereas Nepal is a buffer between India and the Tibetan part of China.[4] Both countries are constitutional monarchies with provision for parliamentary government, but the exercise of voting rights and use of democratic procedures scarcely has begun. The political affairs of each country are dominated by infinitesimally small educated classes from which the hereditary rulers draw their advisors and administrators. Within the boundaries of both countries are found various contrasting and sometimes conflicting ethnic groups for whom the notion of formal citizenship in a national state has not superseded local clan or tribal loyalties.

Transportation

Long-distance domestic traffic in India moves by railways except in the mountains (Map 27), and local traffic moves by buses or carts and by animal carriers or on foot. Inland waterways are developed only in the river plains of eastern India and East Pakistan, particularly in Bengal and Assam (inset, Map 27). International traffic moves by ships through the major seaports of Calcutta, Bombay, Madras, and Cochin in India; Karachi and Chittagong in Pakistan; and Colombo in Ceylon. Coastwise domestic shipping is significant in Pakistan and along the west coast of peninsular India. Airways are important means of transport mainly for passengers arriving from other parts of the world at the large international airports of Karachi, Delhi, Calcutta, Bombay, and Colombo. Regular scheduled flights reach some 50 other places in South Asia, but airways are significant for only the largest inland cities of India and Pakistan, and for the outlying capital cities of Kabul and Katmandu, which are not served by railways.

India and Pakistan inherited from the period of British rule one of the world's great rail networks, consisting in 1946-47 of about 41,140 miles of main tracks or a total of some 57,000 miles, including all tracks. Before partition of India the track mileage was fourth in world rank, being exceeded only by the United States, the Soviet Union, and Canada. The Union of India retained some 34,160 miles of main track, more than twice the mileage existing in mainland China during the late 1940's. Today India and Pakistan each have more fully developed rail nets than any other Asian country except Japan. If it is assumed that land within ten miles of any rail line is economically accessible, then India and Pakistan have one-half to three-quarters coverage in the areas where population density is 100 or more per square mile. There are, respectively, 31 and

---

[4] Nepal has treaty ties to India, provides mercenary troops for the Indian army, and receives an annual subsidy from the government of India.

20 miles of track for every 1,000 square miles of area in these two countries. This is less than half of the average figure for the United States and
less than many countries in western Europe, though in excess of the average for the Soviet Union and Canada.

On account of the quadrilateral outline of South Asia's ecumene,
bounded by mountains and the ocean, the criss-cross pattern of rail lines
forms a closer net covering the inhabited territory than is the case in
Soviet Asia and Canada where the rail lines form tenuous east-west links
through the narrow belts of settlement. Only a score of towns with over
20,000 inhabitants located in the area south of the Himalaya are more
than ten miles from a railway depot. This is not true in the mountainous
borderlands of India, where the cities of Srinagar in Kashmir and Imphal
in Manipur, with more than 100,000 inhabitants, are without rail connections. Afghanistan has never been penetrated by railways, although the
lines passing through Quetta and Peshawar in West Pakistan terminate
almost within sight of the Afghan boundary. The southern boundary of
Nepal is penetrated at three points by railways from India, but the country remains without internal rail transportation. Ceylon inherited 900
miles of railways from the British and is provided with a coarse network
reaching into almost every part of the island except the southeastern
section.

Railway construction began on the mainland in the early 1850's and
was essentially completed by the second decade of the twentieth century.
The rolling stock resembled the British in design of engines, freight cars,
and passenger coaches. During the British period there were seven main
systems, terminating at the four major ports, spreading the length of the
Indo-Gangetic plain from Calcutta through Delhi and Lahore to Karachi
and crossing the Indian peninsula from Calcutta and Bombay, Bombay
to Madras, and Madras to Cochin. Broad-gauge (5 feet 6 inches) tracks
were used for the trunk lines of these systems and for most of the branches
and connecting lines extended over central and northern India as well as
the territory now in West Pakistan. Meter-gauge tracks were used in the
secondary systems built in eastern Uttar Pradesh, northern Bihar, and
Assam and the territory now in East Pakistan, Rajasthan, Bombay, Mysore, and Madras. In the undivided Indian Empire 51 per cent of the
main track mileage was broad-gauge; 40 per cent was meter-gauge; and
the remainder was narrow-gauge (either 2 feet or 2 feet 6 inches), used
for some of the feeder systems and branch lines in the hills and mountains (Figure 111). In the Indian Union only 46 per cent of the railway
mileage is broad-gauge, and 44 per cent meter-gauge; in Pakistan 73 per
cent is broad-gauge and 20 per cent meter-gauge. The lines of meter and
narrow gauges were less costly per mile to build, and they are cheaply
operated; but they are more expensive than broad-gauge lines per ton-

mile of freight hauled. Furthermore, there are freight transfer costs and all the disadvantages that such breaks of gauge imply. Ceylon has 809 miles of broad-gauge railways in operation and an 87-mile narrow-gauge line in the central highlands.

It would be difficult to exaggerate the economic and political significance of railway development in South Asia. Railways represented the largest kind of investment of British capital in India, and they conferred upon the British administration a previously unknown degree of military power. Law and order could be maintained and the frontiers safeguarded. Famines were alleviated and trade was promoted. The railway companies were financed largely by capital raised in London, and the profits were guaranteed by the government of India. Almost from the start they were subsidized by the government whenever and wherever necessary. Certain lines were built and operated by the British government, and almost all the others were eventually taken under government control and management. The large Native States built and operated their own rail

Fig. 111 • The Darjeeling-Himalayan railway, running on tracks two feet apart, climbs on gradients as much as 1 in 20 from Siliguri on the piedmont plain of northern Bengal at about 300 feet above sea level to Darjeeling in the Himalaya of Bengal at about 7,000 feet elevation, a route distance of 51 miles. Steam locomotives, such as the one seen here operating in reverse on the downward run, are being replaced by diesel-driven locomotives. The passenger coaches, divided into compartments of two or more classes with separate outside entrances, typify the larger coaches of the meter- and broad-gauge railways of India and Pakistan. (John- E. Brush.)

Fig. 112 · Two-wheeled oxcarts are the commonest means of hauling agricultural produce and freight in the lowlands of India a .d Pakistan. This cart is carrying a load of *jowar* (sorghum) along a dusty cactus-lined road near Banaras (Benares). The usual yoked pair of oxen is assisted by a bull hitched by a temporary harness in front of the yoke. Water buffaloes also are used to pull such carts. *(Wellington D. Jones.)*

systems, connecting with the British-owned systems. Practically all railways were nationalized by independent India and Pakistan. The old systems have now been reorganized under six regional authorities in India and two in Pakistan.

Other means of land transportation in South Asia are little developed in comparison with the railways. The main highways commonly have graded and rolled laterite gravel surfaces or compacted clay surfaces, but are without adequate bridges or ferries and during the rainy season often become impassable. Even such a famed cross-country highway as the Grand Trunk road running from Calcutta to Delhi is paved only in sections, and traffic is impeded because of inadequate maintenance. Most of the secondary roads in the plains and peninsular uplands are merely tracks worn by cart wheels along village lanes and across fields. In the mountains, as a rule, there are mule tracks or footpaths, although some of the best roads in the subcontinent are found in the Himalaya and other high ranges where the absence of railways and the requirements of resort traffic or military strategy justify the high cost of construction. Only about 86,000 miles of metalled roads exist outside the cities and towns in India and 9,100 miles in Pakistan. In addition, there are 150,000 miles of unmetalled motorable roads in India and 45,000 miles in Pakistan. Ceylon is relatively much better equipped with 14,000 miles of motorable roads, found mostly in the rich estate districts of the central highlands and the southwestern part of the island. The number of automotive vehicles used in Ceylon is more than ten times as high in proportion to the population as the number on the mainland; there is a ratio of one motor vehicle in Ceylon to 180 persons as compared with 2,200 in India and 2,100 in Pakistan.

In the lowlands of India and Pakistan indigenous bullock carts carry practically all commodities moving from village to village and between the villages and the railway stations (Figure 112). Ordinarily these are large, two-wheeled vehicles, drawn by a yoke of bullocks or water buffaloes, capable of carrying about half a ton of goods at a speed of two to three miles per hour and at this pace traveling perhaps 20 or 25 miles a day. India and Pakistan, together, are estimated to have about eight and a half million of these vehicles, approximately one for every 50 persons as compared with one commercial motor vehicle to every 3,100 persons. It is a well known fact that transport cost by bullock cart, although seemingly low in terms of cost per day, is high in terms of ton-miles. Carts are used primarily for short hauls of small tonnages of goods. They often are seen hauling grain or other goods in bulk and travelling in trains of a score or more through areas not accessible by rail.

In rugged hill or mountain areas and sandy deserts, carts cannot be used; the costs of moving freight on the backs of coolies or pack-bullocks, mules, sheep, goats, donkeys, and camels are still greater per ton-mile (Figure 113). In areas like Afghanistan, where only the large towns and cities are connected by graded gravel roads, and accessible for wheeled vehicles of any kind, the cost of local transport by human or animal carriers is a serious deterrent to economic progress.

The vast majority of rural people everywhere in South Asia, if they leave their home villages to go to the local market towns or railway stations, travel on foot. In the cities, the bicycle, trishaw European-style carriage, bus, and electric trolley car are used in addition to the indigenous horse-drawn vehicles, such as the *ekka, tonga,* and *ticca gharry,* but few travelers can afford to use them outside the cities. Increasing numbers of buses are seen on the country roads, and they are proving to be successful competitors to narrow-gauge railways. Generally, the rural bus lines serve as feeders for the railways, which continue to be the primary means of long-distance passenger travel. Improvement of the roads in the well populated areas is followed immediately by a rise in bus and cart traffic.

Fig. 113 • This rough mountain road 6 to 10 feet wide in the western Himalaya of Tehri-Garhwal, Uttar Pradesh, India, is unsuitable for wheeled traffic. Goats and sheep, as well as mules and horses, are used for transport in the mountains. The goats lead the sheep along the road, both kinds of animals carrying loads of grain or salt up to 20 pounds each in small leather bags strapped to their backs. The herdsman can drive the animals 10 or 12 miles a day on the roughest trails, allowing the animals to graze several hours each day. *(John E. Brush.)*

But the iron-rimmed cart wheels deal out such punishment that good highways can scarcely be maintained. Dual-purpose roads suitable for both slow-moving carts and fast-moving motor vehicles are too costly, and segregation of traffic is nearly impossible.

South Asia's primary avenues of foreign travel and of economic intercourse with the rest of the world in modern times have been the seven seaports previously mentioned. Calcutta, which has the heaviest freight traffic, is closest to the densely populated areas of northern India. However, its position with respect to the shipping lanes to Europe through the Suez Canal is less advantageous than that of Bombay, which as a rule ranks second to Calcutta only in terms of tonnage handled and surpasses Calcutta in terms of the value of goods and number of passengers. Calcutta and Bombay together handle three-quarters of the tonnage shipped to and from the Indian Union. Most of the remainder passes through Madras and Cochin. Pakistan's ocean trade is concentrated almost exclusively at Karachi and Chittagong. Ceylon has one great port at Colombo. Landlocked Afghanistan and Nepal depend upon the friendliness of Pakistan and India, respectively, for access to the sea, a very real problem at times in the case of Afghanistan.

From the standpoint of economic nationalism, the lack of home-owned ships and the paucity of modern port facilities are deterrents to progress. Most of the vessels owned and operated by the citizens of India, Pakistan, and Ceylon are small craft, few of which are of modern type (Figure 114). India and Pakistan have encouraged modern shipbuilding, and domestic shipping firms have grown. Yet, during the first decade of independence less than 5 per cent of the foreign seaborne trade of Pakistan, India, or Ceylon was carried in ships owned by their nationals.

The congestion of sea traffic at so few ports has been ascribed to the lack of good natural harbors. It is true that the deep harbors of the west coast of peninsular India were cut off from the interior before the era of railways by the forbidding scarps of the Ghats and that elsewhere the low sandy beaches and the silt-clogged river mouths and shallow waters did not offer good landing places or easy approaches to the coast. Yet it was the historic accidents that determined the sites of early British trading factories, and later the deliberate policies of the railway companies and of governmental harbor-improvement authorities, that were directly responsible for the existence of only a few large ports. India entertains hopes for the rapid development of ocean traffic at the shipbuilding port of Vizagapatnam (Visakhapatnam) in Andhra on the Bay of Bengal and is presently developing the new port of Kandla in Bombay on the Gulf of Kutch (inset, Map 27). Pakistan has added facilities at Karachi and tripled the ship capacity of Chittagong. To supplement these two crowded ports, a new port is proposed for Pasni on the Makran coast in Balu-

Fig. 114 • This small wooden vessel is of the type, resembling Arab trading vessels, used along India's west coast. Note the lateen-rigged mast with the triangular sail furled and the double-ended hull, terminating in a pointed prow-like stern. Teak lumber is being unloaded at Bombay. In the background are the overhead wires of the electric dockside railway and the masts of larger ships. (Wellington D. Jones.)

chistan, and some facilities for steamers already have been put into use at Chalna in East Pakistan. Ceylon will soon find itself in full possession of the port of Trincomalee on Koddiyar Bay, a well protected natural harbor along the east coast of the island which formerly was under lease to Britain as a naval base.

Urbanization

The cities of South Asia have been the focal points of the political and economic changes induced by British rule, and they have nurtured the hybrid Indo-British civilization now evolving. Urban centers are the places where nationalism flourished and whence the directive forces and organizing power of the new nations emanate; whither commerce and factories are attracted; and where educational facilities and specialized skills are most developed. The cities are the centers for diffusion of innovations to the rural areas.

The countries of the subcontinent are, of course, predominantly rural and agrarian, with 80 to 95 per cent of their population living outside cities or towns and with 50 to 80 per cent of their population engaged directly in agriculture. Largely self-sufficient village and hamlet groups still persist as the basic units of economic and social organization. Yet the old village economy was disturbed long ago by the invasion of the railways, bringing foreign factory-made cloth, implements, lanterns, and kerosene oil, and opening export markets for local surpluses of food grains, oilseeds, cotton, jute, tea, and coconuts. The isolation of the rural cultures is being shattered by automotive vehicles, bringing politicians, school teachers, doctors, and agricultural technicians. Although the villages provide the reservoirs of population necessary for urban growth and act as refuges in periods of urban unemployment, the villagers are naturally conservative, and they resist change. Modern urbanism remains something superimposed upon the old folk society.

Yet urbanism as a mode of life has existed in South Asia as long as anywhere else in the world, dating from the towns of the Indus valley civilization some 4,500 years ago. Probably there have been cities in the northern Indo-Aryan culture-hearth area for the past 3,000 years, and the ruins of ancient Patna and Delhi are at least as old as those of ancient Athens and Rome.

The towns of pre-British India commonly were local trade and government centers, not much removed from overgrown villages, and today would rank merely as minor towns with approximately 5,000 to 20,000 inhabitants. Their populations fluctuated during wars or famines and many have vanished or regressed to village status. The largest cities probably were those that grew up around the imperial palaces, like Agra when the Mughals ruled; the most persistent were probably those that grew up at sacred places, like Banaras (Benares), which could survive the fall of empires and attract generation after generation of holy men and pilgrims. The old towns always had bazaars and were the centers of the most highly specialized craft industries, producing the fine textiles and metal wares that were used by the ruling classes and that first attracted European traders. The waterways of the Ganges, Indus, and a few smaller peninsular rivers served as avenues of trade for shallow-draft boats, and there were seaports accessible to the larger vessels, sailing in the monsoon winds to Arabia and Southeast Asia.

The pre-British urban centers were largest and most numerous in the interior regions of semi-arid and arid climate, usually accessible only by land transportation and exposed to local banditry or the transcontinental invasions coming across the northwestern frontier. The military protection offered by the city walls and fortified hilltops encouraged population concentration. Apparently, it has been the habit of farming people in India in the drier regions of low crop-carrying capacity and scanty domestic water supply to concentrate in larger village agglomerations than in the wetter regions, where they have tended to scatter in myriads of tiny hamlets. The custom of dwelling in cities also was a phenomenon of the dry climatic zones of the extratropical northwest and the peninsular interior and was less prevalent in the eastern subtropical and southern tropical humid zones situated farthest from the northwest frontier.

The growth of large modern urban centers in South Asia is associated closely, as elsewhere in the world, with cheap mass transportation made possible by the improvement of facilities for ocean navigation and the inland extension of railways. Four of the six great metropolitan centers with more than a million inhabitants are the major seaports with good rail connections to the interior—Calcutta, where 4,578,000 people (1951) live in 35 geographically contiguous cities and towns along both banks of the Hooghly River; [5] Bombay, 2,839,000 in the city proper and on Salsette island; Madras, 1,416,000 in the city and suburbs; and Karachi, 1,126,000 in the Federal Capital Area. These four metropolitan areas have grown during three hundred years or less from mere villages in pre-British times to rank first, second, third, and fifth, respectively, among the great cities of South Asia. They have been and still remain primarily commercial and transport service centers, although manufacturing supports a large proportion of the population in the Calcutta conurbation and in Greater Bombay, and Karachi's political role has brought most of its recent population upsurge. The only two inland metropolitan centers inhabited by more than one million people are Delhi, 1,384,000 (1951) including New Delhi and adjacent suburbs (Figure 9), and in the Dekkan, Hyderabad, 1,086,000 including Secunderabad. Both were pre-British capitals that secured railway connections and attained renewed political importance under the aegis of Britain.

The seven metropolitan cities in South Asia with between approximately 500,000 and 1,000,000 inhabitants also are located inland and, like the larger centers, are on the broad-gauge railways. Only Kanpur (Cawnpore), 709,000 (1951), arose from humble village beginnings with the coming of the British in the mid-nineteenth century when it was made a major military base and, for a time, was the terminus of the main railway from Calcutta. Kanpur became primarily a manufacturing city. It has none of the past or present political and cultural importance of Lahore, 849,000; Ahmedabad, 794,000; Bangalore, 779,000; Poona, 589,000; Lucknow, 497,0000; and Nagpur, 480,000; although manufacturing has come to play a prominent, if not leading, role in Ahmedabad.

[5] The Calcutta conurbation is outranked in Asia only by Greater Tokyo (estimated 7.3 mil., 1953) and Shang-hai (6.2 mil., 1953) and is eighth in rank among the leading conurbations of the world; being exceeded by New York (12.3 mil., 1950), London (8.3 mil., 1951), Paris (estim. 5.5 mil., 1953), Moscow (estim. 5.2 mil., 1953), and Chicago (4.9 mil., 1950), in addition to the two in Asia.

There are 78 other cities and city clusters in South Asia with population ranging from approximately 100,000 to 400,000. In the Union of India alone 66 cities of this size class are found, containing in sum over 8.4 million people, but India's total population is so great that the 23.5 million people dwelling in all cities of 100,000 or more constitute only 6.6 per cent of the total (see Table XXIV-3). India as a whole has a slightly higher percentage of population in these large cities than Ceylon with the single city of Colombo, 425,000 (1953) in this class, and Pakistan with nine cities over 100,000 in addition to Karachi and Lahore. Kabul, estimated at 200,000 (1953), and Katmandu, estimated at 150,000 (1955), together with nearby Patan, estimated 105,000 (1955), which represent roughly 2 and 3 per cent, respectively, of the total population of Afghanistan and Nepal, are the only other urban centers in this population class. That railways are not prerequisites for cities to reach this size is attested by the existence of the port of Alleppey on the Malabar coast and four other cities in the interior mountain region, including Kabul and Katmandu, without railways. The 73 other urban centers between 100,000 and 400,000 have one or more rail lines, and in all but 16 of them at least one of the lines is broad-gauge. Nine of them are inland cities situated on navigable waterways, but waterborne traffic is important in only three or four instances. Eight others are coastal cities with present-day functions

TABLE XXIV–3

URBAN POPULATION IN SOUTH ASIA

Population in	Per cent of total population			
	Afghanistan	Ceylon	Pakistan	Union of India
Urban places	5.0	15.2	10.0	17.3
Cities over 100,000	2.0	5.2	5.2	6.6
Cities over 1,000,000	——	——	1.5	3.1

Source: *Census of 1951*, Pakistan and India; *Census of 1953*, Ceylon; estimated as of 1952 in Afghanistan.

NOTE: Urban places are defined in the censuses of South Asian countries generally as towns with 5,000 or more inhabitants, but no hard and fast rule is followed because some places over 5,000 have distinctly village characteristics while some towns have less than 5,000 inhabitants. In the Union of India, where the criteria vary somewhat from state to state, 612 of a total of 3,018 urban places were towns under 5,000 that were classified as urban by the local census authorities.

as seaports, however little the traffic may be. Therefore, it becomes clear that the vast majority of cities between 100,000 and about 400,000 in the subcontinent are located inland and depend upon their railway connections, despite the fact that the greatest South Asian metropolitan centers are of maritime origin.

In terms of the proportion of population in urban centers, India is the most urban country in South Asia. (See Table XXIV–3). One among six persons in the Indian Union resides in a town or city, and it is anticipated that in a few decades the ratio will have risen to two or three among six, perhaps as high as in Japan. India's urban percentage is approximately the same as that of the United States in 1850. Ceylon's urban percentage is slightly lower than India's, but Pakistan's 10 per cent figure is considerably lower and is very nearly the same as that of the whole Indian Empire in 1901. Afghanistan's 5 per cent urban population, calculated on the basis of very uncertain estimates, is not unexpected in a nonindustrial nation with almost no modern means of transportation until the 1930's, and doubtless represents a close approximation of conditions in Nepal. The degree of urbanization prevailing today in Afghanistan is lower than the percentage for the Indian Empire at the time of the first complete census in 1881 and could well represent the condition of South Asia as a whole a century ago before the building of the railways.

Economic development

The nations of the modern Asia are aggressively pursuing the goal of economic development, and seek to promote their trade and to transform their primarily agricultural economic systems into more productive industrial systems, while at the same time raising their agricultural output.

The pattern of employment. One method of assessing economic development is to examine the degree to which agriculture, on the one hand, and mining, manufacturing, commerce, transportation and various services, on the other hand, provide employment for the people (see Table XXIV-4). Not many more than 50 per cent of Ceylon's employed people are engaged directly in agriculture, whereas in Pakistan the percentage approaches 77 and in India, 71. Ceylon's economically active population in commerce, transportation, and other services exceeds a combined percentage of 26, whereas in Pakistan the percentage in these three branches together is about 12, and in India about 18. To provide a scale of comparison, it may be noted that in the United States these three branches engage some 52 per cent of the employed population and in Japan, nearly 32 per cent; while agriculture, forestry, and fisheries employ 12.5 per cent of the active population in the United States and about

TABLE XXIV—4

ECONOMICALLY ACTIVE POPULATION IN SOUTH ASIA

Branch of economic activity *	Per cent of active population		
	Ceylon	Pakistan	Union of India
Agriculture, forestry, and fisheries	52.9	76.6	70.6
Mining and quarrying	0.3	0.5	0.6
Manufacturing	⎱ 10.0	6.3	9.0
Construction		⎰ 0.9	1.1
Electricity, gas, etc.			0.5
Finance and commerce	7.9	5.1	5.8
Transport and communication	3.6	1.4	1.9
Services	14.7	5.9	10.6
Not classifiable	10.7	3.8	——

Source: *United Nations Statistical Yearbook 1955*, Table 6. Data from *Census of 1951*, Pakistan and India; *Census of 1946*, Ceylon.

* Nomenclature follows the United Nations' *Standard Industrial Classification of all Economic Activities*. Services include government, community, business, recreation, and personal services.

43 per cent in Japan. In no one of the three South Asian countries does manufacturing industry employ more than 10 per cent of the population, although India appears to be relatively more developed in this respect than Ceylon and has half again as high a percentage in manufacturing as Pakistan. The development of manufacturing in India is vastly greater in absolute terms than in any other part of South Asia. Rapid further development must occur, however, before India can take its place as an industrial nation alongside Japan with some 18 per cent of its employed population in manufacturing, the United States with 30 per cent, or the nations of northwestern Europe with 30 to 40 per cent in manufacturing. In none of the three countries in South Asia is the mineral industry highly developed in comparison to Japan or Europe and North America, but in this respect India is both relatively and absolutely more advanced than Ceylon and Pakistan.

In comparison with the two large South Asian countries, Ceylon's lesser degree of dependence upon agricultural employment and its relatively greater concentration of economically active population in commerce, transportation, and other services indicates a higher level of economic development. This conclusion is upheld by the fact that since 1950 the per-capita foreign trade has totaled from $6 to $7 for Ceylon as compared to about 80¢ per capita for India and about 90¢ per capita for Pakistan. Ceylon's estimated national income per capita is $116 (1953), which is twice India's per-capita national income of $59 (1951) and nearly two-thirds higher than Pakistan's $73 (1951).

Another indication of Ceylon's more intensive economic development is the fact that the percentage of the whole population reported to be economically active is 39, as compared to 30 per cent in India and 29 per cent in Pakistan. Yet there is chronic under- and unemployment, and the island's commercial development has not been accompanied by the development of manufacturing or urbanization to any greater relative degree than on the mainland. Ceylon is an epitome of the tropical countries in which large plantations employ hired labor to grow crops on a mass-production basis for export to middle-latitude countries. Indeed, the people of Ceylon find themselves in the precarious position of depending largely on the exports of three estate crops—tea, rubber, and coconuts—for much of their income and for the means to import one-half to one-third of the rice they consume.

Problems and Programs of Development.   Without undertaking a detailed survey of all aspects of economic development, certain outstanding problems may be mentioned.

(1) During the past 30 to 35 years the rates of population growth in South Asia have increased markedly (see Chapter XXII). The rates of increase in the two countries for which current population estimates are fairly accurate (Ceylon, 2.8 per cent a year, and the Union of India, 1.25 per cent) indicate that the period of rapid growth now well under way could bring annual increments of 5 to 15 million in the whole of South Asia. In Ceylon the death rate has been reduced to 11 or 12 per 1,000 annually, whereas the birth rate remains nearly stable at 39 or 40 per 1,000, yielding annual net gains of nearly 30 per 1,000. If the growth of population in all the countries were as high as 30 per 1,000 in a year, or roughly 30 per cent in a decade, there would be a gain of some 130 million by 1960 on the basis of the numbers reported in the several censuses and estimates from 1950 to 1953, and the total population in the realm would be approaching 600 million. The actual growth rate in the realm as a whole probably is nearer 10 per 1,000 a year, which would mean a gain of about 45 million in a decade and would result in a total population somewhat in excess of 510 million in 1960.

No opportunity exists for relieving the population pressures by emigration. Tropical areas such as Southeast Asia, eastern and southern Africa, and the West Indies, where Indians have already settled successfully, are no longer open to mass immigration, and the middle-latitude countries to which a few Indians have migrated, such as the United States and the

British dominions, admit insignificant numbers. The support of South Asia's future population must be found at home.

(2) The vast majority of the people remain poor, underfed, uneducated and many are underemployed or unemployed. Despite the villagers' hoards of silver and the reputed wealth of India's merchants and princes, the annual average per-capita national income of India and the incomes of the neighboring countries mentioned above, translated into terms of local costs and prices, are little more than sufficient to obtain the minimum essentials of life. The small farmers have been in debt for generations, and the savings of the well-to-do farmers or nonagricultural classes are very limited. The rate of capital formation seems inadequate to support the investment in agriculture and manufacturing necessary to raise the material level of living.

During the period since 1910 the increase of agricultural production in general has been barely sufficient to keep pace with population growth. Food-grain exports from India and Pakistan have diminished or ceased, and in some years the domestic food supply must be supplemented by imports. Judged by scientific nutritional standards ordinary diets are inadequate, even in years of good crop yields and prosperous trade. In India the average size of farm holding has decreased progressively since 1910, and there is chronic underemployment of farmers.

Educational facilities have been increased, but, though in Ceylon the literacy rate has risen to 56 per cent of all persons of school age or older, in India merely 17 per cent are literate, and the percentages must be even lower in the adjacent countries of the mainland. Thus, a large share of the population in these agrarian countries remains ignorant and bound to the soil. Persons who seek work off the farms frequently are unable to obtain it owing to their insufficient education as well as to the lack of job opportunities. In Ceylon it is estimated that under conditions of recent moderate prosperity nearly 5 per cent of the total population, or about 12 per cent of the working population, was underemployed, principally in agriculture, and another 6 per cent of the total population was involuntarily unemployed. In the less developed countries of the mainland, the percentages of underemployment and unemployment must be still greater.

(3) The people are becoming, or have already become, conscious of the inadequacies of their present economic status. The experience of railway travel, whether on religious pilgrimages or in search of nonagricultural work, has opened the eyes of South Asians to things outside their own village areas. The hope, if not the actual experience, of education, and the impact of anti-British agitation spread by their own political leaders have made them unwilling to accept the conditions that their forefathers accepted without question.

Perhaps the masses of people in India and Pakistan are vaguely aware that their condition is in some way connected with the rule of an alien industrial nation for whose own interests it seemed best to keep South Asia agrarian. They are probably unaware that during the past 80 to 100 years real per capita income has not increased significantly. They may not realize that, while they were provided with stable government and with the seaports and railways, the great canal irrigation systems, and other public measures designed to reduce famines and epidemics and promote trade, their economy was being exploited primarily for the benefit of foreigners. They do not have the information to permit them to compare their status with that of the Japanese people, whose careful husbanding of closely limited natural resources and development of domestic capital during the past 80 years stand in sharp contrast to the history of the Indian Empire.

Now that national independence has been attained and the internal political evolution of South Asia apparently is reaching its conclusion, the common people want some tangible economic improvements. They await from the industrial revolution some benefits that will release them from grinding poverty. Economic progress has quickened in India and Pakistan since independence, but the needs for more capital and technological change are still enormous. Ceylon has progressed more than the mainland, but in a lopsided fashion, and today is equally in need of capital and modern technology. Afghanistan and Nepal have lagged in the seclusion of their mountain fastness, and now, ready for change, the people find themselves handicapped more than the people in the lowland countries. The archaic socio-political and economic systems of Afghanistan and Nepal exemplify the conditions that might well prevail today in Ceylon, Pakistan, and the Union of India had it not been for the coming of the European traders and conquerors.

(4) The necessity of foreign economic aid makes the countries of South Asia dependent upon Europe and America, notwithstanding their desire for greater measures of economic freedom and their nationalistic aspirations to greater political influence in world affairs.

Economic aid is obtained through governmental loans and grants as well as through trade and private investment. The main sources of both governmental aid and private investment are those countries to which South Asians sell the bulk of their exports. During the period since 1947-48 the United Kingdom and United States have usually ranked first and second, respectively, in percentage value of all exports from Ceylon, Pakistan, and the Union of India. The same two countries ranked among the first three sources of imports and have supplied most of the foreign public and private funds invested in South Asia. It is to these two countries, also, that South Asians have looked for the scientific and technical training so vital to their progress.

However, new relationships are forming. Pakistan has established reciprocal trade ties with Japan after breaking away as much as possible from dependence upon the Union of India. Ceylon long has obtained most of its rice imports from Southeast Asia and now barters rubber for rice from the Chinese mainland. Afghanistan looks more than ever before·to the Soviet Union to satisfy its import requirements and for technical aid. The Union of India, which has much more diverse relationships with all parts of the world than the other South Asian countries, now has an increasing amount of trade with Eastern Europe and the Soviet Union, whence some technical assistance also is coming.

(5) The programs for economic development now initiated or planned in each of the countries of South Asia entail some, if not all, of the following phases:

(a) Agricultural production is being increased by additions to the cultivated area and by raising the yield and frequency of harvests from land already under cultivation. Major additions to the cultivated area have been made by irrigation works in the arid and semi-arid regions of Afghanistan, West Pakistan, and the Union of India. In the long run more substantial gains probably will result from extension of cultivation in the humid regions of Ceylon, East Pakistan, and India and especially by perennial irrigation, double-cropping, and fertilization which will enhance the returns from land now not used intensively.

(b) High dams are being built for purposes of irrigation, electric power generation, and flood control. Most of the dams built during the period of British rule were "barrages," that is to say, low diversion dams, which brought water from the rivers to the cropland through extensive canal systems but did not create large reservoirs. Consequently, not much water can be obtained during low river stages in the dry season when it is most needed. Only 6 per cent of the river flow in India was being utilized during the early 1950's. The new high dams with reservoirs will capture the floods, more nearly equalize the supply of irrigation water, and increase the output of hydroelectricity. In certain watersheds these multipurpose dams are the basis of comprehensive development schemes involving reforestation, soil conservation, and industrial development, e.g., in the Damodar valley of Bihar and West Bengal.

(c) No civil engineering enterprise would more profoundly affect the villages of South Asia than improvement of roads, especially roads suitable for automotive vehicles. A modern local transportation system to supplement the railway network could help develop the more productive type of rural economy in which cash-crop specialties would replace subsistence crops. The Indian geographer, S. P. Chatterjee, reports in his land-utilization survey in West Bengal [6] that villages located scarcely ten miles from Calcutta are largely cut off from this great urban market for agricultural produce because of the lack of good rural roads. Only in the estate districts of Ceylon and a few mountain localities in India and Afghanistan have road improvements been sufficient thus far to have a marked effect in the rural areas. Certain main roads, of course, are being improved and others are projected, but the expenses of building a net-work on the grand scale necessary to reach all villages in the densely populated lowlands would be so enormous that development must for the present be deferred.

(d) Reform of old semifeudal land-tenure systems is urgently needed for reasons political, if not also economic. Redistribution of excessively large land holdings and consolidation of small fragmented holdings into efficient operating units has long been under way in the Union of India, where it is the responsibility of the constituent states, and reform has begun in Nepal. If thoroughgoing land reform is effected, it may bring about a more equitable distribution of wealth among the agricultural tenants and laboring classes, who now retain of the harvests only half-shares or less. The unhappy fact remains, however, that there is not, and will not be, enough land available to satisfy the demands of every farmer. Future increase in labor productivity and national wealth can come only through shifting a larger proportion of the population out of agricultural occupations.

(e) Public education at all levels, from elementary schools—particu-larly village schools—to universities, is undergoing expansion. Literacy campaigns and agricultural extension services are intended to reach adults in rural areas. About 70 groups of villages in the Union of India have been selected for intensive educational and technical development, led by Indian personnel with foreign aid under the direction of the central gov-ernment. After a term of years when, it is hoped, social and economic re-construction of these villages will be well under way, other village groups will be given aid, and later, others; so that directly or indirectly in time all rural areas will be reached.

(f) Mineral resources are being sought by systematic exploration, espe-cially for petroleum and (in Pakistan) for iron ore and coal.

The known mineral resources and the existing development of mining industries are greatest in the Union of India. The country is self-sufficient in bituminous coal and high-grade iron ore, and the output of coal and iron can readily be increased to meet India's future requirements, al-though a shortage of coking coal is in prospect. India ranks with Japan

[6] S. P. Chatterjee, "Land Utilization Survey of Howrah District," *Geographical Review of India,* Sept., 1952, pp. 1-8.

and China as one of the three leading coal producers and iron manufac-turers in non-Soviet Asia. In certain other respects India is well endowed: mica, in the production of which the country leads the world; manganese, in which India is among the first two or three producers; monazite, the principal ore of thorium, of which the beach sands of Travancore con-tain the world's largest and richest reserves; bauxite, the huge reserves of which India has merely started to exploit. But India's known supplies of copper, lead, and zinc are too scarce to support present demands. The country's known supply and production of petroleum is sufficient to meet only a small fraction of current demand. Nevertheless, India is better en-dowed in minerals than most industrial countries of Europe and has re-sources much superior to those of Japan.

The search for minerals in the other countries of South Asia is under-standably urgent. Aside from the small quantities of chromite once ex-ported from Afghanistan and West Pakistan, and the variable exports of graphite (plumbago) from Ceylon, no commercially significant deposits of metallic minerals have been known. Now the ores of iron and certain other metals have been found, but their successful exploitation remains to be demonstrated. Good resource bases exist for cement and glass in-dustries and some branches of the chemical industry in both Pakistan and India, where so far their development has been most advanced. Low-grade coal is mined in Afghanistan and West Pakistan, and some oil and natural gas are produced in the latter country. Pakistan looks, as does India, to the oil-rich countries of Southwest Asia for petroleum products; Afghanistan looks to the Soviet Union, although geologic formations indi-cate that oil will be found within its territory.

(g) The governments in South Asia are undertaking to establish mod-ern factory industries, particularly in the types of commodities in which private investment is at present inadequate.

In general, the agriculturally based industries and light industries pro-ducing consumer goods are flourishing in India under private ownership. The cotton and jute textile industries, which were initiated in India dur-ing the late nineteenth century, have under private control reached an advanced stage of development. In the primary iron-and-steel industry, which was introduced successfully about 50 years ago, growth has not been so rapid because India's advantages of cheap, conveniently located raw materials are offset by the high cost of importing plant equipment and repair parts, by the large salaries of foreign technical personnel employed at first, the expense of training Indian personnel, the scarcity of indigenous capital, and, not least, the fact that Indian mill labor is not necessarily cheap in terms of output per man-hour, though it is cheap in terms of wages per man-hour. Hence, the Indian government has undertaken to finance and control the new iron-and-steel works being built with foreign aid. Both state and federal governments have assumed the initiative in many fields of steel fabrication and nonferrous metallurgy, and in chemical and pharmaceutical industries. It is of interest to note two parallels to the earlier Japanese industrial development—(1) the prominent role of a few wealthy families, heading industrial combines with interests in a variety of fields; and (2) the importance of government in initiating and guiding industrial development.

Pakistan, where almost no large-scale factory industries existed at the time of partition, has rapidly increased cotton-mill producing capacity, jute manufacture has begun, and a variety of other light industries have been started, largely under private control. The need for speeding up the rate of industrialization is so great, however, that the government has assumed the dominant, if not exclusive, role of financing and operating such industries as paper, chemicals, cement, steel fabrication, and shipbuilding.

In the smaller countries of South Asia little development of modern factory industries has occurred, and the various governments are assuming leadership in promoting and controlling industrialization. Almost no factories exist in Afghanistan, Ceylon, and Nepal, other than those that process local agricultural products such as wheat, rice, sugar, tea, or rubber.

Small-shop and home industries in which goods are made by artisans without the help of mechanical power continue to exist. These craft industries employ more workers and probably produce a larger quantity of goods than all the present large-scale factory industries. Handlooms, producing mostly cotton cloth, but also wool, silk, and rayon goods, employ six or seven million workers in India alone. Wooden furniture, metal utensils, glassware, pottery, leather, and jewelry are produced by other millions of workers according to ancient traditions. Many common requirements of a large percentage of the population come from small workshops in the villages and towns, but such hand industries do not produce a unit of goods as efficiently as factories, and the small entrepreneurs and craft workers are slowly declining in importance.

SELECTED GEOGRAPHICAL BIBLIOGRAPHY

1. Anjaria, J. J. "Industrial Planning in India," *Current History*, February, 1956, pp. 98-103.
2. Anstey, Vera. *The Economic Development of India.* New York: Longmans, Green & Co., 4th ed., 1952.
3. Cohen, Jerome B. "Economic Development in India," *Political Science Quarterly*, September, 1953, pp. 376-395.
4. Crane, Robert I. "Urbanism in India," *American Journal of Sociology*,

March, 1955, pp. 463-470.

5. Fifield, Russell H. "New States in the Indian Realm," *American Jour. International Law*, July, 1952, pp. 450-463.

6. Furber, Holden. "The Unification of India, 1947–1951," *Pacific Affairs*, December, 1951, pp. 352-371.

7. Hartog, Lady Mabel Hélène (Kisch). *India: New Pattern*. London: G. Allen & Unwin, 1955.

8. Kingsbury, Robert C. "India's Industrial Growth," *Focus*, May, 1956, pp. 1-6.

9. Kuriyan, George. "Agriculture in India," *Current History*, February, 1956, pp. 90-97. See also Menon, V. P., *The Story of the Integration of the Indian States*. New York: Macmillan, 1956.

10. Panikkar, K. M. "Indian States Reorganization," *Asian Review*, October, 1956, pp. 247-258.

11. Thorner, Daniel: "The Pattern of Railway Development in India," *Far Eastern Quarterly*, February, 1955, pp. 201-216.

12. ———, and Alice Thorner. "India and Pakistan," in Ralph Linton, ed., *Most of the World*. New York: Columbia Univ. Press, 1949, pp. 548-653.

Comments

The reader will gain a general perspective on India's political and economic history under British rule from Anstey's book, now outdated but still useful, and from the two excellent articles by the Thorners. Fifield presents a concise account of the legal basis of political reorganization in South Asia since the termination of British rule. Furber treats the internal governmental reorganization of the Indian Union, while Panikhar describes the 1956 federal and state reorganization in India. Hartog gives a comprehensive survey of India's public affairs. Cohen analyzes the economic status and trends of development in the new India. Kuriyan discusses the problems of agricultural expansion and pressure on land and briefly outlines the objectives of the local community and river-valley development projects. Kingsbury summarizes the facts on power resources, minerals, and the growth of modern factory industries in India. The Five-Year Plans, their objectives, and questions on public policy in economic development are examined by Anjaria.

Bibliographies specifically concerning Afghanistan, Ceylon, and Pakistan accompany the chapters on these countries.

Northern India and the Himalayan Countries

NORTHERN INDIA AND THE THREE HIMALAYAN STATES OF NEPAL, Sikkim, and Bhutan include some 737,000 square miles of territory, occupied by more than 193,000,000 people. The Indian portion is composed of the seven states of Assam, West Bengal, Bihar, Madhya Pradesh (part only), Uttar Pradesh, Punjab, Rajasthan, and Kashmir; the four centrally-administered territories of Delhi, Himachal Pradesh, Tripura, and Manipur; and the North-East Frontier Agency. This vast area has been divided into eight regions: (1) the Bengal-Bihar industrial region, (2) the Gangetic plain, (3) the trans-Gangetic plain, (4) the Rajasthan desert, (5) the western Himalaya and Kashmir, (6) the central Himalayan countries, (7) the northeast frontier region, and (8) the north-central hills and plateaus. (See Map 29 and Table XXV–1).

The Bengal-Bihar industrial region

The two contrasting physical areas in this region—the plain of West Bengal [1] and the Chota Nagpur

[1] The portion of West Bengal state, located north of Pakistan in the Darjeeling Himalaya and sub-Himalayan plain of Jalpaiguri, is not considered here. Instead, it is included with the northeastern frontier region of India.

plateau of Bihar—are unified by the development here of India's greatest concentrations of mining, metallurgical, and jute textile industries, and by the dominant influence of Calcutta. The Bengalis of the plain and the Biharis of the plateau all have been affected by the commercial and industrial revolution and the associated employment opportunities. Yet in 1951 scarcely 5.5 million persons, or less than 17 per cent of the total population of more than 33.6 million, were residents of urban places. The rural, agricultural way of living still prevails.

Indian Bengalis live in a manner and in an environment that closely resembles that of their Pakistani kinsmen, thus testifying to the artificial nature of the international boundary established during 1947 in the deltaic plain 40 miles east of Calcutta. (See Chapter XXVII). Hindu Bengalis share their mother tongue and—until recently—a proud tradition of Bengali nationalism with Moslem Bengalis, who predominate in East Pakistan. The impact of partition has been less than in the Indian Punjab, adjacent to West Pakistan. In 1951, 20 per cent of the people in West Bengal were Moslems, a relatively small decrease from 25 per cent before partition.

The politico-religious difference between the two Bengals is only one among several, however. The western delta is moribund or dying, largely cut off from the silt-bearing floods of the Ganga and Brahmaputra. The inhabitants are characterized by poor physique and suffer from diseases which they contract from the stagnant streams and open tanks (domestic water storage reservoirs) harboring mosquitoes and intestinal parasites. Rice yields are lower and there is little production of summer and spring crops because in the West the rains are so strictly confined to the four-month period from June to September when the winter crop is grown. Jute yields also are lower here than in Pakistan. Were it not for the high export duties levied by Pakistan on jute shipments to India, probably not even the present 2 per cent of the cropland in West Bengal would be devoted to this cash crop. The general population density is about 880 persons per square mile; rarely does the rural density rise above 1,000 per square mile and never, except in the urban areas, as high as the density of 1,200 to 2,000 per square mile found in East Bengal. Population growth has diminished or ceased in many rural areas of West Bengal.

The West would be less densely populated and much the poorer of the two Bengals were it not for the port of Calcutta on the Hooghly River, the railways, and the huge urban, industrial complex which stretches for 30 miles upriver and 15 miles downriver from Calcutta (Figure 115). One out of every four persons in the West Bengal plain lives in Calcutta and its suburban and satellite towns near the Hooghly (total 1951 population of the metropolitan area, 4,578,071).

Calcutta originated as a transshipping point for ocean and river trade

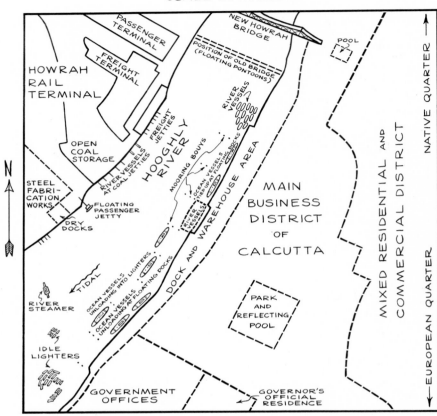

Fig. 115 • Calcutta originated about 1690 on the Hooghly River at a transshipment and warehousing point between ocean sailing vessels and river vessels, plying upstream to the Ganga River. The main business district (lower center of photograph) is situated on the east bank, where the current scoops a pool along the undercut side of the Hooghly bend and offers accommodation for vessels. The floating docks and mooring buoys (seen in the photograph) mark the head of navigation for vessels of 28-foot draft, or about 10,000 tons, the maximum size able to enter the Hooghly estuary. Incoming vessels customarily discharge at the waterfront here, then fall downriver some three miles to receive export cargoes in large artificial docking basins similar to the London docks, shut off by gates from the river's rapid tidal fluctuations.

The industrial portion of the Hooghly waterfront has developed chiefly in Howrah, on the opposite bank from the commercial port, and along both banks above the city. Manufacturing activity has been attracted to the river banks where water is too shallow for modern ocean steamers to dock but deep enough for river steamers. Here fuel and raw materials can be assembled both by railways and by the waterway, connected with the East Pakistan delta. The photograph shows the Calcutta-Howrah bridge and the main terminal yards and coal jetties of the railways which give access to the enormous traffic of the Gangetic plain and the coal-mining and iron-manufacturing region of Chota Nagpur, directly west of the Bengal delta. These and other sections are identified in the diagram. *(Indian Air Survey and Transport Co., Ltd.)*

in the late seventeenth century when small vessels could easily proceed
up the river to the Ganga and thence to Patna, Banaras, and other cities
of the lower Gangetic plain. During the nineteenth century the Hooghly
became a virtually beheaded river, but its estuary was kept open by the
daily tidal fluctuations of 9 to 15 feet and by the flow of the small rivers

entering the delta from the Chota Nagpur plateau. Small country boats ply these rivers and the canals that pass across the plain of West Bengal towards Calcutta. Since 10 miles above the city the Hooghly is only six to eight feet deep and 30 miles above, only three or four, the side-wheeler river steamers of East Pakistan can reach Calcutta only by way of the tidal channels through the Sundarbans swamps and the Hooghly estuary.

The preëminence of Calcutta as India's greatest port is facilitated by continuous dredging to maintain a 28-foot channel. The Hooghly is the sole waterway in Bengal permitting entry of ocean vessels 75 to 80 miles inland. Its floating docks and enclosed docking basins reduce the difficulties caused by tidal fluctuations and tidal bores. Facilities for ocean vessels are confined to the left (east) bank of the river.

The core of the city stands close to the uppermost ocean docks. Around it has grown the city proper, with a population of 2,549,000 in 1951, and a suburban area spreading two or three miles east across the natural levee, five or six miles southward, and an equal distance northward.

Beginning in the 1850's, railways linked the port to a vast hinterland of over 350,000 square miles in the Gangetic plain, central India, and northeastern India, and more than 160,000,000 population, excluding East Pakistan. Two railways approach Calcutta on the northeast. The most important connects with Darjeeling and Assam and carries the bulk of India's tea exports. More important are the three main lines which come from the Gangetic plain, central India, and south India, terminating on the west bank in Howrah (434,000).

The railways paralleling the Hooghly on both sides have had much to do with the continued vitality of the old ports and the growth of new industrial towns upriver. There are 18 satellite towns, ranging from 20,-000 to 140,000 inhabitants (total population 968,000), located along the river within 30 miles above Calcutta. Recent growth is more pronounced 10 to 15 miles below Calcutta. The jute industry, employing perhaps half of all factory workers in the area, is concentrated here because of the economies of assembling raw fiber and fuel by rail and water at factory sites accessible for direct lighterage to ocean vessels. Before partition, British India had almost a world monopoly of jute growing and low-priced burlap production. The effect of partition has been to divert a considerable share of the raw jute to the port of Chittagong and to create jute spinning and weaving mills in the river ports of East Pakistan, but Calcutta still retains world leadership in jute manufactures. Concentrations of many other kinds of manufacturing, notably cotton textiles, food, leather, and paint, chemicals, ordnance supplies, finished metalwares, and fabricated steel, reflect the attraction of India's largest metropolitan market, the advantages of assembling imported raw materials and of distribution to the regional market centers of northern, central and eastern India, and the cheapness of steel delivered by rail from the Chota Nagpur plateau.

Outside the Calcutta conurbation most of the West Bengal plain retains its rural character. The land becomes progressively higher, drier, and less densely settled approaching Bihar. Alluvial surfaces suitable for wet cultivation are narrow strips bordering each small river; the old alluvium of the interfluves between 100 and 300 feet above sea level is composed of infertile lateritic clays, covered with *sal* jungle. Towns are neither large nor numerous, even those with as many as 50,000 to 75,000 inhabitants serving merely as local trade or governmental centers. Kharagpur (129,600), 72 miles west of Calcutta at the junction of the main rail lines from Bombay and Madras, developed as a result of the railway shops established after 1900 and has become the seat of one of India's largest scientific and technical training institutions.

West of the Bengal-Bihar boundary the complex geologic formations of Archean granite, gneiss, schist, and traprock present undulating upland or rounded hill surfaces, generally between 1,000 and 2,000 feet above sea level. The westernmost portion, fantastically eroded tablelands of laterite along the divide between the Son and the Brahmani rivers, reaches 3,600 to 3,800 feet. Elsewhere elevations are below 3,000 feet, aside from a few isolated hills. The valleys are broad and the stream gradients gentle. Most of the drainage is eastward through the Damodar and the other West Bengal rivers.

Chota Nagpur consists of the six southern administrative districts in Bihar state and certain adjacent districts in northern Orissa and West Bengal. So defined, it produces half of India's manganese, roughly two-thirds of the mica, over 80 per cent of the coal, 96 per cent of the iron ore, and 100 per cent of the copper ore. The production of bauxite, limestone, and fireclay is considerable, and there are small workings of chromite and wolframite.

The largest industrial center in Chota Nagpur is Jamshedpur (218,-200) 155 miles west of Calcutta on the main railway to central India and Bombay. The iron-and-steel works here, largest in India and among the larger in non-Soviet Asia, began producing in 1911 under indigenous (Bombay) financial and managerial control. At first American and European technicians played a crucial role. Now there is a body of native technicians and mill workers, and a modern city has been developed. Steel-using industries, such as the tin-plating, wire-cable, and agricultural implements industries, also exist here. Jamshedpur is located neither at the source of its coking-coal supply, the Jharia coalfield 110 miles north, nor at the source of its iron ore, 45 to 80 miles south. It is, however, at a point of minimum ton-mileage necessary for raw-material assembly, close to the essential water supply drawn from the Subarnarekha

River where it descends from the plateau and receives from the south its largest tributary.

Asansol and the associated industrial towns of Kulti and Raniganj (combined population 133,600) in West Bengal form the second largest concentration of heavy industry. Iron smelting began during the 1880's, based on low-grade laterite or on the local ironstone, flux, and fuel taken from the Raniganj coalfield, but the development of modern iron-and-steel manufacturing awaited the utilization of the high-grade iron ores in Singhbhum and the superior coking coal from the Jharia field. The presence of good refractory clay and the availability of pig iron and ingot steel, as well as of cheap coal and thermal-electric power, has attracted a variety of industries manufacturing iron-foundry and steel-rolling-mill products, locomotives, aluminum products, nitrate fertilizer, and firebricks and other ceramic products. Asansol also exploits the relative abundance of water in the Damodar River below the junction of its largest tributary, the Barakar.

Ranchi (106,800), a commercial and administrative center, is climatically attractive because of its elevation over 2,000 feet, but it is the only city over 100,000 besides Jamshedpur. In view of the industrial potential of Chota Nagpur, it is surprising to find that less than 7 per cent of the people live in urban places with populations over 5,000 and that 85 per cent are farmers or farm laborers.

Planned development of the coal and water resources within the Damodar and Barakar watersheds has been undertaken by the government of India, modeled after the Tennessee Valley Authority in the United States. A series of seven dams and reservoirs is being created above the Barakar-Damodar confluence, which will generate power, regulate industrial and irrigation water supply, and prevent floods. The availability of cheap thermal- and hydro-electric power through the high-tension grid in the surrounding plateau region will attract industries, providing steady employment, and perhaps will stimulate dispersion outside the Raniganj coalfield for what some day may become India's "Ruhr." Yet, the region is characterized by improper mining methods, misuse of coking coal, uncontrolled floods, and socio-economic maladjustments associated with mine labor. Many workers are aboriginal tribespeople who live in hovels near the mines.

Agricultural land occupies less than half of the surface and, for the most part, is marginal in productivity. Wet-rice is grown on the best soil in valley bottoms or on low terraced hill slopes (Figure 116). The upland soil of the plateau or hill surfaces is devoted to dry rice, maize, and oilseeds. Each year the equivalent of over 40 per cent of the net sown area is fallowed, and a relatively small fraction of the total cultivated area is either irrigated or double-cropped. A third of the surface

Fig. 116 • Rice fields, seen in West Bengal, 40 miles below Calcutta along the west bank of the Hooghly River, are being harvested during early November. The fields are thoroughly dry a month after the end of the rainy season, although water still stands in the drainage channel, at the upper right of the picture, and fills the excavated storage tank near the two dwellings in the upper left. The rice has been cut by hand with sickles in the center fields and will be allowed to dry before being carried to the threshing floor. Banana plants grow near the tank and vines, probably pumpkin or squash, climb over the thatched roof of one of the houses. Black and white cattle graze on the field borders and roadsides. (R. U. Light, American Geographical Society.)

is forested, but the stand is commonly scrubby owing to grazing, burning, and excessive cutting for mine timbers and firewood. The most important commercial forest product is lac.

Economic development of the region was slight until the nineteenth century, and the thin lateritic soils and the jungles were left largely to the aboriginal peoples. The most numerous of these so-called "primitive" tribes were the Santals and Hos of Munda (Mundari) linguistic affinity and the Oraons of Dravidian affinity. In 1951 in the Chota Nagpur division of Bihar the tribes formed an aggregate of about 3.2 million, or a third of the total population of nearly 11 million. Within recent historic times there has been a progressive upward displacement of Santals from the alluvial valleys in and bordering West Bengal under pressure from the more numerous, so-called "civilized," caste Hindus of the lowlands. Most of the tribes have been or are being absorbed into the Hindu or Indian social system. Several hundred thousand have been converted from tribal animism to Christianity. The opportunity for seasonal employment of perhaps half a million adults in the mines and mills of the region has wrought great changes in tribal society. The rapidity of the economic and social transition is vividly exemplified by the miners or steel-mill operatives whose fathers used bows and arrows to kill jungle game and practiced animistic worship of the trees, streams, and hill fields.

The Gangetic plain

The inland alluvial plain of the Gangetic River system forms a continuous area of good land 750 miles in length and 150 miles in breadth, covering over 115,000 square miles. The eastern limit is taken arbitrarily as the eastern boundary of Bihar state, where the plain narrows to 90 miles width. The western limit of the region is the western boundary of Uttar Pradesh, where it follows the Jumna River. The centrally-administered state of Delhi is excluded, as are the southern upland districts of Uttar Pradesh and Bihar, so that the southern limit of the region is the eroded margin of the peninsular massif. The northern limit is the boundary of Nepal together with the Siwalik hill boundaries of Uttar Pradesh. The aggregate population was some 86 million in 1951 and the average density about 750 persons per square mile, a density exceeding that of any other region in India except Malabar and Bengal.

Although the alluvial lowland is a topographic unit without sharply defined internal subdivisions, the climate and soil are not homogeneous. The lower, or eastern, portion of the plain is wettest, receiving annual average rainfall of 40 to 60 inches or more, and is made up primarily of new alluvial deposits of the northern piedmont fans, known as *terai*, and extensive flood plains, known as *khadar*, along the lower Ganga and the Kosi, Gandak, Ghaghra (Gogra), and Son rivers. The upper, or western, portion of the plain generally receives between 20 and 40 inches of rainfall annually, except in the wetter piedmont section. Most of the area west of Kanpur on the Ganga-Jumna interfluve, or *doab* (= two rivers), is in the semi-arid (*BSh*) climatic zone. Old alluvial surfaces above flood levels are dominant west of the Gumti (Gomati) River. The old alluvium of the upper plain is not lateritic, but it has been partially leached and commonly contains lime nodules which form massive subsoil concretions in some places. Salty efflorescences and alkali crusts exist on the surface in spots where ground water has evaporated, making some soil unfit for crops.

Between two-thirds and three-fourths of the surface of the Gangetic plain is arable and land is used more intensively than in Bengal. (See Table XXV-1.) The ratio of fallow land is under one-tenth of the net sown area, and over one-fourth is sown more than once a year, with the result that the double-cropping ratio is in excess of 115 per cent— higher than anywhere else in India. The highest ratio occurs on the lower plain, where the area sown more than once is close to one-third of the net sown area. The least amount of fallowing is found on the upper plain where only one-twentieth of the arable land is not planted every year. Crop rotation; intertillage of two or more crops in the same field; fertilizers, including leguminous crops plowed under, are characteristic. Light rains from the western cyclonic storms give an inch or less monthly precipitation during December to March; but the water supply would be insufficient for a second crop were it not for the abundance of river and ground water derived from the Himalayan affluents of the Gangetic system. Irrigation by canals and wells of all types appears to be equally common in both portions of the plain, but large perennial canal systems as well as modern tube wells equipped with pumps in the drier west attest to the greater dependence of agriculture here upon irrigation.

Rice is the leading crop of the lower Gangetic plain, where the longer duration of the summer monsoon favors wet cultivation. However, late-maturing rice, the most important variety, needs water applications toward the end of its growth period. Maize, planted during the rainy season on well-drained soil, is a secondary food crop. Sugar cane and jute are cash crops of increasing importance north of the Ganga, but the winter grains, barley and wheat, the leguminous chickpea (gram) frequently interplanted with the grains, and oilseeds, particularly linseed, and other cool-season crops occupy nearly half of the gross area sown. The bulk of irrigation water is obtained from earthen or masonry wells and excavated storage tanks. Canal systems have been built along the Son and other small rivers south of Patna. The Ganga and its large northern tributaries, Gandak and Kosi, are not yet diverted for irrigation. The Kosi, the third largest Himalayan river in volume of flow after the Brahmaputra and Indus, has formed a gigantic alluvial fan 70 miles wide in northern Bihar over which uncontrolled floods and detritus deposits lay waste large agricultural tracts almost every year.

In the upper Gangetic plain rice is not dominant, and cool season (rabi) crops are more important. Wheat is the leading grain, its cultivation being promoted by the lower temperatures from December to March and by sufficient flow in the several large canal systems fed by the Jumna, Ganga, and Sarda rivers to permit three to five applications of irrigation

TABLE XXV-1. POPULATION AND

	Bengal-Bihar Industrial Region		Gangetic Plain	
			Lower	Upper
	W. Bengal Plain	Chota Nagpur Plateau	Gangetic Plain	Gangetic Plain
Total land area (sq. mi.)	25,903	33,160	58,223	57,140
Total population, 1951 (1,000's)	22,779.4	10,866.4	47,246.4	38,901.1
Averape population density (per sq. mi.)	879	328	812	682
Village land area classified (1,000's of acres)	16,510.1	21,175.7	37,096.9	36,582.9
	Per cent	Per cent	Per cent	Per cent
Per cent under forest	6.3	33.6	3.5	1.8
Not available for cultivation	15.9	6.8	10.2	15.0
Other uncultivated land, excluding fallow	10.0	14.0	11.2	14.8
Fallow land ⎫ Arable land	6.7 ⎫ 67.5	13.6 ⎫ 45.6	6.4 ⎫ 75.1	3.6 ⎫ 68.4
Net sown area ⎭	60.8 ⎭	32.0 ⎭	68.7 ⎭	64.8 ⎭
Arable land classified (1,000a.)	11,165.5	9,648.9	27,826.9	25,025.1
Gross area sown (1,000a.)	11,317.8	7,901.8	33,676.6	29,388.1
	Per cent	Per cent	Per cent	Per cent
Crop areas as per cent of G.A.S.				
Rice	76.5	62.1	37.5	12.4
Wheat and barley	1.3	2.2	16.7	27.8
Jowar, Bajra, Ragi	0.1	3.7	1.7	13.7
Other Food Grains	9.7	24.8	34.0	30.7
Foods, other than grain or oilseeds	7.6	1.7	5.8	6.9
Oilseeds	1.9	5.1	2.3	1.3
Fodder crops	0.2	—	0.4	5.7
Cotton	0.1	0.1	0.1	0.5
Jute and other fibers	2.1	0.4	1.3	0.4
Tea, coffee and tobacco	0.3	0.1	0.2	0.3
	Per cent	Per cent	Per cent	Per cent
Per cent of gross area sown, irrigated	15.9	13.1	23.8	24.6
Area sown more than once as per cent of net sown area	12.5	16.4	32.1	25.2
Fallow land as per cent of net sown area	11.0	42.2	9.2	5.6

Source: *Census of India, 1951.* Paper No. 2, *Population Zones, Natural Regions, Sub-Regions and Divisions.* Delhi: 1952.

AND UTILIZATION IN NORTHERN INDIA

Trans-Gangetic Plain	Rajasthan Desert	Western Himalayan Region	Northeast Frontier Region	North Central Hills and Plateaus
79,039	75,310	133,109	99,817	146,703
25,867.4	4,603.8	9,023.6	12,891.3	24,171.3
327	61	68	129	165
38,136.5	8,062.8 [1]	28,161.9 [2]	39,073.0 [3]	80,500.5 [4]
Per cent	Per cent	Per cent	Per cent	Per cent
4.7	0.1	31.0	16.7	14.9
16.0	9.1	38.4	12.0	16.5
13.9	27.2	10.0	48.3	27.2
8.9 } 65.5	26.8 } 63.5	2.0 } 20.3	5.2 } 22.9	5.7 } 41.4
56.6	36.7	18.3	17.7	35.7
24,933.2	5,132.3	5,726.6	8,949.7	33,345.1
25,484.7	3,011.1	6,432.1	7,888.1	31,333.5
Per cent	Per cent	Per cent	Per cent	Per cent
1.6	0.2	19.4	65.5	8.8
20.3	8.1	32.8	0.1	21.6
21.1	42.7	9.1	0.1	18.6
31.5	27.0	30.2	4.7	32.9
4.9	1.4	2.5	10.1	1.7
4.4	7.8	2.9	5.4	8.3
11.9	4.8	0.9	0.1	2.6
2.2	1.4	0.4	0.7	4.9
0.2	0.1	0.2	3.5	0.4
1.8	6.5	1.3	9.9	0.1
Per cent	Per cent	Per cent	Per cent	Per cent
29.6	22.3	19.8	17.2	4.4
18.3	1.5	24.4	14.0	9.4
15.8	72.8	10.8	29.3	16.0

[1] Classified area includes only 17 per cent of total land area.
[2] About 51 million acres of uninhabited land outside 8 million acres of village land excluded in Jammu and Kashmir.
[3] Classified area excludes Manipur and the North-East Frontier Agency.
[4] Classified area includes 86 per cent of total area.

water. Barley and intertilled grains also are important. The commonest oilseeds in addition to linseed are mustard, often mixed with the grains, and rapeseed. Various kinds of pulses and other legumes are grown for food or feed. Grain sorghum (*jowar*) and bulrush millet (*bajra*) are the chief rainy-season (*kharif*) grains grown under dry cultivation in the upper plain, but wet-rice and maize are significant on irrigable land and in the piedmont districts where precipitation amounts to 40 inches. Sugar cane is grown throughout the plain and made into brown sugar by crude processes in the villages. In the piedmont, cane has become a major cash crop for sale to sugar mills. Short-staple cotton is the most widespread cash crop in the drier western and southern districts. It is produced under irrigation and, unless killed by frost, allowed to remain in the fields as long as ten or twelve months to obtain a second picking. A typical three-year crop rotation is the rainy-season crop of sorghum mixed with pulses; followed after a ten-month fallow period by the fall-sown wheat mixed with grain; followed immediately by pulses in the third year. Sugar cane or cotton and other grains or soil-building legumes may be substituted in the rotation.

There are 80 to 90 water buffaloes and cattle of the ordinary north-Indian humped varieties for every 100 acres of cropland in the Gangetic plain. The bovine animal density becomes progressively lower in the upper plain to the west, and the animals are better fed, larger, healthier and more productive than anywhere else in the subcontinent excepting the Punjab and Gujarat. Beef consumption is insignificant, the meat being eaten only by non-Hindus and untouchable castes, but the cows are kept for their milk. The milk is seldom used fresh because it is preferred in the form of curds, or buttermilk after it has been churned to make butter which is clarified and used in cooking. Oxen are used for plowing, pulling carts, and lifting irrigation water from wells. Numerous goats are kept both for milk and meat supply, and thin sheep, which are covered with hair unlike fleece, are reared for mutton. Chickens and pigs live by scavenging and are eaten only by the poorest untouchable castes. Horses are often used for draft purposes. In the subhumid zone near Delhi, camels are fairly common.

Human occupance of the plain is far from uniform. The pattern of rural settlement tends to be dispersed in straggling villages and hamlets in the humid rice-growing east where average population density is highest (800 to 1,000 persons per square mile). In the drier wheat-growing west large compact villages, spaced a mile or so apart, are associated with less dense population (500 to 700 persons per square mile). Prevalent floods, coupled with the high water table and the ease of digging wells, promote dispersion in the eastern plain. Agglomeration of settlement in the western plain is related to the necessity of maintaining deep wells for domestic water supply, and to the historic need before the British conquest 150 years ago for refuge against frequent invasions from the Punjab and central India. These patterns of settlement appear to be related also to fundamental differences in social and economic organization, i.e., the joint-village land tenure and close interdependence of village castes in the west in contrast to the large estates, subdivided into small tenant holdings, and the greater degree of social segregation in the east.

In the region as a whole about 11 per cent of the population resides in cities of over 5,000 inhabitants. Yet in the Bihar portion of the lower Gangetic plain only 7 to 8 per cent of the population is urban, whereas in Uttar Pradesh, the percentage is nearly 15. About 200 urban centers of all sizes exist in the somewhat larger area of the lower plain, spaced at an average distance of 20 miles, while in the upper plain of central and western Uttar Pradesh there are 330 urban centers, spaced at 14-mile intervals. The most highly urbanized portion of the Gangetic region thus coincides with the area of agglomerated village settlement and is related to the long-established tradition of urbanism in the dry climatic zones and their humid borders in India and Pakistan.

The geographic duality of the Gangetic region is apparent in the contrasting historic roles of the wet, rice-growing, less urban eastern plain and the dry, wheat-growing, more urban western plain. The eastern plain has played a less prominent part in recent India's cultural and political development, although in early historic times it was the center of Buddhist civilization. The home of Gautama, the Buddha, was in the wet *terai* belt of present-day Nepal; his religious enlightenment occurred at Gaya, and he preached at Banaras. The emperor Asoka, the great Buddhist and first ruler of all India (except the extreme southern peninsula), had his capital at Pataliputra on the site of modern Patna during the third century B.C. The Gupta dynasty, which united India again after five centuries of division and under which a revival of Brahmanical Hinduism occurred, had Pataliputra as its first capital but later shifted its administrative seat westward to the Jumna. The Jumna-Ganga *doab,* and nearby Delhi and Agra, became the heart of the Hindu Harsha's empire about 640 A.D. and of the various Moslem empires from the thirteenth to fifteenth centuries, culminating in that of the Mughals which lasted from the mid-sixteenth to the nineteenth century. Moslem influence waned under British rule and finally retreated to Pakistan.

Of the 17 cities over 100,000 (1951) within the region, 12 are located in the western plain. Kanpur on the Ganga (Ganges) River is the largest and most rapidly growing place (705,400 including suburbs) and was the only urban center among the 17 not already established as a town in the pre-British period (Figure 117). Lucknow (496,900 including suburbs) was the nineteenth-century seat of Moslem rule in Oudh and is the present capital of Uttar Pradesh. These two large cities, located 40 miles apart, dominate the portion of the western plain farthest from Delhi. Agra (375,600) and Allahabad (332,300), situated respectively on the Jumna and at the Jumna-Ganga confluence near the southern margin of the western plain, had early origins and were fortified strategic centers of Mughal power. The eight other cities, ranging between 100,000 and about 200,000, in the western plain are located west of Kanpur and north of Agra. Meerut, or Mirath (208,100), and Mathura, or Muttra (105,800), had ancient Hindu-Buddhist origins, while Bareilly, or Bareli (208,100), Moradabad (161,900), Saharanpur (148,400), Aligarh (141,600), and Rampur (134,300) are known to have existed as towns during the later Moslem period. Many of the cities retain marks of their pre-British be-

Fig. 117 • A business street in Kanpur, Uttar Pradesh, is being cleaned with water sprayed from a tank cart before the rush of traffic has begun. Later, pedestrians traveling in the street as well as on the sidewalk, cyclists, cycle-rickshaws, carriages, and oxcarts will be numerous. Relatively few private passenger cars will appear, but many persons will ride inside and atop buses of design similar to the public carrier in the photo, which has a body of local construction on an imported truck chassis. The modern-style commercial buildings with residential flats above the ground floor, the advertisements in English and Hindi, and the varied goods and services to be offered when the store fronts open are representative of the new urban life of India in this industrial city of over 700,000 people. (Information Service of India.)

ginnings, such as Moslem forts and mosques or Hindu shrines, and the smaller ones tend to retain the traditional types of craft industries.

The imprint of British rule is shown by separate or reserved areas (cantonments and railway colonies) laid out for military or civilian residential purposes by railways, and by modern commercial and industrial development. All of the large cities in the upper Gangetic plain are served by broad-gauge railways, linking them to one another and to Delhi, as well as to Calcutta and Bombay. Trade, transportation, and services are the basis of most of the current growth. Modern factory industries tend to gravitate to those cities located in the southern and western parts of the upper Gangetic region, but only in Kanpur does modern factory industry (cotton and woolen textiles, leather and shoes, steel fabrication) form the main economic basis of the population.

Banaras, or Varanasi (355,800), and Patna (283,500) are the two largest urban centers in the eastern plain. Both are located on the Ganga River which has served as a medium of transportation from their historic beginnings, but the railways paralleling the river, or crossing it at Banaras, have become more important. Banaras' preëminence rests upon its sacredness to Hindus, who come from all India to bathe in the purifying Ganga and worship in scores of temples. The city is the center of classical Sanskrit teachers and of the famed modern Hindu University's philosophers and scholars. Patna, the capital of Bihar, is the focus of commerce as well as the center of cultural and governmental affairs of the state. The densely settled northern portion of the eastern plain between the Ganga and Nepal, which is provided with meter-gauge railways of the northeastern system, has direct connections to broad-gauge lines at Banaras and various points in the upper plain on the northern system. Since much traffic must be ferried across the Ganga to reach Patna and other places on the broad-gauge eastern system, a bridge is under construction at Monghyr.

The trans-Gangetic plain

Beyond the Jumna, the Indo-Gangetic lowland stretches northwestward without interruption across the Punjab and westward across the broken quartzite ridges of the Aravalli range in Rajasthan to the borders of the Thar desert. Southward are the gneiss and sandstone hills enclosing the small basins of the Chambal River and its tributaries in eastern Rajasthan and northern Madhya Pradesh (formerly Madhya Bharat). This 79,000-square-mile area is the trans-Gangetic plain, arbitrarily limited on the east by the Uttar Pradesh boundary and on the northwest by the Ravi or Sutlej rivers and the Pakistan boundary. Elevation varies from some 600 feet above sea level in the extreme west to 1,000 feet at the base of the Si-walik hills along the northern boundary and to 1,500 feet or more in the southwest where the Aravalli ridges converge near Ajmer. The prevail-ing climate is semi-arid (*BSh*) type with 18 to 35 inches of precipitation annually. The arid (*BWh*) type of climate with only 15 to 18 inches precipitation extends along the Rajasthan border of the Punjab, and nar-row belts of the humid subtropical (*Cw*) type of climate with as much as 40 inches annual precipitation exist in the piedmont portion of the Punjab and in Rajasthan east of the Aravalli range. Most of the surface streams entering or rising in the region dry up and lose their identity. No well-defined divide exists between the watersheds of the Gangetic and Indus systems. The Sutlej and its tributary, the Beas, traverse the extreme northern part of the region and empty into the Indus system. The Chambal and other Jumna tributaries flow northeastward across the southern portion.

In keeping with the dry climate and low crop-carrying capacity of the land, average population density is only 327 persons per square mile, less than half of what it is in the upper Gangetic plain, despite the fact that virtually the same percentage of the surface is arable. Nearly a third of the gross area sown is irrigated, but the ratio of fallowing is higher and the ratio of double-cropping lower than in the Gangetic region (Table XXV-1).

From the standpoint of human occupance the trans-Gangetic region is divided into two sections: (1) the more humid irrigated plain of the Indian Punjab and Delhi, where the majority of the 25.8 million in-habitants are concentrated, and (2) the broken plain of the Aravalli hill country south of Delhi, where dry farming is the rule.

In the Punjab section, fall-sown wheat is the most important grain. Other cool-season crops are identical with those of the upper Gangetic plain. Among the summer crops, cotton and fodder for livestock assume more importance than in the Gangetic region. About half of the land is irrigated by open wells and canals (Figure 118). The canal systems fed by the Jumna and the Ravi were built by the British government a hun-dred years ago and the original Sutlej system, about 70 years ago. The Bhakra and Nangal dams, built on the Sutlej in the Himalaya since India gained independence, permit enlargement of the latter system. Increased diversion of Sutlej water in the Indian Punjab is facing strenuous objec-tions from Pakistan where several canals also are dependent on the Sutlej.

The chief grains produced under dry cultivation in the section south of Delhi are bulrush millet (*bajra*) during the season of scanty summer rains and barley during the still scantier winter rains. Both are drought-resistant crops suited to land where little or no irrigation is possible be-

Fig. 118 • This herd of buffaloes, seen in the piedmont plain of the Indian Punjab, is being allowed to cool almost submerged in water during the mid-day heat. Indian buffaloes are large black or reddish-brown animals, less docile than the common Indian varieties of oxen or cows, strong but slow-moving when employed for draft purposes, and a source of milk with high butter content. These animals and all the similar varieties of domestic buffaloes, ranging from the Mediterranean countries to the Philippines and China, together with the wild water buffaloes of eastern India and Malaya, form a separate species *(Bubalis bubalis)* which does not hybridize with other cattle. *(Information Service of India.)*

cause of the deep water table and the unreliability of stream flow. Some small canals and embanked reservoirs exist, and excavated tanks or wells are not unknown, but water is costly when lifted by draft animals with the aid of leather buckets, if the depth is great, or with Persian wheels, if it is shallow. Plans are being effectuated for modern irrigation development along the Chambal. The one agricultural virtue of this section of the region is the richness of the "black cotton" soils found in the extreme southeast.

The eastern Punjab has served as the gateway to Delhi and the Gangetic plain for about 3,500 years from the beginning of the Indo-Aryan invasions until the arrival of the Mughals, the last conquerors from beyond the Indus, some 400 years ago. It was in the eastern Punjab that the Sikh religious movement made its rapid growth under Mughal rule in the sixteenth century and here that Sikh political and military power had its sources during the early nineteenth century prior to the British conquest of the Punjab in 1849. This area became the main refuge to which Sikhs and Hindus fled from West Pakistan in 1947-48.

The broken country of the Aravallis lies astride the main routes of invasion southward from Delhi and Agra into the Dekkan and through Ajmer into Gujarat. Yet the people are more predominantly Hindu than in either the Punjab or Uttar Pradesh and have remained culturally conservative under the rule of an aristocracy derived from Hindu Rajput princes, who sought refuge here from the inroads of the Moslems in Delhi and Agra, or the Hindu Maratha princes, who came northward from the Dekkan during the decline of the Mughals.

The nodal point of the region, national capital, and greatest inland city of India, is Delhi (1,384,200 including New Delhi and all suburbs). At this site on the west bank of the Jumna or its close environs have been located seven imperial capitals previous to that of the British. The probable location of Indrapat, about 1000-1500 B.C., and the ruins of the Hindu forts dating from the eleventh century A.D., as well as the various Moslem cities built between the twelfth and the sixteenth centuries, are situated south of the walled seventeenth-century Mughal city, which is known as Old Delhi. The military advantage of Delhi's location at a defensible site between the eastward-curving course of the Jumna and the northern extremity of the Aravalli range has been outmoded. Its position in the western zone of political tension near the cultural heartland of India on the Gangetic plain is much more significant. (See Map 27b.) The modern city, New Delhi, planned after Delhi was declared the capital in 1912 and occupied by the British Government of India in the 1930's, spreads north, west, and south over a semicircular area varying from 4 to 10 miles in radius from Old Delhi. The junction of the main broad-gauge railways from Bombay state and Madhya Pradesh with the northern broad-gauge system of Uttar Pradesh and Punjab, together with the meter-gauge net of Rajasthan, give Delhi a preëminent position in the traffic flow and trade of northern India. Craft industries continue to flourish in Old Delhi, and development of modern factory industry is occurring outside the walls, although manufacturing employment remains secondary to government, services, and trade.

In addition to Delhi, seven cities with more than 100,000 inhabitants in 1951 exist in the trans-Gangetic region. Amritsar (325,700), holy city of the Sikhs and location of their chief shrine (The Golden Temple), is the largest commercial and manufacturing center, now handicapped by the fact that it is situated less than 20 miles from the Pakistan boundary of the Indian Punjab. Jullundur, Ludhiana, and Ambala range in population from 145,000 to 170,000 and are situated, like Amritsar, in the rich piedmont plain of the Punjab on the main broad-gauge rail line which runs eastward to the upper Gangetic plain. Gwalior below its ancient fortified rock (and the associated modern towns of Lashkar and Morar; total population, 241,600) in the extreme southeastern corner of the region no longer retains the role of state capital (1948-1956) because of the merger of Madhya Bharat with Madhya Pradesh (Figure 119). The concentration of trade and manufacturing in the city derives from its former role as capital of Gwalior, which was until 1948 an important Native State, and from its location at the junction of narrow-gauge railways built by the state with the broad-gauge line passing through from Agra to Jhansi. Jaipur (291,100), also capital of a former Native State, is a unique planned indigenous city dating from the eighteenth century, now the capital and largest city of Rajasthan state. Ajmer (196,600), until 1956 the capital of the centrally-administered state of Ajmer now

Fig. 119 • This street scene in the city of Gwalior, Madhya Pradesh, illustrates the blending of indigenous and European urban traditions. The arcades of the commercial-residential structures, built in styles copied from European models, are occupied by stores with extended open fronts of the Indian bazaar type, while the upper stories form living quarters, shielded from the light and noise by bamboo mats or glass. In the left foreground is the Indian equivalent of an old-fashioned general store in the United States. Beyond it are other retail shops and personal services, such as tailors and oculists (note eyes with spectacles). The two-wheeled horse-drawn vehicle in the right foreground is a *tonga*, still the common man's taxi in the small cities and towns of northern India. (*Information Service of India.*)

merged with Rajasthan, is served only by meter-gauge railways, as is also Jaipur.

The Rajasthan desert

The great Indian desert, or Thar, may be said to begin at the edge of the irrigated land along the Sutlej, Indus, and Nara rivers in West Pakistan and to reach eastward to an ill-defined boundary along the west flank of the Aravalli range in the vicinity of, but excluding Mount Abu, 5,650 feet above sea level, and various 2,000- to 2,500-foot peaks near Ajmer. On the south is the Rann of Kutch and on the north the semi-arid transition zone of the Punjab. That portion within the nine western districts of Rajasthan, bounded for statistical convenience by West Pakistan, the Indian Punjab, and Bombay and excluding the more humid eastern districts of Rajasthan covers some 75,000 square miles, measuring at the maximum about 400 miles north-south and 300 miles east-west. The climatic classification is almost entirely warm desert (BWh), 90 per cent of the area receiving less than 15 inches of precipitation annually. Yet the region is not sufficiently sterile to exclude some four and two-thirds million people.

The topography is rough; numerous outcrops of wind-carved rocks are interspersed with deposits of loose stones or lime-cemented pebbly soil and wind-blown sand. The dunes of sand are 50 to 100 feet high in the north and rise up to 200 or 300 feet in the south, where they occur in long ridges running in a direction parallel to the strong southwest winds of the summer monsoon period. In the irregular depressions between the dunes are found numerous alkaline ponds and patches of acacia trees, xerophytic shrubs, and coarse grasses. Springs and surface-flowing water are absent, except in the southeast where the Luni River drains the seasonal floods into the salt marshes of the Rann.

The exposed and underlying geologic formations are varied. Metallic mineral deposits are not of economic value, but local quarries yield mica and the high-quality white Makrana marble, used in construction of the famous Taj Mahal in Agra and other buildings in Delhi and Calcutta, and there are lignite mines. The region annually produces 500,000 tons of commercial salt, mainly from lakes in the east, and is the largest inland source of supply for northern India. Gypsum is an important mineral product for which the region is the chief source in India.

It is estimated that 15 to 17 per cent of the desert is cultivable. There are patches of fertile soils in the depressions between dunes and along the Luni and its tributaries. Winter crops of wheat, barley, sesamum, and pulses are obtained. During summer the main crops are the drouth-resistant grains, sorghum and bulrush millet, of which the latter attains its highest relative acreage anywhere in India.

The scarce and extremely unreliable rainfall, averaging 11 inches annually, is received chiefly during July and August from the southwest monsoon. A little rain comes during January and February from cyclonic storms. Irrigation is virtually impossible except in small vegetable patches because the surface water is brackish, if available at all, and good water must be lifted laboriously from wells 200 to 300 feet deep. Double-cropping is negligible, and the percentage of fallowing is high. Dry-farming is essential to conserve moisture in the soil during the fallow periods. The surfaces of fields are scratched with light plows several times with furrows criss-crossed, levelled with harrows and protected from the wind with thorn brush fences. Irrigation of field crops is possible only along the Luni, where alluvial land also is cropped after natural inundation, and in areas adjacent to the Punjab, commanded by canals fed from the Sutlej River. Outside the irrigated areas drouths and famines occur locally once every two or three years and rather generally every eight or ten years.

Pasturage is available at irregular times and places, yet livestock herding is a major occupation. The common livestock kept are, according to the order of their numbers: sheep, goats, cattle, buffaloes, camels, horses, and mules. Some fodder is grown and dairying is given considerable attention with the result that in good years large surpluses of curdled milk and butter are available for shipment out of the region. Hides and low-grade wool are also exported. If the rains fail completely, there is a triple famine of grain, fodder, and water. When this occurs, 50 to 75 per cent of the livestock are lost, and there is wholesale emigration.

With good reason the average population density is but 61 persons per square mile—the lowest among all Indian regions. The majority of the people are concentrated in widely-spaced villages and towns in the eastern half of the region, but many are nomadic herdsmen. Local densities vary from more than 100 per square mile in the less arid east and in the irrigated tracts north of Bikaner, where rapid increases have occurred following canal construction, to only 6 per square mile in the west around Jaisalmer.

The typical walled desert towns of pre-British origin, frequently situated below fortified hills, have preserved the indigenous urban patterns and old culture of north India, little changed by European influences. Traditional craft industries such as cotton and wool weaving, embroidery, leather work, gold and silver smithery, and the making of lacquer and brassware, are flourishing. Over 90 per cent of the people are Hindu. Moslems are 5 per cent, and Jains and Sikhs together are 4 per cent. Hindu Rajput aristocrats and Brahman priests trace their lineage back some 500 years to the Gangetic region when their ancestors sought refuge here from the Moslem invaders. The whole region remained under the rule of native princes during the British period and is known for the social and religious conservatism of its inhabitants. It is also known as the home of the Marwari traders and bankers who have spread throughout the cities of India as a wealthy, enterprising business class.

The only large cities within the region are Jodhpur (180,700) and Bikaner (130,300), both of which were founded by Rajput princes from the Gangetic region in the fifteenth century. Both cities are served by meter-gauge railways which link them and other towns in the region to the Punjab, Delhi, and Bombay state. One rail line crosses the international boundary into Sind and terminates at Hyderabad on the Indus River. Many small places are dependent upon camels and other animals for overland transportation because of the absence of roads suitable for carts and automobiles.

The western Himalaya and Kashmir

India's mountainous borderlands in Uttar Pradesh, Punjab, Himachal Pradesh, Jammu, and Kashmir cover some 133,000 square miles, inhabited by nine million people. Pakistan controls about 27,000 square miles of territory inhabited by 800,000 people in northern and western Jammu and Kashmir, and disputes with India the latter's control of the remaining portions of Jammu and Kashmir. The long-standing conflict between Pakistan and India derives not only from the cultural ties of the inhabitants to both countries, but also from complicated legal questions. Although no wheeled vehicle has passed entirely through the region and no military invaders ever have traversed the high mountains from the north to descend into the plains, the fact that the boundaries of the four most populous countries of the Asiatic mainland come into proximity here gives the region a strategic role.

In the region the land rises from about 1,000 feet above sea level on the plains border to 2,000 or 3,000 feet in the low, parallel Siwalik ridges. Long alluvial-filled valleys at 1,500 to 2,000 feet lie between or adjacent to the Siwaliks. The outer Himalayan ranges, varying from 2,000 to 15,000 feet above sea level, constitute a belt of exceedingly complex terrain 50 to 70 miles wide. The rivers flow in narrow valleys and the only extensive area of level land is the lacustrine basin, or vale, of Kashmir, at about 5,000 feet, embraced between the outer Himalayan Pir Panjal range and the Great Himalayan range on the north. The high Himalaya, 20 miles broad with peaks generally between 18,000 and 25,000 feet, and 100 miles north the still greater 25,000- to 28,000-foot Karakoram, are composed of slate, schist, gneiss, and granite. Along the axes of these main ranges, as well as of the somewhat lower Ladakh and Zaskar ranges between them, tectonic forces have thrown up the earth's surface in mighty waves, as though it were a plastic, viscous mass. The ranges are, of course, deeply scarred by erosion and all except the Karakoram cut by transverse river gorges of which the largest are those of the Indus and Sutlej. Alluvial or lacustrine valley floors and terraces exist along the upper Indus and its tributaries at 10,000 to 12,000 feet between the Himalaya and Karakoram. Limestone and rock salt are of economic importance, and placer gold, hard and soft coal, china clay, gypsum, bentonite, and other minerals have been exploited on a small scale.

Sharp local contrasts in elevation and exposure produce varied climatic conditions. The average vertical temperature gradient up to 11,000 or 12,000 feet is about 3°F. per 1,000 feet in winter, and 2½°F. in summer, the most marked decrease occurring in the first 4,000 or 5,000 feet. The vertical climatic sequence within less than 100 miles from (1) humid subtropical (Cw) in the lower slopes of the outer Himalaya below 8,000 feet elevation through (2) humid microthermal (Dw and Df) up to (3) about 12,000 feet where tundra (ET) extends up to (4) the perennial snow line of the great Himalaya at 16,000 feet, is roughly comparable to the climatic transition from north India to the arctic coast of Siberia, 3,500 miles distant. The annual precipitation is generally between 40 and 80 inches on the south-facing portion of the mountain system. The major source of moisture reaching the southern slopes is the summer monsoon, coming by way of the Gangetic plains, and the maximum amounts (up to 117 inches) are received between 3,000 and 6,000 feet elevation at easterly localities. More than half of the 26 inches received annually at Srinagar in the vale of Kashmir occurs between November and May and is derived from the numerous western cyclonic depressions. It reaches a maximum in March-April and has a secondary maximum in July-August. Most of the snowfall in the high Himalaya and other ranges to the north is believed to come during winter from frontal and orographic lifting in the winter cyclones, but the source of moisture is unknown. Little precipitation is received at any time in the sheltered valleys of the Indus and other rivers beyond the high Himalaya and the temperatures are markedly reduced because of the altitude. For example, Leh at 11,500 feet receives 3 inches of precipitation a year, has a January mean temperature of 17°F., and a July mean of 63°.

The vertical zoning of temperature and the rain-shadow effect of topography are reflected in the vegetation. In the outer ranges a progressive change is observed from subtropical mixed broadleaf evergreen-deciduous forest, from 1,000 to 3,000 feet elevation, to temperate forest from 3,000 to 8,000 feet in which long-needle pine, Himalayan cedar, or *deodar,* and evergreen oak are found in mixed or almost pure stands. Moist temperate forest, in which are mixed other evergreen Himalayan oaks, blue pine, tree-like rhododendrons, and various Himalayan species of birch, spruce, and fir, is found between 5,000 and 11,000 feet. Stunted oaks, rhododendron, birch, and juniper extend to the timberline. Above the forest is alpine tundra, composed of grasses and flowering herbaceous plants in a dense sod cover. Snow falls intermittently throughout the year above 16,000 feet, and temperatures remain almost continuously below freezing. Glaciers begin in cirques at 18,000- to 20,000-foot elevation and descend as low as 13,000 feet. In the valleys beyond the Great Himalaya, which descend below 12,000 feet, there are no forests, only xerophytic shrubs and sparse grasses.

The eroded Siwaliks and gravelly sub-Himalayan fans are little occupied, but the outer valleys are well-peopled, with densities of 100 to 300 persons per square mile. The optimum elevation for agricultural settlement is the moist subtropical zone between 1,500 and 6,000 feet. Within this zone the vale of Kashmir is by far the largest single population concentration—about 1,600,000 in an area 20 by 80 miles, of which over 200,000 are in the city of Srinagar. Dehra Dun (144,200), the only other city over 100,000, is located at the foot of the Himalaya proper at 2,000 feet. Above 6,000 or 7,000 feet and up to 12,000 feet there are many farm villages and some small administrative and trading centers; but beyond the Great Himalaya, settlement becomes sparse and extremely spotty. Summer resorts like Simla are situated on the first ranges of the outer Himalaya which reach 6,000 to 8,000 feet above sea level.

Transportation is primitive except near the summer resorts which are accessible by automobile roads from the rail terminals in the Siwalik foothills or plains border. Narrow-gauge railways penetrate the Himalaya proper in two places, and roads passable for automobiles are being built in several lesser Himalayan valleys, but at no point is the Great Himalaya penetrated by a graded vehicular road. The highest major highway traverses the Banihal pass, 9,300 feet, into the vale of Kashmir from Jammu. The road through the pass and old tunnel at 9,000 feet under it often are blocked in winter by snow. After the Kashmir war of 1947-48, which cut off access to the vale by way of the all-year-round Jhelum River road, India constructed a 1½-mile tunnel at 7,300 feet under the pass in order to assure access by way of the new road (built as a war measure in 1947) through the Jammu foothills. Much use is made of air services connecting Srinagar and Jammu with Amritsar and Delhi.

Arable land, 20 per cent of the area for which village records are available, is found mainly in the valleys of the Siwaliks and lesser Himalaya below 6,000 or 7,000 feet. The ratio of population to arable land is often as high as 1,000 persons per square mile, and land use is nearly as intensive as on the Gangetic plains. Irrigated rice fields are on the alluvial bottomlands and the low natural terraces to which water can be brought by diversion canals. These fields are carefully levelled and irrigated and, after being drained and the rice harvested, often are devoted to winter crops such as wheat, barley, and mustard. The most intensive cropping is the market gardening in the fluvio-lacustrine soils and artificial floating gardens of the vale of Kashmir. Non-irrigable lands are less carefully terraced and produce maize, finger millet, and other millets often grown in mixed stands. The milk cows, or milk buffaloes, and the work oxen are stabled in the villages, their manure being carefully conserved and applied to the fields, and the other cattle of the villages are herded together on the common pastures on the higher slopes unsuitable for cultivation. Firewood is gathered freely, and the lower mountains are usually denuded of tree growth. Forested areas are burned systematically to reduce the undergrowth and to encourage grass for pasturage. Lumber, especially pine and *deodar*, is obtained in sufficient supply not only for the elaborate local type of domestic architecture but also to be floated down to the timberless plains.

Over 7,000 feet the agricultural season is limited to the six or seven months from April to October. The staple crops of wheat and barley are spring-sown, not fall-sown. White potatoes and deciduous fruits, such as apricots and apples, suggest the similarity of the climatic conditions to those of the upper middle latitudes. In the dry region beyond the Great Himalaya in Gilgit and Ladakh every field must be irrigated, and the scarcity of irrigable land has led to intensive utilization. The maximum altitude of cultivation is 12,000 feet. At these heights the yak and yak-cow hybrid (*dzo*) must be used for plowing, and transport is by yaks or by hardy ponies, sheep, and goats. Cattle and even water buffaloes may reach 10,000 feet in the widespread summer transhumance, but sheep and goats are taken as high as 14,000 feet for midsummer pasturage. By September, the livestock descend to valley pastures. The first snowfall finds the villages of the high Himalaya partially or wholly deserted by mass movement of the inhabitants to the lower valleys and plains border where they winter their animals and seek supplementary employment. The inhabitants of Gilgit and Ladakh, like those of Tibet, beyond the high Himalaya do not migrate to lower elevations in winter.

Seasonal migration and transhumance is traditionally accompanied by trade. Small caravans cross the 14,000- to 15,000-foot passes of the Great Himalaya to the market towns of southern Tibet from the Trans-Gangetic plain or from the vale of Kashmir to the towns of Ladakh and Gilgit. The trade in salt, borax, wool, and yaks' tails from Tibet and in grain and manufactures from India has declined since 1950 because of the political ties and improved transportation between Tibet and China proper. Trade across the Korakoram pass (18,550 feet) and the Baroghil pass (15,430 feet) to Chinese Hsin-chiang has ceased entirely. Traffic between Gilgit and the vale of Kashmir also has been impeded by the political conflict between Pakistan and India.

The region is the meeting place of three religions, three language groups, and two racial stocks. Below the limit of the essentially Lamaist Mongoloids of Ladakh, are the Dardic-speaking Caucasoids, mainly Moslems, who dominate Gilgit and Azad Kashmir and who are most numerous in the vale of Kashmir where they have become the basis for Pakistan's claim to all Kashmir. Hindu Dogra (Indo-Aryan) Caucasoids are dominant in Jammu. The Pahari-speaking population east of Jammu in the lesser Himalaya is purely Caucasoid and almost exclusively Hindu, the limit of the Mongoloid racial stock and Tibetan, or Bhotia, dialects being located in or north of the Great Himalaya.

The central Himalayan region

The central Himalayan region is comprised largely of three states: Nepal, Sikkim, and Bhutan. A small portion is in Darjeeling district of West Bengal, India.[2] The total population is estimated to be somewhat over 9 million, or roughly equal to that of the western Himalaya and Kashmir, in an area of only 77,000 square miles. Thus, the average density is nearly 120 persons per square mile, or roughly twice the density of the western Himalaya and Kashmir. Over 2 million of the 8.6 million inhabitants of Nepal, however, live in the submontane plain along the Indian border and half a million in the 230-square-mile valley of Katmandu, a former lake basin. The density in the Nepal mountains, as in Sikkim and Bhutan, is well below 100 persons per square mile. The three largest cities of the region are Katmandu (estimated 150,000) and grouped with it in the same valley Patan (estimated 105,000) and Bhadgaon (estimated 93,000).

The main features of Himalayan physiography, the gently folded foothills, the complexly folded outer ranges, and the high crystalline range, appear in the region. Because the mountain structures are compressed into a belt less than 100 miles in width, the terrain rises abruptly in 70 miles from less than 1,000 feet elevation in the piedmont *terai* to more than 26,000 feet in western Nepal and to more than 28,000 or 29,000 feet, respectively, at Kanchenjunga and Chomolungma (Everest) on the boundaries of eastern Nepal. The rise is almost equally abrupt from 500

---

[2] Darjeeling district, which was ceded in 1835 by the Raja of Sikkim to British India, is included for statistical purposes with the North-East Frontier Region.

feet elevation in the Bengal plain to 24,000 feet on the northern boundary of Bhutan. Many peaks, at least 24,000 feet in altitude, appear to be grouped in a dozen or so tectonic arcs, arranged *en echelon* along the axis of the Himalaya. Streams rising to the north in or near Tibet flow south through transverse gorges and form the headwaters of the major rivers: Sarda, Karnali, Gandaki and Kosi in Nepal; Tista in Sikkim; and Lhobrak in Bhutan.

The racial and cultural boundary of the Mongoloid Tibeto-Burman-speaking peoples descends progressively eastward from about 10,000 feet elevation in Kashmir and in the western Himalaya to 4,000 feet in Nepal and to 1,000 feet or less in the valleys of Sikkim and Bhutan. The boundary of essentially Tibetan, or Bhotia (Bhutia), people is about 8,000 feet in Nepal, and in Sikkim and Bhutan it comes down to about 5,000 feet in the outer Himalaya. Lama Buddhism prevails among all the Tibetan speakers, but below them Buddhism generally gives way to tribal or Hindu traditions. The Newars, who live in central Nepal as low as 4,000 feet, speak a language with Tibetan affinities and also adhere to Buddhist traditions. Mingled with them are the so-called Gurkha Nepali people, whose mixed Mongoloid-Caucasoid racial traits, Pahari (Indo-Aryan) dialects, and semi-Hindu religious practices, show their affinities to the plains people of India proper. The Gurkhas, who conquered Katmandu some 150 years ago and provide the ruling class of Nepal, are spread eastward in the lesser Himalaya as far as Sikkim and Bhutan, but are seldom found above 6,500 feet elevation. The people of the submontane *terai* show some Mongoloid racial admixture but otherwise they are almost identical with those of the adjacent Gangetic plains of India.

Thus, the crest line of the Great Himalaya is no more an ethnic divide than it is a major water divide, and the southern flanks of the range in Nepal, Sikkim, and Bhutan form a cultural as well as a political buffer zone between India and Chinese-controlled Tibet. Until about 1950 the political isolationism of the rulers of Nepal and Bhutan and the lack of roads suitable for wheeled vehicles outside of Darjeeling district had made the region a barrier between Tibet and India, penetrated by one major caravan route from the vehicular highway terminal at Kalimpong, India, through Sikkim across the Jelep pass, 14,400 feet, to the Chumbi Valley in Tibet and ultimately to Lhasa via the Tang pass, 15,200 feet. The trade and transit traffic from India to Tibet has diminished sharply, if not stopped completely, as a result of changes in Tibet since 1950. Meanwhile Nepal, which prior to 1950 had been penetrated by only three short narrow-gauge railways in the *terai*, has been opened to a network of air services from India and a new automobile road has been built across the 8,500-foot Mahabharat range to Katmandu. Sikkim's capital, Gangtok, is accessible by automobile. Bhutan alone remains inaccessible by modern means of transportation. At present India's political and economic influence is paramount in all three central Himalayan states.

Altitudinal climatic zones, similar to but perhaps slightly higher than those prevailing in the western Himalaya, extend eastward into this region. The rainfall of the windward southern slopes becomes progressively heavier to the east and is derived almost entirely from the summer monsoon air current, except in the high Himalaya. The annual rainfall of Katmandu in its somewhat sheltered basin is 56 inches, while Darjeeling on an exposed ridge, 170 miles east at 7,100 feet, receives 123 inches.

Natural forest cover is exceedingly dense except in rain-shadowed valleys. Tree ferns and other species of plants representative of the Indo-Malayan life zone appear in eastern Nepal and Sikkim. Dwarf bamboos form dense brakes on excessively wet exposures; near the timber line there are almost impenetrable rhododendron thickets. Forest growth is dominantly *sal, shisham (Dalbergia sissoo)*, and *haldu (Adina cordifolia)* in the plains border and foothills below 4,000 feet; pine or broadleaf evergreen trees from 4,000 to 6,000 feet, and evergreen oaks from 6,000 to 8,500 feet. Above this are Himalayan species of spruce and fir with birch in zones extending, respectively, to 9,500 feet and 12,500 feet. In the dry valleys above 8,000 or 9,000 feet within the Great Himalaya range and in the Tibetan plateau margins are juniper woodlands and thorn shrub up to 13,000 feet. Alpine tundra grasslands and lichen barrens extend to the perennial snow line at 17,000 feet.

Three distinct agricultural zones exist in Nepal: (1) the submontane *terai* plain below 1,000 feet; this is separated by the gravel fans known as the *bhabar*, and by the foothill ranges, from (2) the outer Himalayan valleys between 3,000 and 6,500 feet; which are in turn separated by gorges and the more rugged high Himalaya from (3) the high valleys and plateau basins, situated at elevations of about 7,000 to 12,000 or 14,000 feet.

The 10- to 20-mile wide *terai* contains perhaps a third of Nepal's estimated five million acres of arable land. Agriculture here resembles that of the humid Gangetic plain to which the surpluses of rice, wheat, jute, tobacco, linseed, and mustard seed are exported and from which the comparatively dense and rapidly increasing population is largely derived. The excellent timber of the piedmont forest zone is being depleted by clearing for agriculture and export to India, but good stands of trees remain in the swampy, malaria-infested *bhabar*, which is still the habitat of the elephant, rhinoceros, tiger, and wild boar.

The most completely utilized zone of agriculture is the outer Himalaya, where cultivation covers the valley floors and natural alluvial terraces and where almost all the gentle slopes are artificially terraced. The best land, as in the western Himalaya, is that which can be irrigated and planted during summer for rice and dry-cropped in winter with wheat, barley, oilseeds, potatoes, broadbeans, peas, or onions. Double-cropping is important in this zone, especially in the valley of Katmandu, but in the country as a whole only 20 per cent of the land yields two harvests a year. Dry upland fields in this zone produce Nepal's second staple crop, maize, which is mainly of flint type, and finger-millet, which is often interplanted in the maize fields and used for brewing an alcoholic beverage rather than as a staple food.

It is reported that Nepal has seven million head of livestock. Half are cows and oxen, concentrated in the villages and overgrazed pastures of the outer Himalaya, where they are utilized for work and milk products and supply manure for the double-cropped fields, but are not butchered. Buffaloes, sheep, goats, and pigs are killed for meat, however. Chickens and ducks are numerous, but there is little egg production.

In the higher zone of agriculture the upper limits of maize (8,500 feet) and winter wheat or barley (10,500 feet) are reached, and the aridity usually makes irrigation essential for any cultivation. Spring-sown grains, potatoes, and buckwheat are best adapted to the short, cool growing season. Barley, mostly of the naked varieties, forms the staple food when roasted and ground into flour. Yaks replace bullocks for plowing and transportation, and yak cows give milk, which is consumed in the form of cheese or butter, mixed with tea, salt, and sometimes barley flour, as a soupy beverage. Yaks and sheep, which provide wool for home-spun clothing, are taken to summer pastures as high as 15,000 feet. Summer trading expeditions across the high passes to Tibet still continue regularly, a rare example of free trade across an international frontier—but winter transhumance and mass migration from the high villages to the foothills does not appear to be as important a feature of the economy as in the western Himalaya. The close linguistic, religious, and economic ties of the highest villages of Nepal with Tibet are a reflection not only of their proximity to Tibet, but also of their comparative ease of access to the plateau.

In Sikkim and Bhutan there is no agricultural zone like the *terai*, the equivalent *duar* belt being in Indian territory. Foothills disappear or become indistinct from the Himalaya proper. Indigenous Lepchas and other tribes of the low outer Himalaya grow upland rice and buckwheat in shifting forest clearings, but immigrant Nepali farmers have introduced wet-rice cultivation on terraced fields. Cattle are grazed in the forest. Cardamoms are a cash crop in Sikkim, and in Bhutan, lac, beeswax, and musk are gathered for sale. In some Bhutanese valleys permanent cultivation of rice, maize, and other crops is established, but population is sparse, and much land in the high valleys is devoted to yak pasturage only.

The northeast frontier region

India's territory eastward from Darjeeling was beyond the recognized border of India until the past century, and people of Hindu affiliations are scarcely half of the total population. One third are tribesmen of Tibeto-Burman or Khasi origin; one-fifth are Moslems of Bengali origin. Assam was an independent semi-Hinduized kingdom, ruled by Shans akin to the people of eastern Burma and southwestern China, in the first quarter of the nineteenth century when it was devastated by Burmese forces in an unsuccessful invasion. In 1824 the British seized Assam during the first Burmese war, and acquired nominal control of the tribal territory in highland Assam between 1830 and 1890. Tripura and Manipur were Native States and now remain separate centrally-administered territories. The former Native State of Cooch Bihar in the plain of northern West Bengal has been absorbed into that state. The sovereignty of Britain was never fully exercised in the frontier tracts, occupied by quasi-independent tribes bordering northern Burma and eastern Tibet, which now comprise the North-East Frontier Agency within Assam.

The region is largely hilly or mountainous. The Himalayan wall, which runs due east-west from Darjeeling and Sikkim through Bhutan, bends northeastward and terminates in the peak of Namcha Barwa, 25,400 feet, towering above the transverse gorge of the Tsangpo, known locally as the Dihang and lower in India as the Brahmaputra. The geological structure of the portion of the range in Assam is unknown, and it is possible that the Himalayan rocks and fold systems extend through Assam eastward into China. However, the topographic barrier which forms the northeastern boundary of India turns southward in an irregular half-circle of mountains to connect with the lower Tertiary and Cretaceous ranges along the Burma frontier. The trend of these simple sedimentary fold structures is northeast-southwest in the rugged 9,000- to 12,000-foot Patkai and Naga ranges; in the 3,000- to 6,000-foot Manipur and Lushai hills the trend is north-south. The Tripura foothills of India show a parallel trend, continuing southward into the Chittagong hills of East Pakistan. The Garo-Khasi hills, extending westward toward the Brahmaputra's entry into Pakistan, are rolling, eroded uplands 3,000 to 5,000 feet in elevation, formed largely of pre-Cambrian crystalline rocks like those of the peninsular massif.

Lowlands in the northeast frontier region form only 30 per cent of the area. The lacustrine basin of Manipur at about 2,000 feet elevation is enclosed by ridges on the north and west and drains into the Chindwin

River of Burma. The main valley of Assam is a 60-mile-wide alluvial trough, extending over 400 miles westward along the Brahmaputra from its upper reaches near Sadiya. The main river is an immense braided stream, averaging a mile in width and much more in flood, navigable as far as Dibrugarh, some 700 miles from the sea.

Land transportation is hampered by the fact that the Brahmaputra is unbridged and that roundabout routes are necessary to link the meter-gauge rail system with the Gangetic plain in India proper. Because of the lack of good rail connections and the discontinuance of through passenger service on the waterways of East Pakistan from Assam to Calcutta since partition, it is not at all surprising that Indian airways now provide the best and most-used passenger and express freight service. Automobile transportation is significant only for short distances. Heavy freight shipments still move by water to and from Calcutta via East Pakistan.

Petroleum and coal are the only important mineral resources exploited. There are probably good reserves of petroleum in upper Assam, but the Digboi and other small fields produce less than 70 million gallons annually—about 5 per cent of India's annual consumption. About 300,000 tons annually of low-grade Tertiary coal are mined in upper Assam for use in the steamers, railways, and tea-processing factories.

The area is extremely wet, and unoccupied land, 63 per cent of the area, is overgrown with dense forests. Weather is characterized by coolness and high humidity, even in the months normally dry elsewhere in India. Pre-monsoonal precipitation is heavy, 20 to 30 inches being received from thunderstorms during March to May. In the period of the southwest monsoon during June to September, 75 to 125 inches or more are received. Thus, the average annual rainfall varies from 75 to 125 inches in most of the region. The wettest areas are the exposed southerly slopes of Bengal and Assam Himalaya, probably receiving up to 200 inches, and the Khasi hills, receiving up to 400 inches (Cherrapunji, 452 inches) on the ridges overlooking the plain of East Pakistan. The driest areas, receiving between 50 and 75 inches, are found in the rain-shadows within the Manipur basin and the Brahmaputra valleys. The climate is humid subtropical (Cw) except in the higher mountains, but on account of the abundance of moisture, the forests are composed of evergreen broadleaf trees—tropical species in the lowlands and hills and temperate species in the mountains. Ridge tops well below the climatic timberline, which is reached only in the Assam Himalaya, may be grassy because of clearing and intermittent cultivation, as in the undulating uplands around Shillong.

The uniqueness of the northeastern frontier region rests in its low population density, merely 100 to 200 persons per square mile in the lowland districts, and the pioneer or even primitive condition of its agricultural development. The demographic anomaly of this region is apparent when it is recalled that the density of the adjacent Bengal delta in East Pakistan is as much as 1,000 persons per square mile. Where else in the humid plains of the subcontinent as late as 1800 were there vast tracts of cultivable land awaiting settlement? Where else could large commercial estates be laid out on vacant land to produce tea, beginning in the 1830's and 1840's? Where else on the mainland was it necessary to bring in contract laborers, mostly Hindus from the Gangetic plain and aboriginal tribesmen from Chota Nagpur, Madhya Pradesh, and the eastern highlands of Madras (now Andhra) to work in the tea gardens and processing factories? Where else outside the Punjab canal colonies has the population doubled in the past 60 years? Today only 23 per cent of the land has been made arable and the pioneer fringe is still expanding. Cropping is generally not intensive, nearly 30 per cent of the arable land being fallow and less than half as much double-cropped annually. Rice is the staple grain, and there are no important cash crops other than tea from estates and jute from peasant farms.

Agricultural settlement in the plains is of two types: large-scale estates and small subsistence farms, maintained by contrasting ethnic groups under different drainage and soil conditions. Except in the Darjeeling Himalaya, tea estates usually are located on the well-drained lateritic soils of the flanks of the hills or on the colluvial slopes and old alluvial terraces. Here on the plains border are concentrated the immigrant laborers, working either on the estates or on small subsistence farms taken up at the termination of their contracts. Land-hungry settlers of a different kind, mainly Moslems of East Bengali origin, have swarmed into the wet flood plains where they have opened up large tracts of wasteland and established their intensive type of rice and jute farming, adapted to seasonal inundation. Nepalis are the most vigorous agricultural settlers in northern West Bengal and they are beginning to make their appearance in Assam. Hindu castemen of old Assamese origin occupy the slightly better drained alluvium between the river land and the piedmont, growing rice, mustard seed, cotton, sugar cane. They hold their own in the upper reaches of the Brahmaputra valley, resenting the intrusion of non-Assamese peoples, particularly the prolific and industrious Bengalis. The number of tea-estate and tea-factory workers in West Bengal and Assam may total 600,000; yet, employment fluctuates according to market conditions, and a relatively small percentage become independent settlers. Well over half a million Bengalis have become permanent settlers in Assam since the turn of the century and, because of the growing pressure on agricultural resources in East Pakistan, migration to Assam continues as long as entry is not severely restricted by India.

Tribal settlement tends to concentrate on ridge tops and well-drained valleys between 2,000 and 6,000 feet elevation. Temporary clearings, known as *jhum*, made by cutting and burning the trees, are planted most commonly in upland rice, maize, finger-millet, and Job's tears with the aid of dibble sticks. Rice growing, especially wet-rice in a few localities, is a relatively recent innovation. The use of maize of flint type, including green ears and pop corn as well as ripe grain, is very ancient and is believed to have been established here before the European discovery of maize among the aborigines in the New World and its dissemination thence to coastal Asia.

North central hills and plateaus

The foreland of peninsular India slopes up gradually from less than 500 feet above sea level on the Gangetic plains border near the Jumna to over 1,000 feet in the Rewa plateau and about 2,500 feet in the Malwa plateau. The successively higher 200- to 400-foot scarps, generally facing west, north, or northeast, are cut by small southern tributaries of the Gangetic river system. The highest and most abrupt escarpment is on the southern margin of the plateaus, where an almost continuous east-west line of hills with local relief over 500 to 1,500 feet overlooks the Narbada-Son trough. South of these rivers, which drain in opposite directions through narrow gorges in their lower valleys, is a more or less continuous parallel line of hills, rising to heights of 3,500 feet above sea level. The headwaters of the Tapti River and those of the Wainganga (Godavari) and Mahanadi rise south of the crests of these hill ranges. In the southwest portion of the region the intricate topography of the Aravalli ranges forms the water divide between the small rivers flowing into the Gulf of Cambay and the southwesternmost tributaries of the Gangetic system.

The broken terrain of the highest ranges marks the traditional cultural limit of northern India and one of the most frequently established political boundaries of pre-British Indian history. In 1956 the southern boundary of the region, as here defined, became the northern boundary of the new and enlarged Bombay state. The region is now largely in Madhya Pradesh state. Five districts of Uttar Pradesh and seven districts of Rajasthan state also are included.

This large area of nearly 150,000 square miles (600 by 150 miles) is inhabited by some 24 million people, whose average density is well below the all-India average of 281 persons per square mile. Settlement and cultural influences have come mainly from the northern Indo-Aryan culture hearth to which this region has served as a marginal area for expansion and an avenue of access to peninsular India. The dominant element in the racial stock is brown Mediterranean, the prevailing religion Hindu, and the commonly spoken languages are dialects of Hindi and Rajasthani. There are small minorities of Moslems and Jains (in Rajasthan) but the most numerous non-Hindu elements in the population are the aboriginal tribes. The region thus includes part of the middle India tribal belt and is the threshold of southern India (Map 28a).

The geology of the region is transitional between the northern alluvial plains and the complex rocks of the peninsular massif. The alluvial mantle is important on the northern margin, where it forms portions of, or upstream extensions from, the Gangetic and trans-Gangetic alluvial belt, and in the upper valley of the Narbada. The underlying rocks are Archean gneisses and granites, exposed chiefly on the margins of the region and weathered into undulating peneplains or rounded hills. Massive sandstone, soft shale, and highly calcareous limestone once covered the old crystalline massif and still remain over extensive areas in the north and east where they form the lower tablelands and scarps. In the south basaltic lava flows have buried the older rocks and have been lifted by vertical crustal movements along fault lines in the vicinity of the Narbada River. Upland soils formed on weathered lava or alluvium derived from it are clayey, dark-colored, and fertile. To a lesser degree this also is true of soils associated with the gneiss and limestone of the region, but the soils resulting from the weathering of granite, quartzite, and sandstone are coarse-textured and infertile.

The old crystalline massif, where it is exposed in Rajasthan and northern Madhya Pradesh, yields manganese, mica, and diamonds. India's only lead-zinc mine was opened in the 1940's in Rajasthan, where the ore had been worked in ancient times. Soapstone, china clay, and brick clay are exploited in various places. Marble is obtained from the metamorphic formations in Rajasthan; easily-dressed sandstone for building and high-grade limestone for lime or cement manufacturing from sedimentary formations in Madhya Pradesh; and good coal of Gondwana age from the same state.

The climate is transitional between subtropical and tropical and between humid and dry. Mean monthly temperatures are between 60° and 65°F. in December-January and light frosts are experienced. The temperature gradient rises southward, and frosts do not occur in tropical peninsular India except at high elevations. Thus, the northern boundary of the winterless savannah-type (Aw) climate runs along the Narbada River, and most of the region is in the subtropical (Cw) zone. But the moisture gradient crosses the temperature gradient at nearly right angles. Annual rainfall is 45 to 55 inches in the east, whereas in the center and north it is below 40 inches and in the west it decreases to only 30 or 20 inches, where the semi-arid (BWh) zone exists. The geographic distribution of moisture is influenced by the terrain, the ranges over 3,000 feet altitude in the south receiving 60 to 80 inches. The eastern half of the region also has heavy persistent rains associated with the passage of weak lows along the "trough of the monsoon" between the dry continental air from the west and the recurving southerly streams of maritime air. The seasonal distribution of moisture is concentrated in the four months from June to September. The climatic regime is in every respect typical of extratropical India, with a distinct hot season during May and early June, when mean monthly temperatures reach 90° to 95°F.

The utilization of land for agriculture is less intensive than in the Gangetic plains but more extensive than in the Himalayan regions. (See Table XXV-1.) The roughness of the land accounts for the fact that less than 42 per cent of the surface is arable as compared with 65 to 75 per cent of the Gangetic plains. The low ratio of double-cropping and the high ratio of fallowing are due to dry farming, especially in the semi-arid western section of the region, and to the problem of obtaining irrigation water from streams deeply entrenched in narrow valleys, many of which stop flowing during the long dry season. Merely 4 per cent of the gross area sown is irrigated—a much lower percentage than elsewhere in northern India. However, the cool-season grains of wheat and barley are planted widely in the region. Indeed, wheat is a more important staple than rice. Cotton production, however, represents the most important cash crop in the region as a whole. The principal *kharif* (rainy season) grains are sorghums, both the large *jowar* and the small *kodon*, and various other millets. In other respects the cropping system of the region resembles that of the adjacent upper Gangetic and trans-Gangetic plains, although oilseeds occupy a relatively larger area and fodder crops less. The density of cattle and small livestock is low, and the animals are allowed to graze more or less indiscriminately on fallow fields, particularly those infested with the weed grass, *kans*. More than a quarter of the surface is uncultivated waste, covered with scrubby trees and coarse grasses or xerophytic shrubs—jungle in the original Hindi meaning of the word. Good stands of *sal* and other deciduous trees are found in the most humid eastern and southern portions of the region, but forests make up only 15 per cent of the total area.

Major routes of transportation traverse the region, but the degree of urbanization is low. Jhansi (127,400), which commands the main railway route into the region from the upper Gangetic plain, and Jabalpur (237,-900), situated at an important junction point in the Narbada-Son trough on the main railway from Calcutta to Bombay via the northern Dekkan, are both new cities which grew up under British rule. The main broad-gauge railway running south from Delhi and Agra passes through the region. Indore (310,900), Ujjain (129,800), and Bhopal (102,300) are indigenous cities located off these main railways in former Native States. Bhopal, the newly-designated capital of Madhya Pradesh, is well situated at a junction of broad-gauge lines between Jhansi and Nagpur and will gain population rapidly because of its political function.

SELECTED GEOGRAPHICAL BIBLIOGRAPHY

1. Ahmad, Enayat. "Rural Settlement Types in the Uttar Pradesh (United Provinces of Agra and Oudh)." *Annals of the Assoc. of Amer. Geogrs.*, September, 1952, pp. 223-246.
2. Brush, John E. "The Iron and Steel Industry in India." *Geogr. Rev.*, January, 1952, pp. 37-55.
3. Chatterjee, S. P. *Land Utilization in the District of 24-Parganas, Bengal.* Calcutta Geographical Society, Publ. No. 6, 1946.
4. Geddes, Arthur. "The Population of Bengal, Its Distribution and Changes." *Geogr. Journ.*, April, 1937, pp. 344-368.
5. Gupta, Debangshu Sen. "Immigration Pattern in Assam Valley." *Geogr. Rev. of India*, June, 1951, pp. 21-27.
6. Karan, Pradyumna P. "Economic Regions of Chota Nagpur, Bihar, India." *Econ. Geogr.*, July, 1953, pp. 216-250.
7. Karan, Pradymna P., and Alice Taylor. "Nepal." *Focus*, June, 1956.
8. Kihara, H., ed. *Land and Crops of Nepal Himalaya.* Kyoto: Fauna and Flora Research Society, Kyoto University, 1955.
9. Kingdon-Ward, F. "The Aftermath of the Assam Earthquake of 1950." *Geogr. Journ.*, September, 1955, pp. 290-303.
10. Kirk, William. "The Damodar Valley—*Valles Opima*." *Geogr. Rev.*, July, 1950, pp. 415-443.
11. Mayfield, Robert C. "A Geographic Study of the Kashmir Issue." *Geogr. Rev.*, April, 1955, pp. 181-196.
12. Singh, R. L. *Banaras: A Study in Urban Geography.* Banaras: Nand Kishore and Sons, 1955.
13. Spate, O. H. K., and Enayat Ahmed. "Five Cities of the Gangetic Plain." *Geogr. Rev.*, April, 1950, pp. 260-278.
14. Svec, Melvina M. "The Dry Lands of Sind and Western Rajputana in North West India." *Jour. of Geogr.*, February, 1935, pp. 45-60.

Comments

The foregoing references on the regions of northern India and Nepal are merely a small selection of recent items from the extensive geographical literature. Chatterjee's monograph on Calcutta and environs and Chapters 1 and 2 by J. Kawakita in the volume edited by Kihara are good examples of studies by Asian geographers based on intensive field work. R. L. Singh's book on Banaras is a thorough interpretive analysis of the city and its tributary region. The articles by Enayat Ahmad and Ahmad with Spate are succinct interpretations of broad regional differences in rural and urban settlement in the cultural heartland of northern India. Gupta and Geddes have mapped and analyzed population changes in Bengal and northeastern India. Karan, Kirk, and Brush have treated the geographic patterns of mineral resources and manufacturing in the areas of greatest concentration of heavy industry. Svec and Karan, with Alice Taylor, present useful summaries of two little-known peripheral regions. The hydrographic and physiographic effect of the most recent major earthquake of India form the theme of Kingdon-Ward's article. Mayfield gives a brief statement of current political and economic problems in Kashmir.

There are two regional atlases with descriptive texts that are helpful in geographic interpretations of two Indian states, together with East Pakistan: S. P. Chatterjee, *Bengal in Maps* (Calcutta: Orient Longmans, 1949); and P. Dayal, *Bihar in Maps* (Patna: K. Prakashan, 1953).

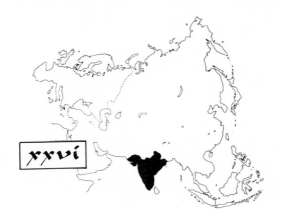

South India

COASTAL AND PENINSULAR INDIA SOUTH OF A LINE DRAWN FROM THE Rann of Kutch eastward to the Bay of Bengal forms 45 per cent of the area of the republic and contains 46 per cent of the population according to the 1951 census. This is tropical India, comprising all of the Dekkan and other peninsular uplands, the interior basins, and the littoral lowlands south of the Tropic of Cancer, exclusive of the west Bengal plain. The total area under consideration, including the Portuguese territories, exceeds 554,000 square miles and is inhabited by some 160,000,000 people. It is divided politically into the seven states of the Union of India: Andhra, Bombay, Kerala, Madhya Pradesh (part only), Madras, Mysore, and Orissa. There also is Pondicherry state, formerly French India, now under the direct administration of Delhi. Southern India may be described in terms of eight regions (numbered consecutively following the regions of northern India on Map 29): (9) the north Dekkan; (10) the Gujarat-Kathiawar coast; (11) the Bombay-Goa coast; (12) the Malabar coast; (13) the Madras coast; (14) the south Dekkan; (15) the Andhra-Orissa coast; and (16) the northeast peninsular uplands.

The north Dekkan

The inland portion of tropical peninsular India which was first reached and most deeply penetrated by the ancient Indo-Aryan settlers and the subsequent Persian, Afghan, or Mughal invaders is the Dekkan, or *Dakshinapatha* (the southland). That part of the Dekkan which is a true plateau of basic igneous rock (lava) weathered into rich black soils and which is inhabited largely by Marathi-speaking people is a politico-geographic region designated as the north Dekkan, in contradistinction to the south Dekkan which is a more rolling, hilly region formed of gneisses and granites with infertile red soils and occupied by Dravidian-speaking peoples.

The north Dekkan, as defined for statistical purposes (Table XXVI-1), consists of 22 administrative districts having a total area over 97,000 square miles with maximum dimensions of nearly 400 miles north-south and east-west and a population of nearly 24 millions. Formerly, Bombay state included only ten of these districts, a section sometimes called Maharashtra. Hyderabad state contained six of the districts in the division officially called Marathwara, while four of the remaining districts, collectively known as Berar, and the Wardha and Nagpur districts were part of Madhya Pradesh. Bombay state now has absorbed all these districts or the largest fractions thereof, excepting one (Bidar) which became part of Mysore, as a result of the 1956 political reorganization of India. The region constitutes the major share of the Marathi-linguistic area,[1] or greater Maharashtra. Its approximate natural boundaries are the great seaward scarps of the Ghats on the west and the crest of the Satpura range on the north; on the southeast no well-defined topographic features exist and the limits of the districts included do not coincide closely with the irregular boundary of the lava, which generally lies 40 to 50 miles farther southeast, beyond the limits of the present Bombay state and predominantly Marathi speech.

The terrain and soils of the region are its most distinctive physical attributes. Both relate to the immense horizontal layers of lava, popularly called traprock, which is augite-basalt. Because the layers vary somewhat in composition and are of unequal resistance to weathering, erosion has produced numerous tablelands (mesas and buttes) with scarped and terraced edges. Soils on the flat tops of the tablelands are lateritic in nature, infertile, and reddish-colored on account of prolonged leaching. The famous black *regur* soils occur on the gentle slopes below the beveled edges of the tablelands or in the alluvial-filled valleys. It appears that the

[1] Marathi and one of its dialects, Konkani, are the dominant languages of Bombay city and three districts along the west coast of Bombay State north of Goa.

TABLE XXVI-1. POPULATION AN

	North Dekkan	Gujarat-Kathiawar Coast	Bombay-Konkan Coast	Malabar Coast
Total land area (sq. mi.)	97,013	71,312	15,713	21,602
Total population (1,000's)	23,868.9	16,101.8	7,516.1	16,328.9
Average population density (per square mile)	246	228	478	756
Village land area classified (1,000's of acres)	61,622.3	31,530.9 [1]	9,774.1	13,277.7
	Per cent	Per cent	Per cent	Per cent
Per cent under forest	12.1	4.3	34.9	23.7
Not available for cultivation	10.3	16.7	15.7	13.4
Other uncultivated land, excluding fallow	2.6	14.5	1.9	17.1
Fallow land ⎱ Arable land	15.0 ⎰ 75.0	11.0 ⎰ 64.5	25.5 ⎰ 47.5	6.7 ⎰ 45.8
Net sown area ⎰	60.0 ⎱	53.5 ⎱	22.0 ⎱	39.1 ⎱
Arable land classified (1,000a.)	46,241.1	19,310.1	4,639.8	6,972.7
Gross area sown (1,000a.)	37,689.2	17,476.7	2,233.5	5,910.9
	Per cent	Per cent	Per cent	Per cent
Crop areas as per cent of G.A.S.				
Rice	2.0	6.4	52.3	41.8
Wheat and barley	4.1	5.4	—	—
Jowar, Bajra and Ragi	44.1	40.7	11.1	0.5
Maize, gram, pulses, etc.	18.2	13.2	12.6	4.7
Foods, other than grains or oilseeds	2.3	2.4	2.4	23.4
Oilseeds	12.1	6.9	2.6	19.0
Fodder crops	5.1	11.4	18.0	0.7
Cotton	11.2	10.9	—	0.3
Jute and other fibers	0.7	0.2	0.3	—
Tea, coffee and tobacco	0.2	2.2	1.2	9.5
	Per cent	Per cent	Per cent	Per cent
Per cent of G.A.S. irrigated	3.7	3.7	2.4	15.4
Area sown more than once as per cent of net sown area	1.9	3.7	3.9	13.9
Fallow land as per cent of net sown area	25.2	20.5	115.9	17.0

Source: *Census of India, 1951*. Paper No. 2, *Population Zones, Natural Regions, Sub-Region and Divisions*. Delhi: 1952.

[1] Data for only 69 per cent of area.
[2] Data for only 76 per cent of area.
[3] Total land area according to the Surveyor General of India.

fertility and other characteristics of true *regur* are maintained only if freshly-weathered mineral particles are added constantly, as on the typical undulating or rolling surfaces with gradients between 1 and 10 per cent, or on the flat valley floors. The highest elevations, of between 3,000 and 4,000 feet above sea level, and the most strongly laterized soils occur in the west on the tablelands which overlook the ghats

LAND UTILIZATION IN SOUTHERN INDIA

Madras Coast (Tamilnad)	South Dekkan	Andhra-Orissa Coast	Northeast Peninsular Uplands	All India
55,421	127,711	48,196	115,582	1,269,640 [3]
30,725.8	31,519.8	21,106.5	18,172.3	356,829.5
554	247	438	157	281
35,337.2	80,621.1	30,059.4	55,853.9 [2]	623,477.1
Per cent	Per cent	Per cent	Per cent	Per cent
14.9	15.3	14.3	30.2	15.0
19.8	18.2	24.6	12.6	16.0
12.8	6.6	12.7	26.9	16.5
14.6 }52.5	15.4 }59.9	10.4 }48.4	3.8 }31.0	9.5 }52.5
37.9	44.5	38.0	27.2	43.0
18,556.6	48,344.4	14,537.7	17,327.4	327,794.2
15,633.4	36,847.6	14,023.1	18,130.9	304,378.9
Per cent	Per cent	Per cent	Per cent	Per cent
32.3	7.5	50.0	54.9	22.9
. 0.1	2.0	0.1	2.1	10.5
25.2	36.4	15.0	4.2	20.5
14.8	24.2	15.7	27.9	24.0
4.3	3.1	4.9	1.8	4.4
15.5	17.1	8.1	7.4	8.1
1.3	1.1	1.9	0.4	3.7
5.0	6.8	0.6	0.3	3.9
0.1	0.4	1.6	0.1	0.7
1.5	1.2	2.3	0.8	1.3
Per cent	Per cent	Per cent	Per cent	Per cent
33.5	8.9	34.0	12.4	15.7
16.7	2.6	22.9	19.3	13.4
38.6	34.7	27.4	14.0	22.1

(passes) leading down to the west coast. The lowest elevations, of about 500 feet, and the deepest black soils are found in the north along the Tapti and its tributary, the Purna, the only river system in the region flowing west. The broad valleys of the Wardha, the Penganga, the Godavari, the Bhima, and the Krishna (Kistna) traverse the region on alignments roughly from west-northwest to east-southeast, falling below 1,000 feet elevation only near their points of exit in the eastern margin of the region. Belts of alluvium derived from lava exist along their courses, and in places the land slopes abruptly down to the rivers. There are tabular hills with local relief of a few hundreds of feet running from west to east between the major rivers. The general upland surface, however, is between 1,000 and 2,000 feet elevation, and dark-colored clayey soils of medium depth prevail.

Almost the entire region is situated in the rain shadow of the Western Ghats, receives merely 20 to 35 inches of precipitation annually, and is classed in the BSh-type (semi-arid) climate. The only well-watered sections, receiving more rainfall and hence being in the Aw (savannah) climatic zone, are in the extreme west, where the orographic effect of the Ghats carries eastward across the crest-line of the range, and in the northeast around Nagpur, where the monsoon lows cause the Bay of Bengal air current to converge with the relatively dry descending air crossing the Dekkan from the Arabian Sea. Two-thirds or more of the annual precipitation comes during four months from June to September. In October and November there is a little rainfall in the eastern and southern sections, derived from the retreating monsoon in the Bay of Bengal. During the period from December to February western depressions pass occasionally over the northern section bringing light rains. Frosts never occur, and the cool season temperatures remain over 65°F. except at elevations over 3,000 feet. March, April and May are the driest and progressively the hottest months. The maximum monthly means of 90° to 95°F. exceed those in the coastal parts of peninsular India.

Natural, or wild, vegetative cover is tropical dry deciduous forest or scrubby thorn trees, interspersed with grass. The steep slopes and summits of the little plateaus, especially in the heart of the rain shadow, may have only a sparse growth of cactus and ephemeral grass, but forests in the wet hills bounding the region on the northeast and west contain good stands of *sal* and teak.

The unusual aspects of agricultural development in the region relate to the scantiness of the moisture and the peculiar properties of the soil. In few other regions of India is so little irrigation practiced, and in no other region is so small a proportion of the land sown more than once a year. Crop yields are low and there is a high ratio of fallowing (Table XXVI-1). *Regur* soils do not lend themselves readily to irrigation on account of their undulating slope phases and their swelling and stickiness when wet. Even in the alluvial areas it is difficult to construct canals to bring water from streams because of the depth of incised valleys and the marked diminution of flow during the dry season.

Only on the upper Krishna and Godavari are there significant canal-irrigated tracts, producing rice and sugar cane. The drought-tolerant millets are the major grains. The percentage of crop acreage in rice, not unexpectedly, is lower in the north Dekkan than in any other south Indian

Fig. 120 • Koreagaon is a small town on the upper Bhima River in north Dekkan of Bombay state about 75 miles east of Bombay city. The compact settlement area is occupied largely by flat-roofed dwellings and surrounded by farmsteads with walled enclosures for livestock. This is evidently a planned settlement originally laid out in a rough grid pattern and fortified by a moat and circular wall, part of which still exists. The predominant crops in the large rectangular fields surrounding the town are grain sorghum and cotton, grown under dry cultivation. *(R. U. Light, The Geographical Review.)*

region. Winter conditions favor some wheat growing, although the great sorghum, *jowar*, is the staple food. Cotton (short-staple varieties) and oil seeds (peanuts, linseed, and sesamum) are outstanding cash crops.

Average population density is less than 250 persons per square mile, well below the all-India average, and settlement is concentrated in compact villages of about 600 to 1,000 persons, spaced at 1½ to 2 mile intervals, as in the semi-arid regions of northern India. Each village, therefore, has within its radius of ¾ or 1 mile, some 2 or 3 square miles of land to support the inhabitants (Figure 120). The density of population in relation to arable land is only 330 persons per square mile, the lowest figure reported anywhere in India. These facts, coupled with the natural fertility of the soil and the emphasis on commercial crops, go far toward explaining the prosperity of the north Dekkan.

The vigor of the Marathi people has been ascribed to their diet of unleavened *jowar* bread and their cohesiveness to the uniformity of their habitat, destitute as it is of dense forests which might afford shelter to aborigines. The most significant linguistic minority is concentrated in and around Nagpur, where a quarter of the people speak Hindi. The most important religious minority is Moslem, which seldom amounts to more than 10 per cent of the local population even in the districts formerly ruled by the Moslem Nizam of Hyderabad.

The north Dekkan stands in the forefront of urban-industrial development in India. No center has approached the size of Delhi, Hyderabad, or the great port cities, but urban population in the region exceeds 4.5 million, a quarter of the total population. Two cities are outstanding: Poona, together with the adjacent cantonments (588,500), and Nagpur, with Kamptee (480,400). Poona was the seat of the Maratha empire for a hundred years, became the rainy-season capital of Bombay Presidency under British rule, and is now headquarters for the western military defense area of India. It is an educational and cultural rather than industrial center, overshadowed by Bombay city only 120 miles distant by railway. Nagpur served as the capital of the British Central Provinces and (after 1948) Madhya Pradesh. Although its political role was lost in 1956, the city retains its importance in manufacturing, particularly textiles, and is the largest commercial and railway center on the broad-gauge line from Bombay to Calcutta. Sholapur (277,100), the next large city south of Poona on the broad-gauge main line from Bombay to Madras, underwent such early and intensive development of the cotton textile industry that it ranks at present with Jamshedpur and Ahmedabad among the first three most industrialized urban centers of India in terms of the percentage of population supported by manufacturing. Nasik with Deolali cantonment (140,000), Kolhapur (136,800), Amravati or Amraoti, with Badnera (124,100), and Ahmednagar with its cantonment (105,-300) are the only other centers having over 100,000 inhabitants in 1951. No one of the four is much industrialized, but among the 37 smaller cities and towns of 20,000 or more inhabitants are some 12 or 15 with highly commercial and industrial character, especially in the rich cotton-growing Tapti valley.

Gujarat-Kathiawar coast

Another distinct region of Bombay state is Gujarat, situated in the lowlands fronting on the gulfs of Cambay and Kutch. Gujarati, like Marathi, is an Indo-Aryan language of the "outer band" (Ch. XXII), having its own script and literature. It is linguistic unity rather than politico-geographic unity which has tended to set apart the region and has permitted the development of the local "nationalism" which gave strong support for the establishment of a separate state of Gujarat in 1956. Prior to 1947 the region had been so divided administratively that no other region in the subcontinent presented such a maze of governmental units. During the year following the achievement of independence the political structure was reorganized in the form of one centrally-administered state, Kutch; one Rajpramukh's State in Kathiawar, called Saurashtra; and the northern section of Bombay (Gujarat proper), enlarged by the annexation of Baroda, all the states of Gujarat Agency, and a portion of the former Rajputana Agency. Further reorganization during 1956 resulted in the formation of 16 districts, all attached to Bombay state. The only political fragments remaining in Gujarat are the Portuguese territories, consisting of the islands of Diu and Panikota off the coast of Kathiawar, with three villages on the mainland, and Damão (Daman) at the mouth of the Damanganga, with 40 villages located 20 miles or more upriver in the enclaves of Dadra and Nagar Alevi.

The physical environment, agriculture, and population distribution in the region are not homogeneous. The best *goradu* and *regur* soils are found along the northern and eastern sides of the Gulf of Cambay on the 50 to 100 mile wide alluvial plain formed where the Sàbarmati and Mahi rivers flow down from the flanks of the Aravalli range and the Malwa plateau and where the Narbada, Tapti, and other rivers debouch from the western Satpuras and northern Ghats. In eastern Gujarat rainfall is relatively abundant (35 to 60 inches), and the main food grains are rice and sorghum; the leading commercial crops, cotton and tobacco. The local breeds of dairy cows and buffaloes are among the best-fed and most productive in India. Population density is 400 to 500 persons per square mile, and agricultural prosperity attains the highest levels of the region. The intensity of land-use diminishes in the rough highlands rising over 1,000 feet along the eastern margin of the region and in central Kathiawar, where elevations rise 2,000 to 3,600 feet above sea level. Most of the terrain in western Gujarat is level, and it is the progressive westward decrease of rainfall from 35 to 20 inches, creating a semi-arid zone (BSh), and in Kutch less than 10 inches in the desert zone (BWh), which makes agriculture precarious. Proceeding westward the soils become less fertile, sandy, and even alkaline, and agriculture reaches an absolute limit at the edge of the salt pans in the Rann of Kutch. Population density declines to only 50 or 100 persons per square mile, and farming depends upon the low and unreliable yields of drought-resistant millets. Irrigation is severely restricted by the lack of good sources of surface or ground water. The prevalence of camels and sheep in western Gujarat signifies the close climatic affinities of this section to the desert zone of adjacent Rajasthan and Sind.

The inhabitants, some 16 million people, show strong racial affinities with those of northern India and West Pakistan, and their cultural origins are diverse. The majority are Hindus, the percentages varying locally between 60 and 75. The upper castes of Hindus (Brahmins and Rajputs) probably stem from the Gangetic plain; some of the lower castes and tribes such as the semi-Hindu Kolis [2] and the Bhils are derived from the aboriginal people. The Gujars (shepherds), whence the term Gujarat, entered from the desert during the 6th century A.D. The Kattis, whence the term Kathiawar, were a conquering tribe which penetrated the region from the Indus plain via Kutch during the thirteenth and fourteenth centuries. Subsequently, the region suffered the Moslem invasions which so deeply affected the Dekkan and all of northern India. To this period are traceable most of the present-day adherents of Islam, generally varying between 10 and 25 per cent of the local population, but some of the Moslems are of Arab or even Somali origin, and the Parsis are the descendants of medieval Zoroastrian refugees from Persia.

The varied ethnic origins and persistent connections of Gujarat with distant overland as well as oversea areas are epitomized by the mixed composition of the urban centers of Gujarat, which contain a third of the inhabitants of the region, and by the wide dissemination of Gujarati emigrants, not only to Bombay island, where perhaps a million live, but also to other places in India and to various parts of Asia and Africa. Among Gujarat's emigrants was Mohandas Karamchand Gandhi, from a Hindu trading caste in Kathiawar, who was educated in England, practiced law in the Union of South Africa, and led the nationalist movement of India for 28 years.

The largest urban centers of Gujarat are situated east of the Gulf of Cambay on the main broad-gauge line of the western railway system by which they are linked on the south to Bombay city and on the west to the Dekkan and northern India. Ahmedabad (788,300), near the terminus of the broad-gauge part of the system, is a junction point with the meter-gauge net which continues northward via the Palanpur gap to Rajasthan and Delhi and serves all of Kathiawar. This great city, located on the east bank of the Sabarmati River but not a port, is the metropolis of Gujarat and sixth largest city in India. The walled city was built by a Moslem ruler on the sites of earlier Hindu towns at the beginning of the

[2] Koli is the general name of the rural low-caste people of the plain north of the Mahi River, many of whom became day laborers in the port of Bombay during the 19th century and were the source of the term "coolie" (*kuli*), which was applied to all laborers of Indian or Chinese origin employed by Europeans in southern and eastern colonial areas of Asia.

15th century and is said to have had a population of 900,000 during the two centuries thereafter, when its textile industries and other crafts flourished and its trade was based on the traffic of the seaport of Cambay at the mouth of the Mahi River and the land routes to Rajasthan and Delhi. Modern Ahmedabad has regained the population it lost during the 18th and nearly 19th centuries and become the foremost inland textile manufacturing city in India, due to the cotton of the rich hinterland and to rail transport and coal power. Surat (223,200), located on the south bank of the Tapti, became the major port of Gujarat in the 17th century. At the end of the 18th century Surat was reported to have had 800,000 inhabitants, but decline set in rapidly during the 19th century. Only in the present century has Surat begun to recover population, due to its rail-borne cotton trade and manufacturing. Baroda (211,400), former capital of the progressive state of the same name, is an active trade and manu-facturing center amid the prosperous eastern Gujarat plain, connected with its local hinterland by a network of narrow-gauge railways.

West of the Gulf of Cambay only meter-gauge railways exist, and most of the seaports are hampered by shallow water. The comparative isolation in modern times of Kathiawar and Kutch is now being overcome by ex-tension of air services and by port development in the Gulf of Kutch. Rajkot (132,000), formerly administrative center of Saurashtra, is the most important inland city of western Gujarat and the cultural and educa-tional center of the Kathiawar peninsula. Bhavnagar (138,000), the larg-est city on the peninsula, has a small port on a badly-silted creek enter-ing the Gulf of Cambay. Jamnagar (104,400), near the Gulf of Kutch, has a small outport with docks, but the modern ports of Okha, located near the western tip of Kathiawar, and Kandla, opened since 1950 in Kutch near the head of the gulf, provide better facilities. Completion of the new meter-gauge railway across the marshes of the Little Rann to Kandla and the opening of new docks to large sea-going freighters helps relieve the congestion in Bombay caused since partition by the diversion of traffic from Karachi.

The mineral resources of Gujarat are not rich except for salt, obtained from sea water and the sub-soil brine of the Rann, about 1,000,000 tons of which are produced a year (one-third of the total Indian production); and the excellent limestone and sandstone, used for building. The de-velopment of modern factory industries, particularly textiles, in the region is based upon coal brought from sources several hundred miles distant.

Bombay-Goa coast

This wet, heavily-forested littoral region, extending 450 miles from about latitude 20° to 14°N., includes north Kanara (now in Mysore state), Portuguese Goa, and the portion of Bombay state known as the Konkan. South of the Daman the coastal lowland narrows to 30 or 50 miles. South of Bombay city, it becomes much broken by hills and sharply differentiated from the Dekkan by the scarps of the Ghats, 2,000 to 3,000 feet above sea level (Figure 121). The annual rainfall increases progressively southward along the

Fig. 121 • A valley in the western Ghats about 40 miles from Bombay city is half encircled by steep scarps of basaltic lava. The layers of successive lava flows (traprock) are seen clearly in the flat tops and dissected slopes of the mountains 2,000 to 3,000 feet above sea level. Although the rainfall here may amount to as much as 100 to 200 inches annually, the uncultivated slopes are not covered with a dense stand of large trees because of deforestation and the rapid rate of erosion. The cultivated alluvial slopes of the valley floor are largely devoted to rice, but only about half of the fields appear to be currently under crops in November toward the end of the growth period following the rainy season. (R. U. Light, The Geographical Review.)

coast from 60 to 80 inches in the savannah-type (Aw) climatic zone of Bombay city to more than 100 inches on the coast and up to 200 or 300 inches on the west-facing slopes of the mountains in the monsoon rain-forest (Am) zone. Historically oriented seaward because of its isolation from the interior, the economic significance of the region today hinges upon the existence of the two ports of Bombay and Mormugão and the railways linking them to the interior. However, there is no lack of sheltered inlets and better transport inland could be provided by improvement of the 10 or 12 old roads traversing the canyon-like valleys up to the *ghats* (passageways, or entrances) leading into the Dekkan. The total population is only 8 million, of which more than a third is in greater Bombay.

The growth of Bombay was favored by the existence of a deep (30 feet) and commodious natural harbor 12 miles by 4 to 6 miles, protected on the west from the wind and waves of the summer monsoon by a double chain of seven basaltic islands (now a single island) on which the port facilities and the city could be built.[3] Bombay's development did not begin until the English acquired the island in 1661-65. Even under British control the port did not become preëminent until 150 years later.

The growth of the city during the century prior to the current upsurge, which in two decades has more than doubled the population from 1,302,-500, including suburbs, in 1931, to 2,839,300 in 1951, shows three major cycles. The first population peak of 816,600 persons, recorded in the census of 1864, was associated with the cotton export boom due to world-wide shortages during the United States' Civil War, and preceded the opening of the Suez Canal. In the 1850's a railroad had been built to the mainland, an express steamer service had been established to England by means of overland transfer across the isthmus at Suez, and a steam-driven cotton mill had been started. Yet, it is incorrect to ascribe the first rapid rise of business and population to the railways connecting the port with Gujarat and the Dekkan because these had been completed only in the previous year. There is no doubt that the city's second peak of population growth to 821,700 in 1891 was aided by these transport improvements, as well as by land reclamation and dock construction begun in the 1870's. The congestion of population under almost unbelievably crowded housing conditions, the proximity of malaria-infested swamps, and the poor sanitary conditions took a heavy toll of life, culminating in the plague epidemics of 1896-1900. Housing and health conditions improved somewhat after the end of the nineteenth century. The cotton textile industry gained rapidly in the first two decades of the present cen-

[3] The name Bombay is not a corruption of the Portuguese words *Bom Bahia* (Fair Bay), attractive as this interpretation may seem, but is derived from the name of the tutelar Hindu deity of the district, the goddess *Bambe Mumbai*, by reason of which the Portuguese themselves at first called the place *Monbaim*, or *Bombaim*.

Fig. 122 • Looking north on Hornby road in the main shopping section of Bombay city known as "The Fort." Little that is Indian in style can be detected in the modified Gothic and Renaissance architecture of these commercial buildings, which might as well be in some western European city. The vehicles, including a local small-scale version of London's double-deck buses, are all foreign and, were it not for the pedestrians wearing loose Indian clothing, one would not think this urban scene to be in India. The main railway terminus of Bombay is two blocks ahead on the right and four blocks to the east is Ballard Pier and Bombay Harbor. Dark rain clouds of the southwest monsoon rise over the city during the morning hours. *(Information Service of India.)*

tury and turned away from earlier dependence on imported coal to sources of hydro-electric power in the nearby Ghats and from spinning yarn for the Chinese market to weaving cloth for the Indian market. The third wave of population growth was evident by 1921, when the census recorded 1,175,900 persons on Bombay island.

Bombay is India's most cosmopolitan metropolis, with an artificially-built waterfront stretching northward 5 miles along the island and expanding to Trombay island at the upper end of the harbor, a central business district on the site of the old fort close behind the original waterfront (Figure 122), the still badly-overcrowded sections, known as *chawls,* inhabited by the laboring classes, elite residential sections to the west on filled land fronting on Back Bay or beyond Malabar Point and on the hills overlooking the Arabian Sea, and large sections in the center and north devoted to railway marshalling yards and to manufacturing plants. The island measures 11.5 miles by 3 to 4 miles and now has 25 square miles of dry land area, as compared with the 22 square miles of Manhattan island, New York. Bombay island has a density of about 100,000 persons per square mile, compared with 87,000 per square mile on Manhattan. Spread of population into residential suburbs is already noticeable as far as 10-15 miles from Bombay proper along the two railways crossing Salsette island, largely included within the expanded political limits of Bombay municipality, *i.e.* greater Bombay. Some 200,-000 passengers are carried daily by the railways from the suburbs, although new suburban industrial development is providing increasing local employment.

Bombay's total annual shipping of about 7 million tons of goods normally does not exceed that of Calcutta, but its import tonnage is greater than Calcutta's and its hinterland of some 500,000 square miles in Madhya Pradesh, Rajasthan, Delhi, and the Punjab, as well as all of Bombay State and portions of Mysore and Andhra Pradesh, is larger than Calcutta's 350,000 square miles. However, its total hinterland population is only about 100,000,000, compared with Calcutta's 160,000,000. Petroleum from the Persian Gulf bulks largest among the imports, and an enormous variety of manufactured goods comes from Europe and North America, including heavy machinery and automobiles (to be assembled). Among the exports, raw cotton is no longer as important as cheap yarn and cotton piece goods, going to Asian and African markets. Other leading exports are oil seeds and manganese ore destined for European and American industrial markets.

As British influence waxed in India, so Bombay prospered; as Portuguese influence waned, so Goa declined. The site of old Goa, the once-flourishing 16th century city of 200,000 on an island along the south side of the Mandavi estuary, 250 miles south of Bombay, is mostly overgrown with jungle and inhabited by a few priests and nuns. Even Nova Goa, or Panjim, its successor as capital of the Portuguese "State of India," located 5 miles west of the old town, is not accessible to large craft at all seasons and has only about 11,000 inhabitants. Still smaller in population is the modern deep-water port of Mormugão and nearby Vasco da Gama on a mainland peninsula six miles south, connected to the meter-gauge net of Mysore in the south Dekkan. The economy of Goa, aside from a little manganese, copra, fish, and salt exported, is based on subsistence agriculture and is kept going by remittances from the mother country and from Bombay.

The coastal region of Konkan and north Kanara is, like Goa, devoted to subsistence agriculture and characterized by poverty and emigration to

Bombay. Traffic into and out of the region moves coastwise through the several small ports. Aside from the unexploited iron and manganese ores known to exist adjacent to Goa, where the basaltic lava formations give way to the Archean crystalline rocks of the peninsular massif, and the little exploited offshore fisheries, the natural resources are limited, and the inhabitants depend upon the local production of rice, coconuts, finger-millet, and pulses. Good land is restricted to small pockets of alluvium found at the heads of bays or in narrow valleys which appear to be in the process of estuarine salt-water encroachment through submergence of the coast. Poor lateritic upland soils are grazed by cattle and are sometimes burned over to be planted in millets. Inclusion of such marginal land in the agricultural statistics for the region explains the exceptionally high ratio of fallow land and high percentage of fodder crops (Table XXVI-1). There is a strong local maritime tradition from the centuries of trade and piracy around the Arabian Sea. Since the suppression of piracy, Konkani sailors have found a place as crewmen (and the Goanese as stewards) on most British vessels plying the Indian Ocean.

Malabar

The 450-mile western littoral region south of latitude 14°N. is known as Malabar (many hills). Geologically recent alluvial and marine formations stretch almost without interruption to Cape Camorin at the southern tip of the Indian peninsula. Seldom out of sight above the flat coastland are the loftiest mountains of the peninsula, 30 to 40 miles inland, their forested slopes enveloped in bluish haze. Quite different from the square-cut, steep-sided heights of the basaltic lava formations north of Goa, these mountains are rounded and undulating in outline because of spheroidal weathering of the massive granite, gneiss, and other crystalline rocks of Archean age. Maximum elevations of some 5,800 feet in Coorg increase to 8,600 feet in the Nilgiri (blue mountains) range of western Madras state. These elevations continue to Palghat, a gap 20 miles in width, 1,100 feet above the sea. Farther south beyond the Cardomom hills is another gap nearly 1,500 feet in elevation; beyond, the southernmost part of the so-called western Ghats rises to a single peak over 6,300 feet and descends to Cape Comorin.

Malabar's population of more than 16 million is crowded into 21,600 square miles of territory in Kerala state and adjacent portions of Mysore, i.e., South Kanara and Coorg; and Madras, i.e., the Nilgiris and the ceded part of former Travancore state west of Cape Comorin. The average population density of about 750 persons per square mile, however, is not a full measure of the actual congestion. Because only 46 per cent of the surface is arable, there are 1720 persons per square mile of cultivated land, a figure considerably higher than that of 1000 to 1100 in the Madras coast and the Gangetic plain and 1260 in the West Bengal plain. Malabar's ratio of fallowing is fairly low, but the ratio of double-cropping is somewhat lower (Table XXVI-1), with the result that only one-third of an acre of land per capita is harvested annually. Unquestionably Malabar has the highest average "nutritional density" among the regions of the Indian republic and faces problems of rural "overpopulation" similar to those of East Pakistan.

The concentration of people in Malabar is possible by reason of the large and reliable rainfall of 80 to 200 inches in the rainforest (Am) zone north of Trivandrum, or 40 to 80 inches in the savannah (Aw) zone near Cape Comorin, and the fertility of the strip of marine and alluvial deposits 5 to 15 miles in width along the low coastland, where local rural densities reach maxima of 2,000 to 4,000 persons per square mile. The outlets of numerous small rivers are blocked by mud and the sandy ridges of old beaches are raised a few feet above sea level. As a consequence, a line of brackish lagoons and backwaters runs parallel to the shore, joined artificially to form a navigable waterway of 200 miles in the southern half of the region. Stream-dissected terraces of older (Tertiary) marine origin lie inland, except south of Trivandrum, and rise 250 to 600 feet above sea level. Inland the leached, lateritic soils of the terrace and hill lands generally support less intensive agriculture, although even in the foothills there are over 1,000 persons per square mile of cultivation. The growth of wild evergreen tropical species of trees, including teakwood and sandalwood, is luxuriant where the stands are protected by the government, but much land is cut over and intermittently cultivated or planted with perennial crops such as rubber, tea, coffee. Above 4,500 feet is a zone of wet, frost-free, subtropical (Cw) type climate in which are found evergreen trees, grasslands, and health resorts built by the British, such as Ootacamund.

Agriculture in Malabar is primarily dependent upon rice and coconuts. In the low coastland wet-rice is easily grown under natural inundation. The normally early arrival of the rains permits a first crop to be planted in April or May and harvested in September; the prolonged season of rains often permits the planting of a second less abundant rice crop which is harvested in January. Some early rice is started on artificial mounds in the shallow brackish lagoons and transplanted after the accumulation of rainfall freshens the water sufficiently. Some late rice is grown in drained and diked fields 3 to 4 feet below the lagoon surfaces. Upland rice is grown without inundation on the inland terraces and hills during the rains. Coconut production is concentrated on the sandy soils of the low coastland, where locally the acreage in coconut groves equals or exceeds that in rice, although in the region as a whole the acreage in coconuts is less than 19 per cent of the gross area in all crops, as compared to 42 per cent in rice. Apart from the consumption of fresh coconuts, the people use and sell the dried meats (copra), the fiber (coir), and the expressed oil and oil cake. Other important crops are cassava, the poor upland farmer's substitute for rice, and pepper or cashew nuts, his chief cash crops. Almost every farmstead has its garden patch with numerous vegetables and fruits for home use, among which are ginger, betel leaf, areca nut, mango, and plantain.

Fishing is important. The maritime fisheries of Malabar, together with those of Konkan, are the best available off India and could be much more intensively exploited. The catch consists largely of sardines, mackerel, and herring, taken from the shallow water 5 to 7 miles offshore. The small lateen-rigged boats ordinarily used cannot be sailed during the season of violent southwest monsoons (May to September), and efforts are being made to substitute power-driven vessels with improved fishing gear. Inland fishing in backwaters, lagoons, and rice fields is engaged in by almost every farmer with the aid of nets, basket fish traps, and crossbows with arrows. Both the sea and freshwater catches are largely consumed locally, with the exception of prawns shipped to Burma.

As is often the case elsewhere in the subcontinent, high rural population density is not associated with a high degree of urban concentration. Less than 15 per cent of Malabar's inhabitants are in cities and towns, nearly all of which are situated in the low coastland. The five large cities of the region are located on or near the shore at fairly large intervals. Mangalore (117,100), now in Mysore state, and Calicut (158,700) in the northern section have open roadsteads and are served by the broad-gauge railway from Madras through Palghat. A branch of this railway reaches Cochin (166,100), the only port in the region capable of accommodating the largest vessels which can pass Suez. The dredging of the 37-foot channel through a sand spit to the deep backwater, the reclaiming of land, and the building of bridges have resulted in trebling the ship traffic since 1920 and increasing the goods handled to well over a million tons. Cochin is the fourth port of India now rivaling Madras and making a strong bid against Colombo for handling transit traffic destined for places on the mainland. Alleppey (116,300) is an old port with an anchorage protected by mudbanks just offshore and good access to the backwater, but without a railway or modern docks. Trivandrum (186,900) in the extreme south, the terminus of meter-gauge rail line, is the largest city, although not a seaport, and retains its former political role in Cochin-Travancore state as capital of the new and enlarged Malayali-speaking state of Kerala.

Manufacturing has a minor part in the economy of Malabar. Yet, there are noteworthy concentrations of industry in Mangalore (roof tile-making), Cochin (soap and cosmetics from copra), and Alleppey (coir-matting), and in Alwaye is the sole south Indian alumina-reduction plant. Hydroelectric power could be increased, and the great reservoir built on the Periyar River to supply irrigation water through a tunnel to the Madras plains possibly could be developed for power. The rich ilmenite, monazite, and zircon sands of the Travancore beaches are used for specialized electrical and chemical products, but their potential for atomic energy is yet to be realized.

The languages and socio-religious system of Malabar exhibit features which are indicative of the peripheral position of the region. Malayalam was the last of the four major Dravidian languages to become distinct in script and literature. Its close connection with ancient Tamil shows in the survival of speech forms which have gone out of use in Tamil and the basic similarity of the script with medieval Tamil. Also, the predominantly Hindu population has been the most caste-conscious in India, adhering to stringent rules of untouchability.

There has been throughout recorded history a contrast between the isolation of Malabar from the main events of Indian history and its close relation by sea with regions outside India: ancient Greece and Rome, China, and pre-Moslem and Moslem Arabia. The Graeco-Romans knew and used the two monsoons in sailing to and from Malabar. There are Jews in Cochin city who trace their establishment to a Solomonic colony and Syrian Christians who trace their origin to the legendary visit of the Apostle Thomas in the first century A.D. (Figure 122a). The Jews are very few, but the Christians form a separate religious community today of some 25 to 30 per cent of the population in southern Kerala. It was the Arabs who mastered the art of sailing vessels against the wind, which enabled them to go to and return from Malabar regularly during the season of the northeast monsoon, not during the violent southwest monsoon. Moslem Arabs had established themselves in the Malabar ports before the year 900 A.D. to deal in local spices and to meet Chinese traders who came this far west, and even during the modern period the trade of Malabar has remained largely in the hands of their descendants.

Madras coast

The region is essentially the area of present Madras state. A better name might be *Tamilnad* (Tamil country) because the boundaries coincide approximately with the limits of predominantly Tamil speech.[4] The region has been incorrectly re-

[4] Telegu-speaking Chittor district in the northwest is included in the region, although it is now part of Andhra. On the other hand, the Nilgiris and the Tamil-speaking portion of former Travancore-Cochin state west of Cape Comorin are excluded, despite the fact that both are in Madras state.

Fig. 122a • Crosses stand in front of and above the entrance to a Syrian Christian church in Kottayam, Kerala, the chief Christian center of Malabar and the see of a bishop of former Travancore-Cochin state. The Christians, known locally as *Nazarani* (Nazarenes), are largely descended from converts to the Syrian church during the period between 500 and 1500 A.D. and their bishops have ties with the patriarchs of Nineveh and Antioch. There are also Roman Catholic and Protestant Christian converts in Kerala. The prosperity and influence of Christians in the region is a striking tribute to long-continued tolerance by the Hindus. *(Information Service of India.)*

ferred to as the Carnatic, a usage established among Europeans during the eighteenth century when the British and French fought against the native rulers from Karnatak in adjacent south Dekkan, now Mysore State. The term Coromandel refers to the entire east coast as far north as the Krishna (Kistna) delta in Andhra.

The Madras coast is the home of the Tamils and their peculiarly Dravidian Hindu culture. Although much of Hindu religion and philosophy was and is held in common with Indo-Aryan India, Tamil poetry, temple art, dance, and music have flourished more or less independently here for at least two millennia. Tamil was the first Dravidian language to be written in a script especially suited to itself, although borrowed from north India. The Madras coast was the center of the earliest known Dravidian political development, and was largely beyond the limit of the north Indian empires. The Tamils reached the zenith of their independent political development from the tenth to twelfth centuries A.D. when the Chola empire was extended to virtually all of Dravidian south India and to Ceylon. Living under direct foreign rule for at least 150 years, the educated classes have learned English or French [5] thoroughly and have assumed the European methods of conducting business and government which have enabled them to benefit from the political and technical advances of the modern period.

The region is an extensive coastal lowland, flanked on the west by the mountains bordering Malabar and on the northwest by the Dekkan plateau. The entire surface slopes eastward, falling abruptly at first from elevations over 2,000 feet and later descending gradually towards the Bay of the Bengal, Palk Strait, and the Gulf of Mannar. The Kaveri (Cauvery) is the chief river, with an extensive delta along 100 miles of coast.

The region may be divided into two sub-regions. To the east the land is below 500 feet and is formed of recent alluvial sediments and wind- or wave-worked deposits, a slightly elevated Tertiary marine terrace belt. Inland is an undulating gneiss plateau. Many isolated hills, rising above the peneplain or projecting like islands through the sedimentary materials, are erosional remnants of the peninsular massif. To the west most of the land is hilly, and elevations rise from 2,000 to 5,000 feet above sea level.

The unusual rainfall regime of Madras lends climatic distinctiveness to the region. The entire area is so completely sheltered by the high orographic features on the west that in the lowlands during the period from June to September the precipitation is merely 1 to 2 inches per

---

[5] Pondichery and Karikal on the coast, respectively 90 and 160 miles south of Madras city, were the most populous and most important parts of French India. See Ch. XXIV.

month. During August and September the rains increase slightly to 2 or 3 inches per month towards the interior, but the coast does not receive increased precipitation until the period from October to December, when the southwest monsoon is in retreat and weak depressions or violent cyclones form in the Bay of Bengal and move onshore. This is the main rainy season in most of a 20- to 30-mile coastal strip, but the interior and the southerly coast are not much affected by these late-season rains and consequently receive very little moisture at any time. About half of the area is classified semi-arid (BSh) with 20 to 35 inches of rainfall, while most of the remainder is savannah (Aw) with a later summer maximum of precipitation. Along the Bay of Bengal coast is found summer-dry savannah (As) with a post-equinoctial maximum. Nowhere, except in the highest mountains bordering Malabar, is the total annual rainfall in excess of 60 inches.

Madras agriculture is noted for intensive fertilization and control of water by means of innumerable tanks (reservoirs) behind earth embankments, from which the moisture seeps into the subsoil, and elaborate stream diversion systems. The prolongation of the dry season and lateness of the rain makes for emphasis either on drouth-tolerant millets or on late rice, planted in September and harvested in January. The best tract of agricultural land is the 4,000-square-mile Kaveri delta, which is irrigated by means of the Grand *Anicut* (diversion dam), originally constructed in the 11th century A.D., and canals leading to the *ayacuts* (irrigated fields). The British government added supplementary dams, extended the canal system, and built the 176-foot-high Mettur dam about 120 miles upstream, which stores water [6] in order to lengthen the irrigation period. The main crop in the delta is rice, but there also are rotation crops of sugar cane and plaintains, demanding heavy fertilization and much labor. In the sandy coastal sections there is specialization on palmyra, a palm from the sap of which is made brown sugar (*jaggary*) or a fermented liquor, called *toddy*. The advent of prohibition in the Union of India now hampers the livelihood of the *toddy*-makers, a particular caste of Hindus living in the palmyra groves. In the medium black soils [7] near Coimbatore cotton is the chief cash crop. Elsewhere, on the thin red loamy or sandy soils of the uplands the chief cash crop is often peanuts, grown for the oil content, and rotated with the three staple grains—bulrush millet (called *cumbu* in south India), sorghum (called *cholam*), and finger millet (*ragi*). Despite the prevalence of dry farming and the fallowing of more than one-third of the arable land every year (Table XXVI-1), upland farmers suffer from drouths and intermittent famines

[6] Mettur (1925-34) was the first combined hydroelectric and irrigation project in India.

[7] These are *regurs* formed in semi-arid piedmont areas on parent material derived from base-rich metamorphic rocks.

due to unreliable rainfall. Only 42 per cent of the region, as a whole, is arable, and the density of population is nearly 1,100 persons for each arable square mile, more than twice the over-all population density.

The Tamils are distinguished among the Dravidian peoples of south India for their high degree of urbanization, some 20 per cent of nearly 55½ million inhabitants, and for the large number and close spacing of their towns—about 15 miles apart. The only other region in India exhibiting both intensive urbanization and high population density is the upper Gangetic plain. These facts are significant in view of the historic cultural and political roles of the two regions, which found expression in their towns and cities. Although relatively little concerned with military strategy and less influenced than the people of northern India by medieval concepts of fortification from Southwest Asia, Tamils have been building well-ordered towns from time immemorial. The most prominent feature is usually a collonaded stone temple, richly carved in tiers of bas-reliefs, standing on the top of a rocky hill or at the intersection of broad avenues used for annual religious processions and fairs. The urban area, spreading out in irregular or sub-rectangular blocks and not carefully planned according to modern concepts, is segregated in sectors determined by socio-religious status, that is, caste and occupation. Side by side or mingled with this traditional urban pattern in the large cities is found the rambling Indo-British pattern of widely-spaced commercial, governmental, and religious edifices and private residences in the midst of tree-shaded gardens and lawns.

The premier city of Madras, however, is not of ancient origin. No special advantage was offered by the site in 1639 when it was granted to the British East India company, except that the low sandy strip of land near the mouth of the little river Cooum (Kuvam) could be fortified and ships carrying up to 50 tons could enter the river. Within a few years ships became too large, and it was necessary for them to anchor a mile offshore and unload into surf boats. Early Portuguese, Dutch, Danish, and French traders occupied at least eight other places on the coast between Madras and Point Calimere, all of which had similarly poor site advantages and problems of access, the only difference being that Madras was more exposed to the full force of waves driven by violent Bay of Bengal storms. The city owed its commercial importance to its position as the first center of British military power in India.

Although by 1773 Calcutta had supplanted Madras as the center of British interests in India, the latter remained until 1947 the seat of administration for all British territory south of the Dekkan and the third largest center of population and trade in all India. During the early nineteenth century a coastal canal was dug to connect Madras and the Kaveri and Godaveri deltas. During the later nineteenth century railways were built along the coastal lowlands north and south and west to the Dekkan, but it was not until the beginning of the twentieth century that the wharves and breakwaters were completed and the harbor dredged to 35 feet. Now these facilities are considered inadequate; the port ranks a poor third in India, is outranked by both Karachi and Colombo, and its traffic is contested in the south by Cochin. The hinterland of Madras is an area of 180,000 square miles with some 70 million inhabitants. The tonnage of exports, consisting chiefly of peanuts, hides or crudely tanned leather, and raw or manufactured cotton is much exceeded by the tonnage of imports, which include rice (and other food grains in years of famine), petroleum products, and manufactures of all sorts. Madras manufactures some cotton and leather, but is not a major industrial center like Calcutta and Bombay. Nevertheless, population in greater Madras (1,416,100) doubled between 1941 and 1951. The previously little-congested urban area extending 3 to 5 miles beyond the closely-built nucleus of George-town adjacent to the harbor is rapidly filling in and the suburbs are becoming contiguously built up.

Ten minor ports, including lately French Pondicherry and Karikal, exist on the Madras coast south of the city. Some, such as Nagapattinam (Negapatam) and Tuticorin, carry on trade in agricultural products and cloth with Europe, or Ceylon and Southeast Asia, but none have facilities to accommodate vessels of more than a few hundred tons burthen. Pondicherry under French rule remained a small city of some 50,000 inhabitants, its trade with India hampered in some respects by customs barriers and, like Karikal, permitting lucrative smuggling. Rameswaram island off the cuspate Ramnad promontory is connected by a meter-gauge railway bridge to the mainland and serves as the rail and ferry terminus across the shallow, coral-blocked, 22-mile strait to Talaimanaar island and the broad-gauge railway of Ceylon. Tamils have always maintained maritime fishing and trading activities in the Bay of Bengal and were among the most prominent medieval Hindu colonizers on Ceylon and in Malaysia. Today they provide the majority of bankers, merchants, and agricultural workers of Indian origin in Ceylon and Southeast Asia.

The seven large cities of Madras state over 100,000 are pre-British centers, located inland and all, except Vellore (106,000), grouped well to the south of Madras city in the heart of the Tamil country. Madurai (361,800), and Tiruchirapalli or Trichinopoly (218,900) are the largest of these old cities served by railways of meter-gauge. Tirunelveli or Tinnevelly (113,500) and Tanjore (100,700), also on the meter-gauge net, are situated in rich alluvial lowlands near the coast. Salem (202,300) and Coimbatore (197,800) are larger places in the middle Kaveri basin with broad-gauge rail connections. All except two or three of them resemble Madras in that trade, services, and professions provide more employment in the aggregate than manufacturing. In Madurai, Salem, Coimbatore, as well as in a number of smaller inland centers, are textile mills, using local cotton. The region is deficient in good quality coal, although extensive deposits of lignite are known, and industry depends for power on hydroelectric stations in development of which Madras state has long been well in advance of India as a whole.

Mineral industries other than cement are little developed. Unsuccessful attempts were made to smelt iron in the 19th century and the large deposits (300 million tons) of magnetite iron ore in the Salem-Tiruchirapalli area have not so far been worked for large-scale steel manufacture.

South Dekkan

The south Dekkan region of 127,700 square miles is an undulating or hilly plateau of Archean crystalline rocks that lies in the states of Mysore and Andhra Pradesh. The average elevation is 1,000 to 2,000 feet above sea level along the northern border and 2,000 to 3,000 feet in the south, with a general slope eastward. The major relief features are the residual heights of land 3,000 to 5,000 feet above sea level in the extreme south and west, the adjacent plateau scarps falling to the Malabar and the Madras lowlands, and the 2,000 to 3,000-foot meridional ranges to the east cut across by the Krishna and Penner rivers on their exit to the Andhra coast. The drainage is almost entirely through the Godavari and Krishna rivers; the Penner and Kaveri rivers respectively rise in and traverse the southeastern and southern portions of the region.

The climate is generally semi-arid (BSh) with less than 35 inches of rainfall. Within 30 or 40 miles of the western Ghats the annual precipitation diminishes sharply from over 100 to only 25 inches. The driest portion of the region is a strip 50 to 100 miles from the Ghats, where the precipitation is only 18 to 20 inches. Annual precipitation is variable, more so in the south where some rain is derived from the southwest monsoon (June to September) as well as from the retreating monsoon (October to November). Rainfall increases to 40 or 45 inches and the climate is savannah-type (Aw) in the high plateau of Mysore in the southeast and near the Godavari River in the northeast. As a result of the scantiness of moisture, the typical wild vegetation of the region is thorny scrub with cactus, open grassland, or scattered stands of acacia trees, but on the wet borders and the crests of the highest mountains tropical deciduous forests are found.

Being similar in elevation, climate, and natural vegetation to adjacent north Dekkan, resemblances might be expected in agriculture and settlement. It is true that dry farming prevails, the staple grains are millets with emphasis upon finger-millet in the extreme south (Table XXVI-1 and Map 26), and the general density of population living in widely-spaced villages is similar. But there are no lava formations in the south Dekkan, except along the northernmost fringe, and red-loam or sandy-loam soils usually overlie the granites and metamorphic rocks. Thus, the dominant upland soils are less fertile and less retentive of moisture than the *regur* of the north Dekkan. The best soils are red-brown or dark brown soils in the valleys of red-soil region or black soils along the rivers flowing from the lava Dekkan. Because of the quality of the soil as well as the latitude, resulting in temperatures over 70°F. in the cool season, wheat reaches its southernmost limit in India and becomes insignificant. Cotton is less important, and there is more emphasis on peanuts, castor seed, and sesamum. Coconut palms reach their farthest inland location and highest elevation in India. More use is made of small reservoirs for irrigation, and on the Krishna and Tungabhadra there are high storage dams and elaborate canal systems. Along the latter stream, modern engineering is succeeding in controlling water in a region where canal irrigation failed when attempted by the British in the 19th century. Still, more than a third of the land is fallowed, and the region is prone to disastrous famines. As in other dry regions of the sub-continent, some land is devoted to fodder crops, and livestock of all kinds are numerous, including small wiry sheep and tough fast Mysore bullocks reared for both local use and sale in Madras.

The south Dekkan is inhabited by 31.5 million people of palae-Mediterranean racial stock—largely Hindu Dravidians, speaking either Kannada (Kanarese) or Telegu. The first of these two ethnic entities is represented by the state of Mysore; the second by Andhra Pradesh. Both states were enlarged in the political reorganization of 1956 and today constitute the only states with territory in the region, although both include territory outside the Dekkan along the west and east coasts, respectively (see Map 28a). The dry climate and open nature of the terrain and vegetation made the region easily accessible to invaders. While the Marathi-speakers gradually occupied the fertile basaltic north Dekkan, the inhabitants of the less fertile south Dekkan retained their Dravidian culture in the face of repeated penetration from northern India. In the 19th century the Kanarese were among the first Dravidian south Indians to undergo political and economic renascence under British aegis, although divided between Bombay presidency and the native state of Mysore. The more numerous Telegus, who were divided between Tamil-dominated Madras presidency and the Moslem state of Hyderabad, were slow to emerge from political and economic subservience. Only in the mid-twentieth century have the Telegus found unity through the partition of Madras and the dismemberment of Hyderabad.

The south Dekkan is important for its various mineral resources. Aside from the coalfields in the Gondwana formation of eastern Hyderabad, which produce about one million tons of bituminous fuel annually, the resources are associated with the ancient crystalline rocks, and most valuable mines are in Mysore, where the government has been successful in its purposeful policy of development. Hematite iron-ore from western Mysore is smelted at Bhadravati with the aid of charcoal and hydro-electricity from the 630-foot Gersoppa falls in the western Ghats to make high-grade steel. In view of the small amount of coking coal available in India and its complete absence in southern India, the development of the iron-and-steel industry at Bhadravati is noteworthy, although production is small in comparison with centers in Chota Nagpur and the northeast peninsular interior. In eastern Mysore are the chief gold mines in India. Other significant mineral exploitation in Mysore includes ores of mag-netite, manganese, and chromite. Manganese output is greatest in that portion of Andhra which was formerly part of Madras, and there is also some production of mica, barytes, asbestos, and steatite.

The contrast between Moslem conservatism and Hindu progressivism is epitomized in Hyderabad and Bangalore. These two cities, fifth and seventh in rank of population in the entire republic and among the five leading urban centers of southern India, are dominant respectively in the Telegu- and Kannada-speaking portions of the region. Neither is situated on the main broad-gauge rail line between Bombay and Madras, but each is served by both the broad and meter-gauge railway nets of the Central and Southern systems. Both were founded in the sixteenth century and served as the seats of indigenous governments of the largest native states of south India, which came under indirect or direct British control during the latter eighteenth century. Thus, each contains a once-fortified native section and a cantonment area where British troops were concentrated and where modified European urban patterns prevail. But with this the points of resemblance end.

Hyderabad is a walled city with Moslem mosques and the Nizam's palaces, populated by small merchants, craftsmen, and service workers along with the retainers of the former ruling class of Moslem aristocrats. The large and growing population of Hyderabad (1,085,700) includes the extramural suburbs and the cantonments Secunderabad and Bolarum stretching 10 miles northeast. Certain modern educational and service institutions exist, and there are a few state-owned factories, but the peo-ple remain almost entirely dependent upon industries without mechanical power or on other occupations, and the urban landscape presents a re-markable spectacle of the peculiar Dekkani Moslem architectural tradi-tion flourishing in the 20th century.

Bangalore is smaller in population (779,000), including the rambling

Indo-British civil and military station, together with the old city and new monotonous gridiron suburbs, spreading over an area 5 to 7 miles in diameter. Yet Bangalore has gained in population at a relatively more rapid rate than Hyderabad since the beginning of the present century. Under both governmental and private auspices, and with the use of abundant hydroelectric power from dams on the Kaveri, it has become a center for textiles, leather, soap, pharmaceuticals, electrical goods, machine tools, and aircraft. Bangalore's greater altitude, 3,000 feet compared to Hyderabad's 1,800 feet, gives it an equable temperature regime and makes it attractive as a place of retirement for the south Indian *intelligentsia*. Its diversified role as a governmental, educational, and leading scientific research center, as well as its commercial and industrial importance, make Bangalore one of the most significant examples of modern industrial India in the making.

The urban component of the population in the south Dekkan is less than 25 per cent and, hence, a lower percentage than in the north Dekkan. Aside from Mysore city (244,300) and Kolar Gold Field city (159,100), the only cities over 100,000 are Warangal (133,100) in northern Andhra and Hubli (129,600) in northern Mysore. Most of the many smaller urban places are local commercial centers, scattered at intervals of 20 miles or more over the uplands of the region.

Andhra-Orissa coast

The region includes all 10 of the coastal districts of Orissa state and Andhra Pradesh between the boundary of West Bengal in the north and Madras state 750 miles south. The average width is 50 to 60 miles, the region being bounded on the west by the slopes of the peninsular highlands which rise 2,000 to 3,000 feet above sea level with some peaks of 5,000 feet. These highlands, mistakenly named by English-speaking geographers the "Eastern Ghats" for no pass here is called a *ghat*, have broad massive crests and present many wide low-level openings to the interior except where the rivers emerge through narrow gorges. The immediate shore is a low strip of river- and wave-deposited sediments, interrupted chiefly in the middle section by small hills of the same hard crystalline rocks which make up the highlands. To the north in Orissa is the triple delta of the Baitarani, Brahmani, and Mahanadi with distributaries beginning as much as 60 miles inland and spreading 120 miles along the seaward face. To the south are the twin deltas of the Godavari and Krishna, each 40-45 miles in radius and spreading 50 miles along the sea. Elsewhere, the lowland narrows to 20 or 30 miles, but is composed, like the deltas, of successive belts of sandy beach ridges, salty swamps, fertile silt and clay deposits, abutting on old alluvial and marine terraces with leached lateritic soils. The rich black soils in the Godavari and Krishna deltas are derived in part from the *regur* of the rivers' upper basins in the north Dekkan. In addition to salty Lake Pulicat on the Madras frontier, two other extensive bodies of water have been formed by alluviation and littoral drift: fresh-water Lake Colair in the depression between the Godavari and Krishna deltas and brackish Lake Chilka, almost cut off from the sea by sand spits south of the Mahanadi mouths.

The climate is humid throughout the region, the annual precipitation ranging from a little less than 35 inches in the south to 60 inches in the north. The rainiest period is from June to September when monsoon depressions are formed in the Bay of Bengal and move west or northwest. North of latitude 18°, 75 to 90 per cent of the total rainfall is received during these four months and October, but in the south scarcely 50 per cent of the total is received before October on account of the lower frequency of depressions and the tendency of the southwest monsoon to blow off the shore or parallel to it. October and November are the rainiest months along the coast of the southern half of the region, where the retreating monsoon lows and violent cyclones move northeastward but not inland. Little or no rain occurs from December until the season of hot weather from March to May at which time occasional thunderstorms bring 5 or 6 inches before the onset of the southwest monsoon. The entire region is far less rainy than the opposite side of the Bay of Bengal, and the southern half suffers from 25 to 30 per cent variability of precipitation year by year, as extreme in percentage terms as the semi-arid zone of the peninsula. Crop failures are as often due to floods as to droughts.

The progressive increase in amount of rainfall and the difference in regimes from south to north are reflected in the cropping pattern. Millets exceed rice in the south, except in the canal-irrigated Godavari and Krishna deltas where the combined long-season and short-season rice crops overshadow all other crops. Rice becomes progressively more dominant proceeding northward, whether dependent on tank irrigation or on simple rainwater inundation as in Orissa (Figure 122b). The chief cash crops are oil producers, particularly peanuts and sesamum, which are more or less widespread south of Orissa; tobacco, which is concentrated near the Krishna River; and jute, which Orissa is producing in increased quantities. The lowland is adapted to coconut, betelnut, and toddy palms, but the concentration of palms is less than that existing farther south in India. Average population density is about 430 persons per square mile, grading from 500 to 700 in the major delta districts down to only 200 or 300 in other districts. The density of population on arable land is 930 persons per square mile, somewhat less than in the Madras coast, although more than half of the surface is not under cultivation.

Fig. 122b • Kutkonda, a village in the district of Visakhapatnam, is located on the alluvial plain of the Andhra coast. The Bay of Bengal is visible on the horizon beyond the wooded sand dune belt. The flat-topped hill near the lagoon between the strand and the alluvial plain and others farther inland are small remnants of the hard crystalline rock of the peninsular massif. The population lives mainly by growing the three palms—coconut, betelnut (areca), and toddy, and cultivating rice, which here is still growing rapidly during November because of the concentration of rainfall during the retreat of the summer monsoon. Sea-fishing by means of nets is an important subsidiary occupation of farmers near the shore. The irregularly grouped conical thatched huts of the village are curiously reminiscent of tropical Africa. *(R. U. Light, The Geographical Review.)*

Slightly more than 27 per cent of the land is fallow each year, but nearly 23 per cent is sown more than once—much the highest ratio of double-cropping is all of south India (Table XXVI-1).

The region overlaps the boundary between the Dravidian and Indo-Aryan languages and forms a transition zone between the lighter colored peoples of northern India and the darker inhabitants of the peninsula. Some 14.4 million, or two-thirds of the region's 21.1 million inhabitants, live in the 35,100 square miles of territory attached to Andhra Pradesh, while only 6.7 million live in Orissa. Thus, the Oriyas are outnumbered two to one by the Telegus and have not pressed southward in recent historic times beyond their linguistic limit fifty miles south of Lake Chilka.

Yet, the coast provided a corridor for migration and cultural diffusion during the early Buddhist and Hindu periods, and the ancient kingdom of Kalinga, located between the major deltas in the northernmost Telegu-speaking section, served as a source of colonization to Burma and Malaya. South Indians in Malaya are still known by the name Kling (Kalinga), whether they speak Tamil or Telegu. The region today is strongly Hindu, tribal animism exists all along the hilly western frontier, and locally tribes comprise more than half the population, but seldom over 5 per cent of the population in the lowlands adheres to non-Hindu faiths, except in the Krishna and Godavari deltas where Christians form 5 to 10 per cent.

The region as a whole has never enjoyed political unity, except when imposed from without. The Moslem invasions had almost no effect here, although the region was included in more than one Moslem empire. Neither the Telegus nor the Oriyas on the coast were able to join with their numerous inland brethren in any form of autonomous internal political union until the present century.[8]

Coastal Andhra and Orissa remained isolated until the twentieth century, despite the fact that more than a dozen small ports have been in use during the past 300 to 350 years and many of the first European trading establishments and territorial acquisitions were situated here during the sixteenth and seventeenth centuries. The isolation was relieved by completion of the broad-gauge railway through the length of the region between Calcutta and Madras in the 1890's and the construction of a deep modern port at Visakhapatnam in the 1930's mainly to serve as an outlet for the local manganese exports and those of the northeastern peninsular interior. The only notable mineral exploited, in addition to manganese, is the mica of the Velikonda hills in Nellore. Visagapatnam (108,000) now ranks fifth in tonnage among the ports of India of goods handled (third in terms of exported tonnage alone) and is becoming a shipbuilding center. Urban development is weak, coastal Andhra being about average for India, while coastal Orissa is as low as 5 per cent urban. Few other cities over 100,000 exist: Vijayawada, or Bezwada (161,200), and Guntur (125,300) in or near the Krishna delta; Rajahmundry, or Rajamahendri (105,300), and Kakinada, or Cocanada (100,000), in or near the Godavari delta; and Cuttack (102,500), Orissa's capital city at the head of the Mahanadi delta.

[8] Orissa was administered by the British as part of Bengal until 1912, then as part of Bihar until 1936. The emergence of Andhra as a state during 1952-56 is described in Chapter XXIV. Ancient Andhra, which existed from the middle of the third century B.C. to about 250 A.D., included much of the Dekkan but only the Godavari-Krishna section of the coast.

The northeast peninsular uplands

The interior basins and high-lands of northeast peninsular India were virtually unknown until the middle of the nineteenth century. The terrain is not forbidding. Yet, throughout most of India's recorded history this 115,000-square-mile region remained isolated; it was avoided by the main routes of migration and trade, and entered little into the political and military affairs of the subcontinent. The river valleys are occupied by Hindus, who speak Indo-Aryan languages, but the highlands are populated by Dravidian and Mundo-Kol tribes, forming the greatest concentration of aboriginal peo-ple in all middle India. The average density of about 160 persons per square miles is lower than in any other region of southern India and is roughly equivalent to the density of the adjacent north central hills and plateaus (Tables XXV-1 and XXVI-1). It is probable that the largest acreages of unused culturable wasteland in India outside Assam are to be found in the region. The known mineral resources offer excellent potentialities for industrial development. At present the northeast penin-sular uplands appear to be the least developed of all regions in the re-public of India.

The main rivers of the region all flow south or southeast across the Andhra-Orissa coast to the Bay of Bengal. A major portion of the area lies within the watershed of the Mahanadi (great river), which is sepa-rated into two basins where its inland alluvial plains broaden to 80 or 100 miles. The uppermost basin, centered around Raipur and Bilaspur, has an elevation slightly below 1,000 feet. It is bounded on the north and south by hills rising 2,000 to 3,500 feet above sea level. The basin of the middle Mahanadi, centered around Sambalpur, is between 500 and 800 feet above sea level and separated from the upper basin by a line of low hills scarcely 500 feet higher. The 200- by 250-mile amphitheater created by these two Mahanadi basins is provided with an entrance in the west across the low divide from the upper Godavari watershed and a lateral passageway on the northeast across the low divide from the Brahmani River. Still lower but narrower corridors provide the outlets for the Mahanadi and Brahmani to the Orissa coastal lowland. Maximum relief is found in the 3,000- to 5,000-foot highlands in southern Orissa, which form the water parting between the Godavari watershed and several short rivers, going directly into the Andhra coastal lowland.

The annual rainfall is 45 to 65 inches, received almost entirely between the first of June and the end of September, and there are no unusual fea-

tures of temperature or precipitation regimes to distinguish the region
markedly from adjacent regions in northern India. In general, December
is the coldest month, but it is frost-free with minima averaging 50° to
55°F., and the monthly mean temperature not under 65°F., except in the
highlands. Thus, the prevailing type of climate in the region is tropical
savannah (Aw), although this borders the humid mesothermal zone (Cw)
at about 2,000 feet above sea level in the bordering highlands. The
Mahanadi is well known for its floods, which may cause a rise of water
65 feet above the winter level at its outlet from the hills above Cuttack
and amount to a maximum flow of almost 2,000,000 cusecs at its mouth,
a volume nearly as large as that of the Brahmaputra where it enters the
Bengal delta. Most certainly it is the wetness of climate, rather than difficulty of terrain, which historically retarded the advance of civilized
plainsmen into the basins of the region and helped to preserve the primitive tribes in the wild, still wetter highlands.

The slow process of settlement by outsiders and cultural assimilation
have been going on for at least 1500 years. The lowlanders here think of
themselves as a separate people, although their dialect shows clearly its
derivation from the eastern Hindi of the Gangetic region. Downstream
in the middle Mahanadi basin settlers from coastal Orissa must have
been entering in medieval times, and today Oriya-speakers are more
numerous than any others in this section. However, the Gond tribes, the
most important Dravidian people north of Kannada and Telegu (Map
28b), evidently did not yield easily to the Indo-Oryans. From the fourteenth to the sixteenth centuries the region was known as Gondwana
(territory of the Gonds) and ruled by independent tribal chiefs; a Hindu
Gond aristocracy became established which has survived to the present
day, but only about half of the 3 million Gonds still speak Gondi, the
others having adopted Hindi or Oriya. The Mughal empire encompassed
the region, and in the eighteenth century the Marattas subjugated the
lowlands by outright conquest; but it is only in the western-most section near Nagpur that Marathi-speakers became more numerous than
any other language group.

When the region came under British hegemony in the 1840's and 1850's
many of the petty feudatory states were allowed to persist. The hill tribes
were not subject to the ordinary law of the land but were left to follow
their own customs. Thus, the most primitive tribes such as the Juang,
whose women until recently wore leaves, and the Bondos, who will
scarcely recognize outside governmental authority, were able to remain
self-sufficient until the twentieth century, living by essentially Neolithic
techniques of food production. The least acculturated tribes are generally
those in the Orissa hills to the east and in the extreme south. The 2 mil-

lion Kols and several minor tribes have linguistic affinities with the Mundari and Santali tribes of Chota Nagpur, the Khasis of Assam, and the Mon-Khmer of Southeast Asia. The oldest racial affinities of the hill tribes are either with the pygmies of insular and peninsular Southeast Asia or with the larger dark-skinned peoples of Australasia (see Chapter XXII).

The consequences of India's independence from Britain have been to increase the pace of tribal assimilation, generally through a semi-official policy of absorption into the lowest levels of Hindu society, and to abolish the feudatory states and tribal agency areas. The numerous petty states were integrated in 1947-48 with former British districts in Madhya Pradesh and Orissa, or Bihar. The reorganization of 1956 left the political status of the region unchanged, except that the two Marathi-speaking districts in the extreme west near Nagpur became part of Bombay state. Of 17 other districts included in the region as here defined, Madhya Pradesh comprises 7, with nearly 10 million inhabitants, and the remainder, with 8 million inhabitants, are in Orissa, land of the Oriyas.

Under British rule the tempo of economic life quickened as railways were built and mines opened. The main broad-gauge line of the Southeastern railway system connects Nagpur with Calcutta by way of the low divides previously mentioned, passing through Jamshedpur en route to the plains of West Bengal. Major branches extend northward to the Bombay-Allahabad line of the central system and south to the Calcutta-Madras line and Visagapatnam port. However, aside from a few spurs and the local narrow-gauge railways south of Raipur and east of Nagpur, no local network exists. The most important aspect of railway construction between the 1890's and the 1930's was the access given to the iron, manganese, coal, and limestone deposits; but urbanization is still slight. All of the towns in the region contain less than 5 per cent of the population and are widely spaced at an average distance of 40 miles from one another. No town had reached 100,000 population at the 1951 census.

Agriculture has not become highly commercial, although the fertile dark-colored soils in the west and the reddish-brown alluvial soils of the eastern basins yield good harvests if the somewhat unreliable rainfall of September is supplemented by irrigation. Water is obtained from river diversion and large storage tanks. Rice is dominant, but wheat, pulses, and linseed are typical crops (Table XXVI-1). Less than a third of the area for which statistics are available is arable land under regular cultivation; nearly as large a proportion is forested, and over a quarter is uncultivated waste. The data belie the fact that much of the land classified as forest has been cut over for railway ties and mine props or degenerated into jungle scrub because of grazing, wood-gathering, and shifting cultivation. It is not known how much more land could be brought into permanent tillage, although the prospects seem good in some sections, poor in most.

One of the purposes of the new dam at Hirakud [9] on the Mahanadi in Orissa above Sambalpur is to expand cultivation by diverting and conserving the great river's floods; but it is the power potential of the Mahanadi and the mineral resources of the region which promise to bring about economic and social transformations as development proceeds. The largest share of India's 2.5 to 3.0 million tons of iron-ore production comes from the enormous deposits of high-grade hematite in the Saranda hills of Bihar and extending into Keonjhar district, Orissa, in a belt 45 miles long and 20 miles wide, where reserves of at least 2.7 billion tons or possibly more are estimated to exist. Nearly all of the remaining iron-ore production is from the small deposits of Mayurbhanj in extreme northern Orissa. But most of the known high-grade ore reserves of 1.5 billion tons are located within the region either in the inaccessible hills of the extreme south or in the more accessible western parts, chiefly in Drug district, Madhya Pradesh.

Three-fourths of India's 30 to 35 million tons of annual coal production comes from the bituminous Gondwana deposits of the Damodar valley in the Chota Nagpur plateau of south Bihar and West Bengal, where half of the country's entire coal reserve of 50 billion tons is believed to be. The line of structural fault-basins containing coal of the same lower Gondwana age extends westward from Chota Nagpur into Madhya Pradesh, where it parallels the upper Mahanadi and sends an offshoot southeastward into Orissa towards Cuttack along the middle Mahanadi and Brahmani rivers. The Gondwana coal formation also breaks into isolated basins westward north and south of Nagpur. The current annual production of all the small Gondwana coalfields in or bordering the northeast peninsular region amounts to some 3 million tons, or about 10 per cent of the country's total. Despite the absence of seams of coking coal, production inevitably will increase as the metallurgical industries develop. India's entire output of flux-grade limestone and furnace-grade dolomite comes from quarries in the upper Mahanadi basin. These facts, together with the localization of the bulk of India's manganese and chromite within or just outside the region, and the potential production of bauxite and limestone from yet untouched deposits, set the stage for heavy industry to be developed.

Plans approved and largely financed by the central government for iron-and-steel works at Rourkela in Orissa on the Brahmani River near the main railway and at Bhilai in the upper Mahanadi basin on the main

[9] This dam, which began functioning in 1957, is the first major multi-purpose project in India to be designed by Indian engineers and built under their exclusive direction.

railway between Raipur and Drug in Madhya Pradesh are being put into effect.[10] The output of steel is intended to be about a million tons annually at each plant and, therefore, probably less than the current expansion will permit at India's oldest steel center of Jamshedpur or in the Asansol area, where a new British iron-and-steel plant at Durgapur will add a million tons of productive capacity. Hydroelectric power from Hirakud, which already is promoting alumina-reduction and other industries in and near Sambalpur, will be transmitted 80 miles to Rourkela. Thermal-electric power will be transmitted over 100 miles from the Korba coalfield, northeast of Bilaspur, to Bhilai.

There is destined to appear a chain of major industrial centers within the northeast peninsular uplands along the main line of railway, which is to be double-tracked, at places near coal or where abundant water is available for power-generation and direct industrial uses. Provision is being made to house 100,000 people at Rourkela. It can be anticipated that Sambalpur, Bilaspur, and Raipur will become cities of more than 100,000 within a decade or two. Thus, it is not unlikely that here as in the Damodar valley and Jamshedpur modern urban-industrial landscapes will arise in the midst of rural villages and wild jungles. The mines and factories will attract an ethnically diverse population from all over India, and tribesmen with a mode of life 5,000 years old will be precipitated into the twentieth century.

SELECTED GEOGRAPHICAL BIBLIOGRAPHY

1. Arunachalam, B. "Bombay City—Stages of Development," *Bombay Geographical Magazine,* December, 1955, pp. 24-39.
2. Christian, John LeRoy. "A Reconnaissance Tour of Western India," *Geographical Review,* October, 1944, pp. 613-620.
3. Deshpande, C. D. *Western India,* Dharwar, 1948.
4. Kuriyan, George. "Some Aspects of the Regional Geography of Kerala," *Indian Geogr. Jour.,* January-March, 1942, pp. 1-41.
5. Sastri, K. A. Nilakanta. *A History of South India,* New York, Oxford University Press, 1952.
6. Simkins, Ethel. "The Coast Plains of South India," *Economic Geography,* April, 1933, pp. 136-159.

[10] It is worth noting that the plant at Rourkela has an excellent economic location, being so close to good water supply, flux, and iron ore that the ton-mileage necessary to assemble raw materials for the blast furnaces, including 175 miles to Damodar valley coal, is even less than in Jamshedpur. Bhilai is less favorable for raw material assembly, being located 250 miles farther than Rourkela from the sources of coking coal and having less adequate water supply. The Rourkela plant is being planned and built by the private German firm of Krupp-Demag; the plant at Bhilai, by the Soviet Union government.

7. ———. *The Agricultural Geography of the Deccan Plateau of India*, Supplement No. 2, Geogr. Teacher, London: Geo. Philip and Son, 1926.
8. Srinivasachari, C. S. "Stages in the Growth of the City of Madras," *Jour. Madras Geogr. Assoc.*, October, 1927, pp. 79-105.
9. Subramanyam, N. "Regional Distribution and Relative Growth of the Cities of Tamil Nad," *Indian Geogr. Jour.*, January-March, 1941, pp. 71-83.
10. Trivedi, A. B. *Post-War Gujarat; An Economic Survey After World War II*, Bombay, 1949.
11. Williamson, A. V. "Indigenous Irrigation Works in Peninsular India," *Geographical Revue*, October, 1931, pp. 613-626.

Comments

The reader will find the detailed treatment of south India's history by Sastri of interest, not merely because of the emphasis on political affairs not usually given much attention in histories covering the whole of India, but also because of the treatment of the regional evolution of society and economy. The books by Deshpande, Simkins, and Trivedi are expositions of portions of the area now included in Bombay State. Kuriyan's article deals with agriculture and population in one part of the west coast; Christian's in a cursory fashion with settlement and land use on the entire west coast; and Simkins' with both coasts in a general fashion. Arunachalam and Srinivasachari provide brief studies of sequent occupance in the south major urban centers of southern India; while Subramanyam analyzes the regional distribution and relative growth of cities in the area of present Madras State. Williamson gives a clear understanding of the types and functions of small irrigation works.

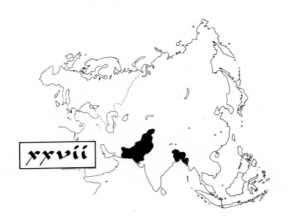

Pakistan

THE CREATION OF PAKISTAN ON AUGUST 15TH, 1947, THRUST two new boundaries upon the map of Asia. The new country, separated as it is into western and eastern parts with some 920 miles of Indian territory intervening, has two frontiers with India. The boundaries of these two Pakistani territories coincide in few places with any natural features such as river courses or breaks in the terrain of the plains across which they are drawn. In the Punjab and in Bengal the India-Pakistan frontiers bisect densely settled portions of the plains and cut across the river systems and railroads, preventing the integrated development of resources and impeding the movements of persons and goods along routes once freely used. The two Pakistans are linked only by the long, costly air and rail routes across northern India or by the slow sea route of more than 2,600 miles around peninsular India and Ceylon (Map 26).

The awkward political geography of Pakistan can be understood only in terms of the secession of the dominantly Moslem territories from the incipient Indian nation. The population of British India as a whole was two-thirds Hindu, but certain provinces or portions of provinces had a relative preponderance of Moslems. The boundaries of the new Islamic nation were established to set apart these territories in which Moslems formed the majority of the inhabitants according to the 1941 census, but

632

boundary lines did not follow exactly the distribution of local Moslem majorities in the partitioned provinces of Bengal, Assam, and the Punjab. In much of the eastern Punjab, where Sikhs were concentrated, no single religious group formed a majority prior to partition. The boundary lines were fixed hastily in mid-1947 by a boundary commission which was charged with compromising the conflicting claims of Hindu, Sikh, and Moslem nationalists. However arbitrary and ill-fitting, the new boundaries have been accepted by both nations, and subsequent emigration of Moslems from India to Pakistan and of non-Moslems from Pakistan to India have increased the relative preponderance of Moslems and non-Moslems in their respective territories. All of the former native states, except Kashmir, have acceded either to Pakistan or to India. In effect, Kashmir also has been partitioned along the 1949 cease-fire line. Never has there been an alignment of such widely separated, disparate territories inhabited by peoples who have in common only the bond of their religious creed.

The two parts of the new nation are of unequal size and show a marked imbalance of population density. West Pakistan comprises an area of 310,236 square miles and had in 1951 a population of 33,779,555. East Pakistan is an area of only 54,501 square miles, less than 15 per cent of the total area of Pakistan, and had 42,062,610 inhabitants in 1951, more than 55 per cent of the country's population. Thus, the larger western part of the country had an average density of only 112 persons per square mile, while the smaller eastern part had an average density of 769 persons per square mile. Much of West Pakistan is a sparsely settled mountain and desert region. The main irrigated areas with population density over 200 persons per square mile are located inland, close to the Indian frontier in the Punjab and Sind. East Pakistan on the other hand is largely a humid delta plain with density of population well over 200 per square mile everywhere except in the hill area along the Assam and Burma frontier and in the seaward fringe of the delta. In the west, the ecumene of Pakistan on the alluvial plains of the Punjab and Sind assumes an attenuated hourglass shape and touches the Arabian seacoast only at Karachi, west of the Indus delta. The ecumene in the east forms a compact area, fronting on the Bay of Bengal and extending along both sides of the Meghna estuary which is the outlet of the combined Ganges and Brahmaputra rivers.

The Punjab

In the west, the Punjab was the most populous province until 1956 when it was merged with the three other adjacent provinces. It is the most prosperous, the most urban, and politically the most influential portion of West Pakistan. Its capital, Lahore, although not Pakistan's largest city, is the outstanding center of Moslem culture in the country. The Punjab was the scene of greatest strife between Moslems and Sikhs at the time of partition and received the greatest influx of Moslem refugees from India after the flight of Sikhs and Hindus to India. From the point of view of political geography, the Punjab must be considered the *raison d'être* of Pakistan, although the province contained only 18,814,000 persons in 1951, less than 25 per cent of the total population of Pakistan.

The real Punjab, the "Land of the Five Rivers," is the plain traversed by the five eastern tributaries of the Indus—Jhelum, Chenab, Ravi, Beas, and Sutlej—to name them in order from northwest to southeast. The old British province of the Punjab once encompassed the five rivers and extended from the Indus River on the west across the Indo-Gangetic divide to the Jumna River on the east. The Pakistani portions of the Punjab contains only four of the five rivers, the Beas having its confluence with the Sutlej east of the political boundary in the Punjab, India. The Pakistani portion, if strictly defined as the plain between these four rivers, is a wedge-shaped area only 100-140 miles in width and 350 miles in length. The province as constituted during the first few years after partition includes the territory westward as far as the Indus and beyond it. Former Bahawalpur state, located in the Thar Desert south of the Sutlej and bordering Rajasthan, India, is closely associated with the Punjab.

The non-alluvial portions of the Punjab are mainly in the extreme northwest. Here the dissected upland between the Jhelum and Indus rivers averages 1,500 to 2,000 feet above sea level and, together with the Salt range which bounds the plateau on the south and forms an irregular escarpment overlooking the Punjab plain, is made up of folded sedimentary rocks laid down close to the base of the Himalaya proper. The plateau region is largely barren, deeply eroded by seasonal streams, and submarginal for agriculture. Within it near the Indus River at Attock is a small oil field, the only producing field in Pakistan. The Salt range has economic significance not only as a source of salt but also as Pakistan's chief source of coal (lignite).

The hills south of the Salt range, near the Chenab River, are geologically parts of the massif of peninsular India. These isolated hills are the only projections of a subterranean ridge which has been detected through gravimetry to run northwestward from Delhi to the Jhelum River at right angles to the course of all the Punjab rivers. It acts as a subsurface dam, dividing the Punjab into two water-table areas of which the northeastern is higher because it is situated upstream and receives the water seeping underground from the Himalayan piedmont.

The surface of the Punjab plain is formed by alluvium brought down from the western Himalaya and adjacent mountain regions in Kashmir, Tibet, and India. The deposits consist of coarse gravelly materials where each river debouches from the mountains and passes through the Siwalik foothill belt. Fans have formed here with gradients near the Kashmir boundary as steep as 15 feet per mile. Towards their outer margins these fans merge into a continuous alluvial plain which slopes southwestward across the province at a gradient of about one foot per mile. The main rivers and the many small torrents descending from the Siwaliks are actively aggrading their beds and often flood the submontane portion of the plain as far as 20 miles from the hills. Farther from the hills floods are confined to narrow belts along the main rivers, which lie 20 to 60 feet lower than the interfluvial surfaces. The high interfluves are natural terraces of old alluvium, dating from the rainy periods of Pleistocene times, when the rivers were larger and capable of performing extensive aggradation. Today only the soils of the fans and the flood plains are naturally well watered and renewed by fresh alluvial deposits.

When the British conquered the Punjab in 1849 the portion of the plain now in Pakistan was sparsely settled except in the extreme north and east. The high interfluves were largely empty tracts covered with tamarisk bushes and scrub acacia. If rain had just fallen, there would be grass for the livestock of nomadic herdsmen, but the average annual rainfall over most of the plain is only 10 to 15 inches—too little to support permanent agriculture. In the submontane section of the plain in the north near Kashmir and in the east near Lahore annual precipitation is as much as 20 to 30 inches, and permanent agriculture had long been established. Sedentary farm population became concentrated here, not only because of the greater intensity of summer monsoon rainfall and the frequency of winter cyclonic rain, but also because of the higher water table and the comparative ease of well irrigation in the interfluvial tracts (Figure 123). Precipitation decreases southwestward in the Punjab to as little as 5 inches near the confluence of the five rivers with the Indus. The only cultivation here in the mid-nineteenth century was made possible by means of small inundation canals, which helped to divert the normally high waters of the summer season onto the flood plains of the main rivers.

This desert landscape has been profoundly altered by large-scale canal irrigation, and the empty plains of the Punjab have now been populated, except in those parts of the Thal desert between the Punjab rivers and the Indus that are beyond reach of modern irrigation systems. In fact, no region in the entire subcontinent benefited more from British rule than the Punjab. The vast network of perennial irrigation canals and the railways built by the British provided the basis for expansion of agricultural settlement and for the achievement of peasant prosperity not seen in the other parts of the Indian Empire. Most of the economic development that took place during the 98 years of British rule now accrues to the Punjab, Pakistan, because it was here that irrigation was most needed and the largest areas of idle land awaited settlement.

The method of diverting water from the rivers at their debouchures from the mountains and distributing it from large canals on the highest parts of the interfluves was not invented by the British engineers. This method had been used earlier by the Mughal kings to bring water from the Ravi to their gardens and palaces at Lahore. Between 1880 and 1930 government engineers diverted water from every major river except the Indus in the western Punjab by means of low dams or weirs and brought nearly ten million acres under cultivation in the area that later became part of Pakistan. Another 2.6 million acres is irrigated by means of private canals, small reservoirs, and wells. Since the total cultivated area in the Punjab, Pakistan, is slightly less than 20 million acres, it can be seen that nearly two-thirds of the cultivated land depends partly or

Fig. 123 • One of the ancient methods of lifting water from a well is by means of a wheel with metal buckets attached. The wheel is turned by means of cogs on the vertical axle which mesh with cogs on the horizontal axle. The animals (an ox and a water buffalo) are yoked to a lever attached to the vertical axle. Such water wheels as this one, seen in Sheikhupura, Punjab, West Pakistan, continue in use although tube wells and modern pumps are also available where water requirements and costs justify installation. *(Stanley E. Brush.)*

wholly upon irrigation, mainly from government canals. Some two million more acres of land are now being brought into cultivation through the construction of the Thal canal system, bringing water from the Indus to the desert lying between this river and the Jhelum.

The Punjab canal colonies are among the more successful examples of dry-land settlement in the world. The success of the colonies must be credited in the first place to the perfecting of irrigation engineering to permit the full utilization of the interfluves, in one instance the water being diverted by means of an aqueduct from the Chenab-Ravi interfluve across the Ravi to be used in the lower Ravi-Sutlej interfluve. The gradients of the main canals were so designed that the silt deposited in them during the summer period of high water would be scoured during the winter low-water period. The success of the colonies must be credited also to careful planning and to the attractive terms of settlement. Hundreds of thousands of peasants migrated from the older submontane regions of dense population and from the more humid eastern plain of the Punjab, now in India. Land grants were made largely to peasant proprietors; at first in return for payment of nominal fees, later on sale to the highest bidder. Land grants were also made to veterans of the British Indian army and to persons agreeing to supply camels or horses for use by the army in wartime. The settlers were usually young farmers, Hindus and Sikhs as well as Moslems, who had lived together in the same village or district in the humid Punjab. The colonists were selected by local government officers and came with their families in groups, which helped to maintain their morale in the face of the hardships of pioneer settlement.

Land was offered in allotments of one or more rectangles, varying in size from 22.5 to about 28 acres, which seemed generous in comparison with the farms of two to five acres typical in the humid Punjab. The rectangles were subdivided into smaller squares of about one acre and each of these was cut into plots of $\frac{1}{10}$ to $\frac{1}{20}$ acre for efficient control of water. The location of branch canals and ditches as well as the allotments having been determined, villages were then planned, each in an area commanded by one or more branch canals, but usually no two villages sharing the same distributaries in order to promote peaceful and orderly use of the water. Towns were planned along the railway lines at larger intervals with streets, like those of the villages, in a rectangular grid. Land was set aside for religious use, for grazing grounds, and for other public use, in addition to the space allowed for the dwellings of cultivators or for tradesmen and service workers. All that remained for the colonists to do was to build their houses, to break the soil, and to bring water to their particular fields from the main ditches. Thus, a rectangular type of settlement landscape prevails, and strangely foreign place names such as Montgomery and Lyallpur occur in the canal colonies of the Punjab.

The creation of a class of small farmers, free from the threat of famine and capable of paying for the cost of the irrigation works through water fees and for the cost of government through land taxes, was the major objective of the British provincial government. The financial objectives of the government were realized quickly when the Punjab began to produce surplus wheat, oilseeds, and cotton to be sold in both domestic and foreign markets. For 70 years (1860-1930) the increase of cultivated acreage and of cash income outstripped the increase of population in the province as a whole. Since 1930, however, the increase of cultivation has been slower, and with the completion of the Thal canal system it must end, while population has continued to grow steadily.

Other problems beset farmers in the Punjab. The size of holdings has decreased because of the subdivision of land in each successive generation. Tenancy has resulted from the loss of land through indebtedness to moneylenders. Evacuation of Sikhs and Hindus from the canal colonies following partition did not relieve population pressure or land-tenure problems because of the influx of Moslems from Indian territory, although there is temporary relief in resettlement of many refugees on the new land of the Thal. The most serious problem in the irrigated land of the Punjab, however, is rapid deterioration of soil through salt accumulation due to excessive seepage from the unlined canals and from the sandy loam soils typical of the cultivated tracts. The water table, which was 25-80 feet deep before irrigation of the interfluves, has risen until in some spots the soil is waterlogged and salts have encrusted the surface, making the land unfit for crops.

The Punjab has two harvests: *rabi,* for which the seed is sown in October-November and reaped in April-May; and *kharif,* for which the seed is sown in June-August and reaped from early September until late December. The principal *rabi* crops are wheat and gram, or chickpea, which together represent almost 55 per cent of the annual crop area planted in the Punjab, Pakistan. Wheat, which alone covers over 43 per cent of the crop area, forms the staple food of the inhabitants and the chief cash crop. The principal *kharif* crops are cotton, 10 per cent of the crop area; *bajra,* or bulrush millet: rice; *jowar;* and maize. The second most important cash crop is cotton, in which in both quality and production the American varieties much exceed the native varieties. Rice also is a cash crop, consumed largely in the cities. *Bajra* is a subsistence crop—a cheap substitute for wheat—grown largely without irrigation. *Jowar* and maize are grown partly for use as food, partly for fodder. Sugar cane and various oil-yielding seeds are minor crops, grown in the humid submontane Punjab, chiefly for household use and some local sale.

The intensity of farming is not high in the Punjab. Yields are low owing to the lack of sufficient manure or other fertilizers, except for sugar cane and vegetable crops. Although there are two harvest seasons and perennial irrigation canals, double-cropping is rare except in the market-gardening areas around the fringes of towns and cities. Each year one acre in every eight acres farmed, or almost 13 per cent of the cultivated area, lies fallow. The high ratio of fallowing is due in part to the scarcity of irrigation water, which is insufficient to reach all fields every year.

Camels, buffaloes and bullocks, goats, and sheep are the common livestock in the Punjab. Camel caravans still can be seen in the western parts of the Punjab and in Bahawalpur. In settled districts camels may be used also for plowing and for grinding cane, but they are greatly outnumbered by some 8.8 million bullocks and water buffaloes. The ratio of cattle to land in crops is about 50 per 100 acres—one of the lowest ratios in the entire Indian subcontinent. The animals are well fed, and the milk buffaloes, at least, are productive. Indeed, the comparatively high output of milk and high per-capita consumption of milk products in the form of *ghee* (clarified butter), curd, and buttermilk place the Punjab in the forefront of the dairying industry in the Indian subcontinent. Goats and sheep are also numerous and provide the chief sources of meat among the Moslem populace, which is without taboos against mutton.

The population of the Punjab is 17 per cent urban, as compared with the 10 per cent urban population in the country as a whole. The three major cities are Lahore (849,476), Rawalpindi (237,219), and Multan (190,122). These are commercial cities and are located, respectively, near the eastern, northern, and southwestern extremities of the province, and on or near the chief routes connecting the Punjab with other parts of Pakistan and the world. Twenty-one other small cities and towns over 20,000 population are located on the railways traversing the agricultural areas and serve as local marketing and shipping centers. Whether they are old towns situated in the ancient settled districts or new towns in the canal colonies, these urban centers experienced rapid and continuous growth during the modern period.

Urban growth of population in the Punjab was accelerated after the inauguration of Pakistan, despite the emigration of Sikhs and Hindus who had comprised before partition as much as 40 to 60 per cent of the urban residents. Refugees tended to concentrate in the large cities such as Lahore, Rawalpindi, and Multan, where in 1951 they formed as much as a third of the population. A number of smaller cities and towns received refugee population amounting in 1951 to as much as two-thirds of their total 1941 population. In the case of Lyallpur (179,144) the number of refugees in 1951 was 174 per cent of the city's 1941 population.

The partition of the Punjab

The intense political antagonism between Moslems and other religious communities in the Punjab is not based upon any racial differences between them. Punjabi racial affinities to the large Irano-Afghan peoples of the highlands to the west can be accounted for by the many historic invasions of the plains. Moslems in the Punjab derive from the same basic Mediterranean stock as Hindus and Sikhs, although the physical appearance of each is distinctive because of their customary styles of clothing and hair dress.

Differences in the written forms of language tended to aggravate the political conflict between religious communities in the Punjab in the period preceding the inauguration of Pakistan. There are two regional Punjabi dialects—Lahnda, or Western Punjabi, and Eastern Punjabi. Both are of Indo-Aryan origin and both were used locally in their respective areas alike by Moslems, Sikhs, and Hindus. The dialects are so similar in grammar and vocabulary that speakers can shift without much difficulty from one to the other. Literate Moslems adhere to the Perso-Arabic script and vocabulary of Urdu, whereas Hindus prefer the Nagari script of Hindi, and Sikhs prefer the Gurmukhi script of their own sacred scriptures. Urdu, as the national language of West Pakistan, enjoys most prestige and is displacing English in higher education, business, and government. In the Punjab, India, Hindi is displacing English only slowly, while Hindus and Sikhs hold to their respective written languages, but speak the Punjabi dialects and, near Delhi, Hindi dialects.

Political antagonism, which necessitated splitting of the old province of the Punjab and resulted in the evacuation of about ten million persons in the Punjab and adjacent areas in 1947, arose from the historic role of Moslems as invaders and conquerors from A.D. 1000 to about 1650 and from the recent intensification of nationalism, colored by religious conservatism. The Moslem aristocracy in the Punjab and Upper Gangetic Plain lost its former influence in the eighteenth and nineteenth centuries as British power increased, and Hindu Brahmins and other high castes developed a new middle-class urban intelligentsia. In the twentieth century, the Moslems' lag and their numerical inferiority to Hindus in India as a whole convinced them of the necessity of forming a separate Moslem national state.

The Punjab became a crucial area. After it was proposed that the provinces in which Moslems were predominant should become autonomous, it became evident that Delhi and Uttar Pradesh province, containing Agra and other former strongholds of Moslem power, could not be part of Pakistan. Moslems made up 57 per cent of the population in the Punjab as a whole in 1941, but in the minor administrative subdivisions they were relatively important only in that part of the province lying west of the Sutlej-Beas line, excluding Amritsar. In Amritsar and in several British-administered districts as well as a number of petty Native States east of the Beas River, Sikhs were numerous, although they rarely formed as much as 50 per cent of the population in any political sub-division. The Sikhs, thus, were concentrated in a critical area between the Moslem-majority area and the Hindu-majority area, which was farther east near Delhi. The partitioners of the Punjab had to take into account the distribution of Sikhs as well as Moslems and Hindus. There could be no completely satisfactory dividing line because of the inter-mingling of all three religious communities.

At the time of partition in August, 1947, the Sikh community aligned itself with the Hindu community, necessitating division of the Punjab at about the eastern limit of the Moslem-majority area. The unhappy compromise line, which followed the Ravi north of Lahore, rather than following the Beas, and gave Amritsar to India, did not satisfy the Mos-lems. Neither did it satisfy the Sikhs and Hindus, who wished to retain Lahore and the prosperous canal colonies to the west. Both sides ac-cepted the boundary, however, and proceeded to eliminate minorities on the wrong side of the line. Villages and towns closest to the new boundary were promptly cleared of minorities of Hindus and Sikhs in Pakistan and of Moslems in India. Unorganized movement by road and railway over longer distances was discouraged by the attacks of raiders in the border zones. Military convoys became necessary as all available means of transport were used. More than a million refugees traveled in each direction on railways under armed guard. In six weeks during Sep-tember and October, 1947, 850,000 non-Moslems walked some 150 miles from the canal settlements around Lyallpur and Montgomery to the border of India. Columns of 30-40,000 persons on foot, accompanied by bullock carts loaded with their possessions and herds of cattle, marched under army escort. In all, about four million Hindus and Sikhs moved to India from West Punjab and another 750,000 from adjacent provinces and states in Pakistan, while five million Moslems left East Punjab and Delhi and entered Pakistan. Shortly thereafter, rail traffic ceased and was not resumed for eight years. The border has been virtually closed to traffic of all kinds because of unfavorable political relations between India and Pakistan.

In 1951, four years after these mass migrations of population, the Punjab, Pakistan, contained 4,882,000 refugees (*muhajirs*) and had gained nearly 20 per cent in total population owing to the difference be-tween this influx and the loss of Hindus and Sikhs, combined with the

Fig. 124 • A pathetic reminder of the mass migrations associated with the partition of the Indian subcontinent is this small, abandoned Hindu temple in Lahore, Punjab, West Pakistan. The building is being used by a Moslem refugee family, probably from India. In the background is a dome associated with one of the numerous mosques of Lahore. Hindu temples vary from small shrine-like structures such as this one to great and complex religious edifices; but the small temple is widely disseminated in India where worship is as much individual as collective. Mosques are somewhat less varied in the sense that all are places for collective worship by the faithful of Islam. *(Stanley E. Brush.)*

natural increase of the remaining population. No Sikhs and only 20,000 Hindus remained in West Punjab (Figure 124). According to the 1951 census, Moslems constituted 98 per cent of some 18,814,000 people in the Punjab, Pakistan. Christians, the only important minority group, numbered 401,000 or about 2 per cent. In Bahawalpur the Moslems formed 99 per cent of the population, which in 1951 totalled 1,823,000.

The economic impact of partition and of population transfer is immeasurable. Not only has the previously integrated system of transportation and trade been severed, but there is interference with the distribution of canal water and hydroelectric power. The sudden uprooting of Hindus and Sikhs from the West Punjab was a hardship to the remaining Moslems because of the important role of Hindus and Sikhs in trade, banking, and manufacturing. Land and houses abandoned by non-Moslems were taken over by their Moslem tenants or redistributed to Moslem refugees. But the influx of destitute Moslem refugees from India could not immediately compensate for the loss of non-Moslem capital, skills, and entrepreneurial knowledge.

The north-west frontier and Baluchistan

On crossing the Indus, one enters a new region of Pakistan in the mountainous borderland adjacent to Afghanistan and Persia. The people are Moslems almost to a man and thus qualify fully as citizens of an avowedly Islamic state, but they have a culture distinctive within Pakistan. Here the mother tongues are Pushtu and Baluchi, affiliated to the Iranian group of languages dominant in Afghanistan and Persia. The modified caste system of social organization and primarily vegetarian diet of the Moslem villagers of the Punjab and Sind identify them with the cultural heritage of lowland India to which Islam has been grafted, but the essentially equalitarian social structure and meat diet of the tribesmen beyond the Indus indicate their similarity to the peoples living west of the political boundary of Pakistan. Although there is no sharp distinction in racial stock between the mountain people and the plainsmen, the light skin color, tall stature, and convex nose of the Irano-Afghan branch of the Mediterranean race are more prevalent traits than on the plains. The ethnic boundary of the Southwest Asian realm, as contrasted to the distinctively South Asian (or Indian) realm, lies between the Indus River and the foot of the mountains rather than at the mountain crests. Indeed, the North-West Frontier and Baluchistan could as well be part of Afghanistan or some southwest Asian state, were it not for the extension of British political power here in the nineteenth century.

Baluchistan covers 134,000 square miles, including the former Baluchistan States Union, and forms somewhat more than one-third of the total national territory. Yet because of the small population, which in 1951 was only 1,174,000, the average density of population is less than 9 persons per square mile. The so-called province of Baluchistan was governed from Quetta (84,343) and formed only two-fifths of the area of Baluchistan, although it contained more than half of the population in the province and states together.

The North-West Frontier covered less than 40,000 square miles, but in 1951 had 5,900,000 inhabitants and hence, the surprisingly high density of 150 persons per square mile. It was divided into the Settled Districts in the valleys and lower hills adjacent to the Punjab, and the Tribal Territory or Frontier Region in the high valleys and mountains adjacent to Afghanistan. The Settled Districts, which comprised about one-third of the area, in 1951 had two-thirds of the inhabitants; they are governed by the provincial administration with its capital formerly at Peshawar (151,776) but now at Lahore. Pakistan's national and provincial laws, however, do not apply in the Frontier Region where 2,647,000 self-governing tribesmen live. Local matters of law and order in the Frontier Region are handled by councils of chiefs or by tribal assemblies in which every adult male takes part. The central government of Pakistan maintains political agents in the Frontier Region who supervise small medical and educational staffs and are responsible for the security of the Frontier. Unlike the former British government, Pakistan maintains no regular army units in the Frontier Region, but there are local militia and scouts trained by the Pakistan army.

If the political geography of this mountainous borderland seems confused, the tribal allegiances and ill-defined citizenship of the inhabitants are yet more so. The primary loyalties of the mountain people are to family and clan, then to tribe, set apart from other tribes by differences of dialect. If a Pushtu-speaking tribesman of the North-West Frontier Region is asked his allegiance, he will identify himself as *Pukhtun,* which is the correct form of the more widely known designation of *Pathan,* but there are many, if not more, *Pukhtun* people across the international boundary in Afghanistan, whence comes the agitation to form *Pukhtunistan,* the "Land of the Pukhtuns." There seems to be little likelihood that such a "nation" will come into existence in the face of the successful administration of tribal affairs on the Pakistan side of the boundary and the increasing economic attraction of life among the tribes' Pushtu-speaking brethren in the Settled Districts.

Certain tribes have languages markedly different. The Dardic tribes in the northern extremity of the Frontier Region in Pakistan, linguistically related to other Dards in Kashmir and eastern Afghanistan, are only distantly related to the Indo-Aryan or Iranian language families. The Brahui tribes found chiefly in eastern Baluchistan are separated by 1,700 miles from the nearest affiliated Dravidian language groups in central India. Some nomadic Baluchi and Pushtu tribes are uncertain of their citizenship because they cross over from the highlands of Afghanistan to winter in lowland Punjab or Sind and have no permanent homes in Pakistan.

The terrain of this borderland of Pakistan is made up largely of rough hills and mountains, rising to peaks as high as 15,000 feet above sea level. The trend of the mountain ranges is mainly north-south, but for some ranges, such as the Safed Koh in the North-West Frontier and the Makran and other ranges of western Baluchistan, it is east-west. The Sulaiman and Kirthar ranges form great arcs, convex towards the Indus and converging near Quetta. Their configuration is probably accounted for by the tectonic pressure against buried promontories of the Indian massif under the Punjab and Sind plains. Being part of the Himalayan-Alpine belt of active mountain-building, the region is subject to violent earthquakes. The typical rocks are limestone and sandstone formations regularly folded and eroded into closely parallel ridges or appearing as small ragged mesas. There are extinct volcanic cones of fairly recent geologic age in western Baluchistan.

The region may prove to be of considerable value for its mineral resources, although little exploitation is going on at present. The only good-quality bituminous coal in Pakistan, used primarily in locomotives, is mined in outcrops and adits along the railways south and east of Quetta. Chromite ore has been mined in the Zhob valley of eastern Baluchistan. Good sources of sulfur have long been known to exist in the volcanic hills of Chagai in western Baluchistan, and iron ore of good quality has been discovered in the mountains north of Peshawar. Exploitation of the sulfur and iron awaits local improvements of transportation and the stimulus of industrial demands within Pakistan. The Sui gas field, discovered in extreme eastern Baluchistan near the Indus, 75 miles north of Sukkur, promises to be of great importance and has been connected by pipeline with Karachi and Lahore.

Climate is subhumid, and precipitation is less than 10 inches a year nearly everywhere, except in the higher northerly portions of Baluchistan and in the North-West Frontier. At Quetta more than 8 of some 9 inches annual precipitation is received during the months from November to May, inclusive, almost all coming from the winter cyclonic storms. At Peshawar the winter and spring are also wet, but about 5 of the nearly 13 inches annual precipitation is received during the summer monsoon period from June to October, inclusive. The maritime air of the summer monsoon system is significant as a source of moisture in the mountains to the north of latitude 32° but not to the south where the dry continental air is dominant, though the Arabian Sea is closer. The mountain heights are partly forested with coniferous trees, especially *deodar* as far south as latitude 30° in Baluchistan, but elsewhere the only trees other than those planted on irrigated land are scrub juniper and pistachio. The traveler in Baluchistan is lucky if he sees even sparse desert vegetation. The rocky land is worn by wind erosion and gullied by the rapid run-off of the scanty rainfall, commonly less than 5 inches, or covered with sand dunes and brittle shiny salt.

Water, of course, is the key to settlement (Figure 125). Innumerable intermittent streams where they parallel the mountain ridges have formed small gravelly fans or sandy braided channels, and where they cut through the ridges they have formed narrow transverse gorges. In Baluchistan water is obtained deep in the stream-laid gravels of fans and brought down the valleys to small villages and cultivated tracts by means of tunnels, known as *karez*. Often in the narrow mountain valleys the only cropland is the moistened soil trapped behind small embankments built across the watercourses. Surface run-off also is stored in small reservoirs

Fig. 125 • Cultivated land under irrigation on the lower slopes of three coalesced alluvial fans in the Sulaiman mountains near the boundary of the Punjab and Baluchistan in West Pakistan. Some of the fields evidently were fallow, some under cultivation, during March at the time of photography. Farmsteads are located on higher portions of the fan slopes. In the middle background are the barren hills of folded and dissected Tertiary strata. In the basin beyond the range a dry stream bed empties in time of flood into clayey salt-encrusted flats where the water evaporates. This is a desert landscape much like that shown in inset D, Map 30. *(Stanley E. Brush.)*

and brought to some towns and forts by means of pipelines. The largest canal-irrigated tracts in Baluchistan are located north of Quetta at Pishin near the Afghan frontier and south of the mountains at Sibi.

No perennial rivers flow out of the whole region except the three Indus tributaries—the Kabul, the Kurram, and the Gomal—which rise in Afghanistan and pass through the North-West Frontier. Each of these rivers has formed an important piedmont plain—the vale of Peshawar, the Bannu plain, and the Derajat, respectively—of which only the first two are well watered and closely cultivated. There is agriculture in the irrigated portion of the Derajat, but some years the water supply is inadequate. In wet years the plain is grassy and is sought eagerly by nomadic herdsmen. The continuous piedmont plain formed by the numerous Sulaiman and Kirthar streams extends in a continuous belt lying partly in the Punjab and Sind provinces that are between these mountains and the Indus River. There is no irrigation and no cultivation in this belt near the Indus except where the plain is within reach of canals fed by the Indus. The large interior basins of western Baluchistan are each occupied by a seasonal lake, known as a *hamun*, and bordered by salt flats. Several small isolated oases are found in extreme southwestern Baluchistan where drainage is to the Arabian Sea.

Agricultural development is extremely varied. The largest block of agricultural land is in the vale of Peshawar, where 750,000 acres are under cultivation. Most of this acreage is irrigated by perennial canals, and about one-third is double-cropped each year. Wheat and maize are the leading winter and summer crops, respectively; sugar cane, *jowar*, rice, cotton, and tobacco are also important. The vale of Peshawar is the most intensively cultivated tract in all of West Pakistan. The Bannu plain, where half a million acres are cultivated, is devoted primarily to winter wheat growing, but the yield is low, and there is a high ratio of fallowing here. The *Pukhtun* tribesmen cultivate innumerable bits of land high in the valleys of the North-West Frontier, and they also herd live-stock. The inhabitants of some of the small mountain villages and forts are without visible means of support and must be maintained either by traditional robbing and pillaging or by remittances from family members working on the plains.

The two leading cities of the trans-Indus region, Peshawar, below the Khyber pass, and Quetta beyond the Bolan pass, are on broad-gauge railways and serve as the major trade centers for this area in Pakistan as well as termini for trade with Afghanistan. The cities, as well as the half dozen smaller trade centers in the region with population over 20,000, have developed in part as military supply centers and have military garrisons. All, except Quetta, suffered a net decline of population following the inauguration of Pakistan owing to the removal of Sikh and Hindu troops and to the flight of the Hindu business and professional groups.

Sind

The former province of Sind, together with Khairpur state, contains Pakistan's greatest oasis, which is sustained by the Indus (or properly *Sindhu*) River. Almost completely surrounded by empty land, Sind is relatively less accessible than the Punjab from the Ganges plain or other parts of India and has suffered less frequently the disturbing effects of invasion and conquest from the west. Aside from the old camel trails to Baluchistan or Rajasthan in India and the shallow channels for native boats provided by Indus River, access to Sind is limited to four rail routes. The two most important routes enter the region at opposite extremities. In the northeast there is the main railway from the Punjab; in the southwest is the railway to the

seacoast and "window to the world" at Karachi. The other two routes
served by railways are located in the northwest, running through the
Bolan pass to Quetta and to the Afghan and Persian borders, and in
the southeast, where the single meter-gauge railway of Sind crosses the
Indian border at Gadra and connects by way of the Rajasthan meter-
gauge net with Ahmedabad and Delhi.

Unlike the Punjab plain, the plain of Sind is made up almost exclusively of new alluvium, subject to flooding and traversed by old river
channels. There are only two fixed sections in the course of the Indus in
Sind, where it is entrenched in hard limestone outliers of the Kirthar
formation. One is at Kotri in the south where the main rail line from
Karachi crosses the river to Hyderabad; the other is at Sukkur in the
north where the second rail crossing is located. Between these narrow
fixed sections the Indus broadens and would annually inundate much of
the land and shift its course frequently, were it not for man-made embankments, dams, and diversion canals.

About one-third of the area of Sind and Khairpur lies between or is
adjacent to the many deltaic distributaries paralleling the main Indus
River. The first distributary channel, the East Nara River, begins on the
left bank about 250 miles inland at the narrows of Sukkur. It runs some
60 to 70 miles east of the Indus, flowing towards the Rann of Kutch but
reaching the Rann only at high flood stage. The West Nara River starts
on the right bank below the Sukkur narrows and flows along a parallel
course 10 to 12 miles west of the main river, ending in a shallow lake between the Indus and the Kirthar range. During the early summer inundation period the lake covers an area of some 200 square miles, overflowing by a short, direct channel eastward into the Indus because flow
southward is blocked by the foothills of Kohistan. Thus, the deltaic plain
of Sind extends along both sides of the main river, bounded by the East
and West Nara rivers. The delta proper, however, begins at a point 110
miles inland just below Kotri and empties the Indus waters into the sea
through seven or more mouths spread along a hundred miles of coastline
between Karachi and the Indian frontier. These shifting, silt-clogged
mouths seem disproportionately small for a river draining an immense
watershed, but the Indus is an exotic stream, like the Nile, and flows for
about a thousand miles in Pakistan through an arid zone, suffering losses
in volume because of seepage, evaporation, and withdrawals for irrigation.

Outside the limits of the river plain are the inhospitable sand-ridge
country of the Thar on the east bordering India and the barren foothills
of the Kirthars which rise abruptly on the west beyond the rocky piedmont fans that mark the limit of perennial irrigation. No permanent
settlements exist in Sind outside the alluvial plain of the Indus except in

the foothills of the Kirthars, where springs in the narrow valleys give rise to little hidden oases or where flood waters are trapped behind earth embankments and in wet years provide sufficient moisture for cultivation on the valley bottoms and fans. In the Thar, nomads dig wells in the hollows between the sand dunes, often finding the water brackish and unfit for use by man or beast. In all, two-thirds of the area of Sind is beyond the reach of irrigation and is virtually unoccupied.

Sind would all be an empty desert or reed-covered swampland were it not for irrigation. The rainfall is less than 10 inches annually near the coast (see Plate C), and less than 5 inches in upper Sind. The scanty 1 to 3 inches of precipitation received monthly during the summer monsoon season from June to August comes usually in the form of irregular thundershowers which may cause local floods and are of little or no agricultural value. Irrigation has been practiced from prehistoric times, probably as early as the period of the Indus Valley Civilization, dated about B.C. 2500 to 3000 and best known from the excavations of the ruins at Mohenjo-daro located near the right bank of the Indus, 60 miles below Sukkur. When the British took control of Sind in 1843 they found it occupied by farming people who tried to control the floods by dikes and at the same time to make use of the water by means of inundation canals. The Sukkur barrage, or diversion dam, built in 1932, will irrigate 5.5 million acres when the canal system is fully developed. It was built at the downstream end of the narrows at Sukkur in order to take advantage of the stability of the river course here. The Lower Sind barrage, under construction at the narrows of Kotri, eventually will add about 2.75 million acres to the cultivated area of Sind. Even without this second barrage, the canals fed by the Sukkur barrage and other canals both above and below Sukkur irrigate about 11.5 million acres of land in Sind—one-third again as much land as is cultivated in all Egypt.

The high ratio of cultivated land per capita—2.3 acres for each of the some 4,928,000 persons in Sind and Khairpur State in 1951—would seem to place this area in the forefront of agricultural development in Pakistan. Sind is Pakistan's only important rice-surplus area, and there also is some surplus of wheat as well as cotton and oilseeds, mainly rape. *Bajra* is an important food grain, grown for local consumption. Rice and wheat occupy about equal acreages in summer and winter, respectively, and together cover 45 per cent of the total area sown, but the annual area sown in all crops is scarcely more than half of the total cultivated area. It is impossible to irrigate much more than half of the cropland each year, and there is only a small amount of double-cropping. In other words, about one acre of cropland is idle each year for every acre cultivated.

Not only is the intensity of agriculture low in Sind, but the economic status of farmers is not generally as satisfactory under the prevailing sys-

tem of farm tenancy as it is in the Punjab canal colonies. Large estates
are the rule in Sind, because of the persistence of holdings established on
land served by the primitive inundation canals before the modern period
of perennial irrigation. No large unoccupied areas were first brought
under cultivation during the British rule, and there was never a land rush
in Sind as in the Punjab. The tenant farmers of Sind usually are unable
to acquire land for themselves and cannot rapidly achieve the level of
prosperity enjoyed by Punjabi peasants.

The people of Sind are much the same basic Mediterranean racial
stock that prevails in Arabia, southern Persia, and western India. The
Sindhi language is derived from Sanskrit roots and is related closely to
the prevailing Indo-Aryan languages of the Punjab and northern India.
Although Urdu is the official language and has a certain prestige value in
Sind, the province lies outside the area in which either Urdu or Hindustani commonly was used before independence. Hence, the adoption of
the West Pakistani national language is slow except in the government
and among the educated upper classes.

The population is not as completely dominated by Moslems as that of
the Punjab. Yet Sind was the first part of the Indian subcontinent to come
under Moslem rule, being conquered by Arabs who came up the river
from the Makran coast during the eighth century. The Moslems in Sind
before partition in 1941 formed only 71 per cent of the population. In
the largest towns Moslems in 1941 formed less than half of the population, owing to the concentration of Hindus and Sikhs in trade and other
urban occupations. The percentage of Moslems in Sind, even after the
exodus of about 640,000 Hindus, Sikhs and others and the arrival of approximately 560,000 Moslem refugees, was only 90 per cent in 1951 as
compared to 98 per cent in the Punjab. All Sikhs fled in 1947-48, but
many Hindus, particularly of the lower castes, did not leave this part
of Pakistan. The 1951 census recorded some 464,000 Hindus still living
in Sind. Khairpur state, too, retained a small Hindu minority. There are
also tiny minorities of a few thousand Christians and Parsis (Zoroastrians)
in Sind.

The cities of Sind, excluding the Karachi Federal Capital Area which
was separated from the province in 1947, are few, and all but one are
small. With the exception of Hyderabad (241,800), the provincial capital
and educational center, the seven towns of 20,000 or more inhabitants
are local agricultural trade centers located on the railways traversing the
irrigated tracts. Since partition only Hyderabad and Sukkur (77,100)
have shown rapid growth, owing to their commercial advantages as
regional centers located at the sole river crossings with rail connections
to both sides of the irrigated plain. Urban population in Sind and Khairpur is only 14 per cent of the total population. Industrialization has been

negligible until recently when refugees introduced craft industries producing consumer goods, such as glass-making. Salt, glass sand, clay, and
limestone suitable for cement-making form the only mineral resources of
Sind at present exploited or likely to be exploited under the government
industrial-development plans.

Karachi

Karachi, the federal capital of
the new Moslem nation, gained over 175 per cent in population between
1941 and 1951 and became the largest city of Pakistan, with 1,068,500 inhabitants. In a hundred years, since the British conquest of Sind, Karachi
has risen from a fishing village and merely local trading port to become
the major seaport in South Asia west of Bombay, with a hinterland including Afghanistan as well as West Pakistan. Karachi's port is on the
island of Kiamari, just off Karachi city. The island, sheltered behind
the Manora sand spit at the mouth of the Lyari River, which enters the
Arabian Sea west of the Indus delta, has provided the basis for development of a modern port with wharves accessible to ships of 27-foot draft;
it is served by the broad-gauge railway coming from the mainland over a
three-mile causeway. The advantages of this location are in the access it
provides by a route on high ground for the rail line to the interior and
avoidance of the deltaic mangrove swamps and shifting silt-laden Indus
mouths, although constant dredging is necessary to maintain the port at
Kiamari.

The changed political status of Karachi has altered its foreign trade and
caused diversification of its functions. The export trade of Karachi first
became important at the time of the world cotton shortage during the
American Civil War and was closely related to the subsequent agricultural development of its hinterland, particularly to the shipment of cotton
and wheat surpluses from the Punjab and Sind. When Karachi became
the capital and only large seaport in Pakistan, its imports increased enormously, especially in cotton cloth, petroleum products, construction materials, transportation equipment, and machinery. Karachi is not only the
port-of-entry for West Pakistan, but it serves as the connecting point by
sea to Chittagong, the port of East Pakistan. The city is provided with
the best airport in Pakistan and has become one of the most important
air terminals in the whole Indian subcontinent. Commercial activity is
rapidly becoming more diversified than in any other city of Pakistan,
except perhaps Lahore. Many new types of manufacturing have been attracted here because of the advantages of Karachi for assembly of raw
materials, either foreign or domestic, and for distribution of finished
goods.

As a result of partition, Karachi's population has become predominantly Moslem, but in other respects it is now more cosmopolitan. In 1941 the city was only 42 per cent Moslem; in 1951 it had become 96 per cent Moslem. Hindus, who before partition constituted 50 per cent of the 386,-700 inhabitants, now form 1.5 per cent. Sikhs were never significant in Karachi, but Christians, who were 3 per cent, are still almost 2 per cent and have actually increased in absolute numbers. Parsis, who form the only other significant religious community, are less than half of one per cent. The Moslems in Karachi are far from homogeneous in race, language, food habits, dress, and other characteristics, because they have come to the national capital from all of West Pakistan, from East Pakistan, and from northern and western India. The influx of refugees from India swelled the population of Karachi beyond all bounds within a few months following partition. The census reported about 460,000 Moslem refugees in 1951, outnumbering the total 1941 population by 120 per cent. Since 1941 perhaps as many as 350,000 other Moslems have also migrated to Karachi. The building of adequate shelter to care for Karachi's newcomers will take many years. Their continued presence constitutes a distressing problem of employment, housing, and sanitation.

Despite the many problems attending the growth of Karachi, South Asia's greatest "boom town," it is rapidly assuming a role in the economic and cultural affairs of Pakistan commensurate with its political role. It is well situated, by virtue of its transportation facilities, to function as the federal governmental center of a bipartite nation, but the rise of such a great city on a desert coast with scarcely any contiguous rural settlement is a never-ending source of wonder.

East Pakistan

East Pakistan was carved out of the old British province of Bengal, with the addition of part of the former district of Sylhet in Assam. The line of partition, determined mostly by the distribution of minor civil divisions that in 1941 contained Moslem majorities, gave to Pakistan the alluvial plain extending along both sides of the combined outlets of the Ganges and Brahmaputra river systems and gave to India the remaining alluvial plain along the Hooghly River around Calcutta, extending westward and northward to the boundaries of Bihar and Orissa and an outlying area in the Himalaya mountains around Darjeeling. Aside from certain Hindu-majority areas given to Pakistan in the delta region along the western margins of East Bengal, the only significant non-Moslem area included in the new province is the Chittagong hill tract along the Burmese frontier in the extreme southeastern part of the province, a region thinly populated by non-Hindu tribal peoples.

The surface of Bengal is nearly all less than 50 feet above sea level and is largely a continuous flood plain dominated by three rivers known locally in East Bengal as the Padma (upstream in India called the Ganga, or Ganges); the Jamuna (Brahmaputra), and the Surma (or Meghna). These rivers ultimately combine their waters and reach the sea through the 70-mile wide Meghna estuary between Barisal and Chittagong. The width of the Bengal delta, including the many distributaries west of the main estuary as far as the Hooghly estuary in India, is 230 miles. The maximum length of the delta, as measured from the open sea to the uppermost distributaries in India along the Ganges or in Pakistan along the Brahmaputra, is 220 miles. The Brahmaputra has a larger maximum discharge than the Ganges, some 2,000,000 cusecs in the former as compared to about 1,500,000 cusecs in the latter. To its flood waters and enriching deposits of silt are added those of the Surma, which has a small but wet catchment area west of the Brahmaputra, and a substantial portion of those of the Ganges which passes into East Pakistan from India and merges with the Brahmaputra above its junction with the Surma.

West Bengal is an area of dead or dying rivers, cut off from the Ganges at the head of the delta and receiving little or no silt. East Pakistan is in an active part of the delta which undergoes deeper flooding and more rapid silting. The concentration of river flooding and delta-building in the east has been observed to become more pronounced during the nearly two centuries of mapping since the British conquest of Bengal in 1757. This tendency is probably due to concentration of flooding and delta-building in the west at some earlier period when the Ganges discharged more water into its now stagnant western distributary channels.

Differences in river discharge and surface elevation create significant geographic variations in soil and drainage in East Pakistan. The Sundarbans is a salty mangrove- and *sundri-* (*Heritiera spp.*) covered belt, extending along the central and western seaward margins of the delta where little or no fresh water is received. Even at the mouth of the Meghna the soil is slightly saline. The best silt loam and clay loam soils extend in fingers along the three major rivers north of latitude 23°. To the north of the main stream of the Ganges, and east of the Brahmaputra, lie two upland tracts of old alluvium, which rise only 40 to 60 feet above the plain but are above flood levels and hence deeply weathered into less fertile lateritic soils under the influence of the warm wet climate. Farther to the east and to the northwest along the boundaries of Pakistan the surface has been partly covered by sand and gravel washed down from the nearby mountains.

The only hilly areas within East Pakistan are in south Sylhet, where the relief does not exceed 1,000 feet, and in the Chittagong hills, where the relief is generally 500 to 2,000 feet. These hilly areas present surfaces characterized by narrow parallel ridges and valleys. The only river of importance outside the delta is the Karnaphuli, draining the Chittagong hills and providing, 11 miles up from its mouth, a good site for Chittagong, the maritime port of East Pakistan.

The climate of East Pakistan is everywhere warm and humid. The southern portion in the delta proper, straddling the Tropic of Cancer, remains warm even in winter; the northern portion has a mild subtropical temperature regime, always frost-free. Rainfall is abundant and comes during the six months from May to October, inclusive. The total annual amount of precipitation varies from 90 to 100 inches in the east to 60 to 70 inches in the west, ranging from 141 inches at Cox's Bazar in the extreme southeast on the coast near Chittagong to 56 inches at Rajshahi in the northwest on the Ganges near the Indian frontier.

The seasonal regime of the climate is controlled by the two monsoons, but there is a less distinct dry season preceding the arrival of the wet monsoon. Thunderstorms occurring from mid-March to mid-May bring 5 to 10 inches or more of precipitation per month and are of great significance in the sowing of early rice and jute. These premonsoonal storms develop in the afternoon hours when humid air from the Bay of Bengal passes inland, becomes heated, and rises to penetrate the dry northwesterly air of continental origin.

The premonsoonal period, as well as the postmonsoonal period, is a season of tropical cyclonic storms of the hurricane type. These storms form in the Bay of Bengal or enter the bay from the Gulf of Siam and pass northward or westward onto the mainland, most of these do not reach Bengal. Quite unlike these violent storms are the weak tropical cyclones, which appear at the head of the Bay of Bengal three or four times a month from June to September and pass westward up the Gangetic plain, causing locally intensified precipitation. Typically, the rainfall is between 10 and 20 inches a month in the period from June to September, in contrast to less than 10 inches a month in the periods preceding or following.

The landscape in East Pakistan presents a verdant and closely cultivated appearance, most of the deltaic surface being 80 per cent under crops (Figure 126). Some 60 per cent, or more than 20 million acres of land, is under cultivation in the whole of East Pakistan. The tropical deciduous or semideciduous monsoon forest, considered to have been originally dominant on the plains of Bengal, has been cleared to make room for rice fields. Wherever land has been kept fallow it has been covered soon with grass. The lowest percentages of cultivation are in the forested Sundarbans district of Khulna and in the Chittagong hill tract. In the hills of the latter area the forest is characterized by tall broad-leaved evergreen trees of the Dipterocarp family. Climbers and epiphytes of all kinds are numerous, and bamboo brake is widespread. Tropical deciduous forest exists in strips along the river banks and on the uplands of old alluvium, where there is a scrubby growth dominated by *sal*. Forests cover only 20 per cent of the surface. Nearly everywhere in this densely populated province the eye rests upon a landscape filled with growing crops and scattered thatch-roofed farmsteads or hamlets, raised on mud plinths above flood levels and half hidden in planted bamboo hedges, surrounded by gardens and groves of tamarind and mango trees, betel-nut palms, and toddy palms, or coconut palms in the saline areas near the coast.

Fig. 126 • An attenuated hamlet cluster near the East Pakistan port of Chittagong is composed of straggling groups of farmsteads sheltered by high bamboo hedges and trees. The numerous reservoirs, or "tanks," conspicuous features near each farmstead, serve as sources of domestic waters during the dry season. Similar storage reservoirs are seen in central and southern India and in many areas of Southeast Asia. Note the difference between the winding streams and the roads, which parallel or go across the streams. The deltaic plain seen here near the Karnaphuli River has been brought almost completely under cultivation. Rice is the major crop; food supplies are augmented from gardens and groves of fruit trees, including coconut and areca palms. (*Indian Air Survey and Transport Co., Ltd.*)

Fig. 127 • The flood plain of the Surma (Meghna) River near Narayanganj, East Pakistan, is devoted to rice cultivation. Natural inundation of the land by the heavy rainfall and by the flooding of the river during the four months from June to September makes canals and irrigation systems unnecessary. In the more deeply flooded areas floating rice may be grown. In areas where the soil remains wet during the dry season, as seen in the foreground of this January view, the late rice may be planted to be harvested in April-May. Jute is the chief commercial crop and it is grown on the highest inundated land during summer. Hamlets and villages of mud-walled thatched huts cluster on the natural levees and artificial mounds, becoming inaccessible except by boat during the rains. *(Wellington D. Jones.)*

The main crop is rice, grown on over 20 million acres annually (Figure 127). There are three rice-harvesting seasons in Bengal: *aman* (winter), *aus* (summer), and *boro* (spring). At least four major kinds of rice are grown, each suited to different flooding conditions. The adaptation of varieties of rice to variations of the environment is more perfect here than anywhere else. Bengal, together with the neighboring areas of India, is also richest in varieties sharing the characteristics of wild rice, and therefore the crop is considered to be native to this part of the world.

The *aman* crop accounts for three-fourths of the rice acreage and is the most likely to be marketed. It is grown during the rainy season, being sown in May-June and harvested in November-December. Two kinds are grown. The long-stemmed kind is sown early on low clayey flood-plain land, where normally the water gets five to 15 feet deep. This rice can grow as much as nine inches a day and keep pace with the rising floods, although too sudden or too deep flooding will damage it. The long-stemmed or "floating" rice is harvested from boats, and the stalks are burned off later. The most widely planted *aman* rice is of three- or four-foot stalk length, and is grown on medium high flood-plain land, but more or less clayey in composition in order to hold the water. This kind of rice is started in seedbeds in or near the villages in April or May and transplanted into embanked fields which have been puddled after the start of the rainy season. No weeding or cultivation is considered necessary. The crop matures after the end of the rains and the fields are dry at harvest time.

The *aus* crop is next in order of acreage. This kind of rice does not survive more than two and a half feet of standing water and hence cannot be grown on much of the land suited to *aman* rice. It is planted during April-May on high flood-plain land, moistened by the premonsoonal rains. It ripens early, being harvested before September, and is followed by a winter pulse or oilseed crop. Exceptionally early broadcast *aus* rice may be followed by transplanted varieties of *aman* rice. *Aus* rice is coarser in quality and its yield lower than *aman* rice. Ordinarily it is consumed by the farmers and does not enter the market.

The *boro* crop is least important, covering only 2 per cent of the delta rice area owing to the limited acreage suitable for it. It is sown during January, mainly in areas too deeply flooded to be planted during the main crop season, but which remain moist through the dry season until the rice is ready for harvest in April-May. This crop also is of low quality and is consumed locally.

Jute is East Pakistan's most important cash crop, and the province produces 75 per cent of the world's supply. It occupies two million acres, or about 8 per cent of the arable land in the province. It grows best along the main rivers where the land is enriched by fresh silt every year, because it is a soil-exhausting crop. Jute competes with *aus* rice on the highest inundated land, but the land must be properly drained during the early growth period. It is sown from March to May during the premonsoonal rains, and harvesting begins in June and extends to October. After cutting, the stalks must be steeped in flowing water and retted in order to separate the fiber from the pith. The cultivation of jute requires greater care and more labor than rice.

There are varied other crops, but none is comparable to rice and jute in importance. Among them are oilseeds (rape seed and mustard), sugar cane, betel nuts, and tobacco, occupying a combined acreage of less than 1.2 million. The entire yield of these crops is consumed normally within Bengal. Tea is a minor crop, cultivated on estates in the upland margins of the alluvial plain in the east and north and largely exported. Coconuts and hill cotton also are locally important. Maize is limited to cultivation in gardens for human consumption. Wheat and barley appear only in the western and northern part of the province as this is the extreme limit of the zone suitable for these winter cereals.

The density of livestock, especially cattle, is high. There are 100 to 110 cattle for every 100 acres sown in Bengal, or one head for every two persons. Only one animal in 25 is a water buffalo, a much lower ratio than in the Punjab. Most of the animals are small, unhealthy, and undernourished on the rice straw that is their usual fodder. The cows produce some milk, and the oxen are used for plowing and, in the dry season, for pulling large two-wheeled carts. Milk production and consumption per capita in Bengal are reported to be at about the lowest levels observed in South Asia. It is estimated that one-third the number of cattle are necessary at the present level of utilization. Other farm animals, chiefly goats and chickens, are of little nutritional value. The province is, however, among the larger producers of raw hides and skins in the world as a result of the high concentration of cattle.

Inland water transportation is more important than land transportation in East Pakistan. Roads are merely cart tracks used in the dry season. The railway system is peripheral, interrupted by unbridged rivers and changes of gauge. The railways of East Pakistan are mostly meter-gauge and serve as a supplement to the network of waterways. During the summer floods, which are normally as much as 10 to 15 feet deep near the main rivers, the farmsteads became tiny islets, linked to other farms and to the towns only by dugout palm-trunk canoes and small wooden boats, propelled with poles or paddles. Larger country boats with decks and high upcurved ends, sometimes propelled with sails, carry goods and people on the interlaced waterways. On the larger rivers there is regular steamer service, connecting most of the towns and cities and forming an inland transportation network centered on Dacca.

East Pakistan is the least urban province of the nation, only 4 per cent of the people being residents of cities and towns in 1951. There are, nevertheless, 23 urban places with over 20,000 inhabitants, only one less than in the Punjab. Two out of every three of these towns are district governmental headquarters, next in rank below the provincial capital, with administrative offices, courts, and the associated concentrations of lawyers and government employees. Trade is the dominant function of nearly all the towns, and all except one are situated on waterways or railways of either broad-gauge or meter-gauge. The population of almost half of these towns declined or failed to grow in the period from 1941 to 1951. The proportion of Hindus in these East Pakistan towns before partition was generally between 50 and 75 per cent. The shifts of Hindus and Moslems to and from India before the 1951 census gave the Moslems numerical superiority in all but one town. Yet, East Pakistani Hindus still formed about a third of the inhabitants.

The two main urban centers of East Pakistan are Dacca (276,033) and Chittagong (145,777). Dacca is the capital and the major commercial and cultural center of the province. Because it is located on a part of the shallow river Burhiganga (Old Ganges), another port, Narayanganj (72,517), has grown at a point nearer the Meghna, ten miles downstream from Dacca and accessible to the largest river vessels. Greater Dacca, including Narayanganj, (total population 411,279), is the third largest urban concentration in Pakistan and grew 29 per cent between 1941 and 1951, but it is not accessible to seagoing vessels. Hence, Chittagong, situated on the Karnaphuli River away from the shifting silt-laden waters of the delta, is the major seaport of the province. Large improvements of the shipping channels, wharves, and warehousing facilities since partition now enable the port to serve the needs of the province more adequately. Greater Chittagong (294,046) seems destined to grow as rapidly as Dacca.

The two major problems confronting the people of East Pakistan are (a) their great density in relation to local resources, and (b) their economic and political relationships to West Pakistan on the one hand and India on the other hand.

The density of population in East Pakistan (769 per square mile) is higher than in any other political unit of this size (54,500 square miles) in South Asia. In the districts of Tippera, Noakhali, and Faridpur density is well over 1,200 per square mile, and in several small tracts in the *rural* parts of Dacca district densities over 2,000 are met with. In India such high densities do not exist outside of Malabar. In all Asia equally high rural densities are found only in parts of southern Japan, in southern China, and in Java.

The growth of population in the old British province of Bengal was rapid from 1901 to 1941. In each decade, except 1911 to 1921, the growth rate exceeded 5 per cent and in 1931-1941 reached a maximum of 20 per cent. Gains were more consistently high in the eastern and northern portions of the province in the territory now included in Pakistan. The multiplication of East Bengalis is ascribed to the greater soil fertility and lower incidence of malaria where the rivers flow rapidly and flood deeply. Bengali Moslems exhibited a higher fertility than the Hindus and were concentrated in the healthier and more fertile parts of the province. By 1941 East Bengalis had not only become extremely crowded in their own territory but had found some outlet for their surplus numbers in the Hooghly industrial region in West Bengal and in the neighboring province of Assam. Half a million Bengalis, chiefly Moslems, had entered the unoccupied flood plains of Assam since the beginning of the century.

The census of 1951 for East Pakistan shows a net loss of half of one per cent during the preceding decade. The population figure for 1941 (42,277,000) may have been inflated owing to the efforts at that time to exaggerate for political purposes the numbers of the Moslem and Hindu religious communities. The decade included the war period and the famine of 1943, when at least one million and perhaps two million lives were lost in Bengal. Post-partition movements of Hindus and Moslems involved several million persons. It is impossible to determine how many Hindus have left East Pakistan permanently because of their tendency to return there whenever there is improvement of Pakistan's relations with India. The net loss of Hindu population is estimated to have been about 1,500,000. Only 700,000 Moslems in East Bengal reported themselves to be refugees from India in 1951, but there are many others who left Calcutta and other parts of West Bengal owing to partition yet were not reported as refugees because they had their original domiciles, or at least family connections, in East Bengal.

The religious composition of the population in East Pakistan, however, changed much less than in West Pakistan as a result of post-partition migrations. The percentage of Moslems in the population of what is now East Pakistan rose from 70 in 1941 to 77 in 1951. The percentage of Hindus fell from 28 to 22, and the percentage of all other communities fell from 2 to 1 per cent. In the last instance, the change is not due to migration but simply to reclassification of partly assimilated Hindu or Buddhist tribesmen who were classified in 1941 with the unassimilated tribal peoples of the Chittagong area. Along the Chittagong coast close to Burma some 150,000 Buddhists form an important local minority. The Hindus of East Pakistan, numbering about 9,239,000 in 1951, form the most important religious minority in the province and in the whole nation. Only one in a hundred of them claimed Indian citizenship at the time of the census.

The balance between food supply and consumption is precarious in East Pakistan. So dense is the population that the arable land available per capita is only half an acre. About one-third of the annual net cultivated area yields two harvests a year, but about one-fifth again as much land that is arable lies fallow. The average production of rice in Bengal is 850 pounds per acre, a low yield typical of the Indian subcontinent, although somewhat above the average. Wheat is insignificant, and animal products or beans and pulses do not form a sufficiently large portion of the diet to provide adequate nutrition. In addition to rice, the people subsist on fish, taken largely from the rice fields and inland waters of the delta. In normal years there is a deficit of rice only in the district around Dacca, but in years when the flood waters rise too rapidly or when a violent tropical cyclone visits Bengal, the shortage of rice necessitates imports from Sind or Southeast Asia.

East Pakistan received from British rule a legacy of industrial backwardness, although in the seventeenth century Dacca was famous for its fine muslins and other handicraft industries. This part of Bengal was in the hinterland of the port of Calcutta, and the jute export served to build up the industry and wealth of Calcutta. In 1947 East Pakistan inherited none of India's 106 jute spinning and weaving mills. It had 50 jute-baling presses, but almost no facilities for exporting jute through Chitta-gong. It had 58 small rice-polishing mills, three sugar factories, and less than a dozen small oil-pressing mills and glass or cement factories. The cotton textile industry had at least made a small beginning at Dacca before partition and has since expanded. A hydroelectric power station and large government-owned paper mill using bamboo have been built above Chittagong on the Karnaphuli River. Jute manufacturing has be-gun at Dacca, Narayanganj, Khulna, and Chittagong, but about half of the raw jute export still moves to Calcutta, and much is still manufac-tured in India.

Were it not for the lucrative jute-export duty and the sustained world markets for jute in the United States and Western Europe, East Bengal would prove to be an economic liability rather than an asset. Competi-tive jute-growing in India or elsewhere and the practice of bulk-loading of ships with grain tend to reduce jute exports from Pakistan. If emi-gration to Assam and West Bengal were restricted, the province would become seriously overpopulated and suffer recurring food shortage, un-less the rice yield could be raised somehow and manufacturing indus-tries developed much more rapidly than heretofore.

East Pakistan already has shown that it can be a political liability to the nation. From the standpoint of East Pakistanis, West Pakistanis might well be regarded as an alien people, so different are their racial characteristics, their foods, their dress, their languages, and their man-ners of living. East Pakistanis, although belonging as do West Paki-stanis to the brown Caucasoid racial stock, have acquired certain Mon-goloid traits through mingling with the tribal peoples, especially in the eastern parts of Bengal. As a group, East Pakistanis are round-headed, short in stature, and light in build. They eat rice and fish, not wheat and mutton. Their women wear the *sari* (long wrap-around skirt and head-covering); their men the *dhoti* (draped breech cloth) or the tight skirt similar to the Burmese *longyi*. They speak Bengali and, if well edu-cated, use the Bengali script and know the rich literature, shared alike by Bengali Moslems and Hindus. English is the preferred second lan-guage of the educated classes; not Urdu with its unfamiliar Perso-Arabic script. They have succeeded in gaining recognition of Bengali as the official language of the province and its acceptance as an alternate na-tional language to the Urdu of West Pakistan.

East Pakistanis resent their inability to wield political power in the federal government commensurate with their numbers, and they are wary of the preference enjoyed by West Pakistanis in the military and governmental services. They also resent the fact, as they see it, that the economy of their province has been exploited to benefit West Pakistan. The problems of integration of national aspirations in the West and East and particularly of finding an acceptable method of representation for East Pakistan in the federal government are the country's most pressing issues.

SELECTED GEOGRAPHICAL BIBLIOGRAPHY

1. Ahmad, Nafis. *The Basis of Pakistan.* Calcutta: Thacker & Spink, 1947.
2. Ahmad, Quazi S. "Distribution of Population in Pakistan," *Pakistan Geogr. Rev.*, 1953, pp. 94-112.
3. Chatterjee, S. P. *Bengal in Maps.* Calcutta: Orient Longmans, 1949.
4. Cohen, Jerome B. "Economic Development in Pakistan," *Land Economics,* February, 1953, pp. 1-12.
5. Fowler, F. J. "Some Problems of Water Distribution Between East and West Punjab," *Geographical Review,* October, 1950, pp. 583-599.
6. Karan, P. P. "Indo-Pakistan Boundaries: Their Fixation, Functions and Problems," *Indian Geogr. Journ.,* January-June, 1953, pp. 19-32.
7. Maron, Stanley. "The Problem of East Pakistan," *Pacific Affairs,* June, 1955, pp. 132-144.
8. Pithawalla, M. B. *An Introduction to Pakistan: Its Resources and Potentialities.* Karachi: 1948.
9. Spain, James W. "Pakistan's North West Frontier," *Middle East Journal,* Winter, 1954, pp. 27-40.
10. Spate, O. H. K. "The Partition of the Punjab and of Bengal," *Geographical Journal,* October-December, 1947, pp. 201-222.
11. Stephens, Ian. *Horned Moon.* Bloomington: Indiana University Press, 1955.
12. Symonds, Richard. *The Making of Pakistan.* London: Faber and Faber, 1950.

Comments

There is an extensive and rapidly growing literature on the geography, economics, and politics of Pakistan. The books by Nafis Ahmad, Pithawalla, and Symonds, written during the first two years of Pakistan's existence as an independent nation, present details of the country's physical basis and political origins. Specific information regarding the determination and effects of the new political boundaries between Pakistan and India is given by Spate and Karan. Fowler, Maron, and Spain treat political and economic aspects of certain regions in the new nation. Quazi Ahmad presents an analysis of the distribution of population according to the 1951 census, and Cohen appraises recent trends in foreign trade and economic development. Chatterjee's maps of Bengal, accompanied by text, in book form show the relationships of East Pakistan to geographic aspects of the old British province of Bengal. Stephens provides a vivid firsthand account of Pakistan's peoples and countrysides eight years after partition.

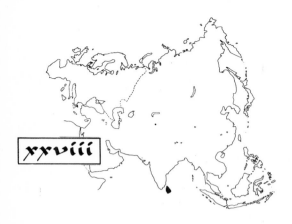

Ceylon

CEYLON HAS LONG HAD INTIMATE TIES WITH THE SUBCONTINENT OF India. It has many characteristics similar to the nearby areas of southern India: a plateau structure the surface of which has been eroded into a complex hill land with a broad coastal lowland; a tropical monsoon climate with high temperatures the year around and heavy rainfall at certain seasons; tropical and monsoon forests on the uplands and scrub and grass lands on the lowlands; and a dense population devoted to rice-dominated subsistence agriculture.

However, certain important features make the island quite distinctive. For example, though Buddhism ceased to be prominent in India many centuries ago, it remains the dominant religion in Ceylon. Also, in recent centuries plantation or estate agriculture has developed in Ceylon and has given the island's economy a distinctive character quite in contrast to that of southern India. Some of these distinctive characteristics have been due to the isolation afforded by a narrow strait, only 22 miles of shallow water.[1] Thus, different civilizations, some originally with strong Indian ties, have flourished and developed in lines divergent from those of their contemporary civilizations on the mainland.

[1] The island is a part of the continental shelf of India. Thus the strait is very shallow, so shallow in fact that ocean-going boats do not go through it, but go around the east coast of the island.

663

Within the island, centers of power and occupance have shifted from place to place. For many centuries one center of occupance was on the irrigated northern plains; a second was along the southeast coast. A few centuries ago, dominance shifted to the protected southcentral mountain and hill lands. In recent decades the center of economic and political activity has been the southwestern coastal regions and the adjacent hill lands closely linked with the coast by transportation lines. This last shift has been occasioned largely by the foreign impact upon Ceylon, which has tended to separate the island even more from the adjacent continent.

As the European commercial nations developed overseas empires, Ceylon, the "pearl of the Orient," became a much desired prize. Its harbors were adequate for the ships of those days, and it had products, particularly cinnamon, much wanted in the European market. Its special strategic value was due to its geographic position at the extremity of the Indian peninsula, athwart the trade routes of Asia. Thus, Ceylon became a pawn in the struggle for empire on the part of the European maritime powers. The Portuguese came in 1505 and obtained a foothold on the coastal plains. A century and a half later the Dutch East India Company took over, after a struggle, from the Portuguese. The Dutch, in turn, were ousted by the British who conquered the Dutch-held coastal lowlands in 1795 and pushed into the hills, where the Sinhalese king at Kandy was overthrown by his subjects, in league with the British, in 1815.

Despite occasional uprisings, the British controlled Ceylon as a colony until after the second World War. Then, culminating a policy under which successively more autonomy had been given to Ceylon, a new constitution was proclaimed, and in 1948 Ceylon became a full-fledged member of the British Commonwealth of Nations. As such, it does not always cooperate with the other members of the Commonwealth and often pursues an independent course. This has been true particularly with respect to trade with the communist-dominated world, which is anxious to obtain Ceylon's rubber. This trade connection with the Soviet bloc reflects the fact that Ceylon is no longer just a way stop on the British "life line of Empire," but is an independent nation in a world that has increasingly close interrelationships.

The island is not large, only 25,332 square miles, less than half the size of the state of Florida. Shaped like a pear, it is roughly 250 miles long and 140 miles wide at its broadest. Much of it is mountainous or in slopes covered with secondary monsoon forest and thorn scrub. The northern part of the island has a long dry season, and irrigation is a necessity. With a population that in 1954 was estimated to be 8,385,000 people, the island as a whole has a density of 316 per square mile. However, densities vary from less than 2 persons per square mile in some of the isolated hilly regions in the southeast and the northernmost plains of the northern and eastern dry zone to 600 to 700 persons per square mile in some of the better rice-growing areas. The port city of Colombo, which in 1953 had an estimated population of 424,000, is the biggest metropolitan center on the island. The growth of population in recent years for the island as a whole has been exceptional, the annual increase being about 200,000 to 250,000 persons, or between 2.5 and 3 per cent.

The rapidly growing population of Ceylon is not only unevenly distributed, but it is made up of diverse elements. The largest group, about 70 per cent of the population, is the Sinhalese, whose ancestors are believed to have migrated originally from the north of India. They are sometimes divided into those who live in the hill country and those in the low country because of variations in their economy and historical background. The next largest group, the Tamils, nearly 23 per cent of

Fig. 128 • The village is the most important unit of occupance in Ceylon. There is relatively little dispersed settlement on the island. This village lies about 20 miles east of Colombo on the eastern edge of the southwest coastal zone. It is populated primarily by Tamils from the south of India, the second largest ethnic group in the country, most of whom in this part of the island are employed as laborers on large estates. The village acts as a market center with many permanent shops as well as temporary stalls. In February, the season shown here, the streets are dry and dusty, but they are paralleled as in much of tropical Asia by trenches that act as both storm and waste sewers. Slabs of stone or wood bridge the sewers. Thatched and also tile roofs are seen here; large tropophilous trees and coconut palms rise above the rooftops. *(Wellington D. Jones.)*

the population, migrants or descendants of migrants from southern India, are about evenly divided between those who have been long settled in the Jaffna peninsula in the north and those relatively recent migrants working on estates and in towns in the hill country and the southwestern coastal region (Figure 128). There are a number of minor groups: the Moors (Arabs) and Malays, many of whom are engaged in commercial enterprises, seven per cent of the population; and composing less than one per cent of the total, Burghers (descendants of the Dutch) and other Eurasians, Europeans, and primitive tribesmen, the Veddas. Finally, there are a few other Asians engaged mostly in trade or services. The differences in ethnic groups are of major importance because they may be the cores of political action groups. Of equal importance are class differences based largely on economic status. The rather small Western-educated elite engaged in government service or employed in larger business concerns is at the top of the social pyramid; below it is a small but growing middle class; at the base of the pyramid is the general mass of the people.

Some of Ceylon's major problems are occasioned by the diversities in distribution and character of the population.[2] A very real concern is to provide a livelihood and give increasing employment opportunities for the continuously increasing population. This is complicated by the important regional differences in both the nature and growth of the population and in the potentialities for economic development. An understanding of these problems demands consideration ot the geography of Ceylon on a regional rather than a national basis (Map 31, P. 514).

The northern and eastern plains (the lowland dry zone)

The early centers of civilization on Ceylon were on the irrigated northern and, to a lesser degree, the southeastern plains. Yet, much of this region became a wasteland, malaria-ridden, and with only a sparse population of farmers many of whom have carried on a primitive migratory form of agriculture, though usually settled in permanent villages.[3] The region comprises more than half the area of the island, but has a population only one-sixth of the

---

[2] Competition and conflict between the Sinhalese and Tamils provides a major threat to Ceylonese unity. The Tamils have been encouraged in their desire for cultural and political autonomy by the successful agitation for linguistic states in India.

[3] However, as Farmer points out, "considerable areas have long been under paddy . . . and the frontiers of cultivation are moving rapidly." Malaria has been controlled with the use of D.D.T. since the second World War, and irrigation tanks are steadily being repaired or built.

total. Its potential for economic development appears relatively great. It is in this region that some of the most encouraging projects for settlement are being attempted. According to one extreme estimate, as many as 20,000,000 people once may have been settled on the irrigated plains, but it appears unlikely that such a large population can ever have been supported within the region.

The region is vast lowland generally with elevations of only 100 to 200 feet, although inland elevations of 500 feet are common. Near the mountainous interior are outliers of hills and mountains, some of them rising very abruptly from the plains. The basic rocks are a complex series of ancient Archean formations which have been greatly metamorphosed. This complex was then eroded so that most of the region has been classed by geomorphologists as a peneplain. Even on the resulting plain there are occasional monadnocks or outliers from the highlands to the south and west. A number of rivers flow down from the mountains and meander across the plain. In the past along some of these rivers tanks or reservoirs were built, and the water was stored and diverted for irrigation. In the rainy months, however, the rivers are in flood, and then in the dry season they become mere trickles of water or chains of pools.

Though the climate differs within the region, the one important characteristic is the existence of a long dry season. During these months some rainfall may occur, but evaporation is so great that the net result is drought. Temperatures (and as a consequence evaporation) are high throughout the year. For example, Trincomalee on the east coast has its hottest month in May when the temperature averages 86.2°F., but December, the month with the lowest average monthly temperature, 78.6°, is still hot. Most of the rainfall (65 inches at Trincomalee) comes during the northeast monsoon season, the months from October through January, when moist air drifts over from the Bay of Bengal. Some areas exposed to the southwest monsoon air drifts of summer and not sheltered by the hill lands have a secondary peak of rainfall during April to June, but they will still have lengthy dry periods. Generally, there is a low amount of total rainfall considering the high temperature and high evaporation.

Under this type of climate deep, leached red soils have developed. These predominantly lateritic soils are not fertile unless well fertilized and limed. The natural vegetation was, perhaps, a tropophilous monsoon forest, but owing to the past use of this region for agriculture both sedentary and shifting and to the land's subsequent abandonment, the present vegetation is mostly secondary forest and scrub with some strips of denser forests along the river valleys. The vegetation is not easy to clear with primitive tools, although the problem is less serious than, for example, that of water supply. People in the area have utilized a system of shifting cultivation for centuries, using the fire-cleared land for crops for two or three years before moving on to new clearings.[4]

Passing through the region today one has difficulty imagining it as densely populated. Yet the northern plains, and to a lesser degree the southeastern plains, were the site of a flourishing civilization with a relatively high standard of living, based upon irrigation agriculture. The development, maintenance, and destruction of the tanks (reservoirs) summarize its history. Permanent settlement of the region began when migrants came into the region about B.C. 500. Buddhism was brought in about B.C. 300, and the numerous temples and shrines which are now mostly in ruins attest not only to the strong hold of that religion, but also to the fact that the economy supported a high state of the arts. During this early period there was a continuing development of irrigation; rice was produced in sufficient quantity to feed the large population with an occasional export surplus for India. Times were not all peaceful, however, for there were many invasions from India. To counter these, in part, there was a movement southward toward the protection of the hill lands. Meanwhile, large dams, tanks, and irrigation canals were constructed. One such dam was 3.5 miles long and 36 to 54 feet high. The canal from this tank extended 54 miles to Anuradhapura, then the leading city.

Later the pressure from India became stronger, and during an eleventh-century invasion Anuradhapura was sacked. The center of government and economic life migrated southward. Tamils from southern India gained a permanent foothold on the Jaffna peninsula to the north. The combination of civil wars, invasions, disruption of the canals, and deterioration of the dams resulted in economic decline. Malarial mosquitoes bred increasingly in the deteriorated irrigation system and gave a final blow to the economy. Jungle encroached upon the fields, and the once-fertile region became a no-man's land between the Tamils in the north and the Sinhalese who had retreated to the mountain lands in the south. The relatively few inhabitants practiced *chena* cultivation.

The area could be redeveloped for agriculture. Such economic redevelopment has been proceeding for three-quarters of a century, but only since the war has it been accelerated by government subsidies. The delay has been due to several factors, among them, the competition for labor in the southwestern region of Ceylon, the hesitancy on the part of the Sinhalese farmers to move from their village homes to an area that has been ridden by malaria, and the lack of sufficient capital for re-

---

[4] This system of agriculture is known as *chena*, and resembles the *rai* of Indochina, the *ladang* of Malaya and Indonesia, the *caingin* of the Philippines, the *jhum* of Assam, and the *kaiden* of Japan.

quired large-scale rehabilitation and new irrigation works. One huge government project, the Gal Oya multipurpose irrigation and power project in southeastern Ceylon is well on the way to completion.

Within the region is the naval base of Trincomalee. Favored by a magnificent natural harbor and a location facing the Bay of Bengal, it has long had a great military and strategic significance. Though it has had an economic effect on the immediately surrounding hinterland, the base has not had much influence on the region as a whole. Like most such bases it tends to be alien to and culturally isolated from the region in which it is sited.

The Jaffna peninsula

Though very small, the Jaffna peninsula is a distinctive region in Ceylon—for two reasons: (1) the underlying structure of limestone rock, which has weathered in places into fertile soils, and (2) the settlement of Tamil farmers from southern India. As a result, unique forms of agriculture and patterns of occupance have developed.

The peninsula, with its peculiar shape and the numerous offshore islands, arose by the elevation of parts of the Miocene limestone beds, which were laid down on the basaltic complex. Where the limestone rock outcrops, lithosols predominate, and the land cannot be used for agriculture. Sand dunes along the coast also are unproductive. Thus, less than a third of the region, where the limestone has been weathered to a brick-red or greyish-white and grey-loam soil, is useful for agriculture. However, these soils must be heavily fertilized to be productive. There are few streams because of the porous limestone structure, and surface water supplies are therefore limited. Wells, however, are common. The climate is dominated by high temperatures which, since the region is close to the subcontinent of India, have a slightly higher range than those in the rest of Ceylon. Rainfall is concentrated during the northeast monsoon season of October through January, though the dry season is not so pronounced as it is in the areas immediately to the south of the peninsula. Drought conditions, however, are more acute because of the porous limestone bedding below the surface.

Over 700,000 Tamils are crowded onto this small area, the productive parts of which have densities of over 1,000 per square mile. Farms average only one-fourth of an acre in size and are little more than gardens. The palmyra palm takes the place of the coconut palm, common in the rest of Ceylon, to provide food, thatching, timber, household utensils, and numerous other useful products. Rice, the major crop, is grown near wells used for irrigation, but much is grown as a dry crop. Vegetable crops are intensively cultivated in an intricate rotation pattern. Tobacco is an important commercial crop grown mainly on the red-loam soils. It must be fertilized with care and is watered twice a day with water from hand-dug wells. Much of the tobacco is exported to India.

In view of the intensity with which the land of the Jaffna peninsula is cultivated, it is difficult to conceive of further agricultural development in this already overcrowded region under existing technologies. The problems of integrating this region, with its close ties with India, into the Ceylonese economy are great. Though they add to the labor force in other parts of the island, most of the Tamil wage laborers in Ceylon do not come from this region but directly from India. Because of their cultural affiliations with Hindu India, they form an important ethnic minority group that increasingly has been a political problem in Ceylon.

The hills

In recent decades, particularly with the introduction of plantation agriculture, the hills of Ceylon have become increasingly important. So great has been the impact of commercial agriculture that the highlands have become economically the most important region on the island. The mountains have been like a fortress set among the surrounding plains. They have served as a place of refuge in historic times, as invaders forced the lowlanders to retreat to them for protection. There is a sudden rise from the lowlands, particularly along the southwest coast where the mountain wall culminates in Adam's Peak, 7,360 feet above sea level and the second highest point on the island. The building of modern roads and railroads over the sharp break from the plains to the hill country and within the hill lands took great engineering skill and effort. It was only with these advances in transportation after the conquest of the Sinhalese that the British were able to develop their plantations within the hill lands.

The hills region of Ceylon is composed of a massive complex of old rocks, mainly gneisses and schists. Though there are different theories about their erosional history, it is thought that the whole area was worn down in the distant past to a gently rolling plain, similar to the northern and eastern lowlands of today. Subsequently, the present mountain mass was uplifted, perhaps in two successive movements. Thus, one can find at the summits, roughly 6,000 to 7,000 feet, a gently rolling surface and again at around 2,000 feet another erosional surface. The mountain mass has been much eroded by rivers and streams, which have dissected the region. As these streams descend from one level to another they form spectacular waterfalls. Though the flat, table-like, erosional levels are visible in places, most of the hill land is a jumble of mountains and small basins, with elevations averaging from 3,000 to 5,000 feet.

The indigenous population of the region is mainly "upland" Sinhalese, whose ancestors moved into the region from the northern plains some 300 to 400 years ago. For centuries they have practiced the cultivation of rice, coconuts, and vegetables. Their homes are simple, and their needs relatively few. They live in the lower basins and along the stream valleys roughly at elevations of 2,000 to 3,000 feet. The original political and religious center for these Buddhist people was Kandy, where the Temple of the Tooth (of the Buddha) was located beside an artificial lake. Here the kings and nobles combined with the monks to keep alive a Buddhist-dominated civilization. Intrigue was rife, and the European powers who came to control the coastal lands played upon internal weaknesses to destroy their independence. Along with the political penetration and conquest came tremendous economic transformations. The introduction of roads and railroads shattered the isolation; new crops for distant markets were grown on large estates cleared from the forests.

The sequence of plantation crops in Ceylon is an interesting example of the varying effects of economic and physical factors. The first commercial crop introduced along the borders of the highlands was cinnamon. Originally, it had been gathered from the forests, but later it was grown as a tree crop. By restricting production, the Dutch, and later the British, were able to maintain artificially high prices and gain profitable revenues. However, other parts of the world started to produce cinnamon; a cheaper substitute, cassia, began to furnish competition; and the industry collapsed. Today, some 26,000 acres of cinnamon gardens indifferently cultivated by Sinhalese farmers in the southwestern part of the island are all that remains of a once-flourishing industry.

As roads were built and the island was opened to English investors, a new crop, coffee, was introduced. The increasing demand in Europe for coffee, the favorable physical conditions, particularly the highland tropical climate,[5] and the importation of Tamil workers from India combined to create a coffee boom, starting in 1835. In 1847 the speculative bubble burst, but the industry recovered shortly thereafter and by 1857 there was an area, mainly around Kandy, of 86,950 acres devoted to coffee trees. Expansion continued particularly to the east deeper in the mountain area; by 1867 the acreage was 168,000, and in 1878 the maximum of 275,000 acres was reached. However, a fungus blight began to take its toll, and production rapidly declined. Brazil began to produce

---

[5] Rainfall in the hills region is everywhere higher than 75 inches annually. Kandy receives 87 inches per year with dual maxima, one in June associated with the southwest monsoon, the second in November associated with the southeast monsoon.

coffee and thus forced the price down in Europe. Today, coffee, is no longer produced commercially; cleared lands in the mountains are mute evidences of the one-time wide extent of coffee plantations.

Cinchona, for quinine, also was grown for a brief period, but the quick saturation of the market owing to overproduction caused a quick collapse of this plantation industry. Fortunately an old product in Asia newly developed on a plantation basis, tea, was established and had a rapid expansion from 1,000 acres in 1875 to 406,000 acres in 1903 (Figure 129). After the flurry of exploitation that accompanied the introduction of new crops in Ceylon had quieted, the tea industry became stabi-

Fig. 129 • A newly planted tea plantation in the highlands of Ceylon south of Kandy at an altitude of about 3,000 feet. Some but not all trees are cleared from the slopes before planting; those spared provide a certain amount of shade for the young plants. Almost all of the tea in Ceylon is raised on large estates owned by Europeans, although some transfer of estates into Sinhalese hands has begun to take place. Acreages are regulated by the International Tea Agreement. Note that almost all of the original forest cover on the misty hills beyond has been removed even on the ridge crests, either for plantations or in the process of shifting cultivation that is common in the area. (Wellington D. Jones.)

lized and for the last half century has provided one of the island's major export crops. In 1933, under the International Tea Agreement, Ceylon received a quota, and the tea acreage has remained relatively constant since that time, though the amount and value of production has fluctuated with world demands. In 1946, 2,308 plantations covered 487,801 acres. These are located mainly south and east of Kandy at elevations from 1,500 to 6,000 feet. The future of the tea industry is not by any means assured, for it depends upon markets far distant from Ceylon, and the island's estates must meet severe competition from other parts of the world. There also is considerable dissatisfaction with the quota system, and Ceylon is clamoring for an increase in its allotments.

The other major plantation crop is rubber. It had a slow start in Ceylon, and only 1,750 acres were in rubber in 1900, but the rubber area increased steadily to 636,936 acres in 1940. During the second World War many of the trees were virtually slaughter-tapped, but the acreage remained almost the same; 653,917 acres were in rubber in 1946. Rubber is grown mainly in the lower elevations of the hills region or in the adjacent lowlands of southwestern Ceylon at elevations below 2,000 feet. The future of the industry is uncertain. Many of Ceylon's estates are old and inefficient producers; labor costs are relatively high; competition, particularly in the postwar period when synthetic rubber has become available as a subsidized product of the United States, is severe. A temporary expedient has been to sell rubber to the Soviet bloc, but this creates many political as well as economic problems, especially in relations with the non-communist West.

The complex sequence of plantation products has transformed the geography of the hills region and in fact all of Ceylon. New railroads and roads have breached the once solitary fastness of the rain forests. The agricultural lands devoted to paddy, coconuts, and vegetables are in gradual transition from a self-sufficient agricultural system to a commercial system, in part to provide food for workers on the estates. New structures, like the multistoried tea factories, dot the landscape. However, it is worth noting that what was once an almost exclusively foreign-dominated enterprise, the estate, is coming gradually into the hands of Sinhalese, Tamils, and other non-Europeans. In addition, native small-holder cultivators of coconut palms and rubber trees are able to produce these products in competition with the large estates, as is true in Malaya and Sumatra, for example. At the same time the consequences of the dual economy associated with the great estate remain—landlessness, uncertain land tenure and landlordism, and rural debt. As in much of Asian Asia, these problems are among the more important facing the new national government.

The southwest coastal zone (the lowland wet zone)

The southwestern part of Ceylon is most characteristic of the new Ceylon. This peripheral region has experienced the greatest impact from the outside world, and it was first to come under the control of the European empire builders. The land itself is not particularly inviting from the standpoint of terrain or climate, but the abundance and the evenness of rainfall have made elaborate water-storage devices unnecessary, although flood-control problems are in turn acute.

At present the multifunctional, essentially Western city of Colombo dominates the region and acts as the major focal point for all of Ceylon.

Fig. 130 • The city of Colombo is the first city, the capital, and the major port of Ceylon. It also is a major stopping point for vessels crossing the Indian Ocean between Suez and the Straits of Malakka. Although the port was deep enough to accommodate the ocean-going vessels of the early period of Western interest in Ceylon, it has long since proven too shallow for large ships. For this reason the loading and unloading of cargoes other than petroleum requires the use of barge-like lighters, one of which is seen here transferring its cargo to a British ship standing about half a mile offshore but within the oval harbor area protected by breakwaters from the sea. Note the small launch moored next to the barge, with its woven bamboo covering. Most of the seamen are Tamil laborers from the south of India. (*Wellington D. Jones.*)

Fig. 131 • Paddy fields and bordering coconut palm groves in Ceylon's rainy south-west coastal zone in March during the drier season. The fields are lying fallow and will not be prepared for paddy planting for at least another month. Almost no double-cropping is practiced in Ceylon; the island, like Malaya, is partly dependent upon imported rice. Almost no fertilizers are used so it is not surprising that rice yields in Ceylon are among the lowest in Asia. Only about half of the paddy areas are under controlled irrigation; the fields shown here depend upon rainfall for their water. The coconut is a major cash and subsistence crop, grown both on estates and by small-holders in association with other crops. *(Wellington D. Jones.)*

Originally only a small fishing and coastal port, it developed as the export of plantation products increased (Figure 130). A long breakwater and harbor and dock facilities enabled Colombo to become a major stopping point for ocean-going vessels; it outstripped Galle, the first major foreign port, which now remains as only a local commercial center. Colombo's major function is that of a commercial port; docks and warehouses line the waterfront; commercial banks and business concerns have imposing buildings in the heart of the city; and there are handsome suburban residential areas with broad streets and gardens. However, most of the people live crowded together along densely packed streets that are lined with bazaars and small commercial enterprises. A limited industry produces items such as matches, paper, chinaware, shoes, and glassware primarily for local consumption.

Along the coast and back toward the hills rice is the dominant native crop; the paddy fields are irrigated by diversion canals bringing water down from the hills or depend upon natural rainfall (Figure 131). The rainfall is heavy, particularly during the southwest monsoon season. Colombo, for example, has an annual rainfall of 93 inches (Plate C).[6] Temperatures are hot the year around. Thus, two crops of rice can be grown during the year, though they rarely are grown on the same fields. Vegetable crops, particularly for the large urban market, are important. Rubber is the most valuable commercial crop and continues on the better-drained lands as an extension of the rubber region within the hills region to the east. Finally, coconut palms, grown in smallholdings around the farm homes or villages and also in relatively large commercial plantations situated along the coasts or in the areas that cannot be irrigated, are extremely important in the rural economy. For the island as a whole coconut palms actually have a greater acreage than rice. Some of the dried coconut meat and oil is exported, but much of the production is for local consumption—the coir fiber for ropes and matting, the leaves for thatch, the meat for food or for cooking oil, and some for toddy and *arrack*, both alcoholic liquors.

Ceylon faces its future as an independent member of the British Commonwealth of Nations with many problems, but also with a considerable potential. The advantages of its insular position are important, and it remains a strategic crossroads for South Asia. Furthermore, although plagued with agrarian problems and population increases similar to those of India, Ceylon possesses a "time cushion" in the form of a sparsely settled Dry Zone which awaits development and resettlement. Nevertheless, its role as a colony, dependent upon overseas markets for its plantation products, is only gradually being modified. It also remains dependent on imports for one-third to one-half of the rice it consumes. Moreover, the threat of a culturally aggressive India is very real to many Ceylonese. As a small country, the island's power position is not great. In part because of this and in part because of its internal needs, Ceylon has been taking an active role in United Nations affairs, particularly in relation to economic development plans. The center for the Colombo Plan, the British Commonwealth plan for economic development, is in Ceylon. The Gal Oya project for irrigation, power, and land reclamation is being used as a testing ground to see what can be done in tropical lands. The beauty of the island remains an important tourist asset; the picturesque mountains, a delightful highland climate, and the

---

[6] The rainfall regime at Colombo is bimodal, with maxima .occurring between the monsoon periods, one in May and one in October. To the northeast, in the lee of the highlands, the southwest monsoon is blocked and only one maximum occurs in winter at the height of the northeast monsoon.

relics of a glorious past, inspired by a Buddhist love of art, are most attractive.

The future here lies in the hands of a people dangerously divided into ethnic and class groups, but full of hope and rising expectations. Marco Polo characterized Ceylon "for its size the finest island in the world." It may once more merit his description.

SELECTED GEOGRAPHICAL BIBLIOGRAPHY

1. *Bulletin of the Ceylon Geographical Society*, printed by the Colombo Apothecaries' Co., Ltd., Colombo, Ceylon.
2. Cook, E. K. *Ceylon: Its Geography, Its Resources, and Its People.* London: Macmillan, rev. edit., 1951.
3. DeSilva, S. F. *A Regional Geography of Ceylon.* Colombo: Colombo Apothecaries' Co., Ltd., rev. and enl. edit., 1954.
4. Farmer, B. H. "Ceylon." Chap. XXVI in *India and Pakistan* by O. H. K. Spate. New York: E. P. Dutton & Co., 1954.
5. ———. "Agriculture in Ceylon," *Geographical Review*, January, 1950, pp. 42-66.
6. ———. "Problems of Land Use in the Dry Zone of Ceylon," *Geographical Journal*, March, 1954, pp. 21-33.
7. ———. *Pioneer Peasant Colonization in Ceylon.* Oxford: Oxford University Press, 1957.
8. Great Britain, Board of Trade. "Ceylon," *Overseas Economic Surveys*. London: Her Majesty's Stationery Office, 1952.
9. International Bank for Reconstruction and Development. *Economic Development of Ceylon.* Baltimore: Johns Hopkins Press, 1953.
10. Jennings, Sir W. Ivor. *The Economy of Ceylon.* Madras, 1951.
11. Livera, Emil J. "Productive Land Use in Ceylon," *Tropical Agriculture*, July, 1954, pp. 188-198.
12. MacFadden, Clifford H. "The Gal Oya Valley: Ceylon's Little TVA," *Geographical Review*, April, 1954, pp. 271-281.
13. ———. "Ceylon and the Colombo Plan," *Focus*, March, 1955, pp. 1-6.
14. McCune, Shannon. "Sequence of Plantation Agriculture in Ceylon," *Economic Geography*, July, 1949, pp. 226-235.
15. Meddegoda, P. N. "Reclaiming the Dry Zone of Ceylon," *British Agricultural Bulletin*. Vol. 6, No. 30, March, 1954, pp. 391-395.
16. Murphey, Rhoads. "The Ruin of Ancient Ceylon," *Journal of Asian Studies*, February, 1957, pp. 181-200.
17. Subramanyam, N. "Tea Industry in Ceylon," *Indian Geographical Journal*, October-December, 1954, pp. 89-105.

Comments

Much of the basic geographic material on Ceylon has been compiled by government agencies. An active prewar mapping program has produced almost complete coverage of the island on topographic sheets. In the postwar period several British and American geographers, for example B. H. Farmer and Clifford H. MacFadden, have been active in the field. Farmer's studies on peasant colonization are particularly valuable. Murphey's article is a fascinating analysis of the factors associated with the occupance and abandonment of the dry zone. A growing group of Ceylonese, also interested in the geography of Ceylon, are organized in the Ceylon Geographical Society which has published a modest but useful *Bulletin*. Much information is summarized in the British Board of Trade report on Ceylon. The World Bank mission to Ceylon, synthesizing material presented to it and developing new material, has analyzed the economic problems of the island in its *Economic Development of Ceylon*. There also are census materials for 1946 and 1953. For use in the schools of Ceylon some excellent texts in Sinhalese and English have been prepared, for example, those of Miss E. D. Cook (recently revised by Mr. H. Kularatnam) and S. F. deSilva.

Afghanistan

IN THE HEART OF ASIA LIES AFGHANISTAN, WEDGED BETWEEN Persia, Pakistan, and the Soviet Union, isolated and little-known to the world. Its existence as a political unit arose mainly from its role as a buffer during the late nineteenth century between the expanding empires of British India and Czarist Russia. It was by agreement between London and St. Petersburg in 1886-87 that Afghanistan's northern boundary was fixed. Britain might well have made the country a protectorate were it not for the threat of Russian intervention in the north and for the fierce resistance of the Pathan or Pukhtun (the Pushtu-speaking) tribes who, under the leadership of the Afghan kings of Kabul, defeated the British invasions of 1838-42 and 1879-80. Indeed, the Pathan tribal area just outside of Afghanistan in the frontier mountains of Pakistan was never fully controlled by the British and remains largely self-governing under their successors, the Pakistanis.

Throughout recorded history, Afghanistan has been a region of transit. Before the rise of the Afghan kings in 1747 from one of the indigenous Pushtu-speaking tribes, the peoples inhabiting the territory had little history wholly their own, being frequently subject to conquest by outside powers. No doubt the early Aryans passed through present Afghan territory on their migrations to India about B.C. 1500. Alexander

679

the Great penetrated the country with his army in B.C. 330-327 and descended to the Indus plains, leaving behind his satraps to rule for 200 years. Kushans, White Huns, Arabs, Turks, and Mughals overran the mountain passes and descended to conquer the plains peoples of India. At intervals, powerful Indian empires such as the Maurya and the Gupta developed and spread their influence into and beyond this northwestern frontier. Although armies composed of Indians have never conquered Afghanistan, Indian culture, notably Buddhism, and Indian goods in part were exported this way to central Asia and China. For at least a thousand years Bactria (Balkh) in northern Afghanistan was one of the more important crossroad cities of Asia where the camel caravan route from India met the routes from Persia and China. More often than not, the territory that is now Afghanistan was part of some larger empire that included territory in the Iranian plateau, the Turanian lowland, or the Indus lowland.

Afghanistan thus occupies a transitional, if not also precarious, position in the great divide between Inner Asia and South Asia. This is true not only in regard to political geography but also in terms of surface configuration and drainage (Map 33). The snow-crusted Hindu Kush (Hindu Killer) and Koh-i-Baba (Grandfather) ranges extend westward from the Pamir plateau across Afghanistan. They form the water divide between the rivers flowing south and those flowing north to the Amu Darya (Oxus), eventually reaching the Aral Sea. Central Afghanistan is crossed only by difficult passes, of which the lowest is 9,800 feet and all of which are covered in winter with heavy snow. In spite of this topographic barrier and the poor state of internal transport, which tend to separate the north from the south, Afghanistan has maintained political unity.

Ethnic composition and economic base

The country's political unity is all the more surprising in view of its ethnic diversity. The Pathan, or Pukhtun, people number some 5.3 million and are dominant in the eastern and southern parts of the country. They belong to the tall, hooked-nosed, high-headed Irano-Afghan branch of the Caucasoid race. The Tadzhiks (Tajiks) form another Caucasoid grouping of about 2.8 million, inhabiting the western region around Herat and spreading through the central and northeastern mountain belt to the headwaters of the Oxus (Figure 132). Their language is closely related to Persian and, like Pushtu, belongs to the Indo-Iranian family of languages. To the north of the Hindu Kush are 1.5 million people of Mongoloid stock—

Fig. 132 • The village of Sirchisma ("head spring"), near the headwaters of the Kabul River, is typical of the many mud-walled villages inhabited by Tadzhiks, an Iranic-speaking people closely related to the inhabitants of Soviet Tadzhikistan and to the Iranians to the west of Afghanistan. The houses are built wall-to-wall and have roofs made of poles, boughs, and straw. The Tadzhiks are Moslems, as are almost all Afghan nationals. Note the forbidding and bleak rock face against which the houses huddle. *(Food and Agriculture Organization.)*

Uzbeks and Turkmen—whose languages belong to the Turkic family and whose closest ethnic ties are with the inhabitants of Russian and Chinese Turkestan.

In addition to these three main groupings, which are estimated in all to be 9.6 million, there are other peoples that together make up perhaps 2 million more. The Hazaras are the seminomadic Mongol tribes of the central highlands west of the Koh-i-Baba, numbering about 1.5 million, who speak a modified form of Persian. The Kafirs are another group of tribes living in the inaccessible south slopes of the eastern Hindu Kush. They are of the same Caucasoid stock as the Tajiks with tendencies toward blondism, but their languages are most closely related to the Dardic family in the neighboring mountain regions of northern Pakistan and Kashmir. In the western part of Afghanistan are found some 400,-000 Persians, and in the south, 50,000 Baluchis.

The chief force integrating the country's varied language groups and races is Islam with its code of law and its powerful religious leaders, the *mullahs*. Except for a few thousand Afghan Jews and a handful of transient European and North American Christians, the people are orthodox Moslems of the Sunni or Shi'a sects. The literate population is also unified by the knowledge of the Arabic language of the sacred Koran and the use of Persian. The official language of the country and the most common idiom of trade is Persian, though the government promotes the use of Pushtu.

Afghanistan's population, estimated variously at from 10 to 12 million, depends primarily upon agriculture and stock-raising. Urban settlements contain only 5 per cent of the people, including nearly all who are engaged in craft industries and trade. Nomadic herdsmen form at least 25 per cent of the population (Figure 133). It is difficult to distinguish clearly between them and the 70 per cent who are farmers, because many of the oasis agriculturists possess herds and practice transhumance while some of the tent-dwelling nomads plant grain and return to harvest it, though they drive their herds of sheep and goats hundreds of miles for pasturage.

The staple food grains are fall-sown wheat and barley. In addition, maize, rice, and cotton are grown in summer, the latter two being the chief cash crops. Alfalfa and clover are important feed crops. Grape cultivation is widespread and there is produced an amazing variety of tree fruits, oilseeds, grain *Leguminosae*, and vegetables.

If the archaeological evidence in Baluchistan may be projected into the adjacent parts of Afghanistan, where scores of ruins await scientific investigators, then Afghanistan appears to have been among the oldest centers of agriculture and the home of some of the world's first sedentary village communities, probably dating before B.C. 3000. Early modification and improvement of the breadwheats and the domestication of peas (for grain), lentils, broad beans (*Vicia faba*), and hemp may have occurred here. It is possible also that the domestication of the goat, fat-tailed sheep, zebu cattle, and the two-humped Bactrian camel occurred in Afghanistan or in the bordering territories.

Whatever may be true of prehistoric evolution in the arts of agriculture and animal husbandry, it is clear that in these respects today Afghanistan is underdeveloped. Here the small-seeded, poor-yielding, hard-to-thresh crop varieties are still accepted by the peasants. Herds are decimated by disease and by lack of pasturage in summer. Cultivation is limited to only about 2 per cent of the area of this arid country's territory.

Afghanistan thus finds itself lagging in the change from its age-old subsistence economy and from its government by religious or tribal tradition into a well integrated and economically productive state. The fact that there is resistance to this transformation is attested by the fall and

Fig. 133 • Camel nomads camped with their black tents along the road to the Shibar pass in the Hindu Kush mountains. In the background trees border the stream from which they obtain their water in an otherwise arid land. Nomadic herdsmen account for about 20 per cent of the population in Afghanistan. Some travel great distances in pasturing their camel (and other) herds; others are only semi-nomadic and practice transhumance in addition to crop cultivation; still others are carriers of goods from one part of the country to another and even across international boundaries. *(Food and Agriculture Organization.)*

exile of King Amanullah in 1929, following his abortive reformations. The processes of adopting Western ways is highly selective. Before the second World War the chief Western educational and cultural contacts were with France, while technology was borrowed from Germany. Since the war, the United States has played a leading role in education and in highway and dam building. But more recently the Soviet Union has sent technicians and basic equipment into Afghanistan.

The Kabul valley and southeastern mountains

From the standpoint of population distribution and political geography, the most significant region of Afghanistan is the southeastern part of the country, specifically in the Kabul valley and in the other valleys opening eastward in the mountains along the Afghan-Pakistan frontier. Here is located the largest city, Kabul, with 200,000 inhabitants, the seat of the national government. The frontier mountains are the stronghold of the semi-autonomous Pathan tribes, the country's most powerful political minority. Though this region accounts for only 10 per cent of Afghanistan's 260,000 square miles, it contains more than one-quarter of the total population and is, therefore, one of the more closely settled areas.

The region lies in the watershed of the Indus. The valleys of the Kabul and of three other Indus affluents—Kurram, Tochi, and Gomal—afford the main lines of approach from the Pakistan plains to the Afghan highlands. Each valley is closed in by a narrow gorge through which the drainage passes on its exit to the Indus plain. It is to avoid the lowest gorge of the Kabul River that the famous Khaibar (Khyber) pass (3,450 feet) is used for the main route from Peshawar to Kabul. Above the gorges the gradient of each of the three smaller rivers is checked sufficiently to cause alluvial filling, and here the best agricultural land is found. The deeply eroded hills of folded sandstone and limestone strata are relieved by landscapes of terraced grain fields with scattered orchards and half-concealed villages. The small intermontane basins that lie in tribal territory on both sides of the Afghan-Pakistan frontier are enclosed by higher ranges, such as the Safed Koh, in which the rivers take their origin and through which passes of 6,000 to 9,000 feet lead westward to Gardez and Ghazni. The Kabul River system flows some 200 miles in Afghanistan, descending from the flanks of the Hindu Kush and Koh-i-Baba through a succession of tectonic basins at different levels which are separated from one another by barren ranges of granite, gneiss, schist, and crystalline limestone and are filled with ancient lake and river deposits. The largest of these basins occur at Kabul (5,800 feet), Charikar

(5,000 feet), and Jalalabad (2,000 feet), each of these cities serving as the center of important agricultural tracts.

The climate of Afghanistan is generally dry, with annual precipitation reaching probably as little as 2 to 6 inches in the southern desert and only 11 inches at Kabul. Precipitation tends to be greatest in the mountains, particularly in the eastern part of the country where 12 to 15 inches or more are received and where the only forests in the country are found. Nearly all the precipitation is of frontal origin and is derived from middle-latitude cyclonic storms that travel eastward during winter from the Black and Caspian seas or the Mediterranean. At Kabul winter precipitation comes in the form of snow, followed by a season of thundershowers in March and the first half of April—the wettest season of the year. Under the influence of northerly winds bringing continental air, cloudless blue skies prevail in summer. However, in Kabul and the southeastern mountains intense rainfall occurs for periods of a few days' duration in July or August when winds shift to the southeast and there is an influx of tropical maritime air from the Indian summer monsoon. Thus the climate may be described as arid or semi-arid with a modified Mediterranean-type regime, except in the southeastern mountains where the secondary summer maximum of rainfall creates locally humid areas.

The temperature regime of Kabul, the only place for which data are available, is continental because of the country's inland position. The winter also is severe because of the high elevation of the city—6,200 feet above sea level. In January the mean is 31°F., and the minimum experienced in this or the following month is zero. Heavy snow, which accumulates to depths of 4-5 feet in the mountains around Kabul, melts rapidly by the end of March. The monthly mean of 77°F. and the daily maximum of only 95° in July, unusually mild for the latitude, are accounted for by elevation.

Progressive upward decrease of temperature in the region creates differences in the length of growing season and brings about important altitudinal zones of agriculture. The so-called "temperate zone" from 4,000 to 8,000 feet, which includes the Charikar and Kabul basins as well as the southeastern frontier valleys, has a growing season of 7-8 months. In this zone are grown chiefly the winter cereals, wheat and barley; also mustard, peas, beans, flax, alfalfa, and clover. There are deciduous fruits such as apples, pears, apricots, mulberries (grown for the fruit), and walnuts. This also is the zone of forests, consisting largely of Himalayan cedar and oak, which bedeck the humid slopes of the Hindu Kush and eastern frontier mountains. In contrast, the basin of Jalalabad is in a subtropical zone below 3,000 feet in which snow rarely falls and monthly mean temperatures are probably 10-15 degrees higher than at Kabul. Here grow sugar cane, rice, oranges, and palms. Wild tree growth is composed of poplar and tamarisk where soil moisture is abundant; otherwise, there is only thorn shrub. Water buffaloes are used as dairy and work animals in the subtropical zone.

Kabul (Sheepfold), court of the kings of the Afghan Durrani tribe, has risen during the past 200 years to eminence. It is the main emporium of trade and the focus of the country's transportation. An ancient political center in the region, Kapisa near Charikar, was founded by Alexander in order to command the most direct routes over the Hindu Kush. In the eleventh century A.D. Ghazni, located some 90 miles southwest of Kabul on the road to Kandahar, assumed short-lived importance as the seat of the first Moslem conquest of northern India. Kabul has the advantage of commanding the route westward to Herat as well as the routes northward and southward. Though the city has no railroad, it has become one of the few centers of modern factory industries, the largest of which produce woolen goods, leather, and matches. Hydroelectricity from three small generating stations within a 60-mile radius supplies power and light to the city.

At a distance of only 200 miles from this focal point of political and economic affairs live the virtually independent tribes—the Pathans and the Kafirs. The latter are found in the wildest and most inaccessible valleys of the Hindu Kush between the Panjshir and Kunar rivers. In their forested fastnesses they preserved their Indo-Aryan speech and pagan religion. The name *Kafir* (Infidel) denotes the fact that they resisted conversion to Islam until the last decade of the nineteenth century. They still enjoy a large degree of seclusion and local autonomy, practicing an intensive though primitive type of irrigated agriculture and living in unique three-storied half-timbered houses.

The most important tribal region is in a belt 75 to 125 miles wide that stretches along both sides of the Afghan-Pakistan frontier extending some 50 miles north of the Khaibar pass and 200 miles south. The inhabitants, known collectively as the Pathans or Pakhtuns, are subdivided into at least a dozen major tribes and many clans; they feud with one another, rob, or take prisoners to be ransomed. They consider themselves subject only to the rule of the tribal council and do not recognize the laws or authority of either Pakistan or Afghanistan. Though they maintain more or less fixed abodes in the several frontier valleys, some of them go to trade or to work in Pakistan during winter. Some tribesmen formerly went on raiding expeditions to the plains and levied tribute on traders crossing the frontier. The British government sought to eliminate the tribal incursions by annual stipends. This arrangement was discontinued after 1947 and their relations with Pakistan are not completely satisfactory. On the other hand, their relations are often strained with the central Afghan government which maintains a special minister for tribal affairs. It is small wonder that there has been agitation in favor of the creation of a new state to be called "Pakhtunistan" to be formed of territory still essentially outside the jurisdiction of either country.

Central Afghanistan and the Hindu Kush

High desolate plateaus and deep canyons, snowy peaks, and rushing gray-green rivers are typical landscape elements of the central mountain belt, which makes up at least one-third of the area of the country. It contains fewer permanent inhabitants than any other region—10 per cent of the population at most. The highlands rise gradually from the west and south towards the northeast, in the region known as Hazarajat, and spread out in high plateaus of 9,000-12,000 feet elevation where the headwaters of the three principal rivers lie. The higher crests of the major mountain chains (Paropamisus, Koh-i-Baba, and Hindu Kush) tower 2,000 to 3,000 feet above these plateaus and run in an east-west axis which forms the main water divide between the north and south in the country. The Hindu Kush proper, east of longitude 68°, has the highest relief with several peaks over 20,000 feet; it includes the only considerable area in the country that is above 15,000 feet and has perennial snowfields and glaciers. On the north and northwest 10-12,000-foot spurs extend into Afghan-Turkestan and Badakhshan, respectively.

As a result of the generally insufficient height and scanty precipitation, glacial development is feeble in the Afghan highlands. All rivers except those flowing from the Hindu Kush itself diminish almost to nothing after the winter snow has melted. The streams are often confined in vertical-walled gorges, but in the heart of the highlands, or towards the margins, the valleys broaden (Figure 134). Here, alluvial or lacustrine material undoubtedly of Pleistocene ice-age origin is now dissected into two or three sharply defined natural terraces.

The geologic structure appears in the main to be an east-west axis of faulting and folding which coincides with the highest elevations and in which igneous and metamorphic rocks are exposed. On both sides of the central axis the flanking plateaus of either crystalline or sedimentary rock exhibit northeast-southwest alignments. Bituminous coal of low grade is mined in small quantities near Doab and Pul-i-Khumri in the upper Kunduz valley, on the north side of the Hindu Kush, and is known to exist elsewhere in the highlands.

Though the shift to rail and ocean transport in Asia has dealt a death blow to overland caravan traffic, the opening of a motor road across the Hindu Kush has stimulated internal traffic between northern and south-

Fig. 134 • The Band-i-Amir valley in central Afghanistan (also known as the Haza-rajat) displays a cultivated valley floor, an alluvial terrace probably dating from the Ice Age, and deeply eroded mountain slopes and precipices—all characteristic of the valleys of this region, cut off from the world by lofty mountain barriers through which only a few high passes run. The only trees visible are associated either with the banks of the river or with points along the lower slopes of the terraces where small alluvial fans funnel the sparse run-off from above. In the foreground are the remains of what appears to have been an earth-walled watchtower dominating the valley below. *(Food and Agriculture Organization.)*

eastern Afghanistan and has become vital to the economic and political integration of Afghanistan. The great north road from Kabul to the rich oases of Afghan-Turkestan, built in the late 1930's, is the shortest link [1] between the two most productive divisions of the country. The distance is 390 miles between Kabul and Mazar-i-Sharif on this well-graded gravel highway over the Shibar pass, 9,800 feet, which is the lowest pass directly through the mountains. By way of the circular road through Kandahar and Herat, the gradient is much easier, for the highest elevation reached is merely 6,000 feet, but the distance between the two cities on this route is 1,210 miles. Daily traffic north of Charikar on the Shibar route averages 100 to 200 vehicles. Trucks carrying chiefly cotton, *karakul* skins, and coal from north of the Hindu Kush move a quantity of goods doubtless much exceeding that formerly transported by camel trains.

Of the four main routes across the Hindu Kush,[2] the Shibar is longest and traverses narrow chasms, but it has the advantage of easier grades and can be kept open even in midwinter. The higher Khawak and Unai routes were much used by the camel drivers because of the open approaches and better forage. The difficult Salang is highest, yet the most direct. It is now proposed either to construct an aerial ropeway over the Salang pass or to tunnel under it at an elevation of 8,400 to 9,800 feet on either of two alignments, 3.9 or 5.3 miles through the Hindu Kush massif, in order to reduce the distance 137 miles between Kabul and the north.

High mountain agriculture is carried to elevations of 11,000 feet where terracing and irrigation are possible. This zone above 8,000 feet is devoted largely to spring-sown wheat, with barley more important towards

[1] It is of interest to note that the road over the Hindu Kush does not provide the shortest route across Afghanistan between the frontier railheads in Soviet and Pakistan territory. The distance by motorable roads is 587 miles from Landi Kotal, above Peshawar in the former North-West Frontier province, by way of Kabul and Mazar-i-Sharif to Termez on the north bank of the Oxus in the Uzbek S.S.R. From Chaman, near Quetta in Baluchistan, it is only 539 miles by way of Kandahar and Herat to Kushka in the Turkmen S.S.R. The latter route has the further advantage of avoiding the high snowy passes of the Hindu Kush.

[2] *Routes Across the Hindu Kush*

Pass	Altitude (feet)	Distance from Kabul (miles)
Khawak	11,640	225 to Khanabad
Unai- Hajigak- Ak Robat	11,000 11,000 10,255	320 to Mazar-i-Sharif via Bamian
Shibar	9,800	390 to Mazar-i-Sharif 327 to Khanabad
Salang	12,000	253 to Mazar-i-Sharif 190 to Khanabad

Fig. 135 • A typical herd of Afghan sheep driven by a boy and girl past a group of travellers engaged in conversation. The sheep population of the country is estimated at 30 million head or about three times the human population. About one-third of the people are engaged partly or entirely in pastoral activities. The sheep supply many of the needs of Afghan life, but are most important to the outside world as a source of *karakul* skins, used as furs. The scanty (and almost invisible) pasturage in the middle background is grazed in winter, but in summer the animals move toward the snow-capped mountains, barely discernible in the far left background. *(Food and Agriculture Organization.)*

the upper limits. Peas, broad beans, flax, turnips, and a few other hardy vegetables also are produced at these heights where winters last 7 to 9 months. The diet consists largely of dried peas, flat bread baked from whole wheat, and goats' milk. A significant historic area of mountain settlement is the basin of Bamian at 8,500 feet where some of the inhabitants live in rock dwellings. As many as 12,000 caves are cut in the red sandstone cliffs, the greater part now unoccupied and some containing Buddha images, carved during the period when Bamian was a monastery center and halfway point on the pilgrim road over the Unai and Ak Robat passes.

Nomadic grazing is the prevailing land use of the central and southern highlands (Figure 135). Every year hundreds of thousands of people with all their belongings on camels and donkeys move their sheep and goats to the sparse mountain pastures. The importance of herding in Afghanistan is obvious when one knows that the sheep population is estimated at 30 million, or about three animals to every person in the whole country. It is possible that one-third of the entire population is nomadic, if all degrees of nomadism be included—from the pasturing of herds by separate families within a short radius of their camps to the migration of whole tribes. The Mongol Hazaras, Turki Uzbeks, and Afghan Ghilzais are the groups most exclusively dependent upon herding. Their autumn and spring migrations to and from the bordering lowlands on routes followed from time immemorial across international boundaries have created problems of jurisdiction, citizenship, and taxation. No migrations are now allowed into the Soviet Union, but they continue undisturbed into Pakistan, and the tribes themselves are under very loose control by the central government.

Northern piedmont

The region of foothills and steppes to the north of the great divide in Afghanistan is in many ways the most favored part of the country. Here about one-third of the total population resides in about 20 per cent of the total area. Here is found more than half of the irrigated land, and here are produced the major surpluses of rice, cotton, and *karakul* skins. The population of this prosperous region is composed of Uzbeks and Turkmens in the section known as Afghan-Turkestan, and Tadzhiks in the extreme east, in the section known as Badakhshan.

Of all the rivers flowing northward into the piedmont, only the Kokcha and Kunduz reach the Amu Darya (Oxus)—master stream of the region and northern boundary of the country. Towards the west such rivers as Murghab and Band-i-Ami spread out in alluvial fans and are lost in the sands of the Kara Kum desert in either Afghan or Soviet territory. Where rivers debouch on the piedmont plain at elevations of 1,200 to 1,500 feet are found the fertile irrigated tracts and a series of important towns. Farther from the foothills arid conditions have prevented the spread of settlement to the south bank of the Amu Darya.

Deep loess deposits mantle the rolling hills which rise 200 to 300 feet above the alluvial surfaces of the piedmont steppe. Thin grass and shrub vegetation of the steppe is renowned for producing *karakuli* sheepskins of superior luster. About five million sheep of this particular breed are concentrated in Afghan Turkestan during winter and spring, but when the pastures have dried in summer the flocks are moved into the highlands southward and eastward. One breeder may own 10,000 sheep, tended by 40 shepherds and divided into units of 500 to 1,000 animals. The lambs must be slaughtered within 24 to 48 hours after birth to obtain skins with the valuable thick curling hair of black, gray, or golden brown. One skin makes a man's hat; 10 to 12 skins a lady's coat. *Karakul,* known to the world as Persian lamb or astrakhan, is exported to New York, which since the second World War has become the world's chief marketing center. Afghanistan is one of three most important sources of *karakul,* the others being South West Africa and the Soviet Union, and the country gains almost half of its foreign exchange in this manner.

Agricultural lands of the northern piedmont are divided into the areas devoted primarily to winter wheat—which can be grown without irrigation here more readily than elsewhere in Afghanistan—and the areas that are watered by means of diversion dams and intricate canal systems and devoted primarily to rice and cotton. Good land with plenty of water is priced high. Average-sized farm holdings are 10 to 15 acres, of which only about one-third can be devoted ordinarily to cash crops (cotton or rice) because of the labor shortage and the necessity of raising wheat and other subsistence crops. Rice, a preferred food among the well-to-do classes, is consumed entirely within the country. Cotton is good quality of the long-staple variety and was exported as early as 1870. Despite economically limited acreage and low yields, there has been a cotton export of 5,000 to 9,500 tons in recent years. Only 2,500 tons are consumed by the domestic spinning and weaving industry. Manufacturing of cotton is concentrated chiefly in one large mill at Pul-i-Khumri, located near sources of coal and hydroelectric power in the Kunduz valley on the road towards Kabul from the cotton-producing region stretching northward around Khanabad. Climate and soil are also adapted to sugar beets, but production is hampered by the severe competition of rice and cotton, and the country's single beet-sugar factory at Baghlan cannot be supplied with a large enough volume for efficient operation.

The hills embracing the northern piedmont are composed of Cretaceous and Tertiary strata with which are associated conditions favorable for petroleum deposits. Oil has been produced for some years just across the Amu Darya at Termez in Soviet territory. It has been decided to drill the first Afghan well in the Ser-i-Pul basin south of Shibargan, although favorable geologic structures have been found also near the Persian border in southwest Afghanistan.

No one city is outstandingly dominant in the northern piedmont, and, although Mazar-i-Sharif (42,000) is recognized as the leading center of trade and handicraft industries, five other cities in the region have populations ranging from 15,000 to 40,000. Near Mazar-i-Sharif stand the ruins of ancient Balkh with walls seven miles in circumference; Balkh was once among the largest cities of Asia and a point of traffic divergence west, south, and east. The eastern route, no longer used, runs through Faizabad and passes into the Wakhan corridor, parallels the upper Oxus, then goes over the Wakhjhir pass (16,150 feet) into China.

Seistan and the southwestern piedmont

A gigantic desert bolson containing playa lakes and immense gravelly or clayey surfaces occupies southwestern Afghanistan. This is the basin of Seistan, parts of which lie in Persia and Pakistan. Similar smaller basins of interior drainage occur along the Persian frontier west of Herat and bordering Pakistan south of Kandahar. These intermontane lands are the most extensive areas of low relief in the country at 1,500 to 3,000 feet above sea level, broken only by a few hills of volcanic rock or sandstone, but nearly useless for agriculture. There is a chain of settlements between the mountains and the deserts, irrigated by the Helmand and other rivers that enter the Seistan depression from the northeast and by the Hari Rud which turns northward into the Caspian depression. The population of these oases, including the cities of Kandahar (77,000) and Herat (76,000) which are the second and third cities, respectively, of Afghanistan, amounts to less than a third of the country's total. The area is 37 per cent of the country.

The floor of the Seistan basin is believed to have been covered by a huge inland sea during the Pleistocene period, and even now at the end of spring floods the Hamun-i-Helmand is a body of water 25 by 100 miles. The driest portions of the basin floor are tabular gravel-capped surfaces, separated from the lower levels by bluffs of 30 feet. The lower levels are traversed by river channels of which the largest is the Helmand. As the lake increases from its late summer depth of 5-8 feet to 15 feet or more, it occasionally overflows from the southern end into a still lower portion of the basin, known as the Gaud-i-Zirreh, lying southeast of the outlet. As a consequence, the latter has become extremely salty, while the Hamun remains fresh.

The most inhospitable aspect of the environment in Seistan is climate. The region is swept by cyclonic storms from December to April with blizzard winds up to 80 miles per hour, bringing all of the 2 to 3 inches of precipitation received annually. A brief season of calm, when swarms of insects rise from the lake flats, terminates in late May with the arrival of the "Wind of 120 Days" which lasts until September. It always comes from one direction, a little west of north, blowing steadily with velocities sometimes up to 70 miles per hour. Wind-scoured troughs 20 feet deep with axes parallel to the direction of the wind are common in the southwestern part of Seistan. Houses are all built with dead walls facing the wind. Migrating sand dunes bury whole villages and force the inhabit-ants to build new houses. The marvel is that anyone stays here. Yet the population of Seistan in the first decade of this century was estimated at 200,000, including settlements outside Afghanistan in Persia south and west of the Hamun-i-Helmand.

Beginning at an unknown time earlier than B.C. 500 and continuing to the tenth century A.D., Seistan was the seat of prosperous and highly civilized peoples, whose cities and towns dot the shifting Helmand delta with countless ruins. Conquered and settled in turn by the Greeks (led by Alexander), Scythians, and Arabs, Seistan was devastated by a Mongol invasion under Genghis Khan in the thirteenth century and again in the fifteenth century by Tamerlane's army. Much of the farm-ing population dependent upon irrigation on the lower Helmand was dispersed, supposedly giving origin to some of the present nomadic tribes of central Afghanistan. Since that time little of the irrigation sys-tem has been restored, sandstorms have wreaked havoc with the soil, and the population has never fully recovered.

Agriculture in the piedmont outside of Seistan proper is much better developed. In the oasis of Herat, supported by water from the Hari Rud, an intensive type of farming is practiced. More than 100 different kinds of truck and field crops are produced. Grains are harvested twice a year; crop rotation with fodder plants, grain *Leguminosae,* and cereals is cus-tomary; and pigeon houses are built for the special purpose of collect-ing dung for fertilizer.

Not as high an intensity of agriculture is observed at oases such as Farah, Girishk, and Kandahar. Though there are two harvests a year (in May, winter wheat, barley, and alfalfa, and then the summer crops, rice, maize, and cotton), and though apricot and peach trees and vineyards are planted, nonetheless the fields are hardly ever manured and lie fal-low two years out of three. Water is scarce; yields are low. Wheat yields vary from 8 to 22 bushels per acre.

The usual method of irrigation in the oases, other than Herat, is by means of a subterranean canal called a *karez* or *kanat* (*qanat*) similar to the *foggara* in the Sahara (Figure 110). A karez in these districts is often 3 to 6 miles long. The method has the advantage of reducing evaporation, but there are great losses of water by seepage, and main-tenance costs are heavy. An oasis farmer carefully watches for the hours when *karez* water is to flow to his land; a rich man is one who has the right to 24-36 hours per week, while a poor man receives water only 1-2 hours. Yet during springtime vast quantities of water flow unused down to the Hamun.

Clearly a great need exists for the improvement of irrigation in south-ern Afghanistan. Some of the possibilities for expansion of agriculture are already being realized,[3] and it is hoped that 20,000 families, to be re-cruited from the nomads, can be settled on land now uncultivated. The Boghra canal, which branches off the Helmand River at the Kajkai dam (330 feet in height), located 63 miles upstream from Girishk and fed from a reservoir 36 miles long, eventually will irrigate 500,000 acres. The Arghandab dam, situated 28 miles northeast of Kandahar, creates another large reservoir and is being equipped with a hydroelectric gen-erating plant to serve Kandahar. The smaller Girishk dam on the Boghra canal will bring water to 155,000 acres. Three other diversion dams to be built along the Helmand in its 400-mile course to the Hamun would add still more acreage. The soils of the Helmand delta are probably superior to soils upstream, but because the delta is split in an awkward fashion between Persia and Afghanistan, problems are anticipated here in the allocation of water. The potentially irrigable land of the Helmand and Arghandab valleys is estimated to be 1.1 million acres; if brought under cultivation it would add 44 per cent to the 2.5 million acres al-ready under intermittent or perennial cultivation in Afghanistan.

Manufacturing and foreign trade

In the present efforts to raise the level of consumption above subsistence and to expand Afghanistan's productive capacity, the basic problems, other than those connected with agriculture and stock-raising, involve manufacturing and foreign trade. There is an uncounted but large output of textiles, ceramics, metalware, and other consumer goods, carried on by craftsmen in the traditional manner. Only seven factories of modern type, employing 100 persons or more, and a few smaller ones exist in the country. These factories are en-gaged exclusively in producing consumer goods also. Although much Afghan cotton and wool is exported, imports of manufactures from these same fibers are increasingly necessary. It is estimated that the internal markets for cotton piece goods, which represent over half of the value of all imports, would permit a tenfold expansion of cotton-mill capacity. The short-term trend is likely to be a shift away from the less efficient, though perhaps more aesthetically satisfying, household crafts to large-scale power-driven mills.

[3] The program was undertaken in 1936, first by the Afghan government alone; later technical assistance was secured from Japan, then from Germany. In 1948 plans were completely revised and construction has proceeded under the direction of a United States engineering firm with financial support largely from Afghanistan itself, but with the aid of a loan from the Export-Import Bank. *United Nations Mission to Afghanistan*, Alphabetical Documentation, Part A, Libraries of the U.N. Secretariat, New York.

The imports of certain consumer goods, such as rayon, tea, sugar, re-fined petroleum products, automobiles, and steel manufactures cannot be replaced readily, if ever, by domestic sources. It is, therefore, vital that Afghanistan should maintain and increase the exports of those commodities for which the country is naturally suited and in which a leading position has already been attained in the markets of South Asia or the world. Chromium and lead-zinc ores of high grade are known but costs of export seem prohibitive. The foremost exports are dried fruits and nuts (40-50 per cent of the value of all exports) and *karakul* (30-40 per cent of the value), which find the best markets in India and the United States, respectively.

Afghanistan's most acute trade difficulty is its lack of direct access to the sea. Goods imported from overseas through Pakistan are subject to transit duty and delays for bureaucratic reasons. Trade with India, America, and Western Europe has to cross Pakistan, as there is relatively little traffic across the Persian frontier. Karachi harbor facilities are already overtaxed by Pakistan's requirements alone, and this outlet to the sea must often be supplemented by Bombay, 500 miles farther away than Karachi from the Peshawar railhead. The opening of the northern frontier to traffic with the Soviet Union may bring about a fundamental change in Afghanistan's foreign trade.

SELECTED GEOGRAPHICAL BIBLIOGRAPHY

1. Barger, Evert. "Some Problems of Central Asian Exploration," *Geographical Journal*, January-February, 1944, pp. 1-8.
2. Cervin, Vladimir. "Problems in the Integration of the Afghan Nation," *Middle East Journal*, Autumn, 1952, pp. 400-416.
3. Clarac-Schwarzenbach, Annemarie. "Afghanistan in Transition," *Geographical Magazine*, September, 1940, pp. 326-341.
4. Franck, Peter G. "Problems of Economic Development in Afghanistan," *Middle East Journal*, July, 1949, pp. 293-314; and October, 1949, pp. 421-440.
5. Fraser-Tytler, W. K. *Afghanistan: A Study of Political Developments in Central Asia.* London: Oxford University Press, 1950.
6. Howland, Felix. "Crossing the Hindu Kush," *Geographical Review*, April, 1940, pp. 272-278.
7. Sykes, Christopher. *A History of Afghanistan* (2 vols.). New York: Macmillan, 1940.
8. Thesiger, Wilfred. "The Hazaras of Central Afghanistan," *Geographical Journal*, September, 1955, pp. 312-319.
9. Westly, David E., and George S. Ayers. *Basic Data on the Economy of Afghanistan.* U. S. Bureau of Foreign Commerce, World Trade Information Series, Economic Reports, Part 1, No. 55-74, 1955.

10. Wilbur, Donald N. "Afghanistan, Independent and Surrounded," *Foreign Affairs*, April, 1953, pp. 486-494.
11. ———, ed. *Afghanistan*. New Haven: Human Relations Area Files, 1956.

Comments

The best descriptive and analytical treatments of Afghanistan's physical, social, and economic geography are published in the French, German, and Russian languages. The foreign books and periodicals containing these source materials are not commonly available to students in the United States. The geographical literature in English concerning Afghanistan consists largely of travel description such as the articles by Clarac-Schwarzenbach and Thesiger. The articles by Barger and Howland are cited for their outstanding descriptive value. Sykes' two-volume work is the most extensive historical account; while Fraser-Tytler's book is less detailed but presents his interpretation of Afghanistan's politico-geographic role. Concise treatments of Afghanistan's postwar internal and external political relationships are presented by Cervin and Wilbur, respectively. Franck's article is a general appraisal of trends in foreign trade and economic development, but more detailed, up-to-date, factual information is contained in the report by Westly and Ayers. Five authors, including Franck and Wilbur, are contributors to the 1956 survey of Afghanistan's social, economic, and political organization.

Southwest Asia

AN INTRODUCTION

THE UNIQUENESS OF SOUTHWEST ASIA IS PRIMARILY IN ITS GEO-
graphic location. A region may be many things to many people, and this
is perhaps true especially of Southwest Asia, but no matter which facets
of its landscape or life are examined, its position as a nexus joining Asia,
Africa, and Europe, cannot be ignored. Since earliest times the region
has served as a route for people, trade, armies, and ideas moving from
Europe eastward to Africa and Asia and from Asia westward to Africa
and Europe. The relative importance of this role has varied from time
to time, but rarely, if ever, has it been insignificant. Because of its location, Southwest Asia has been influenced by Western thought and culture to a greater extent and for a longer period of time than any other
comparable part of the continent, and in turn it has left its indelible
mark upon the West. The region has served as an entryway to the
Orient, but like most portals, the direction of movement could be reversed and often was. Contact with the West has been relatively easy,
though there have been times when it became tenuous or was actually
broken off. The interchange of ideas between the West and the Middle
East can be seen today in almost all aspects of culture—religion, language, science, education, politics, and economy.

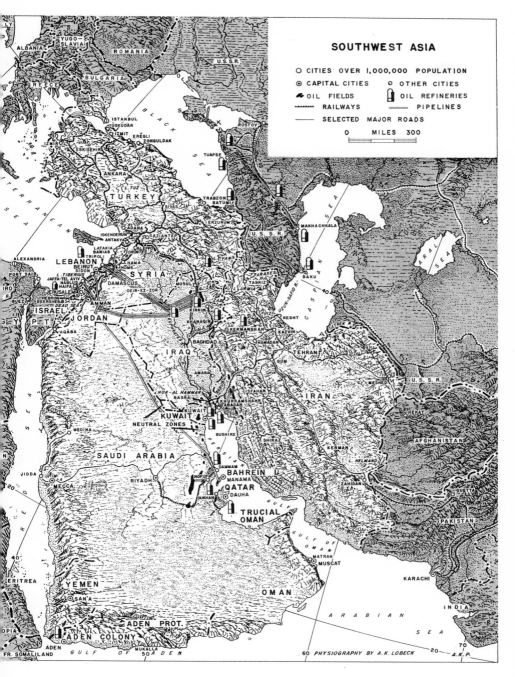

MAP 33

Southwest Asia is more diverse politically than any other major realm of the continent; it contains nine independent states and five dependencies in an area of slightly over 2,000,000 square miles.[1] In contrast to most of Asia it is sparsely populated; its total population is estimated at 52,700,000, which gives it an average density of about 24 persons per square mile. Nowhere in the realm can one find densities of population as great as those found in sections of eastern or southern Asia.

Southwest Asia forms the largest part of the Middle East region, which extends from Iran, on the east, westward to Cyrenaica, and from Turkey, on the north, southward to central Anglo-Egyptian Sudan.[2] Because of the continental scope of this text, Egypt, Cyrenaica, and the Sudan are not considered in detail, but one should remember that these areas, especially Egypt, are parts of an integrated unit, and that their relationship to Southwest Asia is not only obvious but also very close. Egypt is one of the leading countries, politically and economically, of the Middle East; as such it must necessarily be included in many of the discussions on Southwest Asia, even though its location in Africa technically excludes it. For the sake of convenience the term "Middle East" will be used here in general discussion except where the subject deals solely with Asiatic matters.

The importance of the locational factor can, perhaps, be best appreciated by studying a map of the Eastern Hemisphere. It is obvious that the major routes connecting Europe, Asia, and Africa pass through the Middle East. The only land route connecting the European and Asiatic continents that does not cross the Middle East is the trans-Soviet route, which passes north of the Caspian Sea. Much of the complexity of the region, as well as its strategic situation, is directly related to this focus of routes.

Of great importance and interest has been the flow of people, ideas, and goods along these ancient and modern ways. Peoples now long resident in Europe and Africa spent generations in transit; from the east the Seljuk and Ottoman Turks came to conquer but remained to settle; the Mongols under Genghis Khan and Tamerlane conquered and destroyed; Persians, Arabs, Greeks, Romans, British, French, and Americans have come peaceably or with armies. All these have to some degree left their imprint. Out of the Middle East have come the three great monotheistic religions whose beliefs have encompassed the earth. Great variety, if not always great volume, has marked the goods moving through or from this region. Frankincense and myrrh of ancient times,

[1] Turkey, Syria, Lebanon, Israel, Jordan, Saudi Arabia, Yemen, Iraq, and Iran are independent states; Aden and the Aden Protectorate, Oman, Trucial Oman, Bahrein, and Kuwait are dependencies (See Map 33).

[2] W. B. Fisher, "Unity and Diversity in the Middle East," *Geographical Review*, July, 1947, pp. 416-417.

gold, silver, silks, rugs, precious stones, damascene blades, dates, figs, and today's vast flow of oil are examples.

On occasion, conquest of the region has been a necessary prelude to attempted world domination. That Alexander cut the Gordian knot in Asia Minor seems more than pure chance. Neither Napoleon nor Hitler was successful in his ambition, but both tried to conquer the Middle East as a step toward even greater attainment, the control of India. Great Britain, because she controlled the Mediterranean-Suez route and land bases to protect it, was facilitated in the acquisition and maintenance of her Asian and African possessions, and she was at the same time in a position to block attempted penetration into the region by other great powers.

The strategic importance of the Middle East seems greater than ever. Not only is it geographically central, but it has the world's largest known petroleum reserves, at present controlled largely by the United States and Great Britain, and it is the focus of conflicting interests of the United States, Great Britain, France, and the Soviet Union. The outcome of the East-West struggle may well be decided by control of the Middle East.

Thus, the realm of Southwest Asia presents an intricate and complex picture. The area thought to be the original home of man, or at least the one that has been settled continuously longer than any other, contains varied cultures, mixtures of very old and modern. An undeveloped region, it faces many major problems which, together with its geographic location and oil resources, present an ever-present dilemma to the world.

Certain aspects of location already have been cited, but closer examination of some is necessary. The gateway function of the Middle East accounts to a considerable degree for the movement of people into and through the region and for the present ethnic composition of a large part of its population. Among the chief reasons for the movement of people have been (1) the search for new lands because of overpopulation, climatic change, or loss of livelihood, (2) wars of conquest, (3) trade and economic penetration, (4) the spread of religious beliefs or the seeking of religious freedom, (5) the desire for political control, and (6) the need for labor. The importance of any one of these varied from time to time as did the number of people involved, though all together and over a number of centuries the process was fairly continual. The latest manifestation of such movements has been the migration of hundreds of thousands of Jews into Palestine, and later, Israel.

Southwest Asia has been both the source and destination of many peoples. The Semitic peoples who now inhabit much of the realm apparently had their origin in the southwestern part of the Arabian peninsula, moving both toward the north, into the eastern Mediterranean area

and into northern Africa, and northeastward across the desert into Mesopotamia; others reached Egypt and the Sudan by crossing the Red Sea.
From the east, by way of Iran, came successive waves of people, some
of whom, the Iranians, Turks, and Turkmens, are still heavily represented in the present population; others, like the Mongols, had little
lasting effect, except for the destruction they wrought. From the west
came the Greeks, Romans, and Crusaders; and from the south, by way
of Egypt or by sea, came African Negroes. In more modern times various Europeans, especially Greeks, Italians, British, and French, have
settled in relatively small numbers in the various Middle Eastern countries. Intermarriage has altered the original racial types to a considerable
degree, though these normally are still distinguishable. The people
showing least admixture are found in some of the more isolated mountain and oasis communities, or among the nomadic desert tribes.

Although the population of Southwest Asia is heterogeneous, the majority of the people belongs to a few main groups, the largest of which
is the Arab. The population of six of the independent states and that of
all of the dependencies is mainly Arab. Turks, Iranians, and Jews are
the other important groups. In like fashion, although the number of
languages spoken is large, four or five of them account for the majority
of the people—Arabic, Turkish, Persian, and, among the mountain tribes
in Turkey, Iraq, and Iran, Kurdish and Caucasian. Possibly as many
Jews speak Arabic as Hebrew, though the latter is the official language
of Israel. In the larger urban centers foreigners can usually make themselves understood by speaking either French or English.

Weather and climate

Factors of weather and climate
have had a profound effect upon the landscape and life of Southwest
Asia. Not only is this shown in myriad ways in the everyday life of the
people, but it is reflected also in many aspects of the physical scene—in
soils, natural vegetation, and sources of water, both ground and surface.

The most significant factor of the climate for the larger part of the
realm is a deficiency of precipitation (Plate D). The Mediterranean,
Black, and Caspian coastal zones, and some of the hill and mountain
areas, are the only sections that can be classed as humid. Outside of
these, agriculture must be carried on by irrigation or by dry-farming.
Hence the availability of water becomes one of the most vital aspects of
life and one of the greatest problems of the people, the majority of whom
must obtain their livelihood directly from the land. An added handicap
is in the distribution of precipitation; except for a few small areas, the
maximum comes during the cool season. This may allow the production

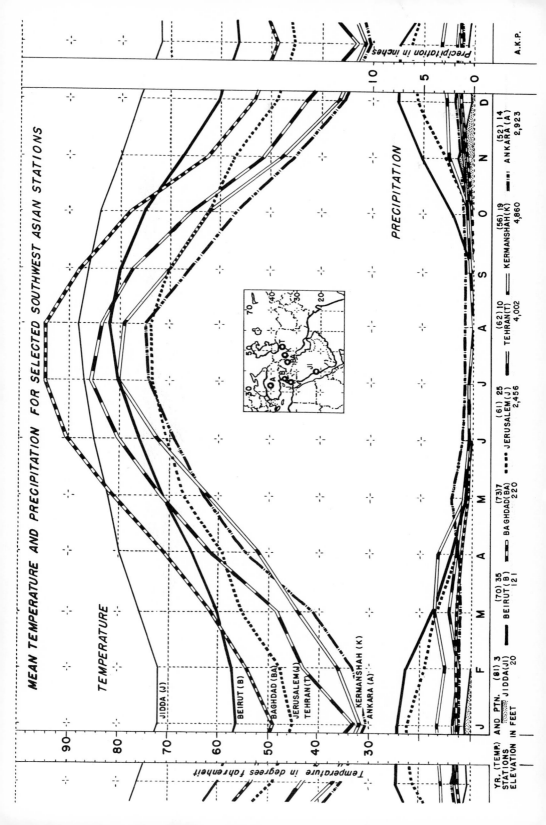

MEAN TEMPERATURE AND PRECIPITATION FOR SELECTED SOUTHWEST ASIAN STATIONS

TEMPERATURE

PRECIPITATION

Temperature in degrees Fahrenheit

Precipitation in inches

A.K.P.

YR. (TEMP.)	(81) 3	(70) 35	(73) 7	(61) 25	(62) 10	(56) 19	(52) 14
AND PTN.	JIDDA (JI)	BEIRUT (B)	BAGHDAD (BA)	JERUSALEM (J)	TEHRAN (T)	KERMANSHAH (K)	ANKARA (A)
STATIONS ELEVATION IN FEET	20	121	220	2,456	4,002	4,860	2,923

JIDDA (J)

BEIRUT (B)

BAGHDAD (BA)

JERUSALEM (J)
TEHRAN (T)

KERMANSHAH (K)
ANKARA (A)

of certain winter crops in the milder areas, but it necessitates irrigation even in some of the areas where conditions are humid, since summers are almost, if not entirely, dry. On the other hand, one advantage of the winter maximum is in the effect it has upon the water supply in mountain and plateau areas. Much of the winter precipitation in the higher mountains is in the form of snow; as it melts during spring and early summer, it replenishes the surface streams and the sources of springs and wells.

Precipitation is characteristically cyclonic in origin, derived from depressions that pass through the Mediterranean region toward the east. Where high mountains lie thwart the direction of prevailing winds, additional precipitation is generated by orographic conditions. The variation in the intensity of cyclones, in the number of storms, and in the position of storm tracks, chiefly accounts for the variability of precipitation from year to year. This condition tends to be most extreme in the drier areas that lie to the south of the storm tracks, but it is of importance in all of the arid and semi-arid areas, and also, on occasion, in the areas receiving relatively ample amounts of moisture.

The major part of Southwest Asia receives less than 10 inches of precipitation a year, large sections as little as 5 inches, and a few under 2 inches. It is possible that interior parts of Arabia and Iran are as rainless as any in the world. The coastal areas of the Mediterranean, Black, and Caspian seas, and the windward slopes of the Pontus, Zagros, and Elburz ranges, are the more humid, receiving between 20 and 40 inches a year. Maximum amounts are reached on the Pontus and Elburz where the yearly totals probably exceed 65 inches. The precipitation gradient in the realm has a general northwest-southeast direction. Sections of the Black Sea coast of Turkey, the Caspian coast of Iran, and the highlands of southwestern Arabia have appreciable summer rain; the last is the sole area with a summer maximum, the result of monsoon-like conditions.

Summers throughout the realm are not only hot but long. With the exception of parts of the Turkish plateaus and possibly northeastern Iran, there are six to nine months of the year with temperatures over 65°F. Hot-month temperatures vary from a high of 100° for one or two stations in southern Iran to the middle or high 70's for stations on the Anatolian and Armenian plateaus which represent the warmer rather than the hot areas. Considerable elevation is necessary to reduce summer temperatures, and even higher latitudes seem to have relatively little effect, or less than is usually normal. In Iran, Shiraz, Kermanshah, and Tabriz have hot-month temperatures of 85°, 80°, and 81° respectively; they are at elevations of 5,000, 4,860, and 4,420 feet, and approximately at latitudes 30°, 34°, and 38°N. Deh Bid, about half a degree of latitude north of Shiraz but at an elevation of 8,000 feet, has a hot-month temperature of only 69°.

Extremes of summer heat are characteristic of southern Iran and also, probably, of interior Arabia, though few figures are available for the latter. In the lowland areas of southern Iran average monthly temperatures of over 90° may be recorded for as many as three or four months; summer daytime temperatures of over 100° have been recorded for as many as 90 consecutive days.

Winter temperatures are much less uniform, though they may be equally extreme. Latitude and elevation seem to play more normal roles. The three Iranian stations mentioned above, Shiraz, Kermanshah, and Tabriz, have cold-month temperatures of 47°, 32°, and 17° respectively, a difference of 30 degrees for winter as compared to 5 degrees for summer. Deh Bid, the mountain station (8,000 feet) just north of Shiraz, has a January temperature of 27°, 10 degrees above that of Tabriz, although its hot-month temperature was 12 degrees less than that of Tabriz. These differences are somewhat less in summer and greater in winter than the normal latitudinal temperature gradient. Interior Turkey and Iran are the major areas having relatively low cold-month temperatures; for the most part, the cold-month temperatures are below 35° (see Tehran on Plate D), and in some instances below 20°. The remainder of the realm has mild to warm, or even hot, winters, with temperatures for the coldest month varying from the 40's to the 60's or 70's depending upon latitude (see Jidda, Beirut, Baghdad, and Jerusalem on Plate D).

Despite the mild or warm winters in the areas of lower latitude, daily minima of 32° or lower have been recorded in practically the entire region with the exception of southernmost Arabia and Iran. Not only is frost quite probable, but snow occasionally falls in the latitude of Baghdad and slightly farther south. As might be expected, the lowest minima occur in the interior areas of Turkey and northern Iran where temperatures well below 0°F. have been recorded, e.g. Tabriz, −18°F. Because of low temperatures, winter precipitation in the northern sections of the realm and in the highlands is largely in the form of snow. The plateaus of Turkey and Iran may have a snow cover for considerable periods of time; high mountains have a heavy accumulation of snow that during the winter often blocks roads for days or weeks and remains on the higher elevations well into late spring and early summer. Only in the most protected spots does snow remain all summer.

A number of other features of weather and climate are of consequence in the use of land. All of the desert areas are subject to dust storms that may be dangerous as well as damaging; Iran and Turkey periodically suffer from severe blizzards in winter; other areas experience hot dry winds, or hot humid winds of great velocity and often of long duration. Torrential rains of short duration clog the *wadis*, washing out irrigated tracts and causing damage to roadways and trails. Rainy spells of more than usual length have brought about the collapse of many buildings made of sun-dried brick, which when saturated simply slump into piles of mingled mud and debris.

The pattern of landforms

The major landforms of Southwest Asia are a singularly important factor, not only in their influence upon weather and climate and certain other natural conditions, but also in their relations to the development of the cultural landscape. Age-old routes of travel, modern lines of transport, settlement patterns, political units, and land use all show varying degrees of relationship to the types of landforms and their areal distribution. Of the major categories of landforms, mountains and plateaus are dominant within the realm; plains are the least in number and areal extent; hill country is usually associated with high mountains as fringe or foothill area, or it occurs as the dissected margins of plateaus (Map 33).

The realm falls naturally into two main divisions based upon major surface features: (1) to the north and east, Turkey and Iran, countries dominated by high mountains and intermontane plateaus, and (2) to the west and south, the Arabian peninsula, the countries of the eastern Mediterranean, and Iraq, areas of continental plateau or tableland, broken locally by hill country or mountains.

The high and generally continuous mountains of Turkey and Iran are segments of the great alpine system of Eurasia. Individual ranges, largely arcuate in outline, coalesce into massive mountain knots, and thus enclose extense areas of plateau. In Turkey the Pontus range or Pontic mountains parallel the Black Sea coast, separated from it only by a very narrow strip of coastal plain which in places is broken by rocky headlands that reach the water's edge. In the south are the Taurus and Antitaurus mountains and associated ranges which form a barrier running almost the entire length of the country. In the east the Pontus and Taurus systems merge into the mass of the Armenian knot, a mountain node which spills into both the Soviet Union and Iran and which, in the east, is dominated by the volcanic cone of Ararat (16,945 feet). The intermontane plateaus of Anatolia and Armenia lie between the bordering mountain chains—Anatolia in the west, Armenia in the east. Small areas of plain are found along the western and southern coasts.

Eastward from the Armenian knot extend the major mountain ranges of Iran, which even more than in the case of Turkey completely encircle the country. The largest and most continuous of these is the Zagros chain which occupies the whole western side of the country from the international boundary in the north to the Strait of Hormuz in the south. Not only are these mountains continuous and rugged, but they are wide as well and in places attain widths of 150 to 200 miles. Along the northern border of Iran are the ranges of Azerbaijan and the Elburz system. Although these differ in structure and appearance from place to place, they form a topographic barrier to and beyond the boundary of Afghanistan in the east, where they eventually merge into the Pamir knot. Although not so massive a system as the Zagros, through much of their length the Elburz are high and rugged. Mount Demavend (18,550), the highest peak in Iran and in the Middle East, is a volcanic cone that towers above the general upland level of the Elburz, just northeast of Tehran. To the east of Hormuz and topographically continuous with the Zagros are the mountains of Makran. This low but relatively rugged range fronts the Gulf of Oman in Iran and western Pakistan. Within Pakistan the system bears northeastward, is joined by the ranges of southern Afghanistan, and ultimately merges also into the Pamir knot. The final segment of encircling mountains are the highlands of eastern Iran, a series of essentially parallel but discontinuous ranges that bridge the gap between the Elburz in the north and the Makran in the south. Lying almost athwart the Iranian-Afghan boundary, they separate the interior plateau-and-basin regions of central Iran from those of western Afghanistan.

Within this peripheral ring of mountain ranges are the intermontane plateaus, most of which are basins of interior drainage. Some of these, such as the Great Kavir and the Southern Lut, cover thousands of square miles and are truly forbidding. Others, much smaller and with more ample supplies of water, are rather well developed agriculturally and have rather high population densities, e.g. Azerbaijan and the Veramin plain.

The plains of Iran are proportionally as small as those of Turkey and are likewise peripheral. The largest, Khuzistan, at the head of the Persian Gulf, is an integral part of the Tigris-Euphrates lowland. In the north a narrow coastal plain borders the Caspian; in the south an equally narrow but more discontinuous plain fronts the Persian Gulf and the Gulf of Oman. Two small areas of steppe in the northwest and northeast complete the list of plains. These are both parts of larger plains that extend into the Soviet Union.

The second major landform region extends from the eastern Mediterranean and Red Sea on the west to the foothills of the Taurus and Antitaurus in the north, and to the Zagros and the shores of the Persian Gulf in the east. It encompasses all of the Arabian peninsula, Jordan, Israel, Syria, Lebanon, and most of Iraq, and is essentially a continental tableland or plateau, highest in the west and lowest in the east where it merges into the Tigris-Euphrates lowland and the coastal plain of eastern Arabia. The high western edge is in the form of hill country and mountains, the result of dissection by streams, local folding, faulting, and volcanism, or of a combination of these. From the crest of the highlands east of the rift valleys, the plateau surface descends gradually to the cliffs overlooking the Euphrates River. A similar condition exists in much of the Arabian peninsula, although the surface there is rather more irregular, broken in places by lava highlands and bold escarpments.

The topography of the hill and mountain areas of the eastern Mediterranean and western Arabia is more varied and complex than that of the plateau to the eastward. Along the eastern Mediterranean from above the Gulf of Iskanderun (Alexandretta) southward to the head of the Gulf of Aqaba there are four distinct and essentially parallel regions from west to east based upon topography—(1) the Mediterranean coastal plain, (2) a western series of hills and mountains, (3) a series of rifts and fault valleys, and (4) an eastern zone of hill and mountain lands.

The Mediterranean coastal plain generally is narrow and north of Haifa is discontinuous, being broken in a number of places by spurs of highlands that reach the sea. Its maximum width in this section is not over four miles. Where Mount Carmel nears the sea at Haifa, the coastal plain is barely wide enough to accommodate a highway and railroad. South of this point the plain gradually widens, to reach its maximum width of 20 miles between Rafah and Beersheba. Between Haifa and Tel-Aviv, the Israeli coastal plain is called the plain of Sharon, while south of Tel-Aviv it becomes the plain of Philistia.

The western of the two hill-and-mountain regions is the better defined and more continuous. In general, these north-south trending ranges composed of folded or folded-and-faulted sediments lie upon a complex crystalline rock basement. Limestone is the predominant type of bedrock. In some areas basaltic lava reaches the surface. This belt of highlands extends the entire length of the Mediterranean coastal area, merging in the north with the Antitaurus mountains and in the south with the dissected plateaus of Sinai. There are only three major breaks in this entire distance that allow relatively easy ingress to the interior—(1) the plain of Esdraelon and vale of Jezreel between Haifa on the coast and Beisan in the Jordan valley, (2) the lowland between Tripoli and Homs, and (3) the valley of the Orontes where it turns westward past Antakya (Antioch) to reach the Mediterranean between the Amanus range and the Jebel Ansarieh. The individual ranges of the western hill-and-mountain area, from north to south, are the (1) Amanus range, (2) Jebel Ansarieh, (3) Lebanon Mountains, (4) hills of Galilee, (5) plateau of Samaria (of which Mount Carmel is an offshoot), and (6) hills of Judea. The highlands of the Negev south of Judea are a northward continuation of the Sinai (See Figure 135a). The highest elevations in the above ranges are found in the Lebanon mountains where one peak is just over 10,000

Fig. 135a • Desert landscape in Southwest Asia: the Sinai. Between the western end of the Fertile Crescent and the Nile valley, the Sinai is characteristic of much of the desert area of Southwest Asia. This view shows some of the low ranges and pebbly plain along the main road from Ismailia, Egypt, to the Negev of Israel. Because of sparseness of vegetation and scarcity of water, the region supports only a few nomads. Ancient monasteries and recent mineral development are other types of human occupance present. (John R. Randall.)

feet above sea level. The ranges vary in width from about 25 miles to as much as 40 miles.

The western hill areas are terminated on the east by a series of rifts and fault valleys which in a like manner extend almost continuously from the Gulf of Aqaba, a drowned rift, to the Antitaurus mountains of Turkey. The best known and most spectacular of the rifts is that of the Dead Sea and Jordan valley, most of which is well below sea level. The northern end of this rift is approximately at the Lebanon-Israeli boundary, where a saddle between the Lebanon and Herman mountains (Jebelesh-Sheik) forms a barrier between the fault valley of the Bekka and the Jordan rift. The northern extremity of the Jordan rift is occupied by Lake Huleh and the Huleh marshes, the surface of Lake Huleh being approximately 230 feet above sea level. From Lake Huleh the Jordan River flows southward in a canyon cut in basaltic lava to enter Lake Tiberias (Sea of Galilee) the

surface of which is 686 feet below sea level. A second basaltic dam marks
the outlet of Lake Tiberias, and southward from there the Jordan rift is
spectacular. The encompassing sides rise sharply from the relatively level
floor of the valley, and the lines of the faults are readily apparent. There
is, however, a difference between the east and west sides. The eastern
side, being the windward one, receives more rainfall and hence is not only
more dissected, but has more vegetation; the western side, being the lee,
is somewhat less dissected and generally much more barren in appearance. The Jordan River meanders below Lake Tiberias and is entrenched
into the floor of the valley so that along much of its lower course terraces
edged with well developed badlands are characteristic.

The Dead Sea occupies the lowest part of the Jordan rift (El Ghor).
The surface of the sea is 1,292 feet below sea level; its greatest depth is
approximately 1,300 feet. Since the highland areas on either side of the
Jordan, south of Lake Tiberias and around the Dead Sea, rise to elevations of between 2,000 and 3,000 feet above sea level in short distances,
the local relief is truly impressive. South of the Dead Sea the rift is continued in the Wadi Araba. The sea-level contour crosses the *wadi* about
40 miles south of the Dead Sea, and the divide between interior drainage
and that of the Gulf of Aqaba is reached some 60 miles from the Dead
Sea. This divide is about 600 feet above sea level and about 45 miles
from the head of the Gulf. The rift south of the divide has a number of
parts, each with a local name. Altogether the Jordan rift is some 250
miles long and varies in width from as little as two miles to as much as
15 miles.

The linear region of rifts and fault valleys northward from the Jordan
is divided into three fairly separate sections. The Bekka, a fault valley
rather than a true rift, lies between the Lebanon mountains on the west
and the Herman and Anti-Lebanon mountains on the east. It is quite distinct from the Jordan rift and cut off from it by a saddle of highland
which connects the Lebanon and Herman ranges near their southern ends.
The Bekka has a width varying between 10 and 15 miles and a length of
approximately 100 miles.

The second section is again a true rift and is the valley occupied by the
middle course of the Orontes River below Hama. Lava has obstructed the
flow of the river in such a way that in winter much of the valley is
flooded, and in summer it is marshy. A few miles above Antakya the
Orontes bends rather sharply towards the southwest and, following a
transverse fault, reaches the Mediterranean. The lowland is continued
northward from the Orontes bend for some 75 miles in a valley that lies
between the Amanus range on the west and the Kurd Dagh on the east.
From its northern end in Turkey to the Gulf of Aqaba, the region of rifts
and fault valleys has a total length of over 400 miles, and with the excep-

tion of the portion containing the Orontes River, these lowlands are hemmed in on both sides by comparatively high ranges.

The eastern region of hill country and mountains (with the exception of the Kurd Dagh, a spur of the Antitaurus) starts well south of its western counterpart. The first ranges of prominence are the folded ranges of central Syria northeast of Damascus. These have a general northeast-southwest trend and extend almost to the Euphrates. The Anti-Lebanon and Herman mountains, also fold ranges, have a more pronounced north-south trend and are generally parallel to the Lebanon mountains facing them across the Bekka. South of the Herman range the continuity of the region is broken by the Hauran, a rolling lava upland contiguous in the east with the large lava-covered areas of southern Syria and eastern Jordan, which reach their greatest height (5,905 feet) in the Jebel Druze, a basaltic dome (Figure 136).

South of the Hauran the highly dissected character of the plateau edge is again resumed and continues without marked interruption to the highlands of the Yemen at the southwestern corner of the Arabian peninsula. Geomorphologically, the head of the Gulf of Aqaba marks the termination of the highlands of the eastern Mediterranean region, but topographically there is no break. The mountains east of the Jordan rift and south of the Houran are still known today by their ancient names: (from north to south) the hills of Gilead, Moab, and Edom.

The highlands that mark the western edge of the Arabian platform along the Red Sea, although topographically continuous with those of Jordan, are composed largely of ancient crystalline rock and lavas rather than sediments, and as a group they are higher and often more rugged than those to the north. Along most of the Red Sea coast the highlands rise abruptly from a narrow alluvial coastal plain and attain their maximum height within a few miles of the coast. In the Hijaz elevations vary from 1,500 to 6,000 feet, though the general crest level is between 2,000 and 3,000. Between Yanbu and Jidda the highlands become noticeably lower, giving easier access to the interior and to the sacred cities of Medina and Mecca. South from Mecca the highlands increase rapidly to attain the greatest height in Arabia. The mountains of Asir have peaks from 7,000 to 9,000 feet and those of the Yemen from 10,000 feet to over 12,000.

The dissected edge of the Arabian platform also extends along three-quarters of the southern border of the peninsula, from Bab-el-Mendab to just beyond Kuria Muria Bay (approximate longitude 57°E.). In keeping with the altitude of the entire platform, the southern edge is highest in the west and descends rather gradually to the plain of southern Oman. Heights of almost 10,000 feet are found in the Aden Protectorate, while at the eastern end the elevation of the Dufar plateau is as little as 2,000

Fig. 136 • The surface of the desolate lava plateau in north-central Jordan. Here the surface rubble is relatively small; in other areas the lava occurs in the form of large boulders. The lava area stretches southward from the Jebel Druze and is crossed by the main highway between Amman and Baghdad.

In the background is Pumping Station H-5 of the Iraq Petroleum Company located on the pipeline to Haifa. There are five such stations between Haditha, on the Euphrates, and Haifa. Since the creation of Israel in 1948, Iraq has stopped the flow of oil through this pipeline. Besides the installations needed for maintenance, each station has housing for employees and a landing strip. Note the water towers silhouetted against the horizon. *(John R. Randall.)*

feet. Fronting the Gulf of Oman in the east are the Oman mountains, an offshoot of the Zagros of Iran. These highlands, an island of green in the desert, counterbalance those of the Yemen in the southwest. For the most part rugged, they reach a maximum elevation of 10,200 feet.

Innumerable instances in the Middle East show the relations between topography and cultural features. More often, however, topography is only one of several factors involved in a given relationship. The Fertile Crescent, one of the most famous routes in the world, undoubtedly developed largely because of the ease of its terrain, but its growth in importance was influenced as well by the availability of water and natural forage. In a similar way other routing of travel, tillage of land, distribution of population, and location of urban centers all show some rather obvious relation to the character of the land surface. Equally understandable is the isolation and defensibility sought by ethnic and religious minorities in their retreat into mountainous regions.

A somewhat more tenuous relationship is seen in the effect of topographic complexity upon the political splintering of Greater Syria.[3] This area, with its large number of small physiographic units, has tended throughout its history to divide into numerous political units, except when under the authority of a strong controlling power, such as Rome. The reverse is seen, however, in the political stability of Turkey, a region of physical compactness in spite of local variety.

The contrast between the Nile valley and that of the Tigris-Euphrates offers another illustration of the influence of landforms. The Tigris and Euphrates lowland, open to the mountains on the east and the plateau on the west, invited invasion because of its abundant waters, fertile soil, and level land. The Nile, on the other hand, was for centuries isolated and undisturbed because invaders could not cross its surrounding deserts, not only because of their dryness, but also because of the difficulty of their terrain.

Adherence to Islam

The last of the major factors that has shaped the realm of Southwest Asia and given it unity has been the adherence of a majority of its inhabitants to Islam. This term is used in three different but mutually related ways: (1) to signify the faith of the Moslems; (2) to designate all the Moslems in the world and the areas they occupy; and (3) to characterize the culture that has developed as a result of adherence to the faith of the Prophet Mohammed. Islamic culture is peculiarly Middle Eastern in spite of the fact that it is found in areas outside that region.

The laws and tenets of Islam reflect nearly all facets of the environment of its homeland, and the people who accepted these have developed a community of spirit and deed that is probably stronger than that of either Christianity or Judaism, though the area encompassed is more restricted than that of the former. Not only is this true of the Arabs of the Middle East, but also of other groups of people who came under the control of the Arabs in the expansion of their empire and who ultimately became Moslems. Thus the Iranians and Turks, ethnically unrelated to the Arabs, are members of the Islamic religious community.

Although it is difficult to judge or to assess the degree of influence Islam has had upon the development of the total culture of the Middle

[3] The area composed of Syria, Lebanon, Israel, and Jordan.

East, it has played an exceedingly important part in the lives and daily actions of a majority of the population. The Qur'an (Koran) and Moslem canon law (Shariah) were the law for centuries in the Islamic world, and in some countries they still are. Thus, Moslems have laws and instructions to guide them for almost every occasion, as well as for every action that an individual or group might conceivably take. These laws are not necessarily or even primarily prohibitions. Many of them are positive actions that are required of all good Moslems such as the Five Pillars of Islam: profession of faith, prayer, alms-giving, fasting, and pilgrimage. Because most Moslems obey the laws of their faith, there results a similarity of action among all these people from place to place despite ethnic and economic differences. This peculiar regional characteristic is of major importance in understanding the Middle East and its many problems.

SELECTED GEOGRAPHICAL BIBLIOGRAPHY

1. Blanchard, Raoul. "Asie Occidentale." Vol. VIII in *Geographie Universelle.* Paris: Librairie Armand Colin, 1929.
2. Coon, Carleton. *Caravan, The Story of the Middle East.* New York: Henry Holt and Co., 1951.
3. Fisher, W. B. *The Middle East, A Physical, Social and Regional Geography.* New York: E. P. Dutton and Co., 1952.
4. ———. "Unity and Diversity in the Middle East," *Geographical Review,* July, 1947, pp. 414-35. See also "South-west Asia: Internal Problems" (Chapter XXVIII) and "Southwest Asia: External Relations" (Chapter XXIX) in W. G. East and A. E. Moodie, eds., *The Changing World.* Yonkers-on-Hudson: World Book Company, 1956.
5. *The Middle East: A Political and Economic Survey,* 2d ed. London: Royal Institute of International Affairs, 1954.

Comments

Blanchard's work on the Middle East is one of the best and most detailed, especially on physical geographic aspects. In spite of the changes that have taken place in the Middle East since its publication, much of the material on culture is still applicable. Fisher's *Middle East* is the only full-scale English-language geography text on the region. It is a college text, valuable, readable, and a handy source of information for anyone interested in the area. The Royal Institute's political and economic survey on the Middle East is a reference volume which contains much nongeographic material, but material nonetheless important for any student of the area.

Fisher's book and the Royal Institute Survey have been used as references in all the chapters on Southwest Asia. In addition, Erwin Raisz has prepared two physiographic diagrams, one of Arabia, the other of the Near East, which are of great value in giving an over-all view of surface features.

Few of the states in the Middle East publish statistical annuals or similar volumes that are readily obtainable in the United States; a number have none at all. Statistical data for the realm and the individual states are difficult to get, often inaccurate, or simply nonexistent. In many cases different sources when reporting a given item will give widely varying figures. In most cases quoted figures should be considered estimates or approximations unless otherwise noted.

Southwest Asia

ECONOMIC PATTERNS

AGRICULTURE, INCLUDING PASTORALISM, IS THE CHIEF ECONOMIC AC-
tivity in the Middle East. By far the largest part of the population is engaged in some type of farming or livestock rearing.[1] For a majority of
the countries the percentage of inhabitants thus occupied is certainly 75;
for all, with the exception of Israel, the percentage is over 60. Relatively
small percentages of the population are engaged in manufacturing of all
types, in trade and services, in the extractive industries, and in tourism
and the pilgrim trade.

| Agriculture and land use

In spite of the preponderance
of agriculture in the total economy, the Middle East is not a region
significant for its agricultural surpluses, nor, with one or two exceptions,
are agricultural products from this area important in international

---

[1] Percentage of population engaged in some type of farming: Iran, 80; Turkey,
over 80; Egypt, 70; Lebanon, 75; Syria, over 70; Iraq, over 60. The percentages for
Saudi Arabia, the Yemen, and Jordan are not available, but they are probably as
high as the highest above.

trade.[2] The major part of the crops and livestock products produced are consumed within the realm. There has been and still is a considerable intraregional trade in farm and livestock commodities.

Subsistence farming is most widespread, and the majority of farmers are tenants or sharecroppers who, while producing crops for the landlord, must at the same time provide enough for their own families. Since in common practice the tenant receives the smallest share of the harvest, he usually achieves only the barest subsistence. This is often true, also, of the small landowner whose farm may not be large enough to supply his minimum requirements. Many of the landlords are interested primarily in a large cash income; few live on their land, and few are concerned about the condition either of the land or of their peasants. Although the capital investment is the landlord's, the percentage of the harvest he receives is all out of proportion to the risks he takes. The peasant, on the other hand, having neither capital nor security of tenure, is in no position to attempt improvement. There is, likewise, almost no chance that he may improve his status. This system of land ownership and tenure has developed over a very long period of time and thus is both complex and difficult to change.

The agricultural system is medieval, similar in many respects to the ancient three-field system of Europe. Small plots of land are cultivated extensively rather than intensively. Although this practice may give a relatively high degree of economic stability, it keeps the peasant at a low subsistence level, is inefficient, and wastes both land and labor. Livestock rearing also is extensive, and where it is carried on in conjunction with cropping there is not enough land available for the production of fodder. Animals must be grazed on the stubble from cultivated fields and on weeds from both arable and fallow land. Community pastures, where they exist, are often poor. Because of climatic conditions most summer cropping other than that in irrigated tracts is done by dry-farming methods. This means that at any given time a large part of the cultivable land is in fallow.[3] Fallowing also is practiced in irrigated tracts to rest and refertilize the soil. Crop land used for winter crops lies fallow in summer.

The methods of tillage and harvest are as antiquated as the system of agriculture. A major part of all the work in the fields is done by hand

[2] The Middle East is the world's major producer of only one relatively important commercial crop: dates. Long-staple cotton, some types of fruit and nuts, and tobacco are other crops that enter international trade in considerable amounts. Turkey recently (1952) became an important exporter of wheat.

[3] The amount of crop land in fallow varies considerably: in Iran it may run as high as 75 per cent; in Iraq, 50 per cent of the winter crop land (wheat and barley) is usually in fallow; in Turkey, about one-third is usually in fallow. In Egypt, land is usually left in fallow at least two months between crops.

with simple implements, draft animals being employed where possible. Plowing is by stick or nail plow; sowing is usually by hand, as is cultivation; reaping and binding are also by hand; and threshing methods are centuries old (Figure 137). The terracing of hillsides, construction of small irrigation canals and tunnels, and much of the lifting of irrigation water onto the fields is likewise done manually. The efficiency of these methods has long been questioned. In a number of cases, however, they may be better than the more modern practices that have been suggested to replace them. In many ways so little is known about soils and soil moisture in relation to climate, weather, and methods of cultivation that unless a change is carefully examined before it is put into effect the farmer may lose even what he has. An example is seen in the use of deep plowing in place of shallow. In several localities where deep plowing has been tried, the results have been unfavorable. Moisture has escaped more readily; soil salinity has increased; and wind erosion has been more prevalent than under the old method. There is, however, little doubt as to the wastefulness of certain tillage practices, and much can be done to improve them.

Labor in the Middle East is cheap. So long as it remains so, the large landowner is loath to invest in machinery; the peasant cannot afford to,

Fig. 137 • Arabs in the Hebron area of Jordan threshing grain with oxen and asses, a method centuries old, wasteful, and inefficient, but used in many parts of the Middle East. After the animals have trodden out the grain from the chaff, the straw is removed, and the grain remains on the threshing floor. The buildings in the background are made of sun-dried brick plastered over with mud, a wide-spread type of construction. The stone enclosure between the buildings and the wall is used for livestock. *(John R. Randall.)*

even if he so desires. Under the present system of land holdings mechanization is hardly feasible. The plots are too small and often too widely separated to lend themselves to any high degree of mechanization. Heavy farm machines are, however, now used in all the Middle Eastern countries (with the probable exception of the Yemen), but their number is still rather small and their use is limited almost entirely to certain types of projects where the land areas involved are large. These are chiefly government projects where new farmlands are being developed and where the farm unit will be larger than that now common. Farm machinery is also used on a number of experimental farms, and there has been an increase in the use of farm machinery on a few of the large estates.[4] One can, however, travel many miles through cultivated areas without ever seeing a sizable piece of farm equipment.

Statistics for cultivated land are only estimates, and in some cases the margin of error may be considerable. No data are available for the Yemen or the dependencies of the Arabian peninsula. Estimates for the remaining countries give Turkey 25 million acres; Lebanon, 500,000 acres; Syria, 4 million acres; Israel, 900,000 acres; Iraq, 6 million acres; Jordan, 1.2 million acres; Saudi Arabia, 125,000 acres, and Iran 41 million acres. These areas of crop land account for only small percentages of the total areas of the countries concerned and in only one case is the percentage higher than that of the United States.[5]

There is little doubt that in most of the countries, with the exception of Egypt, the unused cultivable land equals or exceeds the land that now is cultivated.[6] But it does not necessarily follow that large areas will soon come under cultivation. Indeed, under existing economic conditions it is probable that expansion will be slow and modest. Much of the potentially cultivable land requires irrigation or the improvement of present irrigation facilities; some must be drained. It is also questionable in some areas whether there is a sufficient amount of labor available to till any extra land.

Precipitation is the single most important factor in the use of land for crop production and grazing. Indirectly it also is important in supplying surface and subsurface water for agricultural purposes. There are only three areas in the region that receive enough rainfall to carry on humid farming: the Turkish Black Sea coast, the Caspian coastal plain of Iran,

[4] One estimate gives a total of 49,535 tractors in six of the Middle Eastern countries. No figures are given for the Yemen, Saudi Arabia, Jordan, and Israel. FAO, *Agriculture in the Near East,* 1953, p. 52. In 1950 there were 3,000,000 farm tractors in the United States.

[5] Percentages of crop land in relation to total area: Iran, 10; Turkey, 16; Lebanon, 21; Egypt, 2.2; Syria, 19.0; Iraq, 5.5; Israel, 3; Jordan, 5.2; the United States, 20.2.

[6] Estimates are that cultivated land in Iran, Lebanon, and Syria could be doubled; in Iraq, tripled; in Turkey, increased about 80 per cent; in Egypt, increased from 6 million acres to 7.1 million acres.

and the highlands of the Yemen. Large areas can produce no crops except by irrigation. Between these extremes are the true Mediterranean areas where it is possible to grow winter crops with normal rainfall and summer crops by irrigation. In the cold-winter steppe areas of Turkey and Iran dry-farming is practiced in the summer. In steppe areas where winters are mild, dry farming is practiced during the winter. Winter cropping and summer production by dry farming both entail fallow, and this is the factor that accounts for the high amount of land in fallow at any given period of time. Winters in most parts of the realm are mild enough for fall-sown grains, and wheat and barley here are largely winter crops. Winters in the southern part of the region, in Egypt, Arabia, southern Iraq, and Iran, are warm enough to permit a year-round growing season, provided water is available.

Irrigation is a major feature in the Middle Eastern countries. Its advantages are obvious: (1) increased crop land and crop production, as well as increased variety of crops; (2) the greater stability of farming as a result of an assured supply of water; and (3) the possibility of more intensive use of land. Its disadvantages are possibly more difficult to estimate, but they may be no less significant: (1) destruction of soil by waterlogging and saline accumulation; (2) increased population densities as a result of a more reliable and larger food supply, e.g. Egypt; (3) increase of certain types of disease through the development of perennial irrigation, e.g. bilharzia and malaria; and, in some cases, (4) the loss through the flood-control devices associated with irrigation of the valuable soil increments resulting from flooding of silt-laden rivers.

The obstacles to the increase of irrigated land are manifold, though from country to country they vary considerably. One of the biggest problems involves proper surveys preceding development. There is need for accurate knowledge of soils, water resources, vegetation cover, and rock structure of the areas concerned, as well as an understanding of the economic and cultural changes that will follow irrigation development. To date, too many projects have been started or completed without proper information and as a consequence have failed. There has been a tendency on the part of most countries to plan separately for each project without providing for an over-all or long-range integration into a national developmental program. Moreover, the region lacks the trained technicians to make detailed surveys. Another problem arises in the conflict of water rights within and between the countries concerned. Iraq, in its attempt to increase irrigation facilities and to control floods on the Tigris-Euphrates, must come to an agreement with Iran, Turkey, and Syria, since the two rivers and their tributaries involve these three countries as well as Iraq. Egypt's desire to control the Anglo-Egyptian Sudan stems in part from its need to manage the waters of the Nile.

The distribution of landforms is another major obstacle. With the exception of the Nile valley and delta and the flood plain of the lower Tigris-Euphrates-Karun system, there are few large, relatively level areas in the Middle East with available water that can be developed by large-scale irrigation projects. In some localities such areas are either without water or else stand too high above water to make irrigation profitable. More often, however, because of the nature and distribution of landforms, the areas of irrigable land are quite small, and each one, if it is to be irrigated, must receive costly individual treatment.

Almost every type of irrigation may be found in the Middle East. In valleys of permanent streams there are basin and perennial types; in *wadis* having only temporary water there is flood irrigation, and temporary river water may be impounded behind mud and wattle dams or caught in ponds for basin irrigation; subsurface sources continuously feed ground water through the *qanat* (*karez*) system of underground channels to areas to be irrigated, and also feed artesian wells, springs, and regular wells; some small areas are irrigated from cisterns or tanks whose source of water is surface dainage.

The methods by which water is carried to the fields are also diverse: gravity-flow channels from permanent streams and *qanat* wells; pump irrigation from streams, wells, and springs; the hoisting of water from streams, canals, and wells by a variety of hand- and animal-powered devices (Figure 138), including among others the counter-poised lift, the ox-drawn water lift, the Archimedes water screw, the cog water wheel, and large and small water wheels driven by the current of the stream or canal. Most fields are prepared for irrigating largely in one of two ways. Under the first method fields are furrowed every foot or so, with the soil piled up in ridges between the furrows or runnels. Seeds are planted along the ridges, and water is run down each of the furrows. The second method is to mark off larger beds or sections of field and to surround each with a low dike of earth. Planting is done in the entire bed, and water is led into each area from diversion channels. Although the second method gives a greater area for seed, the first is more widely used, possibly because it seems to be more effective in reaching all of the crops and is less wasteful of water through evaporation. Where terraced lands are irrigated, check dams (in some cases large rocks) are placed in the main gravity-flow channel, and water is led off at each terrace level.

The methods by which water is carried from the streams to the fields often waste both water and time. Most canals and channels are open, allowing substantial loss by evaporation; small channels, carelessly constructed, also allow much seepage. Water is lost, too, in the hoisting process, though this loss may well be less than through seepage and evaporating. Man-powered hoists are slow and inefficient, and some

Fig. 138 • The *saqiya*, a commonly used method, especially in Egypt, for raising irrigation water onto the cultivated fields. The mechanism is a set of cog wheels, one of which has a series of buckets attached to it. The buckets dip water out of irrigation canals and empty it into smaller channels that flow to the fields. Donkeys, cattle, or oxen are the usual motive power; they are blindfolded so they will not try to reach out toward forage beyond their circular track. Similar animal-powerd devices are found throughout the arid lands of South and Southwestern Asia.

In the background is a large canal of the upper delta near Cairo. It is used not only as a source of water but also for transport by motor-driven barges and sailboats. *(John R. Randall.)*

animal-powered types are equally so. The *qanat* system, so widespread in Iran, and one of the oldest methods in the area, is possibly one of the most efficient. The underground channels keep both evaporation and seepage to a minimum, and so long as they are kept in good repair their water is less likely to become contaminated than that in open canals and channels.

Certain countries, of course, depend on irrigated land much more than others do. Egypt and Saudi Arabia, true desert countries, can produce few if any crops without irrigation. At least part of the area and hence part of the crop land of the other countries receives enough precipitation to produce winter crops or to create a possibility of summer crops by dry farming, but Iraq and Israel each have more than half of their cultivated area under irrigation.

Three other factors related to crop production should be mentioned: use of fertilizer, improvement of seed, and pest control. With the exception of Egypt and Israel, the Middle East uses little commercial fertilizer and relatively little animal manure. Fertilizers' high cost and a lack of knowledge about them apparently are the main deterrents to their use. In Egypt they are used extensively for cotton production and in some localities for other crops. Their use here has been made necessary by the development of perennial irrigation, which stopped the annual addition of silt to the fields during flood periods. Western techniques applied to farming in Israel account for the greater use of both fertilizers and manures in that country. Although three or four governments plan to get fertilizers into production, at present only Israel and Egypt are appreciable producers.

Despite the relatively numerous livestock in the realm, little of their manure is consciously applied to the soil to improve it. Because livestock rearing is largely separated from crop production, those areas having the most crop fields have fewer animals. The little animal manure supplied the soil comes from pasturing stock on harvested and fallow fields. In some localities, animal dung is used not as fertilizer but as fuel. The largest numbers of livestock are found in that part of the mountain and desert areas where cultivated land is rare. The development of mixed farming—crops and livestock—in Israel has considerably increased the use of animal manures there.

The use of improved seed and of new varieties of crops also lags. Farmers are not aware of the potential benefits; and trained personnel and facilities for producing good seed and testing new varieties are scarce. Turkey, Egypt, and Israel are the only states that have implemented programs for seed and variety improvement.

Plant pests and disease take a large annual toll of crops, and little has been done on a long-range basis to control these crop bandits. In general, policies for control are short-range; insects are attacked at the local level when they appear, and seeds and varieties are changed only when disease causes acute crop failure. Few states have any over-all plan, nor is there any attempt at intraregional control. Cost, governmental inefficiency, the farmers' ignorance, and isolation are factors that make difficult the stemming of plant pests and disease.

The production of crops and livestock in the Middle East is primarily for food for consumption within the region. Cotton, tobacco, hides, and animal fibers are among the few commodities that could be classed as industrial, that is, not for human food or animal feed. Cereals, fruit, and vegetables are the staple foods. Wheat and barley are the most important and widely grown cereals, but appreciable amounts of rice, corn, millet, sorghum, and rye are produced in localities where physical conditions are suitable or where other more profitable cereals cannot be grown. Most of the well known types of middle-latitude and subtropical fruits are produced, as well as some tropical varieties, such as bananas, dates, and mangoes. The more specialized food crops include sugar beets, sugar cane, nuts, and tea. Peas and beans are grown for food; at times and in certain areas they along with clover serve as fodder. The production of milk and other dairy products varies greatly from country to country, but in general the Middle East is underdeveloped in this respect, not only in production, but also in its adequacy of distribution.

Livestock always have been an important resource in the region for meat and milk, work and transport, and for hides, hair, or wool. Their production has been an occupation of nomadic and semi-nomadic peoples. However, the number of animals has been increasing in areas of sedentary occupance, where draft animals always have been important. One distinction between semi-nomadic and nomadic peoples is that the semi-nomadic groups are characteristically mountain people, and the nomads normally are desert dwellers. Although all mountain regions may not be important for pastoral activities, most of them are, and their distribution may be equated roughly with that of semi-nomadism. The Arabian and Syrian deserts are the principle areas of nomadic cultures.

Sheep and goats are the most numerous as well the most important livestock; cattle are much less important, Turkey being the only country to have any considerable number.[7] Oxen, cattle, mules, donkeys, and camels are the main types of draft animals. Water buffalo are becoming increasingly important, especially in the riverine areas of Egypt and Iraq. Cattle, camels, and water buffalo are utilized for meat, milk, and hides, as well as for work purposes. There are a fair number of horses, most of them used in urban centers for public carriers; in other areas they serve as mounts and for sport. Very few horses are used for farm work. Because of religious taboos almost no swine are found in the region.

Livestock and livestock production could be much improved. They suffer from much the same handicaps as crop production: inefficient methods, disease, and indifference to stock improvement. The use of certain types of animals for both milk production and work purposes is uneconomical. Often meat animals are forced to walk such long distances that they lose much weight; on occasion they are also badly underfed. There is a large annual loss through disease and parasites. In most areas there has been little or no attempt to improve existing strains. Here, as in crop production, there is need for well integrated and long-range programs, in this case to build up the herds and flocks. Disease control, in-

[7] Over 10,000,000 in 1954.

creased veterinarian service, improvement of natural grasslands, and improved breeding practices are among the more immediate needs.

Settlement

Throughout most of the Middle East the sedentary farm or rural population lives in agglomerated settlements; dispersed settlement is found in only a very few localities, as in western Turkey. The size of the village often is a reflection of the amount of water available or of the distance one can walk without too much difficulty to the crop fields. In productive areas, villages are more numerous and closely spaced, and the crop fields of one may lie adjacent to those of the next. In unproductive or undeveloped sections villages may be miles apart and often isolated. Agglomerated settlement is probably the result of a number of interrelated factors: need for protection, availability of water, gregariousness, and, possibly, the conservation of land. These agglomerated settlements are essentially rural, and few of them have any of the functions normally associated with urban centers.

The building materials and types of houses in villages reflect the local natural resources, weather, and climate. The Middle East has few forests to supply timber. Thus wooden houses are rare, except in Turkey along the Black Sea coastal region, and in Iran on the Caspian coastal plain and the north Elburz slope. Most lumber has to be imported, so it is used very sparingly or not at all. The common building materials, depending upon locality, are mud, mud-brick, fired brick, or stone. Mud-covered wattle is also used in some areas. The style of house is in keeping with the construction material used, but also it directly reflects the climate: relatively few openings and thick walls against the summer heat and, often, the winter cold. Many types are flat-roofed. There is great variation in height from low, mud-brick, one-storied huts, through two-storied structures, to the "skyscraper" buildings of the Yemen and southern Arabia, which may have 10 to 12 stories. Rural villages appear very compact and, indeed, there is often little but a footpath or narrow roadway between the houses. In many cases villages stand out bare and unrelieved against the landscape; possibly lack of space or of water precludes tree growth (Figure 139). Many oasis villages in the south, however, are all but hidden by date gardens.

Semi-nomadic people generally have permanent village dwellings similar to those of sedentary folk, but from spring through autumn the larger part of the tribal group is in the highlands with the livestock, living in tents which they carry along with them. Nomadic people have no permanent dwellings, only their tents, though these in winter may be given added protection by wattle and mud siding, or by mud walls. The tents vary in size from those with a single compartment to those that have several. The tent material is usually woven from wool or goat hair. An indication of comparative wealth is often the size of the tent and the elaborateness of its hangings.

Living conditions within the rural village of the Middle East generally are primitive. There is rarely any attempt at sanitation; more often than not the water supply is contaminated. The village as well as the individual house is overcrowded, and the dwellings commonly house both people and stock. The majority of houses in warm areas are without window covering; insects, especially flies, are ubiquitous pests and disease spreaders. Cold winters in northern areas give some surcease from these pests, but summers bring them back. Bright sun and dry air are about the only disinfectants present. Conditions in the encampments of nomads and seminomadic people are little better, though they do have one advantage: they shift periodically to new sites.

Fig. 139 • An Iranian village, like many others, is stark and bare. Flat roofs and sun-dried bricks are typical. The lack of tree growth indicates that the area about the village is not easily susceptible to irrigation. In most villages where irrigation is possible shade trees are grown to give some relief from summer heat. Often rows of poplars are grown on the outskirts of villages to act as windbreaks, to furnish construction material and fuel, and incidentally to afford shade. The construction material here used is sun-dried brick, one of the most widely used of building materials in the rural villages of Iran in those areas where precipitation is slight. Only in the Caspian area is there much wood available for house construction; in the south wattle and mud, and palm are utilized to build huts. (F. A. O.)

Manufacturing

Manufacturing in the Middle East takes one of two forms: (1) the older, more widespread, and probably more important, handicrafts; and (2) modern factory production. Few countries in the region are without some type of modern factory (possibly the Yemen has none), but no country could be classed as either industrial or industrialized.

Home, small-shop, or bazaar production is widespread in the Middle East and probably accounts for most of the goods turned out, excepting petroleum products. There is no way of telling what the total output of such goods is, nor the number of shops or people involved. The shops must be numerous, but each shop employs very few people, from one to about ten, so the percentage of the total population engaged is very small. The tools and devices used in such production are simple and mostly man-powered. Products are diverse, including many types of textiles, rugs, metal ware, leather goods, ceramics, and wood articles; quality ranges from very high to poor. The poor grades are produced for common local use and for the tourist trade. Of the finest of the handicraft arts of the Middle East, some are now represented mostly in museums and private collections; other arts are still being practiced much as they were centuries ago.

The Middle East has not as yet experienced the Industrial Revolution, although factory manufacture is over a hundred years old.[8] The types of factories are those that are most common to nonindustrialized areas: textile, food-processing, and ceramics plants, and establishments for the processing of minerals. The processes of manufacture in such factories are relatively simple, and the complete process is usually done within a single plant. There is no complex division of labor; nor is the value added by the manufacturing process high. The total number of factories in the entire region is small, and the wage earners make up only a small percentage of the total population.[9] Few individual plants employ workers in numbers comparable to those found in innumerable Western factories. For example, Iran at the beginning of the second World War had 250

---

[8] A steam-powered textile factory was opened in Turkey in 1842.

[9] In 1947 about 7 per cent of Egypt's employed population was engaged in manufacturing and the extractive industries. Egypt ranks among the first four countries in factory manufacturing. The others are Turkey, Iran, and Israel. Statistics available for the numbers of wage-earners employed in factories are: (1) Egypt (1947), 708,-776; (2) Turkey (1945) 640,000; (3) Israel (1952) 120,000, including craft as well as factory workers; and (4) Iran (1949-50) 104,000, including 51,000 employees of the former Anglo-Iranian oil company.

factories that could be called modern. A majority of these employed between 30 and 100 workers; ten employed between 100 and 400; 15, between 400 and 1,000; and the two largest factories (other than the refinery of the then Anglo-Iranian Oil Company), both in Tehran, employed 2,500 and 3,300.

The problem of industrialization is very important in the Middle East. It is regarded as a means of raising the standard of living, of becoming less dependent upon imports of finished goods, and of generally developing a more stable economy. But these countries are laboring under tremendous handicaps. The region has relatively little in the way of mineral wealth (oil excepted) upon which to base industrialization; it is not an agricultural surplus area; its people are not experienced with machines, nor are any number of them trained or skilled factory workers, though they show themselves to be apt students when given the opportunity; the purchasing power of the mass of population is almost nil, and Middle Eastern countries find it very difficult to break into already established markets; transportation, both rail and highway, is very poorly developed in much of the area; the Arab countries frown upon foreign investments for fear of economic imperialism, yet local capital hesitates to invest in industry because returns do not come quickly enough and are not immediately so large as those from agriculture; the instabilities of governments and of the general political situation also deter both local and foreign investors. Despite these handicaps and despite the fact that the region has had no gradual development from small-shop production toward industrialization, the countries concerned wish to become industrial in the shortest time possible, telescoping into a few years what took the great industrial powers at least a century to achieve.

Trade and service activities

Trade and commerce long have been of major significance in the Middle East. Today their importance is less, and the people involved make up a relatively small percentage of the population. A threefold division may be recognized: import and export trade; local commerce (such as the sale of food in shops); and the transit trade. This last type may have been the most significant historically, but today it affects relatively little of the region. In times past the prevailing means of transport and the region's geographic position in relation to Europe, Africa, and the rest of Asia, made the Middle East an entrepôt area. By land and sea, cargoes moving from one of the continents to another passed through the region, but in the process were bought and sold, stored, and reshipped by local agencies. A majority of the large cities of the Middle East owe their origin and early growth to this transit trade. With very few exceptions, the commercial function always has been predominant in the large urban centers. The situation of the cities was characteristic: ocean ports—Alexandria, Jaffa, Beirut; land and water crossings—Istanbul and Baghdad; land-route junctions— Damascus and Aleppo; caravansaries on desert routes—Tehran, Mecca, and Kerman.

As modes of transport changed, the transit trade diminished or was more narrowly channelled. Political upheavals and wars closed many routes for varying periods; the North Atlantic replaced the Mediterranean as the primary ocean route; there was a major shift in emphasis from hand-made to machine-made goods; all of these factors had some bearing on the diminution of through trade in the Middle East. With the opening of the Suez Canal in 1869 there began a definite channelling of goods by this sea lane in place of earlier land and sea-and-land routes. Although the Berlin-to-Baghdad railroad followed in part the old Fertile Crescent route, the old traffic did not return. Relatively little of the Middle East now benefits to any considerable extent from transit trade. A number of cities have become major centers on world air routes, but air traffic is mostly in passengers rather than freight.

The commercial function is primary in the large cities, but its importance has become local and regional, rather than international. The cities serve as supply and distributing centers for the areas in which they lie, though they also handle what foreign trade is carried on by their respective countries.

The current foreign trade of the Middle East reflects the primary economic activity, agriculture. The chief export items, with the exception of petroleum, are agricultural products; the main import items are manufactured goods. The value of agricultural exports does not rank high in world trade. Egyptian cotton, Iraqi dates, and tobacco and wheat from Turkey are about the only exports of any importance.

About most of the Middle Eastern countries there is no way of knowing how many people are engaged in the various service and professional occupations, but, as with manufacturing and trade, the number is small as compared to those in farming and pastoral activities. The majority are to be found in the larger urban centers. Few of the rural villages or towns have much in the way of service establishments. For professional and government workers, life out of the cities is the same as exile, and few will leave the city if it can be avoided. Practically all types of services are available in the large cities, both professional and personal.

The extractive industries

For an area as large as the Middle East, the nonagricultural resources are apparently meager—again with the major exception of oil—and a number of them are but little developed. Extractive industries employ few workers even by comparison with the manufacturing and service industries. In Iraq, Saudi Arabia, and Iran the oil industry is the single largest employer outside of government, but the number of workers is not large. For example, in 1952 the total personnel employed in the Iraq oil industry, including the office force, was only 18,767 out of a total population of 5,000,000; in 1953 the Arabian American Oil company employed 28,786 persons in Saudi Arabia.

Mineral production is the most important of the extractive industries, but except for oil, no country has outstanding deposits. Iron, coal, copper, chrome, potash, sulfur, manganese, phosphate rock, and salt are among the mineral deposits being mined at present; building stone is also widely quarried. Excluding oil, more mineral wealth is under exploitation in Turkey than in the other countries. Minerals are known to occur in a number of places, but as yet either they have not been carefully examined or else present conditions do not warrant their exploitation.

Although a number of Middle Eastern countries produce oil, the largest deposits discovered to date lie along the flanks of the great geosyncline that extends through the Persian Gulf area and the Tigris-Euphrates valleys into southern Turkey. Major fields producing, or pools discovered but not yet in production, are found in Iraq, Iran,[10] Kuwait, the eastern neutral zone, Saudi Arabia, Bahrein island, and Qatar. These political units together have the world's largest known reserves of petroleum. New discoveries and constantly increasing production quickly outdate statistics. The known reserves at mid-1956 were 133 billion barrels. The known reserves for the United States, the world's largest producer, were approximately 30-35 billion barrels. The production of Middle East oil in 1955 reached just over one billion barrels, nearly 25 per cent of world production and about one-half that of the United States.

Only Iran has a forest resource that is commercially exploitable, but so far little has been done to develop either a lumber or pulp industry.

[10] Until 1951, Iran had been the largest petroleum producer among the Middle Eastern countries. Nationalization of the oil industry in that year brought about a virtual cessation of production until the fall of 1954 when production began under a predominantly British-American syndicate. In 1950 Iran produced 32,259,000 metric tons; in 1956, estimates were for 23-6 million metric tons.

In the meantime the forest resource is being dissipated by the charcoal industry, which is both wasteful and destructive.

Fishing is carried on in most coastal areas, but the trade in fisheries products is small. Lack of refrigeration and rapid transportation limit the market that can be reached. Although Iran is famous for its caviar derived from Caspian Sea sturgeon, Israel and Turkey have more highly developed fisheries.

The pilgrim trade and tourism

The Middle East has special significance for both pilgrims and tourists. As the region wherein Judaism, Christianity, and Islam had their origins, the area has many holy shrines and cities that are visited periodically or continuously by thousands of pilgrims. These people must be fed and cared for on their journey and at their destinations. Even though many pilgrims are woefully poor, the area generally, as well as the cities of destination, receives a large income from the pilgrim trade.[11]

Holy places can be classified according to degree of importance, from such high-ranking places as Mecca, Medina, Jerusalem, and Bethlehem; through secondary shrines limited to people of one religious faction, or commemorating some event or some person not of major importance; to shrines of tertiary importance, often local in character, perhaps tombs of holy or sainted people, such as Rachels' tomb near Jerusalem, Queen Esther's tomb at Hamadan, or the numerous Imamzadehs of Iran.

Bearing in mind that pilgrimage is one of the five positive tenets of Islam, it is the desire of all good Moslems to make the *hajj* or pilgrimage to Mecca at least once in a lifetime. This lure draws people from far areas of the world and often takes them from home for long periods.

Although tourism is as yet modestly developed in the Middle East, the area has a multitude of attractions for the traveller. There are sites of great historical, archeological, religious, and contemporary interest. There is much scenic beauty: mountains, ocean coasts, and vast desert areas. There is the contrast between the constantly shifting and ever-fascinating life of the large cities and the quiet isolation of the mountain or oasis village. Few people would find unmoving the landscapes and life in the Middle East.

[11] Up to 1940 the pilgrimage fee charged at Mecca is estimated to have provided an annual income of somewhere between five and 20 million dollars. This was one of Saudi Arabia's main sources of income until oil production began.

SELECTED GEOGRAPHICAL BIBLIOGRAPHY

1. Food and Agricultural Organization of the United Nations. *Agriculture in the Middle East.* Rome: 1953.
2. Keen, B. A. *The Agricultural Development of the Middle East.* London: His Majesty's Stationery Office, 1946. See also Kedar, Y. "Water and Soil from the Desert: Some Agricultural Achievements in the Central Negev," *Geographical Journal,* June, 1957, pp. 179-87.
3. United Nations. *Summary of Recent Economic Developments in the Middle East. Supplement to World Economic Report, 1950-51.* New York: 1952.
4. Worthington, E. B. *Middle East Science.* London: His Majesty's Stationery Office, 1946.

Comments

Both Fisher and the Royal Institute Survey listed in the bibliography of Chapter 30 contain good information on over-all economic patterns in the area. The FAO publication has valuable material on the problems of pests and diseases affecting crops and livestock. The Keen work gives a general survey of agriculture with short sketches of its status in each of the political units.

The *Foreign Commerce Yearbook* of the Department of Commerce has much in the way of statistical data gathered from various sources, not all of which are easily obtainable in this country. Some states are omitted, however. Other data may be obtained from the *Statesman's Yearbook,* the U.N. *Statistical Yearbook,* and the U.N. *Demographic Yearbook.*

Southwest Asia

REGIONAL PROBLEMS

TO COMPREHEND THE CULTURAL GEOGRAPHY OF SOUTHWEST ASIA, one must have some understanding of the multiple problems that beset the realm and that either directly or indirectly affect its landscape and its economies. This realm holds no monopoly on such problems. They are not especially unique to it, and whereas many are regional in scope, a number have extra-regional implications.

Political problems

Political problems in Southwest Asia have both regional and international significance. The independent countries are characterized by a governmental instability that has a marked effect upon their political and economic wellbeing and that ramifies into other phases of life as well. With the exception of Turkey, the state-areas of the Middle East are immature and lack any long experience in self-government. Even Iran has for the past 100 years or so been strongly under the influence of both Russia and Great Britain. Growing nationalism, numerous and rapid changes of governments, and mob rule are superficial features that illustrate the basic instability. Having rid themselves of the oppressor, the foreign imperialist power, these states, largely inexperienced in government and characterized by governing elites out of contact with the mass of their populations, lack the ability to fill the void that has been created, and often the consequence has been a political vacuum. Because of their strategic position, any political vacuum becomes highly dangerous not only to the states involved, but also to most of the world.

Internally and interregionally, political instability produces a general tension, as well as dissension, among various groups and countries. This in turn is reflected in the condition of business and in economic relations. People are loath to invest capital or to develop industry or trade when governments and governmental regulations change frequently. Graft and corruption are evils of ancient lineage in the Middle East, but they tend to become more common under weak central governments as the opportunities for their development become more numerous.

The effects of instability are more conspicuous and more recognizable in the urban centers than in the rural areas, since in the cities there is a larger percentage of the people who are politically aware and who have a better chance to know and follow the course of events. Here, conditions also favor the mob. Capitals are especially sensitive spots, but all the larger cities are centers of political change.

The lack of contact between city and village has been notorious. Radio has to some extent reduced the gap, but there has been only a beginning to rural-urban communication. The village or rural dweller is not politically conscious, and his loyalties and ties are to his village and family, not to the central government. The peasant's generally low level of living and his customary ill-health leave neither time nor energy to expend upon political activities, or even on political thought. The result is a marked general disregard of politics. Periodically a strong and forceful personality has penetrated this apathy, but with his passing, it usually prevails once more. The city-village schism is one of the greatest handicaps a central government must overcome in its attempt to achieve the internal organization of the state. Few Middle Eastern countries have been able to accomplish this end.

A second problem is in the political aspirations and the interplay of political relations among the various states. Ethnology and religion as well as politics are involved. Eight of the Middle Eastern states are predominantly Arab and are at present members of the Arab League.[1] Eight states[2] are Moslem with governments that vary from that of Turkey, which is purely secular, to those of Saudi Arabia and the Yemen, which are essentially theocratic. The Lebanon, though Arab, is predominantly

[1] Saudi Arabia, Yemen, Egypt, Jordan, Iraq, Syria, Libya, and the Lebanon. The dependencies and Aden Colony and Protectorate in Arabia are also Arab, but not members of the Arab League.

[2] Turkey, Syria, Jordan, Egypt, Saudi Arabia, Yemen, Iraq, and Iran.

Christian, and Israel is Jewish, though it has a sizable Arab minority. This arrangement and distribution of ethnic and religious groups has led to political intrigue and active hostility among various of the states. An additional factor crops up in the enmity that exists between the ruling families of certain states.

Turkey and Iran, though Moslem, are little involved in this general problem. Turkey now has friendly relations with most of the Arab states, but there is still some feeling against Turkey because of long domination by the Ottoman Empire. Nor are the Turks Arabs. The separation of church and state also has had some effect. Iran is Shia Moslem, whereas the majority of Arab states are Sunni Moslem; Iran also is non-Arab. Iran and Turkey, too, are to some extent physically separated from the remainder of the Middle East. Their stand on the Palestine problem is indicative: neither approved of the creation of Israel, but neither took any active part in trying to stop it, and both have recognized the new state.

All of the Arab states, with the exception of the Yemen, are involved to varying degrees in political rivalry or intrigue among themselves, and this despite their membership in the Arab League.[3] All are hostile toward Israel. The political intrigue revolves around the attempt on the part of the Hashemite House of Jordan and Iraq to form an Arab empire consisting of the Arab countries of the eastern Mediterranean plus Iraq. This ambition dates back at least as far as the first World War, when Husein, Sherif of Mecca and later King of the Hejaz,[4] received promises from the British that such an empire might be forthcoming if Husein and his sons would lead an Arab revolt against Turkey.[5] The Western powers at Versailles did not see fit to fulfill this promise of the British. The idea, however, of a "Greater Syria" did not die, and during his lifetime, Abdullah, King of Jordan, worked toward this goal. There is reason to believe that Iraq and Jordan still might desire a union under the Hashemite dynasty of their two countries, along with Syria and the Lebanon.

The creation of a large Arab state in the eastern Mediterranean has been opposed in various ways by both Saudi Arabia and Egypt. Neither of these countries wants a third state of comparable size and importance in the Middle East. Furthermore, there is enmity between the Hashemites and the House of Saud, since it was King Ibn Saud of Nejd who drove Husein of Hejaz from his throne in 1924 and incorporated the Hejaz

[3] The Arab League was formed in part to show the world that the Arab states were united or could work well in concert.

[4] Husein was the father of King Faisal I of Iraq and King Abdullah of Jordan; great-grandfather of the present king, Husein, and of King Faisal II of Iraq.

[5] The promises are contained in the now famous McMahon Letters. In 1917, through the Balfour Declaration, the British announced the creation of a Jewish Home in Palestine, part of the area included in the projected Arab empire of Husein.

into the present Saudi Arabia. The Lebanon has strongly opposed the idea of union because the Lebanese do not want to become a Christian minority in a large Moslem state. Although certain Syrian groups favor union with Jordan and Iraq, to date all attempts toward this end have been resisted. It is obvious that Israel wants no part of such an arrangement.

The formation of the Israeli state produced one of the most critical political as well as economic problems of the Middle East, a problem important both regionally and internationally. The course of events leading to the creation of Israel was highly complex; the situation that has resulted from it is grave in the extreme.[6] Israel is surrounded by hostile countries; her borders are set solely through armistice agreements with the individual Arab states; her government is recognized by none of the Arab countries; her goods are boycotted by all Arab states; her population has been swollen by recent immigration. She is ever fearful that her neighbors will again go to war in an attempt to bring about her downfall.

The Arabs bitterly resent, and with some justice, the creation of a Jewish state in an area they have considered to be their own for centuries. They resent what they regard as the expulsion of thousands of Arabs from their former homes in Palestine; they are fearful lest Israel try to enlarge its area by force; they distrust the presence of the thousands of Westernized Jews in Israel. They have refused to cooperate in any way with Israel, and they continue their economic boycott against her.

This impasse between the Arab states and Israel has involved the major powers and affected world conditions. Aid to and recognition of Israel by the Western nations has tended to alienate the Arabs; this the West can ill afford because of the strategic importance of the Middle East between East and West, and because of the importance of its petroleum resources. The Soviet Union has used the situation for the furtherance of her own designs, though she too gave Israel early recognition.

Socio-economic problems

Poverty with its attendant social evils is the obvious and most widespread indicator of the low economic status of the large majority of Middle Eastern people. It often is an abysmal poverty the causes and effects of which engender a cyclical condition exceedingly difficult to break. There can be little hope for a

[6] The open warfare that broke out between the Arab states and Israel in 1948 was ended by a series of armistice agreements; there have been no peace-treaty negotiations (1957). Iraq, which signed no armistice, is still technically at war with Israel.

solution of economic and sociological problems in the region until the general level of living is raised.

The Middle East is not a region in which the average inhabitant can easily gain a livelihood, but poverty is more severe than physical conditions warrant. The peasant and laborer almost always have been exploited for the well-being of a very small minority. Arab, Turk, and Iranian, as well as foreigner, have been guilty. There has been little or no concern on the part of the ruling group toward either the economic or the social status of the masses. Hard labor in the fields and towns is ill-paid; security is almost nonexistent; and disease and sickness are widespread.

The loss of man-hours of labor through chronic illness and early death is one of the more important economic problems. Exact figures for such losses are not available, but the total must be appalling. Figures for infant mortality are available only for Egypt and Israel. In Egypt the rate is 135.5 per 1,000; in Israel, 40.6.[7] The rate for other Middle Eastern countries is nearer that of Egypt than that of Israel. A further critical loss occurs through the death of many in late childhood or early maturity. The life expectancy of males up to the age of 21 is strikingly lower than in the United States.[8]

Chronic illness is a social problem of major proportions and accounts not only for much human misery, but also for the loss of countless hours of labor. None of the Middle Eastern countries is exempt, though conditions in Israel are much superior to those in the other states, largely because of the high percentage of Europeans in the population and the work of governmental agencies and private organizations in checking and preventing the further spread of various types of disease.

The diseases that are the most debilitating and often the most commonly found are: malaria, dysentery (especially amoebic), the venereal diseases, bilharzia, and hookworm. The region also suffers periodically from outbreaks of yellow fever, typhus, and cholera. The chronic diseases affect large percentages of the population within the various countries. Malaria is probably the worst and most widespread, but the others are often very prevalent in certain localities. In Egypt estimates are that 70-80 per cent of the *fellaheen* are infected by bilharzia and hookworm and probably 65 per cent by malaria.[9] Incidence in other regions may be lower, but in still others they are certainly higher. Much the same is

[7] The infant mortality rate in the United States is 28.6 per 1,000.

[8] Comparison between Egypt and the United States of male life expectancy:

Age:	less than 1	1	10	20
	35.6–65.9	42–67	46.8–58.7	39.7–49.3

[9] Charles Issawi, *Egypt, An Economic and Social Analysis* (London: Oxford University Press, 1947), p. 155.

true of dysentery and the venereal diseases, though the latter often seem less virulent than in the West.

Disease is fostered and spread through the conditions in which the people live: overcrowded and unclean habitations, use of polluted water, lack of protection of dwellings and food against contamination, and lack of knowledge of personal hygiene. Relatively little has been done to destroy the insects and bacteria or germs that cause or carry various diseases. Malarial mosquitoes breed wherever fields are irrigated, or where swamps and marsh areas occur; bilharzia is directly related to areas where perennial irrigation is practiced, as in Egypt and the lower Tigris-Euphrates valley, and where parasite-carrying snails have gained a foothold. There have been some attempts at malarial mosquito control, but they are few. Facilities for the prevention and cure of illness have increased considerably in the past two decades, but they have as yet made little headway, so great is the problem.

Middle Eastern poverty is no relative matter. Yet, if possible, it sometimes may seem worse than it is through contrast with the extreme wealth and luxury with which it often rubs elbows. People of great wealth make up a very small percentage of the total population, but they wield great power, not only in government, but also over the mass of the people through *control or ownership of land* and business, especially the former. The ownership of large areas of land from which the owner, commonly an absentee landlord, desires as great a return as possible, is one of the main causes of peasant poverty and a backward agriculture, but at the same time it brings to the owner a large annual cash income that allows him to do as he pleases and to live where he pleases. The welfare of his tenants and laborers, wise care of the land, and a more advanced type of farming are of little importance so long as he has a steady income. The peasant is exploited; the land and economy of the country suffer. So long as the wealthy group controls the government, all attempts at serious reform are blocked, and usually any government that tries it is soon toppled. Few Middle Eastern countries have escaped the development of a small group of large landowners.[10]

Closely related to land ownership is land tenure and land inheritance and the set of economic and sociological difficulties to which they give rise. The systems of land tenure in the Middle East are complex and also vary somewhat from country to country. Land may be owned outright, communally owned, placed in trust, or state owned (*mulk, masha, waqf, miri*). Communally owned land usually is redistributed every few years,

---

[10] Among those countries that have escaped the large landowner groups are Israel, Saudi Arabia, and Jordan, largely because of limited amounts of arable land in the latter two and the buying of Arab estates by collective Jewish capital in the former.

and at the same time, it is split up in such a way that each user gets some good as well as some poorer land. This often means that one laborer will have several small plots to cultivate, but they will be widely separated. A similar effect is produced through inheritance laws that divide land equally among sons of the deceased. The land received by each inheritor becomes smaller and smaller, unless he can in some way purchase land from other members of the family. A further difficulty is added through the peculiar ownership of water rights. These do not necessarily go with land holding. It is possible also to have joint ownership of trees growing on someone else's land. The situation may therefore arise where one man owns a plot of land but not the water rights to irrigate it, while at the same time several other people may have joint ownership of trees upon his land. All people involved would have to be in agreement before a change could be made, and no one likes to take real responsibility when a number of others are equally involved. Both land and man suffer as a consequence.

Terms of land tenancy also vary from state to state, but the general result is wealth to the landlord, poverty to the peasant, and harm to the land. Land may be rented outright, or it may be worked on shares. In the first case, the rent will vary depending upon whether the tenant furnishes livestock and implements; in the second case the amount of harvest the tenant receives will vary similarly. In most instances the tenant receives only a meagre share, often as little as one-fifth of the harvest. In addition the tenant often has no security of tenure. Commonly land is rented for one year only and rarely for more than two or three. Under these circumstances it is understandable that a tenant cannot afford to keep up the land, let alone improve it. Landlords and their agents also are often moneylenders and loan at some of the world's most exorbitant rates of interest. The tenant, through debt and the need of land for basic food production, becomes little better than a serf. Since the end of the second World War there have been attempts at land reform and redistribution in some states, but where the landowner group is well entrenched, there has been no instance of its grip being broken.

Southwest Asia, with one exception, is not well endowed with mineral wealth. However, the one exception, petroleum, is indeed spectacular. No other region in the world has as much. Not only has petroleum involved the Southwest Asia deeply in world politics, but it will also ultimately bring about major changes in the life of the people.

The production of Southwest Asian oil is immensely important not only economically, but politically as well. All of the concessions for development and exploitation are in the hands of Western companies, largely

American and British.[11] Southwest Asian oil supplies most Western European needs (85 per cent)and has been vital in postwar reconstruction and rehabilitation in that area. At the same time, it has brought great wealth to the producing countries and companies. Western control of this oil reserve is obviously an asset to the West; but the strategic and vulnerable location of the oil deposits and the political instability of the region are an almost equal liability. There can be little question that the Soviet Union would give much, either to control the oil or to deny its use to the West.

Intraregionally, the income from oil royalties can have tremendous influence on the life of the people of the countries involved and ultimately on the people of the whole Middle East.[12] Concurrently with, or following upon, the nationalization of oil in Iran in 1951, the oil companies increased royalty payments, so that at present the governments granting concessions receive 50 per cent of the profits, plus taxes, on each barrel of oil produced. This, together with the ever-increasing production, has meant great increases in income. The governments concerned all have programs afoot to use a percentage of such income for the betterment of their countries and people. This is true of Iraq and Saudi Arabia, the largest ones, and the ones with the most difficult problems.[13] Both countries have had surveys made of their needs for improvements and have started to implement their programs. The projects include health and sanitation, transportation, flood control and irrigation, land and housing projects for peasants, and a number of others. Provided world conditions do not interrupt these projects, they should before long bring about marked changes within the countries involved. Economies should become more stable; living levels should be raised, and social conditions bettered.[14] The oil industry, of course, gives employment and training to considerable numbers of native people, and the projects contemplated for improvement should give work to many more.

The effect of oil royalties and oil production on the other Middle Eastern countries is harder to judge. At present, Jordan, Syria, and the Lebanon are benefiting directly by allowing pipelines to cross their terri-

[11] French and Netherlands companies and the company of the late Mr. Caluste Gulbenkian hold part control in some concessions, especially that of the Iraq Petroleum Company and its affiliates.

[12] Until recently much of the income from oil royalties had little effect on the masses of the population. It was used by the governments for normal expenses, and there is little question but that some found its way into the pockets of a favored few.

[13] Prior to nationalization, Iran had worked out a detailed program of development, through oil royalties. Kuwait and Bahrein island, both very small countries with small populations, have been able to give more immediate benefits. In Kuwait the problem may well be how to spend so great an income.

[14] Kuwait now levies no taxes, gives free health and medical care, and provides free education to all who show promise, the higher education to be received in any university in Europe or the United States.

Fig. 140 • A nomad encampment in the desert of southern Iraq between Ur Junction and Basra. The characteristic black tents are usually made from goat hair. The picture, taken in early June, shows the sparse vegetation, already dry and brown. During the summer such encampments locate near a permanent source of water and often near a village where food may be obtained if necessary. During the winter, following the rains, when the vegetation is green, the nomads wander widely over tribal areas and change camps as frequently as is needed to obtain forage for their livestock. This section of the desert lies within the Tigris-Euphrates lowland. *(John R. Randall.)*

tories to Mediterranean terminals. Large payments are made to these countries as a kind of annual rent for the land occupied by the pipelines.[15] The oil ports, too, are developments of importance to Syria and the Lebanon. It is conceivable that in time the oil-rich states will be willing to invest money in the other Middle Eastern countries, so that the whole region may benefit.

The *nomadic and semi-nomadic peoples* present another socio-economic and political problem in sections of Southwest Asia. There has never been an accurate count of these people,[16] though they make up a large part of the population in the Arabian peninsula and Jordan; there also are considerable numbers of them in Iraq, Iran, Syria, and Turkey. A distinction should be made between the true nomad or *Bedu,* and the semi-nomad

[15] Jordan receives 60,000 pounds gold annually from the Iraq Petroleum Company for the double pipeline that crosses it, and 40,000 Jordanian pounds from the Trans-Arabian Pipeline Company's Dhahran-Sidon (Saida) pipeline. Lebanon receives about 4.5 million Lebanese pounds annually from TAPline. Syria receives 6.5 million pounds sterling from TAPline for rights to cross its territory. All three countries are pressing for higher payments, and plans for a new pipeline north and west from Iraq through Turkish territory have been prepared, in part to avoid these pressures.

[16] Estimates from various sources give the following: Saudi Arabia, 3 to 3.5 million; Turkey, 1.5 million; Iran, 2 to 3 million; Syria, 150,000; Iraq, 200,000; Egypt, 12,000. Data for other states and the dependencies are not available.

(Figure 140). The true nomad moves from place to place in search of pasture for his livestock; he has no fixed abode, though he may return at intervals to known points. The semi-nomad usually moves seasonally from lowlands to highlands with his livestock. Although he may cover a considerable horizontal distance, his movement is essentially a vertical one. Semi-nomadic people commonly have permanent habitations in their winter lowland quarters and are on the move in spring and summer, returning to their homes with the advent of another winter. Often some members of the tribe remain in the lowland areas all summer so that crops may be grown. The *Bedouin* practice true nomadism, a horizontal movement; the semi-nomadic people practice transhumance, which is a vertical and seasonal shift.

The future of the nomadic and semi-nomadic peoples of Southwest Asia is in doubt. Although their economic activities are of importance to the countries most concerned and to the region as a whole, in many respects they do not fit into the pattern of present-day affairs. They have been encroached upon by peoples of sedentary habits and by the central authority of governments. The age-old warfare between the "desert and the sown" is being resolved apparently in favor of the "sown."

During the long centuries of cultural development in the Middle East, the nomadic and semi-nomadic people have played a major role and have been one of the more virile elements. They have strengthened the sedentary population physically and morally. In the process they have themselves often become sedentary; they have been one of the main sources for the replenishment of populations in urban and settled rural areas. Although this process has been continuous, it also has been slow. Owing to the pressure of population, however, the process has also worked in reverse, and sedentary people have been forced into nomadism. Through time a sort of balance or equilibrium has worked out between these two major groups, and it is this balance that is being tipped permanently in favor of the "sown."

Much of the difficulty seems to arise from the establishment of independent states in the Middle East, the infusion of Western ways and thought, the change from an essentially tribal organization to a national state. The central governments have largely stopped both intertribal war and the raiding of oasis areas, two of the mainstays of the tribal economy. The states, in their attempt to achieve nationality, come into conflict with tribal loyalties and tribal laws and customs. The tribes either do not recognize, or refuse to recognize, national law. Thus, a tribal minority tends to identify itself with a tribe and not with the state, and at the same time it conceivably can be used to weaken the central authority or even rebel openly against it. Hence, the desire on the part of the government to permanently settle these people. Another result of state action in stopping raids has been the lowering of the level of living of tribal groups. Their ability to get food and livestock from raids in part made up for the harshness of the environment in which they existed, and in years when little forage was available such raids often saved them from starvation.

Plans and programs for settling the nomadic and semi-nomadic peoples vary from state to state. It could be questioned whether or not some of the states have carefully considered the problem before acting on it, in spite of its importance to the people involved and to the state. Saudi Arabia, under the leadership of the late Ibn Saud, has had a settlement plan in operation since 1912, which has achieved considerable success, reducing the nomadic population from 80 per cent to somewhere between 50 and 60 per cent of the total. Turkey has attempted to solve its problem by forced assimilation, while Iran under Reza Shah tried, with some temporary success, to bring about the forcible settlement of a number of the semi-nomadic tribes of the Zagros mountains.

The nomadic and semi-nomadic people make up only one of several types of minority groups in Southwest Asia that present problems to their respective countries and to the region. Religious, linguistic, and ethnic groups are the other important types. Although the distinct minorities—especially the religious minorities—are numerous, the problem presented is in general much the same for all of them. They commonly create tensions that tend to weaken the national political structure. Economically, they may be highly important because of the work they do and the products they turn out. The identification of a certain occupation with a certain group has been highly developed in the Middle East, with the result that when such a group is persecuted or expelled the economy may be seriously unbalanced.[17]

Many of these conditions reflect a problem confronting all of the Middle Eastern countries and impinging upon practically every phase of life: the *impact of Western culture*. Although contact and interchange between the West and the Middle East are of great age, developments of the past half century or so have been especially significant. The question posed is how much of Western culture shall be accepted by the people of the states of the region, and what effect will this acceptance have upon their own culture? Much has in part already been accepted—among others, the idea of the state, educational practices, and literature. Degree of acceptance and desire to assimilate differ greatly. Turkey is usually considered the most Western of states and possibly the one most ready to

---

[17] The expulsion of the Jews from Iraq in 1950-1 can be cited as an example. Many of these people were manufacturers, merchants, and financiers.

become thoroughly Westernized; Saudi Arabia, and particularly the Yemen, are least affected and least wish to come under Western cultural influence.

It is impossible to predict what parts of Middle Eastern culture will be kept and what parts discarded, and what phases of Western culture will be adopted. One danger lies in the possibility of accepting the worst features of Western civilization while discarding the best of local culture. But the great integrating factor in the Middle East, Islam, may prove adaptable enough to retain its identity and cultural potency even in the face of the Western impact.

SELECTED GEOGRAPHICAL BIBLIOGRAPHY

1. Arabian American Oil Company. *Middle East Oil Development.* Fourth ed., 1956.
2. Cooke, Hedley V. *Challenge and Response in the Middle East.* New York: Harper and Brothers, 1952.
3. East, W. G., and O. H. K. Spate, eds. *The Changing Map of Asia,* 2d ed., chap. 1, pp. 51-120. New York: E. P. Dutton and Company, 1953
4. Hoskins, Halford L. *The Middle East.* New York: Macmillan, 1954.
5. Hourani, Albert H. *Minorities in the Arab World.* New York: Oxford University Press, 1947.
6. Issawi, Charles. *Egypt, An Economic and Social Analysis.* New York: Oxford University Press, 1947.
7. Tannous, Afif I. "The Arab Tribal Community in a Nationalistic State," *Middle East Journal,* January, 1947, pp. 5-17.
8. ———. "Land Reform: Key to the Development and Stability of the Arab World," *Middle East Journal,* Winter, 1951, pp. 1-20.
9. ———. "Land Ownership in the Middle East," *Foreign Agriculture,* December, 1950, pp. 263-269.
10. United Nations. *Statistical Papers,* Series A, Vol. 5, No. 1, 1953.
11. Warriner, Doreen. *Land and Poverty in the Middle East,* chaps. 1 and 2. London: Royal Institute of Internal Affairs, 1948.

Comments

The political problems so important in the Middle East are discussed with real insight in Hoskins and in East and Spate. The Hoskins work is more detailed, but places somewhat less emphasis on geography.

The social conditions and problems in the realm are covered in Fisher and somewhat more narrowly in Warriner. The Tannous articles discuss certain aspects of larger economic and social problems. Afif Tannous, who has written widely on problems of agriculture, land tenure, and reform, is an outstanding authority in these fields and should be read by anyone desiring a deeper understanding of these subjects.

The Aramco publication is a handy, short resumé of the historical background and present situation of the petroleum industry in all the Middle East oil-producing states. It contains a series of excellent maps.

Turkey

TURKEY,[1] LIKE IRAN, DIFFERS NOTABLY FROM THE REST OF SOUTH-west Asia. Both are separated ethnically and linguistically from the Arab states and from each other, and although diplomatically they are on friendly terms with these states, they tend to remain somewhat aloof from Arab affairs. Turkey's role in the Ottoman Empire has not endeared her to the Arabs, though surface relations are cordial.[2] Both Turkey and Iran have been independent states for many years, despite the interference of Great Britain and Czarist Russia (later, also, the U.S.S.R.) in the internal affairs of Iran and the position of Turkey as the "Sick Man of Europe" during the last years of the Ottoman Empire. This long experience of sovereignty, and all it implies, cannot be matched by any of the Arab states.

Physiographically, Turkey and Iran also are separated from the remainder of the realm. They are areas of high, rugged mountains and extensive intermontane plateaus; their plains are narrow and peripheral. They differ in some other physical aspects as well; both have large areas

---

[1] Turkey: area, 299,893 square miles, 9,257 of which are in Europe; population (1950), 20,934,670.

[2] Except for Syria, which has not forgiven Turkey for accepting the Sandjak of Alexandretta from the French in 1939, while Syria was under French mandate.

that experience cold winters and much snow, and sections that have
heavy precipitation; both have an appreciable forest resource. The strong
ties that bind Turkey and Iran to the Middle East and make them an
integral part of the region are geographic location and a shared Islamic
heritage.

The location of Turkey gives her a strategically commanding position
in the Middle East and in the eastern Mediterranean, but it also has
deeply involved her in the affairs of these regions as well as those of
Europe. The control of the land bridge between Europe and Asia and the
water route connecting the Aegean and Black seas puts Turkey in an
important position, but a vulnerable one. She has been subject to undue
pressure from all sides, and her foreign policy regularly reflects this un-
comfortable state of affairs: she must ally herself with the powers that
are willing to guarantee her control of the straits, for once she loses
them, her strategic significance is lost.[3] Of late, the political and strategic
importance of the straits has greatly outweighed their economic value.

Turkey is a compact country physically and is culturally and ethnically
quite homogeneous. The most important minority groups are the Greeks,
Armenians, and Kurds; but, together with the lesser ethnic groups, they
account for less than 10 per cent of the total population. The number of
Greeks was greatly reduced by migration following the Greco-Turkish
war (1922); a majority of the Armenians have been removed from Turkish Armenia; and the Kurds are being assimilated. With the annexation of
the Sandjak of Alexandretta in 1939, Turkey regained the only sizable
group of Turks adjacent to, but outside the borders of, the republic.
Turkey, through its struggle for independence and consolidation following the first World War and through the vigorous leadership of Kemal
Ataturk after the founding of the republic (1923), became a real nation,
the only state in the Middle East to have achieved this distinction.

In a number of ways, Turkey is the most Western of the Middle Eastern countries, but there is some question of the extent of that Westernization. There is, however, little question as to the intent of the central government to bring it about. Turkey's political revolution dates back to the
"Young Turk" movement of 1908, and it reached its culmination with
the establishment of the Republic in 1923. Following this and the sign-
ing of the Treaty of Lausanne (1923), the country launched into a social
revolution and a process of Westernization that is still in progress. The
principal architect and prime mover behind this revolution was Kemal
Ataturk, and difficult as the process was for the Turkish people, Ataturk,
without doubt, had their fullest confidence.

Ataturk inherited a country with a colonial economy and a debt-ridden

[3] Turkey's acceptance of the Truman Doctrine and her membership in NATO
are examples of this policy.

and corrupt government. Immediately, he initiated a number of far-reaching reforms. By the Treaty of Lausanne, he gained recognition of the republic and an end to all foreign control (including "capitulations"). He brought about the separation of church and state, the abolition of the Caliphate, an end to the wearing of the fez and veil, and the introduction of the Roman alphabet. The constitution was Western in pattern, as was the code of laws. An attempt also was made to bring about a better balance between agricultural and industrial production and generally to improve the social status of the population. Government-owned banks and industries were established and a start was made in improving agriculture, transportation, and the exploitation of natural resources, all under the direct auspices of the central government. As a result Turkey has become the most advanced of the Middle Eastern countries.

Agriculture and the Turkish economy

The mainstay of the Turkish economy today, as in the centuries past, is agriculture,[4] with subsistence farming dominant. Specialized and industrial crops, although of growing importance, occupy less than 20 per cent of the cultivated land. But despite its position of primacy in the country's economy, agriculture has, until recently, received little attention. Methods of husbandry, livestock culture, and irrigation are primitive. Marketing, storage, and transportation facilities are woefully inadequate. The inability to sell produce at a reasonable profit has in turn reduced farm production. This generally unfortunate state of affairs prevailed throughout the period of Ottoman rule, and even under the republic, agriculture, until recently, received less attention than its importance warranted. Only since the end of the second World War has the vital position of agriculture in the general economy been recognized by the state and steps taken to nourish this branch of the economy.

In some ways Turkish agriculture and stock-raising are plagued by the same problems and difficulties that characterize farming in the Middle East in general,[5] but in other ways they are quite different. Although the government under the republic until recently placed a greater emphasis upon industry than farming, it has done much to ease the burden on the peasant and to improve the status of agriculture. Through land reform, land was made available to individual peasant families. Thus, 75 per cent

[4] The percentage of employed population in agriculture is 81.8; in industry and mining, 8.3; in trade and transportation, 4.3; in general services, 5.0; all other, 0.6 (1948). In 1951, agricultural and livestock commodities accounted for 90 per cent by value of the Turkish export trade.

[5] Chapter XXXI, the section on agriculture.

of the some 2.5 million farms are owned by their operators, and only in a few districts is absentee landlordism still a problem. About 97 per cent of the farms are less than 125 acres; the average of this group is probably between 15 and 20 acres. It should be remembered, however, that this acreage is tilled land and does not include pastures or meadows.

Along with land reform, work was started on seed and stock improvement and better methods of tillage. Attempts were also made, with some success, to stabilize farm prices through extension of credit. All of these enterprises were state-instituted and -controlled. Encouragement was given to the production of industrial and cash crops, and much of the industrial development was in the construction of factories for the processing of agricultural commodities. Experimental farms and agricultural schools likewise were a part of the program of betterment. It is perhaps an indication of the backward and primitive state of Turkish agriculture that these policies have shown so few results. Statistical data indicate marked increases in the production of crops and livestock, but it is not known whether they represent actual increases or simply better reporting.[6] Sufficient time has not elapsed to make noticeable a change in the status of the average peasant.

Turkish agriculture, however, is changing and the Cukurova area (Adana plain) in southern Turkey might well be cited as an example, though not as one necessarily to be followed in other areas. This area, recently though still inadequately irrigated, produces over two-thirds of the nation's cotton, as well as grains, legumes, and citrus and other fruits. The farms are large, worked mainly by machinery and managed directly by the owners. It also is one of the few sizable areas where artificial fertilizers are in regular use. Improved communications have made possible the marketing of farm produce, and the construction of factories has given rise to an important cottonseed-oil and cottonseed-cake production. As a result of these improvements, the Çukurova plain has become the best-developed farming area in Turkey.

Topography and climate are the two basic physical influences on the types and distribution of crops and livestock; slope, soils, availability of water for irrigation, and altitude are of varying importance depending upon locale. Large parts of the highlands are too rugged or too high to be utilized for crop land, and in some cases for livestock; local areas of plateau also are too dissected for utilization. The mountains are a major factor as well in determining the amount of precipitation and the condi-

[6] The 1934-38 production of all types of grain was 6,600,000 metric tons; the 1952 production was 11,760,000 tons; and the estimate for 1956 was 13,250,000 tons. Production of wheat: 1927, 1,333,000 metric tons; 1940, 4,068,000 tons; 1951, 5,599,050 tons. Cotton production, up to 1940, approximately 80,000 tons annually; 1944, 60,000 tons; 1951, 151,550 tons. Cattle: 1927, 5,214,000; 1941, 7,935,000; 1951, 10,221,000. Sheep: 1927, 13,632,000; 1941, 18,751,000; 1951, 24,688,000.

tions of temperature. All of Turkey, except the Black Sea coast, has a Mediterranean precipitation regime. Only in the interior basins do the summers tend to be as dry as in other parts of Southwest Asia where a similar regime exists. The range of climatic conditions allows the production of middle-latitude and subtropical crops and a few tropical ones, e.g. bananas and sugar cane.

Of the land area of Turkey (296,185 square miles), 18.4 per cent is classed as cultivated. This includes all land in tree crops and vineyards as well as in common crops. Of the cultivated land, about one-third is in fallow for periods ranging from two to four years. Meadows and pastures, which may be privately, state, or communally owned or controlled, occupy 50.2 per cent of the area. The remainder is forest (15.3 per cent) and unproductive or waste land (16.1 per cent).

Because of the wide range of climatic conditions, the variety of crops produced is considerable,[7] though the largest part of the arable land is in a relatively small number of crops. Grains occupy 80 per cent of the arable land; tree crops and vineyards, 10 per cent; and the remaining 10 per cent is in various specialized and industrial crops and gardens. Of the grains, wheat and barley are first and second respectively in importance, and are grown widely throughout the country. Corn, oats, rye, rice, and the millets, of lesser importance, are more restricted in their distribution. Fruits and vegetables are the other commonly produced food crops; they along with cereals and animal products make up the staple items of the peasant diet. Tobacco, for long the primary industrial crop of Turkey, has recently been displaced by cotton. Other important commercial crops are hazelnuts (filberts), sugar beets, grapes (raisins), olives, figs, opium, and oilseeds (sunflower, linseed and sesame).

Livestock constitute an important part of the agricultural economy. Most sections of the country produce some livestock in conjunction with crops. In a few regions pastoral activities predominate. Sheep and goats are the most numerous, both being widely distributed. Cattle, water buffalo, camels, horses, donkeys, and mules are fewer in number, but of considerable importance. In general, livestock are raised for the immediate use of the peasant family, as an adjunct of subsistence farming. Milk, *laban*, or both, plus wool and animal hair are products of cardinal importance. Sheep, goats, cows, water buffalo, and camels produce milk.

---

[7] Important food, fodder, specialized, and industrial crops include wheat, barley, corn, oats, rye, rice, legumes, cotton, tobacco, sugar beets, grapes, olives, citrus fruit, figs, hazel nuts, apricots, peaches, cherries, plums, bananas, apples, pears, tea, sesame, sunflower seed, flax, millet, pistachio and other nuts, valonia oak, opium poppy, and vegetables. Of the same crops, each of the following accounted for more than $1,000,000 value in Turkish exports in 1951: barley, millet, cotton, cotton seed, beans, lentils, raisins, figs, hazelnuts, pistachio nuts and other nuts, opium, linseed, sunflower seed, olive oil, valonia and valonia extract, and tobacco.

Fresh milk, and butter, cheese, and yoghurt made from milk all are consumed largely on the farms where they are produced. Livestock are not raised primarily for meat, and normally meat makes up only a small part of the regular rural diet. There are few, if any, facilities for preserving meat once the animals are slaughtered.[8] All types of livestock except sheep and goats are used as draft animals and are (besides humans) the main motive power on the farms, since little power-driven machinery is in use. They are also used for hauling produce to market and for powering various contrivances for the hoisting of irrigation water.

Besides those animal products consumed on the farms or in nearby villages, there is a surplus for the country as a whole, as well as for export.[9] Farm animals supply the nonfarm population with wool, mohair, hides, and meat, and with some milk, butter, and cheese.

The agricultural regions [10]

The distribution of agricultural regions in Turkey is closely related to climate and major landforms. Development of modern methods of tillage, irrigation, and transportation may result in a readjustment of the agricultural regions, but as yet there is little to indicate such changes, except in a few subregions. The six major regions, each containing a recognizable grouping of crop combinations, are (1) interior Antolia, (2) eastern Anatolia, (3) the Black Sea coasts, (4) the Mediterranean region, (5) southeastern Anatolia, and (6) interior Thrace. All but two of these (5 and 6) have subregions distinguished by intensity of production, minor climatic differences, and the like.

Interior Anatolia is the largest of the regions and is essentially coextensive with the Anatolian plateau (as distinct from the Armenian plateau to the east, which is often considered a part of the Anatolian plateau). It is a largely treeless steppe with hot, dry summers and cold winters; spring is the period of maximum precipitation. Variability of precipitation from year to year is probably the greatest single hazard to agricultural use. The region is preeminently a grain producer, with 80-90 per cent of its cultivated land (10 per cent of its area) in grains of which

[8] Animals destined for urban areas where meat consumption is higher are driven to the urban slaughtering centers directly from the farms. There is little movement of fresh meat from one city to another because of the lack of refrigeration facilities.

[9] Export of animals and animal products, 1951, (in thousands of dollars): cattle, 2,486; sheep and goats, 4,672; intestines, bladders, and other membranes, 2,389; hides and skins, 4,685; wool, 5,829; and mohair, 5,707. The total value of these products was about 8 per cent of the Turkish export trade in 1951.

[10] Much of the material in this section is adapted from Sirri Erinç and Neçdet Tuncdilek, "The Agricultural Regions of Turkey," *Geographical Review*, April, 1952, pp. 179-203.

Fig. 141 • In cultivated fields and pastures in the highlands of eastern Anatolia, a rugged section of eastern Turkey, livestock-rearing is as important as crop production. Level land is very limited, and the growing season is short. The mountain slopes, largely unforested, offer good grazing for cattle and sheep. The valley pictured here is less isolated than many because of the winding road passing through it. *(Turkish Information Office, N.Y.)*

wheat and barley are the most important. It also is a major livestock producer, but the distribution of animals is not nearly as general as that of the major grains. A majority of the eight subregions of interior Anatolia are delineated on the basis of crops of importance other than grain, and these differences are often the result of variation of climate, topography and soils. Although grain remains the predominant crop in all of them, in various of these subregions grapes, rye, sugar beets, middle-latitude fruits, opium, and tobacco are of major importance. Interior Anatolia is the country's largest producer of wheat, barley, rye, sugar beets, opium, angora goats (mohair), and probably sheep.

Eastern Anatolia (the Armenian plateau) is a high dissected plateau largely surrounded and also broken by mountainous areas. It has the longest and coldest winters in Turkey; the summers are short and dry. Slopes are often steep and badly eroded, with thin soils. The best crop areas are in alluvially filled valleys and basins. Like interior Anatolia, this region is one of grain production, but only from 5 to 10 per cent of it is cultivated, and in sections the percentage is as low as 1. Of its cultivated area 90 per cent is in grain, with spring wheat predominant. Stock-raising is fully as important as crop production (Figure 141). Barley, millet, and winter vegetables are other major crops; cattle and sheep are the principal types of livestock.

The Black Sea coast is relatively small but highly important in Turkish agriculture. The intensity of farming here is not everywhere equal, but the over-all production of commodities is impressive. The region is restricted to the narrow, somewhat discontinuous plain facing the Black Sea in Asiatic and European Turkey and to the lower and intermediate slopes of the Pontic ranges. In a few places, open valleys carry the region inland for some distance (Figure 141a). This coastal zone is generally the best watered in the country. Precipitation varies from 25 inches in the west to over 100 inches in the east, and no part of the year is deficient in moisture. Temperatures, where affected by the sea, are moderate; the low-month temperatures are in the 40's, and the high-month temperatures in the high 60's to middle 70's. There is considerable diversity of crop production in the different subregions of the Black Sea coast, but the predominant crop is corn. Ninety per cent of the country's production comes from this region. The specialized crops of importance are hazelnuts, tobacco, citrus, and tea. Legumes, sugar beets, sunflower seed, wheat, rye, and barley also are grown in varying amounts. The eastern half of the region has numerous cattle and a major part of the country's water buffalo.

The Mediterranean region is composed of the coastal areas facing the Mediterranean, the Aegean, and the Sea of Marmara. The first two are climatically delineated, that is, areas of true Mediterranean climate,

Fig. 141a • Amasya, in northcentral Turkey, lies in the valley of the Yeşil Irmak near the Black Sea. The course of this valley, like that of a number of others in the Black Sea region, has been developed along fault lines that cut the Pontic mountains. These valleys give access to the interior and also allow the penetration inland of the milder coastal climatic conditions. Although level land is limited, it is in most cases intensively utilized. The ruggedness of the Pontic region is apparent here. *(Turkish Information Office, N.Y.)*

whereas the Marmara district is transitional between Mediterranean and Pontic. This region is probably the single most valuable agricultural region of the country, producing significant amounts of several of the major commercial and industrial crops—cotton, tobacco, raisins, figs, and olives. Specialized crops of lesser value are citrus, licorice, flax, and pistachio nuts. Livestock tend to displace crop production in the higher and drier areas that flank the coastal plains. In these sections cattle, sheep, goats, and camels are found in large numbers. The major crop areas of the Mediterranean region are found on the narrow coastal plains and on the floors of the tectonic valleys of the Aegean area, as well as on the lower slopes of the highlands back from the coasts. Vineyards and tree crops, especially, favor the foothills and the lower slopes of the mountains. The upper zones (above 1,200 to 1,800 feet depending upon location) are more important for livestock and have only scattered areas capable of cultivation. Wheat, barley, and the millets are the common crops in these poorer areas. Livestock-raising is carried on by both nomadic and semi-nomadic peoples, as well as by sedentary farmers.

Southeastern Anatolia is the area that lies south of the Antitaurus mountains and between the Tigris and Euphrates rivers. It is a high, dry plateau that drops gradually to the steppes of Mesopotamia. Livestock rearing (sheep and goats) always has predominated over crop production, the latter being restricted largely to oases and the rainier slopes of the mountains. Summers in the region are hot and dry, and winters are cold; spring is the season of maximum precipitation, but there is both a moisture deficiency and a high variability. Grains are the major crops for the areas as a whole, though in the irrigated tracts rice, vegetables, grapes, and other fruits are produced. In spite of poor conditions for farming, the area is one of surplus because of the sparsity of population.

Interior Thrace, semi-arid and steppe-covered, occupies the lowland area of European Turkey and is in its natural features similar to interior Anatolia. This region, however, has the advantage of artesian water, which has brought about marked changes in the agricultural economy. Grains still occupy 80 to 90 per cent of the cropped land (more than 20 per cent of the total area), but the variety is greater than in most parts of the country, and wheat accounts for only 35 per cent of the crop land. Industrial and commercial crops have been gaining—particularly sugar beets, which have become the major source of income for the peasants. Other crops include corn, hemp, sunflowers, tobacco, and grapes.

Industrialization and manufacturing

Turkey commonly is considered to be one of the more industrialized countries of the Middle East, but it is not in any sense an industrial nation.[11] Modern manufacturing may be said to have had its inception after the founding of the republic (1923), although there were a few factories in operation under the Ottoman Empire.[12] For the most part, before the 1920's all locally manufactured goods were produced in the home, in small shops, or in the bazaars, and should be classed as handicrafts.

The government of the republic has attempted to industrialize the country without taking time for industrial evolution; it has endeavored to telescope into three and a half decades what it has taken most industrial countries 100 to 150 years to achieve. The results have been somewhat less than successful. The mass of the population, having had no experience and often even no contact with industrialization, has little or

[11] Approximately 7 to 8 per cent of the total population is engaged in manufacturing, exclusive of handicrafts.

[12] These were largely textile mills and food-processing plants.

no understanding of it. There has been no chance to develop a labor force that has even a rudimentary knowledge of or experience in the use of machines, although the Turks are in no way culturally incapable of developing industrial skills.

The general attitude of the republic toward industrialization is clear only against the historical background of the times. The government greatly desired the development of industry as a means of raising levels of living and making the country more self-sufficient. At the same time, it feared foreign control such as existed under the Ottoman regime and so closed the door on most foreign investment. By ridding itself of some minority groups the country lost many of the people most experienced in business and industry. At the start the government had hopes of getting industry under way through private enterprise, but after the better part of a decade it became clear that Turkish capital would not, or could not, do what the government wished. Private capital was scarce to begin with, and where it was available it was not invested because of unsettled conditions generally and because the government's economic policies were unclear.[13]

Disappointed, the government turned to *étatism,* or state-owned and -controlled industry. This policy was not meant to preclude private enterprise, though in many ways it had that effect. Since the second World War there has been a re-examination of the economy, and *étatism* is on the wane. The government has come to realize that agriculture is the basis of the economy and that industrial development can take place rationally only with the raising of the peasants' levels of living and with advances in transportation. As a result, more emphasis is being placed on agricultural improvements in the hope that these in turn will encourage continued growth of industry.

Turkish industry is difficult to examine because of the lack of detailed information and because of government ownership and control not only of industry, but also of processing and marketing. Ownership of industry is shared about equally by government and private enterprise.[14] The government, however, exercises strict control over much private enterprise. In general, Turkish industrial companies and plants are small and, in the case of numerous government plants, have been located on a basis not so much of economic factors as of factors military, political, or social.

[13] A minor factor that had some effect upon investment of private funds was the Treaty of Lausanne, which until 1928 froze at a low rate the tariffs on imported manufactured goods. Many Turks thought local manufactures could not compete against foreign ones.

[14] Estimates of this division vary; some give 60 per cent to private ownership and 40 per cent to government. Quite possibly this could be reversed. The 50-50 figure is a compromise. Turkey has never had a complete census of manufacturing.

The heavy industries include iron and steel, metal products, cement, building materials, and chemicals. The iron-and-steel industry is state-owned, the only important plant being at Karabuk in the northwest. This plant has two blast furnaces, open-hearth furnaces, coke ovens, three rolling mills, a plate mill, and a cast-iron pipe factory. Coal comes from the Zonguldak coal basin on the Black Sea coast between Zonguldak and Eregli, about 50 miles from the plant but separated from it by a mountain range that makes transportation difficult. The original plan was to run the furnaces on imported ores, but before construction was finished (1940) the amount and quality of the iron-ore deposits of Divrigi were established, and these mines now furnish iron ore for Karabuk, although it must be transported by rail for about 500 miles. The factors that determined both the site and production were more military and strategic than economic.[15]

There are only a few metal-products establishments in the country, and these are privately owned. They turn out a variety of items including tools, wire, stoves, and other relatively simple but small products, some machine-made, but some hand-worked. There are no modern foundries and few facilities for the assemblage of common agricultural implements.

The cement and building-materials industries are in part privately and in part state-owned. There are five cement plants with a collective annual capacity of 400,000 tons. The three privately owned plants are in the Istanbul area and have 78 per cent of this capacity. The state-owned plants are at Sivas and Ankara. The chemical industries are largely allied with state-owned plants producing other items (coke and iron and steel at Karabuk; and paper, cellulose, and viscose at Izmit) and in some cases are by-products of these other processes. The chemicals include sulfuric and hydrochloric acid, superphosphate, and alkalies. Their production generally has been well below capacity, in spite of the need for such items within the country.

The principal consumer-goods industries include textiles, paper, leather and shoes, tobacco, and various processed foods. The textile industry is the oldest and one of the more important. Turkey produces two-thirds of her

---

[15] There is every indication that so far as the country's best interests go, the Karabuk plant was poorly planned. Its pig-iron capacity is too large for its steel-ingot capacity, and this in turn is too large for its capacity for finished steel products (there being no other steel plants in Turkey to produce finished steel products). The capacity of the Karabuk plant is: coke, 300,000 tons; pig iron, 300,000 tons; steel ingots, 150,000 tons; rolled steel and plate, 110,000 tons; iron pipe, 12,000. The production in 1949 (unless otherwise noted) was coke, 292,400 tons; pig iron, 112,700 tons; steel ingots, 101,000 tons, finished steel products (1947), 71,000 tons, and iron pipe, 11,000 tons.

needs in cotton textiles and four-fifths in wool; [16] she also produces artificial fibers, some silk, and rugs. Spinning and weaving are ancient crafts in Turkey, and both raw materials and power are available. The country is self-sufficient in cotton fiber and wool, though much of the latter is low-grade, and some higher grades must be imported.

The manufacture, import, and domestic sales of tobacco, alcohol, alcoholic beverages, matches, tea, explosives, and gunpowder are under the control of the state monopolies.[17] Some of these have been monopoly products for many years; others date only from the founding of the republic. It seems probable that the major objective of the state monopolies is to obtain revenue for the government rather than to supply improved service or products to the consumer.

The production of sugar is not by law a state monopoly; but a single company controls all sugar production without competition.[18] In contrast to a number of the state-owned industries, that of sugar is outstanding for its production and efficiency. As late as 1926 Turkey had to import all the sugar it consumed; by 1946 the country had become self-sufficient and had a small surplus for export, despite an increased consumption and a lowering of retail sugar prices.[19] Almost all sugar produced is from beets, though the company has been experimenting with cane production and processing. It has also done much to improve agricultural production among the beet growers by encouraging crop rotation, supplying high-quality seed, encouraging the use of natural manures (which in Turkey are generally used as fuel), and developing dairying in conjunction with beet production.

The extractive industries

The extractive industries of Turkey are mainly mining, forestry, and fisheries. The first is by far the

[16] That the textile industry cannot supply the entire needs of the country is largely the result of government control of textile marketing. Private textile output is sold to the government at a price determined by cost of production plus profit to the manufacturer. The government then sells to wholesalers (or itself acts as a wholesaler) at prices often much above the purchase price. Retail prices may be as much as double the production price plus profit. At the same time tariff barriers keep out foreign textiles. The profit from textiles is used to subsidize other government industries and activities. This policy has discouraged new private investment in textiles, and high prices have made it difficult for the average consumer to purchase clothing.

[17] The production of salt is a state monopoly, but not its sale. Trade in tobacco leaf is also not controlled.

[18] Although the government has an interest in the Turkish Sugar Refining company, the direction of the company is by a private board over which the government has no real control.

[19] The 1951 production was 186,000 metric tons. The company in 1950 owned and operated four refineries at Alpulla, Eskişehir, Turhal, and Usak.

most important. The mineral endowment of Turkey, with the exception
of oil, is probably greater and more varied than that of any of the other
Southwest Asian countries.[20] However, lack of detailed mineralogical
knowledge, poorly developed transportation, and government policies all
account for the present backward status of mineral development and
production. There has been until recently no over-all coordinated survey
work by competent technicians, and few good topographic or geologic
maps have been produced. Since many of the mineral deposits occur in
isolated or mountainous areas, the lack of good transportation also has
been a serious deterrent to exploitation.

The main handicap to mineral development has been government
policy. As a result of flagrant foreign exploitation under the Ottomans, the
republic ultimately cancelled almost all existing concessions, both foreign and domestic. All minerals are state property, the rights to which
cannot be conveyed, although the government may grant concessions for
a period up to 60 years. That it has rarely done so is the result of rigid
regulations making private development anything but attractive. This
policy gives the government a virtual monopoly in mineral exploration
and exploitation, and although this is what the government desires, it
has meant a slower and often inefficient development of resources.

Turkey's main coal deposit, the Zonguldak basin, lies on the Black Sea
coast between Eregli and Zonguldak. Estimates of its reserves vary from
300 million to a billion tons. Although this field contains ample coal for
the country's needs for many years to come, its production is barely
enough for present-day consumption. Lack of experienced miners and
modern machinery, and no lack of governmental inexperience and inefficiency have plagued the industry. Although production has risen considerably since 1940 when the government took over the mines from foreign owners, both the cost of coal and governmental losses have kept
pace.[21] The average production per miner is very low, approximately one-
half ton per man per eight-hour shift, less than one-tenth the amount
produced by American underground miners in an equal period. The
mines lack facilities for cleaning, grading, and sorting, so that most of the

[20] Turkey produces coal, lignite, iron ore, chrome, salt, and copper. Smaller and
varying amounts of the following minerals are regularly or periodically produced—
sulfur, manganese, lead, mercury, antimony, asbestos, magnesite, borocite, emery,
and meerschaum. Recent surveys by the Mineral Research and Exploration Institute
indicate deposits, as yet unassayed or undeveloped, of bauxite, arsenic, barite, gold,
graphite, gypsum, kaolin, mica, molybdinite, nickel, silver, lead, and talc. The Mineral Research and Exploration Institute (MTA), set up by the government in 1935,
is the first agency to concern itself with mineral resources. It carries on surveys and
mineral exploration, tests deposits, maintains laboratories for analytical and research
work, and trains both technical personnel and mine foremen.

[21] Production in 1940 was approximately 3,000,000 metric tons; in 1954 it had
reached 5,700,000 tons.

production is classed as run-of-the-mine and contains considerable waste material. Yet, Turkey sorely needs coal for her industrial development, and coal remains the major power fuel. Turkey has large deposits of lignite, a number of which are being exploited.[22] This fuel is used on the railroads, for power development, and as industrial fuel.

The iron-ore deposits at Divrigi are the only ones developed and producing. These ores, with a 60 to 65 per cent iron content, furnish the Karabuk blast furnaces.[23] The deposits are estimated at 30 to 40 million tons, but only a third to a half is high-grade ore. The remainder has a sulfur content of 10 per cent, which must be removed before smelting. There are a number of chromium deposits in the country, only a few of which are being exploited. Since Turkey has little use for chromium in its own industries, this ore in concentrate form is an export of major importance, though its market is subject to considerable fluctuation depending upon world industrial conditions.[24] Turkey's copper is produced from two mines, at Erganimadeni and Murgal, both of which are state-controlled.[25] The reserves are estimated at over four million tons. There has been a consistently higher production of ore than the smelters can handle. With one or two exceptions the remainder of the mineral production is not on a par with those above, though the total output is of considerable value.

The forest and fishery resources of Turkey are modest and little developed. Although 15.3 per cent of the country is classed as woodland, the area of commercially exploitable timber is much less. The Black Sea slopes of the Pontic ranges have the major part of the country's best timber; mild temperatures and copious precipitation have given rise to a rather dense forest composed largely of hardwood species. Smaller areas of forest and scattered trees are found in the other highlands. In general, the best stands are in the least accessible areas (hence their preservation). Turkey's forests, like those in other Southwest Asian countries, have suffered from the long period of human settlement and the indiscriminate grazing to which they have been subjected. In 1944 all forests were nationalized, and the government is doing what it can to preserve the pres-

[22] Reserves are probably well over 200,000,000 tons. Present workings are at Soma, Degirmisaz, Tunçhilek, and Agacli. The 1954 production was approximately 2,000,000 tons. Eighty per cent of the lignite is state-produced.

[23] The 1954 production was 371,000 tons. The mines are government-owned and -operated. A second ore deposit of considerable size, much nearer Karabuk than Divrigi but only with 40 per cent iron, has been found at Adapazari, near Izmit, but there is no means of transport available at present.

[24] The major chrome deposits being worked at present are at Guleman and Gazinantep. The 1951 production was 512,000 metric tons. The 1951 export of chrome ore was slightly over 500,000 metric tons, valued at about 16.5 million dollars.

[25] The 1954 copper production was 25,000 metric tons of which about half was exported.

ent resource and to renew it. Only about 40 per cent of the country's timber needs are furnished from domestic forests.

Fishing suffers by a lack of equipment and of proper storage, refrigeration, and transportation facilities. The majority of the people in the interior have little familiarity with fish; thus, there is, or has been, little demand for it. The main catch is obtained from migratory fish passing seasonally through the straits and the Sea of Marmara. Only a small part of the potential resource is caught, and about two-thirds of the annual catch is exported. In recent years the catch has declined.

The pattern of transportation

The lack of adequate and cheap transport has been one of the main handicaps to the economic development of the country and also one of the major factors contributing to the schism between urban center and village. Before 1923 Turkey's railroads were largely foreign-owned or -controlled and had been planned and located more for political or strategic than for economic functions. Moreover, until the end of the second World War neither the Ottoman nor republican governments attempted to integrate rail- and highways into an efficient transportation system. Construction and maintenance of both roads and railroads always have been hampered by difficult terrain and climatic conditions.

The Turkish railroads are state-owned and -operated and have been developed into a trunk system; though superior to that of Ottoman times, it is still inadequate to meet the needs of the country.[26] A majority of the railroads are single-tracked, and a number of the lines are more circuitous than the topography warrants. The system suffers from lack of proper rolling stock, and on occasion rail and roadbed maintenance are sacrificed to keep down operating costs. Cost of transport by rail often is prohibitively high, and this serves to reduce the amount of freight traffic.

The road system of Turkey has been notoriously inadequate, though the need for good roads is probably even greater than that for railroads. In 1951 there were only about 15,600 miles of national roads, many in need of repair. A postwar road program, however, has resulted in a marked increase in road traffic and a decline in highway freight and passenger rates.[27]

[26] There were, at the end of 1952, approximately 4,800 miles of railroad. There were another 280 miles projected. Between 1923 and 1949, the government constructed over 2,170 miles of rail lines.

[27] In 1948 Turkey, in part with American aid, started a nine-year highway construction and improvement program which will produce 13,400 miles of all-weather highway and form the basis of a national highway system. At the time the development program was started, only 7,800 miles of national roads were surfaced.

In spite of its many miles of coast line, Turkey has been only of minor importance in the shipping world. With the exception of Istanbul and Izmir, good natural harbors are rare, and port facilities have been inadequate for modern shipping (Figure 141b). Turkey's ocean-going merchant fleet at the end of 1954 had a gross tonnage of 487,000 tons. Istanbul handles approximately 70 per cent of Turkey's foreign trade and Izmir another 14 per cent.[28] A number of the smaller ports handle considerable amounts of freight in coastwise traffic which is restricted to Turkish vessels.

Turkey has a state-owned airline system, which connects all the major cities and provides regularly scheduled flights in both summer and winter. Foreign lines into Istanbul connect Turkey with the rest of the world.

[28] Iskanderun, however, has been growing in importance as a result of the increased agricultural development of Çukurova and agreements with Iran, Iraq, and Syria that allow those countries rights of export through the port.

Fig. 141b • The port and harbor at Antalya on the Mediterranean coast of Turkey. Antalya is the main center of the Antalya plain, second in size to that of Adana on the south coast. This smaller plain, though productive, is less developed and more sparsely populated than that of Adana because of its isolation. The high, unpierced ranges of the western Taurus block ingress to the Anatolian plateau leaving the sea as the only easy connection with the rest of the country. The harbor at Antalya is one of the few good ones along this section of the coast. Mediterranean fruit and vegetables are the principal crops of the district. (*Turkish Information Center, N.Y.*)

Population and urbanization

In 1950 Turkey had a population of 20,934,670 (in 1955 an estimated 24.1 millions), or approximately 70 persons per square mile. The population density is, however, anything but uniform. The areas of major density (75-100+ per square mile) lie along the Aegean and Black sea coasts and around the Sea of Marmara; the areas of least density (1-25 per square mile) are in the eastern mountains and parts of the Anatolian plateau. Of the total population, 74.8 per cent is classed as rural and 25.2 per cent as urban, although only 6.7 per cent lives in cities having a population over 50,000. Rural settlements consist of some 30,000 villages. Although some villages have large populations, they remain essentially rural, rather than urban, in character.

Although its crude density of population is relatively low, Turkey cannot under existing economic conditions be considered underpopulated. Much of the rural, working population is underemployed, and industrial employment opportunities are too few to absorb the surplus farm population. The 2.1 per cent annual population increase since 1945 will tend in the long run to aggravate the situation, rather than solve it, unless industry and commerce can develop rapidly enough to absorb the increase. It does not seem likely that agriculture can do so, especially as agricultural practices become more efficient.

Turkey had 11 cities in 1950 with a population of over 50,000 and 14 cities that ranged in population from 30,000 to 50,000.[29] The largest cities in 1950 were:

Istanbul	1,000,022	Gazniantep	72,743
Ankara	286,592	Kayseri	65,489
Izmir	230,508	Konya	64,509
Adana	117,799	Erzurum	54,360
Bursa	100,007	Sivas	52,269
Eskişehir	88,459		

Istanbul, though no longer the capital, is the leading city and port of the country, and one of the few truly international cities (Figure 141c).[30] Built on both sides of the Bosporus and around the Golden

[29] The following are cities with a 1950 population of less than 50,000 but over 30,000—Malatya, Diyarbekir, Samsun, Mersin, Urfa, Adapazari, Bahkesir, Zonguldak, Izmit, Maras, Manisia, Trabzon, Antalya, and Edirne.

[30] The site was first permanently settled in B.C. 658 by the Greeks. The Greek city, Byzantium, was renamed Constantinople in A.D. 330. In 1923, after the birth of the Turkish Republic, Constantinople became Istanbul. The Golden Horn, the harbor of Istanbul, is a drowned river valley, tributary to the Bosporus. The Bosporus, Dardanelles, and Sea of Marmara are themselves all the result of subsidence. The Bosporus, on which the city is located, is 18 miles long and in its narrowest part is only 800 yards wide. The current through the Straits from the Black Sea averages three miles per hour, but in some of the narrows it runs to almost six miles per hour.

Fig. 141c • Istanbul and the Golden Horn; a partial view of the city and the harbor looking northward. The main port area is to the right of the Galata bridge shown in the right foreground. The Golden Horn, a drowned valley, separates the old city (the foreground of the picture) from the newer city beyond. The old city was the original site of settlement (Byzantium) and today contains most of the historic buildings. This section of the city is known to Europeans as Stambul. Beyoğlu is the Turkish name applied to that part of Istanbul north of the Golden Horn. The Bosphorus, not visible here, lies beyond the upper right of the picture. *(Turkish Information Office, N.Y.)*

Horn, the city has so incorporated these water bodies into its structure that they have become part of it. Although the Bosporus separates Europe from Asia, Istanbul is a bridge linking them. The major part of the city lies on the European shore, split into an old and new city by the Golden Horn. The old city, colloquially known as Stambul, contains many of the historic buildings of the city—for example, Aya Sofia and the Sultan Ahmed Mosque—and is the European railhead. On the north side of the Golden Horn lies Galata, the business and warehouse section, and beyond that the Beyoglu section which is largely residential. These are parts of the new city. Directly across the straits from Galata is Üsküdar, long the terminus of the Asiatic route to Istanbul. Hydarpasa, south of Üsküdar, is the Asiatic rail terminus. Surburban sections extend northward on both sides of the Straits for almost two-thirds of the way to the Black Sea and southeastward on the Asiatic side toward the Marmara islands that are a part of the province of Istanbul.

Istanbul has long been the cultural and commercial center of the country. Its commercial activity centers around the Golden Horn, an almost perfect natural harbor now hampered by lack of space and by outmoded facilities. The city handles about 70 per cent of the country's foreign trade, as well as much of its coastwise trade. Istanbul also has more industry than any other single Turkish city, though it is by no means an industrial center. Its international character was one reason given by Ataturk for shifting the government to Ankara. Istanbul had too much of the past for a nation that was interested mainly in its future.

Ankara, Turkey's second city and present capital, has a more central

Fig. 142 • Modern Ankara, since 1923 capital of Turkey, has long been the regional center of northern Anatolia. At a much earlier date the site had served as the capital of the Hittite Empire. Although its population was only about 50,000, it was chosen as capital because of its historic associations, because of its location at the areal core of the state, and because the new government wished to be disassociated with Istanbul, considered too cosmopolitan to be truly Turkish. Following the change of government to Ankara, the city grew rapidly, both in population and areal extent, to become a city largely of new buildings with a population over 300,000. The old citadel crowns the hill in the left background. Although Istanbul and Ankara are not the only Turkish cities of size (there are three others over 100,000 in population), most of Turkey's population (78 per cent) remains rural. *(Turkish Information Office, N.Y.)*

location within the country and lies within Anatolia, the core of the state (Figure 142). A provincial center for northern Anatolia until it became the seat of government, the city has grown very rapidly from its 1923 population of only 50,000. Its main function is governmental, and its rapid growth is a reflection of the growing development of Turkey as a nation. As the capital city it has become an important center in the transport system and has acquired some industries. Climatically, it is less pleasant than Istanbul, and it has little of that city's beauty, historical interest, or international flavor.

Izmir, the third city, is the historic center and main port of western Turkey. It handles about 14 per cent of the country's foreign trade. Most of the varied agricultural produce of the Aegean coastal area that enters world trade leaves through Izmir. The city has an excellent natural harbor, but the port facilities, like those of Istanbul, are outmoded.

SELECTED GEOGRAPHICAL BIBLIOGRAPHY

1. Erinç, S. "Climatic Types and the Variation of Moisture Regions in Turkey," *Geographical Review*, April, 1950, pp. 224-35.
2. Erinç, Sirri, and Necdet Tunçdilek. "The Agricultural Regions of Turkey," *Geographical Review*, April, 1952, pp. 179-203.
3. Great Britain, Board of Trade. "Turkey," *Overseas Economic Surveys.* London: Her Majesty's Stationery Office, April, 1950.
4. Helburn, N. "A Stereotype of Agriculture in Semiarid Turkey," *Geographical Review*, July, 1955, pp. 375-84.
5. International Bank for Reconstruction and Development. *The Economy of Turkey, An Analysis and Recommendations for a Development Program.* Baltimore: Johns Hopkins Press, 1951.
6. Lenczowski, George. *The Middle East in World Affairs,* chap. 4. Ithaca: Cornell University Press, 1952.
7. Muntz, T. G. A. *Turkey.* New York: Philosophical Library, 1951.
8. Thornburg, Max W., Graham Spry, and George Soule. *Turkey, An Economic Appraisal.* New York: The Twentieth Century Fund, 1949.
9. Turkey, General Directory of Statistics. *Statistical Abstract, 1951.* Istanbul, 1952.
10. Tümertekin, E. "The Iron and Steel Industry of Turkey," *Economic Geography*, April, 1955, pp. 179-84.
11. Wrigley, G. M. "Turkey," *Focus*, January, 1953, pp. 1-5.

Comments

The economic surveys by Thornburg and the International Bank both provide excellent background for the Turkish economy since the establishment of the republic. The Lenczowski book is largely political and could be cited as background material for the entire Middle East. For the geographer, the Muntz work is of value mainly for the statistical material it contains, not nearly so complete as the *Statistical Abstract* but more readily available in this country than is that official Turkish publication. The British *Overseas Economic Survey of Turkey* contains a wealth of useful information concerning economic conditions in Turkey, and it is a source of valuable statistical data.

The articles of Erinç and Helbrun are valuable for their description of Turkish agriculture, and that by Tümertekin provides a short but authoritative discussion of the Turkish iron and steel industry.

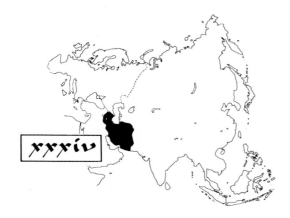

Iran

IRAN, FORMERLY PERSIA, IS THE LARGEST OF THE SOUTHWEST ASIAN states.[1] It is approximately as large as the nine states comprising the Middle West of the United States; it has the highest, most continuous, and most rugged mountain ranges in Southwest Asia; and its climate is more continental, with greater extremes than are found in the rest of the realm. The distribution of its landforms is rather similar to that of Turkey, but the landforms themselves are larger and more extensive.

Economically the country is underdeveloped, and politically it is weak. The general level of living of the peasant population is exceedingly low. Agriculture and pastoral activities are the mainstay of the economy; industry is little developed. Petroleum is the only known mineral resource of major importance. Yet, the cultural heritage of Iran is one of the richest and most varied in the whole realm.

Iran has both gained and suffered from its spatial situation. For centuries it was a routeway (like most of the Middle East) between central

---

[1] Some sources give Saudi Arabia a larger area (at least 900,000 square miles) while others report it at a lower figure (600,000 square miles). The boundaries of Saudi Arabia are indefinite, and its area thus differs according to the way its boundary lines are drawn. Iran, with an area of 628,000 square miles, commonly is considered the larger. The 1956 population of Iran is estimated at 18,944,821, as reported in the preliminary results of the national census.

and southern Asia and the lands to the west. It also has been invaded and conquered from both east and west, though periodically it became in turn the core of vast empires. One of the main strengths of the Iranian people has been their ability to absorb their conquerors without losing their cultural identity. Overwhelmed at different times by Greeks, Arabs, Turks, and Mongols, the Iranians have maintained their national character. Since the sixteenth century, Iran has been a sovereign state, the only country in the Middle East that did not become a part of the Ottoman Empire.

With the expansion of Czarist Russia and the British Empire in the early nineteenth century, there came a shift in the significance of Iran's geographical position. Its importance as a link in the east-west land route declined, and its position as a segment of rimland between the steppe areas on the north and the warm waters of the Persian Gulf and Gulf of Oman on the south (which in turn impinged upon the principal route to India and the Far East) became of primary concern. Russia reached toward these southern waters, while Britain exerted its strength and influence to block her. Persia lost sizable territories in the northwest and northeast to Russia. The central government became weaker as the nineteenth century wore on and thus became an easy prey to the rivalry of Britain and the Czars for influence in the internal affairs of the country. The nadir was reached in 1907 when Persia was divided into zones of influence by Russia and Great Britain.

A further complication arose during the first decade of this century when oil in commercially exploitable amounts was discovered in southwest Persia.[2] In 1914 the British government bought a controlling interest in the Anglo-Persian Oil company in order to insure a supply of oil products for the Imperial Navy. Russian interests obtained concessions in northern Persia, and oil was found, but it never proved commercially profitable.

Until the outbreak of the first World War, Russia continued to interfere in the internal affairs of the country, going so far as to occupy the northern provinces at least twice in order to force the Persian government to give in to its demands. The first World War turned Persia into a battlefield between the Turks on the one hand and the Allied Powers on the other. The country emerged from the war in a chaotic state which continued until the ascendancy of Reza Khan Pahlevi (later, Reza Shah) in 1925. The aftermath of the war at least brought temporary surcease from

[2] The first modern drilling in Persia was done by W. K. D'Arcy, an Englishman, in 1902 in the vicinity of Qasr-i-Shirin. This work did not bring the desired results and the area of exploration was shifted to southwest Persia. Oil in commercial quantities was brought in at Maidan-i-Naftun (Masjid-i-Sulaiman) in 1908. In 1909 the Anglo-Persian Oil company was formed to take over D'Arcy's interests and the concession area which then encompassed some 400,000 square miles of territory.

Russian pressure. The young Soviet Union was in no position to actively interfere in her southern neighbor's affairs.

The inter-war period was one largely of internal development. The Shah attempted to bring about changes in Iran [3] similar to those that Ataturk had achieved in Turkey.[4] Much attention was paid to industry and transportation, but relatively little to agriculture. Although a number of social reforms were put into effect, similar to those in Turkey, the Shah tended to become more dictatorial as time passed, and the people had little voice in the country's affairs.

The liability of Iran's geographical position reasserted itself early in the second World War when Great Britain and the Soviet Union occupied the country and deposed the Shah in an effort to halt German infiltration and influence. The United States later became a third occupying power in order to facilitate the movement of lend-lease goods to the Soviet Union. In most ways Iran benefitted little by the occupation. Its economy was thrown out of gear, and the country was weakened politically when the Soviet Union not only refused to withdraw its occupation forces, but sponsored autonomous regimes in both Azerbaijan and Kurdistan.[5] After the second World War Iran continued to be of great strategic importance and again was caught in a mesh of international rivalries over which she had no control. At the same time the country's economic position worsened especially after the nationalization of her oil fields in 1951. Economic instability and political unrest became the order of the day. Wooed by both Russia and the West, Iran has been reluctant to proclaim herself on any one side for fear of reprisals from the other. There is no question that control of Iran by opposition forces would be a serious blow to the West. The attempts on the part of Great Britain through the Baghdad Pact of 1955 to align Iran, Turkey, Iraq, and Pakistan in defensive alliances is an indication of their importance. Alienation of any of these would allow the Soviet Union to drive a wedge between Asia on the one hand and Europe and Africa on the other. Iran's position is the most sensitive because she is the weakest of the four.

Iran and Turkey are the only countries other than Afghanistan having a common boundary with the Soviet Union that are either not friendly to her or under her domination. Both of them are possible bases for future possible invasion of the Soviet Union. Hence the concern of that country as to their political alignment. The poverty and political weakness of

[3] The official name of the country was changed from Persia to Iran after the deposition of the last Qajar Shah.

[4] Unlike Ataturk, the Shah became an immensely wealthy man as a result of his position.

[5] The question of Soviet withdrawal was the first major question brought before the United Nations for action. As a result, Soviet troops were withdrawn, and the autonomous regimes collapsed.

Iran is wholly advantageous to the aims of the Soviet Union, and anything that the communists can do to foster or continue such weakness is to their benefit. As Haas has said, "Iran occupies a privileged geographical position which is, as all privileges are, heavy with liabilities." [6]

Surface configuration and climate

Deficiency of precipitation, the bane of Southwest Asia, is accentuated in Iran by the distribution of the major landforms. For its latitude, the country has more arid wasteland than its neighbors, the result largely of rain-shadow conditions. The interior plateaus of Iran, the largest part of the country, are virtually ringed by high mountains that effectively cut off sources of moisture. From the northwestern corner of the country to the Strait of Hormuz in the south the Zagros chain extends in an unbroken front. This mountain zone is made up of a series of parallel ranges that are high and rugged, as well as wide. The width of the central and southern sections is as much as 200 miles; the northern part is almost as wide, but much of it lies in Iraq. The second major mountain system, the Elburz and associated ranges, traverses the northern part of the country from the Soviet border eastward to the Afghan border. In only one place, the valley of the Safid Rud, is this mountain wall broken. Lying between the Elburz and Zagros systems in the northwest are the fault-block ranges and volcanic peaks of Azerbaijan. Along the east and southeast are the eastern highlands and the ranges of Makran. These close the circle of mountains and cut off the interior plateaus from the narrow plains along the Persian Gulf and Gulf of Oman, as well as that along the south Caspian shore.

This arrangement of landforms has played an important role in the evolution and development of the country. As mentioned above, the mountains are high enough to block the ingress of moisture, thereby creating a precipitation deficiency in most of interior Iran; at the same time, the windward sides and many summit areas receive ample precipitation, much of it in the form of snow. Although deep snow often blocks roads for weeks during the winter, its slow melting in spring and early summer supplies vital water to permanent streams and springs and also replenishes the ground-water supply which furnishes water for the widespread *qanat* system. In turn the availability of water has a direct influence on the distribution of population. There is a striking correlation between the density of population and the amount of precipitation and the availability of water. Northwestern and northern Iran receive the largest amounts of precipitation and have the largest number of permanent

[6] William S. Haas, *Iran* (New York: Columbia University Press, 1946), p. 42.

streams. Precipitation and permanent streams both decrease toward the southeast. The distribution of population has a remarkably similar pattern, the greatest densities being in the Caspian lowland and Azerbaijan (more than 100 per square mile) and the lowest in southeastern Iran (less than 10 per square mile).

Although the mountains encircling Iran provide a type of natural fortification, they also have tended to isolate parts of the country. The plains areas are cut off from the interior plateaus by mountains difficult to cross and through which it is difficult to build and maintain lines of transport or communication. The Caspian lowland, the most productive part of the country, is isolated by the high Elburz; this in part explains its close economic ties with the Soviet Union. Much the same is true of Azerbaijan. In both cases, it is easier for these areas to carry on trade with the country to the north than with the rest of Iran. The plain of Khuzistan in the southwest, and the narrow coastal strips bordering the Persian Gulf and Gulf of Oman, less productive agriculturally, are likewise isolated from the country as a whole.

Communications are made difficult by forbidding terrain and climatic conditions. Only a few roads are passable in all seasons. Winter rains at lower elevations and snow in the mountains make many roads impassable at that season; extreme heat and drifting sand affect some roads in summer. Iran also has large areas so desolate and lacking in water that few people ever hazard a crossing, and primitive trails are the only lines of travel. The lack of adequate transportation and communications has tended to weaken the central government and depress the national economy. The results have been a periodical rise of autonomy in peripheral regions, the deliberate flouting of the central authority by certain of the mountain tribes, and the close economic ties some regions have developed with other countries, as cited above.

The interior plateaus of Iran occupy almost half its area and contain some of the world's most desolate regions. The plateau character of the interior is everywhere evident, although the surface is broken locally by low mountains and hills that commonly form the divide between the individual basins of interior drainage. These basins vary greatly in size from the two largest, the Great Kavir and Southern Lut,[7] through the medium-sized Jab Murian and Qum-Masileh, to a series of small peripheral basins.

---

[7] These names usually occur on maps as Dasht-i-Kavir and Dasht-i-Lut. The names Great Kavir and Southern Lut are used as being more descriptive of the areas. The term *dasht* applies to a desert surface that is firm, either largely gravel or a mixture of gravel and salt; *kavir* to a surface that is often salt-encrusted but underlain by salt slime and mud and laced by ancient, slime-filled channels called *shatts*. *Lut* refers to the whole desolate interior area, or any generally desolate, uninhabited area of desert. Although the Dasht-i-kavir contains areas of *dasht*, it is dominated by *kavir;* the Southern Lut contains relatively little *kavir* surface.

The alluvial fans bordering the interior basins are the inhabited and productive areas of the interior plateaus.

The Great Kavir and Southern Lut are largely uninhabited. They are practically impassable in winter when temporary lakes are formed; in the summer, heat and glare make life equally insupportable. Although camel caravans may cross in summer, the salt crust of the *kavir* surface often badly damages the animals' feet, and the salt-crusted *shatts* are treacherous dangers that claim the lives of both men and animals. A large area of the Southern Lut has been dissected into a maze of fantastically shaped hills (Shahr-i-Lut) that are exceedingly difficult of passage. Just to the east of the Shar-i-Lut is an even larger area of sand dunes (*rig*) best described as "confused," since they have no apparent general axial alignment. Large areas of the interior basins are devoid of vegetation and of potable water. Where springs exist, they often are too brackish for use.

Whereas the smaller basins are easily avoided or in some cases can be crossed without too much difficulty, the Great Kavir and Southern Lut are major obstacles to travel. No all-weather road crosses them, and through history all important routes have shunned them, seeking higher, more passable ground on their flanks. Thus, the main route from the southeast circles the southern end of the Lut and passes through Kerman, from which it follows the base of the mountains to the west of the basins. The main route from the east enters through Meshed and in a similar way skirts the northern edge of the Great Kavir. The north-south highway in the east follows a route that lies in the mountains. Thus it avoids the heat and lack of water characteristic of the Southern Lut to the west and the Perso-Afghan basins in the east.

The most habitable and productive parts of the interior plateaus are in the northwest where the Zagros and Elburz ranges come closest to meeting, and where piedmont alluvial plains are well developed. There also are a number of small utilized basins in the west. In general, the northern and western parts of the region are the best watered and hence the best developed agriculturally.

The largest part of Iran is deficient in moisture, receiving under 10 inches annually; a sizable part of central and eastern Iran receives less than 5 inches. The precipitation maximum is in the cool half of the year, and precipitation is cyclonic and orographic in origin. Only the provinces of Gilan and Mazanderan in the Caspian lowland have humid conditions throughout the year; some areas in the high northern and central Zagros are probably humid, but few records are available. Iran is characterized by long, hot summers and short, cold-to-mild winters. All parts of the country at elevations below 5,000 feet are hot in summer, generally having temperatures higher than their latitudes would indicate.

Excessive heat is common in the lowlands of the south; the daily maximum temperature is regularly above 100°F. for one to two months and in a few cases for even longer. Except for coastal areas, the humidity is very low. Constant heat, glare, and frequent dust storms plague the inhabitants. Northwestern and northern Iran, with the exception of the Caspian plain, have short but severe winters; frost and snow are common, and temperatures well below zero have been recorded. Southern Iran has mild winters, though only the coastal areas south of Bushire are frost-free.

Agriculture and land-use regions

Iran is typically Asian in that its economy is based largely upon agriculture; as much as 75 to 80 per cent of the population is engaged in some form of farming or pastoral activity. Subsistence farming is dominant, and there is little agricultural surplus.[8] In spite of its importance, agriculture is neither well developed nor efficient. Lack of water, prevailing poverty and illness, uncertain land tenure, lack of knowledge, and custom all conspire to thwart any real improvement in the status of the peasant or his methods of farming. Political instability also has had a crippling effect upon economic development. As a result, the country is one of the more economically retarded in the Middle East.

Iran's economic ills are similar to those in the whole realm. The level of living of its peasants is exceedingly low. Though no statistics give the average annual income of the peasant, the estimated per-capita national product in Iran in 1955 was only 100 dollars (Israel 540, Turkey 276, Iraq 195, Syria 111, the United States, 2,343 dollars). Only Jordan and the non-oil producing countries of the Arabian peninsula have per-capita products as low or lower. Land ownership and tenure and the division of the harvest are the economic factors at the basis of the peasants' plight. Probably less than 30 per cent of the land is owned and operated by the owners, and then in relatively small parcels. The remainder is in the hands of large landowners, the state (approximately 10 per cent), or is *waqf* land. These lands, where cultivated, are worked by share-croppers or tenants, very largely the former. Rent rarely is paid

[8] Apart from petroleum and petroleum products, agricultural products make up the bulk of the so-called commercial exports. Cotton fiber, valued at 26 million dollars, was almost five times as valuable as any other single agricultural export in 1950. Each of the following accounted for a value of over one million dollars in 1950: rice, apricot pulp, dates, raisins, almonds, pistachio nuts, opium, cumin seed, poppy seed, and other oils. The value of petroleum products exported in 1950 was $687,938,000. The total value of all other exports in 1950 was $110,484,000.

in cash, even when the agreement calls for it; payment invariably is in kind.

The usual division of the harvest is determined by the apportionment of five basic items supplied by the landlord or by the peasant—land, water, seed, draft animals, and labor. Since only infrequently can a peasant furnish any of these except labor, the common portion received by the landlord is four-fifths of the harvest. In many cases, dues of another type are also extracted from the peasant—so many bundles of firewood, so much clarified butter.[9] Too often peasants in order to live have to borrow on their share of the harvest before it is produced, so that they have little or nothing left at the end of the crop year. Practical serfdom is the result. To date the government has been able to do little to break the grip of the landowner group. Some governmental, as well as foreign, agencies have attempted to improve methods of tillage and water resources, but there has been no appreciable effect upon the average share-cropper.

Natural as well as economic conditions affect farming adversely. The deficiency of precipitation and the lack of adequate surface- and ground-water supplies force the farmer either to practice dry-farming or to irrigate. Only on the Caspian plain and the lower slopes of the Elburz behind the plain can ordinary farming be carried on with certainty. Dry-farming is common in northwestern and northeastern Iran and in the mountain basins and valleys of the Elburz and the northern and central Zagros. In practicing dry-farming, as much as one-third to one-half, and in some cases three-quarters, of the land is left in fallow for periods ranging from one to four years. The yields from this type of land use are highly variable; yet, over 50 per cent of all cropland is farmed in this manner.

The production of crops during the summer is possible only with irrigation. Obviously, irrigated lands produce more certain harvests and better yields.[10] Yet the development of irrigation faces major difficulties. Water resources are unequally distributed; terrain is unfavorable; planning, if any, often has been shortsighted. There also has been a lack of knowledge concerning soils and the effect of irrigation upon them.

Permanent streams in any number are found only in the Elburz, in Azerbaijan, and in the northern and central Zagros. South of the Karun River system, which empties into the head of the Persian Gulf, only

---

[9] Laws passed in 1952 were designed to reduce the landlord's percentage of the harvest by 20 per cent. Ten per cent of this is to go to the peasant and 10 per cent into a fund for general improvements. All extra dues to the landlord were also abolished. There is little indication as to whether these laws are being enforced. The common four-fifths - one-fifth division varies to some extent with locale, depending upon the type of land farmed and the type of farming practiced.

[10] Estimates of irrigated land vary from 35 to 55 per cent of all land cultivated.

eight or nine permanent streams reach the sea from that point to the Pakistani boundary in the east. These southern streams carry relatively little water. The interior plateaus and eastern highlands are virtually without perennial streams. Not only is there an absence of rivers in much of Iran, but many of those draining from the high mountains into the basins of interior drainage are saline in their lower courses and hence are unusable in the areas where most potentially irrigable land is found, the alluvial fans encircling the basins.

Iran has few large rivers and none with flood plains or deltas comparable to those of the Nile or the Tigris-Euphrates. The Karun, the only navigable river in the country, has the greatest volume, but the plain of Khuzistan, built in part by the Karun and its major tributaries, is not extensive and is a segment of the Tigris-Euhphrates lowland. This plain is, however, the only one in Iran on which a sizable irrigation system might be developed.[11]

In those parts of the country where permanent streams are found, surface configuration often precludes the possibility of irrigation. In a number of instances, the middle or lower courses of the rivers, where volume is most favorable, are in deep valleys or canyons where water is unobtainable and level land is nonexistent. This is true especially of the rivers flowing into the head of the Persian Gulf—the Karkeh, the Diz, and the Karun. On the other hand, considerable amounts of land in the upper reaches of these streams are or could· be irrigated. These rivers and a number of their tributaries flow in open, and often wide, mountain valleys in their upper courses, then turn abruptly and cut transversely across the Zagros ranges in a series of deep canyons to enter the Tigris-Euphrates lowland. Because of the mountainous character and dryness of the country, much of the land that could be irrigated is in the form of alluvial fans, or piedmont alluvial plains. In contrast to major flood-plain or delta areas, these alluvial fans are often relatively small, and in order to obtain any large amount of irrigated land, many small irrigation projects must be developed, a costly venture.

The *qanat* system, one of the oldest in the country, is still one of the most effective, though possibly not efficient by modern standards. This system is limited to alluvial fans. When water is desired on the lower slope of a fan, a source of ground water is found near the base of the mountains by normal well-digging. Once an adequate source of water has been found, a tunnel is dug from the point where the water is desired, up to the source at the apex of the fan. The tunnel has a gradient less than that of the fan, so the outlet will intersect the surface of the fan at the proper point. The diggers first excavate a channel (*haranj*) and then, as they proceed upslope, a tunnel (*qanat*) usually two and a

---

[11] Such a system existed in Khuzistan during Abbasid times.

half feet wide and four feet two inches high. Vertical shafts are opened
as the work proceeds to facilitate the removal of debris and later to aid
in keeping the *qanat* cleaned and repaired. Ultimately, the tunnel reaches
the source of ground water, and this water then flows through the *qanat*
by gravity to its opening. Where the *qanat* passes through soft material,
the tunnel is lined with flagstone or fired brick. Where one source of
ground water does not supply the amount of water needed, a number
of wells may be sunk, each one connected to the main *qanat* by a tributary tunnel. *Qanats* vary greatly in length, depending upon local conditions, from a few hundred yards to several miles. The tunnels are
cleaned and kept free from debris, but when this becomes too difficult,
an entirely new system is built. *Qanats* have decided advantages over
open-flow channels: the water is less likely to become contaminated,
and less is lost by seepage and by evaporation. Although the amount
of water thus supplied varies greatly, a good *qanat* will furnish as much
as four cubic feet of water per second. After the water passes through
the village, it is led to the crop fields. *Qanats* are the main source of
water for human use and irrigation in the fan areas surrounding and
within the interior plateaus and also in many of the mountain valleys
and basins. There is a strong correlation between the size of villages
and the amount of water available; a sizeable village means an ample
water supply and vice versa.

Most crops produced in Iran are for food; industrial and commercial
crops are of comparatively little importance. Cereals, fruit, and vegetables are the main staples of the peasant diet, along with milk in some
form (curdled, as cheese, or clarified butter). An estimated 41,000,000
acres are cultivated or in orchards,[12] and of this about 20 per cent (1951)
is in the three major cereals—wheat, barley, and rice. Cotton is the only
industrial crop having an acreage comparable to that of any of the
cereals.[13]

Livestock rearing is dominant in some areas; in others it is an adjunct
to crop farming. Sheep and goats are the most numerous and important.
Oxen, cattle, water buffalo, camels, mules, and donkeys are used for
draft purposes, and also furnish some of the other animal products. Animal dung is still used primarily as a fuel rather than as fertilizer.

The *major geographic regions of Iran* are based largely on land use
and physiography, whereas subregions reflect primarily the degree of
agricultural development. Seven major regions are commonly recognized:

[12] The major land uses in Iran are: crop land and orchards, 10.15 per cent; potentially cultivable land, 20.17 per cent; forests, 11 per cent; grazing land, 6.2 per cent;
uncultivable or waste, 49.88 per cent; cities, towns, 2.5 per cent.

[13] Production in 1952 (in metric tons) was: wheat, 2,682,000; barley, 1,048,000;
rice, 410,000. Acreages in 1951 were: wheat, 5,189,000; barley, 1,873,000; rice,
476,000; cotton, 371,000; sugar beets, 101,000; tobacco, 39,000.

(1) The Elburz mountains and Caspian plain.
(2) The northwest.
(3) The central plateaus.
(4) The eastern highlands and basins.
(5) The central and southern Zagros.
(6) The Makran and southern coastal strip.
(7) The plain of Khuzistan.

The Elburz mountains and Caspian plain region is agriculturally the most productive in Iran. Although large areas of the highlands are used only for grazing, the Caspian plain, the lower slopes of the north side of the Elburz, and a number of the mountain valleys throughout the region are well developed. Climatically, the Caspian plain and lower Elburz slopes are the most favored; sufficient precipitation and mild temperatures facilitate the production of a large variety of crops. Wet-rice is dominant, but cotton, tea, sugar cane, tobacco, and the opium poppy are grown, as well as many types of fruit. Wheat, barley, and legumes occupy the higher slopes and uplands. Sericulture is also of importance. Sheep, goats, and horses are the principle types of livestock. Water buffalo are common in the rice areas.

Whereas agriculture profits from superior climatic conditions in the plain and on the lower mountain slopes, it is restricted by the dense forest growth that covers the entire area back from the swampy coast. Not only is the forest heavy, but it also supports a dense undergrowth. The relatively small amount of cultivated land indicates in part the difficulty of clearing and in maintaining clearance, and in part the poor drainage of much of the plain. Often crop fields will contain large trees too difficult to remove with available implements. The swampy, marshy character of much of the plain and the presence of flooded paddy fields have made the Caspian provinces of Gilan and Mazanderan the worst malarial areas in the country. Northern Khurasan at the eastern end of the region is one of the principal granaries. The Kuchan-Meshed valley and the basin south of the Binalud range are outstanding, although low precipitation here necessitates dry-farming or irrigation. The variety of crops is large, there being, other than grains, cotton, rice, sugar beets, fruits, and the opium poppy. Within the mountains, generally, where areas of relatively level land occur along the streams or where slopes can be terraced, farming and stock raising are practiced. Level land and the availability of water are the critical factors. The practice of transhumance by semi-nomadic people is common.

Northwestern Iran (Azerbaijan) ranks second in agricultural production. This region, characterized by a series of fault-block ranges and valleys, has a considerable area that can be cultivated, and although dry-farming and irrigation normally must be practiced, the supply of

Fig. 143 • An irrigated valley and cultivated uplands association in Iranian Azerbaijan. Irrigated crops are grown on the near-level valley floor; the rolling uplands produce cereals under dry-farming methods. Fallow fields can be distinguished from cropped ones. The undulating to rolling uplands seen here are characteristic of the less eroded parts of the plateau surface that occur in the headwater areas of such rivers as the Qizil Uzun and its tributaries, the waters of which drain into the Caspian Sea. The stark contrast between the watered valley floor with its green crops and trees, and the drier treeless upland is typical of landscapes in the region. *(F. A. O.)*

water is better than in most of the country (Figure 143). Azerbaijan ranks somewhat above northern Khurasan as a cereal producer and is the major wheat area. Other important crops are similar to those of northern Khurasan. In the northern Zagros or Kurdish mountains, the Kurdish tribes are pastoral and semi-nomadic. Moving seasonally from lowlands and valleys into the mountains with their flocks of sheep and goats, the majority of any tribe are absent through the warm season. The remainder cultivate food and forage crops for the winter. Horses and ponies are an important adjunct to this seasonal migration.

The central plateaus comprise the largest of the regions, but one of the least developed and populated. Large areas are devoid of inhabitants and are trackless wastes. With the exception of a few oases that lie well within the plateaus, the only watered sections lie around the edges. The size and importance of the peripheral oases depend upon the availability of water and the degree to which this resource has been developed. The irrigated fans at the base of the central Elburz and those on the eastern side of the central range (here considered as a part of the Zagros) are the most productive farming sections. The fans eastward from the Veramin plain (the Tehran district) and those along the western side of the eastern highlands are little utilized. Cereals are the most extensively produced crops, though gardens and fruit trees are characteristic of all oases areas. Specialized crop production is relatively unimportant except in the Kazvin-Teheran district. Some dry-farming is carried on in these oases, but results are poor. Mountain streams and *qanats* are the main sources of irrigation water. Livestock production is decidedly secondary except in a few districts.

The eastern highlands and basins are as underdeveloped as much of the interior plateaus. Population and agriculture are scanty and spotty since water is scarce and unevenly distributed. There are few sizable areas of cultivation, but rather a series of small basins and valleys in which cropping can take place. The northern section of the highlands in the vicinity of Qain and Birjand is somewhat better watered than in the south. Food and livestock production is mainly for subsistence. The upper slopes provide some good forage for livestock belonging to the nomadic and semi-nomadic tribes of the region. The basins of interior drainage that straddle the Iran-Afghanistan boundary are largely uninhabited, except for that of Seistan which is the largest and has a good supply of water from the Helmand River. This basin is the only important farming area in southeastern Iran.

The central and southern Zagros region is characterized by a series of northwest-southeast trending ranges, separated by valleys and basins, some of which have interior drainage. It is similar to a folded "ridge-and-valley" region, but on a grand scale. Although this large region is important as a crop producer, it is best known for its pastoral activities. Large numbers of sheep and goats, owned by the semi-nomadic tribes of the region, are taken into the mountain pastures each spring where they remain till autumn. The migration is basically a vertical one, though often a good deal of horizontal distance is covered. Each tribe has a recognized area over which it ranges from its permanent winter base to its summer pasturage. Although Reza Shah tried to break the power of these tribal groups by prohibiting or restricting their movement, he was by no means completely successful; however, a greater percentage of the population now is sedentary.

The distribution of cultivated land in the central and southern Zagros region is uneven. The northern and southern sections contain a number of wide basins and valleys that have a good deal of land either culti-

vated or cultivable. In contrast, the central section has a larger proportion of ranges in which the alternating valleys are quite narrow. There is
a decided decrease in precipitation from north to south, as well as a
diminution of permanent streams toward the south. As a result, many
of the northern valleys and basins are well developed agriculturally.
They not only produce sufficient quantities of food for local consumption, but may have some surplus as well. Dry-farming and irrigation both
are common. Where favorable areas are not cultivated, the reason is
usually a lack of security because of tribal rivalries. In the southern
section the cultivated areas are less numerous because of restricted water
supply. However, where water for irrigation is available, the oases usually are highly productive, and because of milder temperatures the variety of crops is greater. The basins of interior drainage in which Shiraz
and Niriz are located are good examples, as is the much larger Isphahan-
Sirjan trough to the east. Cereals, wheat, and barley with some rice in
favored areas are the dominant crops throughout the Zagros region; in
restricted areas of cultivation they make up the bulk of the produce.
Where larger areas are available the variety of crops increases and specialized ones become more important. Thus in the plains around Kermanshah, cotton, tobacco, the opium poppy, fruits, and nuts are produced, as well as the cereals. In the southern basins, e.g. Shiraz, much
the same is true except that subtropical crops may replace more hardy
varieties. Oases in the far south produce dates as one of the staple food
crops.

The Makran region of southeastern Iran is sparsely populated, and its
agriculture amounts to little. Water is again the most critical element.
The supply is generally small, so that oases are also small and widely
separated. Only a few streams supply water throughout the year, others
only in the winter season. Water is also obtained from *qanats* and wells.
Dates are the main food crop, though cereals are commonly grown
beneath the palms. In a few locations, two crops of wheat a year may be
produced. The narrow coastal plain along the Gulf of Oman, like the
rest of the region, is poorly watered though it does have the advantage
of warm winters.

The plain of Khuzistan in southwestern Iran is the only plain of any
size in the country, having an area of approximately 16,000 square miles.
Its surface is composed of river silts deposited by five Iranian rivers, four
of which are, or have been tributary to, the Tigris or Shatt-al-Arab. The
plain is a segment of the Tigris-Euphrates lowland to the west. The
lowest half of the plain is level, featureless and largely marsh, threaded
by abandoned river channels. In the vicinity of Ahwaz a line of low hills
(the Ahwaz hills) trending northwest-southeast separates the lower,
poorly drained sections from the higher, better drained part. Where the

plain abuts the foothills of the Zagros, it has an elevation of 500 to 600 feet.

Cultivation in Khuzistan is slight considering the amount of river water available. There is little question that at an earlier date this whole area was irrigated by an efficient large-scale system. Like similar systems in the Tigris-Euphrates lowland, that of Khuzistan was smashed during Mongol invasions in the thirteenth century, and though it has at times been repaired, it has never been reconstructed. Today the irrigated lands lie close to the river banks where water is available through free-flow channels or by various types of lifts. Much of the lower plain is inundated during late spring and early summer, precluding cultivation except on the higher land along the river banks. The plain of Khuzistan is, however, the one sizable area of Iran that could be wholly irrigated by the construction of one major system. Cereals (including rice), dates, fruit, and sugar beets are regular crops; smaller amounts of tobacco, cotton, and oilseeds also are produced. Sheep, goats, and camels are important in the farm economy.

Industrialization in Iran

Although Iran is often considered one of the more important manufacturing countries of Southwest Asia, it has very little modern manufacturing by Western standards. A recent estimate (1950) gave the country a total of approximately 250 manufacturing or processing plants, of which 15 per cent were state-owned;[14] of the total almost 75 per cent processed agricultural or livestock products. The most important in number of plants and employees is textiles, followed very closely in number of plants by food processing, though the latter has less than one-quarter the number of employees. With the exception of the state arsenals, there are few metal-products establishments. The state arsenals produce metal products other than armaments: wire, tubes, castings and forgings, and machine tools for other government factories and the railways. Other heavy and construction industries include cement, bricks and tile, glass, and chemicals. The fuel for many factories is oil, though some coal is used, and electric power is generated from oil, coal, and water.

The development of modern industry in Iran dates only from the middle thirties when Reza Shah began a program of industrialization to furnish manufactured products for the home market and to help balance the economy. Relatively little could be accomplished in the few years remaining before the second World War, but the start at least was im-

---

[14] This estimate excludes the processing of petroleum products (see extractive industries below) and the state-owned arsenals.

pressive. Although Reza Shah was following in Ataturk's footsteps, he apparently had better advisors. The state-owned plants—sugar refineries, textile mills, chemical plants—are well located in relation to raw materials and markets and, in general, have been quite successful. Their location was also integrated into the transportation system developed at the same time. Although Iran went in for state ownership, its policy toward private enterprise was more lenient than that of Turkey; from the start, private enterprise was licensed and regulated, but neither prohibited nor discouraged.

Handicrafts still make up the bulk of Iran's manufactured and processed goods. As in all of the Middle East, these products are of great variety in number and quality, and are produced in homes and small shops or bazaars. Rarely are more than ten persons employed in any one shop. Only one handicraft item, rugs, is important in international trade. Iran has been famous for a number of varieties of rugs for many years. This industry, although now in part controlled by large companies, is still carried on by hand in small shops and homes. In value rugs rank second in export commodities ($19,000,000 in 1951) and are the only important manufactured item exported from the country.

The petroleum industry

Iran's extractive resources, other than petroleum, are relatively insignificant both in amount and in value. The country does, however, have fisheries, forests, and a number of other minerals, all of which are exploited to some extent, but these are completely overshadowed by oil production.

The major oil fields of Iran lie in the foothills of the Zagros in the southwestern portion of the country east and northeast of the head of the Persian Gulf and only a short distance from it (between 140 to 160 miles from Abadan). From north to south the structural domes containing the oil pools are at Lali, Masjeed-i-Sulaiman, Naft Safid, Naft Kel, Agha Jari and Gach Saran. All of these are connected by pipelines to the refineries at Abadan and to the loading terminal at Bandar Mashur on the Khor Mashar (a continuation of the Khor Musa on which is located Bandar Shapur, the southern terminus of the Trans-Iranian railroad).

From 1908 when the first well in the Masjeed-i-Sulaiman area was brought in until 1951 when oil production virtually ceased because of nationalization, there had been a gradual increase in the development and production of the industry in southwestern Iran. A similar development took place in the processing establishment and the shipping and storage facilities at Abadan, on Abadan island in the Shatt-al-Arab.[15] By 1950 Iran had attained fourth rank in world petroleum production with a daily output of 660,000 barrels of crude; the Abadan refineries had a daily capacity of 550,000 barrels. The known reserves of oil in Iran are placed at approximately 26 billion barrels.

The production of oil and all its affiliated operations have been of great economic significance to Iran. In the last full year of production, it was estimated that total oil operations, including royalties and wages, brought roughly one million dollars daily to the country. The Anglo-Iranian Oil company was the largest single employer in the country; operations connected with it meant employment for other thousands. A majority of the employees were Persian. The virtual cessation of operations in 1951 was an economic blow. Since the government also was unsuccessful in its attempts to sell oil, one of its major sources of income ceased. The country was brought to the edge of financial chaos and weakened politically. In 1954 an agreement between the Iranian government and a group of foreign oil companies, including Anglo-Iranian, brought about the renewal of oil production. This agreement is for a period of 25 years, with the possibility of extension for three five-year terms beyond that. By this agreement, the Iranian government will receive 50 per cent of the profits of the oil consortium and will hold title to all oil properties and facilities.[16]

A second much smaller oil field, the Naft-i-Shah, is located close to the Iraqi border, northeast of Baghdad. This field was discovered before those in the southwest but has always been of minor importance. Its

[15] This general development was slowed only during the first World War. The various pools were brought into production as follows: Masjeed-i-Sulaiman, 1908; Haft Kel, 1928; Gach Saran 1941; Agha Jari, 1944; Naft Safid, 1945; and Lali, 1948. The first pipelines to Abadan and the refinery there were started in 1909-10 and completed in 1913. By 1950 Abadan was generally considered the largest refining center in the world. Its population had grown from practically none to approximately 140,000. The island prior to development consisted largely of mud flats fringed with date palms.

[16] The oil consortium is composed of the following companies: Anglo-Iranian Oil company, 40 per cent of stock; Standard Oil of New Jersey, Standard Oil of California, Texas company, Gulf Oil corporation, and Socony-Vacuum Oil company, each 8 per cent; Royal Dutch Shell, 14 per cent; and Compagnie de Francaise des Petroles, 6 per cent. Two companies have been formed, one to operate oil-producing properties and one for refining properties. The consortium guarantees to produce 300,000 bbls. of oil daily the first year, 450,000 the second, and 600,000 the third. Thereafter, production will reflect the general supply and demand for Middle East crude oil. The profits to the Iranian government for the first year of full production are estimated at 420 million dollars. Settlements have also been made between Iran and A.I.O.C. for the latter's properties and between A.I.O.C. and other members of the consortium for use of A.I.O.C. installations. In 1955, the name of A.I.O.C. was changed to the British Petroleum company.

output is piped to a small refinery at Kermanshah, and the finished products are marketed mainly in northern Iran. A third field of great potential also has been discovered at Qum, about 75 miles southwest of Tehran. It is to be developed by the National Iranian Oil company, a government corporation, presumably assisted by foreign capital.

Forest resources

Iran's forest resource is restricted largely to the northern slope of the Elburz mountains, facing the Caspian, and to scattered areas in the high Zagros ranges. There are estimated to be eight million acres of hardwood forest from which are produced 28 million board feet of lumber annually. In spite of technical governmental control, the forest resource is being rapidly depleted by cutting for charcoal. Approximately 45 times as much wood is cut annually for charcoal as for lumber, there being 10,000 charcoal kilns in the Caspian forest alone. Recent cutting has amounted to one-half million acres per year. Charcoal burning has also been a serious hazard to natural reforestation in the Zagros. As in most southwest Asian countries, excessive grazing by sheep and goats has also had a serious effect upon the forest areas. The forests and native plants produce a number of items that are used locally and that are exported. Gums exuded by various shrubs are among the more important; others produce vegetable dyes, medicines, and herbs.[17]

Fisheries resources

The developed fisheries of Iran are mainly Caspian, though some are along the south coast and that of the Persian Gulf. Until 1952 the important Caspian fisheries concession was held by a joint Iranian-Soviet company. When the concession expired, it was not renewed. The annual catch from Caspian waters is around 5,000 tons of fish, from which 30 tons of caviar are extracted. About four-fifths of the catch is exported. The government owns small fish canneries on the Persian Gulf and at Bandar Abbas on the Strait of Hormuz. Climate, lack of storage and transportation facilities, and custom all combine to slow the development of important fisheries.

Transportation and trade

Climate and topography are the two natural obstacles that have kept Iran from having a modern sys-

[17] The most important is gum tragacanth whose export value in 1951 was over six million dollars. Other gums include gum arabic, ammoniac, and galbanum. Dye stuffs include acorns, saffron, and madder root; a number of the gums, including asafoetida, are medicinal.

tem of transportation, while the weak economic and political structure of the country is probably the single most important cultural one. Most of what exists today in the way of modern roads and railroads the country owes to the personal force of Reza Shah and to the foreign powers that occupied Iran during the first and second World Wars. The system of routes and roads over which Achaemenid and Sassanian armies and official couriers travelled was, for their time, more advanced than the present system is for Iran today.

The Trans-Iranian railroad, the main line of the Iranian State railways, crosses the country from Bandar Shahpur, on the Khor Musa at the head of the Persian Gulf, to Bandar Shah at the southeast corner of the Caspian Sea. It was completed in 1938 and represents one of the major objectives of Reza Shah. The line was to serve both economic and political ends and was to be integrated into a major, countrywide system of railways and highways. It has not been really successful in either of its objectives, though it does remain an unparalled example of engineering.[18] In addition to the difficult terrain, maintenance is handicapped by excessive heat in gorges; lack of water in summer; hard or saline water in certain sections; steep grades where traction is hard to obtain; heavy snow in winter; and earthquakes. The remainder of the Iranian rail system is as yet not completed. One branch with Tabriz as its objective extends from Tehran to Mianeh; another branch from Garmsar, east of Tehran, to Shahrud, has Meshed as its goal, a third from Qum to Kashan is ultimately to reach Kerman. The utility of these lines is limited.[19]

Modern, all-weather highways in Iran date only from the second World War. Present estimates vary between 17,000 to 23,000 miles for all roads; of these probably not more than 5,000 miles are passable for motor vehicles throughout the year. Roads must cross exceedingly difficult terrain; and once built, both terrain and weather make maintenance a burden physically and financially. Unsurfaced roads are usually

[18] The line largely was reconstructed during the second World War and was taken over first by the British and Russian and later by American forces as one of the main supply lines to the Soviet Union of lend-lease material. The Trans-Iranian railroad crosses in its 861.2 miles both the Zagros and Elburz mountains, the first in its most rugged area. Between Andimeshk and Durad, a distance of 129 miles, the line climbs over 4,000 feet and passes through 125 tunnels which have a total distance of over 35 miles. In this section there are almost as many bridges or trestles where the line has to cross ravines or gorges. Although the distance across the Elburz is less, the construction is equally difficult. Between Pul-i-Safid and Gaduk, a crow-fly distance of 22 miles, there are 69 tunnels totaling almost 12 miles. In the Elburz section there are three instances where the railroad appears at three different levels along a given valley side.

[19] A rail line from Julfa to Tabriz, built by the Russians in 1916, is now part of the Iranian State railways, as is the former Indian line to Zahidan, built by the British during the first World War.

passable only in summer; in winter, snow, mud, or floods commonly close long stretches.

Iran's foreign trade, except for petroleum products, has been relatively unimportant. In 1950 petroleum and petroleum products accounted for 86 per cent of all exports; of the remainder, practically all, except rugs and carpets, were agricultural commodities. The total value of exports in 1950 was just under 800 million dollars, a per-capita amount of $45.62. The main items imported were sugar, cotton goods, and machinery; these amounted to 42 per cent of the total. The value of all imports was approximately 220 million dollars, a per-capita amount of $12.60. Since the end of the second World War, Great Britain, the Soviet Union, the United States, and India have been Iran's best customers for both imported and exported commodities.

Population and settlement

The distribution of Iran's estimated 21,000,000 people is markedly uneven, but shows a strong correlation with the availability and amount of water. The northern and northwest sections, the Caspian provinces and Azerbaijan, have both the greatest densities and the most assured and ample supplies of water. Probably at least half the total population is found in these areas, and densities run well over 100 per square mile. Only in seven other restricted areas do densities run as high—(1) the well watered valleys and basins of the northern Zagros around Kermanshah and Hamadan; (2) Tehran and the well watered Veramin plain to the south of the city; (3) the Ahwaz district, watered by the Karun and the Karkheh rivers; (4) the Shiraz basin; (5) the Isfahan district; (6) the Kerman district; and (7) the Meshed area of the Kuchan-Meshed valley. The last four all receive rather ample water from the mountain areas around them. With the exception of the Ahwaz district, all of the above contain large urban centers which in part account for the higher densities, but they all also have, for Iran, highly developed agricultural districts surrounding them.

Densities for the rest of the country are low, averaging less than 25 people per square mile, and in many areas less than ten, but a detailed picture would show higher densities where water is available, with a corresponding scarcity of population through the mountains and over large, dry, waste areas such as the Great Kavir and Southern Lut. The general gradient of population density is similar to that of water availability: from north and northwest to south and southeast.

Probably not more than one-fifth to one-fourth of the population live in cities having a population of over 30,000. The majority live in small towns and villages (Figure 139), the size of which is commonly indicative of the amount of water available for human use and irrigation. In the drier areas villages may be separated from one another by many miles of undeveloped or waste land. The greenness and shade of these oases after long miles of barren land probably account in part for the widespread fame of "Persian gardens." Only in the Caspian littoral is there any amount of dispersed settlement.

The nomadic and semi-nomadic tribes add another category to Iranian population, one that is even more difficult to estimate. Although there is some semi-nomadism in most parts of Iran, it is fully developed only in the central and southern Zagros, and in the southern section of the eastern highlands. In these areas the members of the semi-nomadic tribal groups outnumber sedentary folk. True nomadism is found apparently only among some of the Baluchi tribes of the southeast. Nomadic and semi-nomadic people may number as high as two or three million out of the total population, but like the figure for total population, this may be quite exaggerated.

Ethnically and linguistically, Iran is not nearly so homogeneous a country as Turkey. The main ethnic and linguistic elements are Persian, Turkish (Azerbaijani), Baluchi, and Arab. No exact figures exist for the proportions of each in the total population, but Persian is certainly primary, with the Turkish element second. When all branches of Persian are combined, this group occupies the Elburz, much of the Zagros, and the peripheral areas of the central plateaus; the northwest is the main Turkish area; the southwest is Arabic; and the south and northeast, Baluchi. In practically every case these groups overlap. There are also numbers of each group living well within the major areas of the others. This last has resulted from forceable resettlement of unruly tribes by government action. Even stronger divisive tendencies spring from religious differences and from those that exist between urban dweller, peasant, or tribesman. Iran is predominantly of the Shia sect of Islam. There is, however, a Sunni minority. Other religious minorities include Jews, Christians, and Parsi. The preponderance of the Shia sect has done much to counterbalance ethnic diversity. The strength of Shia Islam, along with the dominance of Iranian culture, forms a basis for national self-consciousness, a self-consciousness, however, that is as yet hardly realized.

Indeed, the sharp differences between city, village, and tribe are stronger than any sense of nationalism. The urban-village schism is wide in Iran because of the relationship that so often exists between peasant and landowner. Tribesmen and the government also clash frequently since tribal laws and customs are valued above citizenship. Reza Shah did much to break the strength of the tribes, but since his abdication the tribes have regained much of their former power, and at the expense of the central government.

The large urban centers of Iran, with the exception of Abadan, have grown because of their location on trade routes and because of the productivity of the areas they serve. Lines drawn on a map showing the ancient routes would connect practically all the large cities of today. Although these cities have varied over time in size and in importance, they have maintained themselves as sites of urban settlement. Important in this group are (in order of declining size): Tehran, Tabriz, Isfahan, Meshed, Shiraz, Kermanshah, Resht and Hamadan.[20]

Tehran, the capital and largest city, is in some ways symbolic of the changes that have taken place in Iran in recent times. Although the plain at the base of the Elburz, on which the city is located, has had continuous settlement since ancient times and has always been the site of an important city, Tehran was not founded until after the destruction of Rai (five miles south of Tehran) in the early thirteenth century. Thus, it is young in contrast to most of the other large cities. Reza Shah in the late twenties and early thirties tried to modernize the city. He razed its old walls and replaced them with broad streets. He also cut wide avenues through the city and gave it a rectangular street pattern. Many modern buildings were constructed, but these and the wide, paved streets were in some ways only a facade upon the old city, much of which still exists, side by side with the new. Reza Shah neglected to give the city a modern water system, though the present water supply is not so bad as reputation has it.[21] Tehran has more industry than any other Iranian city and is the national rail and highway center as well. Like most of the capital cities of the Asian Crescent, it is a true Primate City, dominating all others in the country.

SELECTED GEOGRAPHICAL BIBLIOGRAPHY

1. Haas, William S. *Iran*. New York: Columbia University Press, 1946.
2. Hadary, Gideon. "The Agrarian Reform Problem in Iran," *The Middle East Journal*, Spring, 1951, pp. 181-196.
3. Hindus, Maurice. *In Search of a Future*, chaps. 1-7. Garden City: Double-day and Company, 1949.

[20] Estimated populations for 1956 are: Tehran, 1,513,164; Tabriz, 290,195; Isfahan, 254,876; Meshed, 242,165; Shirz, 169,088; Kermanshah, 125,181; Resht, 109,495; and Hamadan, 100,029. Cities of over 50,000 but probably less than 100,000 that also are old trade centers include Ardebil, Kerman, Kazvin, Qum, and Yezd. Abadan, 226,103, owes its existence and growth to the oil industry of southwestern Iran. The modern city dates from after the beginning of the present century.

[21] A modern system is being constructed. During the second World War Tehran was the only large city in the Middle East where a supply of pure water was not readily available.

4. Great Britain, Board of Trade. "Iran," *Overseas Economic Surveys*. London: Her Majesty's Stationery Office, April, 1948.
5. Wilbur, Donald M. *Iran: Past and Present*. Princeton: Princeton University Press, 1948.

Comments

The books by Haas, Hindus, and Wilbur, none of them geographers, are all of value to the student of geography who is especially interested in Iran. The Hindus work also contains material on Egypt, Iraq, and Palestine.

The Iran volume of the British *Overseas Economic Surveys* is an invaluable source of factual information about economic and commercial conditions in Iran.

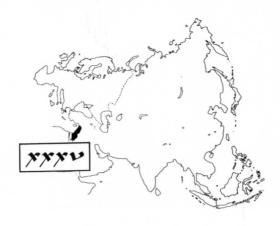

The Fertile Crescent, i

ISRAEL AND LEBANON

THE STATES OF THE FERTILE CRESCENT [1] ARE CHARACTERIZED BY A diversity of physical features and a complexity of cultures, which, along with their location, account for much of their turbulent history and checkered economic and political development. The present division into five states of an area frequently controlled and developed as a unit is the most recent manifestation of a process of fragmentation centuries old.

An introduction to the fertile crescent

The Fertile Crescent extends in an arc from the head of the Persian Gulf northwestward up the Tigris-Euphrates lowland and the upper Tigris valley westward through the steppe lands of northern Syria; then it turns southward along the hill and lowland areas of the eastern Mediterranean to end in the vicinity

[1] Syria, Lebanon, Israel, Jordan, and Iraq. The Fertile Crescent technically excludes the Syrian desert which lies within the prongs of the crescent but is included in Jordan, Syria, and Iraq. The sizes and estimated populations of these states are: (1955) Syria, 70,500 sq. mi., pop., 4,145,000; Lebanon, 3,900 sq. mi., pop., 1,425,-000; Israel, 8,000 sq. mi., pop., 1,748,000; Jordan, 36,700 sq. mi., pop., 1,427,000; Iraq, 171,000 sq. mi., pop., 5,200,000.

of Gaza, where aridity prevails. To the east, northeast, and north, the crescent is paralleled by the high Zagros, Kurdish, Antitaurus, and Taurus mountains, which are breached in few places. Lying within the prongs of the crescent is the Syrian desert, physically a part of the Arabian desert which stretches almost endlessly to the south. In the west the crescent borders the Mediterranean, and in the southwest, the desert of Sinai.

The Fertile Crescent achieved its importance by being well watered, or relatively so, and by having a surface that could be traversed without much difficulty, in contrast to the areas that surround it. It also has a central location within a region that bridges three continents. The greater abundance of water within the Crescent attracted settlers from drier areas, and the availability of water, food and forage, and easy passage brought it into early prominence as a route for armies, traders, and migrating peoples.

Physical conditions within the Crescent vary. The three main subdivisions are: (1) *Mesopotamia,* comprising the flood plain and delta of the Tigris and Euphrates rivers from the latitude of Baghdad to the head of the Persian Gulf; (2) *the rolling steppe of the upper Tigris and northern Syria;* and (3) *the hill country and lowlands of the eastern Mediterranean.*

(1) Mesopotamia, the largest riverine plain in the Middle East, with its abundant water for irrigation, level topography, and fertile soils, proved to be not only attractive to people living in harsher environments, but also readily accessible. It was invaded and occupied time and again from the mountains to the east, the hilly steppe country to the north, or from the deserts on the west and southwest. There also was a continuing and reasonably peaceful infiltration by nomadic peoples from the surrounding areas, who ultimately became sedentary. These, in turn, sometimes reverted to nomadism as a result of circumstances that forced them out of the river plain.

(2) A short distance above Baghdad the topography becomes more rolling and hilly, and the rivers commonly are entrenched well below the general upland. Although in some places strips of level plain are irrigable, the surface generally is too rolling or too high above the streams to be irrigated. This section of the Fertile Crescent, which includes northern Syria, does, however, receive enough rainfall to support steppe grass and to allow the sowing of winter grains. Less productive than Mesopotamia to the south, it has nonetheless been settled continuously since very ancient times.[2] The availability of water, forage, and grains, and

---

[2] The plain of Mesopotamia came into being through river deposition into the Persian Gulf after B.C. 4,000. Archeological evidence indicates that settlement in upper Iraq and Syria antedated that in Mesopotamia. In B.C. 4,000 the head of the Persian Gulf lay some distance north of the present site of Baghdad.

the tractability of the surface made it fairly easy for groups of migratory peoples and armies to live off the land.

(3) The western end of the Fertile Crescent is topographically the most complex and climatically the most advantageous. The north-south alignment of hill and mountain range, coastal plain, and rift valley tends to channel movement and to make an east-west crossing decidedly difficult except at the three points where lowlands or saddles connect the coastal plain with the rift valleys. Only in the north, where the eastern series of highlands is replaced by plateau-like uplands, is passage toward the east possible without an ascent over steep-sloped highlands. The northern route, which connects the steppe area of north Syria with the Orontes valley and the Mediterranean coast, is the "Syrian Saddle."

The areas of coastal plain and the windward sides of the ranges along the eastern Mediterranean have a Mediterranean climate which produces sufficient precipitation for orchards, vineyards, and winter crops, and in much of the area reasonably ample supplies of water are available for irrigation. The precipitation gradients are from north to south (Iskanderun, over 30 inches; Gaza, 14) and from coast (Iskanderun) to interior (Aleppo, 14.6 inches). The same gradients are found in the highlands. The Jebel Ansarieh and Lebanon mountains receive from 40 to 50 inches; the hills of Galilee about 30; and Samaria and Judea, 25 to 15 inches. The eastern zone of highlands, though moister than the areas that flank it, receives 10 to 15 inches less annually than the western zone in similar latitudes. Although water difficulties are present, the Mediterranean region stands out in sharp contrast to the steppe and desert to the east and south; thus, as in the case of Mesopotamia, it always has attracted the desert dweller.

The varieties of surface configuration in the Mediterranean flank of the Fertile Crescent have been a strong influence in its cultural evolution. The compartmentalization of this region into relatively small areas of coastal plain, mountain range, and structural valley, most of which are separated from one another by abrupt natural boundaries, has tended to encourage political fragmentation and attempted economic self-sufficiency. When not united and controlled under a single strong power, each individual range, segment of coastal plain, or rift valley developed as an essentially independent unit under a single tribe or group of tribes. On the other hand, strong political control brought not only economic unity but also public security, and the two together brought general prosperity. With the decline or weakening of control, local autonomy and fragmentation would again prevail.

Another reflection of the diversity of landforms has been the use of the mountain and hill areas as asylums for political, ethnic, and religious minorities. Isolation because of difficult terrain and lack of communications has helped many a group to maintain its identity through long periods without much interference.

The location of the Fertile Crescent area has been a primary factor in its development. The region epitomizes the locational peculiarity of the Middle East; it is the focal point of a larger, intercontinental node. It has served as an arena in which both neighboring and often remote powers have fought out their political and dynastic differences; as a public market in which local and foreign goods were bought, sold, or transshipped; as a forum in which religious faiths were discussed, argued, and fought over; as a haven for persecuted minorities; and as a congeries of cultures.

Through most of its recorded history, powers or dynasties based outside the Fertile Crescent proved stronger and more lasting than those that arose within it. Repeatedly, the region was wholly or in part controlled from outside,[3] and it often constituted the peripheral provinces of the controlling power. At other times it served as the stage for prolonged struggles between powers, with one holding the western side, the other the eastern, and with the Syrian desert as a no-man's land. It also was ravaged by Mongol invasions from the east.[4] When centralized control and security broke down, internecine warfare commonly broke out. Under Roman and early Arab control the region probably experienced its greatest prosperity and economic wellbeing; but under Ottoman Turkey it suffered a slow economic and social disintegration, the results of which are still evident. In some periods, while under foreign domination, sections of the region would prosper, whereas others declined or remained static.

The functions of the region as a trade area also were affected greatly by its location. Commercial importance derived largely from the role of the region as an entrepôt: transshipment and storage frequently were necessary, and the resale of goods was common. The convergence of land and sea routes upon the Fertile Crescent countries created a demand for such services and at the same time often made possible the levy of fees or tribute on goods in transit. A majority of the early cities, such as Palmyra, developed as trade centers, and their relative prominence waxed or waned in proportion to the importance of the route or routes upon which they were located, and with the general condition of the times. Wars or foreign domination did not necessarily bring a halt to trade, though they could dislocate it temporarily or bring about

[3] Among the more important controlling powers were Greece, Rome, Persia, Byzantium, Egypt, Arabia, and Ottoman Turkey. Among ancient dynasties that had their origin within the region were Babylonia and Assyria. The Arab Empire during the Omeyyad and Abbasid times was controlled from Damascus and Baghdad, respectively.

[4] By the grandsons of Ghengis Khan and by Tamerlane.

a change in the status of a given route or routes. A general decline in trade followed the opening of new routes to the Far East in the fifteenth century and the development of the New World and Atlantic routes. The Ottoman Empire's lack of interest in business and trade also was a contributory factor, as was the general economic decline of the areas under Ottoman control.

Islam is the faith as well as the culture of a majority of the inhabitants of the Fertile Crescent countries, though it is the only one of the three predominant faiths that had its origin in another region. Both Judaism and Christianity are native, with Jerusalem as their primary holy city. The three great monotheistic faiths have survived the centuries and grown strong, but they were born in travail and often were disruptive forces within the region. Not only did clashes occur among them, but also within them as a result of internal schisms. At the same time, willingly or not, they lent themselves to political intrigue. Whereas many religious difficulties are of the past, others still remain.

Since from ancient times the Middle East has been a route-area and often a coveted region, it has been subjected to and influenced by many different cultures; its central section has been most affected. No group of people occupying the area for any length of time left the previous culture untouched. Certain cultures have had a lasting influence, but others have had only a temporary effect. The last culture to dominate the entire Fertile Crescent has been the Arabic, which through the spread of Islam and the Arabic language became accepted almost universally. The long term of Ottoman control brought little change, but present Western culture is a major force bearing upon the Middle East.

At the close of the first World War certain Arab leaders hoped that the Fertile Crescent would be unified politically as a result of the collapse of the Ottoman Empire and the promises made by Great Britain. Their hopes were dashed, however, by France, which desired control in Syria and Lebanon, and by the British Balfour Declaration, which allowed the establishment of a Jewish National Home in Palestine. Political fragmentation, with control vested in the mandatory powers, Great Britain and France, was the result. During the approximately two decades of foreign control and the second World War, independence was achieved by Syria, Iraq, Lebanon, and Jordan. In 1948, Israel was created as an independent state out of the British Mandate in Palestine, and the remnants of Palestine were annexed by Jordan. The civil war following the creation of Israel heightened the bitterness between the Jews and Arabs and created the problem of the Arab refugees. Israel, colonized primarily by Jews of Western origin and culture, introduced a new and foreign element into the region.

Since gaining independence, some of the Fertile Crescent states have moved to achieve either unity or confederation. Israel obviously has not participated and is apprehensive lest the Arab states again initiate hostilities. Lebanon has held aloof, partly because of her large Christian population and partly because she does not wish to jeopardize her presently stable economy. The two schemes of union most widely discussed are those of (1) Greater Syria and (2) a Fertile Crescent Union. The first envisions a union specifically between Jordan and Syria, with a possibility of this union being joined by, or closely allied with, Iraq and Lebanon; the second is between Iraq and Syria, with a like possibility of the other two states ultimately cooperating. There also has been some discussion of a union, under the Hashimi family, of Iraq and Jordan. Attempts at union have failed because of political friction within the states involved and as a result of moves on the part of Saudi Arabia and Egypt to block the formation of a state that would be their equal in size and importance.

The political fragmentation following the first World War brought an end to economic unity within the region. With the creation of the mandates and later with independence, each country wished to be economically as well as politically independent. Tariff barriers were raised between all states except Syria and Lebanon, which until 1950 had a customs union. These developments meant costly economic readjustments which the states could ill afford. Furthermore, the formation of an independent Israel was accompanied by a boycott of Jewish goods by the Arab states. Thus, Israel must find its markets beyond the Fertile Crescent, Egypt, and Arabia, and has to pay dearly for imports that could be supplied by the Arab countries. At the same time, Jordan has been hard-pressed by avoiding the use of Israeli ports, which it heretofore had used; Iraq cut the flow of crude oil to the Haifa refinery and stopped construction of its 16-inch pipeline at the Israeli border; Egypt has obstructed the passage through the Suez Canal and the Gulf of Aqaba of Israel shipping. Political policy and nationalism obviously have interfered with economic logic.

Transportation and urbanization in the Fertile Crescent

The road and railroad systems of the Fertile Crescent countries have been reasonably adequate for the needs of the individual countries, though in every case there are areas inadequately served where further development is needed. In general, the main trunk lines have received more attention than the feeder lines. Until recently there have been few detailed surveys made as to the real need for new or improved roads, and there has been no interstate planning. The largest number of hard-surfaced, all-weather roads were built during either the first or the second World War by occupying or allied forces. The creation of Israel and the Arab boycott have stopped all rail and road traffic between Israel and the surrounding Arab countries.

Until 1948 the railroad system served all the countries of the crescent and gave them a connection through Turkey with European railroads; Egypt also was linked with this system (Map 33). North of Aleppo, one line, the Berlin-Baghdad, branched eastward to reach Baghdad; a second passed southwestward through Syria, Lebanon, and Palestine to Cairo where it connected with the Egyptian State railways. During the second World War the coastal line was extended northward from Beirut to Tripoli and thence to Homs. The older interior line, Beirut to Baalbek to Homs, was linked with Damascus and the "Pilgrim" route, with its terminus at Ma'an in Jordan. A second link connected the coast line at Haifa with the Syrian line at Derra, south of Damascus in southwest Syria. Four short branch lines connect important towns with the main line.

The Berlin to Baghdad line, standard-gauge, has its terminus at Baghdad. The other main section of the Iraqi State railways, Erbil-Kirkuk-Baghdad-Basra, is meter-gauge, necessitating costly transshipment at Baghdad. With the exception of the river towns on the Tigris south of Baghdad, the rail system of the Fertile Crescent reached all sizable cities and gave them adequate intraregional service as well as connections with European lines. There is no rail link between Iraq and Iran.[5]

With the creation of Israel, rail connections with the surrounding countries were cut or closed, shutting off from Southwest Asian Arab states not only Israel, but Egypt as well, since its only rail connection with other Southwest Asian countries and Europe was through Palestine.

The road systems of the states of the crescent are the result in part of the economic needs and capabilities of each country and in part of the strategic position and importance of the realm. Until the early part of the present century the need for a modern highway system was not felt, nor, considering the existing conditions, were improved roads necessary. The emergence of the Fertile Crescent from under Turkish rule following the first World War and the changed economic circumstances of the mandatory and postmandatory periods, as well as the second World War, necessitated improved road systems. Most of the hard-surfaced, all-weather trunk highways are the result of the two war periods, when they were needed to facilitate the movement of troops and materiel. Road construction was carried out largely by the British, and during the wars highways were maintained and patrolled by the military. In the interwar

[5] During the second World War (from 1942) there was a rail connection between Tanuma, Iran, and Basra, Iraq, by way of the Hull bridge over the Shatt-al-Arab. This line was dismantled at the end of the war.

and postwar periods, some of the wartime highways have become important through routes and trade channels; others have fallen into disrepair and are only of local importance. The countries involved often have found maintenance difficult and, in some cases, the need too little as compared with the cost of upkeep.

Practically all of the large urban centers of the Fertile Crescent countries are connected by hard-surfaced, all-weather roads, though at any given time sections of highway may be in poor condition. The highway that crosses the Syrian desert through Jordan and Iraq ties the capital cities of the Arab countries by road. There also are highways that connect the Crescent countries with Turkey, Egypt, and Iran. There are an estimated 8,000 to 9,000 miles of such highways in the five countries concerned. The usual surfacing material is tarmac or asphalt; only rarely has concrete been used. Secondary or feeder roads usually are poor and commonly are impassable during the wet season. About 2,000 miles out of 12,000 miles of such roads have a surfacing of gravel or crushed rock; the remainder are either dirt roads or desert tracks.

The improvement of secondary roads and new construction both are necessary. In some areas such as the Jezira of Syria, economic development has been handicapped by lack of roads; in other areas roads may periodically be impassable owing to rains or flooding, e.g., southern Iraq during the spring floods of the Tigris and Euphrates. Through much of the Fertile Crescent new hard-surfaced roads would relieve physical isolation, expedite the movement of goods and produce to market, and facilitate the general social and economic integration of people within individual countries.

Until the first World War the usual carrier in the Crescent countries was either an animal or an animal-drawn cart that could, without much trouble, utilize exceedingly poor roads or trails. Since that war the use of motor vehicles has increased rapidly—though the total is small when compared to those of more advanced countries [6]—and the need for better roads has grown more acute. Lebanon and Israel have reasonably adequate roads; Iraq is in the process of a major road-construction program and has an over-all, long-range road plan to follow; Jordan and Syria, though aware of the problem that exists, have as yet done little to solve it.

The countries of the Fertile Crescent are well serviced by air lines. All of them have international airports served by the major air lines connecting West and East. A number of them can handle the largest commercial planes. All of the countries except Syria also have local air lines oper-

---

[6] In 1954 there were approximately 107,000 registered motor vehicles in Syria, Lebanon, Israel, and Iraq. These figures include private cars, trucks, taxis, and buses. Figures for Jordan are not available.

ating domestic and regional services. Again, as in the case of rail and road transport, there are no air connections between Israel and the Arab countries.

The major urban centers of the Fertile Crescent states, like those of the Middle East as a whole, have developed largely as commercial centers. Although a number of them have several important functions, the commercial one usually is dominant (Figure 144). Every large city, with the exception of Tel Aviv, is old, and its size and importance now as in the past reflects both its position as a junction or terminus and the importance of the trade route or routes upon which it lies. The creation of independent states after the first and second World Wars has increased the importance of the capital cities, all of which have acquired more important governmental functions than they had as provincial centers under

Fig. 144 • Rashid Street, the main thoroughfare of Baghdad, Iraq, looking south. The Tigris River is just behind the buildings on the right. The Regent Palace hotel, the modern, concrete building with the circular balconies, has a back lawn and garden on the river. The custom of siesta, a rest period during the hot part of the day, accounts for the general lack of activity on what is usually a very busy street. The white pillars and arcaded structure of many of the buildings, which provide a shaded sidewalk, is a characteristic feature along much of Rashid street.

Baghdad is by far the largest and most important commercial center of the country, having grown considerably in the past decade; the major changes and additions are away from the center of the city. (John R. Randall.)

Fig. 145 • An aerial view of Old Jerusalem, the walled section of Jerusalem that now lies within Jordan. The rectangular compound at the right-center contains the dome of the Rock mosque. The Jewish Wailing Wall is just above the lower left hand corner of the compound wall. Across the vale of Kedron to the right of the mosque compound is the Garden of Gethsemane.

The armistice line between Jordan and Israel and the no-man's land between these states, passes through the center foreground of the photo, and then skirts the wall of the old city. The vale of Hinnon is in the left foreground. The major part of modern Jerusalem (the Israeli capital) is to the left of the photo. The upper left quadrant of the photo shows, from left to right, the Hadassah hospital, Mt. Scopus with the Hebrew University, the German Hospice, and the Mont of Olives. *(Arab Information Center, N.Y.)*

Ottoman rule. Jerusalem is unique among the cities because of its religious function as the primary holy city for Christianity and Judaism, and a tertiary center for Islam after Mecca and Medina (Figure 145).

Exact population figures generally are unavailable, but most of the larger cities have experienced considerable growth during and since the second World War. This is true especially of a number of the capital cities. Estimates are as follows for cities over 100,000:

1.	Aleppo	339,000
2.	Amman	200,000
3.	Baghdad	550,000
4.	Basra	100,000 (approx.)
5.	Beirut	247,000
6.	Damascus	303,000
7.	Haifa	145,000
8.	Jerusalem	140,000 (Jewish); 54,000 (Arab)
9.	Mosul	302,000
10.	Tel Aviv-Jaffa	325,000

There are between 12 and 18 cities whose population varies from 20,-000 to 100,000. The more important of these are Hama, Homs, Latakia, and Deir ez Zor in Syria; Tripoli and Sidon in Lebanon; Beersheba and Tiberias in Israel; Nablus and Hebron in Jordan; and Kirkuk, Hilla, Amara, and Erbil in Iraq. These cities, like the larger ones, are primarily trade centers, but for more restricted hinterlands. Some also are administrative centers for provinces or districts.

Israel

Israel is small (8,000 square miles) and attenuated, and in general it lacks appreciable mineral wealth. The productive and developed parts of the country lie between Dan and Beersheba; to the south lies the new "promised land" of the Negev, a desert region comprising 60 per cent of the country's area. The northern section has a Mediterranean climate, reasonable water resources, and almost all the plains. This is the part in which, until 1948, most of the modern development took place. It produced most of the agricultural and industrial products, contained the large cities, and supported a majority of the population.

The retention of Samaria and much of Judea by Jordan has produced a bulge in the international boundary between these two states, the western edge of which comes to within about 12 miles of the Mediterranean. In effect this leaves the plain of Sharon as a narrow corridor between northern Israel (Galilee and the plain of Esdraelon) and southern Israel. Not only does this condition hamper transport within Israel, but it presents a constant threat that the country may be severed by an Arab push to the sea.

Israel suffers from an economic structure that is artificial in that it has been based substantially not on its resource endowment and the productivity of its population, but on support from world Jewry and loans from friendly governments. Since its formation in 1948 Israel has been struggling toward a reasonably balanced economy; although it has made remarkable gains in certain directions, it is still far from reaching its goal. Developments in agriculture have been outstanding and have taken place in the amount of production, the area under production, and in methods of farming. The total area under cultivation increased from 412,500 acres in 1948-1949 to 915,000 in 1952-1953. Of this latter total, 145,000 acres were irrigated.[7] During the same period the production of foodstuffs for human consumption doubled and that of feed for livestock and poultry rose from 30 per cent of requirements to 70 per cent. Pisciculture and marine fishing also have increased rapidly. In spite of these increases, approximately 20 per cent of Israel's foreign-exchange budget must be allocated for food and feed imports. Although the area under cultivation and the total production of all crops have greatly increased, the yields of the major grain crops per acre show only slight differences from those of other Southwest Asian countries.[8]

There have been major changes in the methods of farming in Israel since the establishment of the Jewish National Home, which followed the Balfour Declaration of 1917. The ancient, inefficient, extensive system, so widely practiced in the Middle East, has given way to a diversified system in which the raising of livestock and poultry is important. Although cereals, fruit, and vegetables remain the basic food staples, livestock and poultry are the sources of an increasing amount of dairy products, meat, and eggs in the Israeli diet. The production of fodder crops specifically for livestock and poultry is a part of this diversified system. As yet, agricultural production has been geared largely to the needs of the local food market. Citrus fruits are the major commercial crop; grapes (and wine) are a poor second. Citrus production suffered severely during the civil war when many of the citrus groves were badly damaged. Citrus and fruit juices (other than wine) are still, however, the single most valuable export item.[9]

A second feature of agricultural development in Israel is agricultural settlements in which most farm families and agricultural workers live. There are four main types: (1) communal settlements (*kibbutzim*), (2) cooperative settlements (*moshvei ovdim, moshavim, and moshavim shitufiim*), (3) *moshava*, and (4) *maabaroth*.

The *kibbutzim* are entirely communal (Figure 146). No personal property is allowed, and the only concession to privacy is the provision of

[7] The total of cultivated land in Israel is roughly 1,500 square miles. Arab farms account for about 125,000 acres out of the total. In 1954, irrigated land increased to 160,000 acres.

[8] Average yields per acre in Cwt—wheat: Israel, 4.8; Iraq, 6.4; Turkey, 7.3; barley: Israel, 8.9; Iraq, 5.7; Turkey, 8.5; corn: Israel, 9.0; Turkey, 9.8.

[9] In 1947, citrus orchards occupied 59,000 acres; in 1952-53, 35,500 acres. In 1934-8, 300,000 tons of citrus were exported annually; in 1954, 310,000 tons. Between 1951 and 1953 production of oranges and grapefruit increased from 147,000 to 209,000 metric tons. The value of citrus and fruit juices exported in 1951 was just over 19 million dollars; polished diamonds, the second export item in value, amount to 11.7 million dollars.

living quarters for married members. Work is programmed and allotted, each service being performed by those physically capable of doing so. Only the old or very young are excused from work in the fields. There is a regular rotation in personnel doing any particular job, so that all have a chance at most types of work. Certain services are not rotated or are performed by only one group, e.g. medical services, nursing, and child care. The communal settlements are essentially agricultural, but may contain shops and small plants for processing or manufacturing various types of products. The sale of products is through cooperative organizations. In most instances a probationary period of at least year must be fulfilled before a member is taken into the commune.

The various types of cooperative settlements are similar in major aspects, but in general are less rigid in discipline than the *kibbutzim*. Land may be either cooperatively or privately owned, and individually or communally operated; personal property usually is allowed, and family

Fig. 146 • The Jewish settlement of Qiryat 'Anavim, west of Jerusalem, on the Jerusalem-Tel Aviv highway, is a commercial settlement *(kibbutz)*, one of the relatively few pre-partition settlements located in the Palestinian highlands. Most of the buildings and living quarters are new; only a few of those in the original settlement remain. Qiryat 'Anavim specializes in dairy products, poultry and eggs, and fruit. The forest on the hill in the background was planted by the colony. Prior to this reforestation the hill was almost completely denuded by centuries of over-grazing and erosion. Reforestation has been a conspicuous consequence of Jewish settlement in the Israeli landscape. *(John R. Randall.)*

units are separately housed. Produce, whether individually or cooperatively raised, is marketed through cooperatives, and supplies usually are
purchased for the entire settlement through similar facilities.

The *moshava* are normal rural settlements or villages where land is
privately owned and private enterprise is the rule. The *maabaroth* are
temporary settlements where immigrants are placed awaiting removal to
permanent settlements.

The Jewish settlements are agglomerated rural settlements, but in many
aspects they differ remarkably from the average Middle Eastern village.
Once a settlement is well established and paying its way, it evolves into
a well planned, attractive village with most of the services and many of
the attributes of the most modern Western town. Each has its schools,
hospital, and community center. The settlements are clean and sanitary,
and the inhabitants healthy and well cared for.

The number of Jewish rural settlements has almost doubled between
1948 and 1954, bringing the total to approximately 600. There has been
a greater proportionate increase in cooperative settlements as opposed
to *kibbutzim,* since in the cooperatives the family unit can be more easily
maintained and there is a greater freedom of individual action. The development of these settlements has been one of the more remarkable
achievements of the Jews in Palestine and, later, Israel. Since a large proportion of new settlers have been of urban origin, their transformation
into well trained and successful farmers has been no small feat.

Despite these accomplishments the proportion of farm population to
the total is still out of balance, and the state has difficulty in persuading
folk with urban backgrounds to take up farming. In 1954 only 14.7 per
cent of the Jewish gainfully employed were farmers. This is not only the
lowest percentage in this category for any Middle Eastern country, but it
is also considerably lower than the country feels it needs. One method
employed to get more people onto the land and out of the cities has been
the incorporation of farm training into the regular army service, which
applies to all ablebodied men and women.

The most productive agricultural areas of Israel are in the plains along
the Mediterranean (the plains of Sharon and Philistia), the plain of
Esdraelon, the Jordan valley south of Lake Tiberias, and the loessial
area centering on Beersheba. The Sephala, an area of basins and hills
lying between the coastal plain and the Judean upland, also is well
developed and densely populated. A project for draining the marshes
around Lake Huleh has been hampered by border troubles between
Israel and Syria.

The Negev of southern Israel contains the largest part of the state's
potentially cultivable land (three-fifths), and upon its agricultural development the state has placed great hope and stress. Hope for develop-

ment of the Negev is based upon the scientific knowledge of soils and irrigation and on the fact that the Negev once contained both a sizable productive area and a number of large towns. Water brought by pipeline irrigates the Beersheba area; there also are about 150 square miles that are dry-farmed. Whether the Negev indeed becomes a new promised land will depend upon the ability of Israel to bring large amounts of water into the area. Efforts to divert water from the Jordan valley to the Negev are plagued by the unfriendly relations between Israel and the Arab states. Cooperation is needed, since sources of water for the Negev are controlled in part by neighboring countries.

Israeli industrial development faces obstacles even greater than those confronting agriculture. Factory manufacture received its initial impetus during the Mandate period, especially during the second World War when Palestine turned out a variety of products for the war effort. Before the war, handicraft production had been developed and stimulated by various Jewish agencies. Palestinian industry had an advantage because of its political ties with Great Britain and because of the then available markets in the Middle East. Independence and the civil war deprived Israel of these two advantages, and at the same time the war crippled or ended two of Palestine's major industries—oil refining and potash production.[10] Although both the number and the variety of industries have increased since 1948,[11] industrial development has proceeded erratically, and it is still impeded by several factors, among the more important of which are raw materials, governmental regulations, labor, markets, foreign exchange, and internal politics.

Israel lacks the natural resources necessary for industrial development. As late as 1954, 51.5 per cent of the country's total imports were industrial raw materials and another 20.3 per cent industrial equipment. To reduce the costs of these imports, Israel has developed a sizeable merchant marine, grossing about 150,000 tons in 1956; delivery of vessels on order

[10] As a result of the civil war, Iraq stopped the flow of crude oil to the refinery at Haifa and the construction of a 16-inch pipeline. Israel must import oil products from Venezuela or the United States and pay for them from her foreign currency resources, which are slim. Israel has developed potash works at the south end of the Dead Sea, and production started in 1953, following the building of a highway from Sodom to Beersheba. In 1957 a pipeline was completed from Elat at the head to the Gulf of Aquaba to Haifa so as to by-pass the Suez Canal, but its continued use is problematical.

[11] Among the older industries are textiles, fertilizers, oil-refining, diamond-cutting, sanitary equipment, leather products, chemicals, cement, food-processing, tools, machinery and electric appliances; among the newer products are steel piping, radios, refrigerators, light bulbs, rubber products (including tires), diesel engines, plastics, and assembled autos. A further indicator of development is the value of Israel's industrial exports, which in 1953 amounted to 31,350,000 dollars, up from 12 million in 1952.

should raise the total to over 500,000 gross tons by 1962. The lack of coal deposits and the uncertainty regarding petroleum deposits in the Negev have led to much speculation concerning the multipurpose development of the Jordan valley along the lines of the Tennessee Valley Authority, but Jordan, Syria, and Lebanon have not been willing to cooperate with Israel in a program for joint development. Iron-ore deposits have been found in both the Negev and Galilee. Those in the Negev contain only 35 per cent iron and cannot at present be mined profitably; the extent and utility of those in Galilee have not yet been determined. No iron or steel is produced. The Negev and the Dead Sea are the sources of most of Israel's other minerals—copper, rock phosphates, ceramic clays, glass sands, and potash. All of these, excepting copper, are being produced as industrial raw materials.

Also involved is the position of the government in relation to industry and labor. While trying valiantly to foster industry, the government also has hindered its development in some ways. Through a close relationship with the Histadrut, the trade-union federation, a high wage scale has been maintained, whereas another government policy, followed until recently, guaranteed a producer a cost-plus-profit return for manufactured goods. Under this policy production methods were inefficient [12] and production per worker was low. The Histadrut, in which many of the government leaders have worked, not only has as members about 75 per cent of the Israeli labor force, but also is the single largest producing unit in the country, controlling factory industries, wholesale and retail marketing agencies, banks, shipping, and agricultural developments. The cartel-like nature of the Histadrut has tended to discourage private enterprise and foreign investment. The multiplicity of government regulations controlling imports, exports, foreign exchange, raw materials, equipment, and labor, is another obstacle to private and foreign investment.

High wages and the country's dependence upon imported raw materials and fuels price many Israeli goods out of the world market. Furthermore, the Arab boycott has closed what should have become Israel's best and most accessible market.

On the basis of the occupational distribution of her gainfully employed, Israel compares favorably with the highly industrialized and economically stable countries, including the United States. However, there is, in actuality, a maldistribution of labor in Israel. For example, in 1954 public services and the professions accounted for 34.7 per cent of the Jewish gainfully employed. Other categories were commerce and finance, 17.5 per cent; agriculture, 14.7 per cent; industry and crafts, 22.5

[12] Part of this inefficiency stems from the smallness of many of the factory units: 60 per cent of Israeli factories and shops employ less than 50 workers.

per cent; and all others, 10.5 per cent.[13] The high percentage in services
and professions is explained in part by the recent organization of the
Israeli civil service. Even so, the number of persons earning their living
in this group is too high for the country's present needs and often for the
number of positions available. The greatest needs for labor have been in
farming and in industry where certain types of skills are urgently needed.
However, many Jews do not wish to farm; others that might be persuaded
have nonetheless taken jobs in building, road work, and the like, where
wages are high and, to them, the work less onerous. Farm training in
schools and the armed services is the state's best method of ultimately
building up its farm population. The prestige associated with the professions and the civil service also is a factor in the lack of skilled labor in
industry, even though skilled-labor incomes are high. Furthermore, a
majority of the Jews migrating to Palestine, and later Israel, have had no
training in industrial skills.

Another serious problem in the development of Israeli economy and
society is the assimilation of the North African and Asian Jews who have
immigrated since 1948. At that time the Jewish population was almost
solidly Western in culture and origin, and the institutions they had established during the Mandatory period were likewise Western. By 1954 approximately 25 per cent of the population consisted of Jews who had
entered Israel as refugees, largely from North Africa and the countries
of Southwest Asia. For the most part these are unskilled, uneducated,
illiterate, deeply religious, politically innocent, and inarticulate peoples
unfamiliar with Western culture and institutions. The ingathering of
these people has been a tremendous strain upon the new state's relatively
modest resources, and the problem of their assimilation may prove even
more difficult. Israel hopes to achieve this assimilation mainly by edu-
cating the young in Western type schools, a task it hopes to accomplish
within two or three decades, since by that time the non-Western Jews,
characterized by a higher birth rate, may outnumber those of Western
origin.

Lebanon

Lebanon, the smallest of the
Fertile Crescent states, has been rather more progressive than its Arab

---

[13] These percentages do not include 50,000 gainfully employed Arabs, most of
whom are in agriculture. When these are included the breakdown of gainfully employed is as follows: public services and professions, 31.7; commerce and finance,
15.9; agriculture, 21.9; industry and crafts, 20.6; all other, 9.6 per cent. The 1951
figures for Israel and the United States follow (U. S. figures in parentheses): public
services and professions, 29.6 (23.0); commerce and finance, 16.8 (16.1); agriculture, 13.9 (17.6); industry and crafts, 23.6 (25.4).

neighbors. Neither the inadequacies of its physical base nor its domination by foreign powers has kept it from attaining a respected position in the Middle East and the world.

The major landforms of Lebanon have the north-south trend common to the eastern Mediterranean area. The narrow, often discontinuous, coastal plain is backed by the steep, deeply dissected slopes of the Lebanon mountains. The Lebanon,[14] as this range often is called, reaches an elevation of just over 10,000 feet, which makes it the highest in the western arm of the crescent. Dropping steeply on its eastern side, the slope of the Lebanon descends to the relatively level floor of the Bekka, a fault valley that separates this western range from the two eastern ones, the Anti-Lebanon in the north, and the Herman range in the south. These highlands, like the Lebanon, are composed largely of massive beds of folded limestone, but they attain lesser heights—the Anti-Lebanon a little over 7,000 feet, and the Herman, in Mount Herman, 9,200 feet.[15]

The coastal plain and the western slopes of the Lebanon mountains have a relatively abundant supply of water received from both precipitation and springs.[16] Eastward, water becomes the critical factor in land use. The lee side of the Lebanon mountains and the Bekka suffer from rain-shadow aridity. The Anti-Lebanon and Herman ranges receive considerably less precipitation than does the Lebanon, but they are proportionally much drier, since a large part of the moisture soaks rapidly into the porous limestone. Infrequent springs give rise to only small, widely separated, oasis settlements; grazing is the principal type of land use. The floor of the Bekka, where irrigation is possible, has proved agriculturally productive, and there is much more land susceptible of irrigation with proper development.

Despite the paucity of well watered, level land,[17] about two-thirds of the population of Lebanon are rural village dwellers who gain their livelihood directly from the soil. The coastal plain and the western side

---

[14] The rather common use of the term "The Lebanon" for the state of Lebanon is an indication of the importance of this mountain range in the history and life of the Lebanese. The range also was coincident with the Sandjac of the Lebanon, that part of the present state that commonly was autonomous during the Ottoman period.

[15] The Lebanon-Syrian boundary follows the crest of these two ranges.

[16] The geologic structure of the Lebanese ranges is such that the western slope of the Lebanon mountains has a series of springs at 3,000 feet and again at 5,000 feet; only a few springs occur near the base on the eastern side. The largest number of springs in the eastern ranges are found on the eastern slopes and hence are in Syria rather than Lebanon. Precipitation in the Lebanon mountains averages between 40 and 50 inches annually; Beirut, on the coastal plain, receives 37.9 inches per year.

[17] In 1950, 918 square miles (23 per cent) of the total area, approximately 3,900 square miles, were irrigated. Potentially cultivable land was estimated at 17 per cent of the total area; 1 per cent was in pasture, 7 per cent in forests, and 52 per cent was classed as mountains, desert, or marsh.

of the Lebanon mountains are the primary farm areas; the Bekka is a poor second; the eastern ranges are predominantly pastoral lands. Tillage of the mountain slopes is made possible through extensive terracing.

Crop production in Lebanon follows a common Middle Eastern pattern—cereals, fruits, and vegetables for home consumption, with surpluses of certain crops for export.[18] Industrial crops are relatively unimportant. Livestock rearing, either as an adjunct to crop farming or as a mainstay, is widespread.[19] However, the country is not self-sufficient in foodstuffs; wheat, wheat flour, cotton, and sheep are the major agricultural imports.

Small, privately owned landholdings are characteristic in the coastal plain and the Lebanon mountains, particularly in that part north of Beirut where the population is predominantly Christian. Large estates worked by agricultural laborers or tenants are usual in the Bekka and to some extent in the southern section of the Lebanon mountains. Pastoral tribes inhabit the eastern ranges where transhumance is practiced. The Bekka and lower valleys of the Anti-Lebanon and Herman ranges also are used as winter pasture by nomadic tribes from the Syrian desert.

Factory manufacture has a start in Lebanon, but industrial development has just begun. The country conforms to the realm pattern in types of manufactures and in the percentage of inhabitants involved. The leading industries are processors of agricultural and livestock products (textiles, foods, leather) and minerals (cement and petroleum products). The number of wage earners in processing and manufacturing is estimated at only 50,000, of whom half are factory workers. The Iraq Petroleum Company is the single largest employer; it employs 3,300 persons. Most of the manufactured goods used in Lebanon are imported.

The commerce and trade of Lebanon date back at least to the period of ancient Phoenicia and have been, within any given period, of more importance than elsewhere in Southwest Asia. Lebanon normally imports considerably more than it exports.[20] Despite this abnormality, the Lebanese economy has tended to remain stable. This stability results in large part from the so-called "invisible earnings" obtained from various sources

[18] Production of major crops, for year indicated, in thousands of metric tons: wheat (1952), 50; barley (1952), 27; cotton (1951), 1; tobacco (1952), 2; citrus (1952), 90; grapes (1951), 80; maize (1951), 12; paddy rice (1951), 1; sugar cane (1951), 8; figs (1950), 14; vegetables (all types) (1950), 186; deciduous fruit, including peaches, apricots, plums, quince, and pears (1950), 55; and olives (1950), 5. Among crop exports for 1951 having a value of over one million dollars were onions and shallots, citrus fruit, apples, quince, and cotton.

[19] Livestock and poultry (1951) in thousands: goats, 548; sheep, 56; cattle, 46; donkeys, 22; camels, 10; swine, 1; and poultry of all types, 703.

[20] In 1951 value of imports for consumption amounted to $145.12 per capita, while that of domestic exports was $69.96.

—the transit and re-export trade, services, private donations, remittances from Lebanese abroad, capital movements, and tourist trade.[21] Much of the reputation of the Lebanese as a commercial people comes not from the sale of locally produced goods, but from the middleman services of its merchants. The Lebanese have the trading ability so characteristic of the Middle Easterner and, unlike some others, have been in a position to exercise this ability.

During the Ottoman period Lebanon enjoyed considerable political and economic freedom and thus was able to carry on trade and maintain contacts abroad. It also attracted a number of foreign companies that found they could conduct business more freely in Lebanon than in most other Middle Eastern areas. For these reasons and because of the central coastal location of the country, much of the trade of Southwest Asia was funnelled through the Lebanon. The acumen of its traders and their contacts with Lebanese in other parts of the world also were of importance.

The development of Haifa as a port during the Mandate had some adverse effects upon the trade of Lebanon, but with the creation of Israel, Haifa lost all of its Arab business. The customs union between Syria and Lebanon was an advantage to the latter, since practically all Syrian imports and exports passed through Lebanese ports. The end of this union in 1950 and the development of the port of Latakia by Syria and of Iskanderun by Turkey have been disadvantageous for Lebanon, although the two more northern port cities are relatively unimportant in contrast to Beirut. Lebanon, on the other hand, has gained by the construction of oil pipelines to its coast, one with a terminal at Tripoli and another terminating at Sidon. The Lebanese are, however, concerned over the attempts on the part of neighboring countries to develop ports and commercial activities that will compete with their own.

The Lebanese abroad has long been a basic source of revenue to the poorly endowed mother country. In proportion to its size and population, Lebanon probably has had more emigrants during the last century than any other Middle Eastern country. Many Lebanese abroad not only have maintained business connections with home merchants, but also have regularly sent money to their families in Lebanon, or, after a period abroad, have returned home with money earned during their absence.

The tourist trade also is probably as highly developed in Lebanon as in any of the Middle Eastern countries, and both the government and private agencies have done much to promote it. Accessibility, a variety of attractions, and good tourist facilities account for the successful

[21] In 1952 the value of goods re-exported by Lebanon amounted to 8,887,896 dollars; that of goods in transit, 564,802,056 dollars; value of trade in precious metals, 17,994,216 dollars (down from $43,927,392 in 1950). There are no figures available as to the actual profits accruing from this trade.

development. The Lebanon mountains are the major attraction. Their milder summer temperatures are a boon after the often excessive heat of the lowlands; their snowy slopes have given rise to winter sports activities; and their scenery is both rugged and beautiful. Other features to attract the tourist or vacationer are the Mediterranean beaches and many sites of historical importance and interest. Although people from many parts of the world visit Lebanon, the majority of its visitors come from nearby countries, Syria, Iraq, Jordan, and Egypt, especially for the summer months.

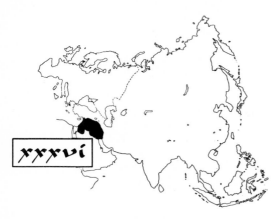

The Fertile Crescent, ii

SYRIA, JORDAN, IRAQ

Syria

Today Syria is characterized by most of the ills that beset the countries of the entire Middle East, and by many to a greater degree: a poverty-ridden peasantry, an inefficient agricultural system, a small, but wealthy landlord class, little industrialization, and a marked instability of government.[1] These conditions have been long-standing, but in Syria, unlike some Arab states of the Crescent, they have become aggravated rather than alleviated. In general, Syria was weakened rather than strengthened under French rule which terminated in 1944. By following a policy of divide and rule, France not only discouraged political training and experience, but also helped lay the foundations of local political enmities and rivalries which have been a major factor in the inability of Syria to govern itself effectively. Economic progress and social reform were slowed, and Syria emerged after the second World War economically weak and politically divided. None of the other mandated states fared quite so badly.

Events since 1945, the Palestinian war, intrigue among the Arab states, and the jockeying for position between Russia and the West in the

[1] Besides several orderly changes in government following independence, there have been four military *coups d'etat* between 1948 and 1954 by which governments were overthrown by force.

Middle East all contributed to the deterioration of a serious economic situation. As a result, plans for agricultural development, land reform, and other similar projects have not, in most cases, been implemented.

Agriculture is the base of Syria's economy, and in normal years it has an agricultural surplus for export. This surplus is more the result of a low level of living and of maldistribution than a reflection of an efficient and productive agriculture. At the same time, Syria is well developed neither industrially nor commercially, nor does it have an easily exploitable nonagricultural resource base. Such industries as it does have reflect its agricultural character.[2] Only recently, by improving port facilities at Latakia, has Syria made any serious attempt to increase its commercial activity and to wrest from Lebanon some share of the regional transit trade.

Aridity is the major physical handicap to farming; inequitable land ownership and tenure, poverty, and lack of transport facilities are some of the more important economic problems. By far the larger part of Syria is too deficient in moisture for humid farming. About 11 per cent of the cultivated area is irrigated. The remaining crop land is winter-sown or worked by dry-farming methods in which one-third to one-half of the land is fallow. Cultivated land makes up approximately 19 per cent of the total area.[3] Except in the irrigated tracts, non-intensive cultivation is the rule. Both physical and cultural factors keep potentially cultivable land from being cultivated. Irrigation projects for which plans have been drawn remain at a standstill because of insufficient funds and governmental instability. Irrigation development for other arid and semi-arid land has never reached even the planning stage. Individual ownership of very large tracts of land and certain types of land tenure also hold arable land idle. Some areas are too distant from markets or too sparsely settled for economic agricultural development.

Approximately two-thirds to three-quarters of Syria's 4,145,000 inhabitants (as estimated at the end of 1955) are rural and gain their living from farming or pastoral activities. The remainder are urban dwellers, most of whom are involved in services, trade and commerce, or industry.[4] The distribution and density of population is correlated with the

---

[2] Among the more important products are cotton textiles, sugar, vegetable oils, food preserving, alcoholic beverages, and tobacco products. Nonagricultural products include glass, cement, and asphalt.

[3] In 1953, of the approximately 9,000,000 acres cultivated, 56.7 per cent were in the following crops: wheat, 36 per cent; barley, 12 per cent; cotton, 4 per cent; sorghum, 2.6 per cent; olives, 2 per cent; and rice, 0.1 per cent. The remaining 43.7 per cent were in minor crops: vegetables, grapes, tobacco, corn, and sugar beets, or it was in fallow. The estimated cotton acreage for 1954-55 was reported to be considerably higher than the 312,000 acres recorded in 1953.

[4] About 500,000 *Bedouin* inhabit the desert areas. No data are available for employment or occupations.

areal distribution of precipitation, western and northern Syria having the largest numbers and greatest densities of people, as well as the highest amounts of rainfall. East of a line from Aleppo to Damascus, population and precipitation decrease rapidly, the one exception being along the northern boundary where steppe conditions continue eastward into Iraq and thus allow some crop farming. The major part of the Syrian desert receives less than 5 inches of rainfall annually. A few oases contain such sedentary population as inhabits the desert region.

The ethnic and religious pluralism of the population in part accounts for the country's difficulties. Although the majority of the population considers itself Arab and is Sunni Moslem, there are sizable minorities of non-Arab people and of other religious groups including non-orthodox Moslems. Complexity is increased by ethnic and religious lines cutting across these groups. The Alawis, Druzes, Ismailis, and Shias, all of whom are Arab, are heterodox Moslems and differ from the Sunni majority not only in religious tenets but also in certain cultural traits. There also are approximately 400,000 Christians, most of whom are Arab. The Kurds, Turkmens, and Circassians, who are differentiated ethnically from the Arabs, are orthodox Moslems; the Armenians and Assyrians, both ethnically distinct, are Christian. In general, religious differences have caused more friction than ethnic ones, in part because the ethnic minorities are relatively small, and in part because minority peoples have in many cases accepted the Arabic language and certain features of Arabic culture.

Both ethnic and religious minorities have had a strong effect upon the social, economic, and political conditions within Syria. In almost every case minority groups have been divided politically as to what course the group should follow, especially in respect to Syrian nationalism. During the Mandate, feelings toward the French were an added divisive factor. The attitudes of some minority groups toward nationalism are closely related to those toward economic and social change. Members of a minority with strong in-group loyalties may also be those who most resist Westernization and socio-economic change.

The agriculturally productive sections of Syria are those where climate and topography have been permissive factors or where water resources have been made available for irrigation. The only outstanding areas of size are the Mediterranean coast and lower slopes of the Jebel Ansarieh, and the steppe area from Aleppo southward to Homs. The Jezira of northern and northeastern Syria is a region of productive soils and steppe climate, but one whose development has been slow. The Hauran, southwest of Damascus, a lava upland long noted as a cereal producer, suffers by rainfall variability and is now less productive than in former times. The Damascus oasis, el Ghouta, is highly developed but small.

The Syrian coastal plain and the gentler slopes of the Jebel Ansarieh have the advantage of relatively abundant rainfall, 20 to 40 inches on the plain and above 40 inches in the mountains, which makes farming more certain than in the country as a whole. The region is characterized by a typical Mediterranean agriculture in which cereals (wheat and barley), fruit, and vegetables are staple crops. It also is the major olive producer, and around the city of Latakia is the only important tobacco area. The production of cotton, potatoes (especially in the highlands), and mulberry for silkworm feeding is of increasing importance. Cereals are winter-sown and unirrigated, as are the olive and mulberry groves. Summer-grown crops, such as tobacco and cotton, must be irrigated.

The region extending from the northern border to the rain-shadow of the Lebanon mountains south of Homs is the best developed, agriculturally, of the steppe regions of Syria. The Jebel Ansarieh, although it has an effect upon the rainfall to its east, is not the barrier that the Lebanons are. The 10-inch isohyet turns sharply west in the latitude of the northern end of the Lebanons and skirts the eastern base of the Anti-Lebanons, creating desert conditions south of the lowland between the Jebel Ansarieh and the Lebanon mountains. The region covers between 7,000 and 8,000 square miles, but it is not everywhere equally well developed.

The reputation of the Aleppo-Homs region as a cereal producer comes more from its size than from its yields, which are no greater than those elsewhere. The farm economy is similar to that of the Mediterranean area, with winter-sown grains and a variety of other crops summer-grown under irrigation. Olives, grapes, and nut trees are common hillside crops grown without irrigation. Cotton and vegetables are the major irrigated crops. Although the amount of land given over to vegetables is small, yields are high.

The distribution of cultivated land is not even throughout the region. Areas of wasteland and fallow are interspersed with productive lands. As the desert on the east is approached, farming becomes less tenable. There are no sizable irrigation projects, but rather numerous small irrigated areas where water and topography may lend themselves to such development. The Orontes River is a major source of water, but even here there is no continuous band of irrigated land along the valley.

The Jezira is considered one of the more promising areas of Syria for agricultural development, although it suffers from lack of transportation, a shortage of labor, and political unrest. It has fertile soils and sufficient rain along its northern side for winter-sown crops. The Euphrates and Khabur rivers are sources of irrigation water for future development. However, irrigation in the Euphrates valley presents difficulties, not only in the Jezira but throughout most of its course in Syria, because of the height of the Euphrates' escarpments.

Until recently the Jezira has been primarily a cereal producer. Cereals are still the major crops, but where irrigation has become available cotton has been introduced. In some instances, cotton has utilized crop land previously devoted to grains. Native grasses and clover furnish some forage, but they have found no important place in the farm economy. Because of the labor shortage some of the large landholders have resorted to mechanization, though the major part of the tilled area is still cultivated by ancient methods.

The Damascus oasis, approximately 400 square miles, is the most extensive irrigated tract in Syria and probably the oldest. Water is obtained from the Barada and its tributaries, streams that have their origins in the Anti-Lebanon and Herman ranges and flow toward the east. During the summer little or no water leaves the oasis, but in winter a small amount drains into a basin east of the city, Bahr el Ataiba. The oasis is intensively cultivated and produces a variety of crops beyond the staple ones, including corn, rice, vegetables, fruit, and olives. Unlike much of Syria, the land in the oasis is individually owned and is in relatively small plots.

The upland of the Hauran, a segment of the lava areas of Syria and Jordan, was an important wheat producer in ancient times, but has lost much of its importance. Its rolling surface and rich soils lack only water to make it one of the more productive sections of the country.

Livestock, chiefly sheep and goats, are produced in Syria both as an adjunct to farming and by nomadic and semi-nomadic peoples.[5] The western highlands are the main centers of transhumance involving sheep and goats; the desert areas of the east are the habitat of Syria's half-million nomads whose main livelihood is camel raising. A few of these tribes, who are becoming semi-sedentary, produce sheep and some crops as well. Southwestern Syria is the major cattle area. Mules, horses, donkeys, and water buffalo are used for work and transport.

Syria's international trade reflects its agricultural economy and lack of industrial development.[6] Exports are largely agricultural products,[7] and about half go to other Middle Eastern countries. Imports consist primarily of foodstuffs and livestock products as well as some manufactured and processed goods and fuels. About 20 per cent of Syria's imports originate in other Middle Eastern countries; most of the rest come from Western Europe (France, the U.K., Western Germany, Italy, and the Low Countries) and the United States. An important hidden

[5] Estimated numbers of livestock, 1954: sheep, 3,955,000; goats, 1,625,000; cattle, 481,000; camels, 106,000; water buffalo, 6,000; horses, 103,000; donkeys, 271,000; mules, 84,000.

[6] In 1954, exports from Syria were valued at £ S459.8 millions; imports were £ S381.7 millions. In dollar equivalents, however, exports were about $129 millions and imports $174 millions, a reflection of the disparity between the official rate of exchange ($0.4525) and the free rate (only $0.2796).

[7] Cotton, grains and flour, and wool are the major ones; others include sheep, cotton seed, and tobacco.

export is the income-producing rights of way granted for the three pipelines that cross Syrian territory (Map 33).

Jordan

The Hashemite Kingdom of Jordan was established in 1923 as Transjordan, a semi-autonomous principality under mandate to Great Britain.[8] Its creation was brought about in part to satisfy Arab aspirations and in part to limit the area open to Jewish settlement. Transjordan, all of which lay east of the Jordan River, had been a part of the Palestine mandatory area, but was never opened to Jewish colonization.

Of the Arab states of the Fertile Crescent, prewar Transjordan was the poorest from the standpoint of resource endowment and numbers of people. The major part of the country was desert with less than 5 inches of rain annually, and there were few natural resources upon which industrialization could be based. Approximately 65,000 of its 400,000 people were nomadic or semi-nomadic. Amman, its capital and largest city, had a population of only 30,000, and other sizable towns and villages were few. The general poverty of Transjordan made necessary its subsidy by Great Britain. It could not have maintained itself without such aid.

The natural poverty of the land was reflected in generally low agricultural development. Of a total area of about 35,000 square miles, only 1,700 (4.8 per cent) were in cultivation.[9] The limiting factors were lack of water and to some extent topography and soils. The height of the highlands west of the Jordan trough allowed only the northwestern corner of Transjordan a rainfall appreciable enough (a minimum of 8 inches) to carry on agriculture without irrigation. At the same time, the width of the rain zone was relatively narrow, since the height of the western edge of the Jordanian highlands was sufficient to throw rain-shadows to their east. Within this area [10] were places where thin, stony soil or rock outcrops precluded cultivation. The irrigated tracts were found along valleys whose streams had their origin in the northern (wetter) section of the highlands (Figure 147). To the east and south of the rain-fed area were marginal lands where crops could be produced only in years with more than average rainfall.

[8] In 1946 Transjordan became independent. Although its name was changed in 1946, the name of *Jordan* did not become current until 1949 when land west of the Jordan was annexed.

[9] The cultivated area was classified as follows: irrigated land, 64,000 acres; vineyards, 19,700 acres; and rain-fed crops, 1,013,000 acres.

[10] The borders of this area approximate the following: on the west the crest of the Jordanian highlands; on the north the Syrian border; on the east a line through Derra, Mafraq, and Amman; on the south a line from Amman due west.

Fig. 147 • This narrow irrigated valley between Amman and Mofraq in the steppe region that lies between the high, relatively humid western edge of the Jordan highlands and the Syrian desert to the east has a grass and brush cover on the hillsides which furnishes low-quality grazing for livestock; little of it even is cropped. The flat-roofed buildings of the irrigated area are mainly on the valley slopes where they will not occupy land that can be irrigated. Sun-dried brick is used in their construction. (*John R. Randall.*)

Although the amount of arable land was small, so was the farm population, some 300,000, so that comparatively the Transjordanian peasant had more cultivated land per capita than his Palestinian Arab neighbor. Winter-sown crops, extensively cultivated, were the rule, and there was little surplus for sale or export.

Increased production was possible more from an intensification of, and improvements in, cultivation than from an expansion of the cultivated area. Settlement of title to land, its survey and registration, which was accomplished during the Transjordanian period, gave the peasant an incentive to increase production. By 1952 title to 2,600,000 acres of land had been settled. One of the major results of title settlement was security of tenure for the landholder, who was now able to develop his land, increase its fertility, and be certain that the advantages from such development would be his. This land-tenure reform accounts for the large number of small landholders and the absence of the large landowner who is so characteristic of some other Middle Eastern countries.

Jordan hardly had attained its independence when it was plunged into the Israeli-Arab war which proved to have far-reaching consequences for the new kingdom. Jordan emerged from the war with an added 2,165 square miles of territory on the west bank of the Jordan River, a population that had more than tripled,[11] and, if possible, a worsened economic situation.

Although the annexation of the remnants of Arab Palestine may have added to the political prestige of Jordan, it also added to its political and economic problems. The people of the east and west banks have been quite successful in presenting a reasonably unified front to any trouble from without, but within Jordan there has been considerable friction between Palestinian and Jordanian Arabs. Jordan's annexation of west-bank territory surprised and outmaneuvered certain groups of Palestinian Arabs and some of the Arab countries and added to intra-regional political tensions. Of the Arab states, Jordan has the longest common frontier with Israel, a frontier lengthened by 125 miles through annexation and almost constantly violated by border incidents. A further aspect of the annexation-frontier situation that causes much concern in Israel is the nearness, 12 miles, of the Jordanian boundary to the Mediterranean. It is here that in the event of renewed hostilities Israel could be severed.

The annexation of west-bank land has tended to increase rather than decrease the economic difficulties of Jordan. The new territory, consisting of much of the thin-soiled and denuded hill country of Samaria and Judea, is poor and infertile. Its present population is all, or slightly more than, the land can support unless the present land-use methods are improved. Attempts to effect such improvements would, however, be a severe drain on the economy of the entire country. With the exception of 7,000 acres of irrigated land, the 342,000 acres of cultivated and cultivable land on the west bank are classed as only second- or third-rate farm land. Every device is used to squeeze a livelihood from the soil. Considering the resources with which they must work, many of the peasants have done well, but in general their level of living remains lower than that of the east-bank farmer.

The Arab boycott of Israel has affected Jordan especially severely. Palestine had been Jordan's best market, and Haifa had served as its main port. New markets in the Middle East, but at greater distances, have been developed to replace those lost, but Jordan still has no port to serve her as well as did Haifa. Aqaba, the only Jordanian port, does not have adequate port facilities. It also is far from the most populous part

[11] To the 1946 population of 400,000 had been added by 1950 400,000 Palestinian Arabs of the west bank; 100,000 Palestinian exiles absorbed into the Jordan economy; and 472,000 Palestinian Arab refugees, who for the most part are located in temporary encampments and who are supported largely by United Nations relief funds.

of the country, and transportation is poorly developed. As a result, Jordan has been receiving the major part of its imports through Beirut, a rather costly alternative for a poor country.[12]

The presence of some 400,000 Arab refugees within Jordan is a disturbing and unstabilizing factor both politically and economically. There is little question that the Arab refugees have been used to some extent for political manipulation in the Arab-Israeli quarrel. Although the U.N. provides the basic support for the refugees, they are on Jordanian soil and will be a disturbing factor until their future is decided.

The present economy of Jordan is still agricultural, though attempts are being made to develop mineral resources, manufacturing, and tourism. Cereals, vegetables, legumes, and animal products are the leading types of farm produce; small amounts of tobacco and sesame also are grown. Only in vegetables is there a regular surplus. Livestock are raised in the desert by Bedouin.[13] Through aid from the United States and Great Britain, Jordan has begun to increase the area of irrigated land, although development is handicapped by lack of agreements with Israel on the use of the Jordan River.

In the Dead Sea Jordan controls a vast and relatively inexhaustible source of mineral salts, of which potash and bromine are the most abundant. The former potash-processing plant and the evaporating pans located at the north end of the Dead Sea were destroyed during the Arab-Israeli war and have not been rebuilt.[14] Jordan is seeking capital with which to reestablish its mineral-salt industry. One big advantage of the north-end location is the source of near-fresh Jordan River water for use in salt processing. The country also has deposits of phosphates and manganese.

Manufacturing is little developed and of a simple nature. The processing of food and other agricultural products leads the meager list.[15] There is a small-scale metal-processing industry making household ware of tin and aluminum. Jordan at present produces enough cement annually (60,000 tons) for its own use. There is likewise a considerable production of handicrafts for local use and the tourist trade.

The state is trying to develop tourism. The country has wide variety of sites of interest to the traveler—the old cities of Jerusalem and Bethlehem, with their religious and historic shrines; the Roman amphitheater at Amman; crusaders' castles; and the fascinating ruins at Petra (Figure

[12] The carrying charges alone for Jordan's imports from Beirut to Amman amount to about one million dinars or 2,800,000 dollars annually.

[13] In 1951 the livestock population was estimated as follows: goats, 358,152; sheep, 266,088; cows, 81,137; and camels, 41,855.

[14] Evaporating pans at the south end of the Dead Sea are in Israel, and there a new processing plant has been constructed.

[15] Vegetable canning, soaps, cigarettes, matches, and alcoholic beverages.

148). Publicity, greater ease of travel, and better accommodations are needed in order to make tourism an important source of income.

What surpluses Jordan may have from her agricultural output are absorbed to some extent by new inhabitants, but there is usually some export annually. Vegetables are the only regular item on the list, but cereals, animals and animal products, and legumes all appear periodically, as may phosphates. Syria, Lebanon, and Iraq have replaced Palestine as Jordan's main markets. Great Britain, Syria and Lebanon, Iraq, Italy and the United States are the main sources of imports. Jordan normally has a large deficit in its balance of trade which must be made up from other sources of income.[16]

[16] Since the second World War met by releases from Jordan's sterling balances, American aid, U.N. expenditures and those of foreign firms and missionaries, and British grants in aid.

Fig. 148 • The ruins of the Roman forum at Jerash, Jordan. These ruins and others at Jerash are one of a number of historic sites that lure the tourist trade. The present Arab town is at the right center.

The barren, stony hills in the background are typical of the poorly watered and denuded areas east of the Jordan highlands. Such upland areas are utilized for grazing, having considerable pasturage on them during the wet season. (*Arab Information Center, N.Y.*)

Iraq

Iraq,[17] the largest of the Fertile Crescent states, is unique among them in having a major reserve of petroleum and an increasing production of oil which brings the state a sizable income. Unlike the others, it can be classed also as an underpopulated state. The similarities between Iraq and the other Arab states of the crescent are numerous, however—an economy that still is largely agricultural; a poverty-ridden peasantry; a small but wealthy landowner group; and a relatively unstable government. Yet Iraq, because of its oil royalties, has real possibilities of overcoming within a reasonable time many of its present problems, something not possible under existing conditions for its Arab neighbors to the west.

Despite the importance of its oil resources and the wealth derived from the production of oil since the late twenties, Iraq still has a predominantly agricultural economy. At least 60 per cent of the population gains its living from agriculture and pastoral activities;[18] outside the large urban centers this percentage rises to 85 or 90.

The distribution of types of agriculture and the density of farm population in general correlate closely with the availability of water and to a lesser extent with topographic features, though local variations result from other factors both physical and cultural. There are four distinct regions based upon agricultural land use: (1) Mesopotamia (the Tigris and Euphrates lowland south of Baghdad), (2) the upper Tigris region, (3) the northeastern highland region, and (4) the western and southern desert region. The last-named region is a pastoral one, inhabited by nomadic tribes who grow no crops.[19]

(1) Mesopotamia is characterized by non-intensive, irrigation agriculture. The cultivated areas, the seasons of cropping, and to some extent the crops themselves are determined by (1) the availability of water from year to year and season to season; (2) the effectiveness of drainage facilities in preventing salification; (3) the need for fallow; and (4) the whim of the landowner or the farm manager. The regimes of the Tigris and Euphrates are similar in that each attains its maximum volume in spring and its minimum in autumn. The Tigris, however, has a larger volume than the Euphrates. Because of the character of their regimes,

[17] Iraq was mandated to Great Britain in 1920 and achieved its independence in 1932. It is thus the oldest state politically in the Fertile Crescent.

[18] The approximately 450,000 gainfully employed in 1950 in fields other than agriculture were as follows: commerce, 110,000; personal and public service, 70,000; manufacturing and handicrafts, 75,000; transport, 45,000; government, 55,000; and other categories, errors, and omissions, 95,000.

[19] The nomad population is estimated at approximately 200,000.

winter cropping is the more important, the amount of water available for the summer being not only considerably less, but also variable.

The last is true as well for the yearly discharge of both rivers. Whereas floods are relatively frequent, years do occur when the total water volume is well under normal. Much of the irrigated land is insufficiently drained, so that salification, after one or two years' cropping, becomes great enough to render the land unusable. Arable land may be left fallow because of lack of water for irrigation or to let the soil renew itself, but at all times there is a large amount (approximately 50 per cent) in fallow, which, however, is often used for pasturage.

Flood, flow, and pump irrigation are all used in parts of the plain; there is little or no real perennial irrigation. The main area of flood irrigation is in the lower valley where great areas are inundated each year. Taking advantage of the flooding, farmers have made summer rice an important crop. Flow irrigation is used wherever the water level in the rivers is high enough to allow the gravity flow of water into canals and thence onto crop land. Flow irrigation is more important for winter crops since during the summer the rivers may be too low. The relative levels of the Tigris and Euphrates have helped in flow irrigation; in the vicinity of Baghdad the Euphrates is at a higher level than the Tigris, and water can be led from the one and drain ultimately into the other. In the lower valley the situation is reversed, with the Tigris being the higher. Drainage, however, is not developed as well as it should be, and low areas become waterlogged or marshy and unfit for cultivation.

A natural type of irrigation is practiced in the date gardens along the Shatt-al-Arab where the tidal rise in the Persian Gulf backs up fresh water which moves through canals onto the gardens, after which it drains back into the river at time of low tide.[20] This natural irrigation occurs twice during each 24-hour period, and the flow into canals is regulated by gates.

Pump irrigation is a rapidly expanding development in Mesopotamia.[21] It is used for both summer and winter crops and has the advantage over flow and flood irrigation of being more certain. Its main disadvantage for the majority of the peasants is its high cost.

Barley and wheat in that order are the most important winter-sown crops. Rice is the single most important summer-sown crop, with cotton a poor second. Minor summer crops include corn, sesame, and millet. There is also a considerable production of garden vegetables by irrigation. Dates are an important crop in all these riverine lands, but the greatest concentration of date palms is along the Shatt-al-Arab (Figure

[20] A similar irrigation technique is practiced along the coasts of Cochin China, although under widely differing physical and cultural circumstances.

[21] In 1921 there were 143 pumps in use in Iraq; in 1944, 3,000; in 1949-50, approximately 3,600. All but about 80 of these were in the Mesopotamian region.

Fig. 149 • Date gardens in the Shatt-al-Arab region of southern Iraq. Date gardens similar to these line the Shatt-al-Arab for the major part of its length, extending back from the river for about a mile and a half. This region produces about 80 per cent of the world's commercial dates, besides furnishing much food and stock feed for local consumption. The village is typical of many in the date area. The chief construction material is the reeds that grow in the poorly drained areas of the south. In the foreground is a drainage ditch that parallels the roadway. (John R. Randall.)

149). Iraq produces about four-fifths of the world production, normally in the neighborhood of 300,000 tons, approximately half of which is exported.

Despite the extent of its flood plains, there are sizable areas in Mesopotamia where no agricultural development has taken place. Poor drainage is the major reason for these underused areas. In the lower valley extensive tracts are in permanent marshes or lakes, e.g. Lake Hammar. Some areas are so situated that they cannot at present be irrigated or are in danger of annual inundation. The eastern, or Tigris, side of the valley has the largest of these tracts. Their utilization is dependent upon the combined flood-control, water-storage, and drainage projects now being developed through the investment of oil royalties.

Although the two agricultural regions north of Baghdad, (2) and (3), exhibit a fair degree of similarity, they are in marked contrast to Mesopotamia. Above Hit on the Euphrates and Samaria on the Tigris, the level

riverine plain gives way in one case to desert upland and in the other
to rolling hill country. To the northeast, along the Iraq-Iran border, are
the northeastern highlands, an extension into Iraq of the Kurdish mountains of Iran.

In general, level land capable of irrigation is limited. The Euphrates
valley is within the western desert region previously mentioned, as is
also a section of the Tigris valley between Samarra and Shargat. The
upper Tigris region consists of that part of the Tigris valley having at
least 15 inches of rain annually; its southwestern boundary is a line extending from Khanaqin, on the Iranian border, through Kirkuk and
Mosul to the Syrian border due west of Mosul. The northeastern highlands receive up to 40 inches of rain in contrast to the 15 or 20 characteristic of the steppe of the upper Tigris.

Crops in these two regions are rain-fed and winter-sown; only in the
restricted tracts is summer planting possible. Livestock-rearing is an important feature of the mountain areas. In contrast to Mesopotamia, a
much larger percentage of farms are small and individually owned and
operated, the percentage in the Kirkuk-Erbil district reaching as high as
75. Barley and wheat are the principal crops. Among those of minor importance are millet, corn, sesame, tobacco, and grapes, the last two being
restricted to the highland region.[22]

Of the problems facing agriculture in Iraq, some can be resolved in
time by a large investment of capital; others are so complex that only
major social and economic changes can solve them. In the first category
are the control, storage, and regulation of the waters of the Tigris-
Euphrates upon which will depend the increase in cultivated land and
the annual use of much land now only sporadically cropped. Estimates
indicate that about 20 per cent of Iraq is cultivable, but that only about
one-third of that percentage is cultivated in any given year.

The regime of the Tigris and Euphrates is such that parts of Mesopotamia, having the largest amount of land potentially cultivable, are
subject alternately to floods and acute shortages of water; other sections
suffer from too much water the year round, that is, they are constantly
marshy or actually covered with shallow water. The solution, then, lies
in projects that will control flooding, store and raise water, and drain off
excess water.

Projects to attain these ends either have been started or are in the development or planning stage (Figure 150). They are under the control
of the Iraq Development Board and are being financed by oil royalties.

----

[22] In 1950 crop production (in thousands of metric tons) was: barley, 800;
wheat, 520; lentils, 6; vetch, 3; rice, 242; cotton, 25; sesame, 10; corn, 21; millet,
19; tobacco, 3 dates, 250. Livestock (in thousands) were: sheep, 7,490; goats,
1,754; cattle, 1,034; water buffalo, 200; camels, 280; horses, 184; mules, 67; and
donkeys, 326.

They entail not only the building of barrages and feeder and drainage canals, but also of high dams on tributary streams and reservoirs for storage of irrigation water and disposal of excess flood waters. The completion of the entire scheme for control of the rivers and the resulting availability of new crop land may take several decades to achieve if there are no major interruptions, but the amount of land that can be cultivated in the country should be doubled. There also will be a major increase in the amount of cultivated land cropped annually, since the obstacles now keeping cultivated land from being regularly cropped will have been removed. Not only will the development projects increase crop land in Mesopotamia, but also to a considerable extent in the valleys above Baghdad and in the valleys of tributary streams. There will be continu-

Fig. 150 • The offices of the Dujaila Land Resettlement project of the Iraq Development Board in Mesopotamia, southeast of Baghdad. This large resettlement project is one of the earliest of the board's developmental schemes to come into being. The project contains approximately 160,000 acres of crop land, much of which has been apportioned between some 1,200 former sharecropping peasants. The new landowners get land and habitations on long-term loans from the government. They also receive aid and advice concerning stock, seed, and farming methods.

The·Development Board has other similar projects started or in the planning stage, with the end in view of creating a class of small landowners who can operate their own farms. (Arab Information Center, N.Y.)

ous areas of irrigated land from well above Sammara to Amara in the south, and for the first time in the modern era the Tigris and Euphrates will have an over-all coordinated irrigation system, rather than a make-shift based largely upon ancient systems. Additional advantages will be derived from the generation of hydroelectric power and the cessation of often devastating floods.

A much more difficult problem is that of land tenure [23] and its at-tendant evils, a landless and debt-ridden peasantry and a small but wealthy land-owning or -controlling group. In law, by far the largest part of all land is state-owned; that owned outright by individuals is mainly in urban centers and makes up only a very small percentage of the total.[24] In practice, the general situation is quite different. Somewhere between 40 and 50 per cent of the agricultural land, though technically state-owned, is held or controlled by private individuals, and, depending upon the type of tenure, rights to it may be sold, exchanged, or inherited. Under these conditions most of the peasants are practically incapable of obtaining land that they themselves can control and operate, especially in Mesopotamia. Large landholdings are held by sheiks (supposedly in the name of the tribe, but in practice often as individual owners) and by city men who have gained control of landholdings through the purchase and maintenance of pumps for irrigation. Although there are variations from one part of the country to another, in general the peasant-serfs who work the land are powerless against the large landholders. Their level of living is exceedingly low; they have few rights to the land they work or the crops they produce; and in time, many of them go deeply in debt to the landholder or his agents. At the same time, a sizable proportion of the large landholders have little interest in the land or the peasants who cultivate it.

On various occasions the government has attempted to establish proper title to land and to make it possible for the peasants to obtain tracts suf-ficiently large to support an average family, but so far most of these attempts have failed. The Cadastral Survey has established title to about half the land in the 14 *liwas* or provinces, but in this process as well a few men have obtained the major amount of the land.[25] Sincere as the government's attempts to establish land titles justly have been, the task

[23] For exact definitions of types of tenure in Iraq see the International Bank for Reconstruction and Development, *The Economic Development of Iraq* (Baltimore: Johns Hopkins Press, 1952), pp. 136-141.

[24] Land held in absolute private ownership is known as *mulk*.

[25] In the areas already covered by the Cadastral Survey 15.7 per cent of the farms are less than 62 acres; 11 per cent are 63 to 310 acres; 6.2 per cent are 311 to 620 acres; 42.8 per cent are 620 to 6200 acres; and 1.1 per cent are 6200 to 124,000 acres.

has proven almost impossible. Yet, a solution to the land-tenure problem will have to be found, especially if maximum benefits are to be derived from new irrigation projects.

Iraq's oil resources are the Aladdin's lamp that may allow the state to finance not only the projects noted above, but also a number of others that will in a similar way affect industry, commerce, education, and public health. Although Iraq's first oil production dates from 1927, total output was limited by the amount of oil that could be moved through the two 12-inch pipelines that reached the Mediterranean coast at Haifa and Tripoli. The only oil that was both produced and processed within the country was the relatively small output of the field at Naft Khaneh on the Iraq-Iran border. This oil, as well as some from Iranian fields, was refined at Khanaqin for internal use. In 1946 two 16-inch pipelines from the Kirkuk field to the Mediterranean coast were started. The one whose terminus was to be at Haifa was not finished because of the Israeli conflict. Also because of the creation of Israel, Iraq stopped the flow of all crude oil to the large Haifa refinery. The second 16-inch pipeline had its terminal at Tripoli. Subsequent pipeline construction included one of 30-32 inches from Kirkuk to Banias in Syria (1952); a 12-inch line from the Ain Zalah field to connect with the Kirkuk system (1952); and 12-inch and 24-inch lines from Zubair to Fao at the mouth of the Shatt-al-Arab.

Following the end of the second World War, renewed exploitation turned up three new fields; pipeline capacity was greatly enlarged; and oil royalties paid the government were considerably increased. In 1955 the following fields were producing—Kirkuk, Naft Khaneh, Ain Zalah, and Basra (Zubair). A new field at Rumaila, southwest of Zubair, had been discovered, but was not yet in production. As result of the increased pipeline capacity and the development of new fields, the daily output of oil jumped from 98,700 barrels in 1947 to 675,000 in 1955. In 1952, in part influenced by oil nationalization in Iran, the Iraqi government and the oil companies concerned drew up a new agreement by which the government would receive 50 per cent of the companies' profits before foreign taxes were paid.[26] This rise in the royalty rate and the increased production of oil account for the large income the government derives

---

[26] The oil companies are the Iraq Petroleum company, the Basra Petroleum company, and the Mosul Petroleum company. These related companies are controlled as follows: British Petrolem company (formerly Anglo-Iranian) 23.75 per cent; Royal Dutch Shell, 23.75; Compagnie Francaise des Petroles, 23.75; Socony-Vacuum Oil company and Standard Oil of New Jersey, each 11.875; and Participations and Explorations corporation (the company controlled by the late Caluste Gulbenkian), 5 per cent. The Khanagin Oil company operating the Naft Khaneh field is a subsidiary of the British Petroleum company.

from oil operations (approximately $175,000,000 in 1955). By law, 70 per cent of the oil income is to be used for developmental purposes.

Although the social and economic status of most of the population of Iraq is low, the probability that it can be raised through the use of oil income is high; thus, Iraq is in a position superior to that of the other Fertile Crescent states. Not only does an assured and sizable oil income make the future appear bright, but it gives the country a stronger political position within the Arab world.

Nonpetroleum resources, industry and trade are not highly developed in Iraq. There are few exploitable nonagricultural resources. The northeastern highlands, in addition to having a meager forest resource, contain deposits of copper, iron, and chromite, the extents of which are unknown.

Industrially, Iraq is similar to the other Arab states of the crescent; only a beginning has been made. The oil industry includes a large labor force (12,000) of well paid workers who benefit from technical training, good housing, and educational and health facilities for employees and their families. Exclusive of the oil-company employees, however, only about 2,000 of the 75,000 gainfully employed in manufacturing work in what can be termed modern manufacturing plants. Most of the labor force is employed in small shops, in bazaars, and in handicrafts.

The pattern of Iraq's foreign trade, other than oil, is also typically Middle Eastern. Imports consist of metals and other processed or manufactured goods; exports, of agricultural and livestock commodities.[27] Iraq normally has an adverse balance of merchandise trade (in 1954, per-capita trade was imports, $41.90; exports, $10.51) which is offset by oil income. The ports on the Shatt-al-Arab—Basra, Ashar, and Maqil—serve the country's ocean trade. Fao, at the entrance of the Shatt, has become the main port for the shipment of crude oil from the Basra fields.

SELECTED GEOGRAPHICAL BIBLIOGRAPHY

1. Ater, M. (ed.) *The Israel Yearbook, 1955.* Tel Aviv-Jaffa: Israel Publications, Ltd., 1955.
2. Boxer, Baruch. *Israeli Shipping and Foreign Trade.* (Research Paper No. 48, Department of Geography, University of Chicago). Chicago, 1957.
3. Cohen, S. B. "Israel's Fishing Industry," *Geographical Review,* January, 1957, pp. 66-85.

[27] Major imports (1954) by value: cotton piece goods, iron and steel, various types of machinery, sugar, and tea. Major exports: grains (especially barley), dates, raw cotton, wool, and live animals.

4. Davies, D. H. "Observations on Land Use in Iraq," *Economic Geography,* April, 1957, pp. 122-34.
5. Deutcher, Isaac. "Israel's Spiritual Climate," *The Reporter,* April 27, 1954, pp. 31-36; May 11, 1954, pp. 20-23.
6. Fish, W. B. "The Lebanon," *Geographical Review,* April, 1944, pp. 235-58.
7. Fisk, B. "Dujaila: Iraq's Pilot Project for Land Settlement," *Economic Geography,* October, 1952, pp. 343-54.
8. Hourani, Albert H. *Syria and Lebanon.* New York: Oxford University Press, 1946.
9. International Bank for Reconstruction and Development. *The Economic Development of Iraq.* Baltimore: The Johns Hopkins Press, 1952. See also International Bank for Reconstruction and Development. *The Economic Development of Syria.* Baltimore: The Johns Hopkins Press, 1955.
10. Iraq, Development Board. *Developments of the Tigris-Euphrates Valley.* Baghdad: Al-'Ani Press, 1954.
11. Kallner, D. H. and Rosenau, E. "The Geographical Regions of Palestine," *Geographical Review,* January, 1939, pp. 61-80.
12. Lebon, J. H. G. "Population Distribution and the Agricultural Regions of Iraq," *Geographical Review,* April, 1953, pp. 223-28.
13. ———. "The New Irrigation Era in Iraq," *Economic Geography,* January, 1955, pp. 47-59.
14. Lehrman, Hal. "Israel without Ideology," *Fortune,* June, 1952, pp. 88-91; 128, 130.
15. Lewis, Norman N. "Lebanon—The Mountain and Its Terraces," *Geographical Review,* January, 1953, pp. 1-14.
16. Patterson, G. "Israel's Economic Problems," *Foreign Affairs,* January, 1954, pp. 310-22.
17. Phillips, P. G. *The Hashemite Kingdom of Jordan: Prolegomena to a Technical Assistance Program* (Research Paper No. 34, Department of Geography, University of Chicago). Chicago, 1954.
18. Skrine, Sir Clarmont. "Economic Development in Israel," *Geographical Journal,* September, 1951, pp. 307-27.
19. Tannous, Afif. "The Village in the National Life of Lebanon," *Middle East Journal,* April, 1949, pp. 151-163.
20. Van Valkenburg, S. "Iraq," *Focus,* January, 1954, pp. 1-5.
21. ———. "The Hashemite Kingdom of Jordan: A Study in Economic Geography," *Economic Geography,* April, 1954, pp. 102-16.
22. Whyte, R. O. "The Phytogeographical Zones of Palestine," *Geographical Review,* October, 1950, pp. 600-14.

Comments

The Fisher, Middle East Survey, and Warriner volumes cited in previous chapters provide the best general background for the fertile Crescent States. The Hourani book probably is the best single general work on the Levant and includes much material of geographical interest.

The Iraqi and Syrian economies are well discussed in the International Bank reports, and the problems progress of Iraq's vast irrigation program is well covered in the Davies, Fisk, and Lebon articles and in the short report of the Iraq Development Board. The Fish article on Lebanon is an excellent survey, as is that of Van Valkenburg on Iraq and Jordan. The best single study of Jordan is that of Phillips.

An extensive literature has developed about Israel of which those cited represent a mere sample. The Boxer study deals with an increasingly important phase of its economy, its merchant marine in relation to trade orientations. The Lehrman, Deutscher, and Patterson articles represent samples of the nongeographic commentary on contemporary Israel.

Each of the Fertile Crescent states publishes official data annually, and yearbooks such as that cited on Israel are important sources of research data.

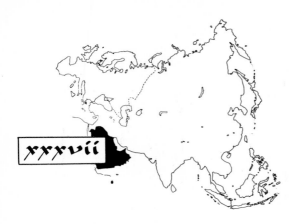

The Arabian Peninsula

THE ARABIAN PENINSULA,[1] OR THE "ARAB ISLAND," OCCUPIES ALMOST half of Southwest Asia and contains a little over a quarter of its population. Although the peninsula is rightly thought of as the core area of

[1] The Arabian peninsula is divided into many political units. Populations and areas are estimates since few boundaries have been demarcated and a number are in dispute, and with the exception of Aden Colony, census data are not available.

Political unit	Area	Population
Saudi Arabia	865,000 sq. mi.	4,500,000
Yemen	74,000 sq. mi.	4 to 5 million
Aden Colony	80 sq. mi.	100,000
Aden Protectorate (Hadhramaut)	112,000 sq. mi.	800,000
Sultanates of Oman and Muscat	82,000 sq. mi.	550,000
Trucial Oman (figures for area and population not available)		
Qatar	8,000 sq. mi.	25,000
Bahrein Island	213 sq. mi.	115,000
Kuwait	6,000 sq. mi.	200,000

Saudi Arabia and Yemen are independent kingdoms; Kuwait, Bahrein, Qatar, Trucial Oman, Oman, and Muscat are British dependencies; Aden Colony is a British Crown Colony, and Hadhramaut a protectorate of Great Britain. There also are two neutral zones in the peninsula: (1) between Kuwait and Saudi Arabia, controlled by these states jointly, and (2) between Iraq and Saudi Arabia, with similar joint control. The inhabitants of these zones largely are nomads who may move into the states on either side of the neutral zone.

831

the Arab world and was the fountain-head of Islam and Islamic culture, it has in some ways remained the most isolated and least-known part of the realm. Only recently has Western culture made any serious inroads into Arabia, where physical conditions have been an important factor in helping its inhabitants remain aloof.

The physique and climate of Arabia

Physiographically, Arabia is a great tilted tableland with a high edge along the Red Sea and a surface that slopes gradually eastward to the Persian Gulf. Only the mountain ranges of Oman in the southeast break this general pattern. Locally, however, there is much diversity. A narrow coastal plain borders the Red Sea, ending abruptly at the base of the west-facing escarpment of the tableland. Stream erosion, diastrophism, and vulcanism have produced a rugged, mountainous topography along this front so that the plateau nature of the tableland is not apparent until one passes beyond the water shed, which lies relatively close to the Red Sea. The elevation of these western mountains varies from around 3,000 feet in the north to a little over 12,000 feet in Yemen. A similar mountain front faces the Gulf of Aden and the Arabian Sea along the south coast of the peninsula from Yemen and Aden to Dhofar, about longitude 56°E. Again, the maximum elevations are in the west, from heights of 10,000 feet in southern Yemen to approximately 4,000 feet inland in Dhofar.

The plateau east of the western highlands is a bleak, rocky upland formed upon the ancient crystalline complex of Arabia. Its surface is broken occasionally by deep *wadis* and extensive lava areas, the latter often strewn with boulders. Some low mountains and local depressions add further variety to the surface. The general upland level of this western section of Nejd lies between 3,500 and 4,500 feet above sea level. Eastern Nejd is almost severed from the larger western portion by long north-south sand ridges. A similar sand-ridge region lies along the eastern edge of the Nejd, separating it from the Persian Gulf area. Eastern Nejd is characterized by a series of west-facing cuestas. In an area some 500 miles long and 200 miles wide there are six to eight cuestas. The resistant members forming the escarpments are limestone; the lowlands are formed over soft shales and sandstones.

The sand ridges noted above connect the two extensive sand areas of the peninsula, the Great Nefud in the north and the Rab al Khali in the south. Both of these are sand wastes with few inhabitants and relatively little vegetation or available water. The Great Nefud covers an area of approximately 22,000 square miles. The Rab al Khali, or so-called

"Empty Quarter," is a basin rimmed on the east, south, and west by mountains. Its area is estimated at 250,000 square miles. Of this probably as much as 80 per cent is covered with sand hills and ridges, some of which attain elevations of at least 500 feet above the surrounding de- pressions. Water is very scarce, and often where it does exist is too im- pregnated with salts to be potable. The eastern margin is the best watered. Water resources of the Rab al Khali are less than those of the Great Nefud; the former supports only a few nomads, but the latter, be- cause of sources of spring water from the higher land to the west, sup- ports a small sedentary oasis population.

Toward the Persian Gulf and east of the sand ridges is the lowest part of the peninsula. The coastal areas are a combination of low flats and sand ridges often interspersed with lagoons, sand dunes, and tidal in- lets. Back from the coast are fairly extensive gravelly plains, broken by occasional rocky uplands and mesas, one of which is large enough to be classed as a plateau.

North of the Great Nefud, and extending to the Jordan and Iraq bor- ders, is a rocky, gravelly upland that is the southern extremity of the Syrian desert. Much of the area is level and has been used for centuries as a route way and as a grazing region by nomadic peoples. It contains the divide between the peninsula proper and the Euphrates drainage basin. On its western edge is the great Wadi Sirhan which is about 200 miles long and as much as 20 to 30 miles wide; on the southeast is the Wadi al Batin which flows toward the Euphrates. Both of these valleys are larger than the present run-off would warrant and probably date from periods of heavier rainfall. Smaller but numerous *wadis* crossing the international boundaries have created a rougher, hilly section along the northern edge of the upland.

The mountains of Oman in the southeast are an extension of the fold ranges of the Zagros mountains of southwestern Iran. Faulting has pro- duced both upthrusts and graben-like valleys. Some of the latter, through subsidence, have produced the long narrow harbors that characterize parts of the coast. Although the main range, the Jebel Akhdar, is high (9,000 feet) and rugged, the major part of the highlands are best de- scribed as plateau-like. The interior slope of the highlands descends to the sandy Rab al Khali.

By far the larger part of the peninsula is tropical desert, with meager amounts of moisture and high temperatures that result in extreme arid- ity. Probably only the highlands and some of the higher escarpments receive as much as or more than 5 inches of rain per year; elsewhere precipitation is very scanty,[2] and a given place may be rainless for sev- eral years. There are no permanent streams in the peninsula, and the

[2] Aden, 5 inches; Bahrein, 2.9 inches; Muscat, 4 inches.

wadis carry water only after the occasional rains. When rain does come, however, it may be very heavy, if of short duration, and the *wadis* fill quickly. The run-off, where impounded behind temporary dams, is utilized for irrigation.

The highlands of Yemen in the southwest receive the largest amount of rainfall, probably as high as 40 inches in the highest areas and as much as 20 inches in the remainder. The mountain front in Asir north of Yemen and Hadhramaut to the east and the mountains in Oman likewise have heavier precipitation, possibly between 10 and 20 inches. West-facing highlands or escarpments in Hejaz and Nejd receive less than those just mentioned, but more than the lowlands and interior areas. The springs and artesian wells of the interior and the Persian Gulf area are undoubtedly fed by the heavier precipitation of the western front of the plateau. The ground water from this source is carried in sedimentary layers which lie upon the ancient crystalline base and dip toward the east.

Arabia, with the exception of Yemen, is characteristically Middle Eastern in that its precipitation comes in the cool season. Rainfall in the Yemen has a summer maximum that is monsoonal in origin. It does, however, have some winter precipitation which in the highlands may be in the form of snow.

Daytime temperatures in summer are high over the whole peninsula, save only the highlands, where elevation has some moderating effect. During the hot months daily maxima are probably in excess of 100°F. and in places may reach 120°, or possibly 130°. Away from the coastal areas there is an appreciable diurnal range of temperature. In the coastal areas the humidity even in summer and in spite of drought conditions is often excessive. The summer season is also the primary period for dust and wind storms. The major part of the peninsula has mean daily minima in winter above 40°, while daytime temperatures are warm to hot. In general, winter is the pleasant season of the year. Probably, however, Arabia's southern coastal area is the only one that does not occasionally record temperatures below freezing.

Relations with the outside world

The forbidding nature of the climate and the terrain, as well as the location of the major routes of travel, have done much to keep large parts of Arabia isolated. Only the peripheries of the "Arab Island" and the water bodies contiguous to them have been important route ways. Land routes have followed the coastal plains or crossed the peninsula between the heads of the

Persian Gulf and Gulf of Aqaba; routes in the interior have been primarily intraregional. Contact with the West until recently also was coastal, as witness the control of such points as Aden and Muscat by European powers. As a result of such isolation, the ways of life of many of the tribes have changed very slowly. Probably the purest strain of Arab is to be found in parts of the peninsula, and certainly nowhere is the nomadic way of life less disturbed, though even here the present century has brought changes.

In contrast to the interior areas, the coastal regions have had contact with the outside world for many centuries. Arab traders from the Persian Gulf and southern Arabia ranged far by sea to India and along the west coast of Africa; there also was contact with Ethiopia and Egypt across the Red Sea. The voyages of Sinbad were not entirely legend. Not only did the coastal Arabs travel widely by ship, but they also acted as middlemen in the movement of goods between Asia and Europe. In this process certain coastal towns became well established entrepôts and flourished as long as trade was possible. Pilgrimage to Mecca and Medina also brought some contact with outsiders, but this tended to be restricted to certain definite routes so that it left unaffected large parts of the peninsula.

The start of the modern period of change, with its increasing contact with the West, may be dated from the rise of the Saud dynasty and the consolidation of a large part of Arabia into the Kingdom of Saudi Arabia. Certainly Arabia underwent marked changes during the lifetime of Ibn Saud who in 1902 recaptured the town of Riyadh, the longtime seat of the Saud family. The consolidation of the state essentially was achieved by 1926; in 1927 Ibn Saud was proclaimed King of the Hejaz and Nejd and its Dependencies; in 1932 this dual kingdom became Saudi Arabia.

Oil has been the major factor in the opening of Arabia to new ideas. Other factors of importance have been developments in communication and transportation, trade, and the general world situation of the Second World War period. It is doubtful, however, that these alone would have had so rapid an effect had they not been sparked by the presence of vast quantities of petroleum in the peninsula.

The traditional economy

Wealth from oil, however, has not had much effect as yet upon the general population. Thus, in many parts of Arabia the people are living now pretty much as they have for centuries past (Figure 151). Their principal economy is a dual one of nomadic pastoralism and sedentary agriculture. Wherever water has been

Fig. 151 • The home of the Emir of Sakaka, a prosperous landowner of northern Saudi Arabia. The flat-roofed buildings are of sun-dried brick and the walls of mud or mud blocks. The main date garden is in the background. The tiny, bunded fields in the foreground, prepared with runnels for irrigation, are planted in cereals.

Although the Emir's home is conspicuously larger than the average, its style is characteristic of oasis architecture in which sun-dried brick is the principal building material. (Parker T. Hart.)

available in sufficient quantities from precipitation, wells, springs, or floods, sedentary farming has developed, and the inhabitants have eked out an existence from crops and livestock. The people of the oases toiled long and with ingenuity to maintain themselves. They also were prey to raids by *Bedouin* when these nomadic people could not get sufficient food or pasturage. Through time, however, a tenuous balance was developed between the "desert" and the "sown."

Because of its greater precipitation Yemen has had fairly extensive areas under cultivation; to a lesser degree the same holds true for the highlands of Oman and Hadhramaut. Oases based upon flood and impounded waters in *wadis* are found in Hadhramaut and in Asir and Hejaz; those based upon wells, springs, and artesian wells in Nejd and Hasa (Figure 152). Of the various types of oases, those based upon large flows of artesian water in Hasa are probably the most extensive. Much of the better watered crop land of Yemen and highland Hadhramaut is on mountain slopes where terracing is necessary. Although humid farming is possible in parts of these highlands, irrigation also is employed.

The production of crops is largely for local consumption. Dates probably are the single most important food staple, followed by wheat and barley; other cereals include rice, corn, oats, millet, and sorghum. Coffee, produced in the highland areas of southwestern and southeastern Arabia, has a world reputation for fine flavor and has been one of the region's few export commodities; the export of dates has varied considerably depending upon local supply and demand and variations in production. Livestock, especially sheep and goats, supply milk, some meat, wool, and hair. Camels and donkeys are the principal draft animals. Although there is some variation in crops and methods of tilling from area to area,

Fig. 152 • Khafs Daghrah in the Nejd south of Riyadh in Saudi Arabia. This oasis has now become a part of the Al Kharj irrigation project. The source of water, likewise, is a limestone pit. The water is raised approximately 70 feet by diesel-powered pumps.

Prior to its development in the early 1940's Khafs Daghrah was a water hole utilized by the *Bedouin* for watering their camels. *Bedouin* still utilize the oasis for this purpose and a number of their camels (dromedaries) and some of their black tents are seen in the foreground. The village buildings of sun-dried brick are typical of this section of the Nejd. The rows of trees in the distance line the irrigation canals. Highlands and dunes are in the far distance. (*Standard Oil of New Jersey.*)

Fig. 153 • The open market place of the village of Sakaka in northern Saudi Arabia. In such markets, the oasis inhabitants do much of their everyday buying and selling and gather to hear news and gossip. These oasis settlements also are used as sources of supply for the *Bedouin* for such needs as cannot be obtained from their animals. The *Bedouin* tribes often own or control oases in order to assure a food and water supply.

The building material is sun-dried brick. Note the camel at the left and the asses in the left middleground. Oil drums at the left are among the principal containers in the Near East. Rush baskets on the ground in the right background are equally common and even more widespread. Several sizable trucks in the background suggest the gradual shift toward motorized transport in much of the area. *(Parker T. Hart.)*

there is far more similarity than diversity. The highland areas produce more subtropical and middle-latitude types of fruit than do the lowland oases; and only in very restricted areas is there scientific agriculture using machinery for cultivation of specialized crops.

Nomadic pastoralism is still of major importance in Arabia so far as numbers of people and extent of area are concerned. The central and northern sections of the peninsula probably are the main regions affected, but hardly any part is without some nomadic activity. The nomadic tribes with their animals shift over reasonably prescribed areas in the search of pasturage. Few of them raise or attempt to raise any crops. Their needs, beyond what is furnished by their animals, are obtained by purchase or barter in the oases settlements (Figure 153). Such a life, considering the environment, is at best a difficult one. It is this factor that has given rise to often long-continued conflict among the tribes over rights to pasturage areas and water holes, and to strife between the tribes and the sedentary population when the former were without food and sufficient pasturage for their animals. Oases were plundered periodically by nomadic tribes and on occasion came under the complete control of a nomadic tribe seeking to assure its food supply.

The camel has been the mainstay of the Bedouins for transport and for milk and other animal products; sheep and goats also are kept in large numbers. Until recently there had been a gradual decline in the number of camels in Arabia, the result largely of a decline in the numbers of nomadic peoples and the introduction of more modern means of transport. In the past decade, however, numerous men, having earned good wages in the oil fields, have returned to their tribes and invested their earnings in camels, since ownership of these animals is not only a sign of wealth but also of prestige. Thus, the development of petroleum resources in Arabia reversed the trend and brought about an increase in the camel population.

Old and honored as may have been the custom of tribal warfare and the pillaging of oases by the *Bedouin,* no state could become stable with these activities continuing. Hence, one of Ibn Saud's first moves was to put an end to tribal feuds and raids. A second was to bring about the permanent settlement of as many *Bedouin* as possible. The first was done by punitive action against unruly tribes; in other cases tribes were brought into line by intermarriage of their leaders with members of the royal house of Saud.

The settlement of many nomads was achieved over a period of years through the creation of the Ikhwan. This colonizing society was composed of adherents of the Wahhabi sect whose allegiance to the king and to the land transcended any tribal allegiance. Through them Ibn Saud not only established sedentary settlements, but at the same time forged a fighting force that ultimately allowed him to establish political stability over the largest part of Arabia. Thus, the nomadic population of Saudi Arabia has been reduced 20 to 30 per cent since the first Ikhwan colony was started in 1912.

Along the coastal areas of the peninsula, trade and fishing have been important aspects of the economy. Trade is both local and transit and today is of relatively less importance, with the exception of oil, than it has been in the past. It has, however, given rise to a number of port cities, among which are Kuwait, Muscat, Mukalla, Aden, and Jidda. These are important transshipment points and supply stations, and in them adjunct industries such as shipbuilding have developed. They are also the production centers and collecting points for handicrafts, the sole type of manufacturing in the peninsula outside of petroleum products.

Fish for local consumption and some, dried, for export are obtained in waters surrounding the peninsula. Because of lack of refrigeration and easy means of transport this industry has not been as important as it might be. Fish, however, are an important item of diet for practically all the coastal peoples, and fishing and the production of boats and nets provide a livelihood for numerous inhabitants. Pearls are the most valuable and spectacular of the products obtained from the coastal waters; the Persian Gulf especially has been noted as a source of some of the world's best natural pearls. Although pearl-fishing has suffered many ups and downs over the centuries, it has continued to be of considerable significance. Change in fashions and the development of cultured pearls are the two factors that have most recently affected the pearl-fishing business. Manama, on Bahrein island, is the center of the pearling industry and trade.

Petroleum and its development

Change in Arabia has been sparked by petroleum. Arabia contains some of the world's largest petroleum reserves. The states of the peninsula with appreciable reserves and production are Saudi Arabia, Kuwait, Bahrein, Qatar, and the Neutral Zone between Kuwait and Saudi Arabia.[3] The Trucial Coast has oil resources, but they had not been brought into production by late 1957. Known reserves in mid-1956 were: Saudi Arabia, 40 billion barrels; Kuwait, 50 billion; Bahrein, 175 million; Qatar, 1.5 billion; Neutral Zone, 390 million; and the Trucial Coast, 50 million barrels; a total for the peninsula of 92.1 billion barrels. In comparison, the United States has known reserves of 30.25 billion barrels. In 1955, production from the Arabian fields was over 812 million barrels, as compared with the United States' 1955 production of 2,485 million barrels.

About two-thirds of this production in 1955 came equally from Kuwait and Saudi Arabia. Most of the production from Kuwait is exported directly as crude, chiefly to refineries in western Europe, via the Suez Canal. About 25 per cent of Saudi Arabia's output is shipped by pipeline to a refinery on Bahrein island, which also processes almost all of the production of Bahrein itself. Another 30 per cent is transported through the 1,068-mile long Trans-Arabian pipeline which terminates at the port of Sidon on the Mediterranean coast of Lebanon. Another 25 per cent is refined within the country in the refinery at Ras Tanura

[3] The known oil fields of the peninsula are, from north to south: (1) Kuwait: Raudhatain, Ahmadi Ridge, Magwa, Burgan; (2) Neutral Zone: Wafra; (3) Saudi Arabia: Safaniya (offshore), Abu Hadriya, Fadhili, Qatif, Damman, Abqaiq, Ghawar (containing the following areas: Ain Dar, Shedgum, 'Uthmaniyah, Huiya, and Haradh); (4) Bahrein: Dukhan; and (5) Qatar: Dukhan No. 1.

(Figure 9). The remaining production is exported by tanker, chiefly through the Suez Canal. These petroleum exports account for about two-thirds of the cargoes passing through the Suez Canal, accentuating the canal's strategic significance to western European and Arabian alike.

The companies holding Arabian concessions are all Western. American companies have full control in Saudi Arabia, Bahrein, and the Neutral Zone; half interest in Kuwait; and 23.75 per cent interest in Qatar and the Trucial Coast. Concessions also have been granted to foreign companies, chiefly British, American, French, Dutch, and German, for exploration and development in the offshore waters of Qatar and the Trucial Coast; Oman, Dhofar;Hadhramaut and Aden; Yemen;

Fig. 154 • Farm workers harvesting carrots on an Al Kharj farm south of Riyodh in Saudi Arabia. Much of the produce from these farms is used by the royal court in Riyodh.

Although Al Kharj is an ancient oasis, its present development is the result of modern technology supplied by the American government and Aramco at the behest of the king. The use of large machines to prepare the fields and of gasoline pumps to raise water from nearby limestone pits has greatly increased productivity. In spite of the use of large-scale machines and powered pumps, much of the work on the farms is still done by hand or with the use of animals. Note the desiccated surface in the background where irrigation has not recently been practiced. *(Arab Information Center, N.Y.)*

and the British islands off the coast of Yemen and their territorial waters.

Royalties paid the rulers of the states concerned amount to 50 per cent of the value of each barrel of oil produced. For both Kuwait and Saudi Arabia the income from this source amounts to over $200 millions annually. The choosing of purposes for which this income will be used is a problem facing each of the Arabian states. In Kuwait and Bahrein, at least one-third of the income is being invested to provide appreciable income for the future when oil reserves are depleted. The remaining two-thirds is used for government, education, health, various types of developmental investment (Figure 154), and for the privy purse of the ruler. In each of these states, with its small area and population, the expenditure of such large sums of money presents a particularly acute problem.

It is not known for what purposes oil income in Saudi Arabia is being used.[4] Some funds have been earmarked for developmental projects, but there apparently is no law regulating their disposal, unlike the situation in Iraq. A part pays for the administrative and defense budgets; the remainder is the king's, to do with as he sees fit.

Since oil royalties have been received for only a few years, it is impossible to forecast their over-all effect upon the economies of the countries receiving them. This is true especially of Saudi Arabia, the largest and most populous of the peninsular states, about the affairs of which the least is known. It is only logical to assume, however, that the continued receipt of immense sums of money ultimately will affect the lives of the peoples of the "Arab Island" and alter their levels and ways of living. Whether or not these benefits will be extended to the Middle Eastern states without petroleum through aid granted by those with it remains to be seen.

There is no uncertainty, however, about the political significance of the petroleum resources of Arabia. The oil-wealthy states, especially Saudi Arabia, have come to exert exceptional influence in the affairs of the Middle East. Their influence in international affairs similarly has come to reflect their control of petroleum reserves in an oil-short world. As a result, the highly industrialized United States has come to share common commercial interests with feudal Saudi Arabia; and Great Britain, the most influential western European state, must treat gently with the miniscule sheikdom of Kuwait which has matured rapidly toward full independence under the tutelage of British Residents. The influence of Saudi Arabia in particular has been reflected in clefts within

[4] Technically all the income is the king's, and he makes the ultimate decisions as to how it is to be used. There is little question that some funds are used to keep the country politically stable, that is, to pacify the various tribes. There has been much publicity about lavish spending by the royal family, but such stories are almost impossible to check.

the Arab world, where competitions among states and dynasties have prevented political unity and often cooperation. In short, whereas the Arabian peninsula had long been a backwash region in the Southwest Asian realm, except for its religious significance as the site of two of the major holy places of Islam, Mecca and Medina, since 1940 it has become a major economic and political focus of the Arab world, of increasing significance as its oil production has mounted.

Within Arabia itself, petroleum has already markedly influenced both the landscape and way of life, nowhere more conspicuously than in the oil-field areas. All the landscape features of an oil-producing area are present—derricks, refineries, pipelines, stabilizers, gas-injection plants, pumping stations, and tank farms. On the coast long jetties project into the shallow waters of the Persian Gulf to facilitate the loading of tankers. New cities and towns have been built to house the many native workers, as well as the foreigners employed by the oil companies. In many ways a settlement such as Dhahran is like an American town transplanted into the Arabian desert. Buildings are modern in construction, and many are air-conditioned. Besides the houses, there are schools, hospitals, office buildings, supermarkets, and a variety of recreational facilities.

In addition to becoming familiar with this setting, the Arab employee of the oil companies has been trained as a technician with pride in his work; he has a good, steady income, and his way of life surely has been altered. Although the Arabs employed in the oil industry form only a minute sample of the total population, their adaptability to Western industrial conditions suggests the vast possibilities for economic and cultural change in the Arab world, given the effective investment of petroleum royalties in economic diversification and industrial development.

SELECTED GEOGRAPHICAL BIBLIOGRAPHY

1. Crary, Douglas D. "Recent Agricultural Developments in Saudi Arabia," *Geographical Review*, July, 1951, pp. 366-383.
2. Izzedin, Nejla. *The Arab World*. Chicago: Henry Regnery Company, 1953.
3. Lebkichen, Roy, George Rantz, and Max Steineke. *Handbooks for American Employees*. New York: Arabian American Oil Company, 1952.
4. Melamid, Alexander. "Political Geography of Trucial Oman and Qatar," *Geographical Review*, April, 1953, pp. 194-206.
5. Sanger, Richard H. *The Arabian Peninsula*. Ithaca: Cornell University Press, 1954.
6. ———. "Ibn Saud's Program for Arabia," *Middle East Journal*, April, 1947, pp. 180-190.
7. Twitchell, K. S. *Saudi Arabia*. Princeton: Princeton University Press, 1947.
8. ———. "Water Resources of Saudi Arabia," *Geographical Review*, July, 1944, pp. 365-86.

9. Vesey-Fitgerald, D. "From Hasa to Oman by Car," *Geographical Review*, October, 1951, pp. 544-60.

Comments

There has been relatively little recent detailed geographical work done in the Arabian peninsula of which the results are available in English. Most materials readily available are more general than precise and contain much information not geographic in nature. The Twitchell book is probably the best of these: the Sanger book is pleasant reading but rather discursive in parts. Books by St. John Philby, not listed here, contain much valuable information on the land, but it must be sorted out from a mass of other material.

The *Handbook for American Employees*, published by Aramco, besides having a good deal of geographic information, contains many excellent photographs and maps.

Quantitative data are not available for the peninsula, and map coverage in general is exceptionally poor.

Russia and Asia

THE EASTERN PART OF THE SOVIET UNION LIES WITHIN THE ASIATIC continent. The Soviet Union, however, as indicated previously,[1] is not an integral part of the Asian world. Nevertheless, it is characterized by a unique relation to Asian Asia: contiguity. This fact, combined with its occupance of most of the northern Asiatic continent, demands a separate treatment of the U.S.S.R., especially in its relation to the countries of the Asian Crescent.

In this chapter the relations between the Soviet Union and Asia will be approached through a brief survey of the maritime and landward boundaries of the Asian Crescent, followed by an analytical description of the broad geographical patterns that characterize the Soviet Union as a whole. Chapter XXXIX will examine each of the major Soviet regions that impinge upon Asia at the common frontier and together constitute Soviet Asia. The chapter will close with a brief comparison of the relations between the Soviet Union and Asia and those between Asia and the non-Soviet Western world.

[1] See Chapter II.

845

The maritime frontier of the Asian Crescent

The Asian Crescent by definition occupies the southern and eastern peripheries of the Asiatic continent. Thus, it possesses both maritime and continental frontiers (Back End Paper).

The Maritime Frontier faces the waters of three great oceans. On the west, portions of Southwest Asia look out over the Mediterranean and its major associated body the Black Sea, both extensions of the Atlantic Ocean. To the south are the waters of the Indian Ocean, and to the East those of the Pacific.

It is characteristic of the sea frontiers that they tend to face not directly upon the oceans themselves, but upon buffering seas that are extensions of the oceans. These extensions reflect the irregularity of the southern Asian coastline and the great promontories, peninsulas, and archipelagoes that rim the Asiatic continent. Most notable of the secondary seas is the Mediterranean, which was the center of maritime transportation for the ancient world and still remains, in association with Suez, one of the world's greatest ocean lanes, as well as a major subcenter of maritime activity in its own right.

To a lesser degree the Indian Ocean reaches the coasts of southern Asia, primarily through less restricted bays and seas. The promontory of the Indian subcontinent separates the Arabian Sea from the Bay of Bengal. More striking is the penetration of the Red Sea almost to the Mediterranean, where the Suez Canal completes the connection that nature failed to make. To the east is the Persian Gulf, rimmed by petroliferous formations; out of this gulf sail some of the world's largest tankers, grossing up to 100,000 tons, laden with black liquid wealth. East of the Bay of Bengal is the Andaman Sea, which lies behind the Andaman and Nicobar islands and shields the coasts of deltaic and Tenasserim Burma and the isthmus of Kra. Only southernmost India at Cape Cormorin, southern Ceylon, and southern Java front directly on the great ocean.

In the east, the Pacific breaks against a shatter zone of lesser seas which penetrate the continental shore—the South China Sea and the Gulf of Siam, together with the lesser seas of archipelagic Southeast Asia; the East China Sea and the Yellow Sea off the coast of middle and northern China; the Sea of Japan along the Korean and maritime Russian coasts; and the Sea of Okhotsk and the Bering Sea to the north. Along the Pacific shore a series of island arcs front upon the great ocean

—Japan in the north; the Ryukyus and T'ai-wan in the center; and the Philippines in the south.

The strategic and commercial significance of these bordering seas and the straits between them has been discussed elsewhere.[2] It bears repeating, however, that communications along the southerly coasts of Asia have long been facilitated by these relatively protected seas. Indeed, Asia may be considered to be seaward oriented, not only in its trade with the world at large, but also with regard to the relations among the Asian nations themselves, although Japan and the Philippines, fronting directly on the Pacific, have been the only Asian countries to develop an important trans-Pacific view. In commercial terms Asian Asia remains a maritime-oriented region, primarily looking westward to the Mediterranean and Europe, secondarily toward the United States. In recent years, however, and especially since the close of the second World War, Asian countries have become increasingly concerned, primarily in political terms, with their land frontiers. This is true of the land boundaries between individual states and even more of those that separate the Asian Crescent countries from the rest of the Asiatic continent.

The continental frontier

The most distinctive feature of the landward boundary of the Asian Crescent countries as a whole is the presence of the Soviet Union along virtually its entire length (Back End Paper). Only where Arabia, Jordan, and Israel on the Asian side and Egypt on the African side meet east of Sinai, and where European Turkey shares a common boundary with Greece and Bulgaria, does Asia as such *not* share a frontier with the U.S.S.R. The importance of this areal relationship is suggested by the political map of the Asiatic continent, which shows the Soviet Union sprawling over the main body of Asian Asia. The figurative pressures that this picture suggests also have literal consequences, for the Soviet Union by its very proximity exerts a notable influence in Asian affairs, and has done so for over two hundred years.

The boundary is distinctive in two other ways. First, it is largely a mountain boundary. Second, it tends to run through areas that, though sparsely settled, are occupied for the most part by ethnic groups belonging neither to the Slavic peoples on the one hand nor to the dominant nationalities to the south on the other. It also is one of the longest land boundaries in the world and extends over 8,000 miles from west to east.

The first great segment of the Russian-Asian frontier extends for nearly

[2] See Chapter 2.

600 miles across the great isthmus that separates the Black Sea from the Caspian (Maps 34 and 36). It begins just south of Batumi on the eastern shore of the Black Sea. For nearly 130 miles it separates Turkey from the Georgian S.S.R., one of the constituent republics of the Soviet Union. On the Turkish side of the border is an area extending along the shores of the Black Sea past Trabzon (Trebizond) for 150 miles or more, which is claimed by Georgians as part of their ancestral homeland, although the present Georgian-related population there (a Moslem people known as Laz) is a minority. The boundary itself does not follow the height of land, but cuts across upland and basin alike. To the east, Turkey shares a 150-mile boundary with Soviet Armenia, which begins east of the Arpa River (a tributary of the Araks River), follows the Arpa to the Araks, and then runs along that river's mountainous course to the Soviet-Persian border. The frontier crosses the Armenian plateau, which is predominantly Armenian in population. The Armenians have claims across the international boundary to what still is known as Turkish Armenia, and Mount Ararat (16,945 feet), sung in Armenian history, lies in Turkish territory. The mutual hostility between Armenian and Turk emphasizes the strategic significance of the border.

Farther east, the boundary separates Soviet territory from Persia. It follows the Araks River almost to the delta that river shares with the Kura River, where it turns southward to enclose within the U.S.S.R. the Lenkoran lowland on the southwestern shores of the Caspian Sea. North of the boundary is the Azerbaijan S.S.R., one of the constituent republics of the Soviet Union, and a panhandle of the Armenian S.S.R., also a constituent republic. To the south is a sector of Persian Armenia and, more important, Iranian Azerbaijan, with a Moslem population predominantly of Turkic origin. Cultural relations between these people and their kinsmen in the U.S.S.R. assumed new political trappings in the form of the short-lived, Russian-supported, Persian Azerbaijan Republic of 1946.

East of the Caspian Sea the border extends for 1,500 miles to China's westernmost frontier. It begins below sea level, but rises quickly to the northern heights of the Kopet Dagh, the mountain range that is a southeastern extension of the Great Caucasus mountains mated with an easterly outlier of the Elburz mountains of northern Iran. To the north lies the Turkmen S.S.R., another constituent republic of the U.S.S.R., and to the south for 500 miles lies Iran. Again the frontier runs through a region inhabited primarily by a non-Slav, non-Iranian people, the Turkmen; Russian claims to northern Iran have been based on Turkmen culture history.

Farther east, the border runs along the foothills of the western outliers of the Hindu Kush, thence into the valley of and along the Amu Darya

(Oxus River) which rises in the high Pamirs. Ultimately, the boundary runs eastward and upward until it touches Chinese territory in the eastern Pamirs. Afghanistan lies south of this entire sector of the frontier. Turkmenistan and Uzbekistan to the north share the western half of this segment of the boundary. Since substantial minorities of Uzbeks and Turkmens, both Moslem peoples, live in northern Afghanistan, there is a distinct parallel with the Soviet Azerbaijan-Iranian juxtaposition. The parallel is equally striking and perhaps of greater strategic importance along the eastern portion of the Afghan-Soviet border, which separates the Tadzhik S.S.R., another constituent republic of the Soviet Union, from northern Afghanistan with its substantial Tadzhik (Tajik) minority. The Tadzhiks, unlike the Turkic-speaking Uzbeks and Turkmens, speak Persian dialects. These people extend well across northern Afghanistan to the Persian boundary, and they have played an important role in Persian-Russian relations. Although the Soviet boundary actually does not touch India and Pakistan, being separated from them by a narrow, 25-mile-wide panhandle of Afghan territory, the distance between them is so slight that Tadzhik (and Kirgiz) minorities in those two countries may be considered of similar importance to those in Afghanistan and Iran.

The international boundary turns northward and northeastward after its initial junction with China, and for about 1,400 miles separates Soviet territory from that of China's Hsin-chiang province. Three constituent republics impinge on this sector of frontier. On the southwest is the Tadzhik S.S.R.; just north of it is the Kirgiz S.S.R.; farther north yet is the Kazakh S.S.R. which borders more than half of this frontier segment. The boundary itself runs over the eastern Pamirs, northeastward along the T'ien Shan, north across the Ili valley up onto the Ala Tau (mountains), thence across the lower Dzungarian Gate, over the crest of the Tarbagatay mountains, and finally to the crest of the western Altai mountains.

In Hsin-chiang province is a great mixture of peoples, largely of Mongoloid extraction, with substantial numbers of Chinese in the oases and towns and true Mongols in the northeast nearer the Outer Mongolian border. The Kirgiz are an important minority near the Kirgiz S.S.R. Also, there are more than half a million Kazakhs near the Kazakh S.S.R. In addition, Hsin-chiang contains over three million Uighurs, a Turkic-speaking, predominantly Mongoloid people, who form a substantial minority (100,000) in Soviet Middle Asia,[3] although they do not have an autonomous political organization of their own in Soviet territory. Lastly, there are Chinese-speaking Moslems, the so-called Dungans,

[3] Soviet Middle Asia is here used to refer to the five union republics—Kazakh S.S.R., Uzbek S.S.R., Kirgiz S.S.R., Tadzhik S.S.R. and Turkmen S.S.R.

PHYSIOGRAPHY AND REGIONAL DIVISIONS OF THE U.S.S.R.

Physiography by A.K. LOBECK   A.K.P.

who appear both in Chinese and Soviet territory. The existence of all of these culturally non-Chinese, non-Slav peoples on both sides of the frontier has been a major element in the expansion of Russian influence in far western China.

In sum, the international boundary that separates Soviet Middle Asia from Turkey, Iran, Afghanistan, and western China, like the border segments to the west, crosses mountainous terrain and runs through regions occupied by relatively homogeneous peoples on both sides of the boundary. For centuries, until very recent times, the boundary has been more a zone of passage and flux than a divide. Only since about 1935 has the boundary begun to partake of the greater rigidity of international boundaries long characteristic of the more highly developed parts of the globe.

The fluxing quality of the regions through which the boundary passes is indicated clearly by the racial qualities of the peoples within them. All are racial mixtures. The Turkmens and Tadzhiks may be classified as primarily Caucasoid in race with strong Mongoloid intermixtures. The Uzbeks, Kirgiz, and Kazakhs may be considered primarily Mongoloid; many of them are descendants of the Mongol tribesmen who spread over much of northern Eurasia under Genghis Khan and his descendants. In these cases, also, there are strong intermixtures, however, and non-Mongoloid physical characteristics often dominate locally.

East of the 87th meridian, the boundary takes a major easterly rather than northeasterly trend, crossing the highland zone, including the Tannu Ola and eastern Sayan mountains, which separate western Outer Mongolia from Soviet territory. Thence it traverses the treeless Selenga River valley and the forested uplands east of Lake Baykal to the foothills of the Kentei mountains of northeastern Outer Mongolia and into the upper Amur River basin. Northwest of the border on the Soviet side is Tannu-Tuva, inhabited by a people related to the Kirgiz, which formally was annexed to the U.S.S.R. in 1944. To the northeast are the Buryat or Northern Mongols. South of the border is the predominantly Mongol population of western Manchuria, politically organized under the Peking government into the Inner Mongolian Autonomous Region. Again the frontier passes through rugged highland country, transitional between the taiga of Siberia and the arid steppes and stony deserts of Mongolia. Although the ribbon of predominantly Russian settlement that follows the Trans-Siberian railway comes nearer to the frontier here than anywhere to the west, the political boundary scarcely can be termed an ethnic one, since it divides areas inhabited by Mongol peoples.

At longitude 118°E. just east of the western terminus of the Trans-Manchurian or Chinese Eastern Railway, the Argun River acts as the boundary until it joins the Shilka River to become the Amur or Hei-lung

Chiang. The Amur acts as an international boundary to a point near the 135th meridian where it is met by its last major affluent, the Ussuri River. The Argun and Amur together form a boundary some 1,150 miles in length. At the Ussuri the frontier turns southward along that river, passing through Lake Khanka, and then over the hilly forested lands to the southwest until the Tumen River is reached, a total distance of some 540 miles. This stream forms the international boundary between Korea and the U.S.S.R. for a distance of 12 miles until it enters the Pacific. It forms, therefore, the Pacific terminus of the Soviet Union's landward frontier with Asia.

The Amur-Ussuri sector of the frontier, however, differs markedly from the rest of the frontier in two strategically significant respects. First, rivers and not mountains demarcate the greater part of the border in this sector, although the Amur and its tributaries flow through uplands for much of their length, and the Amur is effectively cut off from the central Manchurian lowlands to the south by the Great and Little Hsing-an mountains. Second, the non-Western peoples near the border are relatively few and are of minor political or economic importance. Chief exceptions are the Chinese and Koreans, some 300,000 in number, who live in the southernmost portions of the maritime Far East, but many of these migrated into Russian territory *after* the Russians had obtained the territory from China in 1860. It was they who crossed the frontier, not the frontier that divided them.

In general, the frontier that separates Asia from the Soviet Union is characterized by great length, by an association with uplands and mountains, and by its division of similar ethnic groups into differing political spheres. This third characteristic has been used by the Soviet Union to extend its influence into Asia, especially into those countries wherein reside minorities related to those on the Soviet side of the border. The Mongol minority within China can be identified as being of particular interest to Russia; the activities of Kazakhs in Hsin-chiang province are of great interest to the Khazakh S.S.R. and the authorities in Moscow; similarly, the policy of the Iranian government toward Persian Azerbaijan is regarded as of direct interest to the Russians because of their Azerbaijanian minority. Conversely, the problems and wellbeing of minorities in Russian territory are of intense concern to their kinsmen across the border in Turkey, Iran, Afghanistan, and China. As the state of wellbeing of the Russian minorities varies, so is the effectiveness of Soviet propaganda likely to vary among the related peoples across the frontier. The political strategic significance of this fact underlies much of the increasing concern of the Asian countries with their landward frontiers.

In spite of its greatly increasing importance, the Russo-Asian frontier is crossed by surprisingly few transportation routes. This may be taken as a measure of the negative and separatist character of much of central Asia.[4] It is noteworthy that there are only six rail crossings of the boundary (Back End Paper). One leads from Soviet Armenia into Turkish Armenia and after a break of gauge meets the Turkish railway system. A second branches southward from Soviet Armenia into Iran and joins the broad-gauge Persian line which terminates at Tabriz and eventually will reach Tehran. The next crossing is some 5,000 boundary miles to the east,[5] where a branch of the Trans-Siberian railway leads southward to Ulan Bator, the capital of Outer Mongolia, and thence to Peking. Another branch to the east extends southward into easternmost Outer Mongolia. Both of these, however, cross a portion of the frontier that separates a known Russian satellite from the senior country. There is one rail crossing of the frontier between Outer Mongolia and China, much of which traverses the barren Gobi: the new railroad southward from Ulan Bator to Peking. Another crossing takes place near the Russian–Outer-Mongolian–Manchurian border, where a branch of the Trans-Siberian passes into Chinese territory and becomes what was known originally as the Chinese Eastern Railway.[6] The last rail crossing occurs where the Chinese Eastern or Trans-Manchurian line crosses into Soviet territory northwest of Vladivostok. A number of roads cross the frontier, but few are all-weather roads and few, if any, are paved. The volume of traffic that moves across them, therefore, can be assumed to be small,[7] although their ancient function as caravan routes continues to provide links across the frontier, which in cultural and political terms are all out of proportion to their small economic importance.

The physical patterns of the Soviet Union

The U.S.S.R. is the largest country in the world, roughly the size of all of North America. With an

---

[4] What is meant here is central Asia as a zone of sparse settlement and limited opportunities for large-scale permanent occupance on the one hand, and of diminishing Russian and Chinese cultural influences on the other.

[5] Two branch lines in Soviet Middle Asia reach the Afghan frontier, but there is no Afghan rail system with which they can connect.

[6] It is probable that the break-of-gauge, from Russian 5 foot to Chinese 4 foot 8½ inch, at the border remains, although occasional reports suggest that the main-line Manchurian rights of way may have been broadened to Russian gauge.

[7] Certain of these roads are ancient caravan routes that cross the high mountain passes along the western Hsin-chiang and Outer Mongolian boundaries. One of these is the old Roman silk route, which leads to Kashgar. More important in modern times, is the road that follows the Ili river valley eastward from Alma Ata in Kazakhstan to Ti-hua in Hsin-chiang's Dzungarian basin. A 1,400-mile pipeline is reported to follow this same route from Alma Ata to the oil fields of Kan-su province.

area approximating 8.5 million square miles it extends more than 6,000 miles from east to west and some 3,000 miles at its maximum width from north to south. Within this vast land mass, which occupies northeastern Eurasia, there are great variations in natural conditions. However, despite these variations, the Soviet Union may be described in terms of a relatively small number of major natural regions. Extreme variations of climate or topography are restricted for the most part to the margins of the country.

Most of the western half of the Soviet Union is a great lowland extending from its western borders to the Yenisei River in central Siberia (Map 34). This lowland is not level but is undulating to rolling in places and broken markedly at points. The most conspicuous break occurs at the Ural mountains, commonly used to distinguish Europe from "Asia." These are old mountains, extending some 1,500 miles from near the Arctic Ocean to the vicinity of the Aral and Caspian seas. Although at their highest they rise to 6,200 feet, their mature and rounded topography provides little barrier to communications, and at their center they form hills no more than 1,000 feet above sea level. West of the Urals the lowland plains are broken by hills west and southwest of Moscow, which are lower than 1,000 feet, and the hill country of southern Ukrainia, which is lower still. East of the Urals is the west Siberian plain, the largest near-level area on earth. The great lowland extends to the Caucasus in the south and far into Soviet Middle Asia in the southeast, where it lies below sea level along the margins of the Caspian Sea.

The mountain borders of Iran and Afghanistan and the mountain complex of the Pamirs, T'ien Shan, Altai, and associated ranges bound the lowland on the southeast. West of the Altai the great Kazakh upland, which rises to over 4,600 feet, extends out onto the lowland. On the east it is limited by the central Siberian plateau, through which flow the eastern tributaries of the Yenisei River, and by the mountains west of Lake Baykal.

The great mountain ranges are generally peripheral to the main body of the country and are associated markedly with the international boundary, except in northeastern Siberia. East and northeast of Lake Baykal a series of ranges rising to nearly 10,000 feet extend to the northeastern limits of the country. These mountains are drained by great river systems, of which the most extensive are the Lena and the Amur.

Although two-thirds of the boundary of the U.S.S.R. is maritime, the country is conspicuously continental in character. Most of the ocean frontage is in the north along the shores of the seas that rim the Arctic Ocean, frozen in whole or in part for nine to ten months of the year. To the west is the Baltic Sea with its narrow outlet into the North Sea and the Atlantic; to the southwest is the Black Sea with its still narrower outlet through the Bosporus into the Mediterranean and thence into the Atlantic at the Straits of Gibraltar. In the far east, a more direct frontage on the Pacific exists through the Sea of Okhotsk and the Sea of Japan.

In European Russia several major streams drain into the White and Barents seas of the Arctic on the one hand and into the Baltic on the other. The major streams of European Russia, however, rise either in the hills that break up the western lowland or in the Urals, and drain either into the Black Sea—the Dniester, Bug, Dnieper, and Don—or into the inland Caspian Sea—the Volga, Ural, and Emba. In Soviet Middle Asia two of the major rivers—the Syr Darya (the Jaxartes) and the Amu Darya (the Oxus)—drain into the inland Aral Sea, after rising in the high Pamirs and T'ien Shan. Most of the great rivers of Siberia, however, flow northward into the Arctic—the Ob and its affluent the Irtysh, the Yenisei, and the Lena. One great river, the Amur, flows eastward out of eastern Mongolia into Pacific waters.

The continentality of the Soviet Union is most clearly reflected in its climate. Cut off from the southern seas by lofty mountain barriers and without the equivalent of a Gulf of Mexico, most of the country is characterized by sparse precipitation. Only a few areas receive more than 20 inches of rainfall (Map 2). For the most part moisture is carried in air masses of Atlantic origin, which move eastward in cyclonic lows across the country. Thus, rainfall decreases to the east and southeast. At Moscow the mean annual precipitation is 21 inches; near the Aral Sea it is less than 6 inches; at Tomsk it is under 20 inches; and at Irkutsk it is only 14 inches. In the far north rainfall is also low, being less than 14 inches in most places. The cold and often frozen Arctic adds little moisture to the country south of it. Rainfall becomes more plentiful, however, in the southeastern Pacific littoral where the monsoon effect of East Asia comes into play, and Vladivostok receives 22 inches of rainfall each year.

Temperatures display great variations, and only a very small part of the country, along the northeastern and eastern shores of the Black Sea, is subtropical.[8] Average January temperatures are well below freezing in most of the country, with markedly lower averages to the north and east (Plate E). Whereas the January mean is 13° at Moscow, it is 3° in the Middle Urals, −6° at Irkutsk on the shores of Lake Baykal, and −46° at Yakutsk in northeastern Siberia. Soviet Middle Asia has a more severe climate than its latitudinal position would suggest, again because of its continentality. Tashkent has a January mean of 32°, as compared with 45° at Rome in approximately the same latitude. July temperatures display much smaller variations. The July mean at Moscow is 64°; at Irkutsk it also is 64°; at Tashkent, 81°; at Yakutsk, 66°. The more continental

---

[8] Along the eastern Black Sea shore orographic effects bring the highest rainfall in the U.S.S.R. Batumi receives 93 inches annually.

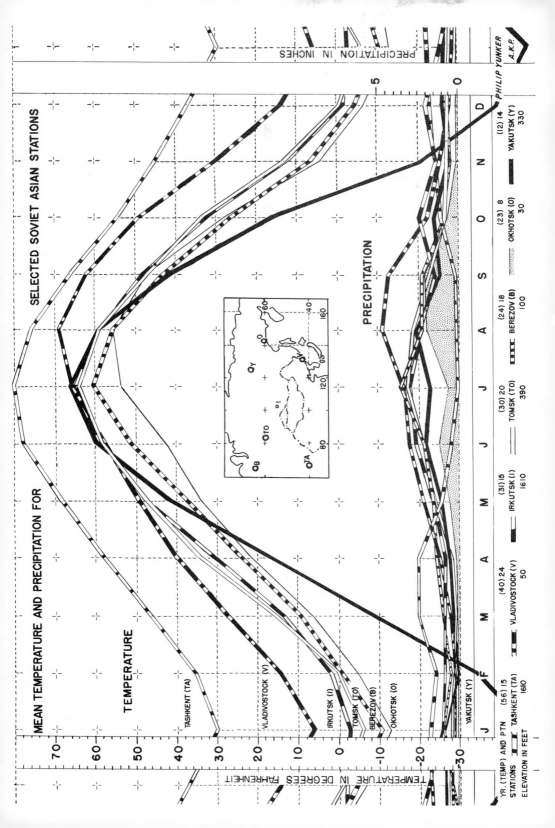

MEAN TEMPERATURE AND PRECIPITATION FOR SELECTED SOVIET ASIAN STATIONS

PHILIP YUNKER · A.K.P.

stations, such as Yakutsk, where the range is 112 degrees, display the greatest range between January and July means. At both the eastern and western margins of the country, however, tempering maritime influences keep the range to within 60 degrees. This compares with a 50-degree range in Chicago.

In general, winters in the Soviet Union are cold and long. Only near the Black Sea and to a lesser extent in southern Soviet Middle Asia, especially in the protected valleys are the winters mild and short. The location about Lake Baykal of a great semipermanent high-pressure area in winter results in cold winds sweeping outward over most of Asiatic Russia, even down into Soviet Middle Asia. Summers in general are short, shortest in the far north and northeast and longest in the south. Except in a few areas, precipitation is low and is one of the major limiting factors on Soviet agricultural development.

The natural vegetation cover of the country reflects climatic conditions and falls into a distinctly zonal pattern. In the far north is the tundra along the Arctic shores, characterized by dwarf woody vegetation and lichens and mosses—a dreary landscape cover. To the south the tundra blends into a great belt, broken by swamp, of northern coniferous forests, the taiga, which covers northern European Russia and most of Siberia. Pine and fir in the west become mixed with larch in the east, and birch and alder also are common. Mixed forests, composed of both coniferous and deciduous species, such as oaks and maples, lie south of the taiga in European Russia and in the maritime Far East. South of the mixed forests is a transitional belt of wooded steppe, of forest stands alternating with grasslands. This zone extends well into Siberia. South of it is the true steppe, a vast grassland which covers much of southern European Russia, extends across northern Kazakhstan, and appears also just east of Lake Baykal north of the Mongolian frontier. Most of Soviet Middle Asia and the northwestern shores of the Caspian Sea are desert or semidesert regions. These are temperate rather than hot deserts and are characterized by scattered brush vegetation in the north and sand deserts in much of the south. In the subtropical Black Sea areas and Transcaucasia, Mediterranean-type evergreen forests are found. In the peripheral mountains, vegetation ranges in an altitudinal progression from desert to shrub, deciduous forest, coniferous forest, meadows, and in some cases perennial snow cover.

Soils correspond in general to the vegetation cover, which both reflects and modifies soil conditions. Much of the tundra and part of the taiga are underlain by permanently frozen ground, about 40 per cent of the total land area of the U.S.S.R. (Map 35). The soils may thaw to a depth of several feet in summer. Most of them are acid, contain little humus, are highly podzolized, and are infertile. More fertile podzols and podzolics underlie the other forested regions of the U.S.S.R., and about a third of the agricultural area is located on soils of this type. In the transitional areas between forest and steppe, the soils become deeper, darker, and more fertile, much as in the transition from east to west in the central United States. The steppe soils are rich and black and are known by the name *chernozem*. These are among the more fertile soils in the world; they are in effect storehouses of fertility derived from the humus laid down by the decaying grass cover. The drier steppe is underlain by fertile chestnut-brown soils, and these blend into grey desert soils in the still drier regions. Some of the desert soils, or *sierozem*, are quite productive when irrigated. Others are highly alkaline or saline, and therefore unproductive.

The broad pattern of settlement

A population map of the Soviet Union (Back end paper) shows that its people live within only a small part of the vast areas under Soviet domination. Most of Siberia remains a sparsely settled region of forests and tundra desert, and much of northern European Russia falls into the same classification. Soviet Middle Asia for the most part also is sparsely settled, a temperate desert land little suited for permanent occupance except where mountain-originated rivers cross it, carrying life-giving water for irrigated agriculture. The Soviet ecumene consists of a vast triangle with its short base running along the western borders of the country, between the Baltic and the Black seas (see the agricultural triangle in Map 35). The apex of the triangle lies far to the east of Novosibirsk and beyond Lake Baykal, drawn out along the thread of the Trans-Siberian railway. A major population outlier exists along the southeastern margins of Soviet Middle Asia; a second, less densely populated, is found in the Soviet Far East near the Pacific terminus of the transcontinental railway. In all, this triangle is estimated to cover about one-fourth of the U.S.S.R.

The population of the Soviet Union in 1956 was estimated at 200 millions. Of these, approximately 150 millions are Slavs, chiefly Great Russians who number more than 100 millions. Ukrainians and Byelorussians account for the balance. The remaining 25 per cent of the population of the U.S.S.R. consists of a myriad of ethnic groups. In the northwest are the Baltic peoples; in the Caucasus and Transcaucasia are Georgians, Armenians, and Azerbaijanians, as well as numerous lesser groups; in Soviet Middle Asia are the numerous Turkic and Iranian peoples; and to the east are those of Mongol and Tungus stock. The more numerous of these are organized into constituent republics bearing their names which

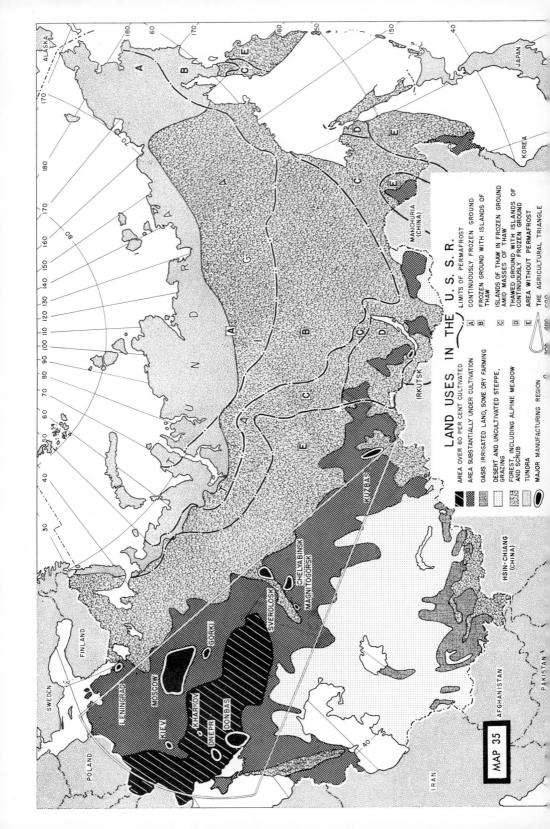

LAND USES IN THE U.S.S.R.

LIMITS OF PERMAFROST

- Ⓐ CONTINUOUSLY FROZEN GROUND
- Ⓑ FROZEN GROUND WITH ISLANDS OF THAW
- Ⓒ ISLANDS OF THAW IN FROZEN GROUND AMID MASSES OF THAW
- Ⓓ THAWED GROUND WITH ISLANDS OF CONTINUOUSLY FROZEN GROUND
- Ⓔ AREA WITHOUT PERMAFROST

THE AGRICULTURAL TRIANGLE

AREA OVER 60 PER CENT CULTIVATED

AREA SUBSTANTIALLY UNDER CULTIVATION

OASIS IRRIGATED LAND, SOME DRY FARMING

DESERT AND UNCULTIVATED STEPPE, GRAZING

FOREST, INCLUDING ALPINE MEADOW AND SCRUB

TUNDRA

MAJOR MANUFACTURING REGION

MAP 35

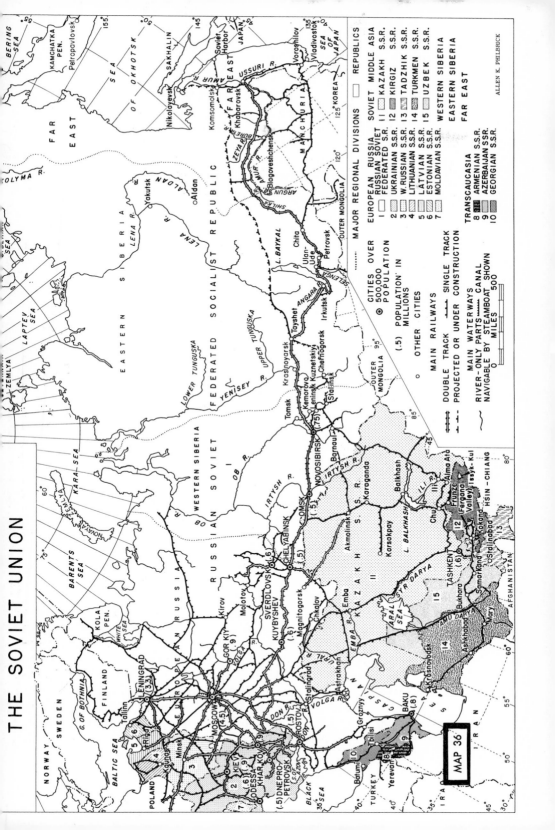

THE SOVIET UNION

MAP 36

ALLEN K. PHILBRICK

MAJOR REGIONAL DIVISIONS

EUROPEAN RUSSIA
RUSSIAN SOVIET
 FEDERATED S.S.R.
1
2 UKRAINIAN S.S.R.
3 W. RUSSIAN S.S.R.
4 LITHUANIAN S.S.R.
5 LATVIAN S.S.R.
6 ESTONIAN S.S.R.
7 MOLDAVIAN S.S.R.

SOVIET MIDDLE ASIA
11 KAZAKH S.S.R.
12 KIRGIZ S.S.R.
13 TADZHIK S.S.R.
14 TURKMEN S.S.R.
15 UZBEK S.S.R.

WESTERN SIBERIA
EASTERN SIBERIA
FAR EAST

TRANSCAUCASIA
8 ARMENIAN S.S.R.
9 AZERBAIJAN S.S.R.
10 GEORGIAN S.S.R.

REPUBLICS

⊙ CITIES OVER
    500,000
    POPULATION

(.5) POPULATION IN
      MILLIONS

○ OTHER CITIES

MAIN RAILWAYS
——— DOUBLE TRACK
——— SINGLE TRACK
----- PROJECTED OR UNDER CONSTRUCTION

MAIN WATERWAYS
——— RIVER-ONLY PARTS
——— CANAL
NAVIGABLE BY STEAMBOAT SHOWN

0   MILES   500

together compose the U.S.S.R. Lesser groups in general are organized
into semi-autonomous political units subordinated to the constituent republics. Approximately 47 million people inhabit what can be called
Soviet Asia—Transcaucasia, Soviet Middle Asia, Siberia, and the Far
East—but many of these are not of Asian but of Slav origin.

Fifteen republics compose the U.S.S.R. (Map 36). Table XXXVIII-1
lists their areas and estimated 1956 populations.

TABLE XXXVIII–1 °

Republic	Area (square miles)	Population (1956 est.)
1. Russian S.R.S.R.	6,592,300	112,600,000
2. Ukrainian S.S.R.	232,000	40,600,000
3. Byelorussian S.S.R.	80,300	8,000,000
4. Estonian S.S.R.	17,400	1,100,000
5. Lithuanian S.S.R.	25,100	2,700,000
6. Latvian S.S.R.	24,700	2,000,000
7. Moldavian S.S.R.	13,100	2,700,000
8. Georgian S.S.R.	27,800	4,000,000
9. Armenian S.S.R.	11,500	1,600,000
10. Azerbaijan S.S.R.	33,600	3,400,000
11. Kazakh S.S.R.	1,067,900	8,500,000
12. Uzbek S.S.R.	154,000	7,300,000
13. Kirgiz S.S.R.	76,400	1,900,000
14. Tadzhik S.S.R.	54,800	1,800,000
15. Turkmen S.S.R.	188,400	1,400,000
Total	8,599,600†	200,200,000

° Source: *The National Economy of the U.S.S.R. A Statistical Compilation.* (Moscow, 1956). In English.

† Includes the White Sea and the Sea of Azov, 50,193 sq. mi. Excluding seas,
the total area is 8,549,400 square miles.

The constituent republics are in turn composed of lesser administrative
subdivisions. Many of these subdivisions are based on the principle of
ethnic autonomy. Senior among them are the so-called Autonomous Republics (A.S.S.R.). Apart from ethnic administrative units such as these,
the constituent republics are divided into major subunits, based largely
on economic regional considerations, known as *oblasts* or *kray*, terms
which can be interpreted loosely as provinces.

One of the striking features of population change in the Soviet Union
has been the rapid increase in urbanization and the growth of cities. In
1914, the urban population accounted for 14.6 per cent of the total population. In 1926, this percentage had risen to 21 per cent. In 1939, it was
32 per cent, and by 1950 it is likely that it had risen to 40 per cent. Much
of this increase in urban population took place in established centers of
urbanism within European Russia. Moscow's population, for example, increased from two million in 1926 to over four million in 1939. However,
great increases took place also through the creation of new cities both

within and without European Russia. Great industrial cities have risen in the Urals, in western Siberia, in Soviet Middle Asia, and elsewhere, more often based on old towns, sometimes created out of what had been sparsely settled steppe or forest. Such cities as Karaganda (220,000) in Kazakhstan and Magnitogorsk (200,000) in the Urals are examples of the new industrial city.

The gross pattern of agricultural production

The distribution of population in the U.S.S.R. conforms closely to the distribution of agricultural land. Nearly two-thirds of the Soviet population, 125 millions, live in rural areas. The agricultural triangle of the Union is virtually identical with that of the population triangle and is in effect the Soviet ecumene. Again, there are major outliers in the southern parts of Soviet Middle Asia and in the Far East. The northern part of the agricultural triangle includes areas that still are partly or have been forested and that are underlain with podzol and podzolic soils. The southern part of the triangle is associated with the fertile steppe lands underlain with *chernozem* soils.

As the triangle narrows to the east, it is pinched from the north by the environmental pressures of excessive cold and poor soils; from the south it is pressed by limitations of aridity and drought. These limitations are suggested by the low percentage of the Soviet land area that actually is under cultivation, some 7 per cent in 1940 (373 million acres). The percentage of land area believed suitable for permanent cultivation is only 10.6 per cent of the total. In addition, about 19 per cent is considered suitable for pasturage. In comparison, about 17 per cent of the land area of the United States actually is under cultivation. It is doubtful whether there can be a major expansion of Soviet agricultural production through an expansion of cultivated acreages, although in 1954 a mammoth plan to bring some 70 million acres of virgin, semi-arid land under cultivation was initiated in western Siberia, Kazakhstan, and the lands north of the Caspian Sea. Most of the land best suited for cultivation already is under cultivation; the balance is marginal. Even some of the better lands, especially in the south, suffer from severe droughts, much as do the wheatlands of Kansas, Nebraska, and the Dakotas, but to perhaps an even greater degree. Although only a small percentage of the total land area of the U.S.S.R. is under cultivation, in European Russia about 43 per cent of the land is in crops. Further expansion of cultivated land there is unlikely. Soviet Asia, exclusive of Transcaucasia, has only 2 per cent of its land area in crops. Further expansion is possible, but is growing excessively difficult and costly.

Soviet agriculture is based upon grain production. Grains occupy about 80 per cent of the total cropped acreages in the Union. In 1952, 130 million metric tons were reported harvested.[9] Wheat is the most important grain crop, accounting for 30 per cent of the total acreage cultivated and for about half the grain produced. Wheat acreage has been expanding northward from the steppes of European Russia into northerly agricultural regions (the non-*chernozem* regions) which are still more noteworthy as growers of rye, potatoes, hemp, forage crops, and flax. Wheat also is the most important crop in Siberia. Yields, however, are modest to low, averaging 12 bushels per acre for spring wheat. Yields for winter wheat, grown primarily in the Ukraine, are slightly higher, but bear no comparison to yields in northwestern Europe where they may average 30-40 bushels per acre. Winter rye rivals wheat as a major grain and is grown primarily in central-northern European Russia. Oats, barley, millet, buckwheat, corn ,and grain sorghums also are widely grown in the drier regions. In fact, the U.S.S.R. ranks first or second in the world in the total production of rye, oats, and wheat. The importance of grains in Soviet agriculture, however, is not necessarily an indication of wealth, but may be the reverse, since the Soviet diet depends heavily on high-calorie grain foods and starchy tubers, as is true in most lesser developed regions.

Industrial crops occupy only about 8 per cent of the cropped area, but are of greater economic importance than this percentage suggests. Cotton production in Soviet Middle Asia, especially Uzbekistan, Transcaucasia, and southeastern European Russia tripled between 1914 and 1937 and doubled again to reach 4,000,000 tons in 1951. By 1954 production was reported to have reached 5,000,000 tons from 2.5 million acres, and the goals for 1958 were over 6,000,000 tons. The country is self-sufficient in the low and medium grades of cotton. Sugar beets are a basic crop in the Ukraine and western Siberia, and Russian acreages are largest in the world. Flax and hemp are staple crops of the northern agricultural zone. Sunflowers are expanding rapidly into the more arid regions. Subtropical industrial and food crops are restricted to the shores of the Black Sea and the oases of Soviet Middle Asia.

Livestock are almost universally distributed. In European Russia they form part of a highly integrated crop-livestock association in which fodder crops play a major role, although in the absence of a "Corn Belt" type of climatic region, the corn-hog association of the American Middle West conspicuously is lacking is most areas, or when it appears, is highly localized. In the more arid regions to the southeast, natural or cultivated pasturage is much more important, and the transition has not long since

---

[9] Since Russian crop production figures are based on crops standing in the fields, not on actual harvests, they tend to be high.

been made from a state of nomadic herding to a form of collectivized livestock ranching. In some peripheral areas, as in the Mongol country southeast of Lake Baykal, true nomadic herding still is practiced. The total cattle population, however, in 1955 had not increased from the 67 million head in 1928. This resulted partly from the replacement of work cattle by tractors and partly from losses incurred during collectivization, especially in Soviet Middle Asia. The result in any case has been a nationwide shortage of meat.

Irrigation is becoming increasingly important in Soviet agriculture, but despite the low rainfall that characterizes most agricultural regions in the U.S.S.R., irrigation is practiced primarily as a form of oasis agriculture in the Caucasus and Transcaucasia and in Soviet Middle Asia. An estimated 15 million acres are irrigated, but plans call for a 20 per cent increase in this acreage by 1960.

Fishing is another source of foodstuffs. About one-fourth of the total fish catch (sturgeon are the most important species) comes from the Caspian Sea, the waters of which are enriched by the outflow of the Volga among other rivers. Before 1914, the Caspian furnished two-thirds of the total fish catch. About a fourth comes from the Far Eastern fisheries, which have been developed on the basis of an export market in competition with Japan. Another fourth comes from the Barents Sea fisheries based on Murmansk, which are an extension of the North Atlantic and Norwegian Sea fisheries. Neither the Arctic Ocean nor the Black Sea has important fisheries, in the first case because of adverse conditions of cold, in the latter in part because of accumulations of hydrogen sulfide in the lower depths and extreme temperature and salinity variations nearer the surface. Total production in 1951 was estimated at 2.5 million metric tons, about the same as that of the United States and second only to that of Japan.

The patterns of mineral and energy resources

The Soviet Union, in keeping with its great size, is one of the wealthiest countries of the world in terms of energy and mineral resources. Only the United States, and possibly China, exceeds the U.S.S.R. in mineral wealth and energy resources. The Union is said to contain 23 per cent of the world's supplies of inanimate energy. However, only a fraction of these energy resources are of contemporary economic significance, since most of them are inaccessible, peripheral, or probable rather than known.

The U.S.S.R. contains coal reserves estimated at some 1,645 billion tons. About 40 per cent of these estimated reserves, however, are in the upper basin of the Lena River in the Tunguska region of eastern Siberia, and are both remote and conjectural. The greatest single deposit, some 450 billion tons, is in the Kuznets basin of western Siberia, the second largest producing center. The largest area in terms of output is the Donets basin of the southeastern Ukraine, with 90 billion tons of high-grade coal reserves, the more accessible measures of which are being depleted rapidly. The so-called Donbas produces about one-third of Soviet production, whereas the Kuzbas produces nearly 20 per cent. A third major field is at Karaganda in northern Kazakhstan, with reserves of 50 billion tons. Other reserves are found just west of the northern Urals, east of the Kuzbas in the Minusinsk basin of western Siberia, northwest of Lake Baykal, east of Vladivostok, and near Tashkent in Uzbekistan. Sakhalin island was a major producer under the Japanese and in the mid-war period supplied Japan with about 15 per cent of her coal requirements. Russia also contains huge reserves of peat, and this low-quality fuel, together with lignite, is mined extensively near Moscow. In 1955, coal production (including peat) was scheduled at 390 million metric tons, equivalent to that of the United Kingdom, France, and Western Germany combined.

In addition there are great reserves of petroleum, variously estimated at 5 per cent to 59 per cent (according to Soviet sources) of the world's reserves. Production in 1955 was 70 million metric tons, about 11 per cent of the world's total. Production is centered in the fields near Baku in the Azerbaijan S.S.R. and in the fields north of the Caucasus centering about Grozny. A third major area composed of three fields lies between the Urals and the Volga and is known as the "Second Baku." Lesser but important producing areas are the salt domes northeast of the Caspian Sea along the Emba River and in northern Sakhalin island.

Other sources of energy are fuelwood, which is consumed in enormous quantities, especially in northern and eastern Russia, and hydroelectric energy of which the U.S.S.R. possesses an enormous potential. Most of the hydroelectric resources are located in peripheral regions, in the Caucasus and Transcaucasia, along the outer border of Soviet Central Asia, and in the distant northeast. Less than 10 per cent of the total electric output (170 billion KWH planned for 1955) [10] was derived from hydro sources.

Nonfuel minerals are found in similarly large quantities, although thorough mineralogical exploration of the country is far from complete. Almost all metallic minerals are found within the country. Known iron ore reserves approximate 11 billion tons. Still vaster quantities of ore exist in the form of low-grade ferruginous quartzites, of which 250 billion tons lie 100 miles north of Kharkov. The primary deposits are at Krivoi Rog

[10] Nearly four times the electrical output in Japan.

in the southern Ukraine; in the Kerch peninsula of the Crimea; and in the central and southern Urals, especially at Magnitogorsk. The Krivoi Rog ores are of very high grade, but like those of the Mesabi in northern Minnesota, are becoming depleted, and more intensive use must be made of the lower-grade ores such as those at Kerch. The Ural deposits are of relatively high grade and are expected to last, although signs of depletion are evident. Lesser deposits are worked near the Kuznets basin, in the Far East, near Lake Baykal, in southern Soviet Middle Asia, and in Azerbaijan. Production in 1955 was estimated at close to 50 million metric tons.

Ferro-alloy metals are especially well supplied. Manganese is mined in the southern Ukraine and in Georgia, and there is a surplus for export. The Urals supply manganese, gold, platinum, and more important chrome, vanadium, nickel, and copper. Most copper, however, comes from low-grade deposits in central Kazakhstan, which account for 75 per cent of known reserves. Nickel is also found amply in the northern Yenisei valley and in the far northwest. Lead, zinc, molybdenum, and tin are among the metals present in limited supplies. Bauxite and other aluminum-bearing minerals are present in limited quantities near Leningrad, in the Urals, in the far northwest, and in the far north. Production of aluminum in 1950 was estimated at 200,000 metric tons, one-third that of the United States in the same year.

Nonmetallic mineral resources are abundant. Industrial salts are found in unlimited quantity in the Caspian depression. Apatite, a source of phosphate fertilizers, is found in huge deposits in the far northwest. Potash comes from the northern Urals and asbestos from the central Urals. Only high-quality talc, corundum, quartz crystals, and diamonds are known to be in notably short supply.

The location of industry

The Soviet Union is the second greatest industrial country in the world, as measured in terms of heavy industry and the output of basic raw materials. In 1955 the output of crude steel, a generally reliable index for measuring industrial capacity, was 45 million metric tons, as compared with about 50 million tons in the United Kingdom, France, and West Germany combined. Similarly, electrical output, another reliable index of industrial growth, was set at 170 million KWH for 1955, as compared with a 1955 output of 180 million KWH in these three countries. At present rates of increase the U.S.S.R. will soon equal the heavy industrial productive capacity of all of Western Europe, even including the rapid postwar expansion of West Germany.

The industrial growth of the U.S.S.R. is all the more unusual in light of the predominance of its agricultural population. The explanation lies in the fact that Soviet industry is predominantly heavy; that the so-called light industries which produce consumer goods have in large part been neglected. About 70 per cent of the total industrial output consists of producers' goods rather than consumer goods. This means that a higher level of living for the average man has been sacrificed for a forced investment in basic industrialization. The capital for investment is, in effect, derived from the personal sacrifices and discomfort of the Soviet citizen.

There are, however, centers of light industry, and such industry is scattered widely throughout the country (Map 35). Leningrad, Moscow, and certain of the larger, older cities such as Kharkov and Kiev in the Ukraine are centers of textile, clothing, and other consumer goods industries. Apart from these centers, the localization of industry is associated closely with the distribution of natural resources. The major industrial region, producing about 35 per cent of all steel, is composed of the Donets basin, the southern Ukraine, and a ring of industrial centers near the margins of the region. Cities such as Stalino, Krivoi Rog, Voroshilovsk, and Dnepropetrovsk lie within the area. Stalingrad lies to the east, Rostov to the southeast, Kharkov to the northwest, and Zhdanov to the south.

The second major industrial region lies in the central and southern Urals near the great deposits of iron ore, ferro-alloy metals, and lesser minerals contained within that vast storehouse of mineral wealth. Low-grade coal is produced locally, but higher-grade coals are brought from Karaganda in Kazakhstan, nearly 700 miles *ESE* of Magnitogorsk, and from the Kuznetsk basin, 1,300 miles to the east. The long rail haul of coal between the Kuzbas and the Urals, economically dubious, has been made possible by the loading of Ural iron ore for the return trip to the Kuzbas, where steel mills also have been established.

The third major industrial region is the Kuznetsk basin, or Kuzbas. Here high-grade coal is the basic source of energy. Some iron ore is mined at Gornaia Shoriia to the south of the basin and, though limited in quantity, accounts for most of the ore now used in the Kuzbas mills. Immediately to the east in the Minusinsk basin there are more iron ores and coal, as yet little developed. Other metallic ores, including lead and zinc, are found to the southwest of the basin in northeastern Kazakhstan.

The fourth major industrial area is the co-called Central Industrial region centered about Moscow; a fifth centers about Leningrad. Here heavy industry is of secondary importance, and the textile, machinery, and automobile industries are of prime importance. Textiles and food-stuffs, as well as light machinery and farm equipment, also are processed or manufactured widely in regional subcenters. Heavy industries are developing at Karaganda, and there are steel mills in operation or under construction near Tashkent in Uzbekistan, in the Georgian S.S.R., and at Petrovsk east of Lake Baykal. Komsomolsk in the Far East also produces steel from local ores and coal, as well as numerous manufactured goods. Vladivostok is another regional manufacturing center in the Far East.

Although industrial development on the borders of and east of European Russia has taken place at an extremely rapid pace, the fulcrum of industrial production remains west of the Urals. The industrial core with its major regions is triangular in shape and closely resembles both the population and agricultural triangles. However, the central location of the Ural industrial region and the easterly location of the rapidly expanding Kuzbas give the industrial triangle an easterly bias which the other two still lack. In terms of nonagricultural resources, moreover, the future of the country may lie east of the Urals rather than west, and a gradual eastward shift of industry not only seems possible but also is being planned. The major limiting factors to this eastward movement appear to be agricultural resources, since climate, surface configuration, and soils, the natural triune, conspire to restrict agricultural opportunities where mineral and power resources are abundant.

Patterns of transportation facilities

The great distances that characterize the U.S.S.R. make the development and operation of efficient transportation facilities of special economic and strategic importance. They also make them costly. Harris estimates that in 1951 the railroads of the Union, which accounted for 90 per cent of the total freight tonnage carried in domestic commerce, consumed the equivalent of more than 100 million metric tons of coal, about 35 per cent of the total coal and lignite production in that year. In short, the U.S.S.R. must devote a far greater percentage of its energy resources to transportation (estimated at 20 per cent in 1937) and the conquest of distance than does the United States (in that same year, 12 per cent). Thus, the size of the country, which in certain respects may be considered a great advantage, is in transportational terms a major disadvantage. The enormous distances that separate the major industrial regions illustrate some of the problems involved. Coal and iron ore moving between the Kuzbas and the southern Urals must travel more than 1,300 miles; even Karaganda coal lies some 700 miles from the Ural industrial region; and the oil of Baku is about 1,500 miles by ship and river barge from the Central Industrial region about

Moscow. Cressey states that fast express trains take 9.5 days to cross the country from the Polish border to Vladivostok; and it takes 3.5 days from the Black Sea northward to the Arctic Ocean. In contrast, express trains take less than 3 days to travel from Boston to Seattle.

The Soviet railway system forms the backbone of the transportation services (Map 36). Rivers, to be discussed below, are important, but highways are distinctly underdeveloped, and only a small mileage is fully paved outside of the metropolitan areas. The railways generally are broad-gauge—5 feet. Mileage was estimated in 1956 to be 73,000 miles, of which 36,300 miles had been constructed under the Czarist empire. Most of the mileage is concentrated within the population triangle and therefore lies west of the Urals. A highly developed rail net serves every major city and almost all of the lesser towns of European Russia. The lines characterized by the highest ton-mileage west of the Urals connect the Southern Industrial area with the Central Industrial area and the rail hubs at Moscow and Leningrad. Transcaucasia is connected with the rest of the country by lines that skirt the mountains along the shores of the Black Sea on the west and the Caspian Sea on the east. A lengthy spur of the main rail net extends to the northwestern margins of the Urals and taps the coal fields there. A number of post-revolutionary lines have been constructed that further connect European Russia proper with the Urals, and these have been essential in integrating the Ural industrial complex into the national economy.

The rail pattern east and southeast of the Urals in 1914 centered about (1) the Trans-Siberian line, which runs from Omsk in western Siberia through Irkutsk to Vladivostok, and (2) the Trans-Caspian line, which runs from the southeastern shore of the Caspian Sea eastward across the desert to the oasis of southeastern Soviet Middle Asia. An extension of this line, the so-called Central Asian line, ran northwest from Tashkent to Uralsk on the Ural River. Much of the post-1917 Soviet railway construction has consisted of additions to and connections among these main rail lines. The chief achievement was the construction of the so-called Turk-Sib (Turkestan-Siberia) line which connects the Trans-Caspian, Central Asian, and Trans-Siberian railways. Branches from the Turk-Sib line reach to the major oases and mining regions of Soviet Middle Asia. The Trans-Siberian also has its branches. One of them passes through Karaganda south to the shores of Lake Balkhash, with an extension to the western copper belt of Kazakhstan. A line from Karaganda northwest to the Urals also has been completed, which saves 200 miles on the coalhaul to Magnitogorsk.[11] Branches into the Kuzbas also have been built.

[11] This route is the westernmost segment of the so-called South Siberian railway, which roughly parallels the Trans-Sib to the Kuznets (the railway has been completed to Stalinsk) and Minusinsk basins, east of which it will join the Trans-Sib at Tayshet.

East of Lake Baykal two southerly branches have been extended into Outer Mongolia, one of them connected in 1955 with China's railway system, and several have been pushed into the hinterlands along the north bank of the Amur River. Certain of these latter branches may have been connected at their northern termini so as to provide by-passes for portions of the overloaded Trans-Siberian line, which itself has been double-tracked. An extension of the great line also has been constructed eastward from Komsomolsk to the Pacific at the new port of Sovyetskaya Gavan (Soviet Harbor).

The rivers of the U.S.S.R. play a relatively minor role in national transportation, but locally they may be exceptionally important. Development of river transportation is hampered by excessive winter cold in most of the country, by aridity and lack of sufficient water in Soviet Middle Asia, and by unfavorable directions of flow and outlets in much of the country. The Volga is the major inland waterway and carries more than half the total river and canal tonnage. Petroleum from Baku is a major northward cargo; other bulky commodities such as grains, coal, salt, sands, gravels, and timber are other important cargoes. A canal connects the Volga near Stalingrad with the Don River which flows into the Sea of Azov, an arm of the Black Sea, thereby giving the Volga basin an indirect oceanic outlet. The upper Volga also is connected via a system of canals and lakes northwest of Moscow with the Neva River system, Leningrad, and the Baltic Sea. Moscow is connected by canal with this system and is reachable by small sea-going as well as river vessels. Another canal system connects Leningrad and the Baltic with the White Sea, an arm of the Barents Sea and the Arctic. It is possible, therefore, to travel from the Black Sea to the Arctic, the north-south extent of Russia, by inland waterways. The Volga, however, is closed to navigation by ice for four or five months of the year, and the northernmost canals and rivers are closed for longer periods.

In Siberia, the major rivers run almost entirely in the "wrong" direction, that is, northward toward the Arctic. Furthermore, they are frozen for more than six months of the year. Nevertheless, the Ob, Yenisei, Lena, and their tributaries provide the major transport facilities for most of northern Siberia. The Amur River drains into the Pacific and is a major transport artery in the Soviet Far East, though it too is closed to traffic by ice five months of the year. A tributary of the Amur, the Sungari, is the longest navigable waterway of northern China, and the two streams form a navigable waterway over 1,000 miles in length. The rivers of Soviet Middle Asia are of relatively little importance for transportation because of their shallowness and shifting channels, although the lower Amur Darya carries some river traffic. In addition, water transportation is locally important on the Aral Sea, Lake Balkhash, and Lake Baykal.

Coastal shipping serves the Black Sea, the Caspian, and the Baltic Sea of the northwest. It also is significant in the Far East, where Kamchatka, Sakhalin, and the Maritime Territory are joined by regular shipping services. Vladivostok, however, is the only port open all year; in winter, ice-breakers keep it free of solid ice. Among the coastal routes is the so-called Northern Sea Route which follows the shores of the Arctic seas. Although open to traffic only two and a half months of the year and then by the use of specially constructed ships and ice-breakers, this route has become of exceptional strategic importance. Its economic significance may be questioned, however, except for the seasonal movement of timber and minerals out from the drainage basins of the great Siberian rivers.

Most of the U.S.S.R. is covered by an air net of regular services, estimated at 150,000 miles in 1956. Russian air lines also extend into the satellite countries including China, which are not served by the airlines of the non-Soviet world. Russian outposts in the far north and northeast are especially dependent upon air services. The speed of air communications will do much to overcome at least for passengers the negative qualities of the Soviet Union's excessive space. Even when vastly expanded, however, air transport cannot be expected to carry more than a minute fraction of the volume of freight now carried by rail and water facilities.

Soviet Asia

THOSE REGIONS OF THE SOVIET UNION THAT BORDER THE ASIAN CRES-
cent are of particular importance to the Asian world. They also form
parts of a large segment of the U.S.S.R., which occupies the northern half
of the Asiatic continent. Most Soviet statistical information is presented
in terms of the great administrative-territorial blocs that compose this
segment, although these blocs may not be geographical regions in a
strict sense. Therefore, the following descriptions will deal with the
major territorial blocs recognized by the Russians themselves, rather than
simply the relatively narrow zone that impinges directly upon the frontier. These vast regional blocs are (1) the Soviet Far East, (2) Eastern
Siberia, (3) Western Siberia, (4) Soviet Middle Asia (including the
Kazakh S.S.R.), and (5) Transcaucasia.[1] Together they constitute the
realm known as Soviet Asia.

Soviet Asia covers 75 per cent of the total area of the U.S.S.R. Within
its confines live some 47 million people, nearly one-fourth of the population of the U.S.S.R. Only 17 million of these are of non-Slav stock. Therefore, in considering the relation of Soviet Asia to Asian Asia, it is necessary to note that most of its population is not related to the Asian peoples,
but is Slavic. Nevertheless, one of the more significant factors in evalu-

[1] These regional blocs are shown on Map 34.

873

ating Russia's place in the Asian scene, as indicated in the previous chapter, is the distribution of her non-Slav minorities and their relations with the countries along her borders.

The Soviet Far East

The Soviet Far East covers more than a million square miles on the northeastern margins of the Eurasian land mass. The most significant fact about this great area is its marginal location and its frontage on the Pacific Ocean. By virtue of possession of the region, the U.S.S.R. makes its claim to being a Pacific power. It is not correct, however, to regard Russia's expansion to the Pacific as a direct consequence of a rational policy directed by, for example, a desire for warm-water ports. It was, in fact, a somewhat accidental consequence of Russian interest in furs, silver, and gold. The early Russian attitude toward Siberia and the Far East was one of doubt and indifference, just as the acquisition of the western half of the Mississippi drainage basin was regarded with scepticism in the United States at the time of the Louisiana Purchase. There is an even more marked resemblance to the course of America's later expansion to the California littoral.[2]

The Soviet Far East may be divided roughly into two parts, a north and a south, unequal in terms of both area and population. The northern region beyond the 55th parallel contains more than three-fourths of the area and less than a fifth of a total population estimated at 3.5 millions. The southern sector, conversely, contains one-fourth of the area and the vast bulk of the population.

The northern subregion begins north of the 7-8,000 foot Stanovoy Mountains of eastern Siberia, which separate the Amur drainage system from that of the Lena and others of the north-flowing rivers. Most of the northern subregion may be regarded as a mountainous extension of the eastern Siberian region to the west. A series of young mountains, the highest of which rise to more than 10,000 feet, appears *en echelon* in the far northeast. This vast upland, a region of tundra blending into taiga and of intense cold, is drained on its western flank by tributaries of the Lena and on the north by a series of lesser rivers of which the Kolyma is perhaps the best known. Since the eastern coastal mountains rise precipitously out of the Bering Sea and the Sea of Okhotsk, the streams that empty into Pacific waters are in general short and of rela-

[2] Russian expansion reached a major peak in the middle of the seventeenth century when Russian adventurers first reached the Pacific. However, control of the Pacific maritime region was not assured until after treaties with China in 1858 and 1860, whereby the lands north of the Amur and east of the Ussuri were brought formally under Russian rule.

tively little importance to the area. The chief products are gold, timber, reindeer, and fish. The Kolyma basin in the farthest north has been the scene of a modern gold rush. The outlets for the north utilize the Northern Sea route of the Arctic seas. However, a rapidly growing port has been established at Magadan on the Sea of Okhotsk, which acts as a base of supply and a transhipment center for the interior.

Although it fronts on two great oceans, or arms of them, the climate of the northern subregion is little modified by its oceanic proximity. The Sea of Okhotsk is of slight importance as an ameliorating climatic element, because of prevailing wind directions and because it is frozen for several months of the year.

The Kamchatka peninsula displays somewhat different characteristics, however, since it fronts directly on the relatively open and deep Bering Sea. Two longitudinal volcanic ranges, divided by a lowland that opens on to the Bering Sea, rise well above the 10,000-foot level, and numerous volcanoes are active. Kamchatka's climate is milder, especially on the east coast, and rainfall along the southeastern littoral is much higher than it is elsewhere because of the moisture-bearing winds of summer which come off the Pacific. Petropavlosk, a port with a great natural harbor on the southeast coast of the peninsula, is closed to shipping for five months of the year, but its January mean temperature is only 13°F., and its annual rainfall averages 35 inches. Fishing is the major industry, and exports, especially of higher-grade canned products such as crabmeat, go mainly to the southern part of the Soviet Far East for re-export either to western Russia or abroad. Sealing, fur trapping, and lumbering round off the major occupations.

The southern subregion of the Far East lies south and southeast of the Stanovoy range. Most of it lies within the drainage basin of the Amur River. The Amur is formed by the junction of two rivers, the Shilka, upon which Chita city is situated, and the Argun, which rises in Mongolia and forms part of the boundary between the Eastern Siberian region and Chinese territory. The Amur itself acts as the boundary between the U.S.S.R. and Manchuria approximately as far east as the 135th meridian. Its two major northern tributaries in Soviet territory are the Zeya and the Bureya; its major tributary in Chinese territory is the Sungari (Sunghua), which with its tributaries drains most of central and northern Manchuria. Near the 135th meridian the Amur is joined by the north-flowing Ussuri River, which forms nearly two-thirds of the boundary between eastern Manchuria and the Russian so-called Maritime Territory. The Amur and its tributaries are navigable for nearly seven months of the year, and they provide a natural means for integrating much of the southern Far East into an economic region (Figure 155).

The middle course of the Amur is bounded on the south by the hill-

Fig. 155 • Here at Khabarovsk, near the junction of the Amur and Ussuri rivers, is one of the major river ports of the Soviet Union. Vessels from the upper reaches of the Ussuri and from the Sungari (Sung-hua), the major Manchurian tributary of the Amur, reach Khabarovsk and characterize an integrated river transport system over which bulk cargoes of all sorts move during the seven months the rivers are unfrozen. The several types of vessels in the photograph suggest the variety of shipping which patronizes the port—large barges which move in barge trains; long, shallow-draft steamers bearing a vague resemblance to Mississippi river boats; ferries from points bordering the streams in the vicinity; a river gunboat; and a number of tiny rowboats and river tugs. In the short summers, when this picture was taken, the river banks are used as beaches, and then as well as at other times of the year fishing is a major recreational as well as livelihood occupation. *(Sovfoto.)*

like Little Hsing-an mountains of northern Manchuria, which rise to heights of over 3,000 feet. To the north is a great lowland across which the Zeya and Bureya also flow. This is one of the better agricultural regions in eastern Siberia, and wheat and other grains form the basis for a traditional Russian agricultural economy. The climate is severely continental, but the maritime-originated winds of summer bring precipitation during the warm summers. These contrast with the blasts of polar air that in winter originate in the continental high-pressure area to the northwest. Parts of the lowland are marshy, and this creates special drainage problems which are met also in other parts of the southern subregion. To the southeast the Amur receives the Sungari River amidst huge expanses of marshland which on the Russian side are included within the Jewish Autonomous Oblast (province), sometimes known as Birobidjan after the two minor northern tributaries of the Amur that cross it. This marshy country continues downstream for much of the remainder of the river's course, and agriculture tends to be restricted to areas either immediately adjacent to cities or on the grassy uplands just beyond the flood plain of the river.

The Ussuri also flows through a marshy lowland in much of its lower course, and poor drainage characterizes the areas northeast of Lake Khanka, on the international boundary to the south, from which it drains. The Khanka-Ussuri lowland has been brought under cultivation, in part by Chinese and Koreans, and the relatively mild summers and ample rainfall permit the cultivation of some rice in addition to wheat, millet, kao-liang, soybeans, and oilseeds. The climate is similar to that of Hokkaido, though somewhat less humid. At Vladivostok, which receives 22 inches of rainfall annually, the January temperature mean is 7°F. and the July mean is 65°. The eastern part of the Maritime Territory is covered by a little-explored mountain range, the Sikhota-Alin range, which rises abruptly out of the Sea of Japan to heights of 7,000 feet and more.

Across from the mouth of the Amur and separated from it by the Strait and Gulf of Tartary is Sakhalin island. This meridionally elongated island extends for some 600 miles, and is composed of two major mountain ranges with a lowland in between. The northern part of the island experiences exceptionally cold winters and very short summers. In the south the climate is milder, and some cultivation of hardy grains, potatoes, and vegetables takes place in the central lowland. Sakhalin experiences very heavy snow cover, however, in contrast to much of the Soviet Far East wherein snow cover is thin, though of long duration. The southern half of the island had been ceded to Japan by Russia in 1905 and was given the name Karafuto by the Japanese. The Japanese depended heavily upon Karafuto for timber, pulp, coal, and fish, and in the prewar period it accounted for over 3 per cent of Japan's overseas imports by value. After the close of the war, Karafuto, with its population of about 350,000 Japanese,[3] was returned to Russia, and it has become integrated with the rest of the Far East region.

East of Sakhalin and extending southward in a great arc from Kamchatka are the Kurile islands, called Chishima or the Thousand Islands by the Japanese, which also were returned to Russia at the close of the second World War. For the most part these islands (there are only 36) are volcanic and of little commercial value except as centers for fishing and sealing industries. Their strategic importance, however, is very great, since they are separated from Hokkaido by the very narrow Nemuro Strait and provide excellent air bases along the Pacific approaches to the

[3] Most of the Japanese were repatriated after the close of the Pacific war, but an unknown number still remain.

Far East. The Japanese used these islands as military and air bases during the Pacific war, and it was from them that the Japanese mounted their offensives across the Bering Sea against the Aleutians and Alaska.

The chief nonagricultural resources of the southern Far East region consist of fisheries, timber, and mineral resources. The Bering Sea, Sea of Okhotsk, and the Sea of Japan coasts of the U.S.S.R. all are important bases for fisheries operations. The Okhotsk Sea formerly was an important Japanese fishing ground, but since the war it has been barred to the Japanese. Numerous fishing ports dot the Soviet coast. The lower Amur also is a major fresh-water and tidal fishery zone. The Far Eastern fisheries account in all for a quarter of the catch of the U.S.S.R. The more valuable species are canned and shipped out of the region. Others are iced and consumed within the region. Still others, chiefly herring from the Okhotsk Sea and the Sea of Japan, are processed into fertilizers.

The timber resources of the region are enormous, even discounting the vast taiga to the north. Pine and larch forests of the southern taiga give way to mixed and then deciduous forests in the south, especially in the Maritime Territory. Manchurian cedar, oak, birch, maple, and various fruit trees, similar to the associations found in the eastern and northern Manchurian forests, predominate, although conifers are more important at higher altitudes. Lumber and paper-and-pulp mills located within the area supply a surplus for export to other parts of the country or abroad. The output of wood products has been boosted by the confiscation of Japanese mills on Sakhalin, among which was the largest pulp-and-paper plant in the former Japanese Empire.

Mineral resources are perhaps most important among the resources of the region. Reserves of coal total some 32 billion tons, almost twice the size of Japan's reserves. The largest coal measures lie north of the Amur in the middle Bureya River basin. These are coals of coking quality, and they are being mined despite their relative inaccessibility. Coal also is mined along the middle Amur. Important mines are located in the vicinity of Vladivostok, where both low- and high-grade coals have been mined for many years. In fact, Vladivostok was long known as a major coaling station in eastern Asia. Petroleum deposits are found on northern Sakhalin; these were exploited both by the Russians and by the Japanese, the latter on a lease basis, before the war. Reserves are estimated to be about those of Middle Asia exclusive of the Emba fields, and production is of the same order. However, in oil-short eastern Asia, as well as in the Russian Far East, such reserves and production are of great significance. Tankers bring the petroleum up the Amur to a refinery at Komsomolsk, and it is reported that a pipeline has been built from Sakhalin across the Strait of Tartary to that city.

Metallic ores are less plentiful, but exploration of the region has yet to be completed. Iron ore is mined near the mouth of the Amur and in the southeastern part of the Maritime Territory. Tin, lead, zinc, and silver are other important minerals mined in the maritime area. Gold, however, is the most important metal in terms of value, and it is found chiefly in the uplands north of the Amur. Industries based on these mineral resources have been developed. At Komsomolsk is the only iron-and-steel mill in the Far East. It depends primarily upon local coal and iron ore, although the ore is low-grade.

The main transportation net of the southern subregion hinges on the Amur system already discussed and the railway network of which the Trans-Siberian railway is the backbone. The Trans-Sib tends to parallel the Amur, though running as much as 90 miles north of its marshy floodplain. It then curves southward up the Ussuri valley and terminates at Vladivostok. A connection with the Trans-Manchurian railway exists northwest of Vladivostok at Sui-fen-ho. Several branch lines fan out from Vladivostok. A connection with the Trans-Manchurian railway exists and northwestward to the Chinese border on the shores of Lake Khanka. A major branch of the Trans-Sib follows the lower Amur to Komsomolsk, and a secondary eastern branch extends from Komsomolsk to the new port, Sovetskaya Gavan, on the Gulf of Tartary. This port has been developed to avoid the navigational difficulties and channel restrictions for ocean vessels of the lower Amur at Nikolaevsk. One branch of the Trans-Sib has been built to the Bureya coal fields. Three others extend southward to the Amur River. Only at one point, opposite Blagoveschensk, has there been a Chinese railway to which connections across the frontier might be made, but the Chinese line, dismantled during the war, has not yet been rebuilt. A northern Siberian railway also is reported under construction northwest of Komsomolsk. Roads are of local importance only, as in much of Siberia, but a major highway extends northward from a point on the railway north of the great bend of the Amur to the interior gold fields at Aldan in the Eastern Siberia region.

As in any rapidly developing region, cities have grown rapidly. Vladivostok (300,000) is the most important, being the terminus of the Trans-Siberian railway and a major world port. Though sheet ice forms in the excellent natural harbor in winter, ice-breakers keep it open all year round. To the north of it is Voroshilov (150,000) in the center of the Khanka-Ussuri agricultural area, a regional commercial center and the site of numerous light industries. Khabarovsk (300,000), located where the Trans-Siberian crosses the Amur, resembles Vladivostok in that it is not a new city, but it also has grown rapidly and is the acknowledged regional capital for most of the region outside of the Maritime Territory itself. It also is an important industrial center. Downstream 180 miles is the new city of Komsomolsk (150,000), founded in 1932. Chiefly an industrial center, it is pointed to as a model of Soviet developmental enterprise. To the west are several smaller cities of which the most important is Blagoveschensk (60,000). It is a regional center for the agricultural area along the middle Amur and uses agricultural raw materials and timber from the hinterland in a diversity of industries. Like Khabarovsk, Komsomolsk, and Vladivostok, it builds ships and provides services for both rail and water transport facilities.

The tendency in Far Eastern regional development has been toward a high degree of autonomy. Both before and during the war the Far East was regarded as a virtually self-contained regional unit despite a food deficit, and it possessed military forces characterized by a marked degree of independence from Moscow. This trend has since been reversed, but the vast distances that lie between the Far East and the rest of the country make intimate integration difficult and costly. On the other hand, the population of the region is too sparse to conceive of its ever counterbalancing the great mass of European Russia and western Soviet Asia to the west. Its strategic value, however, remains very great. Primarily, it provides Russia with a window on the Pacific. It places her in a position of actual and potential great influence upon Japan. It necessarily gives Russia so-called "special interests" in Manchuria, and it does provide an excellent warm-water port upon the Pacific. It contains the best agricultural lands in the eastern half of Siberia. All of these factors suggest that in time the Soviet Far East will become an increasingly important region in terms of both Soviet and East Asian affairs.

Eastern Siberia

Eastern Siberia is by far the largest of the five regions of Soviet Asia, encompassing 2,800,000 square miles. It includes the drainage basins of the Yenisei and Lena rivers, two of the greatest rivers in the world, both of which flow northward into the Arctic Sea after rising in the mountain borderlands of southern Siberia. The headwaters of the Yenisei in fact rise across the international boundary in central and western Outer Mongolia; the river has a maximum length of 2,400 miles. The Lena rises just northwest of Lake Baykal and flows for a distance of some 2,600 miles. Both streams carry enormous volumes of water derived from the melting of frozen ground in the spring and summer.

The central and northern part of the region is sparsely settled, and the population density is less than 2 per square mile. Excessive cold has restricted permanent occupance to a few places such as Norilsk, near the mouth of the Yenisei, where valuable deposits of nickel, platinum, and polymetallic ores are mined; or Igarka, on the lower Yenisei, where timber is floated down for transport out of the region via the Northern Sea route. Some agriculture is practiced, especially in the valley of the middle Lena about the city of Yakutsk, capital of the Yakut A.S.S.R., where hardy grains and vegetables are grown. At Aldan, 400 miles north of the great bend of the Amur, settlement has centered about rich gold fields. To a large degree, however, the raising of reindeer by people of Eskimo-like habits is the most common livelihood along the Arctic fringe. Farther south, lumbering, trapping, and mining are the chief livelihood activities.

Fig. 156 • A great belt of forest extends from east to west across Siberia. Known as the *taiga,* it is virtually unbroken except by stretches of swampy lowland, the water table of which lies almost at the surface. Here is a stretch of taiga along the Amur-Yakutia highway which links the Amur basin with the middle Lena basin, the core of the Yakut A.S.S.R. Larch, pines, fir, and birch are the major species in the taiga, found generally in large unmixed stands except where local variations in surface configuration, soils, and drainage influence vegetation. The road itself, though the main land connection to the outside world of Yakutia, can be described as an all-weather road only by stretching the definition, since access along it is limited during much of the winter, and washouts and snow and mud slides are common. Since the difficulties of highway construction and maintenance are great, as they are throughout the Soviet northlands, reliance is on seasonal river navigation, as along the Lena downstream from Yakutsk to the Arctic, for contact with outside areas. There is also navigation upstream to the railhead at Ust-Kut where a branch of the Trans-Siberian railway reaches the Lena. *(Sovfoto.)*

The bulk of the region consists of the eastern Siberian upland, drained
by tributaries of the Yenisei and the Lena, which rises to 4,500 feet above
sea level in places. Within and along the margins of this upland are vast
deposits of coal, estimated at as much as 450 billion tons of reserves, although verification of this figure will demand further mineralogical exploration. A modest production is used for space-heating and as fuel for
Lena riverboats. The northern part of the area is tundra; the vast remainder of it is covered by taiga, vast coniferous forests in which larch is
most widespread, but with stretches of pine, fir, and birch (Figure 156).
The climate is most severe and continental. In the far northeast of eastern
Siberia, where a series of high, glaciated mountain ranges form the northeastern Siberian mountain belt, some of the lowest temperatures in the
world are experienced. At Verkhoyansk, the January temperature mean
is −58°F., but the July mean rises to 60°. Most of the area is underlain
by permanently frozen ground which melts during the short summer to
depths up to 10 feet where the vegetation cover has been removed. Of
potentially great importance to the Soviet Union because of its resources
of coal, timber, and metallic minerals (such as lead, zinc, tin, gold, and
platinum), this great northern subregion of eastern Siberia remains one
of the least developed areas in the country.

Most of the population of eastern Siberia, in total 5.5 million people,
live south of the 58th parallel. The southwestern sector of the southern
subregion consists of the Sayan mountain system, the Minusinsk basin,
and a small portion of the west Siberian plain. The Minusinsk basin is
drained by the Upper Yenesei and is a major center for current agricultural and industrial development. Like the Kuznets basin just to the
west, it contains vast deposits of coal, estimated at 20 billion tons, with
some associated reserves of iron ore destined for development in part to
supply the steel mills of the Kuzbas. Manganese and gold are the other
two major minerals known to exist in the area and to be under exploitation. Agriculture based primarily on wheat has been expanding rapidly
in the Minusinsk basin and on the margins of the west Siberian plain near
Krasnoyarsk, where wooded steppe and true steppe form a narrow zone
along the Trans-Siberian railway. Krasnoyarsk is a regional agricultural
and mining capital with a population estimated at 300,000 persons. South
from it runs the branch rail line into the Minusinsk basin, which in time
will be connected with the uncompleted South Siberian railway. The
new railway undoubtedly will strengthen the connections of the area with
the regions to the west. Although the climate is not as severe in this
sector as it is in the north, except in the high highlands, it is notably
continental. Rainfall averages slightly more than 10 inches per year, although in the mountains averages of 35 inches and more have been
recorded. Farming is possible in the lowlands, however, despite the low

Fig. 157 • Siberia contains most of the undeveloped water power resources of the Soviet Union. Here at the Padun rapids of the Angara River at Bratsk, 400 miles from Irkutsk, is being constructed an enormous dam and hydroelectric station with an installed capacity of 3.2 million kilowatts. Another hydroelectric installation was well on its way to completion near Irkutsk in 1957. The Angara carries enormous quantities of water, which do not change markedly from season to season by virtue of the natural storage reservoir of Lake Baykal and which do not freeze solid in winter because of the river's steep gradient. The development of water power and other energy resources is being pushed rapidly as part of a general program of development in the so-called eastern regions where the greater part of the mineral and other non-agricultural resources of the U.S.S.R. are found. With sources of energy assured, there will follow the development of power-oriented manufactural industries and aggregations of population which in the long run may alter substantially the population geography of the country. (Sovfoto.)

rainfall, since relatively low temperatures lower the evapo-transpiration rate. In the intermontane Tannu Tuva basin to the south of Minusinsk, inhabited chiefly by a Turkic-speaking people numbering less than 100,-000 persons, agriculture and pastoral activities are the chief bases for livelihood.

Between the southwestern sector and Lake Baykal to the east is a highland area extending eastward from the Sayans. The tectonic disturbances to which these highlands have been subjected have resulted in the formation of Lake Baykal, a graben lake, the deepest in the world (5,700 feet) and one of the largest (13,300 square miles). The area is cut by the valley of a major tributary of the Yenisei, the Angara River, which drains Lake Baykal from its southwestern shore (Figure 157). For this reason it possesses an enormous and regular water flow, which makes it one of the more promising rivers for hydroelectric power generation in

Asia.[4] In addition, vast coal deposits are found within the area northwest of Irkutsk, where reserves of 79 billion metric tons have been determined and where most of the East Siberian coal production originates. Gold is another important mineral resource, and iron ore exists along the Angara. In addition, the mountains are covered with magnificent forests of pine and larch, which have scarcely been tapped. Fur-trapping and fishing on Lake Baykal also are important activities.

Irkutsk, with a population of 300,000, is the oldest and largest city of Eastern Siberia apart from Krasnoyarsk. It lies 30 miles northwest of Lake Baykal and was a major center from which the Trans-Sib railway was constructed. The railway itself runs diagonally from northwest to southeast through the region. One branch departs from the main line at Tayshet, the terminus-to-be of the South Siberian railway, and continues to the headwaters of the Lena, where it connects with river transportation along that river. It is planned to extend this eastward-running branch north of Lake Baykal across Eastern Siberia to the Soviet Far East, thereby providing a strategic route parallel to the overburdened Trans-Sib line.[5] The rainfall at Irkutsk measures 15 inches annually. The January temperature mean is −6°F., and the July mean 64°. Virtually the same temperature figures hold for Yeniseisk, 150 miles north of Krasnoyarsk.

East of Lake Baykal is the subregion known as Transbaykalia. Most of this region resembles the areas west of the lake, and it is crossed by a series of complex hill-and-mountain ranges trending toward the northeast. In the south, however, near the Outer Mongolian boundary, the Mongolian steppe crosses into Soviet territory, and many of the valleys and lower hills are unforested. Gradually, however, as the hills become mountains, the forest cover increases and shortly becomes taiga of great potential value. The mountains act as a divide between the headwaters of the Yenisei (via Lake Baykal), Lena, and Amur river systems. The chief stream is the Selenga, which rises in Outer Mongolia and flows into Lake Baykal.

Western Transbaykalia is occupied by the Buryat Mongol A.S.S.R., with a population of 600,000 persons of whom only 44 per cent are Mongols; Slavs are a majority. In addition to its forest resources, the republic contains considerable reserves of brown coal mined southwest of Ulan-Ude, the capital. Iron ore, gold, tungsten, molybdenum, and some petroleum are found within the republic. Ulan-Ude (150,000) possesses

[4] In 1956 the 660,000-kilowatt capacity power station near Irkutsk was under construction. A much larger development of 3,200,000-kilowatt capacity is projected downstream at Bratsk, where the Angara joins the Upper Tunguska River, and another has been begun at Krasnoyarsk on the Yenisei.

[5] Reports that this second Trans-Sib or North Siberian line has been wholly or in part completed have been circulating since 1942, but reliable evidence is unavailable.

other industries based chiefly upon local agricultural and livestock products; it also is a railroad center. From Ulan-Ude a branch of the Trans-
Sib railway runs southward across the international boundary to the
capital of Outer Mongolia, Ulan Bator, which lies in a highland basin
drained by a tributary of the Selenga River, and ultimately to Peking.
Most of the Buryat Mongol population is engaged in animal husbandry
which formerly took the form of nomadic herding, but, as in Soviet Middle
Asia, it has become partly sedentary. Wheat-growing along the Trans-
Sib is largely a Russian occupation.

The eastern half of Transbaykalia lies almost entirely within the Amur
drainage basin and is populated largely by Russian settlers concentrated
in a narrow band along the Trans-Siberian railway. Wheat and rye are
grown in lowlands which receive monsoonal rainfall from the Pacific,
but the growing season is short, and winters are long and severe. At
Petrovsk, near the boundary of the Buryat Mongol A.S.S.R., there exists
a small, modern iron-and-steel plant dependent upon local supplies of
coal and iron ore. Lead-zinc-silver ores and gold also are important. Low-
grade coal deposits are mined on the outskirts of the regional capital
Chita (150,000). Most of the proven tin reserves of the U.S.S.R. also are
located in the area and are mined in the southeast. Since 1942, other
and larger reserves of tin ore have been identified in far northeastern
Siberia, but these are not yet reported in production. East of Chita the
Trans-Siberian railway, chief transportation artery of the area, bifurcates,
the northern part turning northeastward and following the Argun River,
chief tributary of the Amur. The southern branch extends southeastward
into the Inner Mongolian region and thence across Manchuria as the
former Chinese Eastern or Trans-Manchurian railway. A narrow-gauge
line leads from this southern branch to the mines near the southeast frontier and into eastern Outer Mongolia.

In sum, eastern Siberia is one of the least well developed regions
within the Soviet Union, but it is at the same time one of the wealthiest
in terms of forest, mineral, and power resources. Its severe climate and
lack of arable land, however, will continue to impede development. Even
more important is the inaccessibility of many of its most valuable resources, especially those of the northeast. Despite its sizable Asian
minorities, the area can be expected to experience increasing increments
of Russian population and rapid Russification as economic development
proceeds.

Western Siberia

Western Siberia is the least
Asian and the most Russian of all the regions of Soviet Asia. Nearly a

million square miles in size, it consists of the greater part of the basin of
the Ob River. The Ob flows northward to the Arctic for 3,200 miles from
its source in the western Sayan mountains, which form part of the international boundary between Russia and Outer Mongolia. A major tributary of the Ob, the Irtysh, rises in the Altai mountains to the south of the
Sayans. About ten million people live in this territory, giving a density
of over 10 per square mile. Only 7 per cent of the population is non-Slav,
and the entire territory, like eastern Siberia and the Far East, is included
within the Russian Soviet Federated Socialist Republic.

The middle and lower Ob and Irtysh rivers flow across the northern
sector of a great plain of compelling flatness, the west Siberian plain, in
which ill-drainage has created vast marshlands of forbidding accessibility. In the farthest north is the tundra belt; south of it is the wooded
tundra and then the vast taiga, predominantly in Siberian spruce, larch,
and fir, but with sizable areas of birch and aspen among others. The chief
industry of this sparsely settled area is lumbering, and timber is floated
down the Ob to the Arctic. Large quantities also move upstream for use
in the more densely settled south. The climate is harsh and continental.
Winters are long and cold with temperatures down to −40°F.; summers
are very short and mild. Much of the area is underlain by permanently
frozen ground, and agricultural development, though widely publicized
because of its significance to the settlement possibilities of arctic regions,
is slight.

South of the taiga at about latitude 56° the wooded steppe begins, and
it shortly becomes true steppe, with a narrower transition zone than in
European Russia. The steppe itself also is narrower than in the west, and
patches of desert and salt flat appear soon after it enters Kazakhstan.
This zone is the eastern extension of the agricultural triangle, which
tapers rapidly in Siberia under pressure from excessive cold in the north
and undue aridity in the south. It is a subregion primarily of Russian
settlement, which produces a surplus of foodstuffs and provides the industrial regions of western Siberia and the Urals with much of their
sustenance. Climate within the area is continental and semi-arid, with
rainfall averaging 14 inches at Barnaul. Relatively low mean temperatures reduce evaporation and make dry-farming more practical than the
rainfall figure would indicate, despite occasional dessicating winds that
sweep across the steppe. January mean temperatures are well below
0°F., while summer temperatures reach 70°. The growing season is limited to five months. About five million acres, 18 per cent of the total in the
U.S.S.R., is sown to spring wheat, which in turn accounts for half of the
region's cultivated land. Rye is second in importance; sugar beets, sunflowers, and other grains make up most of the balance. The area also has

supplied Soviet Middle Asia with some of its grain needs, since Middle Asia has been undergoing a transformation into a cotton-oriented agricultural region. Together with the adjacent areas of Kazakhstan, which are climatically and edaphically similar, the Siberian steppe region has accounted for about 30 per cent of the total Russian area sown to spring wheat. In addition, dairying is an important industry, and in the drier steppe livestock raising for meat is important. It is not surprising, therefore, that each city and town in this agricultural area possesses indusrties based on the processing of agricultural products—canneries, granaries, and flour mills, meat-packing plants, and tanneries. In addition, agricultural machinery and tools are produced locally.

The southeastern part of western Siberia is a mountain rimland, consisting chiefly of the Altai mountains and associated ranges. The Altai is a great range comparable in size to the T'ien Shan but (on the average) lower, with elevations seldom exceeding 10,000 feet. The trend of the range is from northwest to southeast, and most of it actually lies in Outer Mongolia. There is a permanent snow line in the Altai above 8,500 feet, and the headwaters of the Ob system rise in lakes fed by these melting snows and the glaciers that lie above them. These are valuable sources of hydroelectric power, already partially developed. To the northeast of the Altai, but connected with it by a continuous upland, are the Western Sayan mountains to the north and the Tannu Ola, along which the international boundary runs, to the south. Vegetation is zoned vertically from grasslands to forests to alpine meadows.

The most significant fact about this mountainous subregion is its high degree of mineralization. Reference will be made again to the mineral wealth of the Altai where it enters northeastern Kazakhstan. Polymetallic ores of lead, zinc, and silver, as well as iron, manganese, and rare metallic ores all are found in this upland complex. Most important, however, are the coal reserves of the Kuznetsk basin (Kuzbas), which lies between two northward extensions of the Altai, opens in the north onto the west Siberian plain, and is drained by the Tom River, a tributary of the Ob. The Kuzbas coal deposits are estimated at 450 billion metric tons. They are the largest known coal reserves in the Soviet Union and are in large part high-quality coking coals. They provide the basis for the development of an iron-and-steel industry within the basin, which produced 11 per cent of Soviet steel in 1950. Kuzbas coal is used to fire the blast furnaces at Magnitogorsk, and in return iron ore from the Urals is transported by rail to the mills in the basin. The utilization of local iron-ore from the Urals is transported by rail to the mills in the basin. The utilization of local iron-ore deposits to the south of the main mills at Stalinsk has lessened the dependence upon Ural iron ores, and at the same time

the use of Karaganda coal by the Ural complex has lessened the need for
Kuzbas coal.[6] Manganese also is mined within the basin, and large deposits are known east of the basin in the Minusinsk area. In that area
also large deposits of good-quality ores, just being developed, may
further lessen Kuzbas dependence on distant ore supplies. In association
with the iron-and-steel industry and the coal deposits, chemical industries using coal gas as a source of energy and as a raw material have
been developed, and many metal manufacturing plants have arisen both
within the basin and in nearby cities of the western Siberia region. For
the most part, production is for consumption in that part of the U.S.S.R.
east of the Urals; the industrial products of the area find their way primarily into Middle Asia to the southwest and to Eastern Siberia and the
Far East.

One of the characteristics of the Western Siberian region has been the
tremendous growth of cities. There are as many as ten cities in the region
with populations over 100,000, whereas in 1926 there were only two such
cities. The largest possess multifunctional urban characteristics. These,
together with their populations for 1946-8 as estimated by Shabad, are
Novosibirsk (750,000), Omsk (500,000), Barnaul (200,000), and Tomsk
(150,000). Each is a trade center, industrial center, and cultural center
for large hinterlands. Within the Kuzbas itself several large cities also
have developed, among which Stalinsk and Kemerovo, each with 200,000
population, are the largest and most important.

The main transportation route is the Trans-Siberian railway, which
runs east-west through the southern part of the region. At Novosibirsk,
the main rail center, the Turk-Sib railway joins the Trans-Siberian, and
a branch of the latter extends southeastward into the Kuznetsk basin.
Among the railway construction under way or planned is a continuation
of the so-called South Siberian railway which roughly parallels the
Trans-Sib line from a point 120 miles north of Karaganda in Kazakhstan
eastward through Barnaul into the Kuzbas, and thence will continue
farther east into the Minusinsk basin of eastern Siberia where both coal
and iron ore are found. The completion of this railway should strengthen
the connections of the Kuzbas industrial area with western Russia, and
may alter its primary function as the industrial developmental center for
Siberia.

[6] There is major disagreement as to the extent to which the Kuzbas is dependent
upon Ural iron ores. Shabad states that in 1947 local ores contributed 75 per cent
of all the ore used in the Kuzbas. However, Shimkin states that as late as 1949 the
area was "still dependent upon Magnitogorsk ore output." Clark agrees with Shabad.

Soviet Middle Asia

The most Asian region of the Soviet Union is Soviet Middle Asia.[7] This southernmost part of the U.S.S.R. includes 17 per cent of the total surface area of the country and is occupied by 8.5 per cent of the total population, 17 million persons. The chief material importance of the region is its production of cotton and minerals. Its significance in political-geographical terms reflects the composition of its population.

Only 30 per cent of the total population in Soviet Middle Asia is Slav in origin, and these Russians and Ukrainians have for the most part immigrated to the region within the past half century. They form a substantial part of the population of Kazakhstan, but in other areas they are confined largely to cities. Russian control over the area was not consolidated until 1880. The bulk of the population is of Turkic stock, with a substantial Persian minority and lesser groups of Mongols and Chinese Moslems. Islam is the religion of the area, the oasis cities of southern Middle Asia being among the more famous centers of Islamic culture. As noted previously, similar peoples live on the other side of the international frontier, and the welfare of the Soviet nationals is of great importance in assessing the loyalties of their kinsmen across the frontier, since most of these are minorities in the bordering nations as well.

The Soviets have pursued a policy of ethnic autonomy throughout their domain, and Middle Asia is no exception. The region is composed of five republics, each named after the majority ethnic group within its territory. Each republic is a union republic, one of the 16 of which the Soviet Union is composed (Map 36). The largest of these, the *Kazakh S.S.R.*, lies to the north and accounts for two-thirds of the area and nearly 40 per cent of the population of the region. The Kazakhs, like most of the people of Middle Asia, are primarily of Mongoloid extraction with considerable Caucasoid intermixture; they account for about 60 per cent of the population of their republic. The republic extends 1,850 miles from a point just east of the Volga mouth to the Altai mountains in the east. From north to south it measures some 1,050 miles, from the steppes of Siberia to the westernmost outliers of the T'ien Shan, the Alai mountains. It includes the northeastern shores of the Caspian Sea, the lower Ural and Emba rivers, the northern shores of the Aral Sea, and most of the lower Syr Darya and Lake Balkhash; it also includes the southern outliers of the Ural mountains. Its capital, Alma Ata, with an estimated population of close to 300,000, lies to the southeast, like most of the capitals of the

[7] Soviet Middle Asia is the term applied to Kazakhstan plus the four republics commonly termed Soviet Central Asia.

Middle Asian republics, on the very periphery of the republic's territory. The city possesses special strategic importance as the westward terminus of a major trade route which runs eastward through the Ili River valley into Hsin-chiang province.

The second most populous republic lies to the southwest of Kazakhstan, the *Uzbek S.S.R.*, or Uzbekistan. Its 157,400 square miles contain about 40 per cent of the population of the region. The dominant ethnic element is the Uzbeks, a Turkic-speaking people also of mixed racial origin, but differing from the Kazakhs in that their tradition has not been primarily nomadic and warlike, but sedentary. Uzbekistan does not reach the Caspian Sea, but does include the southern shores of the Aral Sea and the delta of the Amu Darya. Its predominantly northwest-southeast axis is extended to the northeast by an irregularly shaped proboscis which extends into the fertile Fergana valley of the upper Syr Darya. Only a small stretch of boundary adjoins Afghan territory. For the most part, Uzbekistan is surrounded by its related Soviet republics.

To the northeast of Uzbekistan and southeast of Kazakhstan is the *Kirgiz S.S.R.*, only 76,100 square miles and with a population of 1,500,-000 persons. The Kirgiz are a people related to Kazakhs. They are traditional pastoralists, occupying the high lands of the T'ien Shan and its related ranges, both in Russian and Chinese territory. Kirgizia itself is primarily a mountain country, and only along its northwestern and western borders are there lowlands of any size for cultivation.

South of Kirgizia and southeast of Uzbekistan is the *Tadzhik S.S.R.*, or Tadzhikistan, smallest of the republics, with an area of only 54,900 square miles and a population of less than 1.5 millions. Most of the inhabitants are of Caucasoid rather than Mongoloid stock, and the language of the Tadzhiks is Persian rather than Turkic. Most of the republic lies in the high Pamirs, the roof of the world, and the highest points of the Soviet Union are located within its borders. A northern extension of the republic protrudes northward into the Fergana valley, which it shares primarily with Uzbekistan and incidentally with the Kirgiz S.S.R. In addition to these fertile lowlands, there are river valleys tributary to the Amu Darya which forms the international boundary between Tadzhikistan and Afghanistan. Although Pakistan and Kashmir lie only 30 miles to the southeast, a long finger of Afghanistan territory separates Russian territory from that of South Asia.

Last of the five republics in Soviet Middle Asia is the *Turkmen S.S.R.* (Turkmenistan), 187,200 square miles and with a population of 1.5 millions. It lies between Uzbekistan on the north and Afghanistan on the south, but shares its far northwestern boundary with the Kazakh S.S.R. Its western boundary is the Caspian Sea. The Turkmens are also of mixed racial stock, with perhaps a stronger Caucasoid element than the Kazakhs, Kirghiz, and Uzbeks. Turkmenistan contains minorities other than Slavs, as do all of the other Middle Asian republics.

Middle Asia as a whole is one of the regions of the Soviet Union least well suited to permanent human occupance despite its fertile and densely populated areas. Its population density is less than 11 to the square mile. By far the greater part of the region is semi-arid and arid, and about half consists of true desert, much of it sandy waste. Rainfall in the far northern portions of Kazakhstan may reach 18 inches per year, but this figure decreases rapidly to the south. In the Caspian lowland of western Kazakhstan, precipitation diminishes to less than 5 inches annually, and rainfall averages of less than 10 inches characterize most of the region. Except for the north, where dry-farming is practiced on the black-soil extensions of the west Siberian steppe, the chief economic use of land

Fig. 158 • The types of irrigation practiced in Soviet Middle Asia differ from place to place. Here in the South Kazakh region of Kazakhstan in the broad valley of the Syr Darya considerable areas of land which previously had been dry-farmed are being brought under partial irrigation. Temporary channels are shown being cut into a previously dry-farmed area. This type of rather extensive irrigation may be contrasted with that in the more intensively cultivated and irrigated cotton regions in Uzbekistan (Fig. 159). The photograph also suggests the type of country, somewhat better watered naturally, which is being brought into cultivation for the first time or is being cultivated once more after long periods of fallow in northern Kazakhstan and the steppes of southwestern Siberia. In these regions irrigation is not being practiced, and the threat of drought is fully as great as it is along the western margins of the Great Plains in the United States. (Sovfoto.)

is for grazing; the Kazakhs were long a nomadic people, moving from pasture to pasture with their herds. In addition, irrigated agriculture is practiced wherever supplies of surface water are available (Figure 158). Winter temperatures are quite low, and polar continental air masses plunge southward into the region, diminishing in intensity as they travel. Thus, all of the region experiences winter temperatures below freezing, and the northern part of the Aral Sea, Lake Balkhash, and even the mouth of the Amu Darya freeze in winter. In summer, temperatures increase rapidly to the south where hot spells with temperatures of over 100°F. are common. Vegetation cover conforms quite closely to climatic zoning. In the north the wooded steppe rapidly becomes steppe, then semi-arid short grassland, and then desert, some bare, some covered by feather grass, and some by the tree-like, leafless *saksaul*. Soils vary from the *chernozem* of the steppe zone, to grey *sierozem* that is of some fertility when irrigated, to undifferentiated clays and sands; alkaline soils are found in ill-drained depressions.

The western border of the region is the Caspian Sea, the largest inland sea in the world and the lowest of any size, the surface being 85 feet below sea level. The northern part of the sea is shallow, nowhere more than 165 feet deep. It is kept fresh by the waters of the Volga, its chief tributary, and shallow by the silt that the Volga pours into it. In its southern portion, however, depths reach 3,200 feet and salinity is higher, although the salinity of the sea as a whole, 10-15 per cent, is not high considering the rate of evaporation, which is estimated to remove a meter of water from the surface of the sea each year. The rate of evaporation is greatest in the shallow eastern arm of the Caspian, the so-called Kara-Bogaz-Gol, which therefore draws water from the rest of the sea. Since the northern part of the sea is shallow, fresh, and enriched by materials emptied into it by the Volga, it is a famed fishing ground, sturgeon being the most famous of its fish products. The shallow waters of the north have made it necessary, however, to create an outport for the Volga delta city of Astrakhan. This outport is about 20 miles from the city and is the break-of-bulk point at which petroleum tankers from Baku transfer their cargoes to Volga river barges. The Aral Sea lies east of the Caspian and is separated from it by a low plateau, the Ust Urt. Less than 25,000 square miles in area, the Aral Sea also is shallow, averaging 10 to 20 meters. It lies above sea level and formerly was connected with the Caspian Sea by an arm of the Amu Darya.[8] It also is an important fishing area, al-

[8] Among the various schemes designed to utilize these channels is a gigantic proposal to dam the Ob River below its junction with the Irtysh, thereby creating a great inland sea in part of the west Siberian lowland, and to divert the water through an intricate system of canals to the Aral and Caspian seas. In Middle Asia old stream channels would be used to connect the larger waterbodies and to distribute water for large-scale irrigation.

Fig. 159 • A cotton field at first watering in one of the irrigated areas along the Syr Darya in Uzbekistan in May. Note the small plots separated by irrigation channels into which the cotton fields are divided and the hand cultivation and plot-trimming that is practiced. The irrigated oasis type of agriculture common to this region has long been a center of cotton cultivation in the Soviet Union. In recent years the irrigation systems have been greatly expanded, and nearly three-quarters of all the cotton acreage in the Soviet Union is associated with them. As a result, the Soviet Union has become virtually self-sufficient in cotton, except for some of the highest grades of long-staple cotton which still are imported in modest quantities from Egypt. *(Sovfoto.)*

though like the Caspian its northern part is frozen in winter.

The eastern and southeastern borders of Soviet Middle Asia are mountainous. The Kopet Dagh form the southern boundary for much of its length, and the Pamirs the remainder. The T'ien Shan, Altai, and associated ranges form most of the eastern boundary. Extensions of the Pamirs on the south and the T'ien Shan in the middle east rise abruptly from the arid lowlands, receiving greater rainfall and covered by vegetation that ranges within relatively short distances from shrub to forest, meadow, and tundra. High intermontane basins provide summer pastures, but in winter snow covers most of the highlands. To the northeast the region is bordered by arms of the Altai mountains, rich in minerals. A western extension of the Altai system occupies much of eastcentral Kazakhstan, a partly levelled hill land known as the Kazakh upland, also an area of mineral wealth. Another major upland area appears in northwestern Kazakhstan, an extension of the southern Urals, which again is highly mineralized.

Between the lowlands, plains, and low plateaus that cover much of Middle Asia and the high mountains that rim it on the south and east is a narrow belt of densely populated (up to 1,500 persons per square mile) irrigated oases which have long been renowned as centers of Islam in Asia. The names of cities such as Samarkand, Tashkent, Mary or Merv, Kokhand, and Bukhara are famous in Central Asian history as literal oases of plenty in the dry world of Moslem Asia. It is on the basis of these and other oases that Soviet Middle Asia has come to fulfill one of its major functions, the production of high-grade cotton (Figure 159). About 70 per cent of all cotton acreage in the Soviet Union is found in these oases, and before the war they produced 80 per cent of the national output. Most of them are located where mountain streams debouch onto the lowland, and the essential waters have long been canalized into irrigated fields. In some cases, covered canals (*karez* or *qanat*), similar to those used in Iran, Afghanistan, and Hsin-chiang, were constructed at great cost.

Since 1928 the irrigation system has been modernized and greatly expanded, and this expansion is still going on. Large dams and canals such as the Great Fergana Canal, 200 miles long, have been constructed. The most important of the oases is the Fergana valley, drained by the Syr Darya, which is divided primarily between Uzbekistan and Tadzhikistan and includes Kokhand and Leninabad. Just to the north is the Tashkent oasis on a branch of the Syr Darya. Other agricultural centers are about the irrigated lands near Ashkhabad, Tedzhen, and Mary (Merv) along the Murgab River, which flows northward from Afghanistan into the desert known as Kara Kum (Turkmenistan). Others are in the Vakhsh valley of southwestern Tadzhikistan, in the Zeravshan oasis near Bukara, in the Chu and Ili river valleys (especially near Alma Ata) of Kazakhstan and Kirgizia, and in the lower reaches of the Amu Darya. In addition to cotton, wheat is a major crop, but it is grown primarily on nonirrigated land. Sugar beets, sesame, vegetables, dried fruits, rubber-producing shrubs, flax, tobacco, rice, and alfalfa are other important agricultural products. Uzbekistan, with the greatest number of major oases, is the largest agricultural producer, accounting for about 60 per cent of the total cotton production in the U.S.S.R.

Animal husbandry was the chief industry of the region before the revolution and still remains important. Kazakhstan is one of the largest producers of meat in the U.S.S.R., and the drier areas support flocks of sheep from which karakul fur is derived. Camel herds reflect the arid nature of the region. However, the nomadic pattern of occupance was forcibly altered by the Russians, and pastoral activities have been collectivized. This in fact has not eliminated transhumance, but has resulted in the creation of fixed bases of operations and the end of tribal nomadism. In the process of collectivization, and after 1928, the livestock population of the region declined sharply; by 1950 it had just begun to reach its pre-collectivization level. Animals may still be taken to the mountain pastures during the summer months, but the extent to which feeding depends on forage crops has greatly increased.

The Soviet emphasis on cotton and other specialized crop production resulted in a stagnation of grain production in southern Middle Asia, although the main development of its mineral industries did not take place until the thirties and thereafter. Some of the largest deposits of coal in Russia are found at Karaganda, with reserves of 50 billion tons, in the Kazakh uplands of central Kazakhstan. Around these deposits has grown a city of 220,000 people, engaged in industries dependent on local coal. Other coal deposits are found in and around the Fergana valley near Tashkent (Figure 160), and at the western edge of the Kazakh upland.

Fig. 160 • The strip mines at Angren near Tashkent supply about 40 per cent of the coal consumed in Uzbekistan. Seams lie near the surface and can be mined by strip or open-cast methods, as shown here. The coal is largely lignitic and cannot be used for coking purposes. Thus, the steel mills in the region are dependent upon imports of coal from the Kuzbas for coking purposes. Note the traces of snow visible on the mountain tops in the background in the early fall, and the barrenness of the middle and lower slopes. This is a desert region, dependent upon irrigation for agriculture. (Sovfoto.)

Reserves of petroleum also are great. One of the primary producing areas in the country lies along the Emba River of western Kazakhstan where salt-dome structures predominate. Pipe lines carry the crude oil northeastward to Orsk for refining, but a refinery is located also at Guryev at the mouth of the Ural River. A second oil belt of anticlinal structure lies far to the south, with fields at Nebit Dab near the shores of the Caspian Sea in Turkmenistan, and in the Fergana valley.

The hydroelectric potential of the region is very high. Development has taken place particularly in the far northeast of Kazakhstan, in association with copper-refining industries in the western Kazakh uplands and the southern Urals, and further construction is under way.

The region is also especially well endowed with metallic mineral resources and ranks with the Urals as a primary metallic mineral region of the U.S.S.R. In northeastern Kazakhstan lead-zinc-silver ores have long been mined about Leninogorsk (formerly Ridder). The largest reserves of copper in the Soviet Union are found in the Kazakh uplands, and major producing areas are in the western uplands at Dzhekazgan and near Kounradsky, just north of Lake Balkhash. Manganese also is found in the area. About half the nickel in the U.S.S.R. is located in the projection of the southern Urals that enters northwestern Kazakhstan. Chrome and copper are also major metallic resources in Kazakhstan.

In the southern republics rich metallic mineral resources are found all along the mountain border belt, but especially on the margins of the Fergana valley. Lead, zinc, antimony, vanadium, copper, molybdenum, tungsten, and iron are among the ores found within the southern area. These areas also contain the most important uranium-ore deposits in the country.

Nonmetallic minerals also are important. Industrial salt from the eastern Caspian, sulfur from the Kara Kum desert, arsenic, and phosphorite, particularly in the northwest near Aktyubinsk, are noteworthy.

Refining industries based upon regional ores and local coal supplies and hydroelectric power are found widely distributed over the region. Phosphates are manufactured in the northwest; nitrates near Tashkent where hydroelectric power is used. Copper refineries are based in the Kazakh uplands where both local coal and hydroelectric power resources have been developed. Lead and zinc refineries in the northeast also are based on hydroelectricity. Conversion steel mills at Jemir Tau near Karaganda and at Begovat south of Tashkent in Uzbekistan use some local coal [9] and, when blast furnaces are added, will use local iron ores at least in part. Total industrial production in the region in 1940 was

---

[9] Coke from Karaganda coals needs mixing with higher-grade Kuzbas coke. Most of the coal in the south is too poor for coke conversion, and most of the coke required comes from the Kuzbas as well.

Fig. 161 • This is the Frunze branch of the Turk-Sib railroad in the gorge of the Chu River, on the right, which drains the Issyk-Kul, a large mountain lake in the T'ien Shan of northern Kirgizia. Note the barren slopes, the telegraph and power lines which parallel the line, and the relatively poor but all-weather road which extends from Frunze, the capital of the Kirgiz S.S.R. to a point east of the lake. As its name suggests, the Turk-Sib railway was designed to link Russian Turkestan with western Siberia. It also connects the major cities of the Middle Asian republics and provides a direct linkage between them and the Kuzbas. Like most Russian railways, the line is single-track and broad-gauge. A branch line east of it, under construction near the eastern edge of Lake Balkhash eventually will link up with a Chinese line gradually inching its way westward across Hsin-chiang province to the Sino-Soviet border. *(Sovfoto.)*

estimated at 3.7 per cent of the national total, but this figure probably rose significantly during and after the second World War. Industries other than metallurgical industries are in the aggregate equally important; they are based primarily on locally produced agricultural products. Cotton- and woolen-textile plants, beet-sugar factories, and meat-packing and fruit-preserving plants are among the more important types of industrial establishments.

The basic transportation routes have been the four major railway lines—Trans-Sib, Trans-Caspian, Central Asian, and Turk-Sib (Figure 161). The latter three join at Tashkent. Numerous branch lines connect the oases and mining centers in the southeast. Under construction is a second Trans-Caspian line which will run northwestward from Chardzou on the present Trans-Caspian, along the Amu Darya valley, across the Ust Urt plateau between the Caspian and Aral seas, and through the Emba oil district to connect eventually with the European Russian rail net southeast of Saratov. It has been completed (1957) to Kungrad just southwest of the Aral Sea. This new line will make the lower Amu Darya and the southernmost oases more easily accessible from European Russia. In Kazakhstan a railway has long linked the north shore of Lake Balkhash with the Trans-Siberian at Petropavlovsk via Karaganda. A branch also extends westward to the copper areas near Dzezkazgan. A shorter route to the Ural industrial area has been constructed west from the Karaganda branch line. As noted previously, this basically east-west line is being extended eastward, parallel to the Trans-Sib, to and through the Minusinsk basin.

Rivers are a minor part of the transportation picture, although the Irtysh is used for navigation, as are the lower Ural and Amu Darya. Both Lake Balkhash and the Issyk-Kul of Kirgizia similarly are utilized, as are the Caspian and Aral seas. Road transport is primarily of local significance, although several major trade routes pass over the mountain frontier into China and Afghanistan.

It appears certain that the economic development of Soviet Middle Asia has been a material success. Output for the region and in per-capita terms on the whole has vastly increased; authorities differ as to whether this accomplishment required major imports of capital from the rest of the country. The growth of great cities within the region also is evidence of increasing industrialization. However, the nonmaterial aspects of development are more questionable, since the collectivization of agriculture and the industrialization had a higher cost in human life, animal life, and traditional cultural values than in many other areas in the U.S.S.R. undergoing economic development and cultural change.

Transcaucasia

In terms of area, Transcaucasia, with some 74,000 square miles, is the smallest major region of Soviet Asia. Long associated with the West and therefore not so clearly Asian as is Soviet Middle Asia, the region nevertheless is populated primarily by people who are non-Russian and whose cultural ties lie well within the Mediterranean culture world and in Southwest Asia. The region occupies the southern half of the 300-mile-wide isthmus that separates the Black from the Caspian seas. Its chief importance to the Soviet Union as a whole is threefold: (1) it is a major producer of petroleum, in fact the

leading producing area; (2) it is the most important producer of specialized subtropical agricultural products; and (3) its ethnic composition is important in influencing the course of Soviet foreign policy in
Southwest Asia.

Although there are a number of ethnic groups in Transcaucasia and
the region is noted as a cultural "melting pot," three are numerically and
politically more important than the rest—the Georgians, the Armenians,
and the Azerbaijanians. Of the regional population of over eight million,
about 27 per cent are Georgians, 25 per cent are Azerbaijanians, and 14
per cent are Armenians. Kinsmen of all these peoples are found on the
other side of the international frontier, and the U.S.S.R. has long used the
lure of ethnic autonomy to attract members of these nationalities to
Soviet territory. For example, after the end of the second World War
some 100,000 Armenians migrated to the Soviet Union, attracted by
promises of Soviet citizenship and promised tax exemptions. Among the
less numerous peoples are the Kurds, an ethnic group widely distributed
in the highlands of Iran, Iraq, and Turkey.

In line with Soviet ethnic policy, Transcaucasia is divided into three
republics, corresponding roughly to the distribution of the three major
population groups. Largest in population is the *Georgian* S.S.R. with a
population of 3.6 million and an area of 29,400 square miles. Of this
population 61 per cent are Georgian, the remainder consisting of Armenians, Russians, Ukrainians, and other minorities. As the birthplace of
Stalin, himself a Georgian, Georgia has been of particular interest to the
Bolsheviks, and was one of the earliest areas of vigorous communist, as
well as later anticommunist, activity. The capital of Georgia is Tbilisi
(Tiflis) in the southeastern part of the country, a city of some 550,000 and
an important cultural as well as administrative, industrial, and commercial center.

Second of the republics is the *Azerbaijanian* S.S.R., with an area of
33,100 square miles and a population of 3.1 millions, of whom some 63
per cent are Azerbaijanians. Across the international frontier in Iran to
the south is Persian Azerbaijan, inhabited by kinsmen of the Soviet
Azerbaijanians. Russian influence, always strong in northern Iran,
reached its zenith shortly after the close of the second World War when
an autonomous Azerbaijanian republic was established in northern Iran.
Short-lived, it fell shortly after Soviet troops withdrew from the area in
1946. However, the Soviet government continues to speak of "Northern"
Azerbaijan in connection with Soviet territory and "Southern" Azerbaijan in connection with Iranian territory, and thus keeps the threat of
Russian expansion alive in the area. The chief material importance of
Azerbaijan is associated with its petroleum resources, which supply about
40 per cent of the total petroleum production of the U.S.S.R. The capital

of the republic is Baku, on the Caspian Sea, a true metropolis with a population of some 800,000 persons. It ranks as the sixth largest city in the Soviet Union.

Third of the republics is *Armenia*, smallest in area with 11,500 square miles and in population with 1.4 millions. Of the three it also is the least well endowed with natural resources, and is the only one that does not front on a major water body. About 85 per cent of the population is Armenian, though people of Armenian ancestry are more widely distributed both in the U.S.S.R. and in the world at large than any other Soviet Asian nationality apart from the Slavs themselves. The relatively high levels of education and sophistication that characterize the Armenians have long made them of special utility to Russia, czarist and communist alike. It is clear that an attempt has been made to establish the Armenian S.S.R. as a sort of homeland for the Armenian diaspora, much as was attempted by the Russians in establishing a Jewish autonomous political area in eastern Siberia. The capital of the republic is Yerevan, with a population approaching 255,000, in the southwestern part of the country.

Transcaucasia is primarily a mountainous region, and it is estimated that 80 per cent is unsuited for agricultural uses because of the slope factor. Most of the northern boundary of the region follows the Great Caucasus mountains which extend in a northwest to southeast line from the Black Sea to the Caspian. These are young mountains of great height and impressive beauty. Many glaciers and permanent snow fields cap the higher peaks, of which Mount Elbrus in the northwest corner of the Georgian S.S.R. is the highest (18,480 feet). Although folded ridges predominate, there is much volcanic intrusion, as evidenced by Mount Elbrus, itself an extinct volcano. The rivers that drain northward enter the Sea of Azov on the one hand and the Caspian on the other. Their waters are used for irrigation along the foot of the north slopes of the range. The rivers to the south include the Kura and the Rion, two of the three more important streams of Transcaucasia. Vegetation ranges vertically from desert, to steppe, to oak steppe, to deciduous forest, alpine meadow, and then the snow line. As one goes farther east the uplands are less well forested and present a denuded aspect, a consequence primarily of lower rainfall.

Southern Transcaucasia consists largely of the so-called Little Caucasus mountains, really part of the faulted Armenian plateau which extends well into Turkey and Persia. In its southeastern sections the range averages over 10,000 feet and culminates in the famed Mount Ararat (16,-945 feet) which lies across the frontier in Turkish territory. This range is characterized by considerable past volcanic activity, as evidenced by numerous extinct volcanoes and wide areas underlain by volcanic rocks.

Present physical instability is indicated, as in the Great Caucasus mountains, by numerous earthquakes. Block-faulting is the explanation for Lake Sevan in eastern Armenia. Vegetation again varies with altitude and resembles that of the Great Caucasus, but to the south the forested areas are smaller and may be characterized as open forest and shrub with xerophytic species prominent. There is no permanent snow line.

Running north-south between the two ranges in the western half of the region is the Suram range which connects the two major mountain masses. Most of the range is under 6,000 feet, and the Kura River cuts through its modest barrier. East of this range is the valley of the Kura River, largest of the Transcaucasian lowlands and most important. The headwaters of the Kura rise in Turkey, flow through Georgia, and then cross a broadening valley, the heartland of Azerbaijan, before entering the Caspian Sea. To the west of the Suram mountains is the lesser valley of the Rion, which flows into the Black Sea across a marshy lowland, the Colchis of Greek mythology. The third major river system is that of the Araks, which rises in Turkey and flows generally eastward, south of the Little Caucasus range, as an international boundary until it joins the Kura with which it shares a common delta. Vegetation in the Rion valley and the western coastal plain is exceptionally lush; rainfall is heavy. In the drier eastern half of the region it varies with altitude, but is predominantly steppe and semidesert. Most of the population of Transcaucasia is centered in these three river basins.

Climatically, Transcaucasia is one of the mildest parts of the Soviet Union, although its highest uplands reflect altitudinal influences and possess an alpine-type climate. The main Caucasus range tends to block the coldest winds from the north. On the west the climate is especially mild in the Rion lowland. Average January temperatures are 43°F. (at Batum, and summer temperatures and humidity are both high. The Suram mountains block and lift moist air coming from the Black Sea. Thus, Batumi receives 93 inches of largely orographic rainfall, with a maximum in the fall and winter months. The reverse conditions characterize the lee of both the Great Caucasus and Suram ranges. Rainfall at Baku is a mere 9 inches; mean January temperatures seldom fall below 40°F. Low rainfall also characterizes the Armenian highlands and the upper Araks River basin, which have a continental climate with relatively cold winters and hot summers. The average rainfall is 12-14 inches. The southeastern part of Azerbaijan is the so-called Lenkoran lowland along the southwest shores of the Caspian Sea. This area receives more rainfall for orographic reasons, and humidities are high.

The chief mineral resource of the region is petroleum. The main fields lie north of the eastern lowland, close to Baku. Production from these fields is estimated at just above 40 per cent of the total production of the country. Lesser fields are exploited in eastern Georgia. A pipeline along the Kura valley and across the Suram range connects Baku with Batumi on the Black Sea. Oil is also shipped to the mouth of the Volga, where it is transshipped to river barges for transport to the Central Industrial Region. Refineries exist at Baku, Batumi, and near the east Georgian fields. North of the region an important petroleum region is centered about Grozny. Coal is mined at several places, the most important being in central Georgia, and good coking coal is mined in northwestern Georgia. Hydroelectric power is a major source of energy in each republic. It is most important in Armenia, where a tributary of the Araks draining Lake Sevan is the site of an enormous hydroelectric installation, already partially completed. Power installations also have been built on the Rion and are being constructed on the middle Kura River.

Transcaucasia also is the second most important source of high-grade manganese ore in the U.S.S.R. and perhaps in the world. The chief mines are at Chiatura in central Georgia, where measured reserves total 146 million metric tons of ore. Some of the ore is smelted with local coal; most is exported. Other metals such as antimony, molybdenum, tungsten, and copper also are mined in significant quantities. Iron-ore deposits in western Azerbaijan are being exploited for the new iron-and-steel plant at Rustavi in southeastern Georgia. In association with the metallic industries and abundant power resources, manufacturing industries have been established, ranging from machinery and automotive plants to food-processing and textile industries.

The region specializes in crops that cannot be grown in most of the country. In the east, cotton is grown under irrigation, together with rice and alfalfa. In the western lowlands and on the mountain slopes, tea, mulberry (for silkworms), tobacco, citrus fruits and other fruits, and grapes for wines and brandies are important products. Wheat and corn are the major grains; sugar beets and potatoes are making rapid headway. In the Armenian basins to the south, especially about the capital, Yerevan, cotton, fruits, wines, and tobacco are important products. In all republics animal husbandry is an important and traditional occupation, producing wool, meat, milk, cheese, *laban* (yogurt), and skins.

Communications center about the rail system, the core of which is the Baku-Batumi line which crosses the region from southeast to northwest. In the west it is connected with the south Russian rail system by a line paralleling the Black Sea; in the east it connects with a line to the northern Caucasus which follows the Caspian Sea shore. From Tbilisi, capital of Georgia, a line extends south into Armenia, through Yerevan, and then along the Araks River eastward to the Kura valley and Baku. Three major roads also cross the main Caucasus range, but these are primarily of military importance. Rivers are navigable only for short distances. However, both the Caspian and the Black seas provide major channels through which commerce moves into and away from the region.

Like Soviet Asia's other semi-colonial region (Middle Asia), Transcaucasia is undergoing rapid and major economic development. Stresses within the indigenous societies resulting from these changes have yet to be evaluated, but that they are extreme is certain. The region continues to possess a special importance as part of the zone of transition between Europe and Asia. Its transition from an underdeveloped to a more highly developed status is watched with interest by Asian peoples across the international frontier.

The gross pattern of political orientations

The regions of Soviet Asia are extensions of a Soviet political organization that centers on Moscow and allows these regions little leeway in their roles in world and Asian affairs. They also happen to occupy the vast area known as the Heartland, which, as defined originally by Sir Halford Mackinder, provided a fortress core within which a continental power could be safe from maritime and naval penetration. Mackinder's theories have become obsolescent, if not archaic, but they are still of great value in understanding the role of the Soviet Union in Asia. Modern Russia remains to a large degree what it was in 1900—a huge continental power occupying the core of a vast land mass and surrounded on all sides by numerous countries along the more peripheral and therefore martime margins of the continental land bloc. The fact that on the west a buffer of satellite states lies between Russia and the Atlantic-oriented West may obscure but does not fundamentally alter this picture.

In large-scale terms, there exists a balance of political power between the countries on the peripheries of the continent and the U.S.S.R. The strength of these collective states varies with the degree to which they are allied and cooperative. It is to the Russian interest, therefore, to do what it can to discourage a grand alliance of the states that rim the Eurasian continent. In this connection, Russian foreign policy runs squarely against that of the United States and (to a lesser degree) Great Britain, which are pursuing a policy of virtual containment of the Soviet Union and its allies through the organization of the states along or near its frontiers. The Marshall Plan, NATO, SEATO and the Baghdad Pact, among other policy programs, may be considered aspects of this predominantly American and British policy.

The Mackinder hypothesis, however, did not necessarily conceive of the Heartland as an independent and solitary political unit. Indeed, greatest concern long centered about the possibility of Germany gaining control of the Heartland. This fear rose to new heights during the German drive into Russia in the second World War. In effect, the possibility of an alliance between German might and Russian massiveness came to be regarded as the greatest potential threat to the other countries of Europe and the United States.

Since 1949, however, a somewhat similar situation has developed along the eastern rather than the western frontiers of Russia. China has passed under the control of a Communist government, closely allied with that of the U.S.S.R., and to a major degree the two are acting in concert. There has arisen a formidable amalgam of Russian massiveness (including also considerable technological experience) and Chinese human and physical resources. The Heartland thus has become associated with a great marginal state, full of problems to be sure, but a power of potential greatness. The democratic West's loss of China has meant a shift toward Russia in the balance of power between Russia and the marginal powers, since the largest of the latter has been brought into the Russian orbit.

The Sino-Russian border, therefore, has been brought into new perspective. Though still qualifying as both a physical barrier along much of its course and a neutral ethnic zone between Russian and Chinese civilizations, it has become much more a zone of passage over which Sino-Russian trade and communications pass at an increasing rate. This new function is suggested by the initiation in early 1954 of the Moscow-Peking express, the first direct scheduled service between the capitals of the two countries.

At the same time, Russian influence in East Asia is buttressed by the special privileges accorded Russian shipping in the port of Dairen. More important, Russian influences in Hsin-chiang province have continued strong; they were vastly increased with the completion of the Turk-Sib railway, branch lines of which are much nearer to the center of the province than is any railhead in China itself. In Outer Mongolia Russian influence has been established firmly, although the significance of the Sino-Russian relationship upon the Mongols is less clear. Furthermore, Japan no longer blocks Russian expansion into the Pacific theater, and Japan's postwar situation has become increasingly precarious, as the entire East Asian mainland, except for South Korea, has come under Communist control.

The defection of China to the Communist camp also has had grave repercussions on the countries of the Southeast Asian realm, since for the first time since the eighteenth century Chinese cultural and economic imperialism has been combined with an even more potent political imperialism. Russian influences, as filtered through Chinese forms and cultural patterns, have been brought to bear much more directly on Southeast

Asia than ever before. Similar pressures weigh increasingly heavily on South Asia as well. The consolidation of Chinese sovereignty over Tibet in 1951 brought Russo-Chinese power right to the northern gates of India.

Russian relations with Southwest Asia are more direct. Here a number of independent states exist in close proximity to Soviet territory. Russia's policy of fomenting disunity among its border nations is no more clearly illustrated than in Southwest Asia. This is all the more important since substantial Russian oil reserves are near the frontier, and the lure of Middle Eastern oil also remains strong at all times.

From the standpoint of Asia, external relations with the Soviet Union and the communist bloc have increased greatly in importance since the close of the second World War. Before the war the ties with the western European nations and the United States were strongest, being symbolic of the colonial relationship that existed between the more and less advanced countries. These ties still remain, but they have greatly lessened with the rise of nationalism in Asia and the acquisition of independence by many of the formerly dependent territories. Indeed, in many instances, as in the case of Indonesia, the reaction against the former imperialistic powers has resulted in a virtual rejection of the sorts of technical and economic assistance that the former mother countries (and the U.S.) can provide. In this sense the relative importance of the Soviet Union, even apart from the associated change of government in China, has increased. In short, the motives and methods of the Soviet Union in developing its "colonial" territories in Asia are to most Asians less familiar than those of their former overlords. Being less familiar, they usually are considered no worse, and by extension often better.

For these reasons the burden of proof with regard to the possibilities for economic betterment in the underdeveloped territories has come anomalously to weigh upon the democratic West, rather than upon the relative unknown, Russia. The apparent success of the U.S.S.R. in the economic development of Soviet Asia has vastly impressed Asians, who may not be familiar with the totalitarian methods employed in that development. Current economic development programs in Soviet Asia and more especially and more recently in communist China are observed with intense interest by other Asian countries, from Turkey to Japan. Many of the individual nations have cast their lots for the time being with the United States and Western Europe, Turkey and Iraq being notable examples. However, there also has arisen a "third force" concept centering about India, which proposes that a foreign-policy middle course be followed between the democracies and Russia. Antipathy toward the former imperialist countries, with which the United States often is identified, and the rise in nationalist aspirations have made many of the Asian countries particularly susceptible to any policies that are anti-European, ethnocentric, and nationalistic. By extension, they have become more concerned with both the problems and possible advantages of a closer affiliation with the great power to the north.

The Asian Crescent is perhaps in greater political and economic ferment than any other part of the globe, with the possible exception of Africa south of the Sahara. Insofar as this ferment can be allayed, moderated, and eliminated by rapid economic progress and the development of democratic institutions, there will be a bloc of countries along the Asian rimlands, apart from China, clearly independent of the Russian orbit. If these conditions fail to materialize, the massive weight of the Russo-Chinese combine cannot fail to bear increasingly heavily upon the countries of Asia.

SELECTED GEOGRAPHICAL BIBLIOGRAPHY

1. Balzak, S. S., V. F. Vasyutin, and Ya. G. Feigin. *Economic Geography of the U.S.S.R.*, C. D. Harris, ed. New York: Macmillan Company, 1949.
2. Bergson, Abram, ed. *Soviet Economic Growth.* Evanston: Row, Peterson and Company, 1953.
3. Bulik, J. J., G. B. Cressey, N. Jasny, D. B. Krimgold, M. Y. Nuttonson, and S. Schwartz. "Soil Conservation in the U.S.S.R.," *Land Economics,* November, 1949, pp. 333-64.
4. Caroe, Olaf. *Soviet Empire.* London: Macmillan Company, 1953.
5. M. G. Clark. *Economics of Soviet Steel.* Cambridge: Harvard University Press, 1956.
6. Harris, C. D. "Ethnic Groups in Cities of the Soviet Union," *Geographical Review,* July, 1945, pp. 466-73.
7. ———. "Growing Food by Decree in the Soviet Union," *Foreign Affairs,* January, 1955, pp. 1-14.
8. ———. "U.S.S.R. Resources: I—Heavy Industry," *Focus,* February, 1955.
9. ———. "U.S.S.R. Resources: II—Agriculture," *Focus,* May, 1955.
10. ———. "Soviet Agricultural Resources Reappraised," *Journal of Farm Economics,* May, 1956, pp. 258-73.
11. Kolarz, W. *Russia and Her Colonies.* London: George Philip and Son, Ltd., 1952.
12. ———. *Peoples of the Soviet Far East.* London: George Philip & Son, Ltd., 1954.
13. Jackson, W. A. D. "The Virgin and Idle Lands of Western Siberia and Northern Kazakhstan," *Geographical Review,* January, 1956, pp. 1-19.
14. Lorimer, Frank. *The Population of the Soviet Union.* Geneva: League of Nations, 1946.
15. Mandel, W. *The Soviet Far East.* New York: Dial Press, 1944. See also Mills, D. R., "The USSR: A Reappraisal of Mackinder's Heartland Concept," *Scottish Geographical Magazine,* December, 1956, pp. 144-53.
16. Mozley, A. "The Ponds, Lakes, and Streams, of the Kirghiz Steppe," *Scottish Geographical Magazine,* January, 1937, pp. 1-10.

17. *Oxford Regional Economic Atlas: The U.S.S.R. and Eastern Europe.* Oxford: The Oxford University Press, 1956.
18. Schwartz, Harry. *Russia's Soviet Economy,* 2d ed. Englewood Cliffs, N. J.: Prentice-Hall, Inc., 1954.
19. Shabad, T. *Geography of the U.S.S.R.* New York: Columbia University Press, 1951.
20. Shimkin, D. B. *Minerals: A Key to Soviet Power.* Cambridge: Harvard University Press, 1953. See also Wheeler, G., "Recent Developments in Soviet Central Asia," *Geographical Journal,* June, 1957, pp. 137-47.
21. Wilhelm, W. "Soviet Central Asia: The Development of a Backward Area," *Foreign Policy Reports,* February 1, 1950, pp. 218-28.

Comments

The preceding bibliography refers to both Chapter XXXVIII and Chapter XXXIX. It is a highly selective listing and does not pretend to include the voluminous literature on the Soviet Union, which has appeared especially since 1946.

Among the numerous general geographies on the Soviet Union, Balzak, Vasyutin, and Feigin is one of the more useful, although it is based upon pre-war data and contains much political bias. When used in conjunction with Shabad, it brings the reader relatively up to date concerning the broad patterns of Soviet geography.

The problems of Soviet agriculture and its expansion into Siberia and Middle Asia are discussed in the several articles by Harris and by Jackson. Mandel gives a rather superficial description of the Soviet Far East. Wilhelm discusses the course of economic development in Middle Asia. Kolarz gives a useful description of the non-Slav territories in the U.S.S.R. though not on a wholly systematic basis. Caroe deals almost entirely with Middle Asia.

Bergson and Schwartz give non-geographers' appraisals of the Soviet economy. These may be augmented by Shimkin's detailed study of minerals and Clark's careful examination of the Soviet steel industry. Both become more meaningful when associated with Lorimer's classic study of Russia's population in the prewar period.

As a general reference tool, the Oxford atlas on the U.S.S.R. and Eastern Europe is invaluable, especially for its economic data and distributions. For more detailed work the student is referred to the *Great Soviet World Atlas* (not listed above), Volume I, copies of which are in the major American reference libraries. The atlas, published in Moscow in 1938, contains numerous plates showing economic distributions in the Soviet Union. Volume I was followed by Volume II, which is not, however, available in this country. A translation of the plate legends was made under the direction of Professor Cressey and published by Syracuse University in 1940.

Index

Index

A

Abaca, 318, 330
Abadan, Iran, 783
Abdullah, King, 735
Afghan Jews, 682
Afghanistan, 536-37, 679-96
  agriculture, 513, 685-86, 689-92
  boundaries, 527
  Central Region, 687-91
  climate, 685
  ethnic groups, 680-84, 686
  history, 679-80, 682-83, 686
  northern piedmont, 691-93
  politics, 526-55
  population, 682, 687, 691
  rainfall, 687
  topography, 684, 691
Agriculture (*See also* Cropping systems;
  Fertilizers; Irrigation; Livestock;
  Soils; names of specific products):
  Afghanistan, 513, 685-86, 689-92
  Arabia, 835-39
  Asia, 15
  Burma, 447-52
  Ceylon, 669-73
  China, 53, 168-86, 267-69
  East Asia, 55-57
  East Pakistan, 654-58
  India, 564-65, 583, 590, 593, 603, 610,
    616
  Indonesia, 366

Agriculture (*cont.*):
  Iran, 773-81
  Iraq, 821-27
  Israel, 800-804
  Japan, 86-99, 105
  Java, 359
  Korea, 135, 137
  Malabar, 611
  Malaya, 378-81
  Mongolia, 198
  Nepal, 586
  North China, 209-10
  North Korea, 142
  Outer Mongolia, 281-83
  Pakistan, 635-39, 647
  Philippines, 324-37
  Seistan, 694
  Sind, 649-50
  South Asia, 510-21
  South China, 217, 226, 230
  South India, 600-601, 628-29
  South Korea, 147-48
  Southeast Asia, 316-19
  Southwest Asia, 716-31
  Soviet Asia, 896, 901, 904
  Syria, 812-15
  T'ai-wan, 234-35
  Thailand, 395, 397-402, 407
  Tibet, 203
  Turkey, 747-54
  U.S.S.R., 865-67
  Yemen, 836-38
Ahmedabad, 546

911

C